The
Complete
Antiques
Price
List

Books by Ralph M. and Terry H. Kovel

The Complete Antiques Price List

Know Your Antiques

American Country Furniture 1780–1875

A Directory of American Silver, Pewter and Silver Plate

Dictionary of Marks—Pottery and Porcelain

The Complete Antiques Price List

A guide to the 1969 market
for professionals, dealers, and collectors

by Ralph M. and Terry H. Kovel

CROWN PUBLISHERS, INC., NEW YORK

175662

INTRODUCTION

Selling or buying an antique is no different from selling or buying any other product. It is a matter of supply and demand. What is needed is information about the demand, and this book has been written to fill that need.

The value of an antique can be judged in many ways: by its intrinsic value if it is made of silver or another precious metal or stone, by its historic or nostalgic value to the owner, or by its sale value in a recognized sale or auction. This book records the "asked for" prices of antiques in auctions, ads, and antique shows. Each price indicates an actual piece that was offered for sale, and the piece is described by the seller. If identical antiques were offered at different prices, a range has been given which includes the highest and lowest prices indicated. Each price listed in the book has been taken from an antique offered for sale between July 1967 and June 1968. No price shown is just an estimate or even a suggested figure.

Antiques sell at varied prices in different parts of the country. The West Coast market is higher for bottles and for pioneer relics. The East Coast seems more interested in regional items. Buffalo pottery, for example, is sold at its highest prices in the New York State region. The antique trading newspapers and the advertisements in magazines have equalized the market in many respects, and mail-order antiques have become big business. If a price in the book appears low or high, perhaps the regional difference has influenced the seller.

The prices in this book are as accurately reported as possible. Each item is recorded as it was offered. There has been no attempt made to determine the accuracy of the seller's description. All items are considered perfect unless otherwise noted. The authors and the publisher cannot be responsible for any loss incurred because of any error in the price list.

This first listing includes the antiques and "almost antiques" most frequently offered by the antique dealers of the United States. Many of the pieces are less than one hundred years old, the legal definition of a duty-free antique. The average collector knows that the majority of items offered at antique shows are less than a hundred years old. Most bottles, all art glass, art pottery, art nouveau, most jewelry, souvenir spoons, and many other categories are in this group.

This book does not include an extensive gun section, although some guns are included under the heading "weapons." Formal paintings, museum-quality furniture, and other antiques of limited interest have also been omitted.

A computer was used in order to produce this list as accurately and quickly as possible. The subject headings and certain punctuation marks were needed as guides to the computer program. All pressed glass patterns, for example, are listed under "pressed glass" and not under the pattern name. If you do not find an item in the alphabetic listing under a particular heading we suggest you try a different category; for example, all music boxes and phonographs are listed under the heading "music," and all fabrics such as clothing, paisley shawls, and coverlets are listed under "linens."

Photographs of particular antiques were not included because there are so many good books available that have large color pictures. We felt a collector of Tiffany glass knows what it is, and the noncollector could not make a positive identification from a small black-and-white picture. Over 30,000 items are listed in this book. Each piece is worthy of a special picture.

We are sorry, but it is impossible for us to answer any requests for appraisals by mail.

To all of the dealers who knowingly or unknowingly added to this book by offering antiques for sale, our thanks. We hope this compilation will prove a help to all buyers and sellers.

RALPH AND TERRY KOVEL

The
Complete
Antiques
Price
List

ABC PLATES or children's alphabet plates were popular from 1780 to 1860.
The letters on the plate were meant as teaching aids for the children who were
learning to read. The plates were made of pottery, porcelain, metal, or glass.

ABC ACORN & LEAF PLATE,JEANNETTE GLASS,RAINBOW IRIDESCENT...	30.00
ABC ALPHABET PLATE WITH JUMBO IN CENTER,TIN.................	5.00
ABC ALUMINUM PLATE..	3.00
ABC CHILDS PLATE,FISHERMEN & BULL.........................	28.00
ABC CHILDS PLATE,HUNTER & DOGS...........................	28.00
ABC CHILDS PLATE,PICTURE & RHYME IN BOTTOM................	12.00
ABC CHINA PLATE,LETTERS IN RELIEF WITH GOLD,STABLES & 4 HORSEMEN..	20.00
ABC CLEAR DISH,CLOCK IN CENTER...........................	5.00
ABC CLOCK FACE 7 IN. PLATE...............................	13.50
ABC CUP & SAUCER WITH HENS & ROOSTER,PINK LUSTER BAND.......	15.00
ABC EMMA PLATE...	13.00
ABC FEEDING DISH,LITTLE RED RIDING HOOD & FOX..............	9.50
ABC GLASS PLATE WITH CLOCK CENTER........................	16.00
ABC MUG,BLUE,CHILD AT DESK,CHILD AT CHRISTMAS TREE..........	15.00
ABC PINK LUSTER CHILDS CUP & SAUCER......................	9.50
ABC PITCHER,WHITE WITH GOLD,GERMANY......................	8.50
ABC PLATE,6 IN.,DOG IN CENTER...........................	9.00
ABC PLATE,6 IN.,NEGROES GATHERING COTTON.................	12.50
ABC PLATE,6 IN. TIN....................................	6.00
ABC PLATE,7 IN.,ANIMALS ON BORDER......................	6.50
ABC PLATE,A SIOUX INDIAN CHIEF,STAFFORDSHIRE.............	12.50
ABC PLATE,CARNIVAL GLASS ORANGE.........................	35.00
ABC PLATE,CHILDS..	12.00
ABC PLATE,CLEAR,DOG HEAD CENTER.........................	12.50
ABC PLATE,DUTCH GIRLS & BOYS DANCING....................	6.00
ABC PLATE, GREEN GLASS TO VASELINE, LITTLE BO PEEP.........	18.00
ABC PLATE,HIGBEE MARKED,CLEAR,DOG PORTRAIT...............	10.00
ABC PLATE,HUNTER RIDING TO HOUNDS.......................	7.50
ABC PLATE,MAN FISHING,8 IN..............................	23.00
ABC PLATE,MILK GLASS....................................	7.50
ABC PLATE,NATIONS OF THE WORLD,7 IN.....................	15.00
ABC PLATE,RAISED LETTERS WITH SCENIC CENTER.............	9.00
ABC PLATE,ROBINSON CRUSOE,ENGLISH MARK..................	18.00
ABC PLATE,SIOUX INDIAN CHIEF,7 IN.......................	23.00
ABC TIN PLATE...	4.50
ABC TIN PLATE,HI DIDDLE,DIDDLE..........................	9.00

ADAMS CHINA was made by William Adams and Sons of Staffordshire, England.
The firm was founded in 1769 and is still working.

ADAMS,BOWL,PINK BOLOGNA.................................	8.50
ADAMS,COOKIE JAR,HUNT SCENE,SIGNED JASPERWARE..............	50.00
ADAMS,CUP & SAUCER,PAIR,QUEEN ELIZABETH,CHARLES,ANNE,ENGLISH BONE CHINA..	4.50
ADAMS,CUP & SAUCER,PICKWICK PAPERS,GIANT,ENGLAND..........	11.00
ADAMS,JAR,COVERED,BLUE WITH WHITE HUNTING SCENE,IMPRESSED JASPERWARE..	68.00
ADAMS,MUG,DOMINION OF CANADA,TUNSTALL ENGLAND MARKED BLUE JASPER...	35.00
ADAMS,PLATE,1939 WORLDS FAIR,BLUE & WHITE,MADE FOR TIFFANY & CO..	8.50
ADAMS,PLATE,CURRIER & IVES MIDNIGHT RACE ON THE MISSISSIPPI,10 IN.......................................	22.50
ADAMS,PLATE,DICKENS CHRISTMAS EVE AT MR. WARDLES...........	15.00
ADAMS,PLATE,GREEN & TAN BORDER,10 IN.,ENGLAND.............	10.00
ADAMS,PLATE,LANDSCAPE,BLUE & WHITE,7 IN...................	3.50
ADAMS,PLATE,ORANGE & TAN BORDER,10 IN.,ENGLAND............	3.50
ADAMS,PLATE,PINK ANDALUSIA,8 IN.........................	12.00
ADAMS,PLATE,SIR JOHN FALSTAFF,10 IN.,ENGLAND.............	7.00
ADAMS,PLATE,SOUVENIR SERIES,HOME OF PRESIDENT COOLIDGE,PLYMOUTH,VT...................................	10.00
ADAMS,PLATE,SOUVENIR SERIES,THE UTAH,10 IN..............	10.00

ADAMS,PLATTER,COLUMBUS,BLUE...................................... 25.00
ADAMS,PLATTER,SCENE BUILDINGS,BLUE & WHITE,HEXAGON.......... 15.00
ADAMS,SALT DIP,WHITE ON BLUE,JASPER............................ 7.25
ADAMS,SAUCE,TEMPLE PATTERN,BLUE & WHITE,CIRCA 1830.......... 9.50
ADAMS,TEA POT,ACORN PATTERN,RED BAND & GOLD TRIM,ROYAL IVORY 20.00
ADAMS,TOOTHPICK,WHITE ON BLUE,3 HANDLED,JASPER.............. 11.75
ADAMS,VASE,BULBOUS,8 IN.,MARKED............................... 18.00

AGATA GLASS was made by Joseph Locke of the New England Glass Company
of Cambridge, Massachusetts, after 1885. A metallic stain was applied to New
England peachblow, and the mottled design characteristic of Agata appeared.
AGATA SUGAR & PITCHER......................................2,250.00
AGATA VASE,CRANBERRY WITH BLUE MOTTLING...................... 600.00
AGATE CARVED BOTTLE,PEARLY MOONSTONE COLOUR,MAN & DOG CARVED 125.00
AGATE SNUFF BOTTLE,CREAMY WITH AMBER & BLACK MARKINGS,METAL
    COLLAR.. 75.00
AGATE SNUFF BOTTLE,MOTTLED BROWN & AMBER,,2 IN. HIGH........ 70.00

AKRO AGATE GLASS was made in Clarksburg, West Virginia, from 1932 to 1951.
Before that time the firm made children's glass marbles. Most of the glass is
marked with a crow flying through the letter A.
AKRO AGATE 3 IN. VASE,FLUTED ,CREAM & ORANGE ,MARKED........ 7.50
AKRO AGATE BLUE CREAMER....................................... 2.00
AKRO AGATE BLUE SLAG CIGARETTE HOLDER......................... 3.00
AKRO AGATE CUSTARD ASHTRAY.................................... 1.00
AKRO AGATE DISHES,CHILDS...................................... 42.50
AKRO AGATE DISHES,DOLL,GREEN,5 PIECES,MARKED.................. 9.50
AKRO AGATE GARDEN DISH.. 8.00
AKRO AGATE GREEN PLATE.. 5.00
AKRO AGATE GREEN VASE,DAFFODIL PATTERN........................ 4.00
AKRO AGATE MARKED FLOWER POT,BLUE............................. 3.50
AKRO AGATE MARKED TOOTHPICK HOLDER............................ 6.00
AKRO AGATE RECTANGULAR GARDEN DISH,5-PETAL FLOWERS,GREEN.... 10.00
AKRO AGATE RECTANGULAR GARDEN DISH,5-PETAL FLOWERS,ORANGE... 10.00
AKRO AGATE SIGNED DOLL DISHES,10.............................. 17.00
AKRO AGATE VASE... 5.00
AKRO AGATE YELLOW PLATE....................................... 4.00

ALBUMS were popular in Victorian times to hold the myriad pictures and cutouts
favored by the collectors. All sorts of scrapbooks and albums can still be found.
ALBUM,BROWN EMBOSSED LEATHER PHOTO,TIN TYPES................. 4.00
ALBUM,FAMILY IN LEATHER COVER,PICTURES 1884.................. 4.00
ALBUM,GUTTA PERCHA
    7.50 TO.. 12.50
ALBUM,GUTTA PERCHA DAGUERROTYPES,BLACK....................... 6.00
ALBUM,LEATHER DATED JUNE 6,1882.............................. 15.00
ALBUM,LEATHER PHOTO,BATES COLLEGE CLASS 1881,SILVER CLASP... 8.50
ALBUM,MINIATURE 1 IN. TIN TYPES WITH 100 TIN TYPES.......... 10.00
ALBUM,OLD POST CARDS,USED & UNUSED,1900...................... 3.00
ALBUM,PHOTO... 1.50
ALBUM,PHOTO,2 METAL CLASPS,EMBOSSED.......................... 5.00
ALBUM,PHOTO,STANDING,CELLULOID COLOUR WITH BETSY ROSS &
    WASHINGTON... 18.00
ALBUM,POST CARD CIRCA 1907,125 CARDS......................... 10.00
ALBUM,POSTCARD GERMANY WITH 40 VIEWS......................... 5.00
ALBUM,RED PICTURE... 3.00
ALBUM,RED SHIRRED PLUSH,GOLD EMBOSSED,HEART SHAPED MIRROR IN
    CORNER... 30.00
ALBUM,RED VELVET PICTURE...................................... 6.00
ALGER BOOKS... 1.00
ALLERTON PORTIA PATTERN,6 PLATES,2 PLATTERS,BLUE
    BORDER,FLOWERS... 58.00
       ALPHABET PLATE SEE ABC..............................

AMBER GLASS is the name of any glassware with the proper yellow-brown shade.
It was a popular color after the Civil War.

```
AMBER,BOTTLE,SIGNED STUART ENGLAND.........................      22.00
AMBER,BOWL & CANDLESTICK WITH ENAMEL FLOWERS...............      45.00
AMBER,BOWL,FLOWER FLANGE FOOTED............................      12.00
AMBER,BREAD TRAY,OVAL,DARK SHEAF OF WHEAT..................      14.50
AMBER,BUTTER,COVERED,FLOWER & FLANGE WITH DEWEY
  FINIAL,GREENTOWN.........................................      24.00
AMBER,CRACKER JAR,SWIRLED PATTERN,SILVER COVER & BAIL HANDLE     18.00
AMBER,GAS GLOBE............................................       5.00
AMBER,GAS GLOBE,DRAPE & PANELS.............................      18.00
AMBER,GOBLET,1000 EYE......................................       9.00
AMBER,GOBLET,BEADED OVAL...................................      12.00
AMBER,LIQUEUR SET,ENAMEL FLORAL DECOR,6 MATCHING MUGS.......      48.00,
AMBER,PLATE,BLUE PANELLED HOBNAIL,7 IN.....................       9.50
AMBER,PLATE,POINTED HOBNAIL,6 IN...........................       9.00
AMBER,ROLLING PIN..........................................      11.50
AMBER,ROLLING PIN WITH CORK,16 IN..........................      12.50
AMBER,TIE BACKS,PAIR,LACY GLASS,IRON SCREWS................      18.00
AMBER,TOOTHPICK,INVERTED THUMBPRINT........................      15.00
AMBER,TOOTHPICK,RED SMALL PANELLED TOP WITH INITIALS E.J....       6.00
AMBER,VASE,CELERY,3 PANEL,FLUTED RIM.......................      12.50
AMBER,VINEGAR CRUET,BLOWN STOPPER,ROUGH PONTIL.............      22.50
AMBER,WITCH BALL,INVERTED THUMBPRINT DESIGN,BLOWN GLASS.....     22.00
```

AMBERINA is a two-toned glassware made from 1883 to about 1900. It was patented by Joseph Locke of the New England Glass Company. The glass shades from red to amber.

```
AMBERINA,BASKET,SMOOTHED PONTIL,LOOPED HANDLE...............      45.00
AMBERINA,BERRY BOWL,POINTED PETAL EDGES....................      10.00
AMBERINA,BERRY DISH,FOOTED,DIAMOND DESIGN,4 IN. SQUARE......      48.00
AMBERINA,BON-BON,3 FOOTED,SIGNED LIBBEY....................     240.00
AMBERINA,BOWL..............................................      20.00
AMBERINA,BOWL,DIAMOND QUILTED,NEW ENGLAND..................      60.00
AMBERINA,BOWL,FLUTED & RIBBED,FUCHSIA COLOURING,3 IN. HIGH..     145.00
AMBERINA,BOWL,FLUTED TOP...................................     135.00
AMBERINA,BOWL,SIGNED C IN TRIANGLE,10 IN. DIAMETER.........      42.50
AMBERINA,BUD VASE,FUCHSIA COLOUR,PEDESTAL BASE,LIBBEY SIGNED    265.00
AMBERINA,BUD VASE,FUCHSIA,HANGING IN SILVER HOLDER.........      95.00
AMBERINA,CANDLESTICKS,PAIR.................................      15.00
AMBERINA,CARAFE,INVERTED THUMBPRINT,FUCHSIA TO AMBER AT
  TOP,9 IN................................................      95.00
AMBERINA,CARAFE,INVERTED THUMBPRINT,REVERSE COLOUR FUCHSIA..     95.00
AMBERINA,CELERY VASE,INVERTED THUMBPRINT,REVERSE FUCHSIA,5
  SIDED TOP...............................................     105.00
AMBERINA,CELERY,INVERTED THUMBPRINT,SCALLOPED TOP..........      48.00
AMBERINA,CHEESE DISH......................................     175.00
AMBERINA,CREAMER,FOOTED,LIBBEY............................      22.50
AMBERINA,CREAMER,FUCHSIA..................................     190.00
AMBERINA,CREAMER,INVERTED THUMBPRINT,FUCHSIA,SQUARE TOP.....    187.00
AMBERINA,CRUET............................................       5.00
AMBERINA,CRUET,AMBER TO FUCHSIA,AMBER STOPPER..............      70.00
AMBERINA,CRUET,INVERTED THUMBPRINT,APPLIED REEDED HANDLE....    175.00
AMBERINA,CUSPIDOR,CRANBERRY TO AMBER......................     110.00
AMBERINA,FINGER BOWL......................................      25.00
AMBERINA,FINGER BOWL,THUMBPRINT...........................      55.00
AMBERINA,FRUIT BOWL,MIDWESTERN............................      38.00
AMBERINA,ICE BUCKET.......................................      37.50
AMBERINA,JUICE GLASS,SET OF 4.............................      75.00
AMBERINA,LAMP,HALL,FRENCH.................................     245.00
AMBERINA,LAMP SHADE,HANGING,PLATED,14 IN. DIAMETER........... 4,500.00
AMBERINA,LAMP SHADE,SWIRLED PATTERN,CRIMPED FLARED TOP......     50.00
AMBERINA,LEMONADE GLASS, INVERTED THUMBPRINT..............      30.00
AMBERINA,MILK PITCHER,CUFF TOP............................      98.00
AMBERINA,MILK PITCHER,INVERTED THUMBPRINT.................     135.00
AMBERINA,MUG,SWIRL,APPLIED RIBBED HANDLE..................      40.00
AMBERINA,PERFUME BOTTLE...................................      85.00
```

AMBERINA,PICKLE CASTOR,SILVER PLATE FRAME & LID,PEACOCK EYE & SWIRL	145.00
AMBERINA,PITCHER,8 IN. TALL	240.00
AMBERINA,PITCHER & 4 TUMBLERS,INVERTED THUMBPRINT	225.00
AMBERINA,PITCHER,INVERTED THUMBPRINT,WHEELING,CLEAR REEDED HANDLE	92.50
AMBERINA,PITCHER,REEDED HANDLE,5 IN. TALL	98.50
AMBERINA,PUNCH CUP 35.00 TO	45.00
AMBERINA,PUNCH CUP,BABY THUMBPRINT,FUCHSIA,1885	55.00
AMBERINA,PUNCH CUP,DIAMOND PATTERN,NEW ENGLAND,2 IN. TALL	65.00
AMBERINA,PUNCH CUP,DIAMOND QUILTED,AMBER REEDED HANDLE	59.00
AMBERINA,PUNCH CUP,DIAMOND QUILTED,FUCHSIA,REEDED HANDLE	65.00
AMBERINA,PUNCH CUP,QUILTED,FUCHSIA TO AMBER,AMBER REEDED HANDLE	65.00
AMBERINA,PUNCH CUP,RIBBED & DIAMOND QUILTED,AMBER REEDED HANDLE	72.50
AMBERINA,SALT & PEPPER SHAKER,PAIR,INVERTED THUMBPRINT,FUCHSIA	28.50
AMBERINA,SAUCE,DAISY & BUTTON,FUCHSIA,SQUARE,1 IN. HIGH	65.00
AMBERINA,SAUCE DISH,DAISY & BUTTON PATTERN,5 IN. SQUARE	48.50
AMBERINA,SAUCE DISH,DAISY & BUTTON,SQUARE 28.00 TO	48.50
AMBERINA,SHADE,DIAMOND QUILTED,RUFFLED EDGE	225.00
AMBERINA,SHADE,IRIS EMBOSSED,RUFFLED TOP	35.00
AMBERINA,SHAKER,PLATED	485.00
AMBERINA,SUGAR,OPEN,SIGNED LIBBEY	80.00
AMBERINA,TOOTHPICK HOLDER,DAISY & BUTTON,FUCHSIA,FOOTED	125.00
AMBERINA,TOOTHPICK HOLDER,DIAMOND QUILTED,BARREL-SHAPE	85.00
AMBERINA,TUMBLER,DIAMOND QUILTED,RED	39.50
AMBERINA,TOOTHPICK HOLDER,INVERTED THUMBPRINT	40.00
AMBERINA,TUMBLER 15.00 TO	38.00
AMBERINA,TUMBLER,BABY INVERTED THUMBPRINT	28.50
AMBERINA,TUMBLER,BABY THUMBPRINT	36.00
AMBERINA,TUMBLER,DIAMOND PATTERN,FUCHSIA,MT.WASHINGTON	85.00
AMBERINA,TUMBLER,DIAMOND QUILTED,FUCHSIA 50.00 TO	75.00
AMBERINA,TUMBLER,INVERTED THUMBPRINT 40.00 TO	48.00
AMBERINA,TUMBLER,RED	39.50
AMBERINA,TUMBLER,SWIRL	70.00
AMBERINA,TUMBLER,THUMBPRINT	35.00
AMBERINA,TUMBLER,VENETIAN DIAMOND,GOLD AMBER TO FUCHSIA	50.00
AMBERINA,TUMBLER,WATER,DIAGONAL RIBBED,CRANBERRY TO AMBER	30.00
AMBERINA,VASE,CLASSIC DESIGN,1 IN. FLOWER BANDS,10 IN. HIGH.	110.00
AMBERINA,VASE,DIAMOND QUILTED,FUCHSIA,6 IN	125.00
AMBERINA,VASE,FAINTLY RIBBED PATTERN,TRI-SCALLOPED RIM,11 IN.,BLOWN	95.00
AMBERINA,VASE,PAIR 8 IN.,SWIRL PATTERN,ENAMEL DECORATED	130.00
AMBERINA,VASE,PAIR,SWIRL PATTERN,RUFFLED TOP	140.00
AMBERINA,VASE,SWIRL RIBBED,AMBER RIGAREE ON RIM	140.00
AMBERINA,VASE,THUMBPRINT	150.00
AMBERINA,VASE,TRUMPET,PAIR,AMBER TO RED,11 IN. HIGH	310.00
AMBERINA,WATER PITCHER,INVERTED THUMBPRINT	135.00
AMBERINA,WATER PITCHER,SWIRL	250.00
AMBERINA,WATER TRAY,ROUND	60.00

AMETHYST GLASS is any of the many glasswares made in the proper dark purple shade. It was a color popular after the Civil War.

AMETHYST, SEE ALSO CROESUS	
AMETHYST,BARBER BOTTLE,WHITE ENAMELED PICTURE OF LADY	27.50
AMETHYST,BASIN,BLOWN,14 IN. DIAMETER	150.00
AMETHYST,BOTTLE,VIOLIN,10 IN	7.50
AMETHYST,BOWL,BERRY WREATH,8 IN	18.00

AMETHYST,BOWL,COIN DOT,9 IN.	13.50
AMETHYST,BOWL,FLOWERING ALMOND,6 IN.	55.00
AMETHYST,BOWL,OPALESCENT,WATER LILY DESIGN	13.50
AMETHYST,BOWL,RAYED INSIDE	14.00
AMETHYST,BOWL WITH TWISTED CANDLEHOLDERS,CAMBRIDGE	33.00
AMETHYST,BUTTER DISH,COVERED,DOME TOP,GOLD & WHITE ENAMEL	27.00
AMETHYST,CANDLE HOLDER	5.00
AMETHYST,CANDLE HOLDER,BLACK	2.50
AMETHYST,CANDLE HOLDER,VENETIAN,DOUBLE	35.00
AMETHYST,CANDLESTICKS WITH SILVER DESIGNS,PAIR	40.00
AMETHYST,CELERY,BLACK,LOVING CUP STYLE WITH HANDLES,EMBOSSED NYMPHS	7.00
AMETHYST,COLOGNE BOTTLE CASED IN SILVER GILT FILIGREE	56.50
AMETHYST,COMPOTE,PAIR,OPEN,BAR & FINE CUT	35.00
AMETHYST,CONSOLE SET,BLACK	32.50
AMETHYST,CUP,SAUCER & DINNER PLATE,PURPLE	5.00
AMETHYST,DARNER,BLOWN MOLD	7.50
AMETHYST,DECANTER,GOLD DECORATIONS,SQUARE	12.50
AMETHYST,DECANTER,SHAPE OF BUNCH OF GRAPES	29.00
AMETHYST,DISH,THREE LEAF CLOVER,8 IN.	6.00
AMETHYST,DRESSER BOTTLE & STOPPER,BLOWN	11.00
AMETHYST,FINGER BOWL	8.00
AMETHYST,MATCH HOLDER,SOUVENIR AYER MASS.,SCALLOPED TOP,GOLD RIM	6.50
AMETHYST,PERFUME BOTTLE,CAMPHOR,CUT TO CLEAR	13.50
AMETHYST,PERFUME BOTTLE,PAIR,BLACK,WHITE FLOWER,BLOWN,NUMBERED	10.00
AMETHYST,PLATE,BLACK,HANDLED,SQUARE	5.00
AMETHYST,PLATE,BLACK,OCTAGON,8 IN.	3.50
AMETHYST,POWDER BOX WITH BRASS BAND,HINGE & CATCH	12.50
AMETHYST,ROSE BOWL,LOUISA	16.00
AMETHYST,SUGAR BOWL,BLACK	3.00
AMETHYST,TOOTHPICK HOLDER	9.00
AMETHYST,TUMBLER	10.00
AMETHYST,TUMBLER,IRIS,4	12.50
AMETHYST,VASE,BLACK	5.00
AMETHYST VASE,BLACK,SILVER DEPOSIT,10 IN.	22.50
AMETHYST,VASE,BOOT BOUQUET	42.50
AMETHYST,VASE,CUT TO GREEN,10 IN.	85.00
AMETHYST,VASE,FROSTED,SIGNED CHARDER LE VERRE FRANCOIS	55.00
AMETHYST,VASE,PAIR,OVERLAY,8 IN.	50.00
AMETHYST,VASE,PEACHES PULLED LOOP,9 IN.	12.00
AMETHYST,VASE,RIBBED,BLOWN,12 IN. TALL	8.50
AMETHYST,VINEGAR CRUET,HOLLOW BLOWN STOPPER,ROUGH PONTIL	22.50
AMETHYST,WATER SET,12 IN. PITCHER & 6 TUMBLERS	95.00
AMETHYST,WATER TUMBLER,DECORATED,WHITE ENAMEL & BLUE	10.00
AMETHYST,WINE GLASS HOLDER,HINGED	26.00
ANDIRONS,BRASS SIGNED J MOLINEUX BOSTON	200.00
ANDIRONS,BRASS SIGNED R WHITTINGHAM,NEW YORK,CHIPPENDALE STYLE	200.00
ANDIRONS,IRON PAIR,PENNY-FOOT	35.00
ANDIRONS SHIPS ANCHOR	32.00
ANIMAL DISHES, COVERED, SEE MILK GLASS, DISH	
ARGY-ROUSSEAU SIGNED GREEN,BLUE & WHITE PAT-DE-VERRE VASE,CATS FACES	240.00
ARMOR,16 PIECES OLD THEATRICAL	145.00
ARMOR,JAPANESE SUIT OF	350.00
ART GLASS, SEE SEPARATE HEADINGS SUCH AS BURMESE, MOTHER OF PEARL, SATIN GLASS, TIFFANY, ETC	

ART GLASS means any of the many forms of glassware made during the late nineteenth century or early twentieth century. These wares were expensive and made in limited production. Art glass is not the typical commercial glassware that was made in large quantities, and most of the art glass was produced by hand methods.

ART GLASS,APPLIED VASE,AMBER RUFFLED TOP & BELL FLOWERS & LEAVES.. 130.00
ART GLASS WHITE RUFFLED PITCHER,APPLIED HANDLE,4 TUMBLERS... 95.00
ART NOUVEAU TRAY,PORCELAIN PLAQUE ,GIRL & FLOWERS,HANDLED METAL FRAME.. 60.00
ASHWORTH CHINA CHINESE PATTERN MILK PITCHER................. 10.00
ATTERBURY BLUE MELON & LEAF DATED SPOONER.................... 20.00
   AURENE, SEE ALSO STEUBEN................................

AURENE GLASS was made by Frederick Carder of New York about 1904. It is an iridescent gold glass, usually marked "Aurene" or "Steuben."

AURENE,ATOMIZER,BLUE,9 IN................................... 105.00
AURENE,ATOMIZER,GOLD WITH RED IRIDESCENCE................... 55.00
AURENE,ATOMIZER ON WAFER BASE,GOLD WITH PINK & BLUE HIGHLIGHTS.. 65.00
AURENE,BOWL,BLUE IRIDESCENT,PEDESTALED,SIGNED.............. 225.00
AURENE,BOWL,GOLD,SCALLOPED RIM............................. 45.00
AURENE,BUD VASE,GREENISH GOLD,FOOTED,5 IN. TALL,SIGNED...... 145.00
AURENE,CANDLESTICK,BLUE,GOLD,TWISTED MIDDLE,SIGNED,7 IN. TALL... 135.00
AURENE,CANDLESTICK,GOLD,8 IN. HIGH,SIGNED.................. 105.00
AURENE,CANDY DISH,RUFFLED STRETCHED EDGE,SIGNED & NUMBERED.. 65.00
AURENE,CANDY OR NUT BOWL,ROLLED IN TOP,4 IN. DIAMETER....... 45.00
AURENE,CENTERPIECE,GOLD IRIDESCENT,FOOTED,9 IN.,SIGNED...... 75.00
AURENE,CENTERPIECE,SIGNED................................. 325.00
AURENE,COMPOTE,GOLD,10 IN. HIGH,SIGNED & NUMBERED.......... 250.00
AURENE,COMPOTE,GOLD,TWISTED STEM,SIGNED & NUMBERED........ 165.00
AURENE,COMPOTE,GOLD WITH STRETCH FINISH,BLUE,OVAL,RUFFLED TOP,SIGNED... 195.00
AURENE,CONSOLE BOWL,BLUE,SIGNED........................... 200.00
AURENE,CORDIAL,GOLD,TWISTED STEM,SIGNED & NUMBERED......... 110.00
AURENE,CREAMER,MINIATURE,WISHBONE HANDLE,PEDESTAL BASE,SIGNED... 240.00
AURENE,DECANTER,GOLD...................................... 315.00
AURENE,DISC,BLUE,14 IN. ACROSS............................ 225.00
AURENE,FERN BOWL,GOLD,SIGNED STEUBEN...................... 72.50
AURENE,FINGER BOWL,GOLD,SIGNED,5 IN. BY 2 IN.............. 125.00
AURENE,GOBLET,GOLD,TWISTED STEM,SIGNED & NUMBERED......... 150.00
AURENE,LIGHT SHADE,GOLD & CALCITE,RIBBED,3................ 35.00
AURENE,MASTER SALT,BLUE,GOLD,SIGNED....................... 65.00
AURENE,PERFUME,BLUE,MELON SHAPED BODY,6 IN. HIGH,SIGNED.... 395.00
AURENE,PERFUME,GOLD,MELON RIBBED,STEUBEN,SIGNED & NUMBERED.. 135.00
AURENE,PLATE FOR UNDER SHERBET,GOLD,SIGNED................ 95.00
AURENE,PLATE,RAINBOW IRIDESCENCE,RUFFLED,STRETCHED,SIGNED... 65.00
AURENE,ROSE BOWL,GOLD IRIDESCENT,RUFFLED.................. 45.00
AURENE,SALT DIP,GOLD IRIDESCENCE WITH PINK & BLUE HIGHLIGHTS,SIGNED...................................... 45.00
AURENE,SHADE,GOLD,IRIDESCENCE,MARKED FLEUR DE LIS,PAIR...... 60.00
AURENE,SHADE,GOLD,RIBBED.................................. 20.00
AURENE,SHADE,GOLD,RIBBED.................................. 18.00
AURENE,SHERBET & PLATE,GOLD CALCITE....................... 105.00
AURENE,SHERBERT & UNDERPLATE,STEMMED,GOLD WITH CALCITE...... 125.00
AURENE,TUMBLER,GOLD....................................... 45.00
AURENE,VASE,BLUE,BULBOUS,4 IN. HIGH,SIGNED................ 375.00
AURENE,VASE,BLUE WITH MIRROR BOTTOM,RUFFLED TOP........... 350.00
AURENE,VASE,GOLD,4 BLUE DIMPLES IN BASE,STRETCHED TOP,4 IN.. 95.00
AURENE,VASE,GOLD,BLUE HIGHLIGHTS,RUSTIC,3 PRONG,SIGNED...... 225.00
AURENE,VASE,GOLD IRIDESCENCE,CLASSIC,APPLIED HANDLES & BASE,11 IN. HIGH....................................... 125.00
AURENE,VASE,GOLD IRIDESCENT,BLUE HIGHLIGHTS,CLASSIC SHAPED,SIGNED.. 145.00
AURENE,VASE,GOLD,SIGNED................................... 275.00
AURENE,VASE,GOLD WITH SILVERY GREEN-BLUE HIGHLIGHTS,SIGNED.. 225.00
AURENE,VASE,PINCH... 50.00

AURENE,WATER GOBLET,GOLD,TWISTED STEM,SIGNED.................. 165.00
AUSTRIA MARKED VASE,BROWN & GOLD TRIM,BUST OF WOMAN.......... 12.00
AUSTRIA PLATTER,CRABAPPLE DECOR............................. 9.50
AUSTRIAN CHINA CANDLE HOLDER,BLUE & WHITE,HANDPAINTED........ 4.50
AUSTRIAN CHOCOLATE POT,6 IN.,TWIG HANDLE,BLUE & WHITE,GOLD
FLOWER.. 9.50

AUTO PARTS and accessories are collectors' items today.

AUTO,1950 HUDSON 4-DOOR..................................... 225.00
AUTO,BEVELED GLASS REAR VIEW MIRROR FOR 1915 FORD........... 12.50
AUTO,BOYCE MOTOR METER...................................... 10.00
AUTO BRASS TIRE PUMP HAS FORD NAME.......................... 7.50
AUTO,DODGE RAM RADIATOR CAP................................. 7.00
AUTO,ESSEX RADIATOR & MOTORMETER............................ 75.00
AUTO,FORD SCRIPT WRENCH..................................... .50
AUTO,FRANKLIN LION RADIATOR CAP............................. 15.00
AUTO,GREEN GLASS FLOWER VASE WITH HANGER,ETCHED FLORAL...... 9.50
AUTO HEADLIGHTS MODEL T PAIR................................ 25.00
AUTO,HUB CAP FROM FRANKLIN.................................. 4.00
AUTO,KLAXTON HORN MARKED WARNING HORN,MODEL 114A,STEWART &
WARNER.. 20.00
AUTO,KLAXTON PUSH HORN T MODEL.............................. 27.50
AUTO,LAMP WITH HANDLE....................................... 39.50
AUTO,LUGGAGE RACK,RUNNING BOARD TYPE........................ 5.00
AUTO,MARBLE GEAR SHIFT KNOB................................. 7.50
AUTO,MODEL T HEADLIGHTS ,2.................................. 25.00
AUTO,MODEL T JACK... 12.50
AUTO,MODEL T SPARK PLUG & HEAD WRENCH....................... 2.50
AUTO,MODEL T SPARK PLUG WRENCH.............................. 2.50
AUTO,MODEL T STEERING WHEEL................................. 7.50
AUTO,PAIR 12 IN. COACH LIGHTS............................... 60.00
AUTO,PENNA.PORCELAIN LICENSE PLATES,1915.................... 7.00
AUTO,PRE 1931 OVERLAND HEADLIGHT LENS....................... 2.00
AUTO,REAR VIEW MIRROR FOR 1915 FORD......................... 12.50
AUTO,RUNNINGBOARD LUGGAGE CARRIER
3.00 TO... 8.00
AUTO,RUNNING BOARD TIRE PUMP................................ 4.00
AUTO,SPARTON A HORN... 27.50
AUTO,STUDEBAKER HEADLAMPS................................... 20.00
AUTO VASE,TERRE-COTTA,WHITE KITTEN & BIRD.IMPRESSED CHINA... 25.00

BABY CARRIAGE,VICTORIAN,WICKER,SHELL DESIGN WITH PARASOL.... 75.00

*BACCARAT GLASS was made in France by Le Compagnie des Cristalleries de
Baccarat located about 150 miles from Paris. The factory was started in 1765.
The firm went bankrupt and began operating again about 1822. Famous cane
and millefiori paperweights were made there during the 1860–1880 period. The
firm is still working near Paris making paperweights and glasswares.*

BACCARAT,ATOMIZER TOP & SQUEEZE BULB,PEWTER TOP,AMBERINA.... 26.00
BACCARAT,BOWL,AMBER LACE EDGE............................... 10.00
BACCARAT,BOX,GREEN & RED WITH GOLD,STERLING LID,CUT,SIGNED.. 165.00
BACCARAT,CANDLESTICK,12 IN. HIGH,BRASS TOPS,PAIR........... 50.00
BACCARAT,CANDLESTICKS,DIAMOND-POINT,MARKED,PAIR............. 45.00
BACCARAT,CARAFE WITH TUMBLE-UP,AMBERINA,FRENCH,SIGNED....... 40.00
BACCARAT,CHAMPAGNE,FINE CUT DIAMOND BODY,GOLD LEAF TRIMMED,8 120.00
BACCARAT,COGNAC BOTTLE,APPLIED FLEUR DE LIS
MEDALLIONS,SIGNED... 15.00
BACCARAT,COLOGNE BOTTLE,6 IN. TALL,RUBINA SWIRLED........... 17.50
BACCARAT,COLOGNE BOTTLE,SWIRL RUBINA........................ 25.00
BACCARAT,COLOGNE BOTTLES,CLEAR TO ORANGE RED,SWIRLED,PAIR... 35.00
BACCARAT,COLOGNE,ST.LOUIS,CRANBERRY & GOLD CAMEO FLORALS.... 125.00
BACCARAT,COMPOTE,GREEN,SWIRLED.............................. 15.00
BACCARAT,COMPOTE WITH PLATE,AMBERINA SWIRLED,FOOTED &
COVERED,SIGNED.. 110.00
BACCARAT,DECANTER,CLEAR GLASS,APPLIED PUNTS OF FLEUR DE LIS. 35.00

BACCARAT,DECANTER,PEACH COLOURED,FLAME STOPPER............... 25.00
BACCARAT,DECANTER,WINE,CLEAR SWIRLED RIB,OBLONG TRAY........ 21.00
BACCARAT,DISH,LOW,FOOTED,AMBERINA.......................... 28.00
BACCARAT,DRESSER SET,SWIRLED CRANBERRY,6 PIECES............. 140.00
BACCARAT,FINGER BOWL,RUBINA SWIRL,SIGNED................... 15.00
BACCARAT,GOBLET,GOLD ENCRUSTED,FRENCH TASSLE,REVERSIBLE
  STEMS.. 12.50
BACCARAT,INKWELL,SWIRL..................................... 33.00
BACCARAT LAMP,BRASS BASE,BANQUET,FILIGREE FONT,BALL
  SHADE,SIGNED... 125.00
BACCARAT,KNIFE RESTS,DUMB-BELL,SIGNED,PAIR................. 18.50
BACCARAT,PAPERWEIGHT,CANDY CANES,SIGNED................... 35.00
BACCARAT,PAPERWEIGHT,RED BACKGROUND,POPE PIUS.............. 97.00
BACCARAT,PAPERWEIGHT,RED,WHITE & BLUE ARROW CANES,4
  CONCENTRIC CIRCLES...................................... 130.00
BACCARAT,PAPERWEIGHT,SULPHIDE,TEDDY ROOSEVELT.............. 100.00
BACCARAT,PAPERWEIGHT,ZODIAC................................ 39.50
BACCARAT,PERFUME BOTTLE,CRANBERRY TO CRYSTAL SWIRL......... 28.00
BACCARAT,PERFUME BOTTLE,IN SWIRLED RUBINA GLASS........... 17.50
BACCARAT,PERFUME BOTTLE,PLAIN WITH STOPPER,SIGNED,PAIR..... 12.00
BACCARAT,PLATE,7 IN.,AMBERINA SWIRL,SIGNED................. 20.00
BACCARAT,PLATE,7 IN.,SIGNED............................... 40.00
BACCARAT,PLATE,LACY GLASS,SIGNED.......................... 15.00
BACCARAT,RING TREE,3 IN. CENTER POST,ROSE AMBER SWIRLED
  PATTERN,SIGNED.. 18.00
BACCARAT,TRAY IN SWIRLED RUBINA GLASS,SIGNED.............. 17.50
BACCARAT,TUMBLER,AMBERINA,SIGNED.......................... 15.00
BACCARAT,TUMBLER,CLEAR SWIRL AMBER DAISIES................ 12.50
BACCARAT,TUMBLER,FOOTED................................... 50.00
BACCARAT,TUMBLER,LACY,FOOTED,CIRCA 1840.................. 600.00
BACCARAT,TUMBLER,LACY,MINIATURE,CIRCA 1840,FOOTED......... 55.00
BACCARAT,URN,ENAMELED GOLD BIRD,FLOWERS IN SATIN,2
  HANDLED,SIGNED.. 65.00
BACCARAT,VASE,10 IN. HIGH,BLUE GOLD CRANES,PAPER MARK,PAIR.. 80.00
BACCARAT,VASE,GREEN TRIPLE HANDLED,HANDLES APPLIED & TWISTED 30.00
BACCARAT,WINE BOTTLE,CRYSTAL,GREEN TO CLEAR,FLOWERS & LEAVES
  IN GOLD... 85.00
BADGE,DEPUTY-INSPECTOR OF OILS,OHIO STATE.................. 16.00
    BANK, SEE ALSO BANK, MECHANICAL.......................
BANK,3 LITTLE PIGS TIN.................................... 2.50
BANK,ALWAYS DID SPISE A MULE.............................. 135.00
BANK,AMERICAN EAGLE CERAMIC,IMMIGRANTS SAVINGS BANK......... 5.00
BANK,ARMY TANK.. 8.00
BANK BARREL... 2.00
BANK,BARREL,ROCKINGHAM,STILL.............................. 9.00
BANK,BEAR,EMBOSSED TEDDY,STILL,CAST IRON.................. 25.00
BANK,BEAR,STANDING,CAST IRON.............................. 6.75
BANK,BEAR TREE.. 150.00
BANK,BEE HIVE..1,000.00
BANK,BELL,MARIGOLD.. 4.50
BANK,BILLIKEN,IRON.. 15.00
BANK,BILLIKEN,STILL,CAST IRON............................. 10.00
BANK,BOTTLE,LINCOLN....................................... 1.00
BANK,BOY,DUTCH,STILL...................................... 8.00
BANK,BOY SCOUT,6 IN. HIGH,CAST IRON....................... 14.50
BANK,BUILDING,2 STORY MARKED CITY BANK,IRON............... 24.75
BANK,BUILDING,5 IN. TALL,STILL,CAST IRON.................. 18.50
BANK,BUILDING,BANK,WITH STEPS & CUPOLA,STILL,IRON.......... 14.00
BANK,BUILDING,FIRST NATIONAL
  BANK,HAYLAND,NEBRASKA,OVAL,METAL........................ 4.00
BANK,BUILDING,GOLD TOP,IRON............................... 6.00
BANK,BUILDING,NEW YORK FLATIRON,STILL,IRON................ 10.00
BANK,BUILDING,NEW YORK TIMES,STILL,IRON................... 12.00
BANK,BUILDING,NINE STORY,STILL............................ 8.00
BANK,BUILDING,TRIANGLE SHAPED,5 IN.,STILL,CAST IRON........ 8.50

```
BANK,BUILDING,WOOLWORTH,STILL,IRON....................................   10.50
BANK,BUILDING,YELLOW & RED PAINT,STILL................................    6.50
BANK,BULLDOG,SITTING,STILL,IRON.......................................   14.50
BANK,BUST OF LINDBERGH................................................    9.50
BANK,BUST OF THOMAS JEFFERSON,STILL...................................   10.00
BANK,BUSTER BROWN & TIGE,STILL........................................   25.00
BANK,CAPTAIN KIDD CAST IRON STILL.....................................   18.00
BANK,CAR MODEL,DIE CAST...............................................    6.00
BANK,CASH REGISTER DATED 1905.........................................   11.00
BANK,CAT,BLACK,STILL,IRON.............................................   25.00
BANK,CAT ON TUB,STILL,IRON............................................   17.00
BANK,CAT SITTING,IRON.................................................   15.00
BANK,CHINA LINCOLNS CABIN.............................................    5.00
BANK,CLOCK,PATENTED 1925,GREEN METAL FINISH...........................    4.50
BANK,CLOCK,STILL,IRON.................................................   16.00
BANK,COCKER SPANIEL,STILL,CAST IRON...................................   10.00
BANK,COIN DEPOSIT,COMBINATION,........................................   15.00
BANK, COLUMBIAN.......................................................   75.00
BANK,COMICAL DOG,CAST WHITE METAL WITH KEY............................    4.50
BANK,DEER WITH ANTLERS,STILL..........................................    9.50
BANK, DIME REGISTERING BUSHEL BASKET DATED 1902.......................   12.50
BANK,DOLL EMERGING FROM EGG...........................................   85.00
BANK,DOVETAILED,WALNUT HANDMADE.......................................   16.50
BANK,DUCK IRON STILL..................................................   14.50
BANK,EAGLE & EAGLETS MECHANICAL DATED 1883............................  125.00
BANK,ELEPHANT.........................................................   12.50
BANK,ELEPHANT BOTTLE..................................................    4.25
BANK,ELEPHANT,GREY PAINT,RED & GOLD,STILL,IRON........................    9.00
BANK,ELEPHANT MECHANICAL..............................................    4.00
BANK,ELEPHANT,RED PAINT,CAST IRON.....................................    8.50
BANK,ELEPHANT SEMI-MECHANICAL,MARKED SECURITY-BANK....................   10.50
BANK,ELEPHANT STANDING,NICKEL PLATED,STILL,IRON.......................   16.00
BANK,ELEPHANT WITH HOWDAH,IRON........................................   17.50
BANK,ELEPHANT WITH LOWERED TRUNK & HOWDAH,STILL,CAST IRON.............   14.00
BANK,ELEPHANT WITH SEAT,5 IN. LONG....................................    5.50
BANK,ELEPHANT WITH SEAT & FANCY TRAPPINGS,CAST IRON...................   10.50
BANK,ELK,STILL........................................................   28.00
BANK,EMBOSSED DATED 1879,STILK,CAST IRON..............................   12.50
BANK,GILT PRANCING HORSE..............................................   15.00
BANK,HAPPY DAYS TIN BARREL............................................    3.00
BANK,HAT,PASS AROUND THE HAT,CAST IRON................................    7.50
BANK,HAT,STOVEPIPE,PASS AROUND THE HAT,STILL,IRON.....................   16.00
BANK,HORSE,BLACK BEAUTY,STILL,IRON....................................   15.00
BANK,HORSE,IRON.......................................................    1.00
BANK,HORSE PRANCING,STILL,IRON........................................   12.50
BANK,HORSE REARING ON PEDESTAL BASE,STILL,CAST IRON...................   18.00
BANK,HORSESHOE,STILL,IRON.............................................   14.00
BANK,HOUSE,IRON.......................................................    4.00
BANK,IDEAL COMBINATION SAFE...........................................   13.50
BANK,I.O.O.F. MATCH SAFE,PAT.1/12/04..................................    4.50
BANK,INDIAN CHIEF STILL,GOOD PAINT....................................    7.50
BANK,IRON,WHITE CAST SETTING..........................................   15.00
BANK,JACKASS PENNY,WHITE METAL........................................   15.00
BANK,JOLLY NEGRO CAST IRON............................................   45.00
BANK,JOLLY NEGRO MECHANICAL...........................................   50.00
BANK,JOLLY NIGGER.....................................................   55.00
BANK,JOLLY NIGGER,ENGLAND 1892........................................   37.50
BANK,JOLLY NIGGER MECHANICAL,NEGRO BUST...............................   55.00
BANK,JOLLY NIGGER MECHANICAL PAT.1882.................................   65.00
BANK, JUMBO...........................................................  215.00
BANK,KITTEN SITTING,STILL,IRON........................................    6.00
BANK,LIBERTY BELL,CLEAR GLASS.........................................    1.50
BANK,LIBERTY BELL IRON................................................   10.00
BANK,LINCOLN BOTTLE
   2.00  TO...........................................................    8.00
```

```
BANK,LION,CAST IRON.........................................    8.50
BANK,LION ON ALL FOURS,GOLD,STILL,CAST IRON.................   14.00
BANK,LION,STANDING,CAST IRON................................   12.00
BANK,LION,STANDING,STILL,IRON,3 IN. HIGH....................    8.50
BANK,LION,STILL,CAST IRON...................................   10.00
BANK,LOG CABIN IRON.........................................   17.50
BANK, MAGIC MAN.........................................2,000.00
BANK,MAIL BOX,U.S.,STILL,.....................................    6.50
BANK,  MAINE................................................   60.00
BANK,MAMMY,COMPOSITION TRAP.................................  100.00
BANK,MECHANICAL 4 COIN RECORDING KINGSBURY..................   25.00
BANK,MECHANICAL,BOYS STEALING WATERMELONS...................  125.00
BANK,MECHANICAL,EAGLE FEEDING EAGLETS.......................  100.00
BANK,MECHANICAL ELEPHANT....................................   40.00
BANK,MECHANICAL GLOBE ON STAND..............................   35.00
BANK,MECHANICAL IRON DONKEY IN STABLE.......................   85.00
BANK,MECHANICAL,NOVELTY,PAINTED,FIGURE,.....................   75.00
BANK,MECHANICAL SITTING PIG.................................    9.00
BANK,MECHANICAL TAMMANY.....................................   45.00
BANK,MECHANICAL ,TAMMANY BANK 1873..........................   42.50
BANK,MECHANICAL TEDDY & THE BEAR............................  150.00
BANK,MECHANICAL TRANSVAAL MONEY BOX.........................   65.00
BANK,MECHANICAL,TRICK PONY..................................  130.00
BANK, METAL CAT.............................................    8.50
BANK, METAL DOG.............................................    9.50
BANK,METAL SANTA............................................    8.00
BANK,MILK GLASS LIBERTY BELL................................   35.00
BANK,MULE,IRON..............................................   15.00
BANK,MUTT & JEFF,IRON
  15.00  TO.................................................   30.00
BANK,NASHS JOLLY JOE GLASS,TIN TOP..........................    4.00
BANK,NEGRO ALUMINUM.........................................   55.00
BANK,NEGRO MAMMY STILL IRON.................................   16.00
BANK,ORGAN,CAT,DOG & MONKEY.................................   90.00
BANK,ORGAN GRINDER..........................................   95.00
BANK,OWL,7 IN. FIGURE OF ROOSTING OWL,SIGNED ROYAL RUBY,....   25.00
BANK,OWL ON STUMP,BE WISE,SAVE MONEY,IRON...................   11.75
BANK,PATRONIZE THE BLIND MAN................................  700.00
BANK,PAY PHONE..............................................  150.00
BANK,PENNY,CAST IRON LION...................................    9.00
BANK,PENNY,C.I.BLACK BEAUTY HORSE...........................   10.00
BANK,PENNY,ELEPHANT WITH A HOWDAH...........................    7.50
BANK,PENNY,PRANCING HORSE...................................    8.50
BANK, PENNY, TINY ELEPHANT WITH A HOWDAH....................   12.50
BANK,PIG....................................................   13.50
BANK,PIG,MARIGOLD...........................................    4.50
BANK,PIG,SITTING,IRON.......................................    8.75
BANK,PIGGY,ORANGE CARNIVAL..................................    5.00
BANK,PINK PIG IN GREEN SUITCASE.............................    8.50
BANK,PONY,5 IN.,IRON........................................   12.50
BANK,PORCELAIN MONKEY,12 FIGURES............................   75.00
BANK,PRANCING HORSE STILL...................................   12.00
BANK,PRESSED STEEL POSTAL SAVINGS PAT.1902,ORIGINAL GLASS &
  PAPER....................................................   28.00
BANK,PUP,FLOP-EARED, BROWN & WHITE,STILL,CAST IRON..........   60.00
BANK,RABBIT SITTING,STILL,IRON..............................   12.50
BANK,RABBIT STANDING........................................  150.00
BANK,RADIO,IRON.............................................   17.50
BANK,REFRIGERATOR,ELECTROLUX,WHITE,4 IN. HIGH,IRON..........    3.75
BANK,REGISTER,UNCLE SAMS DIME,STILL.........................    3.00
BANK,ROOSTER STILL,SILVER WITH RED..........................   12.00
BANK,ROUND BUICK FIREBALL...................................    1.50
BANK,ROYAL SAFE DEPOSIT,IRON................................    7.75
BANK,SAFE,CAST IRON.........................................    6.00
BANK,SAFE,FILIGREE IRON 1897................................    8.00
```

BANK,SAFE,IRON,COMBINATION LOCK,MARKED KENTON BRAND PAT. 1911	7.95
BANK,SAFE,MARKED,STILL	8.00
BANK,SAFE WITH COMBINATION LOCK,CAST IRON	12.50
BANK,SAFE WITH COMBINATION LOCK,IDEAL SAFE DEPOSIT,CAST IRON	9.50
BANK,SETTING ELEPHANT,DATE 1930,CAST WHITE METAL DULL PINK	4.50
BANK,SHELL	15.00
BANK,SITTING ELEPHANT PENNY,5 IN. HIGH CAST WHITE METAL DATED 1936	4.50
BANK,SITTING PIG	15.00
BANK,SITTING PIG,IRON	5.00
BANK,SLIPWARE PIG	17.50
BANK,SOUTHERN COMFORT MECHANICAL,CONFEDERATE SHOOTS PENNY INTO BOTTLE	18.00
BANK,SPEAKING DOG	100.00
BANK,SQUARE COMBINATION SAFE,MARKED STAR SAFE	12.50
BANK,SQUARE,MARKED,CAST IRON	15.00
BANK,STANDING LION,CAST IRON	12.00
BANK,STATUE OF LIBERTY,STILL,IRON	14.00
BANK,STEAMBOAT ON 2 WHEELS,STILL,IRON	30.00
BANK,ST.BERNARD DOG,CAST IRON	10.75
BANK,STEEL,SHAPE OF BOOK,REPLICA ON NEW YORK LIFE INS.BLDG	4.50
BANK,STEEPLE	5.00
BANK,STOLLWERK	250.00
BANK,STUMP SPEAKER	150.00
BANK,TAMMANY MECHANICAL	50.00
BANK,TAMMANY PENNY	55.00
BANK,TAN BULLDOG,BUMBLEBEE	16.50
BANK,THREE MONKEYS TOOTHPICK,STILL,SOAPSTONE	4.50
BANK,TIN GLOBE	3.50
BANK,TIN NATIONAL	2.50
BANK,TREASURE SAFE,J & E STEVENS 1897	22.50
BANK,UNCLE SAM CASH REGISTER,TIN	6.00
BANK,UNCLE SAM PENNY,PAINT,KEY	105.00
BANK,UNCLE SAMS BANK	20.00
BANK,UNCLE TOM ORIGINAL MECHANICAL	100.00
BANK,U.S.MAIL	7.50
BANK,U S TANK	10.00
BANK,WOOLWORTH BUILDING,CAST IRON	12.00

BARBED WIRE is collected and displayed in 18-inch pieces. The value is determined by the rarity of the type of wire, the earliest dating from about 1867.

BARBED WIRE,RIBBON TYPE,SAWTOOTH,21 IN. PIECE	1.00
BAROMETER & THERMOMETER IN CARVED CASE	30.00
BAROMETER CIRCA 1820,BURLED WALNUT CASE	95.00
BAROMETER,ENGLISH,ANEROID,33 IN. TALL,OAK	35.00

BASALT is a black stoneware made by mixing iron and oxides into a basic clay. It was very hard and could be finished on a lathe. Wedgwood developed his famous black basalt in 1769, which was an improvement on a similar ware made in Staffordshire, England, as early as 1740. Basalt is still being made in England and on the Continent.

BASALT BLACK FIGURINE,WOMAN,SPRING,11 IN. TALL,IMPRESSED WEDGWOOD	300.00
BASALT BLACK TEAPOT ,SQUATTY	10.00
BASALT SQUATTY CREAMER,BASKETWEAVE PATTERN	22.00
BASALT TEA POT	38.50

BATTERSEA ENAMELS are enamels painted on copper and made in the Battersea district of London from about 1750 to 1756. Many similar enamels are mistakenly called Battersea.

BATTERSEA BOX,PRIZE FIGHTERS ON PINK ENAMEL	165.00
BATTERSEA CARD DISH CIRCA 1770	325.00
BATERSEA ENAMEL OVAL BOX,HANDPAINTED WOMAN HOLDING BIRDCAGE.	120.00
BATTERSEA TYPE ENAMELED BOX,FLORAL DECOR	22.50

BAVARIA was a district where many types of pottery and porcelain were made for centuries. The word "Bavaria" appears on many pieces of nineteenth-century china, the words "Bavaria, Germany" appeared after 1871.

BAVARIAN, SEE ALSO PORCELAIN............................	
BAVARIAN 4 PIECE DRESSER TRAY,YELLOW FLOWERS,GREEN LEAVES...	35.00
BAVARIAN 7 IN. BLUE & GOLD DISH WITH LADY HOLDING VASE OF FLOWERS...	4.00
BAVARIAN 11 IN. PLATE SIGNED PIERRE,HANDPAINTED ROSES.......	15.00
BAVARIAN ALHAMBRA 9 IN. PLATE..............................	12.50
BAVARIAN BOUQUET GOBLET....................................	7.50
BAVARIAN CHINA FRUIT SET,8 IN. COMPOTE,6 PLATES,GOLD TRIMMED	65.00
BAVARIAN CHINA GREEN GREEK KEY 6 IN. PLATE,12..............	10.00
BAVARIAN CHINA HANDPAINTED LUNCHEON SET,WHITE,BLUE WITH GOLD	38.00
BAVARIAN CHOCOLATE POT.....................................	7.50
BAVARIAN CHOCOLATE SET,ROSE DESIGN,HANDPAINTED,............	100.00
BAVARIAN CHOCOLATE SET,YELLOW WITH BLUE BANDS..............	45.00
BAVARIAN CREAMER & COVERED SUGAR,GOLD HANDLES & FINIAL......	18.00
BAVARIAN CREAMER & COVERED SUGAR,GOLD HANDLES & RAISED SCROLL..	16.00
BAVARIAN CUP & SAUCER,BLUE & AMBER.........................	4.00
BAVARIAN CUP & SAUCER,RANSOM PATTERN.......................	4.00
BAVARIAN DESSERT PLATE,6 IN.,HANDPAINTED...................	3.50
BAVARIAN DRESSER SET,SIGNED,BLUE,GOLD INITIAL..............	15.00
BAVARIAN DRESSER TRAY,PINK FLOWERED........................	7.50
BAVARIAN FLORAL SHAVING MUG................................	5.25
BAVARIAN GAME PLATE,GERMANY,MALE PHEASANT & BROWN HEN.......	10.00
BAVARIAN GAME PLATE,GOLD RIM,PIERCED FOR HANGING...........	12.00
BAVARIAN HANDPAINTED CHINA BASKET,VIOLET DECOR,GOLD HANDLE..	7.50
BAVARIAN HANDPAINTED FLOWER BASKET.........................	4.00
BAVARIAN HANDPAINTED HUMIDOR WITH PIPE ON COVER............	25.00
BAVARIAN HANDPAINTED PLATE,9 IN............................	5.00
BAVARIAN HANDPAINTED ROUND 13 IN. PLATTER MARKED,MULTI COLOUR ROSE..	18.50
BAVARIAN HANGING GAME PLATE,BIRD IN CENTER,4 BIRDS ON BORDER	10.00
BAVARIAN HATPIN HOLDER 10.00 TO..	20.00
BAVARIAN MARKED 8 IN. CHINA BOWL,ROSES PATTERN.............	4.75
BAVARIAN MARKED 8 IN. OPEN HANDLED BREAD PLATE,GIVE US THIS DAY...	8.00
BAVARIAN MARKED PEERLESS MARLBORO ARCHER ON HORSE PLATE,6...	25.00
BAVARIAN PANCAKE DISH,GOLD DETAIL,LAVENDER ROSES,HANDPAINTED	9.50
BAVARIAN PICARD ARTIST SIGNED PLATE,GOLD TRIM,POPPIES ON GROUND..	12.50
BAVARIAN PICARD PLATE,POPPIES ,SCALLOPED GOLD TRIM,SIGNED ARTIST..	12.50
BAVARIAN PIERCED PLATE,BROWN,HORSE HEAD....................	12.75
BAVARIAN PLACE SETTING FOR EIGHT,GOLD TRIM.................	140.00
BAVARIAN PLATE,CAKE,LAVENDER GENTIANS,OPEN HANDLED.........	38.50
BAVARIAN PLATE HANDPAINTED ROSES WITH GOLD GEOMETRIC RIM,SIGNED...	4.00
BAVARIAN PORCELAIN VASE SIGNED TUNHILL,BUTTERFLIES ON BLUE..	9.00
BAVARIAN ROSE BOWL,SCALLOPED EDGE,ALTERNATE GREEN & YELLOW..	18.00
BAVARIAN ROYAL MUNICH CHINA 10 IN. GAME PLAQUE,DUCKS........	68.50
BAVARIAN SET OF 6 7 IN. PLATES,ASTERS & GOLD...............	12.50
BAVARIAN SIGNED & DATED TEAPOT,YELLOW,PINK FLOWERS,GREEN LEAVES,GOLD..	6.00
BAVARIAN SIGNED A.KOCH,CLOSED-HANDLED CAKE PLATE,MARKED J & C LOUISE..	19.00
BAVARIAN SIGNED RENE HANDPAINTED PLATE,,ROSES & GREEN LEAVES,GOLD BAND..	15.00
BAVARIAN SILVER RESIST ON BLUE CUP & SAUCER................	8.00
BAVARIAN TEAPOT,4 CUPS & SAUCERS,R/C MALMAISON.............	32.50
BAVARIAN TRAY,EMBOSSED SCROLLS & ENAMELED GREEN & WHITE.....	12.50
BAVARIAN TRAY,RAISED ENAMELS,PINK ROSES,BLUE BACKGROUND,GOLD HANDLES..	8.00

```
BAVARIAN WHITE LUSTRE 3 IN. SALT & PEPPER SET,GOLD ON TOP...    4.00
BAYONET & SCABBARD,BRITISH,MARK IV.............................    1.75
BAYONETS,WOODEN GRIPS,22 IN. OVERALL,DATED 1907..............    1.25
```

BEAM BOTTLES are made to hold Kentucky Straight Bourbon made by the James B. Beam Distilling Company. The Beam series of ceramic bottles began in 1953.

```
BEAM BOTTLE,1955 DUCKS & GEESE................................   10.00
BEAM BOTTLE,1955 WHITE ASHTRAY
  29.50  TO....................................................   70.00
BEAM BOTTLE,1956 DONKEY.......................................   12.50
BEAM BOTTLE,1960 DONKEY.......................................   15.00
BEAM BOTTLE,1960 ELEPHANT.....................................   15.00
BEAM BOTTLE,1960 FOX..........................................   15.00
BEAM BOTTLE,1960 POLITICAL DONKEY.............................    6.50
BEAM BOTTLE,1960 POLITICAL ELEPHANT...........................    6.50
BEAM BOTTLE,1960 REPUBLICAN...................................   15.00
BEAM BOTTLE,1961 GRECIAN......................................   10.00
BEAM BOTTLE,1961 PHEASANT.....................................   12.50
BEAM BOTTLE,1963 EXECUTIVE....................................   32.00
BEAM BOTTLE,1963 ROYAL ROSE...................................   40.00
BEAM BOTTLE,1964 BICENTENNIAL.................................   13.00
BEAM BOTTLE,1964 DONKEY.......................................   12.50
BEAM BOTTLE 1964 ELEPHANT.....................................   12.50
BEAM BOTTLE,1964 EXECUTIVE....................................   20.00
BEAM BOTTLE,1964 FAIR.........................................   15.00
BEAM BOTTLE,1964 MUSICIANS....................................   10.00
BEAM BOTTLE 1964 OHIO.........................................   12.50
BEAM BOTTLE,1964 WORLDS FAIR..................................   14.50
BEAM BOTTLE,1965 WORLDS FAIR..................................    8.75
BEAM BOTTLE,1965 ZIMMERMAN GREEN 2 HANDLED JUG................   70.00
BEAM BOTTLE,1966 EXECUTIVE....................................   20.00
BEAM BOTTLE,1966 ZIMMERMAN GRAY OATMEAL JUG...................   60.00
BEAM BOTTLE,1967 EXECUTIVE IN PRESENTATION BOX,..............   24.50
BEAM BOTTLE,1967 GOLD PORTRAIT................................    4.00
BEAM BOTTLE,1967 GREEN EXECUTIVE..............................    2.00
BEAM BOTTLE,1967 HAWAII.......................................   50.00
BEAM BOTTLE,1967 ZIMMERMAN,BLUE...............................   12.50
BEAM BOTTLE,ALASKA............................................    9.25
BEAM BOTTLE,ALASKA PURCHASE...................................   10.50
BEAM BOTTLE,ALASKA PURCHASE CENTENNIAL........................    8.75
BEAM BOTTLE,ANTIOCH...........................................   22.75
BEAM BOTTLE,ANTIOCH INDIAN HEAD...............................   25.00
BEAM BOTTLE,ANTIOCH JUBILEE...................................   75.00
BEAM BOTTLE,ARTIST............................................    5.00
BEAM BOTTLE,BLACK CANASTA.....................................   49.50
BEAM BOTTLE,BLACK CAT.........................................    9.25
BEAM BOTTLE,BLACK HORSE.......................................   22.00
BEAM BOTTLE,BLACK RAVEN.......................................   25.00
BEAM BOTTLE,BLUE BOY..........................................   10.00
BEAM BOTTLE,BLUE MAJESTIC,1966................................   30.00
BEAM BOTTLE,BLUE SAILBOAT.....................................   10.00
BEAM BOTTLE,BLUE SHEPHERD.....................................    4.00
BEAM BOTTLE,BROWN CAT.........................................   15.00
BEAM BOTTLE, CAMEO............................................    3.00
BEAM BOTTLE,CAMEO BLUE........................................    6.50
BEAM BOTTLE,CAT...............................................    9.00
BEAM BOTTLE,CATS..............................................   10.50
BEAM BOTTLE,CHEYENNE..........................................   10.00
BEAM BOTTLE,CHEYENNE CENTENNIAL...............................    8.00
BEAM BOTTLE,CHEYENNE RODEO....................................   20.00
BEAM BOTTLE,CIVIL WAR.........................................   27.50
BEAM BOTTLE,CIVIL WAR NORTH...................................   40.00
BEAM BOTTLE,CIVIL WAR SOUTH...................................   40.00
BEAM BOTTLE,CLEOPATRA.........................................    4.00
BEAM BOTTLE,CLEOPATRA RUST....................................    5.00
```

```
BEAM BOTTLE,COFFEE SERVER,GOLD HANDLE.........................   5.00
BEAM BOTTLE,COFFEE WARMER.....................................   4.75
BEAM BOTTLE,COLORADO..........................................  20.00
BEAM BOTTLE,DANCING SCOTS.....................................  12.00
BEAM BOTTLE,DEER..............................................  22.50
BEAM BOTTLE,DELFT BLUE........................................   4.00
BEAM BOTTLE,DOE...............................................  30.00
BEAM BOTTLE,DOG...............................................  75.00
BEAM BOTTLE,DOMESTIC..........................................   5.00
BEAM BOTTLE,DONKEY............................................   8.00
BEAM BOTTLE, DUCK.............................................  15.00
BEAM BOTTLE,EAGLE.............................................  10.50
BEAM BOTTLE,ELEPHANT..........................................   8.00
BEAM BOTTLE,GREEN JUG.........................................   4.00
BEAM BOTTLE,GREY CAT..........................................  10.50
BEAM BOTTLE,GREY HORSE........................................  20.00
BEAM BOTTLE,GREY NEW JERSEY...................................  20.00
BEAM BOTTLE,FISH..............................................  45.00
BEAM BOTTLE,FLOWER BASKET EXECUTIVE...........................  45.00
BEAM BOTTLE,FOX...............................................  20.00
BEAM BOTTLE, EMPEROR..........................................   7.50
BEAM BOTTLE, GENIE............................................   3.00
BEAM BOTTLE,GRAY CASK.........................................  12.50
BEAM BOTTLE,GRECIAN...........................................   4.00
BEAM BOTTLE,GREEN & GOLD DUELING PISTOLS,PAIR.................   7.50
BEAM BOTTLE,GREEN PUSSY WILLOW................................  10.00
BEAM BOTTLE,GREEN SPECKLED....................................   8.00
BEAM BOTTLE, GREEN XMAS.......................................   3.00
BEAM BOTTLE,HAROLDS CLUB......................................  20.00
BEAM BOTTLE,HAROLDS CLUB SLOT MACHINE.........................  35.00
BEAM BOTTLE,HAROLDS PINWHEEL..................................  50.00
BEAM BOTTLE,HORSE.............................................  10.00
BEAM BOTTLE,HORSES............................................   8.00
BEAM BOTTLE,JEANNIE...........................................   5.00
BEAM BOTTLE,KANSAS............................................  45.00
BEAM BOTTLE,KATZ CAT..........................................  40.00
BEAM BOTTLE,KATZ
  40.00  TO...................................................  50.00
BEAM BOTTLE,KATZ DRUG STORE CAT...............................  45.00
BEAM BOTTLE,KENTUCKY..........................................   8.95
BEAM BOTTLE,KEYSTONE..........................................  11.50
BEAM BOTTLE,KITTEN............................................   8.95
BEAM BOTTLE,LAUGHING CAVALIER.................................   5.00
BEAM BOTTLE,MAJESTIC..........................................  25.00
BEAM BOTTLE,MARBLE FANTASY....................................  30.00
BEAM BOTTLE,MARINA CITY.......................................  20.00
BEAM BOTTLE,MARK ANTHONY...................................... 125.00
BEAM BOTTLE,MASTER............................................   4.00
BEAM BOTTLE,MASTERPIECE IN GREEN LEATHERETTE CABINET,,22K
  GOLD.......................................................  24.00
BEAM BOTTLE,MINIATURE,LABEL...................................   3.00
BEAM BOTTLE,MONTANA...........................................  30.00
BEAM BOTTLE,MUSICIANS ON BARREL...............................   8.00
BEAM BOTTLE,MUSICIANS ON WINE CASK............................  10.00
BEAM BOTTLE,NEBRASKA..........................................   8.75
BEAM BOTTLE,NEBRASKA CENTENNIAL...............................  20.00
BEAM BOTTLE, NEVADA...........................................  15.00
BEAM BOTTLE,NEW JERSEY........................................  16.00
BEAM BOTTLE,NEW JERSEY,YELLOW.................................  13.50
BEAM BOTTLE,NEW YORK..........................................  22.50
BEAM BOTTLE,NEW YORK FAIR.....................................  12.00
BEAM BOTTLE,NORTH DAKOTA......................................  25.00
BEAM BOTTLE,OHIO..............................................   8.75
BEAM BOTTLE,OLD MASTERS.......................................   5.00
BEAM BOTTLE,OLYMPIAN..........................................   7.50
```

BEAM BOTTLE,ON THE TERRACE	10.00
BEAM BOTTLE,OREGON	20.00
BEAM BOTTLE,PENNSYLVANIA	15.00
BEAM BOTTLE,PENNSYLVANIA PHEASANT	15.00
BEAM BOTTLE,PHEASANT	20.00
BEAM BOTTLE,PHEASANTS	12.50
BEAM BOTTLE,PINBALL	3.75
BEAM BOTTLE,PIN BALL 56-61	4.00
BRIDES BASKET,PINK APPLIED HANDLE,3 IN. TALL	25.00
BEAM BOTTLE,PINK SPECKLED	200.00
BEAM BOTTLE,PINWHEEL	20.00
BEAM BOTTLE,POLITICIANS	27.50
BEAM BOTTLE,PUSSY CAT	9.00
BEAM BOTTLE,PUSSYWILLOW	5.00
BEAM BOTTLE,RED SAILBOAT	6.00
BEAM BOTTLE,REDWOOD	15.00
BEAM BOTTLE,ROYAL CRYSTAL	12.00
BEAM BOTTLE,ROYAL DI MONTE	65.00
BEAM BOTTLE,ROYAL OPAL	10.00
BEAM BOTTLE,ROYAL ROSE	45.00
BEAM BOTTLE,RUBY CRYSTAL	10.00
BEAM BOTTLE, SAILBOATS	3.00
BEAM BOTTLE,SANTA FE	195.00
BEAM BOTTLE,SELF-PORTRAIT CAVALIER	5.00
BEAM BOTTLE,SHEPHERD	5.00
BEAM BOTTLE,SIAMESE CAT	11.00
BEAM BOTTLE,SMOKED CRYSTAL	10.00
BEAM BOTTLE,SMOKEY CRYSTAL	5.00
BEAM BOTTLE,SPACE NEEDLE	37.50
BEAM BOTTLE,ST. LOUIS ARCH	9.50
BEAM BOTTLE,THE DOE	22.00
BEAM BOTTLE,THE EAGLE	12.50
BEAM BOTTLE,THE FOX	17.00
BEAM BOTTLE,TROPHY CATS	7.75
BEAM BOTTLE,TURQUOISE URN	8.50
BEAM BOTTLE,VAN GOGH	6.00
BEAM BOTTLE WHITE CAT	9.25
BEAM BOTTLE,WHITE HORSE	9.25
BEAM BOTTLE, W. VIRGINIA	25.00
BEAM BOTTLE,WYOMING	40.00
BEAM BOTTLE,YELLOW NEW JERSEY	18.00
BEAM BOTTLE,YOSEMITE	15.00
BEAM BOTTLE,ZIMMERMAN,CHINA,BLUE RAISED FLOWERS WITH WHITE	15.00

BEEHIVE, Austria, or Beehive, Vienna, china includes all the many types of decorated porcelain marked with the famous Beehive mark. The mark has been used since the eighteenth century

BEEHIVE 12 IN. BRASS CANDLESTICK,PAIR,PUSHUP	30.00
BEEHIVE MARKED COVERED URN,BLUE UNDERGLAZE,9 IN. TALL,GOLD BOAR HEADS	35.00
BEEHIVE PAIR 10 IN. PLATES,GOLD RIMS,CENTER MEDALLION	27.00
BEEHIVE PLATE,GOLD PORTRAIT,10 IN.,SIGNED WAGNER	95.00
BEEHIVE PLATE,JULIET SIGNED,9 IN.,PAIR	65.00
BEEHIVE PORTRAIT BOWL SIGNED KAUFMANN	55.00
BEEHIVE SALT & PEPPER,PAIR	18.00
BEEHIVE SIGNED NAPOLEON & JOSEPHINE PLATES,PAIR,10 IN	60.00
BEEHIVE URN,PAIR,PEDESTAL,RED,GREEN & GOLD,PORTRAIT MEDALLIONS	150.00
BEEHIVE URN,SIGNED KAUFFMANN,RED MARK	150.00
BEEHIVE VASE,12 IN.,SIGNED KAUFFMANN,AUSTRIA	60.00
BELL, SEE ALSO BRASS	
BELL,1 IN. DIAMETER,NICKEL ON 7 FT. STRAP	10.00
BELL,2 IN. BRASS SHOP BELL	6.00
BELL,2 IN. BRONZE,EMBOSSED ANIMALS & BIRDS	9.50
BELL,3 BRASS IN BRASS FRAME	15.25

```
BELL,3 IN. BRASS SCHOOL HAND..................................  10.00
BELL 3 IN. HIGH GREEN PEDESTAL FOOT FLOWER HOLDER............  45.00
BELL,4 BRASS SWEDISH ON 16 IN. STRAP........................  32.00
BELL,4 FOOT STRING OF ENGRAVED BRONZE SLEIGH,12 POLISHED
  CAST......................................................  35.00
BELL,4 HAND.................................................  15.00
BELL,4 IN. BRONZE WITH IRON CLAPPER.........................   9.50
BELL,4 LARGE BRASS SWEDISH,ON 3 X 16 IN. STRAP..............  32.00
BELL,4 ON METAL STRAP,GRADUATED.............................   6.50
BELL,5 IN. BRASS MISSION,NAMES OF DESCIPLES.................  35.00
BELL,5 IN. HIGH CAST BRASS MISSION,FILIGREE BAND OF
  LION,ANGEL................................................  35.00
BELL,5 IN. HIGH STERLING SILVER TABLE.......................   5.00
BELL,5 IN. IRON,OVAL BASE,EMBOSSED FLOWERS..................   8.25
BELL,5 IN. TALL CAST IRON & PLATED BRASS
  TAP-BELL,JEWISH-HARP SHAPE.................................  12.50
BELL,6 MOUNTED ON STRAP.....................................  18.00
BELL,7 GRADUATED BRONZE SLEIGH ON STRAP MARKED G & A........  20.00
BELLS,7 IN. FOOT STRAP OF 20 HEAVY NICKEL...................   1.00
BELL,7 IN. SCHOOL...........................................   6.00
BELL,10 GRADUATED ON FELT PADDED LEATHER STRAP..............  30.00
BELL,16 BRASS RIVETED TYPE ON LEATHER STRAP.................  24.00
BELL,20 NICKEL SLEIGH BELLS ON 7 FOOT STRAP.................  10.00
BELL,22 BRASS RIVETED TYPE ON LEATHER STRAP.................  27.50
BELL,22 GRADUATED BRASS ON LEATHER STRAP,COTTER PIN TYPE....  38.50
BELL,23 SLEIGH TIN RIVETED ON LEATHER STRAP.................  23.00
BELL,25 SLEIGH ON STRAP & BUCKLE............................  18.50
BELL,30 BRASS COTTER PIN TYPE ON LEATHER STRAP..............  45.00
BELL, 30 BRASS SLEIGHBELLS ON 7 FT. STRAP...................  18.00
BELLS, 30 ON 7 FT. STRAP....................................  15.00
BELL,30 SLEIGH NICKEL ON 7 FOOT STRAP.......................  15.00
BELL,42 BRASS SLEIGH ON 78 IN. LEATHER STRAP................  35.00
BELL,42 BRASS SLEIGH ON 84 IN. LEATHER STRAP................  35.00
BELL,42 BRASS SLEIGH ON LEATHER STRAP,80 IN. LONG...........  40.00
BELL,ART GLASS DINNER,AMBER WITH FROSTED BIRD & PINE........  24.00
BELL,BLUE PULL-UP PATTERN ON OVERLAY GLASS..................  95.00
BELL,BOHEMIAN RUBY GLASS,DEER,CASTLE........................  16.00
BELL,BRASS ,3 IN. HIGH,STANDING VICTORIAN LADY..............  10.00
BELL, BRASS ,4 SWEDISH ON LEATHER STRAP.....................  32.00
BELL,BRASS 6 IN. TALL HAND..................................   6.50
BELL,BRASS 10 IN. HIGH SCHOOL...............................  25.00
BELL,BRASS & IRON DOOR,PULL TYPE,PAT.1868...................   7.00
BELL,BRASS COW..............................................   7.50
BELL,BRASS DINNER,SEA MONSTER EMBOSSED......................   7.50
BELL,BRASS ELEPHANT,ENAMEL DECORATED........................   4.00
BELL,BRASS ELEPHANT,ENAMELLED BAND,PRONGED BASE.............   4.50
BELL,BRASS EMBOSSED WITH MALTESE CROSS & ACANTHUS LEAVES
  DATED 1878................................................  12.50
BELL,BRASS,FISH HANGS FROM CLANGER..........................  15.00
BELL,BRASS HAND.............................................   2.00
BELL,BRASS HAND,HANDLE IS 5 IN. TALL FULL-FIGURE STANDING
  CRANE.....................................................  11.00
BELL,BRASS ,HAND SCHOOL, 5 IN.DIA.,WOOD HANDLE..............  25.00
BELL,BRASS HAND SCHOOL
  5.00  TO..................................................  18.00
BELL,BRASS HAND,WOODEN HANDLE...............................  17.50
BELL,BRASS HANDBELL,WOOD GRIP...............................  12.00
BELL,BRASS HORSE WITH STRAP
  3.95  TO..................................................   4.75
BELL,BRASS,IRON HEART HANDLE................................   4.50
BELL,BRASS LADY IN EARLY COSTUME............................  12.50
BELL,BRASS LION & EAGLE EMBOSSED HANDLE,BRUSSELS BOY STATUE.  18.00
BELL,BRASS LITTLE RED RIDING HOOD...........................   9.00
BELL,BRASS MISSION,BEARING NAMES OF DISCIPLES...............  35.00
BELL,BRASS NAUGHTY LITTLE BOY SQUIRTER MARKED BRUXELLES.....  15.00
```

```
BELL,BRASS,OVAL BASE EMBOSSED FLOWERS.......................      7.25
BELL,BRASS PAIR SHAFT CHIMES,4 BELLS ON EACH,METAL STRAP....     22.50
BELL,BRASS PLANTATION......................................     35.00
BELL,BRASS SCHOOL , 6IN....................................      3.50
BELL,BRASS SCHOOL,6 IN. WOOD HANDLE........................      4.00
BELL,BRASS SCHOOL,7 IN.....................................     10.00
BELL,BRASS SCHOOL,POLISHED & BURNISHED.....................     25.00
BELL,BRASS SCHOOL WITH WOODEN HANDLE.......................     15.00
BELL,BRASS SCHOOLMASTER HAND,WOODEN HANDLE.................     12.75
BELL,BRASS SET OF 4 SWEDISH ON A STRAP.....................     32.00
BELL,BRASS SLEIGH ,40 ON STRAP.............................     25.50
BELL,BRASS SLEIGH ON 7 FOOT STRAP..........................     35.00
BELL,BRASS STORE WITH COIL SPRING..........................      6.75
BELL,BRASS TEACHERS........................................     12.50
BELL,BRASS WAGON MARKED WITH EMBOSSED LETTERS WILLIAM MC
  KENNA....................................................      9.00
BELL,BRASS WITH BLACK WOODEN HANDLE........................      8.00
BELL, BRASS WITH CAT AS HANDLE,CHESHIRE CAT WRITTEN ON FRONT     7.50
BELL,BRASS WITH HEAD OF ELDERLY WOMAN,WARRIOR ON
  HORSEBACK,MARKED.........................................     20.00
BELL,BRASS WITH NICKEL PLATE,HOTEL DESK....................     11.00
BELL,BRASS,WOODEN HANDLE...................................      7.25
BELL,BRISTOL HOLLY LEAVES & BERRIES........................     24.00
BELL BRONZE,4 IN. DIAM.TOP FOR STRAP.......................      8.50
BELL,BRONZE,17 IN. ,BUCKEYE BELL FOUNDRY,1878..............    195.00
BELL,BRONZE COUNTRY STORE..................................     11.50
BELL,BRONZE SHIP...........................................     20.00
BELL,BUDDHIST WITH METAL WORK ON HANDLE....................     19.00
BELL,CAST BRASS, DUTCH MAID, 5IN. HI.......................     10.75
BELL,CAST BRASS FROM STEAM LOCOMOTIVE,125 POUNDS,YOKE &
  PLATFORM.................................................    275.00
BELL,CAST IRON WITH YOKE,DINNER............................     20.00
BELL,CHINESE GONG WITH MALLET..............................      7.50
BELL,CHINESE ,HEXAGONAL SHAPED WITH PEKING ENAMEL,YELLOW &
  BROWN JADE...............................................     45.00
BELL,CHINESE TEMPLE GONG,4 FEET HIGH ON CARVED TEAKWOOD....    250.00
BELL,CHURCH................................................     60.00
BELL,CHURCH,BAROQUE 1753,435 POUNDS.....................2,500.00
BELL,CLEANED COPPER COW....................................      5.00
BELL,COLONIAL..............................................      4.50
BELL,COW...................................................      5.50
BELL,COW,IN LIGHT IRON,A,OVAL SHAPE,RESEMBLES POUCH,4IN.
  DIA.....................................................      7.50
BELL,CRANBERRY GLASS,7 IN. TALL,CRYSTAL HANDLE.............     22.00
BELL,CUTLER,SET OF 3 NICKEL ON IRON STRAP..................      7.50
BELL,DESK,BRASS ON IRON STAND..............................      5.00
BELL,DESK SCHOOL TAP.......................................      2.50
BRASS DESK TAP BELL PAT.1896...............................      5.95
BELL,DESK,WOODEN HANDLE....................................      3.50
BELL,DINNER,STERLING SILVER HANDLED........................      2.75
BELL,EL CAMINO REAL,SAN DIEGO PAT.1914.....................     15.00
BELL, ENAMEL CHINESE, CRYSTAL HANDLE KNOB..................     20.00
BELL,FARM ,BRASS,WROUGHT IRON U SHAPED STANDARD,CHAIN TO
  RING....................................................     75.00
BELL,FRENCH BRASS,ELIZABETHAN LADY,LEGS ARE STRIKERS.......     15.00
BELL,GAMEWELL FIRE ALARM BELL,BRASS MOUNTED ON MAHOGANY....     35.00
BELL,GLASS.................................................      3.50
BELL,GLASS,AMBER...........................................     25.00
BELL,GLASS AMBER,THREADED HANDLE...........................     20.00
BELL,HALLMARKED SILVER HANDLE CALL.........................      8.00
BELL,HAME,3,BRASS ON IRON SHAFT............................     65.00
BELL,HAND,GLASS,5 IN. TALL.................................      8.50
BELLS,HAND SCHOOL..........................................     10.00
BELL,HAND SCHOOL,CAST BRASS................................     35.50
BELL,HANDPAINTED CHINA,TWISTED GOLD HANDLE.................     12.50
```

```
BELL,HANDPAINTED WITH VIOLETS................................    6.00
BELL,IRON,20 IN. DIAMETER,HANGING BAR & RINGING BAR.........  110.00
BELL,IRON COW...............................................    4.00
BELL,IRON TABLE,4 IN.,PRESS LEVER AT SIDE TO RING...........    6.50
BELL,LEATHER STRAP WITH 34 BRASS SLEIGH BELLS...............   30.00
BELL,LITTLE GIRL,BRASS......................................    7.50
BELL,METAL DINNER,WOMAN.....................................    4.50
BELL,MILKY GLASS SMOKE......................................    7.00
BELL,NEW ENGLAND COW........................................    2.50
BELL,OPAQUE WHITE BLOWN GLASS SMOKE,CRANBERRY RIM...........   12.00
BELL,ORIENTAL,4 GRADUATED,BRASS FITTINGS FOR
  CONNECTIONS,COPPER........................................   45.00
BELL,ORNATE CAST OPENWORK BRASS,ANIMALS,BIRDS,INSCRIPTION...   10.00
BELL,PAIR RUSSIAN SADDLEBELLS...............................   55.00
BELL,PERSIAN CAMEL CHIME WITH BLUE BEAD & TASSELS,4 BELLS...   35.00
BELL,RANCH TYPE DINNER BELL,TRIANGLE OF IRON................   10.00
BELL,RUMP ON STRAP,BRASS....................................   20.00
BELL,SADDLE,NICKEL ON BRASS,MOUNTED ON MARBLE...............   39.00
BELL,SCHOOL.................................................    3.00
BELL,SCHOOL,4 IN. TALL......................................    4.00
BELL,SCHOOL,5 IN. BRASS.....................................   25.00
BELL,SCHOOL,7 IN...........................................,    8.50
BELL,SCHOOL MASTERS,5 IN....................................   10.50
BELL,SCHOOL TEACHERS BRASS,WOODEN HANDLE....................    7.50
BELL SCHOOLMASTER HAND,WOODEN HANDLE........................    3.75
BELL,SCHOOLMASTER HAND,WOODEN HANDLE,6 IN. HIGH.............    6.75
BELL,SET OF 4 GRADUATED ON STRAP...........................    25.00
BELL,SIAMESE BRONZE TEMPLE BELL,2 SIDED FIGURES.............   70.00
BELL,SILVER 7 IN. TALL......................................    7.50
BELL,SILVER,CONTINENTAL,HANDLE FORMED BY GOD MERCURY........   65.00
BELL,SILVER PLATED..........................................    4.50
BELL,SLEIGH,20 NICKEL ON 7 FOOT STRAP.......................   10.00
BELL,SLEIGH,BRONZE,,25 NO. 2 BELLS..........................   30.00
BELL,SLEIGH,BRONZE,EMBOSSED,MOUNTED.........................   42.00
BELLS,SLEIGH ON BRASS BAR...................................    7.00
BELL,SLEIGH ON STRAP,10,GRADUATED...........................   47.00
BELL,SLEIGH,STRING OF IRON..................................   20.00
BELL,SMOKE MILK GLASS.......................................    5.00
BELL,SOUTHERN BELLE,BRASS...................................   17.00
BELL,SPANISH MISSION 1810...................................   65.00
BELL,STERLING HANDLE........................................   12.50
BELL,STERLING SILVER HANDLE.................................    8.00
BELL,STOVE BRASS,BENT ON CURLED SHEET IRON WITH SPRING......   22.50
BELL,STRAP WITH 21 SLEIGH...................................   16.00
BELL,STREET CAR 10 IN. BRASS,CLAPPER........................   14.00
BELL,STRING OF 12 BRASS SLEIGH..............................   15.00
BELL,STRING OF 13 SLEIGH ON LEATHER STRAP...................   24.75
BELL,STRING OF 22 BRASS ON LEATHER..........................   20.00
BELLS,STRING OF  25 BRASS SLEIGH,POLISHED...................   30.00
BELL,STRING OF 29 ,LEATHER..................................   32.50
BELL,STRING OF 30 UNIFORM STEEL BELLS ON LEATHER............   15.00
BELL,STRING OF BRONZE SLEIGH GRADUATED,30 BELLS.............   77.50
BELL,STRING OF SLEIGH 44 IN. LONG,12 ENGRAVED BRONZE CLOSED
  BELLS.....................................................   35.00
```

BELLS have been made of china, glass, or metal. All types are collected.

```
BELL,STRING SLEIGH..........................................   15.00
BELL,STRING SLEIGH,25 GRADUATED ON STRAP....................   60.00
BELL,SWISS BRASS............................................    7.50
BELL,TABLE,RUBY BOHEMIAN GLASS..............................   16.00
BELL,TIN SMOKE..............................................    1.50
BELL,TOWN CRIERS BRASS HAND.................................   20.00
BELL,TWIST DOOR BELL........................................    7.50
```

BELLEEK CHINA was made in Ireland, other European countries, and the United

States. The glaze is creamy yellow and appears wet. The first Belleek was made in 1857.

BELLEEK BLACK FERMANAGH MARK HONEY JAR,BASKETWEAVE PATTERN..	48.50
BELLEEK BLACK MARK 2 HANDLED TUB,SHAMROCK DECORATION........	19.50
BELLEEK BLACK MARK 3 IN. TALL PITCHER......................	22.50
BELLEEK BLACK MARK 4 IN. SHAMROCK CREAMER....................	18.00
BELLEEK BLACK MARK CLOVERLEAF ON BASKETWEAVE TEA SET........	55.00
BELLEEK BLACK MARK NUT DISH.................................	3.25
BELLEEK BLACK MARK TEAPOT,CREAMER & SUGAR...................	55.00
BELLEEK BLACK MARK TUB WITH SHAMROCK DECOR..................	22.50
BELLEEK BOWL,BLACK MARK.....................................	19.00
BELLEEK,BOWL,LENOX,HANDPAINTED,CLAM SHELL COLOURING WITH YELLOW...	6.00
BELLEEK,BOWL,LENOX,PRESENTATION,9 IN.,STERLING OVERLAY......	25.00
BELLEEK COFFEE SET,BANDS OF PINK ROSES......................	45.00
BELLEEK CREAM & SUGAR,BLACK MARK WITH SHAMROCK DECOR........	30.00
BELLEEK CREAMER & SUGAR.....................................	25.00
BELLEEK CREAMER & SUGAR,BLACK CASTLE MARK...................	29.50
BELLEEK CREAMER,BACCHUS WITH GRAPES BLACK MARK CIRCA 1915-40	25.00
BELLEEK CREAMER,BLACK MARK,CIRCA 1857-1890.................	60.00
BELLEEK CREAMER,HANDPAINTED BLUE BORDER,SIGNED..............	12.00
BELLEEK CUP & SAUCER,BLOCK DOT MARKING,CUP IS BEEHIVE.......	18.50
BELLEEK CUP & SAUCER,HARP,HOUND & TOWER MARK,6 IN. PLATE,WHITE LUSTER..	18.00
BELLEEK CUP & SAUCER,SHELL PATTERN.........................	15.00
BELLEEK FERMANAGH BLACK SHAMROCK CREAMER...................	15.00
BELLEEK GREEN FERMANACH MARK SITTING PIG...................	22.50
BELLEEK HANDPAINTED VASE....................................	35.00
BELLEEK HEART SHAPED DISH MARKED...........................	20.00
BELLEEK HARP & HOUSE TEA SET,FOOTED TEAPOT,CREAM & SUGAR....	55.00
BELLEEK IRISH CREAMER & SUGAR..............................	50.00
BELLEEK IRISH CUP & SAUCER.................................	20.00
BELLEEK,IRISH DINNER SERVICE FOR 12,BLACK MARK,BASKETWEAVE-SHAMROCK..................................1,250.00	
BELLEEK IRISH GREEN MARK SWAN..............................	9.50
BELLEEK IRISH PAIR DISH....................................	12.50
BELLEEK LENOX LUSTER SALTS,6...............................	11.50
BELLEEK LENOX RAMEKIN IN STERLING PIERCED HOLDER...........	8.50
BELLEEK OPEN SALT,SET,LENOX WITH PALETTE,HANDPAINTED PINK ROSES...	32.00
BELLEEK PITCHER,4 IN. HIGH,BASKETWEAVE & SHAMROCK PATTERN...	13.50
BELLEEK PLATE,5 SIDED FLUTED AND SCALLOPED RIM,GREEN........	7.50
BELLEEK ROSE BOWL,FLORAL DESIGN............................	45.00
BELLEEK ROSE BOWL,WILLETS,GOLD HANDLES & TRACERY DESIGN.....	25.00
BELLEEK SET OF 6 HANDPAINTED SALTS,HANDPAINTED,ROSES,PINK...	32.00
BELLEEK,SHAKER,LENOX,PAIR,WHITE WITH GREEN,COIN GOLD TOPS & TRIM...	6.00
BELLEEK SHELL CANDLESTICK,BLACK MARK,PEDESTAL HOLDER,SHELL & CORAL...	55.00
BELLEEK SHELL PATTERN ON SHELL FEET GREEN & WHITE TEA SET...	118.00
BELLEEK SHELL SALT,BLACK MARK,2 FEET.......................	10.00
BELLEEK TOY SUGAR & CREAMER,SNAIL PATTERN,WHITE WITH YELLOW.	27.50
BELLEEK SUGAR AND CREAMER,BLACK MARK.......................	27.50
BELLEEK TEAPOT,BLACK MARK,SHELL PATTERN....................	32.00
BELLEEK TEAPOT,CREAMER,SUGAR,IVORY COLOUR,BLACK MARK.......	100.00
BELLEEK TEA POT,OPEN SUGAR & CREAMER,SHELL PATTERN,GREEN TRIM..	75.00
BELLEEK TEA SET,HARP & HOUND MARK,FOOTED TEAPOT,CREAM & SUGAR...	60.00
BELLEEK TUMBLER,IVORY COLOUR,BLACK MARK....................	35.00
BELLEEK VASE 4 IN. OPEN,5 IN. HIGH,SWIRL...................	25.00
BELLEEK,VASE,LENOX,WOODBARK,8 IN. TALL,4 IN. SCALLOPED OPENING...	5.50
BELLEEK,WILLETS 12 IN. VASE,FLORAL DECOR...................	35.00
BELLEEK WILLETS POWDER BOX,................................	14.50

BENNINGTON WARE was the product of two factories working in Bennington, Vermont. Both firms were out of business by 1896. The wares include the brown and yellow mottled pottery, parian, scroddle, stoneware, graniteware, yellow ware, and Staffordshire-like vases.

BENNINGTON 2 QUART PITCHER,PEACOCK,TREES,BEADED DECORATION..	49.50
BENNINGTON 7 IN. TEAPOT,REBECCA AT THE WELL..................	28.00
BENNINGTON 8 IN. PEACOCK PITCHER,MOTTLED BROWN & TAN........	27.00
BENNINGTON 8 IN. PITCHER,PEACOCK DESIGN.....................	28.00
BENNINGTON 8 IN. VASE,ROSE BOUQUET IN WHITE PARIAN..........	25.00
BENNINGTON 9IN. DIAMETER PIE PLATE, MOTTLED BROWN...........	18.00
BENNINGTON 13 IN. BOWL,MARKED...............................	62.50
BENNINGTON BAKING DISH 9 IN.................................	20.00
BENNINGTON BIRD WHISTLE.....................................	12.00
BENNINGTON BOOK BOTTLE......................................	35.00
BENNINGTON BOWL...	5.00
BENNINGTON BROWN BOOK FLASK,1 QUART.........................	50.00
BENNINGTON BROWN MOTTLED COVERED BOWL.......................	15.00
BENNINGTON BROWN MOTTLED SPITTOON...........................	8.50
BENNINGTON BROWN TEA POT 1881,METAL BOTTOM,SPOUT,PEWTER LID.	25.00
BENNINGTON CANDLESTICK......................................	90.00
BENNINGTON COACHMAN BOTTLE 1894 MARK........................	225.00
BENNINGTON COVERED BOX,.....................................	40.00
BENNINGTON CUSPIDOR	
7.00 TO..	12.00
BENNINGTON DISH...	4.00
BENNINGTON DOOR KNOB,3 SETS.................................	5.00
BENNINGTON DOOR KNOBS,PR....................................	5.00
BENNINGTON FLINT ENAMEL CANDLESTICKS........................	48.00
BENNINGTON FLINT FLASK......................................	300.00
BENNINGTON FLINT PINT BOOK FLASK............................	135.00
BENNINGTON GOLD BAND CUP & SAUCER...........................	12.00
BENNINGTON GOOD SAMARITAN PITCHER...........................	32.50
BENNINGTON INVERTED THUMBPRINT AMBER SUGAR..................	4.00
BENNINGTON OPEN SOAP DISH,HOLES TO DRAIN....................	10.00
BENNINGTON OVAL BOWL,BROWN MOTTLING.........................	17.50
BENNINGTON OVAL BOWL, MOTTLED BROWN, 7IN....................	20.00
BENNINGTON OVAL PLATTER.....................................	75.00
BENNINGTON PARIAN BLUE & WHITE CREAMER......................	40.00
BENNINGTON PARIAN BLUE & WHITE SWAN VASE....................	60.00
BENNINGTON PARIAN PITCHER,WHITE.............................	25.00
BENNINGTON PIE PLATE 8 IN...................................	20.00
BENNINGTON PITCHER,8 IN.,PEACOCK PATTERN,MOTTLED BROWN & TAN	28.00
BENNINGTON PITCHER,FLINT ENAMEL,BROWN & GREEN...............	145.00
BENNINGTON PITCHER,PEACOCK DESIGN...........................	28.00
BENNINGTON PLATE..	18.75
BENNINGTON POODLE...	500.00
BENNINGTON,ROCKINGHAM BROWN & YELLOW PITCHER,TULIP PATTERN..	32.00
BENNINGTON ROCKINGHAM DARK SLIP SITTING POODLE..............	125.00
BENNINGTON ROCKINGHAM FOOT WARMER...........................	125.00
BENNINGTON ROCKINGHAM OVAL PICTURE FRAME....................	110.00
BENNINGTON ROCKINGHAM POTTERY SALT BOX,HANGING..............	42.00
BENNINGTON ROCKINGHAM ROUND SOAP DISH PANELLED..............	18.00
BENNINGTON ROUND BOWL,BROWN MOTTLING........................	18.00
BENNINGTON SHOE BOTTLE......................................	43.50
BENNINGTON SIGNED E & P NORTON STONEWARE 3-GALLON JUG.......	17.50
BENNINGTON SIGNED E.NORTON & CO.STONEWARE 1 & HALF GALLON	
HANDLED CROCK..	12.50
BENNINGTON SIGNED J.NORTON & CO. STONEWARE 2 GALLON	
CROCK,HANDLED..	22.50
BENNINGTON SOAP DISH..	5.00
BENNINGTON SPITTOON...	6.50
BENNINGTON SPITTOON,MOTTLED BROWN...........................	12.50
BENNINGTON SPITTOON,SHELL PATTERN...........................	15.75
BENNINGTON TANKARD WATER PITCHER............................	16.50
BENNINGTON TOBACCO JAR,EAR HANDLES	40.00

```
BENNINGTON TYPE BATTER PITCHER,BROWN MOTTLED GLAZE..........     20.00
BENNINGTON TYPE BEAN POT,1 HANDLE,COVERED...................      4.75
BENNINGTON TYPE BOWL,EMBOSSED DESIGN,BROWN.................      12.50
BENNINGTON TYPE BROWN GLAZE DOUBLE DOOR KNOB................      8.00
BENNINGTON-TYPE BROWN MOTTLED CUSPIDOR......................     14.50
BENNINGTON TYPE COFFEE POT,BROWN WITH TAN...................      8.75
BENNINGTON TYPE CUSPIDOR....................................     18.00
BENNINGTON TYPE CUSPIDOR,RED BROWN..........................      6.50
BENNINGTON TYPE DOOR KNOB...................................      3.50
BENNINGTON TYPE MOTTLED GREEN & BROWN SALT..................      3.25
BENNINGTON TYPE MIXING BOWL WITH POURING LIP................     45.00
BENNINGTON TYPE PITCHER,RAISED DESIGN,MAN WITH STEIN,BROWN..     22.50
BENNINGTON TYPE POT,COVERED,RED BROWN.......................      3.75
BENNINGTON TYPE REBECCA AT THE WELL TEAPOT..................     28.00
BENNINGTON TYPE SOAP DISH,OVAL,RAISED DECORATION............     18.00
BENNINGTON TYPE SOAP DISH,OVAL WITH SCALLOPED EDGE..........     16.00
BENNINGTON TYPE SPITTOON....................................      9.00
BENNINGTON TYPE SPITTOON,TAN & BROWN MOTTLED,RAISED SCALLOP
   & PANEL...................................................      6.75
BENNINGTON TYPE TOBY MUG....................................     35.00
BENNINGTON TYPE VASE,2 HANDLED,RAISED LEAF,GREEN
   DESIGN,BROWN,GLAZE.......................................      5.75
BICYCLE,HIGH WHEEL..........................................    175.00
BICYCLE,MANS,CIRCA 1890.....................................     85.00
BICYCLE,WOMANS,LOZIER,YOST,THE GIANTESS.....................    135.00
```

*BILSTON ENAMELS were painted on copper as early as 1760 in Bilston, England.
Several factories worked in the area*
```
BILSTON ENAMEL ON GOLD PERFUME CIRCA 1810,SHEPHERDESS &
   SHEEP...................................................    185.00
```

*BING AND GROHNDAHL is a famous Danish factory making fine porcelains from
1853 to the present. Their Christmas plates are especially well known (see
under CHRISTMAS PLATES).*
```
BING AND GRONDAHL, SEE ALSO CHRISTMAS PLATE.............
BING & GRONDAHL 8 IN. PLATE,PIERCED,BLUE & WHITE,KING
   CHRISTIAN IX............................................     20.00
BING & GRONDAHL PORCELAIN FIGURE OF LONG EARED PUPPY,WHITE
   GLAZE...................................................     32.00
```

*BIRD PLATES are any plates decorated with pictures of birds. Sets were often
made with a different bird on each dish. The design was popular for many years
but reached its height from 1870–1890.*
```
BIRD PLATE MARKED FRANCE,OVAL,SIGNED BY ARTIST LUC,.........     22.50
```

*BISQUE is an unglazed baked porcelain. Finished bisque has a slightly sandy
texture with a dull finish. Some of it may be decorated with various colors.
Bisque gained favor during the late Victorian era when thousands of bisque
figurines were made.*
```
BISQUE 5 IN. BONNETED GIRL FIGURINE........................      6.00
BISQUE 6 IN. CURLY HAIR GIRL,MARKED GERMANY................      5.00
BISQUE 7 IN. FIGURAL VASE,BOY WEARING PASTEL COLOURED
   CLOTHES..................................................     65.00
BISQUE 15 IN. FIGURINE,YOUNG MAN...........................     60.00
BISQUE BABIES,1 SMILING,1 CRYING,5 IN......................     52.00
BISQUE BABIES IN TUB,GIRLS & BOY IN ROUND BATH TUB.........     20.00
BISQUE BABY BOY & GIRL SITTING.............................     35.00
BISQUE BABY,CRAWLING BABY,BLONDE,SHORT WHITE DRESS..........     20.00
BISQUE BABY IN DIAPER SWING................................     15.00
BISQUE BABY,LYING DOWN,2 IN. LONG,TINTED FACE,BLOND HAIR....      8.50
BISQUE BABY,PIANO
   4.50  TO................................................     38.00
BISQUE BABY,SITTING UP,2 IN. TALL,HOLDING SHOE,TINTED
   FACE,BLOND...............................................      8.50
BISQUE BABY,SITTING UP WITH ARMS UPRAISED,TINTED FACE,BLONDE     8.50
```

BISQUE BANK SHAPE OF BEEHIVE...................................   6.50
BISQUE BOWL,FROGS FOR HANDLES..................................   12.00
BISQUE BEAR NODDER,5 IN. TALL HOLDING TENNIS RAQUET.........   17.00
BISQUE BOX,FAN DESIGN IN RELIEF...............................   10.00
BISQUE BOY & GIRL CANDLESTICKS IN FRONT OF 3-CANDELABRA,PAIR   60.00
BISQUE BOY PUSHING A WHEELBARROW,FLORAL DECORATION..........   12.00
BISQUE CHINESE NODDERS,PAIR,SEATED WITH LEGS CROSSED,5 IN.
   TALL..   50.00
BISQUE COURT LADY DOLL HEAD....................................   8.00
BISQUE COW LYING DOWN..   3.50
BISQUE CRYING BABY MATCH HOLDER................................   7.00
BISQUE DOG,LITTLE BOY IN BLUE..................................   12.00
BISQUE FIGURE,14 IN. TALL,PAIR,GIRL IN BRIMMED HAT,BOY WITH
   TAM...   125.00
BISQUE FIGURE,LITTLE GIRL READING TO CHILD....................   9.00
BISQUE FIGURE OF BOY IN KNEE BREECHES,BASKET,FISH............   25.00
BISQUE FIGURINE,11 IN. TALL,BOY & GIRL,GERMAN MARK..........   100.00
BISQUE FIGURINES,PAIR,NUDE BABIES SITTING,GERMANY...........   12.00
BISQUE FRENCH FIGURINES,LITTLE GIRL,BOY HOLDING WALKING
   CANE,PAIR...   45.00
BISQUE FRENCH FIGURINES,PAIR,GIRL,BOY HOLDING FALCON........   65.00
BISQUE FRENCH FISHERMAN COUPLE 8 IN. HIGH,STICK BODIES......   75.00
BISQUE FRENCH PLAQUE IN OFF WHITE ,DISCOVERY OF PLANETS
   JUPITER & MARS..   45.00
BISQUE GERMAN 7 IN. PIANO BABY................................   16.50
BISQUE GERMAN STANDING BOY HOLDING HOLLY SPRAY..............   10.50
BISQUE GIRL ON OVAL BASE BESIDE BASKET,DRESSED,PINK & WHITE.   25.00
BISQUE GIRL ON OVAL BASE BESIDE LARGE BASKET,KATE GREENAWAY
   DRESS...   25.00
BISQUE GROUP OF BOY & 2 GIRLS,PASTEL COLOURS WITH GOLD
   BEADING TRIM..   10.00
BISQUE INDIAN HEAD TOBACCO JAR,FEATHERED HEADDRESS COVER....   19.50
BISQUE KEWPIE SITTING IN BISQUE BATHTUB.......................   22.00
BISQUE LION...   8.00
BISQUE LITTLE CLOWN MATCH HOLDER..............................   8.75
BISQUE MARKED HEUBACH MOTHER & CHILD FIGURINE,12 IN. TALL...   45.00
BISQUE MARKED HORNBERG BABY IN SITTING POSITION.............   35.00
BISQUE MATCHHOLDER,3 IN. HIGH, BUST OF GIRL..................   12.00
BISQUE NODDER IN SHAPE OF COW WITH BOY DRESSED IN FARMER
   CLOTHES...   35.00
BISQUE NODDING LADY,6 IN. HIGH,GOLD TRIMMED,BLOND SMILING
   LADY..   55.00
BISQUE NOVELTY BEAR,SITTING ON HEAD...........................   12.50
BISQUE OWL ,GREY & WHITE FACE,BLUE BOW,BROWN EYES,INNER
   CANDLE HOLDER...   42.00
BISQUE PAIR 12 IN. TALL FRENCH BOY & GIRL....................   100.00
BISQUE PAIR BOY & GIRL FLOWER SELLERS.........................   65.00
BISQUE PAIR BOYS SITTING ON LOG,GREEN CLOTHING,BLONDE HAIR..   25.00
BISQUE PAIR FIGURINES,MAN WEARING BOOTS,WOMAN CARRYING DUCK.   65.50
BISQUE PAIR FRENCH CAVALIER & LADY IN WHITE & YELLOW........   85.00
BISQUE PAIR FRENCH FIGURINES IN DANCING POSITIONS,GIRL &
   BOY,PAIR..   48.00
BISQUE PAIR GERMAN GREENAWAY TYPE BOY & GIRL SWINGING.......   22.50
BISQUE PIANO BABIES,3 BLOND TOTS,BOY IN BLUE,GIRL IN
   PINK,BABY IN WHITE...   60.00
BISQUE PIANO BABIES,BOY & GIRL SITTING ,6 IN. HIGH..........   30.00
BISQUE PIANO BABY,10 IN. LONG.................................   35.00
BISQUE PIANO BABY,BOY SITTING DOWN WITH LEGS
   UPRAISED,COLOURING...   14.00
BISQUE PIANO BABY,GIRL IN BLUE & WHITE NIGHTIE,RECLINING ON
   SIDE..   14.00
BISQUE PIANO BABY,GIRL LYING DOWN IN BEAR SKIN RUG..........   38.00
BISQUE PIANO BABY,LITTLE GIRL,SITTING UP.....................   22.50
BISQUE PICKANINNIES JAPAN PAIR................................   7.50
BISQUE PINK PIGS TOOTHPICK HOLDER.............................   8.50

```
BISQUE PINKISH WEE MAMA PIG & 2 BABIES MARKED GERMANY.......    8.00
BISQUE PLANTER,4 IN. HIGH,ROSES & BOY.....................   12.00
BISQUE SEA CAPTAIN FIGURINE...............................   35.00
BISQUE SHOE SHINE FIGURINE,ITS A SHAME TO TAKE MONEY......    6.50
BISQUE SKULL TOOTHPICK HOLDER.............................    5.00
BISQUE TOOTHPICK HOLDER...................................    4.00
BISQUE TOOTHPICK HOLDER,BOYS HEAD.........................    5.00
BISQUE TOP HAT,BRONZE BAND................................    4.00
BISQUE VICTORIAN FIGURINE MATCH HOLDER,BOY IN BLUE JACKET...  15.00
BISQUE YELLOW BASKET WITH CAT,NIGHT LIGHT WITH CANDLE.......  45.00
BISQUE YELLOW COVERED CHICK...............................    4.50
```

BLACK AMETHYST GLASS appears black until it is held to the light, and a dark purple can be seen. It was made in many factories from 1860 to the present time.

```
BLACK AMETHYST PITCHER 6IN................................    6.00
BLACK AMETHYST SALT & PEPPER SHAKER SET...................    4.50
BLACK AMETHYST SUGAR,FLOWERED DESIGN......................    4.00
BLACK GLASS ROSE BOWL 6 IN. HIGH..........................    4.50
```

BLOWN GLASS was formed by forcing the air through a rod into the molten glass. Early glass and some forms of art glass were hand blown. Other types of glass were molded or pressed.

```
BLOWN GLASS GREEN PITCHER,FLUTED TOP......................   28.00
  BLUE ONION, SEE ONION...................................
```

BLUE WILLOW PATTERN has been made in England since 1780. The pattern has been copied by factories in many countries including Germany, Japan, and the United States. It is still being made. Willow was named for a pattern that pictures a bridge, birds, willow trees, and a Chinese landscape.

```
BLUE WILLOW BOWL,VICTORIAN,WEDGWOOD.......................   22.50
BLUE WILLOW BUTTER DISH,COVERED,ROUND,ENGLAND.............   25.00
BLUE WILLOW BUTTER DISH,OAK...............................   14.50
BLUE WILLOW BUTTER PAT,SET OF 6...........................   15.00
BLUE WILLOW COMPOTE,OAK...................................   20.00
BLUE WILLOW CREAMER & COVERED SUGAR,WOODSWARE,............   15.00
BLUE WILLOW CREAM PITCHER,ALLERTON........................    3.75
BLUE WILLOW CUP & SAUCER,ALLERTON MADE IN ENGLAND.........    4.50
BLUE WILLOW CUP & SAUCER,BLUE & WHITE,BOOTH...............    4.50
BLUE WILLOW CUP & SAUCER,SET OF 6,WOODSWARE...............   28.00
BLUE WILLOW CUP MARKED MAAESTRICHT,SAUCER MARKED ALLERTON...   6.50
BLUE WILLOW DISH,BONE,SET OF 6............................   35.00
BLUE WILLOW DISH,COVERED,SQUARE,9 IN.,STEVENSON,ENGLAND...   12.50
BLUE WILLOW DISH,RELISH,ALLERTON..........................    6.75
BLUE WILLOW DISH,SAUCE,ALLERTON...........................    2.75
BLUE WILLOW DISH,VEGETABLE,COVERED,SQUARE,GREAT BRITAIN...   18.75
BLUE WILLOW DISH,VEGETABLE,COVERED,SQUARE,RIDGWAYS........    8.00
BLUE WILLOW DISH,VEGETABLE,FLAT TYPE,BELGIUM..............    7.50
BLUE WILLOW DISH,VEGETABLE,OBLONG,MARKED GREAT BRITAIN....    6.00
BLUE WILLOW DISH,VEGETABLE,OVAL,OPEN,MAAESTRICHT,HOLLAND..    6.75
BLUE WILLOW EGG CUP,DOUBLE ENDED..........................    5.75
BLUE WILLOW GRAVY BOAT,ASHWORTH BROS.,HANLEY,ENGLAND......    5.75
BLUE WILLOW GRAVY BOAT,WINCANTON,WOODS WARE...............    8.00
BLUE WILLOW JUG,MILK,TOBY,GRAY HAIR,BLACK HAT,ORANGE VEST &
  PANTS...................................................  125.00
BLUE WILLOW KNIFE REST,BLUE...............................   20.00
BLUE WILLOW LID,OBLONG....................................    3.75
BLUW WILLOW PLATE,6 IN.,JOHN STEVENSON,ENGLAND............    1.00
BLUE WILLOW PLATE,7 IN.,ENGLAND...........................    2.50
BLUE WILLOW PLATE,8 IN.....................................    .25
BLUE WILLOW PLATE,8 IN.,MARKED MAASTRICHT,WILLOW HOLLAND..    2.00
BLUE WILLOW PLATE,8 IN.,SCALLOPED EDGE WITH GOLD..........    2.50
BLUE WILLOW PLATE,9 IN.,ALLERTON..........................    1.50
BLUE WILLOW PLATE,9 IN.,BROWN,STEVENSON...................    1.25
BLUE WILLOW PLATE,9 IN.,JOHN STEVENSON & SON,BURSLEM,ENGLAND  2.75
BLUE WILLOW PLATE,10 IN...................................   10.00
```

BLUE WILLOW PLATE,10 IN.,LAUGHLIN U S A......................	4.00
BLUE WILLOW PLATE,10 IN.,SOFT PASTE,CIRCA 1820...............	8.50
BLUE WILLOW PLATE,12 IN.,JOHN STEVENSON &	
SONS,BURSLEM,ENGLAND.......................................	4.75
BLUE WILLOW PLATE,ALCIK,BATAVIA IMPERIAL STONE MARKED.......	7.50
BLUE WILLOW PLATE,ALLERTON.................................	2.25
BLUE WILLOW PLATE,CAKE,10 IN.,MARK INCISED,CLOSED HANDLES...	3.75
BLUE WILLOW PLATE,DIVIDED,SILICON CHINA....................	5.25
BLUE WILLOW PLATE,ENOCH WOOD & SONS,BLUE...................	10.00
BLUE WILLOW PLATE,FRANCE...................................	6.00
BLUE WILLOW PLATE,OAK,7 IN.................................	13.50
BLUE WILLOW PLATE,RIDGEWAY.................................	2.00
BLUE WILLOW PLATTER,19 X 15 IN.............................	18.00
BLUE WILLOW PLATTER,ALLERTON,ENGLAND,17 X 13 IN............	18.50
BLUE WILLOW PLATTER,BOSTON,18 IN...........................	100.00
BLUE WILLOW PLATTER,IRONSTONE..............................	14.50
BLUE WILLOW PLATTER MARKED GREAT BRITAIN...................	5.75
BLUE WILLOW PLATTER,OBLONG,SCALLOPED EDGE..................	8.00
BLUE WILLOW PLATTER,OVAL,GRINDLEY,ENGLAND..................	3.75
BLUE WILLOW PLATTER,STEVENSON,SQUARE SHAPE WITH SCALLOPED	
CORNERS..	10.50
BLUE WILLOW PLATTER,TURKEY,BLUE,MARKED.....................	15.00
BLUE WILLOW PLATTER,TURKEY,OVAL,PINK & WHITE,FLORAL	
BORDER,MARKED WOODS..	24.00
BLUE WILLOW PLATTER,WOOD & SONS,16 X 13 IN.,LAKE GEORGE,NEW	
YORK...	200.00
BLUE WILLOW SAUCE,OAK,THUMB HANDLE.........................	6.00
BLUE WILLOW SAUCER...	1.50
BLUE WILLOW SAUCER,3,DAY PATTERN,WOOD & SONS...............	2.50
BLUE WILLOW SAUCER,5 IN....................................	1.50
BLUE WILLOW SOUP PLATE,MAASTRICHT..........................	3.50
BLUE WILLOW SUGAR BOWL,ALLERTON............................	3.75
BLUE WILLOW TEAPOT,SADLER ENGLAND..........................	10.00
BLUE WILLOW TEA SET,3 PIECES,COPELAND SPODE,ENGLAND,GOLD	
EDGES..	18.75
BLUE WILLOW TEA SET,CHILDS,JAPANESE........................	10.00
BLUE WILLOW TEA SET,CHILDS,JAPAN MARK,15 PIECES............	8.00
BLUE WILLOW TEA SET FOR 4,CHILDS...........................	23.00
BLUE WILLOW TUREEN,VEGETABLE,COVERED,ENGLAND...............	27.50

BOEHM (EDWARD MARSHALL) made pottery in Trenton, New Jersey, starting in 1949. His bird figurines have achieved worldwide recognition.

BOEHM,ROBIN WITH DAFFODIL....................................1,800.00	
BOEHM SQUIRREL...	325.00

BOHEMIAN GLASS is an ornate, overlay splashed glass made during the Victorian era. It has been reproduced in Bohemia, which is now a part of Czechoslovakia. Glass made from 1875 to 1900 is preferred by collectors.

BOHEMIAN AMBER DECANTER,ETCHED CLEAR WITH AMBER STOPPER.....	17.50
BOHEMIAN AMBER VASE WITH CLEAR FROSTED DEER & PINE	
TREE,ETCHED,...	30.00
BOHEMIAN BLOWN 14 IN. TALL LUSTRE,ORIGINAL PRISMS...........	43.00
BOHEMIAN CRYSTAL STEMMED GOBLET,INTAGLIO CUT TO CLEAR.......	10.00
BOHEMIAN DECANTER,PAIR,CUT AROUND BASE & BODY IN HONEYCOMB..	95.00
BOHEMIAN DISH,WINE COLOUR,VINTAGE PATTERN..................	30.00
BOHEMIAN GLASS 9 IN. BOTTLE WITH 6 LIQUOR GLASSES ON TRAY...	75.00
BOHEMIAN GLASS BOWL,RED,OVAL,HUNTING SCENES,CIRCA 1830......	175.00
BOHEMIAN GLASS DECANTER	
16.00 TO...	36.00
BOHEMIAN GLASS DECANTER,RED,VINTAGE PATTERN & CLEAR PANELED	
ON SIDES...	42.00
BOHEMIAN GLASS PAIR DECANTERS,VINTAGE PATTERN..............	95.00
BOHEMIAN GLASS PAIR WINE GOBLETS...........................	37.00
BOHEMIAN GLASS RED COMPOTE,ETCHED TO CLEAR FLOWERS & LEAVES.	19.50
BOHEMIAN GLASS RED MUG WITH HANDLE,ETCHED FLOWERS & FORGET	

```
ME NOT.............................................................    8.50
BOHEMIAN GLASS RED WINE BOTTLE,WHITE FROSTED GRAPES & LEAVES        21.00
BOHEMIAN GLASS STEMMED WINE,CRANBERRY & GOLD AMBER...........       22.00
BOHEMIAN GLASS VASE,FOOTED,AMBER COLOUR,ETCHED LEAVES &
  GRAPES..........................................................  195.00
BOHEMIAN GLASS WINES,6,FLARED TOPS,FROSTED WHITE ON RED.....        45.00
BOHEMIAN GREEN GLASS RING TREE,PEDESTAL BASE................        18.00
BOHEMIAN MAROON MUFFINEER WITH HANDLE,SCROLL DECOR..........        55.00
BOHEMIAN PAIR AMBER & CLEAR GLASS VASES CIRCA 1830,HUNTING
  SCENES.........................................................  225.00
BOHEMIAN PAIR COLOGNE BOTTLES,RED SWIRL IN CUT STOPPER......        37.50
BOHEMIAN PAIR DECANTERS,CUT FUGIRES OF BOY & GIRL...........        95.00
BOHEMIAN PAIR LUSTRES,GREEN CRYSTAL,ENAMELLED WITH FLORALS..       200.00
BOHEMIAN PAIR RED VASES....................................         45.00
BOHEMIAN RED CASTLE & DEER PATTERN DECANTER WITH 6 STEMMED
  CORDIALS.......................................................   35.00
BOHEMIAN RED FLASHED VASE,BIRD & LEAVES IN CLEAR OVAL ON
  SIDE...........................................................   12.50
BOHEMIAN,RED MUG,TO MY DAUGHTER.............................        10.00
BOHEMIAN RUBY & CLEAR WINE BOTTLE..........................         16.50
BOHEMAIN RUBY CARAFE,BLOWN,SNAPPED OFF PONTIL,GRAPE VINE
  DESIGN.........................................................   24.00
BOHEMIAN RUBY CRUET,DEER,CASTLE,BIRD.......................         20.00
BOHEMIAN RUBY CUT 13 IN. BOTTLE,RUNNING DEERS & CASTLES &
  SCROLLS........................................................   35.00
BOHEMIAN RUBY CUT TO CLEAR VINTAGE COVERED CANDY...........         27.50
BOHEMIAN RUBY ETCHED TUMBLER...............................         15.00
BOHEMIAN RUBY GLASS CHAMPAGNE GLASS........................          8.00
BOHEMIAN RUBY GLASS DATED 1904 DECANTER & 6
  WINES,CASTLE,DEER..............................................   70.00
BOHEMIAN RUBY GLASS JUICE GLASS............................          7.00
BOHEMIAN RUBY GLASS SUGAR BOWL & CREAMER...................         30.00
BOHEMIAN RUBY MANTLE LUSTRES,12 IN. TALL,PAIR..............        135.00
BOHEMIAN RUBY PITCHER,PAIR,ENGRAVED IN GOLD WITH BIRDS &
  FLOWERS........................................................   50.00
BOHEMIAN RUBY WINE SET,DECANTER & 6 STEMMED WINES DATED 1896       125.00
BOHEMIAN STEM WINES,LARGE SIZE.............................          4.50
BOHEMIAN TYPE THIN BLOWN COVERED POWDER JAR & PAIR
  BOTTLES,GOLD...................................................   35.00
BOHEMIAN VASE,RED CUT TO CLEAR.............................         45.00
BOHEMIAN VINEGAR CRUET,AMBER DEER..........................         20.00
BOHEMIAN VINEGAR CRUET WITH STOPPER,RUBY DEER..............         15.00
```

BONE CHINA was made in England since 1748. It is a very white ware and is still being made today.

```
BONE HANDLE FORK...........................................          1.00
BONE HANDLED SET OF 4 SHEFFIELD STEEL KNIVES...............          4.00
BONN GERMANY 3 PART HANDLED DISH,PINK FLOWER DECORATION.....         6.00
  BOTTLE. SEE ALSO BEAM, COCO COLA, INKWELL, ETC...........
```

BOTTLE COLLECTING has become a major American hobby. There are several general categories of bottles such as historic flasks, bitters, household, figural, and others.

```
BOTTLE,3 CORNERED AMBER POISON.............................          2.00
BOTTLE,3 MOLD BLACK BEER...................................          3.50
BOTTLE, 3 MOLD HONEY AMBER WHISKEY.........................          5.00
BOTTLE,3 PIECE BLOWN WHISKEY...............................          7.50
BOTTLE,3-PIECE MOLD 1860 9 IN. BLACK GLASS.................          4.00
BOTTLE, 3-SIDED COBALT LAXOL,CASTOR OIL....................          7.00
BOTTLE,3-SIDED FREDERICK STERNS AMBER......................          7.00
BOTTLE, 3 SIDED SHARP & DOHME..............................          2.00
BOTTLE, 4 IN. AMBER SNUFF..................................          4.00
BOTTLE, 5 GAL. SOUTH JERSEY HAND-BLOWN DEMIJOHNS...........         15.00
BOTTLE,5 IN. RECLINING SCENT,4-PRISM SHAPED,GREEN &
  GOLD,BRASS CAP.................................................   55.00
```

```
BOTTLE,6 IN. CLEAR OVERSHOT GLASS COLOGNE,MELON BOTTOM,GOLD
  CAPPED.....................................................    7.50
BOTTLE,6 LOG AMBER PLANTATION BITTERS......................   23.50
BOTTLE,7 IN. BALL FRUIT JAR,AQUA,PORCELAIN LINER...........    2.00
BOTTLE,7 IN. BALL MASON ,AQUA,PORCELAIN LINER..............    2.50
BOTTLE,8 IN. AQUA CATHEDRAL,IRON PONTIL....................   10.00
BOTTLE,8 IN. GREEN WINE....................................    1.25
BOTTLE,OWL,9 IN. TALL INCLUDING JIGGER.....................   11.00
BOTTLE,10 IN. APOTHECARY SQUARE,WIDE MOUTH,2 IN. STOPPER....    9.50
BOTTLE,10 IN. ONION-SHAPE GREEN BENEDICTINE................    7.00
BOTTLE,11-PANEL AQUA,2 IN. TALL............................    3.00
BOTTLE,12 IN. BLOWN BASE,PAINTED TRAPEZE PERFORMERS RED BAND
  AT TOP...................................................   18.00
BOTTLE,12 IN. BLOWN ,PAINTED TRAPEZE PERFORMERS RED BAND....   18.00
BOTTLE,1858 HALF GALLON MASON JAR..........................    7.50
BOTTLE, 1858 MASON,ZINC LID................................    1.50
BOTTLE,1858 QUART MASON JAR................................    6.00
BOTTLE,ABOTTS BITTERS......................................    5.00
BOTTLE,A D ASHLEY RED SEA BALSAM,12 SIDED..................    6.50
BOTTLE,AMBER 8 IN. HIGH,WALTHERS PEPTONIZED PORT,PITTSBURGH.   10.00
BOTTLE, AMBER AROMATIC SCHNAPPS 9 IN.......................   15.00
BOTTLE, AMBER BALL MASON SQUARE 2 QUART....................    9.00
BOTTLE,AMBER BAY RUM WITH ORIGINAL LABEL...................    6.00
BOTTLE,AMBER BEER..........................................    1.25
BOTTLE,AMBER BEER,1836-86,MC KEE & CO......................   12.50
BOTTLE,AMBER BIMAL EMBOSSED ST.ANNE DE BAUPRE..............    5.00
BOTTLE,AMBER COCA-COLA.....................................    9.00
BOTTLE, AMBER COKE.........................................   25.00
BOTTLE,AMBER DEEP COLOR FRUIT JAR,1/2 IN. NECK BAND,1886 1
  1/2 GAL..................................................   12.50
BOTTLE AMBER DEEP COLOR FRUIT JARS, 1/2 IN. NECK BAND,1886 1
  QT.......................................................   14.50
BOTTLE AMBER DEEP COLOR FRUIT JARS, 1/2 IN. NECK BAND,1886 2
  PINTS....................................................   16.50
BOTTLE,AMBER DOYLES HOP BITTERS WITH LABEL.................   19.00
BOTTLE,AMBER DRAKES PLANTATION BITTERS.....................   22.50
BOTTLE,AMBER FISH,9 IN.....................................   15.00
BOTTLE,AMBER GLOBE TOBACCO JAR,PAT.1882....................    6.00
BOTTLE AMBER GUITAR........................................    6.00
BOTTLE AMBER HEARTS, NO LABELS.............................    5.00
BOTTLE, AMBER HOSTETTERS STOMACH BITTERS...................    6.50
BOTTLE,AMBER JOHNSON-JOHNSON,4 IN..........................    4.50
BOTTLE,AMBER KEPLER........................................    3.50
BOTTLE AMBER LIGHTNING QT. JAR.............................   25.00
BOTTLE,AMBER POISON........................................    3.50
BOTTLE,AMBER QUART MILK BOTTLE.............................    4.00
BOTTLE,AMBER RAILROAD FLASK,SUCCESS TO THE RAILROAD........   95.00
BOTTLE,AMBER,RECTANGULAR,SCALES & FISH EMBOSSED ON FRONT....    4.50
BOTTLE,AMBER RUSS ST.DOMINGO BITTERS WITH LABEL............   48.50
BOTTLE,AMBER SNUFF.........................................    6.00
BOTTLE,AMBER STODDARD DOUBLE EAGLE 1 HALF PINT FLASK.......  100.00
BOTTLE,AMBER SYPHON DR.PEPPER..............................   27.50
BOTTLE,AMBER WARNERS SAFE KIDNEY & LIVER CURE..............   15.00
BOTTLE,AMERI-PIECON BITTERS................................   12.00
BOTTLE,AMETHYST BARBER BOTTLE..............................   42.50
BOTTLE, AMETHYST, BUBBLY PUMPKIN SEED, 5 OZ................    8.50
BOTTLE,AMETHYST PINCH DECANTER,CLEAR STOPPER...............   10.00
BOTTLE,APOTHECARYS HAND ENGRAVED BEAKER....................   12.50
BOTTLE,AQUA ATLAS STRONG SHOULDER QUART FRUIT JAR..........    3.00
BOTTLE, AQUA ATWOODS JAUNDICE BITTERS......................    4.00
BOTTLE,AQUA BALL MASON QUART...............................    1.00
BOTTLE,AQUA BALL QUART.....................................    1.00
BOTTLE,AQUA BEER BOTTLE....................................    2.00
BOTTLE, AQUA-BLUE HALF PT. SCROLL..........................   35.00
BOTTLE,AQUA BURDOCK BLOOD BITTERS..........................   14.50
```

```
BOTTLE,AQUA CANNING,JOHN AGNEW & SONS,PGH.,PA...............    3.00
BOTTLE,AQUA DR.MC LEANS CORDIAL..........................    3.50
BOTTLE,AQUA DR.PIERCE FAVOURITE PRESCRIPTION................    5.00
BOTTLE,AQUA FOR PIKES PEAK 1 HALF PINT,REVERSE EAGLE WITH
  RIBBON.................................................   26.00
BOTTLE, AQUA HALF GAL. RED KEY MASON.....................   12.50
BOTTLE,AQUA KINGS 25 CENT BITTERS........................   29.00
BOTTLE, AQUA MISSION BELL MASON JAR......................    6.00
BOTTLE,ARGUS HANDLED WHISKEY.............................   16.50
BOTTLE,ATLAS PINT JAR,GLASS TOP..........................    4.00
BOTTLE,ATLAS SQUAT PINT,AQUA WITH COVER..................    4.00
BOTTLE, ATLAS WHOLEFRUIT,CLEAR,LID & WIRE CLAMP,QUART OR
  PINT..................................................    2.50
BOTTLE ATWOODS GENUINE BITTERS , 5STAR...................   15.00
BOTTLE, ATWOODS JAUNDICE.................................    6.00
BOTTLE,ATWOODS JAUNDICE BITTERS,12 SIDED.................    4.75
BOTTLE ATWOODS QUININE TONIC BITTERS.....................   40.00
BOTTLE,BABY ,FLAT BOTTOM.................................    2.00
BOTTLE,BABYS NURSING,SWANSON & THOMPSON..................    7.50
BOTTLE,BALL IDEAL 1908...................................    1.50
BOTTLE,BALL IDEAL CLEAR HALF PINT........................    2.50
BOTTLE,BALL IDEAL DATED QUART,GLASS LID..................    3.50
BOTTLE, BALL IDEAL QUART,AQUA WITH CAP...................    1.00
BOTTLE, BALL IDEAL,WIRE BAIL,GLASS LID,1908
  PAT.DATE,CLEAR,QUART...................................    2.00
BOTTLE,BALL PERFECT MASON AQUA QUART.....................    1.75
BOTTLE,BALL PERFECT MASON QUART,ZINC LID,BLUE,1888-1930....    3.00
BOTTLE, BALL SQUARE MASON,QUART..........................    5.00
BOTTLE, BARBER, BLUISH WHITE HOBNAIL.....................    5.00
BOTTLE,BARBER ,MILKY.....................................   10.00
BOTTLE,BARBER,VASELINE OPALESCENT,RIBBED.................   35.00
BOTTLE,BARBER ,WHITE MILK GLASS..........................   20.00
BOTTLE, BARBER,WHITE WITH STOPPER........................   11.50
BOTTLE,BARBER WITH ENAMELED FLOWERS......................   25.00
BOTTLE, BARKER, MOORE & MEIN, PHILADELPHIA...............    2.50
BOTTLE, BARRARDIN PINT...................................    3.50
BOTTLE,BARREL MUSTARD....................................    3.50
BOTTLE, BARREL SHAPED VINEGAR,APPLE PIE RIDGE ON BOTTON....   10.00
BOTTLE,BEEFEATER.........................................   25.00
BOTTLE, BEGGS DANDELION..................................   42.50
BOTTLE,BELLSHAPED EMERALD GREEN BARBER WITH ENAMELED FLOWERS   45.00
BOTTLE, BERNADINE MASON,PINT.............................    3.50
BOTTLE, BERNADINE MASON,QUART............................    2.50
BOTTLE,BIG CHIEF COKE....................................    3.75
BOTTLE,BILLY GOAT........................................    5.00
BOTTLE,BITTERQUELLE,OLIVE GREEN..........................    6.00
BOTTLE,BITTERQUELLE WITH WHITTLE MARKS...................    9.00
BOTTLE, BITTERS, DR. MAPES HERB STOMACH BITTERS,AQUA.........   50.00
BOTTLE, BITTERS, FENNERS CAPITOL.........................   42.50
BOTTLE,BITTERS,LOG CABIN,DRAKE PLANTATION................   26.00
BOTTLE,BITTERS,MILK GLASS................................   40.00
BOTTLE,BITTERS,MILK GLASS,EMBOSSED
  HARTWIG,KANTOROWICZ,POSEN,HAMBURG......................   60.00
BOTTLE,BITTERS,VERMO STOMACH BITTERS.....................   35.00
BOTTLE BLACK, DK. GREEN, KUMMEL BEAR.....................   45.00
BOTTLE, BLACK GLASS BEER IN 3-MOLD WOODEN MOLD ,1860........    4.00
BOTTLE,BLOB TOP AMBER QUART BEER,A.HAAS & CO,HOUGHTON
  MICHIGAN...............................................    1.50
BOTTLE,BLOB TOP AMBER QUART BEER,HANCOCK,MICHIGAN........    1.50
BOTTLE,BLOB TOP AMBER QUART BEER,PARK BREWING CO,HANCOCK
  MICHIGAN...............................................    1.50
BOTTLE,BLOB TOP AMBER QUART BEER,PHIL SCHEURMANN.........    1.50
BOTTLE,BLOB TOP AMBER QUART BEER,UPPER PENINSUAL
  BREWERY,MICHIGAN.......................................    1.50
BOTTLE,BLOB TOP SODA,CLEAR WITH METAL STOPPER,EMBOSSED
```

HACKETTSTOWN.. 6.00
BOTTLE,BLOWN CLEAR GLASS NURSING........................ 18.50
BOTTLE,BLOWN DRUGGIST JAR,4 IN. SQUARE MOUTH............ 4.00
BOTTLE, BLUE BARBER WITH MUSHROOM TOP................... 16.50
BOTTLE,BLUE BARBER WITH OPALESCENT FERN PATTERN......... 30.00
BOTTLE,BLUE COLOGNE,WHITE & YELLOW ENAMELED DAISIES..... 35.00
BOTTLE BLUE DELFT, NO LABELS............................ 5.00
BOTTLE,BLUE GOOCHS SARSAPARILLA......................... 8.50
BOTTL,BLUE-GREEN BALL IDEAL PINT........................ .75
BOTTLE,BLUE-GREEN BALL IDEAL QUART...................... .75
BOTTLE,BLUE-GREEN BLOB TOP,A.W.MEYER 1885 SAVANNAH,GA... 14.00
BOTTLE,BLUE-GREEN DATED BALL IDEAL PINT................. 1.00
BOTTLE,BLUE-GREEN DATED BALL IDEAL QUART................ 1.00
BOTTLE,BLUE-GREEN RUMFORD,GOTHIC ARCH................... 5.00
BOTTLE,BLUE HARDENS HAND GRENADE FIRE EXTINGUISHER...... 25.00
BOTTLE, BLUE PINT TELEPHONE JAR......................... 10.00
BOTTLE,BLUE VIOLIN,10 IN................................ 5.00
BOTTLE,BLUMENTHAL BICKART WHISKEY....................... 2.75
BOTTLE, BRELLE PINT, DATED GLASS LID,1912, NO CLAMP..... 10.00
BOTTLE,BRISTOL DOUBLE PERFUME,BRASS CAPS................ 12.00
BOTTLE,BRISTOLS SARSAPARILLA............................ 10.00
BOTTLE,BROMO-CEDIN FOR HEADACHES,EMBOSSED,COBALT BLUE... 5.50
BOTTLE BROPHYS BITTERS NOKOMIS ILL. BLUE GREEN 7IN...... 15.00
BOTTLE,BROWN HICKS CAPUDINE,5 BN.,CROOKED NECK.......... 4.00
BOTTLE BROWN IRON BITTERS TWO LABELS.................... 30.00
BOTTLE, BROWNS IRON..................................... 25.00
BOTTLE, BUBBLY AQUA QUART ROOT MASON.................... 4.00
BOTTLE,BUDDA.. 5.50
BOTTLE, BULLDOG CANDY CONTAINER, SCREW ON BASE.......... 15.00
BOTTLE,BURDOCK BLOOD BITTERS............................ 15.00
BOTTLE,BURDOCK BLOOD BITTERS,AQUA....................... 16.00
BOTTLE BURDOCKS BLOODBITTERS AQUA....................... 15.00
BOTTLE, CALDWELLS SYRUP PEPSIN.......................... 1.00
BOTTLE, CALIF. FIG SYRUP................................ 1.00
BOTTLE,CARBOY,APPLIED LIP,AQUA BUBBLES.................. 40.00
BOTTLE,CARRIE NATION
   5.00   TO.. 7.50
BOTTLE,CARTER BLUE INK.................................. 14.00
BOTTLE,CARTERS BLUE CATHEDRAL INK ,QUART................ 9.50
BOTTLE,CARTERS HOUSEHOLD INK,LABEL..................... 3.00
BOTTLE,CARTERS PURPLE INK............................... 1.00
BOTTLE,CARVED IVORY,SAGE & SERVANT IN RELIEF,INTAGLIO CARVED   85.00
BOTTLE, CASE GIN BLACK GLASS EMBOSSED BLANKENHEIN & NOLET... 12.00
BOTTLE,CAT,E.J.BURKE.................................... 4.00
BOTTLE CATHEDRAL COBALT PT. CARTERS INK................. 22.00
BOTTLE, CHAMBERLAINS COLIC, CHOLERA, DIARRHEA REMEDY.... 3.00
BOTTLE, CHAMBERLAINS COUGH REMEDY....................... 2.00
BOTTLE, CHINA WHISKEY ,LOAF O BREAD..................... 10.00
BOTTLE, CHINA WHISKEY,PILGRIMS BOTTLE................... 10.00
BOTTLE, CHINA WHISKEY,TAMALE............................ 10.00
BOTTLE,CHINESE GREEN GLASS.............................. 8.00
BOTTLE,CHINESE MEDICINE................................. 4.00
BOTTLE,CHINESE SNUFF OVERLAY RED LEAF CARVED BACK TO CAMPHOR   21.00
BOTTLE,CHINESE SNUFF,TURQUOISE WITH MATCHING STOPPER.... 70.00
BOTTLE,CHINESE WHISKEY JAR,BROWN GLAZE.................. 5.00
BOTTLE, CHRISTIAN MOERLEIN, CINCINNATI.................. 2.00
BOTTLE,CLEAR 11 IN.,THE HAYNER DISTILLING CO.,DAYTON,... 3.75
BOTTLE,CLEAR ATLAS EZ SEAL QUART........................ 1.00
BOTTLE,CLEAR BALL IDEAL 1 HALF PINT..................... 1.00
BOTTLE,CLEAR BALL IDEAL PINT............................ .75
BOTTLE,CLEAR DATED BALL IDEAL PINT...................... 1.00
BOTTLE,CLEAR DATED BALL IDEAL QUART
   .75   TO.. 1.00
BOTTLE,CLEAR ECONOMY.................................... .75
BOTTLE,CLEAR FOSTER SEALFAST PINT....................... 1.00

```
BOTTLE CLEAR FRENCH CHANTICLEER,HEAD IS STOPPER............     30.00
BOTTLE,CLEAR GLASS FAT BOY,8 IN.............................      5.00
BOTTLE, CLEAR GUN BOTTLE, CAP...............................      5.00
BOTTLE, CLEAR HALF PT. CHESTNUT OVERALL HOBNAIL DESIGN,
  POISON FLASK..............................................     45.00
BOTTLE,CLEAR PANEL OLD RYE,10 IN............................      8.50
BOTTLE,CLICQUOT CLUB SIDA,CLEAR,EMBOSSED....................      2.00
BOTTLE,CLIMBING MONKEY ON GREEN.............................      6.00
BOTTLE,CLOWN................................................      2.50
BOTTLE,COBALT BARBER WITH WHITE & YELLOW ENAMEL FLOWERS.....     18.00
BOTTLE,COBALT BLOB TOP,MEINCKE & EBBERWEIN 1882,MINERAL
  WATER....................................................     15.00
BOTTLE,COBALT BLOWN,BULBOUS BODY,COBALT APPLIED SNAKE TRIM
  ON NECK..................................................     55.00
BOTTLE,COBALT BLUE 9 IN. INK ,32 OUNCES,LIPPED.............     20.00
BOTTLE, COBALT BLUE INK DIAMOND SHAPE, SCREW CAP...........      3.00
BOTTLE, COBALT BLUE PEPTENZYME.............................      3.50
BOTTLE,COBALT CARTERS QT.INK...............................     15.00
BOTTLE COBALT CASTOR OIL...................................     18.00
BOTTLE,COBALT JOHN WYETH & BROS,,MEASURING CUP & TIMER.....     12.00
BOTTLE,COBALT POISON, SKULL AND CROSSBONES.................     10.00
BOTTLE,COBALT POISON,SMOCKED FRONT,STOPPER SAYS POISON.....     12.50
BOTTLE, COBALT QT. CARTERS INK.............................     15.00
BOTTLE, COBALT SODA,WIRE BAIL..............................     12.00
BOTTLE,COFFIN FLASK........................................      3.00
BOTTLE,COLDWATER BOTTLING COMPANY SODA.....................      2.00
BOTTLE,COLOGNE WITH STOPPER................................      6.50
BOTTLE,COLUMBIA PINT.......................................      2.00
BOTTLE,CONE INK,AMBER......................................      4.50
BOTTLE,CONE INK ,AQUA......................................      3.00
BOTTLE,CROCKERY BEER.......................................      4.50
BOTTLE,CROCKERY GINGER BEER JUG,11 IN. WITH SPIGOT AT BOTTOM    10.00
BOTTLE, CROWN MASON,PINT...................................      3.00
BOTTLE, CROWN MASON,QUART..................................      2.50
BOTTLE,CROWN QUART FRUIT JAR...............................      5.00
BOTTLE,CUT GLASS COLOGNE,CANE PATTERN......................     17.50
BOTTLE,DAISY PINT FRUIT JAR................................     12.00
BOTTLE DAMIANA BITTERS.....................................     35.00
BOTTLE DANCING SCOT, TALL..................................     20.00
BOTTLE, DAVIS VEGETABLE PAINKILLER.........................      2.00
BOTTLE,DAVOL BABIES DELIGHT NURSER.........................      2.00
BOTTLE, DECKERS IOWANA,JULY 14, 1908,QUART,CLEAR...........      5.50
BOTTLE,DELAGE GUITAR.......................................     12.00
BOTTLE,DIAMOND FRUIT JAR,IMPROVED GLASS LID,CLEAR..........      2.75
BOTTLE,DICKEL POWDER HORN
  9.00  TO................................................     10.00
BOTTLE, DODSONS LIVERTONE..................................      1.00
BOTTLE,DOERFLINGER,COLOUR DESIGNS IN STOPPER & BASE,6 IN.
  FOOTED..................................................    175.00
BOTTLE,DOUBLE DUTY CLEAR PINT WITH COVER...................      3.00
BOTTLE,DOYLE HOP BITTERS...................................     18.00
BOTTLE, DR. BELLS PINE TAR HONEY...........................      1.00
BOTTLE,DR. D JAYNES ALTERNATIVE............................      7.50
BOTTLE DR. FLINTS QUAKER BITTERS...........................     25.00
BOTTLE,DR.FLINTS QUAKER BITTERS,AQUA.......................     25.00
BOTTLE DR. HARTERS WILD CHERRY BITTERS.....................     35.00
BOTTLE, DR. HASKELLS ELECTRIC OIL..........................      3.00
BOTTLE, DR. HAYDENS VIBURNUM...............................      2.50
BOTTLE DR. HOPKINS UNION STOMACH BITTERS...................     40.00
BOTTLE,DR. HOSTETTERS BITTERS,AMBER
  1.50  TO................................................      4.50
BOTTLE,DR. J. HOSTETTERS BITTERS...........................      8.00
BOTTLE,DR.JAYNES EXPECTORANT...............................      3.50
BOTTLE, DR. KILMERS........................................      2.00
BOTTLE DR. LANGLEYS ROOT, HERB BITTERS, SMALL 99 UNION.....     20.00
```

```
BOTTLE, DR. PIERCES , AQUA, IRIDESCENCE.....................   4.50
BOTTLE, DR. PIERCES GOLDEN MEDICAL DISCOVERY................   2.50
BOTTLE,DR.SIEGERTS BITTERS..................................   5.00
BOTTLE, DR. TRUES ELIXIR ,EST. 1851 AUBURN,MAINE,AQUA
  BUBBLES...................................................   3.50
BOTTLE DR. VAN HOFS CURACOA BITTERS.........................  50.00
BOTTLE,DR.W.B.CALDWELLS MONTICELLO,ILL......................   1.00
BOTTLE DRAKES PLANTATION 4 LOG..............................  27.50
BOTTLE,DRAKES PLANTATION BITTERS............................  25.00
BOTTLE,DREY IMPROVED EVER-SEAL CLEAR QUART WITH CAP.........   2.00
BOTTLE,DREY PERFECT MASON HALF GALLON,CLEAR.................   3.00
BOTTLE,DREY PERFECT. MASON QUART,CLEAR......................   2.50
BOTTLE,DRUGGIST JAR,THUMBPRINT,PEDESTAL BASE,...............  13.00
BOTTLE, EAGLE...............................................  10.50
BOTTLE,EAGLE QUART FRUIT JAR,MISTY..........................  15.00
BOTTLE,ECONOMY GLASS LID....................................   2.50
BOTTLE,E.G.BOOZE LOG CABIN,AMBER,6 IN.......................   5.75
BOTTLE, ELECTRIC BITTERS,AMBER,APPLIED LIP..................  15.00
BOTTLE,ELECTRIC BRAND BITTERS...............................   9.00
BOTTLE, ELECTRIC BRAND BITTERS,EMBOSSED PLUS 2 FULL LABELS..  15.00
BOTTLE ELECTRIC BITTERS, SMALL, TWO LABELS..................  14.00
BOTTLE,ELYS BALM............................................   2.50
BOTTLE,EMBOSSED MILK........................................   1.50
BOTTLE,EMBOSSED PATENT MEDICINE.............................   1.00
BOTTLE, EMERALD GREEN QUART CONGRESS WATER SPARKLING........  16.00
BOTTLE, EMERALD GREEN SCENT, 2 IN...........................  23.00
BOTTLE, EMPIRE MEDICINE, KNOXVILLE..........................   2.00
BOTTLE,ENAMEL SNUFF,PORTRAIT MEDALLION FRONT & BACK,FLOWERS. 200.00
BOTTLE, ENOS FRUIT SALT DERIVATIVE..........................   2.50
BOTTLE,E R DURKEE RINGED ,CONE SHAPE........................  37.50
BOTTLE,ERVEN LUCAS BOLS,HOLLAND,DELFT.......................   9.50
BOTTLE,FAT MAN,7 IN.,CLEAR,PAINTED..........................   6.00
BOTTLE,FIGURAL,BROWN POTATO OVER MILK GLASS.................  27.50
BOTTLE,FISH,SITS LENGHTHWISE,ABOUT 14X7.....................   7.95
BOTTLE,FLACCUS UNCLE SAM WITH RIFLE.........................  28.50
BOTTLE,FLAT THIN CASTOR OIL.................................    .25
BOTTLE,FOGERTY DRUGGIST.....................................   3.00
BOTTLE, FOUR COMPARTMENT DECANTER, 2 RINGS AROUND NECK,.....  25.00
BOTTLE,FRAIELLE-BRANCA-MILANO...............................   3.50
BOTTLE,FREE BLOWN OIL,AQUA..................................   5.00
BOTTLE,FRENCH PERFUME,PAIR AMBER BLOWN GLASS 6 IN. HIGH.....  30.00
BOTTLE,FROSTED WASHINGTON FIGURE............................  16.00
BOTTLE, FRUIT, ONE HALF PINT, GLASS TOP.....................   4.00
BOTTLE, FRUIT,PINT,GLASS LID................................   2.00
BOTTLE, GALIANO & DICKEL POWDER HORN........................  10.00
BOTTLE,GALIANO SOLDIER......................................  17.50
BOTTLE,GAMBLER..............................................   6.00
BOTTLE,GARRETT BROWN SNUFF..................................    .50
BOTTLE,GEM 2 QUART FRUIT JAR................................   8.00
BOTTLE,GENUINE PHOSPHATE GIN................................   4.00
BOTTLE,GERMAN HOP BITTERS,IRIDESCENCE.......................  35.00
BOTTLES GINGER BEER C.1900 FROM ENGLAND.....................   2.75
BOTTLE,GLASS OIL LEVER CLOSE FRUIT JAR,12...................  12.00
BOTTLE,GLASS FIGURAL,PAINTED BOY CHARACTER..................   7.00
BOTTLE,GLASS ROLLING PIN....................................   3.00
BOTTLE GLOBE TONIC BITTERS WITH 2 LABELS....................  62.50
BOTTLE, GLYCO-HEROIN, AMBER MEDICINE........................   5.00
BOTTLE,GOFFS HERB BITTERS,LABEL & CARTON....................   8.00
BOTTLE,GOLDRUSH LIQUOR,.....................................   2.50
BOTTLE,GOLDRUSH POTTERY BROWN & CREAM SHADED SODA
  POP,STAMPED KENNEDY.......................................   4.50
BOTTLE, GOOD HERB BITTERS...................................  12.00
BOTTLE,GREEK WARRIOR HEAD,BLUE WITH SILVER METALIZED
  HELMET,6 IN...............................................   1.25
BOTTLE,GREEN 10 SIDED SIPHON,PEWTER TOP & HANDLE,COCA COLA
```

```
IN SCRIPT.................................................   7.50
BOTTLE,GREEN BLOWN BARBER BOTTLE,ENAMEL DECORATED...........  38.50
BOTTLE, GREEN CAPER, 8 INDENTED PANELS, RING NECK...........  15.00
BOTTLE GREEN CARTERS INK,POUR SPOUT.........................   7.00
BOTTLE,GREEN CLAW 11 IN. HIGH...............................  24.00
BOTTLE,GREEN GLASS CORN,LOOKS LIKE EAR CORN.................  22.00
BOTTLE,GREEN INK............................................   9.00
BOTTLE,GREEN MOSES FIGURE,10 IN.............................   4.75
BOTTLE, GREEN MOSES POLAND WATER FACSIMILE, 6IN.............  15.00
BOTTLE,GREEN ONION-SHAPED BENEDICTINE.......................   5.00
BOTTLE,GREEN PEPPERSAUCE,SPIRAL RIDGED......................  17.50
BOTTLE,GREEN ROUND CAPERS...................................   5.00
BOTTLE,GREEN RUMFORD CHEMICAL...............................  16.50
BOTTLE,GREEN TURN MOLD BEER.................................  10.00
BOTTLE,GROVES TASTELESS CHILL TONIC
   1.00  TO...............................................    3.00
BOTTLE,GUITAR,16 IN.........................................  10.00
BOTTLE,GUITAR AMBER 16 IN...................................  10.00
BOTTLE,GYPSY DANCER,8 IN.,CLEAR,PAINTED.....................   7.00
BOTTLE,H.J.HEINZ FLUTED PRESERVE JAR,HAZEL GLASS CO.,PURPLE
   MARK....................................................    4.50
BOTTLE, HALF PINT AMBER UNION OVAL..........................   4.00
BOTTLE,HALF PINT HINGED LID,CLEAR JAR.......................   1.00
BOTTLE,HALLIDAY DRUG CO.,SALT LAKE..........................   2.50
BOTTLE,HALLS CATARRH CURE...................................   3.00
BOTTLE,HANDLED POTTERY MINERAL WATER........................  10.00
BOTTLE,HARDENS FIRE EXTINGUISHER,BLUE.......................  20.00
BOTTLE HARROLDS CLUB PINWHEEL...............................  30.00
BOTTLE,HAYNER WHISKEY
   5.00  TO...............................................   10.00
BOTTLE,HAYWARDS HAND FIRE GRENADE 1871......................  20.00
BOTTLE, HERO IMPROVED.......................................   6.00
BOTTLE, HICKS CAPUDINE......................................   2.00
BOTTLE,HIGGINS PURPLE INK...................................   1.00
BOTTLE,HILLBILLY ON BARREL WITH RIFLE.......................  12.50
BOTTLE,HOFFS GERMAN LINIMENT,5 IN.,BIMAL,12
   PANELLED,AQUA,BUBBLY.....................................   3.00
BOTTLE,HOM PAK MASON QUART,METAL LID........................   3.00
BOTTLE,HOODS SARSAPARILLA...................................   3.50
BOTTLE,HOODS SARSAPARILLA,APOTHECARIES ON BACK..............   6.00
BOTTLE,HOODS SARSAPARILLA,8 IN.,BIMAL,AQUA..................   4.00
BOTTLE, HOOKERS THROAT & LUNG REMEDY........................   4.50
BOTTLE,HORLICKS MALTED MILK.................................   3.00
BOTTLE,HOSTETTERS...........................................   5.00
BOTTLE,HOSTETTERS BITTERS
   6.50  TO...............................................    8.00
BOTTLE,HUMPHREYS MARVEL OF HEALING..........................   3.00
BOTTLE,IMPERIAL FLASK,......................................   3.00
BOTTLE,INDIANAPOLIS BREWING CO,EMBOSSED WOMAN...............   3.00
BOTTLE,INGRANS MILK WEED LARGE..............................    .75
BOTTLE,INK,MILK GLASS.......................................   6.00
BOTTLE, INK, TOLL TIN CONTAINER.............................   2.50
BOTTLE,IRISH MIST SOLDIER
  17.50  TO...............................................   25.00
BOTTLE,ITALIAN MAN SITTING ON BARREL........................  17.50
BOTTLE,J.W.DANT POT BELLY STOVE.............................  15.00
BOTTLE,J.W.PALMER WHISKEY SOLD BY J.W.SEAY,HALF PINT PURPLE.   4.50
BOTTLE,JAMAICA GINGER FLASK.................................   4.00
BOTTLE,JASPERWARE WITH 2 FACES,GREEN & WHITE................  12.00
BOTTLE,JENNY LIND,4X9 BUST IMPRESSED ON BOTTLE..............   4.99
BOTTLE JEWETTS HEALTH RESTORING BITTERS PONTIL..............  35.00
BOTTLE,JOHNSONS LINIMENT....................................   3.00
BOTTLE, JOHNSONS TONIC......................................   1.50
BOTTLE, K.C.MASON PINT......................................   3.50
BOTTLE, KATONKA, THE GREAT INDIAN REMEDY....................   3.50
```

```
BOTTLE KENNEDYS PRAIRIE WEED.................................  22.50
BOTTLE,KERR SELF-EASLING 1915..............................   1.50
BOTTLE,KING SOLOMONS BITTERS...............................  100.00
BOTTLE, KINSELLA 1874 TRUE MASON, CLEAR....................  17.50
BOTTLE,KNIGHT ON HORSE,CLEAR...............................  15.00
BOTTLE,LANGLEYS ROOT & HERB BITTERS,AQUA...................  22.00
BOTTLE,LAQUE BURGUATE SNUFF,SIGNED,INLAID SHELLS,GOLD &
   SILVER FOIL.............................................  275.00
BOTTLE,LASHS BITTERS.......................................   3.00
BOTTLE,LASHS BITTERS,2 LABELS..............................   5.00
BOTTLE, LASHS BITTERS,KIDNEY & LIVER.......................  10.00
BOTTLE,LASHS BITTERS,SAN FRANCISCO.........................  10.00
BOTTLE,LASHS BITTERS,SAN FRANCISCO SCREW TOP...............   4.00
BOTTLE,LASHS KIDNEY & LIVER BITTERS,AMBER BIMAL............   6.00
BOTTLE,LEOTRIC PINT FRUIT JAR..............................   8.00
BOTTLE, LEOTRIC QUART AQUA.................................   5.00
BOTTLE,LESTOIL FLASK,SHIP,BLUE & AMETHYST..................   4.50
BOTTLE, LIGHTNING JAR, AQUA................................   6.00
BOTTLE,LIGHTNING PINT FRUIT JAR............................   5.00
BOTTLE,LIGHTNING PUTNAM,AQUA,GLASS LID.....................   5.00
BOTTLE,LIGHTNING QUART FRUIT JAR...........................   5.00
BOTTLE,LIME TO MAUVE PERFUME,TEAR DROP APPLIED THROUGH BODY. 450.00
BOTTLE,LINCOLN BANK........................................   4.00
BOTTLE,LOG CABIN COVERED LUTTEDS COUGH DROPS...............  25.00
BOTTLE,LOWENSTEIN CORN WHISKEY.............................   4.00
BOTTLE,LUSTRE,DEEP AQUA,NO LID.............................   3.00
BOTTLE,LYDIA PINKHAM BIMAL AQUA............................   3.50
BOTTLE,LYDIA PINKHAM MEDICINE 14 OUNCE GREEN...............   3.50
BOTTLE,MADONNA FIGURINE,HAND BLOWN,DATED 1932,COBALT BLUE...  4.00
BOTTLE,MAN IN MILITARY UNIFORM,CLEAR.......................  18.00
BOTTLE MANDRAKE BITTERS....................................  10.00
BOTTLE, MARCHANDS PEROXIDE OF HYDROGEN.....................   1.00
BOTTLE, MARION MASON HALF GAL. JAR.........................  12.50
BOTTLE, MASON, DATED 1858, QUART, AQUA WITH ZINC LID.......   5.50
BOTTLE,MASON JAR DATED 1858................................   9.50
BOTTLE,MASON PINT FRUIT JAR................................   5.00
BOTTLE,MASONS 1858 QUART KEYSTONE 1 HALF GALLON............   6.00
BOTTLE,MASONS 1858 QUART MALTESE CROSS ,1 HALF GALLON......   6.00
BOTTLE,MASONS IMPORVED PAT. 1870 AMBER GLASS QUART
   JAR,AQUA,TIN LID........................................   9.50
BOTTLE,MASONS PAT.1858 QUART,AQUA..........................   5.00
BOTTLE,MASONS PAT. 1858 QUART,AQUA WITH CAP................   3.50
BOTTLE, MASONS PAT. 1858 WITH MALTESE CROSS................   5.00
BOTTLE,MC DONALD NEW PERFECT SEAL QUART,AQUA...............   2.50
BOTTLE,MC DONALDS AQUA,COMPLETE............................   3.25
BOTTLE,MELLINS FOOD........................................   2.75
BOTTLE,MELVIN BADGER COBALT BLUE...........................   7.50
BOTTLE,MILK................................................   1.50
BOTTLE, MILK BOTTLE, HALF PINT.............................   1.00
BOTTLE,MILK GLASS ALE......................................   6.50
BOTTLE,MILK GLASS CREAM JAR................................    .50
BOTTLE,MILK GLASS HOGANS MAGNOLIA BALM.....................   5.00
BOTTLE,MILLVILLE ATMOSPHERIC FRUIT JAR,AQUA,QUART..........   4.50
BOTTLE,MILLVILLE ATMOSPHERIC PINT FRUIT JAR................   6.00
BOTTLE,MINIATURE 3 IN. DEMI-JOHN,OLIVE GREEN...............   5.00
BOTTLE,MOSES IN BULRUSHES..................................  24.00
BOTTLE, MR. BOSTON PRESIDENTIAL INAUGURATION WHISKEY.......  25.00
BOTTLE MR. CARTER INK......................................   9.00
BOTTLE,MR.LINCOLN BANK,CLEAR,TOP FORMS HAT.................   4.50
BOTTLE,MR.PICKWICK.........................................  13.50
BOTTLE,MRS.BUTTERWORTH AMBER 10 IN.........................   3.00
BOTTLE, MRS. WINSLOWS SOOTHING SYRUP.......................   1.25
BOTTLE, MTA IN SHIELD,QUART,RECTANGULAR,LID................   4.50
BOTTLE, N&B LINIMENT.......................................   1.00
BOTTLE, NATIONAL REMEDY....................................   1.00
```

```
BOTTLE,NEW ENGLAND SAILING WIDOWS TEAR DROP VIAL............    10.00
BOTTLE,NICHOLAS LUTZ,6 IN. HIGH,BLUE & GREY SWIRLS..........    45.00
BOTTLE,NITRATE MAGNESIUM,PORCELAIN TOP......................     2.00
BOTTLE,OCTAGON PRESERVE JAR,AQUA............................     3.00
BOTTLE OLD DR. WARRENS QUAKER BITTERS.......................    50.00
BOTTLE, OLD MILK GLASS PAIR OF DICE.........................     8.00
BOTTLE, OLD QUAKER EMBOSSED,SCREWTOP........................     4.00
BOTTLE,OLD TAYLOR DISTILLERY................................    10.00
BOTTLE,OLIVE GREEN BLOB SEAL PERNOD FILS....................    12.00
BOTTLE,OLIVE GREEN PINT CHAMPAGNE...........................     2.50
BOTTLE,OLIVE GREEN QUART CHAMPAGNE..........................     2.00
BOTTLE,ORANGE CARNIVAL CANADA DRY...........................     7.00
BOTTLE, ORANGE CRUSH, PAT. JULY 20, 1920....................     9.00
BOTTLE,PAINE CELERY COMPOUND,AMBER..........................     7.50
BOTTLE,PAINES CELERY COMPOUND...............................     4.00
BOTTLE,PAINTED SNUFF ,WHITE GLASS STOPPER,RED OVERLAY ON
   SIDES....................................................    27.50
BOTTLE,PAIR DUELING PISTOL,GREEN WITH GOLD SCROLLWORK.......     9.95
BOTTLE,PAIR ORIENTAL SAKI ,& 5 CUPS.........................    16.00
BOTTLE,PAIR PINK HOBNAIL TOILET,6 IN. TALL,GROUND STOPPERS..    12.50
BOTTLE,PENGUIN,HEAD IS TOP..................................     8.50
BOTTLE,PERFUME,BACCHUS GLASS,SIGNED,6IN.H.,CREAM BODY.......   195.00
BOTTLE,PERFUME,FLORAL,TALL STOPPER..........................     7.50
BOTTLE,PERFUME,GREEN & WHITE OVERLAY WITH GILT..............   125.00
BOTTLE,PICCADILLY GIN,CRACKLE GLASS.........................     4.00
BOTTLE,PICKLE JAR...........................................     2.50
BOTTLE PIERCE INDIAN RESTORATIVE BITTERS....................    25.00
BOTTLE,PINT,CLEAR,FOSTER SEALFAST...........................     1.50
BOTTLE, PINT, GLASS LID, BLUE, BALL IDEAL...................     1.50
BOTTLE,PINT,GLASS LID,CLEAR ATLAS E-Z SEAL..................      .50
BOTTLE,PINT,GLASS LID,CLEAR,BALL IDEAL......................     1.00
BOTTLE,PINT,GLASS LID,CLEAR,DOUBLE SAFETY...................     1.50
BOTTLE,PINT,GLASS LID,CLEAR,PLAIN...........................     1.50
BOTTLE,PINT,PORCELAIN LID,BLUE ATLAS STRONG SHOULDER MASON..     4.50
BOTTLE,PINT,PORCELAIN LID,BLUE MASON........................     4.50
BOTTLE,PIRATE PISTOL,METALIZED GOLD,10 IN...................     1.25
BOTTLE, PISO, EMERALD GREEN.................................     3.00
BOTTLE,PITCHERS CASTORIA....................................     1.25
BOTTLE,PITKIN TYPE PINT FLASK,MIDWESTERN,OLIVE GREEN,RIBBING
   TO RIGHT.................................................   115.00
BOTTLE,PLAIN AMBER 3 PC. MOLD WHISKEY,QT....................     6.00
BOTTLE,PLAIN AMBER LADYS LEG WHISKEY QT. 3 PC. MOLD.........    12.00
BOTTLE,PLUTO WATER..........................................     2.00
BOTTLE,PONDS BITTERS,AMBER..................................    21.00
BOTTLE PONDS BITTERS , TWO LABELS...........................    45.00
BOTTLE, PONDS EXTRACT, 1846.................................     3.00
BOTTLE,POP,LOOSE MARBLE SEALED IN NECK,WITH DESING..........     8.50
BOTTLE,POWDER & SHOT CASTER ,...............................     7.50
BOTTLE,POWDER FLASK,GREEN,GAME..............................    30.00
BOTTLE,PRE-PROHIBITION BEER,EMBOSSED........................     2.00
BOTTLE,PRETZEL-SHAPED.......................................    15.00
BOTTLE PRICKLEY ASH BITTERS.................................    40.00
BOTTLE,PUMPKIN SEED.........................................     7.50
BOTTLE,PUMPKIN SEED PURPLE 5 OZ.............................     5.00
BOTTLE,PURPLE CURTICE BROS.KETCHUP..........................      .50
BOTTLE,PURPLE SHOO-FLY......................................     5.00
BOTTLE,PURPLE WHITE PINE COUNTY MILK........................     3.00
BOTTLE,QUART ECONOMY JAR 1903-10,PURPLE.....................     5.00
BOTTLE, QUART, GLASS LID, AMBER, PUTMAN.....................    12.50
BOTTLE, QUART, GLASS LID, BLUE, ATLAS E-Z SEAL..............     2.50
BOTTLE, QUART, GLASS LID, BLUE, BALL IDEAL..................     2.00
BOTTLE, QUART, GLASS LID, BLUE, BALL IDEAL, SQUARE..........     2.50
BOTTLE, QUART, GLASS LID, CL. FOSTER SEALFAST...............     2.00
BOTTLE, QUART, GLASS LID, LIGHT, LIGHTNING..................     1.50
BOTTLE,QUART MASON JAR 1858.................................     2.00
```

BOTTLE, QUART, PORCL. LID, BLUE, PLAIN....................... 4.50
BOTTLE, QUART, PORCL. LID, BLUE, BALL MASON.................. 2.00
BOTTLE, QUART, PORCL. LID, BLUE, MASONS PAT.,............... 4.50
BOTTLE, QUART, PORCL. LID, BLUE, MASONS PAT. NOV. 30, 1858,
  HIGH RELIEF... 5.50
BOTTLE,QUART SIZE GREEN WAVY BLOWN GLASS WINE,RECESSED
  BOTTOM.. 2.50
BOTTLE,QUART WHISKEY,AMBER.................................. 1.00
BOTTLE,QUART WHISKEY,CLEAR.................................. 1.00
BOTTLE,QUEEN FLORIDA....................................... 3.75
BOTTLE,QUEEN IMPROVED PINT,GLASS LID....................... 3.25
BOTTLE,QUEEN WIDE MOUTH ADJUSTABLE QUART AMETHYST.......... 3.50
BOTTLE,RED AMBER LIQUID MALT EXTRACT....................... 3.75
BOTTLE RED DELFT, NO LABELS................................ 10.00
BOTTLE,RED KEY MASON PINT FRUIT JAR........................ 8.00
BOTTLE, RED RAVEN SPLITS AMBER............................. 2.25
BOTTLE,REDDISH AMBER BARREL BITTERS,KEYSTONE BITTERS....... 150.00
BOTTLE,ROLLED NECK GIN..................................... 40.00
BOTTLE,ROUND BOTTOM,AQUA................................... 3.50
BOTTLE,ROUND BOTTOM POP.................................... 4.00
BOTTLE ROUND, CLEAR LASHS BITTERS.......................... 7.50
BOTTLE,ROUND COBALT INK.................................... 6.50
BOTTLE, ROYAL RUBY ANCHOR GLASS 9IN........................ 15.00
BOTTLE,ROYAL RUBY SCHLITZ BEER,7 OZ. WITH LABEL............ 12.00
BOTTLE ROYAL RUBY RED BEER................................. 7.50
BOTTLE,RUBY DOUBLE SCENT BOTTLE............................ 45.00
BOTTLE,RUBY RED QUART BEER................................. 9.00
BOTTLE,RUBY RED SPLITZ..................................... 12.00
BOTTLE RUSHS BITTERS....................................... 30.00
BOTTLE RUST CLEOPATRA...................................... 10.00
BOTTLE,S.3.RICHARDSONS BITTERS,SMOOTH BASE................. 20.00
BOTTLE,S.C.DISPENSARY,PALMETTO,AQUA HALF PINT UNION FLASK... 19.00
BOTTLE, SAILOR... 20.00
BOTTLE,SANFORDS INK.. 1.00
BOTTLE,SANFORDS PURPLE INK................................. 1.00
BOTTLE,SAPPHIRE BLUE 6 IN. BARBER.......................... 9.50
BOTTLE,SAPPHIRE BLUE 9 IN. ,FLORAL ENAMEL & GOLD DECORATION. 35.00
BOTTLE,SAPPHIRE BLUE COGNAC,CUT & FACETED STOPPER.......... 28.00
BOTTLE,SARSAPARILLA,AQUA BELLS............................. 12.50
BOTTLE,SARSAPARILLA,AQUA BRISTOLS GENUINE.................. 9.50
BOTTLE,SARSAPARILLA,AQUA DANAS............................. 6.00
BOTTLE,SARSAPARILLA,AQUA HOODS............................. 3.00
BOTTLE,SAUCE.. 1.50
BOTTLE,SCOTTS EMULSION
  1.50   TO.. 2.75
BOTTLE,SCOTTS EMULSION,AQUA,COD-LIVER OIL IN BASE.......... 4.00
BOTTLE,SCOTTS EMULSION,FISH ON BOTTOM,9 IN................. 3.50
BOTTLE, SHEARED TOP CHINESE OPIUM.......................... 2.25
BOTTLE,SHOE POLISH,ROUND................................... 1.25
BOTTLE, SHOO FLY FLASK..................................... 5.00
BOTTLE SHORT PIN.. 10.00
BOTTLE, SKELETON POISON.................................... 15.00
BOTTLE,SLIPPER.. 3.50
BOTTLE,SMALLEY FULL MEASURE MONOGRAM QUART,METAL LID....... 6.50
BOTTLE,SMALLEY ROYAL PINT FRUIT JAR........................ 4.00
BOTTLE SMOKED CRYSTAL...................................... 4.00
BOTTLE,SNUFF,INSIDE PAINTING............................... 18.00
BOTTLE,SNUFF,PORCELAIN,BLUE & WHITE,UNDERGLAZE
  CRACKLED,1722-1735...................................... 95.00
BOTTLE,SODA POP BLOWN WITH MARBLE INSIDE PINCHED-IN NECK.... 12.00
BOTTLE,SODA WITH SPRING & WHITE PORCELAIN STOPPER.......... 3.50
BOTTLE,SOMCO GENUINE MASON,CLEAR QUART..................... 1.50
BOTTLE SONOMA WINE BITTERS................................. 10.00
BOTTLE,SPANISH BULLFIGHTER,8 IN.,CLEAR,PAINTED............. 7.00
BOTTLE, SQUARE, 6 STARS ON SHOULDER, EMBOSSED SODA

```
WATER,DATED..........................................    4.50
BOTTLE SQUARE AMBER LASHS KIDNEY LIVER BITTERS...........   14.00
BOTTLE,STODDARD DEMI-JOHN 11 IN. HIGH,PONTIL,............   35.00
BOTTLE,STORE SQUIRREL BRAND SALTED PEANUT,YELLOW STENCIL
  COVER..................................................    5.00
BOTTLE,STUBBY PIN BOTTLE,WOOD STOPPER....................   50.00
BOTTLE,SWAYZEES IMPROVED MASON QUART,AQUA................    5.00
BOTTLE, TAN & BROWN POTTERY ,STAMPED PORTO BELLO........    5.50
BOTTLE,TAYLOR DISTILLERY WITH RED VELVET BASE...........   17.50
BOTTLE,TAYLOR VINEGAR BITTER............................   10.00
BOTTLE,TEACHERS HIGHLAND CREAM..........................    1.50
BOTTLE,THE GREAT DR.KILMERS SWAMP,SPECIFIC..............    6.50
BOTTLE,TIPPECANOE,AMBER,DATED...........................   25.00
BOTTLE,TOBY.............................................    7.50
BOTTLE,TORPEDO SODAS BLOB TOP...........................    3.00
BOTTLE, TRADE MARK LIGHTNING AQUA,REGISTERED US PATENT
  OFFICE................................................    5.00
BOTTLE, TRADE MARK LIGHTNING,REGISTERED US PATENT OFFICE....    2.00
BOTTLE,TRAGER WHISKEY FLASK,AMBER.......................    4.50
BOTTLE, TROMMERS, BROOKLYN..............................    2.00
BOTTLE,VAN SCHUYVER....................................   12.00
BOTTLE,VARIANT BURDOCKS BLOOD BITTERS...................   14.50
BOTTLE,VINAL EMBOSSED DATED CHESTNUT-SHAPED AMBER.......    4.00
BOTTLE,VIOLIN SCROLL HISTORICAL FLASK...................   60.00
BOTTLE,WAHOO BITTERS,PAPER LABEL........................    8.00
BOTTLE,WALKERS KILMARNACK WHISKEY.......................    4.00
BOTTLE, WARNER, 4 IN....................................    2.00
BOTTLE, WARNERS SAFE....................................    7.50
BOTTLE, WARNERS SAFE CURE...............................   15.00
BOTTLE, WARNERS SAFE,SAFE EMBOSSING.....................    8.50
BOTTLE, WELZ & ZERWECK, BROOKLYN.......................    2.00
BOTTLE,WEYMANS SNUFF JAR................................    7.00
BOTTLE,WHISKEY,AMBER BIMAL LIQUOZONE...................    1.50
BOTTLE,WHISKEY,AMBER QUART,BM,RECTANGULAR,EMBOSSED
  CHAS.DENNEHY & CO.....................................    3.50
BOTTLE,WHISKEY,CLEAR QUART BIMAL,3 IN. SQUARE,MORLEES BAUCHU
  GIN...................................................    6.00
BOTTLE,WHISKEY,CLEAR QUART BIMAL,KIDNEY GIN,TAPERED
  RECTANGULAR...........................................   10.00
BOTTLE, WHISKEY, CROWN DISTILLERIES.....................   10.00
BOTTLE, WHISKEY, DAVY CROCKETT..........................   50.00
BOTTLE,WHISKEY FLASK,CLEAR..............................    2.50
BOTTLE, WHISKEY, GOLD DUST KENTUCKY BOURBON.............   75.00
BOTTLE, WHISKEY, HAYNER, TROY, OHIO.....................   10.00
BOTTLE, WHISKEY, J.E.BRADY,MILL VALLEY..................   22.50
BOTTLE, WHISKEY, J.H.CUTTER.............................   15.00
BOTTLE, WHISKEY, JESSE MOORE HUNT,S.F...................   12.00
BOTTLE, WHISKEY,KELLOGGS................................   35.00
BOTTLE, WHISKEY,MONOGRAM................................   20.00
BOTTLE,WHISKEY,OLIVE GREEN QUART BIMAL,STRAUSS BROS. CO.....    4.50
BOTTLE, WHISKEY, QUAKER MAID,GILT EDGE,SQUARE...........   10.00
BOTTLE, WHITE ENAMELED LARGE VODKA BEAR.................   15.00
BOTTLE, WHITE HOUSE VINEGAR, HOUSE EMBOSSED, PAT. MARCH 6,
  1909..................................................    7.00
BOTTLE,WHITE SITTING BEAR...............................    6.00
BOTTLE,WHITNEY MASON QUART FRUIT JAR....................    5.00
BOTTLE, WILSONS WA-HOO BITTERS,PAPER LABELS & CONTENTS......    9.00
BOTTLE,WINE FLAT PINT,AMBER,SCREW TOP,EMBOSSED GRAPES.......    2.00
BOTTLE,WORLDS FAIR......................................   15.00
BOTTLE,WYETH FRUIT SYRUP,ORIGINAL LABEL.................    4.00
BOTTLE YERBA BUENA BITTERS..............................   85.00
BOTTLE, YUENGLING, POTTSVILLE, PA.......................    2.00
```

*BOXES of all kinds are collected. They were made of thin strips of inlaid wood,
metal, tortoiseshell, embroidery, or other material.*

BOX   36   BRASS ART NOUVEAU

BOX, SEE ALSO STORE, BOX, TIN.............................
BOX, ART NOUVEAU SHAPED JEWEL BOX LINED IN PINK, GOLD.........   22.50
BOX, BLACK LACQUER 4-SECTION WITH GOLD DESIGN, CIRCA 1840.....   95.00
BOX, BURNT WOOD HINGED, 8 IN. BY 8 IN.........................   5.00
BOX, FRENCH JEWEL AND RING, HINGED, BEVELED GLASS SLANTED
   COVER, BRASS...   16.00
BOX, GLOVE, BLACK LACQUER, ORIENTAL FIGURES IN GOLD...........   25.00
BOX, GREEN CINNEBAR STAMP BOX, 4 X 2 X 1......................   17.50
BOX, JEWEL CASE ON BRASS FEET, BEVELLED GLASS, 8 IN. BY 6 IN...   75.00
BOX, JEWELRY, GOLD PLATED, LIKE MINIATURE LOUIS XVI 2 DRAWER
   CHEST...   35.00
BOX, OVAL SPLINT, 7 IN. BY 3 IN. FROM CONN. PAINTED DESIGN....   8.00
BOX, PATCH, , 2 X 1 IN. GOLD WASHED FRAME, BLOODSTONE IN LID..   22.00
BOX, RUBY RED GLASS HINGED COVERED, LEAF & BERRIES & GOLD TRIM   48.50
BOX, SEA CAPTAIN DITTY, VENEER PANELS, PAPER LINED, MIRROR IN
   LID...   5.50
BOX, TRINKET, 2 PART COVER, GIRL FEEDING CAT, OVAL MIRROR.......   25.00
BOX, TRINKET, FANCY LID..   10.00
BOX, TRINKET, HAND..   28.00
BOX, TRINKET, LITTLE RED RIDING HOOD & THE WOLF...............   35.00
BOX, TRINKET, OVAL BASE, WHITE SWAN COVER.....................   20.00
BOX, TRINKET WITH COVER, MILK GLASS...........................   7.00
   BRANDING IRON, SEE IRON...................................

BRASS had been used for decorative pieces and useful tablewares since ancient
times. It is an alloy of copper, zinc, and other metals.
   BRASS, SEE ALSO BELLS, BRONZE, MINIATURE, TOOLS.........
BRASS 2 IN. HORSE BRIDLE ROSETTES.............................   6.50
BRASS 2 PAN SCALES...   15.00
BRASS 3 BRANCH GIRANDOLE, PAUL & VIRGINIA, MARBLE BASE, 5
   PRISMS..   47.50
BRASS 3 IN. DOOR KNOCKER.....................................   6.50
BRASS 3 SOCKET CANDELABRA , LIONS, PAIR......................   25.00
BRASS , 4 BELLS CLOSED ON LEATHER STRAP......................   7.50
BRASS 4 FOOTED INKWELL, LIFT UP COVER, WHITE CHINA INSERT.....   4.75
BRASS 4 FOOTED TRIVET, OPENWORK & FLOWER DESIGN, MARKED CHINA.   2.75
BRASS 4 IN. HARNESS BUCKLE...................................   2.00
BRASS 4 LEVER 1891 PADLOCK...................................   3.00
BRASS 5 BRANCH CANDALABRA, ARMS SWING........................   10.00
BRASS 7 IN. DOOR LATCH.......................................   2.00
BRASS 7 LIGHT MENORAH CANDLESTICK, 9 IN. HIGH................   9.75
BRASS 8 IN. TALL ELEPHANT....................................   15.00
BRASS 9 IN. CONVERTED KEROSENE LAMP, DURAND SHADE, GOLD LINED.   45.00
BRASS 9 IN. SPUN CANDLESTICK, REEDED STEM....................   8.00
BRASS 11 IN. BARBER BOWL, NECK NOTCH.........................   45.00
BRASS 12 X 14 FLORENTINE EASEL FRAME........................   18.00
BRASS 12 IN. SHOVEL..   15.75
BRASS, 18TH CENTURY JAGGING WHEEL............................   9.50
BRASS 18TH CENTURY PASTRY JIGGER, IRON & BRASS IMPLEMENTS....   15.00
BRASS & COPPER 17TH CENTURY DUTCH TOBACCO BOX................   85.00
BRASS & COPPER TEAKETTLE.....................................   15.00
BRASS & COPPER TIN LINED CHAFING DISH........................   12.00
BRASS & IRON TURTLE SPITTOON.................................   75.00
BRASS & NICKLE PLATED FIRE HOSE NOZZLE.......................   5.00
BRASS & ROCOCO BEVELED GLASS MIRROR WITH 2 CANDLEHOLDERS....   38.00
BRASS & SILVER PLATED SHAVING STAND,.........................   15.00
BRASS & TORTOISE SHELL CALLING CARD CASE.....................   4.00
BRASS ADJUSTABLE POCKET PITCH PIPE...........................   22.50
BRASS ADVERTISING LETTER OPENER..............................   4.50
BRASS ADVERTISING MATCH SAFE, LOCOMOTIVE & EAGLE, MARKED
   ANHEUSER BUSCH..   7.50
BRASS ANDIRONS PAIR 19 IN. HIGH, URN FINIALS.................   25.00
BRASS APOSTLE BELL WITH INKWELL INSIDE MADE OF WHITE
   PORCELAIN, MARKED.......................................   18.00
BRASS ART NOUVEAU 4 FOOTED TRAY, FIGURE OF SLEEPING GIRL.....   3.75

```
BRASS ART NOUVEAU EASEL-TYPE MIRROR,LADY IN FLOWING ROBE AT
    SIDE.................................................   11.50
BRASS ASTRAL LAMP WITH PRISMS...........................   75.00
BRASS AUTO BULB HORN,FLEXIBLE HOSE......................   58.00
BRASS BACK SADDLE BELL..................................   25.00
BRASS BALINESE HAND HAMMERED TRAY,20 IN.,SCALLOPED EDGES....   35.00
BRASS BALLS RESEMBLING CHESTNUTS,......................   12.50
BRASS,BAROMETER INK STAND,GLASS DOME,IRON SCROLL WORK HOLDS
    PEN.................................................   15.00
BRASS BASE LAMP WITH DRAGON HANDLES,PINK & GREEN SHADE......   48.00
BRASS BASEBALL MITT.....................................   10.00
BRASS BASKET............................................    9.00
BRASS BASKET FROM TRAIN COACH RESTROOM..................   15.00
BRASS BED WARMER,WOODEN HANDLE..........................   45.00
BRASS BEEHIVE CANDLESTICKS,PAIR,ENGLISH CIRCA 1830,OCTAGONAL
    BASE................................................   48.00
BRASS BEER PAIL WITH SPOUT..............................   15.00
BRASS BELL,DUTCH BOY & GIRL.............................    8.00
BRASS BELL,EMBOSSED,JADE TOP............................   10.00
BRASS BELLS ON BRASS STRAP,4 BELLS......................   12.00
BRASS BELL ON LOOSE SPRING..............................    6.00
BRASS BELL,QUEEN ISABELLA...............................    9.00
BRASS BELL STANDING LADY WITH HOOP SKIRT................   18.00
BRASS BELL STANDING LADY WITH MUFF......................   22.00
BRASS BELL STANDING LADY WITH SUNBONNET.................   12.00
BRASS BIRD CAGE,GABLE TOP,TWISTED ORMOLU UPRIGHT,GREEN ONYX.   25.00
BRASS BIRD CAGE,RED & BLACK TRIM WITH RED WOOD FINIALS......   35.00
BRASS BIRD WHISTLE,THIN.................................    6.00
BRASS BOOK ENDS,CHARLES LINDBERGH,PAIR..................   20.00
BRASS BOOK,ETCHED SCROLL WORK WITH CAMEO PROFILE OF WOMEN ON
    COVER...............................................   15.00
BRASS BOWL,CHINESE WITH DRAGON AND KEY DESIGN,9 IN. DIA.....   32.50
BRASS,BOWL DIPPER WITH WROUGHT IRON HANDLE..............   22.00
BRASS BOWLED LADLE,IRON HANDLE..........................   12.50
BRASS,BOX,IRON WITH INNER SLUG..........................   25.00
BRASS,BOX,POZZANIS COMPLEXION POWDER,ART NOUVEAU SCROLL WORK    8.00
BRASS BREAD CRUMB TRAY..................................    3.50
BRASS BRONZE CANDLESTICKS,PAIR,10 IN. TALL,.............   30.00
BRASS BUCKET TOOTHPICK..................................    5.50
BRASS BURMA VASE,5 IN. TALL,GEOMETRIC ,DESIGN..........    5.00
BRASS BUTTON,PICTURE,1 IN.,OPEN-WORK,KATE GREENWAY CAT ON
    FENCE...............................................    8.50
BRASS CANDELABRA,PAIR...................................   35.00
BRASS CANDLE SNUFFER,10 IN..............................    5.00
BRASS CANDLE SNUFFER,11 IN..............................    5.00
BRASS CANDLE SNUFFER,ORNATE.............................   12.50
BRASS CANDLESTICK,7 IN.
    10.00  TO...........................................   11.00
BRASS CANDLESTICK,11 IN.................................   20.00
BRASS CANDLESTICK,CHINA.................................   10.00
BRASS CANDLESTICK,PAIR..................................   15.00
BRASS CANDLESTICK,PAIR,ROUND BASE,TRUMPET,PUSH-UP.......   30.00
BRASS CANDLESTICK WITH SILVER FILIGREE IN EGYPTIAN
    DESIGNS,PAIR........................................   20.00
BRASS,CANDLESTICKS,7 IN.,UNSCREW,PAIR...................   12.00
BRASS CANDLESTICKS,22 IN. TALL WITH SPIKE TOPS,PAIR.....   25.00
BRASS CANDLESTICKS,PAIR,13 IN. HIGH.....................   42.00
BRASS CANDLESTICKS,PAIR,BOTTOM MARKED CHINA,6-SIDED
    BASE,ENGRAVING......................................    8.00
BRASS,CANNON,11 IN. SHOOTER.............................   15.00
BRASS CANNON CARRIAGE,BRASS WHEELS,BRASS BARREL.........   75.00
BRASS CARRIAGE LAMP,PAIR................................   45.00
BRASS,CAST DOUBLE STANDING PICTURE FRAME................   17.50
BRASS CAST EAGLE HEAD NUT CRACKER.......................    9.00
BRASS CASTERS, SMALL....................................    3.00
```

BRASS CHAMBERSTICK,OVAL SAUCER WITH HOOK ,LONDON CIRCA 1820.	28.00
BRASS CHESTNUT ROASTER,WROUGHT IRON HANDLE	30.00
BRASS CHINESE BOWLS,3	6.00
BRASS CHINESE DINNER GONG,BELL HANGS FROM BRASS PAGODA	12.00
BRASS CHINESE JARDINEIRE,FOOTED SEPARATE BASE	45.00
BRASS CHINESE WALL DINNER CHIMES,4 TUBULAR PIPES	22.50
BRASS CHURCH -TYPE 7 ARM CANDELABRA,34 IN. TALL	50.00
BRASS,CIGAR CUTTER,MOOSE HEAD HANDLE	12.50
BRASS CIGAR HUMIDOR	6.00
BRASS COFFEE URN,BULBOUS WITH FAUCET,ON CURVED FEET	30.00
BRASS,COMPASS,8 IN. WIDE	55.00
BRASS CONDUCTORS CAP BADGE,P & R F RY,MAINE	5.00
BRASS CONE SHAPE BELL	4.25
BRASS CONTAINER FOR FASTENERS 1889	2.50
BRASS COOKING STOVE ,DOME TOP,PIERCED CENTER SECTION,FLUTED BASE	120.00
BRASS-COPPER 2 HANDLED VALVE SPOUT COFFEE POT	15.00
BRASS CORONATION 3 IN. DOOR KNOCKER DATED 1953	10.00
BRASS CUSPIDOR,2IN.HI	3.00
BRASS CUSPIDOR,FLARED TOP 5IN	15.00
RASS CUSPIDOR WITH PRESENTATION PLAQUE & SEAL,MINIATURE	7.50
BRASS DATED SOLAR CARBIDE BICYCLE LAMP	12.00
BRASS DESK TRAY,RAISED SIDED,2 OPEN HANDLES,DRAGONS	10.00
BRASS DINNER GONG ON PEDESTAL	2.50
BRASS DOOR HINGES,PR.10 IN	12.50
BRASS DOOR KNOCKER	18.00
BRASS DOOR KNOCKER FOR BEDROOM,WISE OLD OWL	6.00
BRASS DOOR KNOCKER WITH BELL ON END AS STRIKER MARKED BELLS OF SONIA	5.00
BRASS DOOR PULLS	5.00
BRASS DOUBLE INKWELL & PEN REST, HINGED LID,FOOTED	5.00
BRASS DOUBLE LEMON TOP ANDIRONS	145.00
BRASS,DRAWER PULLS,METAL HANDLES	2.00
BRASS EAGLE DOOR KNOCKER,LAUREL SWAG IN BEAK	45.00
BRASS EAGLE ON MARBLE STAND	20.00
BRASS EAGLE ON ROUND BLACK WOODEN BASE	18.00
BRASS EASEL PICTURE FRAME	1.00
BRASS ECCLESIASTICAL CANDLEHOLDERS,FOUR,3 CLAW FEET	275.00
BRASS ELEPHANT,5 IN	6.00
BRASS EMBER CARRIER,WOOD HANDLE	45.00
BRASS ENAMELED NAPKIN RING	1.50
BRASS ENGLISH CHESTNUT ROASTER,PIERCED HANDLE,EMBOSSED SHIP DECOR	24.50
BRASS,ENGLISH-TYPE LOCOMOTIVE,18 FLANGED WHEELS	75.00
BRASS ENGRAVED HOT-COAL PIPE TONGS,4IN	12.50
BRASS ENGRAVED TIFFANY MARKED PEN WIPER	25.00
BRASS EWER,HANDPAINTED FLOWERS & LEAVES,MARKED B & H	8.00
BRASS EXTENSION BOOK RACK,OWL ON EACH END	18.50
BRASS FIGURAL BELL OF FRIAR HOLDING BABE	32.50
BRASS FIREMARK,WASHINGTON MUTUAL	48.00
BRASS FIREPLACE FENDER,62 X 12 IN.,OPEN FRET SHEET BRASS	75.00
BRASS FIRE PLACE ROASTING FORK	8.50
BRASS FIRE TRUCK BELL	65.00
BRASS FISH PAPER CLIP,3 IN	8.00
BRASS FOOTED INKWELL STAND WITH HOLDERS FOR 3 PENS	18.00
BRASS FRAME,OVAL CURLY-Q WITH EASEL,11 X 9 IN	15.00
BRASS FRENCH CHARACTER BELL,ELIZABETHAN LADY	16.00
BRASS GLASS BLOWERS PUNTY ROD,BUGLE TYPE MOUTH PIECE	20.00
BRASS GOLD-COIN SCALES,6 IN. BEAM,2 IN. PANS	13.00
BRASS GONG & STAND ,8 IN. DIA	39.50
BRASS GOOSE NECK TODDY KETTLE,BUTTON FEET	35.00
BRASS HAMMERED BOOK-ENDS	2.50
BRASS HAND BELL	2.00
BRASS HAND BELL,10 IN. H	28.50
BRASS HAND DOOR KNOCKER FROM SPANISH HOUSE	20.00

```
BRASS,HAND MIRROR,RAISED CUPID,LEAVES,SCROLLS...............    12.00
BRASS HANDLED CANDLESTICK WITH FILIGREE BRASS SHADE.........    12.50
BRASS HANDMADE 5 IN. CANDLESTICK,ROUND BOTTOM..............     4.75
BRASS HANDMADE PADLOCK WITH KEY............................    16.00
BRASS HAND MIRROR WITH FLOWERED PORCELAIN BACK.............     8.00
BRASS HARNESS KNOBS,PAIR...................................     3.50
BRASS-HEADED WOODEN-HANDLED PARADE TORCH...................    17.50
BRASS,HEAVY 11 IN. CANDLE STICK...........................     20.00
BRASS HENS FOOT & FEATHER LETTER OPENER....................     4.00
BRASS HORSESHOE DOOR KNOCKER WITH BRASS STRIKER PLATE.......    3.95
BRASS HORSESHOE SHAPE PADLOCK DATED JUNE 24, 1879..........     5.00
BRASS HUMIDOR..............................................     2.50
BRASS INCENSE BURNER,FOOTED,FOO DOG........................    10.00
BRASS,INDIA,DECANTER,3 IN. TALL............................     3.50
BRASS INDIAN HORNS.........................................     7.00
BRASS INDIAN VASE,ENGRAVING WITH BUDDHAS,2 COBRA HANDLES....    25.00
BRASS INKSTAND CIRCA 1770..................................   165.00
BRASS INKSTAND,ROCOCO PATTERN,HINGED BRASS LID,FEET WITH
    TRAY...................................................    23.00
BRASS INKWELL,GLASS INSERT.................................    20.00
BRASS INKWELL,LIFT-UP COVER,GLASS INSERT...................     3.75
RASS INKWELL,ORNATE........................................    65.00
BRASS INKWELL STAND & PEN REST.............................     4.75
BRASS INKWELL WITH GLASS INSERT............................     4.00
BRASS INKWELL,VIKING DESIGN,6 IN. TALL,HINGED COVER........    12.50
BRASS INKWELL WITH OPAL MILK GLASS LINER...................    12.50
BRASS JAMB HOOKS,PAIR,FOR HOLDING FIRE PLACE TOOLS..........    25.00
BRASS JAPAN 11 IN. CANDLE HOLDERS,CORKSCREW STEM,PAIR.......     3.00
BRASS JARDINIERE...........................................    10.00
BRASS,JARDINIERE,9 IN. ACROSS,3 BALL FEET..................     8.00
BRASS JARDINIERE AND BASE,LIONS HEAD HANDLES,SEPARATE 25 IN.
    PEDESTAL...............................................    57.50
BRASS JELLY KETTLE,14 IN. DIAMETER.........................    25.00
BRASS JELLY KETTLE,IRON HANDLE.............................    15.00
BRASS JEWEL BOX,VELVET LINED,PICTURE UNDER GLASS OF NOBLE
    WOMAN..................................................    15.00
BRASS JEWELED EASEL FRAME..................................    15.00
BRASS JEWELED EASEL FRAME,OPEN FLORAL DESIGN...............    15.50
BRASS JEWELED PICTURE FRAME,7 X 5 IN.......................     9.50
BRASS KEY..................................................     2.00
BRASS KNIFE,US WWI HANDLE TRENCH,MKD. US 1918..............    22.50
BRASS LADIES LEG 8 IN. SHOE HORN...........................     3.00
BRASS LADLE WITH ROLLED RIM,IRON HANDLE....................    35.00
BRASS LAMP STAND,SQUARE BOWED LEGS,WHITE MARBLE TOP........    47.50
BRASS LAP SPITTOON.........................................    13.00
BRASS LEATHER COVERED TRAVELING INKWELL....................     2.75
BRASS LETTER OPENER,GODDESS OF FERTILITY...................     3.50
BRASS LETTER OPENER,KNIGHT HANDLE..........................    15.00
BRASS,LETTER OPENER,SHAKESPEARE HANDLE.....................     6.50
BRASS,LETTER RACK,BURNISHED & LACQUERED....................    65.00
BRASS MAIL BOX,CORBIN......................................    12.50
BRASS MARINERS SPY GLASS...................................    30.00
BRASS MARKED AUTO TAIL LAMP PATENT DATE 1897...............    65.00
BRASS MASTHEAD LIGHT,17 IN.,360 DEGREES....................   110.00
BRASS MECHANICAL PENCIL,GREEN JEWEL AT TOP,RETRACTABLE,19TH
    CENTURY................................................     3.50
BRASS MEDALLION OF GENERAL LA·FAYETTE,LACQUERED FRAME.......    15.00
BRASS MINIATURE BELL.......................................     1.00
BRASS MINIATURE BOWL ON STANDARD...........................     2.00
BRASS MINIATURE CARAFE.....................................     2.00
BRASS MINIATURE COVERED COMPOTE ON STANDARD................     4.00
BRASS MINIATURE COVERED GYPSY KETTLE AND TRIPOD............    10.00
BRASS MINIATURE DOUBLE BOILER..............................     3.00
BRASS MINIATURE FRY PAN....................................     2.00
BRASS MINIATURE HANDLED COOKING PAN........................     2.00
```

```
BRASS MINIATURE HANDLED MUG..................................   1.00
BRASS MINIATURE HANDLELESS CUP & SAUCER......................   3.00
BRASS MINIATURE LOG BASKET...................................   4.00
BRASS MINIATURE PAIR CANDLE STICKS...........................   3.00
BRASS MINIATURE SALT & PEPPER SHAKER SET.....................   3.00
BRASS MINIATURE SALT SHAKER..................................   1.00
BRASS MINIATURE TRAY,HANDLED.................................   4.00
BRASS,MINIATURE WINE GOBLET..................................   2.00
BRASS MINIATURE WINE JUG & STOPPER...........................   3.00
BRASS MIRROR STAND WITH OVAL MIRROR,4 ANGELS IN DESIGN.......  26.50
BRASS MORTAR & PESTLE,3 IN...................................  18.00
BRASS MORTAR & PESTLE,5 IN. TALL.............................  27.50
BRASS MORTAR & PESTLE........................................  20.00
 RASS MORTAR & PESTLE,4 IN...................................  15.00
BRASS MORTAR & PESTLE WITH 2 HANDLES.........................  20.00
BRASS NATIONAL CASH REGISTER,RESISTERS TO $3.99,.............  65.00
BRASS NICKEL PLATED CHAFING DISH WITH BURNER.................   8.50
BRASS NICKEL PLATED SPITTOON.................................  10.50
BRASS NUT CRACKER SHAPE ROOSTER,2 HANDLES,5 IN. LONG.........   4.95
BRASS OBLONG DOOR KNOCKER....................................  35.00
BRASS OCTAGONAL PAIR CENTER PUSH-UP CANDLESTICKS WITH TURNED
  POSTS.......................................................  25.00
BRASS OIL CAN WITH CHAIN HELD SCREW CAP......................   3.00
BRASS ON BLACK ENAMEL CIGARETTE BOX,WOOD LINED,HINGED COVER.    4.00
BRASS OPERA GLASSES,CHEVALIER OPTICIAN.......................   3.50
BRASS OPIUM PIPE LINER.......................................   7.50
BRASS OVAL BREAD TRAY........................................   3.00
BRASS OVAL BASKET WEAVE FOOTED CARD TRAY WITH HANDPAINTED...    2.75
BRASS OVAL DISH,5 X 10 IN....................................   3.75
BRASS OVAL TRAY,11 X 8 IN.,2 HANDLES.........................   4.50
BRASS OWL PAPER CLIP.........................................   3.50
BRASS PADLOCK................................................   5.00
BRASS PADLOCK & KEY 1882.....................................   5.00
BRASS PAGODA SHAPE BUILDING,7 STORIES,MARKED CHINA...........   7.95
BRASS PAIL,E.MILLER & CO.MERIDEN CT.PAT.AUG.1868,LACQUERED..  30.00
BRASS,PAIR 3 CANDLE HOLDER WALL CANDLESTICKS.................  85.00
BRASS PAIR 7 IN. CANDLESTICKS................................  11.00
BRASS PAIR 8 IN. CANDLESTICKS,TWISTED STEM...................  25.00
BRASS PAIR 10 IN. CANDLEHOLDERS..............................  20.00
BRASS PAIR 12 IN. BEEHIVE CANDLESTICKS.......................  27.50
BRASS PAIR BALL TOP ANDIRONS,SLIPPER FEET....................  85.00
BRASS PAIR BEEHIVE CENTER PUSH-UP CANDLESTICKS...............  35.00
BRASS PAIR CANDLESTICK,HOLDS 3 CANDLES,2 LIONS ON EACH.......  40.00
BRASS PAIR CANDLESTICKS,27 IN. HIGH,RELIGIOUS FACES ON BASE.  85.00
BRASS PAIR CANDLESTICKS,ANCHOR BASES.........................  28.00
BRASS PAIR CANDLESTICKS,CHINA................................   4.00
BRASS PAIR CANDLESTICKS ,OVAL BASE,PUSH-UP ,LONDON CIRCA
  1820.......................................................  25.00
BRASS PAIR CANDLESTICKS,SAUCER BASE..........................  25.00
BRASS PAIR CANDLESTICKS,SQUARE BASES,PUSHUPS.................  32.00
BRASS PAIR CAST 10 IN. GEORGIAN CANDLESTICKS.................  75.00
BRASS,PAIR CENTER PUSH UP CANDLESTICKS.......................  30.00
BRASS PAIR CLOCK ROASTING JACKS..............................  28.00
BRASS PAIR DOOR HINGES.......................................  20.00
BRASS PAIR DOOR KNOCKERS,MAN ON HORSE........................   8.00
BRASS PAIR DOUBLE WALL CANDLESTICKS,CARVED JADE INSERTS......  85.00
BRASS PAIR DOUBLE WALL SCONCES CIRCA 1900....................  75.00
BRASS PAIR EARLY AMERICAN PUSH UP CANDLE HOLDERS.............  15.00
BRASS PAIR 18TH CENTURY 3-BRANCH SCONCES,LYRE BACKS.......... 300.00
BRASS PAIR ELLIPTICAL EMBOSSED INTERIOR DOOR KNOBS...........   7.00
BRASS PAIR EMBOSSED WALL SCONCES,GERMAN,2 MOVABLE HOLDERS...  18.00
BRASS PAIR FRENCH LAMP SHADES,FLEUR DE LIS IN RELIEF.........   5.00
BRASS PAIR GIRONDOLES,MARBLE BASES,20 U-DROP PRISMS,MARY &
  HER LAMB....................................................  38.00
BRASS PAIR MATCHED INDIA VASES...............................  10.00
```

```
BRASS PAIR PUSH-UP BEEHIVE CANDLESTICKS,SQUARE BASES........    38.00
BRASS PAIR QUEEN ANNE TAPERSTICKS............................    75.00
BRASS PAIR RECTANGULAR BASE PUSHUP CANDLESTICKS..............    21.00
BRASS PAIR SAUCER TYPE RING HANDLED CANDLESTICKS.............    19.50
BRASS PAIR SCONCES,6 IN.,OPEN-WORK FLOWERS WALL BRACKET.....   150.00
BRASS PAIR SPIRAL CANDLESTICKS,14 IN. HIGH...................    37.50
BRASS PAIR TRUMPET VASES,4-SIDED,ENGRAVED....................    12.50
BRASS PAIR TURNED CANDLESTICKS,18 IN. HIGH...................    60.00
BRASS PAIR VICTORIAN PUSH UP CANDLESTICKS....................    35.00
BRASS PAIR WALL SCONCES,DOUBLE ARMS..........................    32.50
BRASS PAPERWEIGHT SHAPE DOLPHIN..............................     2.50
BRASS PARROT NUT CRACKER.....................................     5.50
BRASS PEDESTAL BOTTOM CHINESE CANDLESTICKS WITH PEG TOP,8
  IN. HIGH...................................................    35.00
BRASS PICTURE BUTTON,BIRD OF PARADISE........................     2.50
BRASS PICTURE BUTTON,LUSTER,ALLIGATOR ON KNOLL IN MARSH.....     9.50
BRASS PICTURE BUTTON,MEDUSA..................................     9.50
BRASS PICTURE BUTTON,PHAETON DRIVING CHARIOT THROUGH SKIES..    12.00
BRASS PICTURE FRAME,TIN BACK.................................    12.50
BRASS PIERCED TRAY WITH DOUBLE HANDLES,10 IN.................     7.50
BRASS PIE WHEEL TYPE CRIMPER.................................     6.00
BRASS PISTOL POWDER FLASK,SHELL DESIGN.......................    19.00
BRASS PLANT STAND WITH CARAMEL SHADED MARBLE INSERTS TOP &
  BOTTOM....................................................    35.00
BRASS PLATED METAL NUDE KNEELING 8 IN. TALL,FELTED BOTTOM...     4.50
BRASS PLATED VICTORIAN JEWEL BOX,4 LEGS......................     6.50
BRASS PLATED WALL BILL CLIP SHAPE OWL,4 IN. LONG.............     5.95
BRASS PLATE WALL MATCH SCRATCHER.............................     2.00
BREAD PLATTER,13 IN. SHELL & TASSEL..........................    20.00
BRASS PLEATING IRON IN IRON FRAME,SCREWS TO TABLE............    20.00
BRASS POCKET MATCH SAFE,RUNNING HORSE,PABST BREWING,STATUE
  LIBERTY...................................................     8.00
BRASS POCKET PITCH PIPER.....................................    20.00
BRASS,POT,OPEN HANDLES,ENGRAVED,MARKED CHINA.................     5.00
BRASS POWDER FLASK...........................................    16.00
BRASS POWDER FLASK,6 IN.,EMBOSSED DOG & TURKEYS..............    18.00
BRASS POWDER FLASK,FLUTE DESIGN,EMBOSSED,ORIGINAL PATINA....    15.00
BRASS,POWDER FLASK,MEDALLIONS ON SIDES WITH GAME BIRDS &
  DOGS......................................................    20.00
BRASS POWDER FLASK,PERSIAN...................................    40.00
BRASS POWDER MEASURE,WOOD HANDLE.............................     3.50
BRASS PUSH-UP CANDLESTICKS,PAIR,10 IN. HIGH..................    48.00
BRASS ROASTING FORK,FIGURES OF HENRY VIII & SHAKESPEARE.....    15.00
BRASS ROSETTES,CAVALRY.......................................     4.00
BRASS ROUND ANIMAL BELL......................................    10.00
BRASS ROUND BUCKET WITH COPPER ON UPPER RIM,WROUGHT IRON
  HANDLE....................................................    60.00
BRASS ROUND BUCKET WITH WROUGHT IRON SUPPORT ON UPPER RIM &
  HANDLE....................................................    68.00
BRASS ROUND TRAY,...........................................    52.50
BRASS RUSSIAN TEA POT 4IN. DIA. BASE TAPERING TO 2IN. AT TOP    25.00
 RASS BRASS SADIRON MARKED CHINA,CHINESE,IVORY CARVED HANDLE    28.00
BRASS SALESMAN SAMPLE CARRIAGE LIGHT.........................    25.00
BRASS SALOON CUSPIDOR........................................    15.00
BRASS SALOON CUSPIDOR,FLARED TOP.............................    15.00
BRASS SALTER FIREPLACE CLOCK ROASTING JACK...................    19.00
BRASS SANTA FE RAILROAD LOCK WITH KEY........................     8.50
BRASS SAUCER CANDLESTICK,18TH CENTURY,PUSH-UP & SNUFFER.....    45.00
BRASS SCHOOL BELL,WOODEN HANDLE..............................    10.00
BRASS SCISSOR TYPE CANDLE SNUFFER & TRAY.....................     3.50
BRASS SEAMANS BELL CIRCA 1830,10 IN. HIGH....................    28.00
BRASS SET OF CAST ANDIRONS,TURNED POSTS,URN FINIALS.........    35.00
BRASS SHAKER,POUNCE..........................................     5.00
BRASS SHAKER TYPE BIBLICAL BELL..............................    22.50
BRASS SHIPS INKWELL..........................................     4.00
```

```
BRASS SHIP WHEEL,TELEGRAPH,.....................................  20.00
BRASS SHOE SHINE FOOT STAND.....................................  15.00
BRASS SHOT FLASK,FLEUR DE LIS TYPE RAISED DESIGN.............  18.00
BRASS SIGNED RUSSIAN POTS,1890-1914,BULBOUS BODY............  25.00
BRASS SIGNED RUSSIAN POTS 1890/1914,LION MASK,HANDLES,3 KNOB
    FEET........................................................  35.00
BRASS SKIMMER,HAND WROUGHT HANDLE DATED 1835.................  18.00
BRASS SNUFFER..................................................   6.00
BRASS SNUFFER & TRAY..........................................  18.00
BRASS SNUFFER & WICK TRIMMER ON CHAIN FOR WHALE OIL LAMP....  12.50
BRASS, SPIRIT LAMP & KETTLE...................................  28.00
BRASS SPITTOON................................................  12.50
BRASS SPITTOON,9 IN. TALL.....................................  16.50
BRASS SPURS,WORLD WAR 1.......................................   6.50
BRASS SQUARE PILLAR CHAMBER CANDLESTICKS,PAIR................  22.50
BRASS STAND,ONYX INSETS,29 IN. TALL,FILIGREE BORDER.........  75.00
BRASS STAND WITH MARBLE TOP & SHELF,TURNED LEGS WITH CLAW
    FEET........................................................  95.00
BRASS STANDARD ART NOUVEAU PAIR CANDELABRA WITH MILK GLASS.. 125.00
BRASS STEAM WHISTLE...........................................  35.00
BRASS,STEAM WHISTLE,THREADED FOR PIPE.........................  20.00
BRASS STOVE VENT COVER,HANDPAINTED SNOW SCENE.................   6.00
BRASS STREET CAR HAT & BAGGAGE RACK...........................   7.50
BRASS STUDDED OAK BELLOWS.....................................  25.00
BRASS SUNDIAL CIRCA 1800,INSCRIBED HOUR GLASS & DIAL CIRCA
    1800.......................................................  100.00
BRASS SUNDIAL,N.S.E.W.,I COUNT NONE BUT THE SUNNY HOURS,V TO
    VII.........................................................  32.50
BRASS TABLE BELL,WALNUT HANDLE................................  10.00
BRASS TEA CADDY,BRASS ON COPPER OVAL HANDLED TRAY............  16.50
BRASS TEAKETTLE
    10.00  TO...................................................  20.00
BRASS TEAKETTLE,13 IN. BY 11 IN...............................  35.00
BRASS TEAKETTLE,BAIL HANDLE...................................  15.00
BRASS TEAKETTLE,EMBOSSED FLORAL ,MARK 1890....................  19.00
BRASS TEAKETTLE WITH HANDLED BRASS TRIVET,KOREA...............  15.00
BRASS TEAPOT..................................................  25.00
BRASS TEAPOT,BLACK WOODEN HANDLE,ALCOHOL BURNER...............  24.00
BRASS TEAPOT,CAST,............................................  14.50
BRASS TEAPOT ON STAND.........................................  18.00
BRASS TEAPOT ON STAND WITH ALCOHOL BURNER,TIN LINED..........  15.00
BRASS TEAPOT WITH STAND.......................................  40.00
BRASS TEA STRAINER............................................   3.00
BRASS THIMBLE.................................................   3.00
BRASS,THUMB LATCH & DOOR PULL.................................   7.50
BRASS TOASTING DOG FORK.......................................   6.00
BRASS TOKENS,20 ASSORTED AMUSEMENT,LOT........................   2.00
BRASS TRAY,5 X 7 IN.,ETCHED,HANDMADE..........................   5.00
BRASS TRAY,6 CUTOUTS,EMBOSSED FLOWERS,BERRIES.................   6.50
BRASS TRAY WITH APPLIED SHRINERS INSIGNIA AND 3 JEWELS.......   2.95
BRASS TRAY WITH CANDLE SNUFFER,SCISSORS TYPE.................  12.50
BRASS TRAY WITH ORIENTAL DESIGN MARKED CHINA.................   9.00
BRASS TRIANGULAR INK WELL.....................................   7.00
BRASS TRIVET,3 LEGS,SHIP CUT OUT TOP.........................  30.00
BRASS TRIVET,4 LEGS,OBLONG....................................  22.00
 RASS TRIVET,POLISHED.........................................  10.00
BRASS TRIVET,PRESIDENT ADAMS,SHIELD,CANNON
    BALLS,CANNONS,CROSSED SWORDS...............................  15.00
BRASS TRIVET SIGNED WILTON....................................  12.50
BRASS TWISTED STEM CANDLESTICKS,11 IN. HIGH,AMERICAN.........  40.00
BRASS UMBRELLA HOLDER.........................................  14.00
BRASS UMBRELLA STAND,LIONS HEAD HANDLES.......................  15.00
BRASS US NAVY AZIMUTH CIRCLE IN WOODEN CASE,10 X 10 IN.......  22.50
BRASS VASE, 12 IN. , ENGRAVING................................   6.50
BRASS VASE,RED JEWELED ENAMEL.................................  55.00
```

```
BRASS VIGIL LIGHTS FROM AN OLD CHURCH,SWIRLED GLOBES........    40.00
BRASS WALL PLATE,COBALT BLUE MAJOLICA WITH PINK & COLOUR
  CENTER..................................................    45.00
BRASS WALL PLATE,HAND HAMMERED...........................    45.00
BRASS WASHBOARD..........................................     3.50
BRASS WATER CAN, 2 HANDLES AND COVER.....................    28.50
BRASS WEIGHT SET,8 WEIGHTS,1-50 GRAMS IN VELVET LINED WOOD
  BOX....................................................    18.00
BRASS WEIGHTS FOR DRUGGIST SCALE IN WOOD BASE, SET OF
  15,MARKED..............................................    27.50
BRASS WELSH JELLY PAN ,BALE..............................    15.00
BRASS WITH CHINESE CHARACTERS ASH TRAYS,4................     6.50
BRASS WOODMAN CONVENTION BADGE...........................     2.00
    BREAD TRAY, SEE SECTIONS CARNIVAL,MILK GLASS,PRESSED
  GLASS, ETC.............................................
```

BRIDES' BASKETS of glass were usually one-of-a-kind novelties made in any of
the American and in some European glass factories. They were especially popular about 1880 when the decorated basket was often given as a wedding gift.
Cut-glass baskets were popular after 1890. All brides' baskets lost favor about
1905.

```
BRIDES BASKET,7 IN. LOOP HANDLED CUSTARD,HONEY-COMB & DAISY
  DECORATED..............................................    52.00
BRIDES BASKET,9 IN. HANDLED ,HEXAGONAL...................    19.00
BRIDES BASKET,13 IN.,ETCHED FLOWERS......................    12.50
BRIDES BASKET,AMBER,3 IN.,2-HANDLED......................    10.00
BRIDES BASKET,AMBER RIBBED MOLD BLOWN,APPLIED COBALT BLUE
  HANDLE & RIM...........................................    29.00
BRIDES BASKET,ART GLASS CASED,PINK & WHITE SPATTERINGS,WHITE
  LINED..................................................    32.00
BRIDES BASKET,ART GLASS CASED SPATTER GLASS,BLUE & WHITE,RED
  & GREEN................................................    30.00
BRIDES BASKET,ART GLASS,OPAQUE LEMON YELLOW OUTSIDE,SPATTER
  INSIDE.................................................    40.00
BRIDES BASKET,ART GLASS ,PINK OVERSHOT,BLUE APPLIED FLOWERS.    25.00
BRIDES BASKET,ART GLASS,WISHBONE HANDLE,DOUBLE UMBILICATED
  WATERMELON.............................................   115.00
BRIDES BASKET,BLACK ACID FINISH MILK GLASS HANDLED..........    22.00
BRIDES BASKET,BLUE & YELLOW GREEN SPATTER GLASS,MOLD BLOWN..    27.00
BRIDES BASKET,BLUE GLASS,ENGLISH REGISTRY MARK..............    15.00
BRIDES BASKET,BLUE,RUFFLED EDGE.........................    45.00
BRIDES BASKET,CARNIVAL GLASS MARIGOLD BEADED,5 IN. HIGH.....    12.00
BRIDES BASKET,CARNIVAL GREEN OPAL BLUE GREEN BUSHES MARKED..    18.00
BRIDES BASKET,CHINA MARKED GERMANY,LAVENDER,BLUE & GOLD.....     8.50
BRIDES BASKET,CLEAR GLASS WITH DAISIES,ETCHED,10 IN. HIGH...    10.00
BRIDES BASKET,CRANBERRY OPALESCENT,......................    47.00
BRIDES BASKET,CUT GLASS,.................................    75.00
BRIDES BASKET,CUT GLASS,SILVER PLATE OVERHANDLE,HOLDER......    75.00
BRIDES BASKET,GLASS,ENGRAVED & PRESSED DESIGN,ROPE HANDLE...    15.00
BRIDES BASKET,GLASS,HANDLE,8 IN. TALL....................     3.50
BRIDES BASKET,GREEN GLASS,SWIRL PATTERN,9 IN.............     8.00
BRIDES BASKET,HANDLELESS,BASKETWEAVE OUTSIDE,BLACKBERRIES
  INSIDE.................................................    15.00
BRIDES BASKET,HEISEY MARKED,ROUND,CLEAR CUT FLOWERS........    30.00
BRIDES BASKET IN SILVER PLATE FRAME,BLUE CRISS-CROSS PATTERN    62.50
BRIDES BASKET,MINIATURE,SATIN FINISH,CRANBERRY RUFFLED EDGE.    40.00
BRIDES BASKET, OLD ROSE, 9 IN. ACR. SILVER HOLDER, PEARPOINT    69.00
BRIDES BASKET,OVAL THREADED GLASS,13 X 6 IN.,HANDLE.........    20.00
BRIDES BASKET,PANEL THISTLE 7 IN........................    16.50
BRIDES BASKET,PIGEON BLOOD,SILVER PLATE HOLDER.............    95.00
BRIDES BASKET,PINK & VASELINE BLOWN.....................    35.00
BRIDES BASKET,PINK GLASS,BLACK EDGING & HANDLE.............    38.00
BRIDES BASKET,PINK OPALESCENT,RUFFLED TOP,APPLIED HANDLE....    30.00
BRIDES BASKET,PINK RUFFLED TOP,THORNY HANDLE..............    28.00
BRIDES BASKET,PRESSED CLEAR GLASS,LOOP REEDED HANDLE,DAISY &
```

```
FOLIAGE..............................................................  11.25
BRIDES BASKET,PRESSED HONEY AMBER GLASS,PANELLED CRYSTAL
  PATTERN............................................................  11.25
BRIDES BASKET,SANDWICH GLASS,BUTTERSCOTCH SPANGLE...........  56.00
BRIDES BASKET,SANDWICH GLASS WITH HANDLE,PINK WITH FLUTED
  GREEN..............................................................  30.00
BRIDES BASKET,SATIN GLASS,BLUE TO WHITE,RUFFLED
  ENDS,STERLING FRAME................................................ 185.00
BRIDES BASKET,WHITE AT BASE TO CRANBERRY.....................  25.01-
BRIDES BASKET,WHITE OVERLAY GLASS,CLEAR RUFFLED EDGE.........   7.50
BRIDES BASKET,WHITE TO PURPLE................................  95.00
BRIDES BOWL,10 IN.,SHIRRED,SCALLOP,PINK SHADES...............  25.00
BRIDES BOWL,CRANBERRY,BASKET.................................  47.50
BRIDES BOWL,ORNATE...........................................  39.00
BRIDES DISH,VASELINE OPALESCENT,RESILVERED FRAME.............  60.00
BRIDLE,CAVALRY...............................................   5.00
BRIDLE ROSETTE,OLD GLASS DOMED,ROSES.........................   3.75
BRIDLE ROSETTE,PONY EXPRESS..................................   2.00
BRISTOL 4 IN. VASE,BIRD FLORAL ON GREY,PEDESTAL SILVER PLATE
  HOLDER.............................................................  15.00
BRISTOL 6 IN. BLUE OPALESCENT VASE,BLOWN,ROUGH PONTIL.......   8.75
BRISTOL 6 IN. HANDPAINTED COLOGNE BOTTLE.....................   8.00
BRISTOL 6 IN. VASE,CARAMEL WITH PAINTED FLOWERS..............  10.50
BRISTOL 7 IN. ENGLISH VASE,ENAMELED BIRDS,FLOWERS...........  13.50
BRISTOL 7 IN. SMOKE BELL WITH FLUTED EDGE....................   5.00
BRISTOL 8 IN. VASE,CASED PINK ON WHITE,BLUE & WHITE FLOWERS.  18.00
BRISTOL 9 IN. FROSTED COLOGNE BOTTLE,FLOWER SPRAY...........  12.50
BRISTOL 9 IN. VASE,CYLINDER,OPALINE,ENAMEL BIRD RESTING ON
  LIMB...............................................................  15.00
BRISTOL 9 IN. VASE,PINK SHADING,MOSAICS IN GOLD &
  PASTELS,FROSTED....................................................  30.00
BRISTOL 9 IN. VASE,FRUIT DESIGN..............................  17.00
BRISTOL 11 IN. VASE,HANDPAINTED WITH ENAMELS & OILS.........  17.50
BRISTOL 12 IN. PINK CASED GLASS VASE,ENAMEL FLOWERS.........  28.00
BRISTOL 12 IN. VASE,GREEN BACKGROUND,MAROON & WHITE FLOWER &
  LEAF...............................................................  12.50
BRISTOL 2 PIECE HANDPAINTED 8 IN. DRESSER TABLE PIECE.......  14.00
BRISTOL,3 PIECE PINK DRESSER SET,GOLD TRIM...................  55.00
BRISTOL BELL SHAPED BARBER BOTTLE,GOLD TRIM..................  12.50
BRISTOL,BLUE 7IN . VASE, ENAMELLED FLOWERS...................  12.50
BRISTOL BLUE BUD VASE,BELL SHAPE,WHITE ENAMELED SPRAYS ON
  SIDES..............................................................  16.00
BRISTOL BLUE CASTOR IN METAL HOLDER,CORALENE DECORATION.....  37.50
BRISTOL BLUE EWER,GOLD & YELLOW ENAMEL,APPLIED HANDLE.......  28.00
BRISTOL BLUE GOLD DECORATED CALLA LILY VASE..................  25.00
BRISTOL BLUE HAND VASE.......................................  45.00
BRISTOL BLUE VASE,10 IN. ENAMELED FLOWERS & LEAVES..........  35.00
BRISTOL BLUE VASE,COSMOS FLOWERS IN ROSE,YELLOW,GREEN,TAN...  32.50
BRISTOL BLUE VASE WITH LEAVES & FLOWERS ENAMELED IN
  WHITE,SILVER TRAY..................................................  20.00
BRISTOL BOTTLE,ALICE BLUE WITH RUFFLED STOPPER...............  26.00
BRISTOL BOTTLE,HANDPAINTED SCENE ON FRONT....................  20.00
BRISTOL CANDLESTICK WITH MATCHING TRAY & CANDLE..............  20.00
BRISTOL CLAMBROTH VASE,HANDPAINTED GOLD FLOWERS,RUFFLED TOP.  10.00
BRISTOL COBALT BLUE MUG,WHITE ENAMEL REMEMBER ME............  35.00
BRISTOL CRACKER JAR,BLUE & PINK FLOWERS,GREEN LEAVES........  50.00
BRISTOL CRANBERRY RED MAGNUM DECANTERS,PAIR,CIRCA 1820...... 295.00
BRISTOL CUSTARD COLOUR CRACKER JAR,ENAMELLED LEAF
  DESIGN,SILVER COVER................................................  37.50
BRISTOL DECORATED OVERLAY PAIR VASES,ENAMELLED BLUE
  CORNFLOWERS........................................................  50.00
BRISTOL EGG FOR DARNING......................................   3.00
BRISTOL FLORAL TUMBLER.......................................  12.75
BRISTOL FLORETTE PINK GLASS COOKIE JAR,SILVER BAND
  TOP,COVER,HANDLE...................................................  41.50
```

BRISTOL GLASS was made in Bristol, England, after the 1700's. The Bristol glass most often seen today is a Victorian, light-weight opaque glass that is often blue. Some of the glass was decorated with enamels.

BRISTOL GLASS EPERGNE,WHITE BOWL,PINK SHADING,RUFFLED EDGE..	39.00
BRISTOL GLASS GREEN BASKET,CLEAR GLASS THORN HANDLE.........	42.50
BRISTOL GLASS PAIR VASES,CAFE-AU-LAIT.......................	55.00
BRISTOL GLASS PAIR VOTIVE LIGHTS,BLUE SHADES,BRASS NICKEL PLATED..	28.50
BRISTOL GLASS VASE,APPLIED VASELINE THORN EDGE..............	38.00
BRISTOL GLASS VASE CASED VICTORIAN FORM,ENAMELLED BIRD......	18.00
BRISTOL GLASS WHITE PITCHER & 4 TUMBLERS,BLUE WINDMILL SCENES..	40.00
BRISTOL GREEN MANTEL SET...................................	75.00
BRISTOL HANDPAINTED 2 PIECE 8 IN. DRESSER TABLE PIECE,BLUE HANDLED..	8.00
BRISTOL HANDPAINTED HINGED JEWEL BOX,BRASS BOUND,..........	25.00
BRISTOL HANDPAINTED VASES,PAIR,............................	110.00
BRISTOL HANDPAINTED VASE,WHITE.............................	10.00
BRISTOL HINGED POWDER BOX WITH HOUSE & BRIDGE SCENE ON COVER	15.00
BRISTOL MEAT PLATTER.......................................	50.00
BRISTOL MUG,3 IN. ,REMEMBER ME.............................	15.00
BRISTOL OPAQUE WHITE 3-PIECE TOILET SET,GREEN & ORANGE......	25.00
BRISTOL OVERLAY VASE,BLUE WITH PINK,RUFFLED RIM.............	25.00
BRISTOL PAIR 6 IN. CLAMBROTH VASES,CORALINE DECOR RED ROSES & GREEN...	35.00
BRISTOL PAIR ENAMELED & JEWELED VASES,GOLD ,COLOUR & WHITE..	60.00
BRISTOL PAIR FROSTED VASES.................................	26.00
BRISTOL PAIR GLASS 12 IN. VASES,DECORATED SCENE.............	48.00
BRISTOL PAIR GREEN COLOGNE BOTTLES.........................	36.00
BRISTOL PAIR PINK LUSTRES,WHITE INSIDE,CUT PRISMS...........	125.00
BRISTOL PAIR PINK VASES,LEAF FLOWER DECORATED..............	25.00
BRISTOL PAIR ROUND BULBOUS VASES,8 IN. TALL,BLUE TO WHITE,ENAMELED...	45.00
BRISTOL PAIR SATIN VASES,BULBOUS SHAPE,FLARED TOP,FLORAL & BIRD..	18.00
BRISTOL PAIR SMOKEY VASES,11 IN. TALL,FLARED TOP,LILY OF VALLEY ENAMEL..	37.50
BRISTOL PAIR VASES,HANDLED,LAVENDER LUSTER WITH LEAVES......	65.00
BRISTOL PAIR VASES,PINK,ENAMELED...........................	55.00
BRISTOL PAIR VASES,PORTRAIT OF GIRL........................	55.00
BRISTOL PAIR WHITE RUFFLED TOP BLOWN VASES,MARKED..........	16.00
BRISTOL PAIR WHITE VASES,12 IN. TALL,LAVENDER DECORATION....	40.00
BRISTOL PASTEL HAND DECORATED VASE.........................	10.00
BRISTOL PINK CASED 8 IN. VASE,RUFFLED & CRIMPED TOP,FLORAL..	18.00
BRISTOL PINK VASE,9 IN.,GOLD & WHITE DECOR.................	55.00
BRISTOL PORTRAIT VASE,7 IN.,RUFFLED TOP....................	15.00
BRISTOL PORTRAIT VASE,7 IN. TALL,SIGNED,CHILD,.............	16.50
BRISTOL PORTRAIT VASE,ARTIST SIGNED,CREAM WITH ENAMELING,PAIR...	25.00
BRISTOL ROBINS EGG BLUE VASE,9 IN.,HIGH,RUFFLED TOP........	25.00
BRISTOL SET OF 12 GREEN WINE GLASSES CIRCA 1790............	145.00
BRISTOL TAN HANDPAINTED & ENAMELLED VASE,..................	17.00
BRISTOL,TUMBLER,ENAMEL PAINTING............................	14.00
BRISTOL,TUREEN & PLATTER...................................	125.00
BRISTOL VASE,6 IN.,CAFE AU LAIT,ENAMEL BIRD IN TREE........	10.00
BRISTOL VASE,7 IN.,FLORAL DECOR,CLAM BROTH.................	10.00
BRISTOL VASE,BLOWN,PASTEL GREEN,1 PANEL HANDPAINTED FLOWERS.	8.00
BRISTOL VASE,HANDPAINTED COLOURFUL FLORAL DESIGN...........	15.00
BRISTOL VASE,HANDPAINTED PANSIES WITH BIRD.................	22.00
BRISTOL VASE,OPAQUE,SCALLOPED TOP,TURQUOISE WITH ENAMELED FLOWERS..	14.00
BRISTOL VASE,PAIR..	26.00
BRISTOL VASE,PAIR HANDPAINTED FLOWERS & BLUE BIRDS..........	20.00
BRISTOL VASE,YELLOW BACKGROUND ON WHITE CASING,HANDPAINTED FLORAL..	22.00

```
BRISTOL VASE,WHITE 12 IN.,ENAMELLING.........................      25.00
BRISTOL WHITE 7 IN. VASE,.....................................      10.00
BRISTOL WHITE BLOWN VASE......................................      10.00
BRISTOL WHITE OPALESCENT SMOKE BELL,RUFFLED RIM...............      12.50
BRISTOL WHITE RUFFLED TOP PITCHER,4 TUMBLERS,BLUE WINDMILL..      40.00
BRISTOL WITH SATIN FINISH COVERED TRINKET BOX,BRASS
  EDGING,ENAMELED.............................................      32.00
BRONZE,4 PIECE DESK SET,PORCELAIN LINED INKWELL,.............      18.00
BRONZE 7IN.H. WATER FOWL BIRD,SIGNED J.MOIGNIEZ,GILT PATINA.     195.00
BRONZE 9 IN. FIGURE OF LITTLE GIRL WITH BANGS...............      16.50
BRONZE,9 IN. WALL PLAQUE,ADAM & EVE DRIVEN FROM PARADISE....      28.00
BRONZE 11 IN. VASE,BLACK ENAMEL HAND WORK...................      10.00
BRONZE 1910 GREEK BOY SCOUT BUCKLE..........................      10.00
BRONZE & ENAMEL PAIR CANDLESTICKS,RAISED DESIGN,1J IN. TALL.      75.00
BRONZE & GILT ROUND FOOTED BOX ON BALL FEET,MYTHOLOGICAL
  MOTIFS....................................................     225.00
BRONZE ARMADILLO............................................      45.00
BRONZE,AUSTRIA BIRD-DOG,ENAMELED............................      32.50
BRONZE,AUSTRIAN ENAMELED,2 ARABS COOKING DINNER.............     150.00
BRONZE,AUSTRIAN MINIATURE EQUESTRIAN SET OF 6 FIGURES,FOX
  HUNT......................................................     100.00
BRONZE BEAR,8 IN. TALL......................................      16.50
BRONZE BIRD & BUCKET........................................      75.00
BRONZE,BOAR,7 IN. LONG......................................      60.00
BRONZE BOAT,ON STAND........................................      22.00
BRONZE BOOK ENDS,ALTAR OF LOVE,LOVERS IN EMBRACE WITH CHERUB      38.50
BRONZE BUDDHA,BRASS TURBAN,HAND-CARVED,3 PIECES.............      75.00
BRONZE BULL,12 X 8 IN.,MEME,SIGNED..........................     300.00
BRONZE BUST,MAN IN TRI-CORNE HAT,PEDESTAL ON RED MARBLE BASE      35.00
BRONZE BUST PROFILE OF WASHINGTON...........................      25.00
BRONZE,CAST,11 IN. WALL PLAQUE,KOREA,19 NATIVE MEN..........      18.00
BRONZE,CENTENNIAL STATUE HONOURING REMINGTON FIREARMS
  CO.,1816-1916.............................................     250.00
BRONZE,CHARIOT & 2 HORSES ON FRENCH BASE....................     150.00
BRONZE CHINESE IRON,GREEN JADE HANDLE.......................      17.50
BRONZE,CLASSICAL 25 IN. DISCUS THROWER SIGNED A ROHRICH.....     325.00
BRONZE,CLASSICAL 35 IN. MERCURY.............................     185.00
BRONZE,CLASSICAL VENUS......................................     300.00
BRONZE COWBOY ON HORSE,VIENNA,5 IN. HIGH....................     300.00
BRONZE CRUCIFIX ON OAK BASE.................................      18.00
BRONZE DEMI-TASSE SPOON MOLD................................      10.00
BRONZE DOG CARRYING BOOT....................................      35.00
BRONZE DOG NUTCRACKER.......................................      15.00
BRONZE DOOR STOP,OLD SAILING SHIP PAINT GOOD................       8.00
BRONZE EAGLE,7 IN. WINGSPREAD...............................      65.00
BRONZE,ELEPHANT,6 IN. LONG,STANDING.........................      10.00
BRONZE ELEPHANT,PAIR,5 IN. HIGH.............................      90.00
BRONZE,ENGLISH SPARROW......................................      45.00
BRONZE FIGURE OF ORIENTAL FISHERMAN, 15 IN. H...............     115.00
BRONZE FIGURE OF ORIENTAL FISHERMAN SITTING ON STOOL........      50.00
BRONZE FOO DOG CIRCA 1620...................................     200.00
BRONZE,FRENCH CARRIAGE CLOCK................................      80.00
BRONZE FRENCH HANGING WALL PLAQUE,TAVERN SCENES.............      20.00
BRONZE FRENCH INKWELL,HINGED JOCKEY CAP,FOOTED PLATFORM.....      27.50
BRONZE FRENCH STAMP BOX,FOOTED,HINGED COVER,RAISED FLOWERS &
  CUPIDS....................................................      20.00
BRONZE,FRENCH TITLED LE FORGERON PARIS BY MEDNAT,12 X 9 X 6
  IN........................................................      88.50
BRONZE FROG WEARING SHORTS PLAYING BALL.....................       5.00
BRONZE GOLD MASTER SALT CIRCA 1780,MARBLE BASE,MEDIEVAL
  ANIMAL....................................................     195.00
BRONZE,GROUP OF 4 PLAYING FOO DOGS..........................      70.00
BRONZE HOUND DOG,6 IN.......................................      45.00
BRONZE HUNT CUP, REMOVABLE COVER, 15 IN. , SIGNED P.J.
  MENE-1849.................................................     248.00
```

```
BRONZE INCENSE BURNER,BAND OF CLOISONNE ON SIDE,ROSEWOOD
  STAND.............................................................  65.00
BRONZE INCENSE BURNER CIRCA 1765,FOO DOG ON TOP,LOTUS LEAF
  HANDLES...........................................................  45.00
BRONZE INCENSE BURNER,EAGLE FINIAL,LION HEAD LEGS,7 IN. HIGH        6.75
BRONZE,INCENSE BURNER,FOO DOGS ON SIDES AND COVER,SIGNED....       39.00
BRONZE INCENSE BURNER IN FORM OF FAT QUAIL...................       40.00
BRONZE INCENSE BURNER IN SHAPE OF DUCK,JAPANESE.............        40.00
BRONZE INCENSE BURNER,SHAPE OF SAMURAI WARRIORS HELMET......        45.00
BRONZE INCENSE JARS,10 IN. H. ,6 IN. DIA.,FOO DOG FINIAL....       110.00
BRONZE INDIA DOG,GOD & MAID IN EROTIC EMBRACE,15TH CENTURY..        50.00
BRONZE LETTER OPENER,HANDLE HERCULEAN FIGURE SLAYING LION...        10.00
BRONZE LINCOLN BOOKENDS,AMOR BRONZE CO,TAUNTON MASS.........        18.00
BRONZE LION BEARING SEAL OF EMPEROR HSUAN TE,1426-1435,3 IN.
  LONG..............................................................  50.00
BRONZE MACAW,10 IN. HIGH....................................        85.00
BRONZE METAL LEAF-SHAPED TRAY...............................         6.00
BRONZE MIRRORED WALL SCONCES,DOLPHINS TAILS URN
  BORDER,22IN.H. 7IN.W.............................................   75.00
BRONZE MOOSE,4 IN...........................................        55.00
BRONZE MORTAR & PESTLE,16 CENTURY SPAIN.....................        85.00
BRONZE MOUNTAINEER,4 IN. LONG,MARBLE MOUNTAIN...............        22.00
BRONZE ORIENTAL FOO DOG.....................................        75.00
BRONZE PAIR COVERED METAL STATUES,BEETHOVEN & MOZART,7 IN.
  TALL..............................................................  18.50
BRONZE PAIR CHINESE CANDLESTANDS,ROUND BASE,CURVED LEGS OF
  LION HEADS........................................................ 265.00
BRONZE,PAIR PORT & STARBOARD SHIPS RUNNING LIGHTS,GREEN &
  RED...............................................................  65.00
BRONZE PAIR VIKING SHIPS,11 IN. HIGH........................        27.50
BRONZE PANELS,17IN.L,4IN.W.,RAISED FIGURE OF WOMAN,SIGNED
  F.BARBEDIENNE.....................................................  110.00
BRONZE PLAQUE,9 IN.,TALL,PARTIALLY DRAPED VENUS & CUPID.....        25.00
BRONZE PLAQUE,BUST OF WASHINGTON............................        20.00
BRONZE PLAQUE,CAST,TEDDY ROOSEVELT,SIGNED FRASER 1920.......        30.00
BRONZE PLAQUE,EMBOSSED DUTCH BOATS & WINDMILLS ON CANAL.....        15.00
BRONZE PRESIDENTIAL MEDAL ,BUST OF CHESTER A ARTHUR DATE
  1881..............................................................  10.00
BRONZE ROOSTER 3 IN. HIGH...................................        45.00
BRONZE ROOSTER,VIENNESE.....................................        22.50
BRONZE SET OF CHESS IN STYLE OF PHILLIPE OF SPAIN...........       110.00
BRONZE SETTER DOG, 12 IN. L. SIGNED P.J.MENE................       150.00
BRONZE SHRINERS ASH TRAY,PYRAMID TEMPLE.....................         4.00
BRONZE SIGNED FRENCH OF YOUNG BOY,ON MARBLE BASE............        45.00
BRONZE SIGNED MENE IRISH SETTER.............................       125.00
BRONZE SIGNED ON MARBLE BASE 3 BOYS SINGING.................        35.00
BRONZE STAG,BLACK METAL BASE................................        45.00
BRONZE,STANDING ELK ON BASE.................................        15.00
BRONZE STATUE MISS LIBERTY,4 FOOT,2 3-ARM ELECTRIC TORCHES..       495.00
BRONZE TURTLE CIRCA 1850,3 IN. LONG,........................        14.00
BRONZE URN WITH COPPER LINER,CLASSIC GREEK FIGURES IN
  RELIEF,45 LBS.....................................................  250.00
BRONZE VASE,FLARES OUT AT TOP,DESIGN OF POINTS AT BASE &
  TOP,9 IN. HIGH....................................................  16.50
BRONZE VASE,INLAID SILVER,ART NOUVEAU MOTIF,8 IN. TALL......        21.00
BRONZE VASE IN SHAPE OF FISH LEAPING FROM WAVES,CIRCA 1820..        85.00
BRONZE VASE WITH STERLING SILVER DECOR......................        12.00
BRONZE,VIENNA ARAB LEADING CAMEL,HITCHED TO WATER BARREL....        50.00
BRONZE,VIENNA BIRDS,INKWELLS,MOTHER OF PEARL SHELL & BRASS
  PEDESTAL..........................................................  85.00
BRONZE WALL BRACKET,12 IN...................................        20.00
BRONZE WALL PLAQUE SIGNED ARTIST MIAULT,3 SWALLOWTAIL
  BUTTERFLIES.......................................................  36.00
BRONZE WILL ROGERS FIGURE,15 IN.............................         7.50
BRONZE WOLF 6 IN. TALL WITH MARBLE BASE.....................        22.00
```

BUFFALO POTTERY was made in Buffalo, New York, after 1901. The firm marked its wares with a picture of a buffalo and the date of manufacture. Deldare ware, the khaki-brown pottery decorated with hunting scenes, is the most famous product of the factory.

```
BUFFALO POTTERY 6 WHITE BONE DISHES,GOLD BAND................    9.00
BUFFALO POTTERY 9 IN. PLATE,THE GUNNER,GREEN.................   12.00
BUFFALO POTTERY 10 IN. PLATE,BLUE,CAPITOL
  BUILDING,WASHINGTON.........................................    9.00
BUFFALO POTTERY 1907 DUTCH JUG,CASTLE SCENE,DUTCH
  WINDMILL,LADY & CHILD.......................................   39.50
BUFFALO POTTERY 1909 BLUE WILLOW COVERED VEGETABLE DISH.....   15.00
BUFFALO POTTERY,1914,BLUE WILLOW 9 IN. PLATE,DIVIDED,12.....   60.00
BUFFALO POTTERY,1914,BLUE WILLOW ,4 PLATES,CREAMER,SUGAR &
  GRAVY......................................................   40.00
BUFFALO POTTERY ABINO 6 IN. CAKE PLATE,DUTCH SCENERY,SIGNED
  1912.......................................................   20.00
BUFFALO POTTERY BLUE WILLOW COVERED SUGAR...................    9.00
BUFFALO POTTERY BLUE WILLOW PINT BOWL.......................    7.50
BUFFALO POTTERY,BLUE WILLOW ROUND COVERED VEGETABLE TUREEN..   18.00
BUFFALO POTTERY CINDERELLA MILK PITCHER....................   68.50
BUFFALO POTTERY,CREAMER,BLUE FOR-GET-ME-NOT PATTERN.........    8.00
BUFFALO POTTERY CREAMER,WILLOW DATED 1907...................   12.50
BUFFALO POTTERY DELDARE 2 HANDLED COVERED SUGAR.............   60.00
BUFFALO POTTERY DELDARE,6 IN. PLATE,AT YE LION INN
  20.00  TO.................................................   35.00
BUFFALO POTTERY DELDARE 6 IN. PLATE,THE FALLOWFIELD HUNT....   42.50
BUFFALO POTTERY DELDARE 7 IN. PLATE,YE VILLAGE STREET,SIGNED   25.00
BUFFALO POTTERY DELDARE 7 IN. PLATE,YE VILLAGE
  ST.1908,SIGNED............................................   50.00
BUFFALO POTTERY DELDARE 8 IN. PLATE,YE TOWN CRIER...........   36.00
BUFFALO POTTERY DELDARE 8 SIDED PITCHER....................  115.00
BUFFALO POTTERY DELDARE 9 IN. PLATE,DR.SYNTAX INTRODUCTION..   85.00
BUFFALO POTTERY DELDARE 9 IN. PLATE YE OLDEN TIMES..........   55.00
BUFFALO POTTERY DELDARE 12 IN. HANGING CHARGER,YE LION INN
  PATTERN...................................................  110.00
BUFFALO POTTERY DELDARE 12 IN. PLATE,AT YE LION INN.........   20.00
BUFFALO POTTERY DELDARE 12 IN. PLATE,BREAKFAST AT THE 3
  PIDGEONS..................................................   75.00
BUFFALO POTTERY DELDARE 12 IN. PLATE FOR HANGING,FALLOWFIELD
  HUNT......................................................   75.00
BUFFALO POTTERY DELDARE 12 IN. PLATE,THE FALLOWFIELD HUNT...  125.00
BUFFALO POTTERY DELDARE 13 IN. PLATE,AN EVENING AT YE LION
  INN.......................................................  125.00
BUFFALO POTTERY DELDARE 1909 MINUET TRAY...................  130.00
BUFFALO POTTERY DELDARE ARTIST SIGNED 9 IN. PLATE,THE
  FALLOWFIELD HUNT..........................................   58.00
BUFFALO POTTERY DELDARE ARTIST SIGNED 9 IN. PLATE,THE START.   58.00
BUFFALO POTTERY DELDARE ARTIST SIGNED 9 IN. PLATE,YE OLDEN
  TIMES.....................................................   56.00
BUFFALO POTTERY DELDARE BOWL,9 IN..........................  110.00
BUFFALO POTTERY DELDARE BOWL,INCURVED,YE LION INN,8 IN.
  DIAMETER..................................................   67.50
BUFFALO POTTERY DELDARE COVERED HANDLED SUGAR,SCENES OF
  VILLAGE LIFE..............................................   75.00
BUFFALO POTTERY DELDARE CREAMER,VILLAGE LIFE................   45.00
BUFFALO POTTERY DELDARE CUP & SAUCER,YE OLDEN DAYS..........   35.00
BUFFALO POTTERY DELDARE HAIR RECEIVER,VILLAGE STREET........   85.00
BUFFALO POTTERY DELDARE MUG,THE FALLOWFIELD HUNT,2 IN. TALL.   40.00
BUFFALO POTTERY DELDARE MUG,YE LION INN PATTERN.............   50.00
BUFFALO POTTERY DELDARE PITCHER,THE FALLOWFIELD HUNT 1908,9
  IN. HIGH..................................................  140.00
BUFFALO POTTERY DELDARE PITCHER,RETURN OF THE CURTSY.......   60.00
BUFFALO POTTERY DELDARE PLAQUE WIRED FOR HANGING,YE LION INN  135.00
BUFFALO POTTERY DELDARE PLATE,THE FALLOWFIELD HUNT.........   57.50
BUFFALO POTTERY DELDARE PLATE,THE FALLOWFIELD HUNT,THE START   85.00
```

BUFFALO POTTERY DELDARE PLATE,THE DEATH...................... 57.50
BUFFALO POTTERY DELDARE PLATE YE TOWN CRIER.................. 36.00
BUFFALO POTTERY DELDARE SIGNED HAIR RECEIVER................. 12.00
BUFFALO POTTERY DELDARE SUGAR & CREAMER,SCENES OF VILLAGE
  LIFE.. 65.00
BUFFALO POTTERY DELDARE,TEA TILE,TRAVELING IN YE OLDEN DAYS. 9.00
BUFFALO POTTERY DELDARE TEA TILE,TRAVELING IN YE OLDEN
  DAYS,SIGNED... 37.00
BUFFALO POTTERY DELDARE TANKARD THE FALLOWFIELD HUNT THE
  HUNT SUPPER... 95.00
BUFFALO POTTERY DELDARE TRAY DANCING THE MINUET.............. 90.00
BUFFALO POTTERY,DR.SYNTAX DISPUTING BILL WITH LANDLADY IN
  BLUE.. 8.00
BUFFALO POTTERY FEEDING DISH,SCENE,BOY & GIRL,BROKEN DOLL... 16.50
BUFFALO POTTERY GAME SET,PLATTER & 6 PLATES,SIGNED BECK..... 100.00
BUFFALO POTTERY GRAVY BOAT,BLUE FOR-GET-ME-NOT PATTERN...... 8.00
BUFFALO POTTERY,GREEN NIAGARA FALLS PLATE................... 6.50
BUFFALO POTTERY MARKED 7 IN. BLUE & WHITE & GOLD RIM
  PITCHER,1909.. 95.00
BUFFALO POTTERY MARKED 1907 8IN. H. JOHN PAUL JONES PITCHER. 75.00
BUFFALO POTTERY MARKED GEORGE WASHINGTON PITCHER,HELMET
  SHAPED 1909... 95.00
BUFFALO POTTERY MILK PITCHER,PANSIES........................ 20.00
BUFFALO POTTERY MILK WHITE PITCHER,PINK & YELLOW ROSES...... 28.50
BUFFALO POTTERY NIAGARA FALLS PLATE,10 IN................... 8.00
BUFFALO POTTERY,PATRIOTIC SERIES,INDEP. HALL,10 IN.
  PLATE,MARKED.. 15.50
BUFFALO POTTERY PITCHER,5 IN. HIGH,BLUE SWALLOWS............ 7.50
BUFFALO POTTERY PITCHER,PURPLE BUFFALO MARK,ROSE PATTERN,7
  IN. TALL.. 10.00
BUFFALO POTTERY PITCHER,ROBIN HOOD.......................... 38.50
BUFFALO POTTERY SUGAR,BLUE WILLOW........................... 6.00
BUFFALO POTTERY WILLOW WARE TRAY 1909....................... 7.50
BUGGY,DOCTORS... 575.00
BUGGY,SEAT,WAGON WITH SPRINGS............................... 22.00

*BURMESE GLASS was developed by Frederick Shirley at the Mt. Washington
Glass Works in New Bedford, Massachusetts, in 1885. It is a two-tone glass,
shading from peach to yellow. Some have a pattern mold design. A few Burmese
pieces were decorated with pictures or applied glass flowers of colored Burmese
glass.*

BURMESE 5 IN. VASE,BULBOUS BASE OPENS TO QUILTED............ 350.00
BURMESE 8 IN. DECORATED VASE,ACID FINISH.................... 425.00
BURMESE ACID MT.WASHINGTON TUMBLER.......................... 185.00
BURMESE BOWL-VASE,OGEE BODY,ACID FINISH..................... 320.00
BURMESE CREAMER,PINK,YELLOW APPLIED HANDLE.................. 295.00
BURMESE DECORATED VASE,PINK AT TOP TO RED................... 325.00
BURMESE FINGER BOWL,RUFFLED EDGE............................ 165.00
BURMESE GLOSSY FINISH 5 IN. VASE,BULBOUS BASE OPENS TO
  QUILTED NECK.. 375.00
BURMESE HANDLED LEMONADE.................................... 175.00
BURMESE LILY VASE,6 IN. TALL,YELLOW EDGE.................... 225.00
BURMESE MELON RIBBED VASE,ACORNS & LEAVES................... 325.00
BURMESE MINIATURE ROSE BOWL................................. 220.00
BURMESE,MT.WASHINGTON ACID FINISH TUMBLER................... 210.00
BURMESE MT.WASHINGTON ACID TUMBLER.......................... 165.00
BURMESE MT. WASHINGTON BUD VASE,10 IN. TALL................. 245.00
BURMESE MT.WASHINGTON CREAMER,RUFFLED TOP................... 375.00
BURMESE,MT.WASHINGTON DIAMOND QUILT TOOTHPICK............... 225.00
BURMESE MT.WASHINGTON MUSTARD POT,HINGED COVER,RIBBED BARREL
  SHAPE... 80.00
BURMESE MT.WASHINGTON RIBBED BOWL,RECTANGULAR MOUTH......... 195.00
BURMESE MT.WASHINGTON SQUARE TOP TOOTHPICK.................. 195.00
BURMESE MT.WASHINGTON TUMBLER IN ACID FINISH,PINK 3/4 WAY
  DOWN.. 225.00

```
BURMESE MT.WASHINGTON TUMBLER,PINK TO YELLOW,POLISHED PONTIL   150.00
BURMESE MT.WASHINGTON VASE,11 IN. TALL,MATTE FINISH,PINK....   350.00
BURMESE PITCHER,5 IN. TALL,PLEATED TOP.....................   375.00
BURMESE RIBBED SALT SHAKER,ACID FINISH.....................    69.00
BURMESE TOOTHPICK HOLDER,SATIN FINISH,YELLOW & WHITE DAISIES  300.00
BURMESE TUMBLER
  200.00  TO................................................   265.00
BURMESE VASE,5 IN. TALL,PURPLE & YELLOW,ENAMEL DECORATED....   650.00
BURMESE VASE,GOLD,PRUNUS BLOSSOMS,ACID FINISH..............   500.00
BURMESE ,WEB VASE ,COLLARED STAR SHAPED TOP,2 IN. T.2 IN. D.  195.00
```

BUTTER CHIPS or butter pats were small individual dishes for butter. They were in the height of fashion from 1880 to 1910. Earlier, as well as later, examples are known.

```
BUTTER CHIP ROUND PORTRAIT LADY ON DARK BACKGROUND..........   20.00
   BUTTER MOLD, SEE WOODEN MOLD, BUTTER..................
```

BUTTERMILK GLASS is a regional name for some custard glass.

```
BUTTERMILK GLASS EUREKA PATTERN FOOTED.....................     7.50
BUTTERMOLD.MINIATURE,BIRD DESIGN...........................     4.50
```

BUTTONS have been known through the centuries, and there are millions of styles. Only a few of the most common types are listed for comparison.

```
BUTTON,1 IN. BIRD ON NEST FEEDING YOUNG....................     2.75
BUTTON,1 IN. MEDIEVAL VILLAGE..............................     2.50
BUTTON,1 IN. SHEPHERDESS & LAMBS...........................     2.25
BUTTON,1 IN. WOODCHOPPER...................................     9.50
BUTTON,2 DOLLAR SIZE HANDPAINTED ROSES PORCELAIN...........     1.00
BUTTON,2 HANDPAINTED FLORAL................................     4.00
BUTTON,2 PIECE,CONVEX,1815 EAGLE...........................     1.50
BUTTON,2 PIECE,DOUBLE ANCHOR,BRASS,PARIS...................     1.25
BUTTON,6 SILVER HALLMARKED OPENWORK FLOWER IN PRESENTATION
CASE.......................................................    48.00
BUTTON,10 AMERICAN LEGION,MARKED PAT. 1919.................    10.00
BUTTON,40 BLACK GLASS......................................     1.25
BUTTON,68 BRASS UNIFORM BUTTONS............................     3.50
BUTTON,75 VEGETABLE IVORY..................................     1.25
BUTTON,88 BRASS UNIFORM....................................     3.50
BUTTON,BRASS,THE WINNER....................................     4.50
BUTTON,BRASS BIRD,5........................................     1.00
BUTTON,BRASS MOLD,AMERICAN EAGLE...........................     5.00
BUTTON,BRIDLE,ROSES UNDER GLASS............................     3.50
BUTTON,CAPE COD COTTAGE ,TREES & FENCES....................     2.50
BUTTON,CARMEN & TOREADOR 1 IN..............................     3.75
BUTTON,CATS EYE,4..........................................    25.00
BUTTON,CONFEDERATE STAFF OFFICERS COAT BUTTONS.............     8.00
BUTTON,DOORKNOCKER,LION WITH RING IN MOUTH TO KNOCK........     9.50
BUTTON,8 FIRE DEPARTMENT SUIT BUTTONS......................     4.00
BUTTON,FRENCH ENAMEL.......................................     4.00
BUTTON,FRENCH PAPERWEIGHT..................................     4.50
BUTTON,GENERAL CUSTER EAGLE BUTTONS,12.....................     2.00
BUTTON,HANDPAINTED CHINA DRESS,ROSES,5.....................    15.00
BUTTON,LADY IN WINDOW GIVING LETTER TO BIRD................     3.75
BUTTON,MERRY CHRISTMAS CELLULOID SANTA CLAUS...............     1.50
BUTTON,METAL,CRESCENT HELMET MACE..........................     3.75
BUTTON,METAL,CUPID ON SWALLOWS.............................     2.75
BUTTON,METAL,EMPEROR CHARLES...............................     3.25
BUTTON,METAL,HOUSE IN PINES 1723...........................     3.25
BUTTONS MILITARY , 3 DIFFERENT.............................     1.00
BUTTON,NEPTUNE TRIDENT.....................................     2.25
BUTTON,NUDIE,SQUARE........................................     3.50
BUTTON,PINK ROSE ,LEAVES,PAPERWEIGHT,1870.................     9.50
BUTTON,PONY EXPRESS BRIDLE ROSETTES,PAIR...................     2.00
BUTTON,PORCELAIN,LEEDS.....................................     1.00
BUTTON,UNION 1 COAT BUTTONS................................     2.00
```

BUTTON,WORLD WAR I... .75

CALCITE GLASS was made by the Steuben factory to be used with colored Aurene glass. It was usually used as the liner (see STEUBEN).
CALCITE, SEE ALSO STEUBEN...............................
CALCITE COMPOTE,GOLD WITH APRICOT IRIDESCENCE............... 95.00

CALENDAR PLATES were made in the United States from 1906 to 1929. A few were produced in the years since then; a calendar, the name of a store, a picture of flowers, a girl or a scene were featured on the plate.
CALENDAR PLATE,8 IN. FLORAL BORDER,1895..................... 7.50
CALENDAR PLATE,9 IN.,1920................................... 12.00
CALENDAR PLATE,10 IN. MILL HOUSE BY STREAM 1909............. 8.00
CALENDAR PLATE,10 IN.,1953,GOLD & WHITE..................... 3.00
CALENDAR PLATE,1906
   10.00   TO... 26.00
CALENDAR PLATE 1907,SANTA AT CHIMNEY........................ 17.50
CALENDAR PLATE,1908... 14.50
CALENDAR PLATE,1908,PINK ROSE............................... 6.00
CALENDAR PLATE,1908,THOMPSON,PA............................. 8.00
CALENDAR PLATE 1909
   6.50   TO.. 12.50
CALENDAR PLATE 1909,4 SEASONS............................... 7.00
CALENDAR PLATE,1909,8 IN.................................... 8.00
CALENDAR PLATE 1909,CHERRIES IN CENTER,FLORAL DECOR......... 9.00
CALENDAR PLATE,1909 CRESCENT CITY,ILL....................... 6.00
CALENDAR PLATE 1909 FLOWERS................................. 6.50
CALENDAR PLATE,1909 GIBSON GIRL............................. 17.50
CALENDAR PLATE,1909 GIBSON GIRL,GREEN MONTHS................ 8.50
CALENDAR PLATE 1909,GREEN,WOMANS HEAD....................... 6.00
CALENDAR PLATE 1909,PINK & GREEN,BENTON HARBOR,MICHIGAN..... 8.50
CALENDAR PLATE 1909,POPPIES................................. 6.50
CALENDAR PLATE 1909,RED & GREEN CHERRIES ADVERTISING
   MILWAUKEE... 7.50
CALENDAR PLATE 1909,RED ROSE CENTER......................... 8.75
CALENDAR PLATE,1910
   6.00   TO.. 15.00
CALENDAR PLATE,1910,8 IN.................................... 10.00
CALANDAR PLATE,1910,8 IN. D.,RED & PINK ROSES............... 4.75
CALENDAR PLATE 1910,BETSY ROSS.............................. 9.50
CALENDAR PLATE 1910,BROOK,FRUIT TREES IN BLOOM,HORSESHOE
   FRAME... 8.00
CALENDAR PLATE 1910,CHERUBS................................. 5.50
CALENDAR PLATE,1910 CHERUBS RINGING BELL.................... 15.00
CALENDAR PLATE 1910,COMMERCIAL HOTEL........................ 8.50
CALENDAR PLATE 1910,COUPLE DRIFTING IN CANOE SIGNED CHRISTY. 12.00
CALENDAR PLATE 1910,FAMILY GROUP............................ 5.50
CALENDAR PLATE 1910,GIBSON GIRL CENTER...................... 9.00
CALENDAR PLATE,1910,GIBSON GIRL SIGNED...................... 18.00
CALENDAR PLATE,1910,2 HORSES HEADS,7 IN..................... 7.50
CALENDAR PLATE,1910,LIGHTHOUSE & SHIPS...................... 5.00
CALENDAR PLATE 1910,NIAGARA FALLS........................... 9.00
CALENDAR PLATE 1910,PLUMS................................... 13.00
CALENDAR PLATE 1910 SCHWARTZBURG CHINA ,PINK ROSES.......... 9.50
CALENDAR PLATE 1910,VIOLETS................................. 10.00
CALENDAR PLATE 1910,WASHINGTONS HOME........................ 9.50
CALENDAR PLATE ,1911....................................... 9.50
CALENDAR PLATE 1911 ,21 CLOCKS SHOW TIME AROUND WORLD....... 5.25
CALENDAR PLATE,1911,CARRIAGE GIRL........................... 16.00
CALENDAR PLATE,1911,CLOCKS OF WORLD,VIOLETS................. 8.50
CALENDAR PLATE 1911 CUPIDS & ROSES.......................... 8.00
CALENDAR PLATE,1911-1912,FARMHOUSE SCENE.................... 12.00
CALENDAR PLATE,1911,FALL FRUITS............................. 6.75
CALENDAR PLATE 1911,DUCK.................................... 7.50
CALENDAR PLATE,1911 SEASCAPE,PINK ROSES..................... 7.00

```
CALENDAR PLATE 1911,WHITE SWAN,WATER LILIES...................   10.50
CALENDAR PLATE 1911,WILD ROSES,TREES..........................    6.51-
CALENDAR PLATE 1912...........................................   15.00
CALENDAR PLATE,1912,8 IN.,HUNTING SCENE.......................    7.50
CALENDAR PLATE,1912,DOG ROUSES NEST OF GAMEBIRDS..............    8.50
CALENDAR PLATE 1912 FLOWERS SIGNED............................    8.50
CALENDAR PLATE,1912,FRUITS,FLOWERS............................    6.50
CALENDAR PLATE 1912 VASE OF PINK ROSES........................    8.00
CALENDAR PLATE,1913
   5.50   TO.................................................    8.50
CALENDAR PLATE 1913 BLACK SWANS,WHITE LILIES..................   10.50
CALENDAR PLATE 1913,HARVEST SCENE ,GOLD TRIM..................    7.50
CALENDAR PLATE 1913,WAVING FLAG...............................   11.00
CALENDAR PLATE, 1914 BOY IN TORN CLOTHES......................   16.75
CALENDAR PLATE,1915...........................................    7.50
CALENDAR PLATE,1915,ADVERTISING XMAS..........................    .6.50
CALENDAR PLATE 1915,DUTCH CHILDREN,BUTTERFLY BORDER...........   13.00
CALENDAR PLATE,1915,MAP OF PANAMA CANAL ZONE..................    6.00
CALENDAR PLATE 1915,PANAMA CANAL
   6.50   TO.................................................   11.75
CALENDAR PLATE,1915,PANAMA CANAL,BLUE & GOLD BORDER,8 IN. D.     9.75
CALENDAR PLATE 1915,STRAWBERRIES & LEAVES IN CENTER...........    5.00
CALENDAR PLATE,1916 MAN IN CANOE..............................   42.00
CALENDAR PLATE 1916 PINK EDGE INDIAN BRAVE IN CENTER..........   12.50
CALENDAR PLATE,1917,VIOLETS...................................    8.75
CALENDAR PLATE,1919,9 IN......................................   10.00
CALENDAR PLATE,1919,PINK FLOWERS & FLAGS OF
  BELGIUM,FRANCE,ENGLAND......................................   25.00
CALENDAR PLATE,1919,WORLD WAR I,AMERICAN FLAG.................   25.00
CALENDAR PLATE, 1920..........................................   12.50
CALENDAR PLATE,1920 PEACE.....................................   11.00
CALENDAR PLATE 1920,THE GREAT WAR.............................   10.50
CALENDAR PLATE,1920,THE PEACE PLATE...........................   10.00
CALENDAR PLATE 1920,VICTORY,WORLD GLOBE,4 FLAGS,PEACE DOVE..    11.50
CALENDAR PLATE,1921,GRAPES,BLUE BIRDS.........................    7.50
CALENDAR PLATE 1921,REDHEAD IN RED ROADSTER WAITING FOR RED
  LIGHT......................................................   18.75
CALANDAR PLATE, 1924,PEARS....................................    9.75
CALENDAR PLATE,1928,BLUE & WHITE..............................   22.00
CALENDAR PLATE 1950...........................................    2.50
CALENDAR PLATE,1951
   2.00   TO.................................................    3.25
CALENDAR PLATE 1952...........................................    2.50
CALENDAR PLATE 1953
   2.00   TO.................................................    3.00
CALENDAR PLATE,1953 WINDMILL BOATS............................    3.75
CALENDAR PLATE 1954...........................................    2.50
CALENDAR PLATE,1954 WINDMILL BOATS............................    3.75
CALENDAR PLATE 1955...........................................    2.50
CALENDAR PLATE 1956...........................................    2.50
CALENDAR PLATE 1957
   2.00   TO.................................................    3.00
CALENDAR PLATE,1957,PINK......................................    2.75
CALENDAR PLATE 1958
   2.00   TO.................................................    3.00
CALENDAR PLATE 1958 PINK......................................    2.75
CALENDAR PLATE 1959
   2.00   TO.................................................    2.95
CALENDAR PLATE,1959,PINK......................................    2.75
CALENDAR PLATE 1960
   2.00   TO.................................................    3.00
CALENDAR PLATE,1960,PINK......................................    2.75
CALENDAR PLATE 1961...........................................    2.50
CALENDAR PLATE,1961,PINK......................................    2.75
CALENDAR PLATE 1962...........................................    2.50
```

```
CAKENDAR PLATE,1962,PINK........................................  2.75
CALENDAR PLATE 1962,BROWN COTTAGE & SIGNS OF ZODIAC.........  9.50
CALENDAR PLATE 1963..........................................  2.50
CALENDAR PLATE,1964..........................................  4.00
CALENDAR PLATE 1965..........................................  2.50
CALENDAR PLATE 1966..........................................  2.50
CALENDAR PLATE,1966,SQUARE GLASS.............................  1.25
CALENDAR PLATE 1967
  1.95  TO...................................................  2.50
CALENDAR PLATE,CENTRALIA,ILL.................................  6.00
CALENDAR PLATE,DOUBLE,1911 & 1912............................  9.00
CALENDAR PLATE,GIBSON GIRL................................... 40.00
CALENDAR PLATE,HISTORICAL.................................... 12.50
CALENDAR PLATE TIN 1955,BLUE & GOLD DUTCH SCENE..............  4.00
CALENDAR PLATE ,TIN 1956.....................................  4.00
CALENDAR TILE 1905,SEPIA SHOWING STEPHENSONS LOCOMOTIVE
  ROCKET 1829...............................................  7.50
CALENDAR TILE,JONES,MC DUFFEY & STRATTON CO 1896............ 18.50
CALENDAR TILE,JONES,MC DUFFEY & STRATON CO 1912............. 15.00
```

THE CAMBRIDGE GLASS COMPANY made pressed glass in Cambridge, Ohio.
It was marked with a C in a triangle before 1906. The words "Near-Cut" were
used after 1906.

```
CAMBRIDGE AMBERINA BOWL MARKED,QUILTED...................... 52.50
CAMBRIDGE CLEAR TO AMETHYST NUDE GIRL BELL.................. 20.00
CAMBRIDGE GLASS 2 HANDLED BASKET,AMBER,FOOTED,BASKETWEAVE... 18.00
CAMBRIDGE GLASS AMBER SUGAR & CREAMER,PINK,3 PLATES......... 12.00
CAMBRIDGE GLASS COLONIAL PATTERN MARKED COMPOTE.............  6.00
CAMBRIDGE GLASS COLONIAL PATTERN MARKED FRUIT BOWL..........  4.50
CAMBRIDGE GLASS NUDE HOLDING AMETHYST PLATE................. 27.00
CAMBRIDGE ICE BUCKET,SILVER COLOURED HAMMERED HANDLE........  6.00
CAMBRIDGE MARKED 12 IN. BOWL,CLEAR GLASS 10 PANELLED........  4.50
CAMBRIDGE MARKED PINK GLASS TABLE SET,11 IN. BOWL,4 CANDLE
  HOLDERS................................................... 15.00
CAMBRIDGE OPAQUE GREEN GOBLET,SHAPED VASE,DOLPHIN HANDLES... 12.50
CAMBRIDGE OPAQUE HORSESHOE GOBLET........................... 10.00
CAMBRIDGE PAIR MARKED GLASS AMBER 8 IN. PLATES.............  3.50
CAMBRIDGE PINK CUP,SAUCER & PLATE.......................... 10.00
CAMBRIDGE PINK PLATE.......................................  2.50
CAMBRIDGE SIGNED TOPAZ ICE BUCKET,ALUMINUM HANDLE & TONGS... 12.00
```

CAMEO GLASS was made in layers in much the same manner as a cameo in
jewelry. Part of the top layer of glass was cut away to reveal a differently colored
glass beneath. The most famous cameo glass was made during the nineteenth
century.

```
   CAMEO, SEE ALSO LISTED UNDER ARTISTəS NAME..............
CAMEO 3-COLOUR CARVED BOTTLE............................... 150.00
CAMEO 5-COLOUR CARVED SNUFF BOTTLE......................... 125.00
CAMEO 6 IN. VASE SIGNED RICHARD, FLOWERS ON ACID ETCHED
  BACKGROUND ..............................................  65.00
CAMEO 9 IN. LEGRAS VASE,EMBOSSED SIGNATURE,CARVED RED
  OVERLAY................................................. 135.00
CAMEO BARREL SHAPED VASE SIGNED DEGUE,FRENCH,RED SCROLLS.... 225.00
CAMEO BOWL,LA VERRE FRANCAIS FRENCH SIGNED CHARDER..........  85.00
CAMEO CARVED VASE.......................................... 120.00
CAMEO CERISE RUBY VASE,CUT TO GREEN CINTRA,12 IN. HIGH......1,250.00
CAMEO CHAMPAGNE SIGNED EHRENFELD,GREEN CLOSED STEM..........  75.00
CAMEO COVERED BOX,FLORAL,RED ON CHARTREUSE,SIGNED DE LATTE.. 135.00
CAMEO CUT VASE SIGNED HAWKES ,BLACK,7 IN. HIGH,ORIENTAL
  DESIGN..................................................  37.50
CAMEO FRENCH DE LATTE NANCY VASE,BURGUNDY & RED ACORNS &
  LEAVES.................................................. 105.00
CAMEO FRENCH GLASS MULLER FRES LUNEVILLE VASE,GREEN & PURPLE
  FLOWERS.................................................  95.00
CAMEO FRENCH GLASS,LE VERRE FRANCOIS GOBLET SHAPE ON
```

```
PEDESTAL BASE VASE...................................   95.00
CAMEO,FRENCH VASE,25 IN. HIGH,SERPENT TWINED AROUND
  NECK,SIGNED DAMON..................................  650.00
CAMEO FRENCH VASE,ACID CUT BACK FLORALS,3 COLOURS SIGNED
  VERRE FRANCAIS.....................................   60.00
CAMEO FRENCH VASE,GOLD ACCENTED AMETHYST,CUT POPPY ON
  FROSTED............................................   30.00
CAMEO FRENCH VASE,RED CARNATIONS,SIGNED VESSIERE.....  180.00
CAMEO FRENCH VASE SIGNED LA VERRE FRANCOIS,YELLOW,ORANGE &
  BROWN..............................................  175.00
CAMEO GLASS BOWL VASE,PASTEL WITH GREEN PINE CONES,SIGNED...   85.00
CAMEO GLASS D ARGENTAL VASE,CUT RED & BURGUNDY ROSES........  115.00
CAMEO GLASS GALLE TOOTHPICK HOLDER,CUT GREEN FLOWERS &
  LEAVES.............................................   65.00
CAMEO GLASS GALLE VASE,CUT PURPLE BERRIES,LEAVES & STEMS....   70.00
CAMEO GLASS GALLE WITH STAR VASE,CUT GREEN SATIN LEAVES,....   55.00
CAMEO GLASS,MULLER FRES LUNEVILLE VASE,13 IN.
  HIGH,SIGNED,PASTORAL...............................  450.00
CAMEO GLASS SIGNED CHARDER & LE VENE FRANCAIS 9 IN. VASE....   80.00
CAMEO GLASS SIGNED HONESDALE ART NOUVEAU VASE,WISTERIA AND
  GOLD...............................................  145.00
CAMEO GLASS SIGNED MONT JOYE 9 IN. VASE,STIPPLED FROSTED
  BACKGROUND.........................................   58.00
CAMEO GLASS TRI-CORNER VASE,SIGNED PEYNAUD,ACID CUT BACK....   42.00
CAMEO GLASS VASE SIGNED GALLE,GREEN & PINK FLORAL DESIGN....   62.00
CAMEO GOLD RUBY TO GREEN CINTRA A C B VASE,,12 IN. HIGH....1,250.00
CAMEO HANDLED MUG,BARREL SHAPED,1900 PARIS EXPOSITION,ACID
  CUT................................................  225.00
CAMEO LAMP,SCENIC SIGNED T.MICHELL,PARIS,BRONZE,GREEN &
  YELLOW.............................................  275.00
CAMEO LE GRAS 8 IN. TREES,FOLIAGE,ORANGE MARBELIZED
  BACKGROUND.........................................   90.00
CAMEO,LE GRAS,CHARTRUESE WITH BROWN CHESTNUTS & LEAVES,GOLD
  STAND..............................................  175.00
CAMEO LE GRAS VASE,8 IN.,CUT IN LAYERS AND ENAMELED.........   35.00
CAMEO LE VERRE FRANCAIS 14 IN. VASE,MOTTLED BROWN OVERLAY ON
  ROSE...............................................  135.00
CAMEO LE VERE FRANCAIS VASE,9 IN.,3 COLOURS................   85.00
CAMEO LE VERRE FRANCAIS VASE,ORANGE LEAF DESIGN CUT TO CREME   85.00
CAMEO SIGNED C.VESSE
CAMEO SIGNED CHARDER 8 IN. VASE,ORCHID GEOMETRIC DESIGN.....   70.00
CAMEO SIGNED D ARGENTAL VASE,GREEN UNDERCASED WITH CORAL....   70.00
CAMEO SIGNED DEVEZ PIECE,BLUE INSIDE,TORTOISE SHELL OUTSIDE.  110.00
CAMEO SIGNED G.ARGY ROUSSEAU,PATE DE VERRE 2 HANDLED
  CHALICE,BLUE.......................................  425.00
CAMEO SIGNED MULLER FRERES SCENIC VASE,6 IN. HIGH...........  150.00
CAMEO SIGNED PANTIN CYLINDRICAL PLUNGER FRENCH TYPE PERFUME
  ATOMIZER...........................................   95.00
CAMEO SIGNED RICHARD SCENIC VASE,AMETHYST ON AMETHYST &
  FROSTY............................................. 110.00
CAMEO SIGNED RICHARD SCENIC VASE,TREES,MOUNTAINS & WATER.... 110.00
CAMEO THOS.WEBB CORAL ROSE VASE SIGNED..................... 450.00
CAMEO VASE, ARSOLL, SIGNED, PINK W. GREEN , 8 IN...........   84.00
CAMEO VASE,BLUE WITH ROSE BUD ETCHING,GOLD TRIM............   75.00
CAMEO VASE,CARVED RED LILIES ON GREEN ,SIGNED F. DE LATTIE
  HANDEL.............................................   85.00
CAMEO VASE,D ARGENTA,CRANBERRY COLORED BERRIES & LEAVES ON
  YELLOW.............................................   97.50
CAMEO VASE,DEGUE SIGNED,TAPERED & WAISTED OVOID,SATIN YELLOW  210.00
CAMEO VASE,FLOWERS WITH GOLD ON FRONT,DRAGON FLY ON BACK....   45.00
CAMEO VASE, FRENCH, TROUVENIN......................... 145.00
CAMEO VASE,LE GRAS SIGNED,6 IN. HIGH,LAMBS SCENE........... 110.00
CAMEO VASE,LE GRAS SIGNED,BUTTERSCOTCH,5 IN. HIGH.......... 135.00
CAMEO VASE,LE VERRE FRANCAIS,FROSTED WHITE TO RASPBERRY,3
  CARVED BIRDS.......................................   75.00
```

```
CAMEO VASE,NANCY,5 IN. HIGH,ORANGE,GREEN & RED...............   45.00
CAMEO VASE,PURPLE IRIS IN FROSTED BACKGROUND................   32.00
CAMEO VASE,SIGNED ARSOLL,PINK FLOWERS.......................   95.00
CAMEO VASE SIGNED C.VESSIERE FRENCH,12 IN. TALL,HAND
  DETAILED THISTLES.........................................   85.00
CAMEO VASE SIGNED D ARGENTAL,BLACK,THISTLES ON GOLD ACID
  BACKGROUND................................................   85.00
CAMEO VASE SIGNED D ARGENTAL,PEDESTALED,RED TULIPS & LEAVES
  ON YELLOW.................................................  150.00
CAMEO VASE SIGNED D ARGENTAL,RED LEAVES ON YELLOW...........  125.00
CAMEO VASE SIGNED DAUM NANCY WITH CROSS OF LORRAINE,GREEN
  BACKGROUND................................................  195.00
CAMEO VASE SIGNED DELATTE,FRENCH,WHITE ROSES WITH BLACK
  FOLIAGE...................................................  125.00
CAMEO VASE SIGNED HONESDALE,13 IN.,FLARING,AMBER CUT TO
  FROSTY ICE................................................   60.00
CAMEO VASE SIGNED HONESDALE,GREEN CUT TO IRIDESCENT
  BACKGROUND................................................  135.00
CAMEO VASE SIGNED LE GRAS..................................  100.00
CAMEO VASE SIGNED LE GRAS,GREEN HOLLY VINES & LEAVES,RED
  CHERRIES..................................................  175.00
CAMEO VASE SIGNED LE LOTTE,BLACK SHINY LEAVES ON GREEN,9 IN.
  HIGH......................................................  165.00
CAMEO VASE SIGNED PEYNAUD,10 IN.HIGH,LEAVES,POPPIES.........   75.00
CAMEO VASE SIGNED RICHARD,3 IN. TALL,GREEN & BLUE CUTTING TO
  ORANGE....................................................   60.00
CAMEO,WEBB 4 IN. BULBOUS VASE IN SAPPHIRE BLUE,CARVING IN
  WHITE.....................................................  365.00
CAMEO WEBB PERFUME,WHITE FERNS CUT ON BLUE GROUND,STERLING
  HINGED TOP................................................  135.00
        CAMPAIGN, SEE POLITICAL CAMPAIGN...................
```

CAMPHOR GLASS is a cloudy white glass that has been blown or pressed. It was made by many factories in the Midwest during the mid-nineteenth century.

```
      CAMPHOR, SEE ALSO PRESSED GLASS.......................
CAMPHOR DIAMOND SHAPED PERFUME BOTTLE,CUT GLASS STOPPER.....    5.00
CAMPHOR GLASS,3 IN. TALL,HAND HOLDING TOOTHPICK HOLDER......    9.00
CAMPHOR GLASS 7 IN. BULBOUS COLOGNE,HANDPAINTED PANSIES.....    9.50
CAMPHOR GLASS 7 IN. COVERED HEN DISH.......................   15.00
CAMPHOR GLASS,7 IN. HEAVY VASE, EMBOSSED FISH, SEAHORSE
  HANDLES...................................................   17.50
CAMPHOR GLASS 8 IN. FIGURE CANDLE HOLDER...................    9.00
CAMPHOR GLASS,8 IN. PITCHER,SIX GLASSES,ACID
  FINISH,RIBBED,DECORATED...................................   40.00
CAMPHOR GLASS BANK WITH WATERMELON RIBBED & HOBNAIL.........   32.00
CAMPHOR GLASS BOWL,CHRYSANTHEMUM...........................   40.00
CAMPHOR GLASS BUD VASE,FOOTED & FLARED TOP,ENAMEL DECORATION    7.00
CAMPHOR GLASS CAKE PLATE,11 IN. EMBOSSED...................    5.00
CAMPHOR GLASS CAR VASE,9 IN. IN METAL FRAME................   14.50
CAMPHOR GLASS CAT,2 IN.....................................    5.00
CAMPHOR GLASS CAT PLATE,OPEN LATTICE,3 KITTENS.............   10.00
CAMPHOR GLASS CRUET,WILD ROSE BOW KNOTS....................   18.00
CAMPHOR GLASS DISH,COVERED SWAN,PANELLED BASE,8 IN.........   24.00
CAMPHOR GLASS DRESSER TRAY, 11X8 IN. RUFFLED EDGE,GOLD EDGE.    8.00
CAMPHOR GLASS DUCK DISH,YELLOW BEAK........................   12.50
CAMPHOR GLASS EASTER OPENING PLATE.........................   10.50
CAMPHOR GLASS EMBOSSED POWDER BOX..........................    8.50
CAMPHOR GLASS FROSTED NOBNAIL CREAMER & OPEN SUGAR.........   42.00
CAMPHOR GLASS GREEN SATIN COMPOTE,ROPE STEM................   10.50
CAMPHOR GLASS HEN..........................................   15.00
CAMPHOR GLASS PAIR HANDPAINTED VASES ON PEDESTAL,1 ROOSTER,1
  PHEASANT..................................................    7.50
CAMPHOR GLASS PAPERWEIGHT & MATCHHOLDER,CHICK & EGG.........   14.00
CAMPHOR GLASS PINK COVERED BOWL,BULLDOG FINIAL.............   14.00
CAMPHOR GLASS PINK HEART DISH WITH HANDLE..................    6.50
```

CAMPHOR GLASS PITCHER & 5 TUMBLERS...............................	20.00
CAMPHOR GLASS ROSE BOWL8 LARGE SIZE,4 LEGS,EMBOSSED, TRACES OF PAINT...	8.00
CAMPHOR GLASS SLIPPER WITH BOW.............................	10.00
CAMPHOR GLASS STEMMED LIQUORS,3,GOLD DRAPED DESIGNS RED BUDS	20.00
CAMPHOR GLASS SWAN MASTER SALT.............................	12.00
CAMPHOR GLASS THREE KITTEN PLATE..........................	7.50
CAMPHOR GLASS TOILET WATER BOTTLES,PAIR,PAINTED COLOURED FLOWERS..	27.00
CAMPHOR GLASS VASE,7 IN. HIGH,BLOWN PINK...................	18.00
CAMPHOR GLASS VASE ON BASE,3 CUT OUT TINED YELLOW LEAF SPRAY	11.00
CAMPHOR GLASS WHITE COVERED POWDER BOX....................	5.50
CAMPHOR-SATIN GLASS POWDER BOWL,PINK,2 NUDE MAIDENS ON COVER	16.50
CAMPHOR SATIN HINGED JEWEL BOX,HANDPAINTED ENEMELED FLORALS,BRASS...	15.00
CANARY GLASS CREAMER AND COVERED SUGAR IN DEWEY PATTERN.....	32.50
CANDLE HOLDER, SEE ALSO BRASS, CANDLESTICK, PEWTER, PRESSED GLASS,..	
TIN, ETC..	
CANDLE HOLDER,BRASS,HEXAGONAL BASE,ETCHED ,MARKED CHINA ON BASE,PAIR..	7.00
CANDLE HOLDER,BRASS,PAIR,7 BRANCHES.........................	33.85
CANDLE HOLDER,BRASS,SAUCER BASE,BELL SHAPED STEM,PAIR.......	12.50
CANDLE HOLDER,BRASS,SQUARE SIDES,ETCHED DESIGN ON SIDE......	2.75
CANDLE HOLDER,BRASS,THREADED AT BOTTOM,6 IN. HIGH...........	3.75
CANDLE HOLDER,BRASS,THREADING...............................	1.50
CANDLE HOLDER,COPPER & BRASS,PAIR SAUCER TYPE,SERPENT HANDLE	9.75
CANDLE HOLDER,COPPER & BRASS,SQUARE BASE....................	2.00
CANDLE HOLDER,PAIR 8 IN. HIGH COPPER & BRASS................	9.75
CANDLESTICK, SEE ALSO BRASS, CANDLEHOLDER, PEWTER, PRESSED GLASS,..	
CANDLESTICK,BRASS BEEHIVE,PUSH UPS,SQUARE BASE..............	29.00
CANDLESTICK,IRON 8 IN. DRAGON,PAIR.........................	14.50
CANDLESTICK,IRON HOG SCRAPER,PUSH UP & HOOK.................	12.50

CANDY CONTAINERS, especially those made of glass, were popular during the late Victorian era.

CANDY CONTAINERS, 5 IN. GLASS STATION WAGON.................	4.50
CANDY CONTAINER,AIRPLANE...................................	5.00
CANDY CONTAINER,AIRPLANE MARKED ARMY BOMBER 15P7............	3.50
CANDY CONTAINER,AMBER DOG..................................	7.50
CANDY CONTAINER,AMBER LIBERTY BELL,TIN BOTTOM..............	15.00
CANDY CONTAINER,ARMY TANK,USA ,MARKED......................	6.00
CANDY CONTAINER,AUTO WITH SCREW CAP IN BACK................	5.00
CANDY CONTAINER,AUTOMATIC PISTOL	6.00
CANDY CONTAINER,AUTOMOBILE.................................	3.50
CANDY CONTAINER,BABY DEAR MINIATURE GLASS NURSING BOTTLE....	8.75
CANDY CONTAINER,BLUE GLASS RABBIT..........................	6.00
CANDY CONTAINER,BOAT.......................................	4.50
CANDY CONTAINER,BOOT	2.00
CANDY CONTAINER,BULLDOG,USA,BULLDOG........................	6.50
CANDY CONTAINER,CANDY PISTOL...............................	4.00
CANDY CONTAINER,CAR WITH TIN WHEELS........................	10.00
CANDY CONTAINER,CHICKEN ON BASKET..........................	5.00
CANDY CONTAINER,CHICKEN ON NEST............................	3.00
CANDY CONTAINER,CLEAR GLASS PUPPY..........................	2.50
CANDY CONTAINER,CLEAR HEN..................................	4.00
CANDY CONTAINER,COUGAR.....................................	4.00
CANDY CONTAINER,DOG..	1.25
CANDY CONTAINER,DRESSER WITH MIRROR........................	20.00
CANDY CONTAINER,ELECTRIC IRON..............................	3.25
CANDY CONTAINER,ENGINE.....................................	3.50
CANDY CONTAINER,FIRE ENGINE................................	3.75
CANDY CONTAINER,FIRE ENGINE & DRIVER.......................	6.00
CANDY CONTAINER,FIRE ENGINE DRIVER ON CYLINDER MARKED	

```
USA,TIN BASE.......................................... 7.00
CANDY CONTAINER,FIRE TRUCK............................ 2.50
CANDY CONTAINER,GIRL WITH DUCKS....................... 7.50
CANDY CONTAINER,GLASS 14 IN. TALL DISPLAY............. 25.00
CANDY CONTAINER GLASS ARMY TRUCK...................... 3.50
CANDY CONTAINER,GLASS AUTO
   3.00   TO......................................... 5.00
CANDY CONTAINER,GLASS BOAT............................ 3.50
CANDY CONTAINER,GLASS BOOT............................ 5.00
CANDY CONTAINER,GLASS CAP............................. 5.00
CANDY CONTAINER,GLASS CAR............................. 3.50
CANDY CONTAINER,GLASS CHICKEN ON NEST................. 6.00
CANDY CONTAINER,GLASS FIRE ENGINE
   3.50   TO......................................... 4.50
CANDY CONTAINER,GLASS GUN
   5.00   TO......................................... 6.00
CANDY CONTAINER,GLASS IRON............................ 5.00
CANDY CONTAINER,GLASS LANTERN
   5.00   TO......................................... 8.00
CANDY CONTAINER,GLASS LOCOMOTIVE...................... 4.50
CANDY CONTAINER,GLASS LOCOMOTIVE,PAINTED BLACK........ 2.00
CANDY CONTAINER,GLASS OPEN TRUCK...................... 3.50
CANDY CONTAINER,GLASS PEANUT MAN PENNY................ 2.50
CANDY CONTAINER,GLASS PENNY,BANK...................... 22.00
CANDY CONTAINER,GLASS PENNY,STANDING SANTA CLAUS...... 15.00
CANDY CONTAINER,GLASS PENNY,SWEEPER................... 22.00
CANDY CONTAINER,GLASS PISTOL.......................... 5.00
CANDY CONTAINER,GLASS PISTOL WITH CAP................. 10.00
CANDY CONTAINER,GLASS RABBIT WITH BASKET.............. 6.00
CANDY CONTAINER,GLASS SANTA BOOTS..................... 8.50
CANDY CONTAINER GLASS SEDAN CAR....................... 3.50
CANDY CONTAINER,GLASS SITTING PUPPY................... 1.95
CANDY CONTAINER,GLASS SITTING RABBIT.................. 7.50
CANDY CONTAINER,GLASS SITTING RABBIT,4 IN............. 8.00
CANDY CONTAINER,GLASS SPEED BOAT...................... 3.50
CANDY CONTAINER GLASS STEAM LOCOMOTIVE................ 3.50
CANDY CONTAINER,TANK
   3.00   TO......................................... 3.50
CANDY CONTAINER,GLASS TANK-TYPE FIRE ENGINE........... 4.00
CANDY CONTAINER,GLASS TELEPHONE....................... 5.00
CANDY CONTAINER,GLASS WINDMILL........................ 6.00
CANDY CONTAINER GLASS UPRIGHT TELEPHONE WITH WOODEN RECEIVER
   ON CORD........................................... 3.50
CANDY CONTAINER,GLASS WITH ORIGINAL CANDY,AIRPLANE.... 8.50
CANDY CONTAINER,GLASS WITH ORIGINAL CANDY,ARMY TANK... 3.00
CANDY CONTAINER,GLASS WITH ORIGINAL CANDY,LANTERN..... 8.50
CANDY CONTAINER,GLASS WITH ORIGINAL CANDY,MUSICAL TELEPHONE. 8.50
CANDY CONTAINER,GLASS WITH ORIGINAL CANDY SCOTTY...... 8.50
CANDY CONTAINER,GLASS WITH ORIGINAL CANDY,SEDAN CAR... 3.00
CANDY CONTAINER,GLASS WITH ORIGINAL CANDY,STEAM LOCOMOTIVE.. 3.00
CANDY CONTAINER,GLASS WITH ORIGINAL CANDY,TELEPHONE... 8.50
CANDY CONTAINER,GLASS WITH ORIGINAL CANDY,UPRIGHT TELEPHONE. 3.00
CANDY CONTAINER IN SHAPE OF MILITARY OFFICER.......... 15.00
CANDY CONTAINER,JUMBO PENCIL.......................... 4.00
CANDY CONTAINER,KETTLE................................ 7.50
CANDY CONTAINER,LADYS CINDERELLA TYPE SLIPPER......... 4.50
CANDY CONTAINER,LANTERN
   1.50   TO......................................... 7.50
CANDY CONTAINER,LANTERN,TIN TOP & BASE................ 5.00
CANDY CONTAINER,LANTERN WITH SHAKER TOP............... 4.00
CANDY CONTAINER,MANTEL CLOCK.......................... 12.75
CANDY CONTAINER,MINIATURE LANTERN..................... 2.00
CANDY CONTAINER,MINIATURE PHONE....................... 2.25
CANDY CONTAINER,MOTOR BOAT............................ 5.00
CANDY CONTAINER,RAILROAD LANTERN...................... 5.00
```

```
CANDY CONTAINER,ROLLS ROYCE.......................................    5.00
CANDY CONTAINER,SANTA
  8.50  TO.......................................................   18.00
CANDY CONTAINER,SANTAS BOOT......................................    7.50
CANDY CONTAINER,SANTAS BOOT,ORIGINAL CANDY,LABEL MARKED
  MERRY CHRISTMAS................................................    4.50
CANDY CONTAINER,SANTA IN CHIMNEY.................................   11.00
CANDY CONTAINER,SANTA,SCREW ON METAL BASE........................   10.50
CANDY CONTAINER,SCOTTY...........................................    7.50
CANDY CONTAINER,SEDAN CAR........................................    5.00
CANDY CONTAINER,SITTING DOG......................................    5.00
CANDY CONTAINER,SITTING DOG WITH WHISTLE ON TOP..................    3.00
CANDY CONTAINER,SPIRIT OF GOOD WILL..............................    8.50
CANDY CONTAINER,STOP & GO SIGNAL.................................    4.00
CANDY CONTAINER,SUITCASE
  6.00  TO.......................................................    8.00
CANDY CONTAINER,TELEPHONE........................................    1.50
CANDY CONTAINER,TELEPHONE,METAL BASE.............................    8.00
CANDY CONTAINER,TRAIN
  4.00  TO.......................................................    6.00
CANDY CONTAINER,TRAIN ENGINE MARKED 1028.........................    5.50
CANDY CONTAINER,WILLYS JEEP TRUCK................................    7.00
CANDY CONTAINER,WINDMILL.........................................    4.50
CANDY CONTAINER WITH ORIGINAL CANDY,FIRE ENGINE..................    4.50
```

CANTON CHINA is a blue-and-white ware made near Canton, China, from about 1785 to 1895. It has a hand-decorated Chinese scene.

```
CANTON 4 IN. DEEP DISH,11 IN. SQUARE,4 CHARACTERS IN CENTER.       40.00
CANTON 7 IN. PLATE..............................................   14.00
CANTON 8 IN. PLATE..............................................   18.00
CANTON BIDET,FLORAL,FRAME.......................................  400.00
CANTON BLUE & WHITE 9 IN. PLATE.................................   14.50
CANTON BLUE & WHITE 9 IN. PLATE,TREES,BIRDS,LITTLE MEN..........   18.50
CANTON BLUE & WHITE CREAM PITCHER,4 IN. HIGH....................   85.00
CANTON BLUE & WHITE CREAM PITCHER...............................   40.00
CANTON,BLUE CREAMER,5 IN. HIGH..................................    5.00
CANTON CHINA 3 PIECE TEA SET....................................   62.00
CANTON COVERED BOWL,TWISTED HANDLES,GOLD TRIM,BERRY FINIAL..       75.00
CANTON COVERED GINGER JAR,PAIR,GREY & BLUE......................  135.00
CANTON COVERED VEGETABLE CIRCA 1820.............................  135.00
CANTON CUP & SAUCER,TEA-HOUSE MOTIF,SET OF 4....................   40.00
CANTON DEMI-TASSE CUP & SAUCER,4................................   85.00
CANTON EGG CUP..................................................   27.00
CANTON HANDLELESS CUP,ORIENTAL TREE.............................    6.50
CANTON HOT SERVING DISH.........................................   58.00
CANTON HOT WATER DISH...........................................   50.00
CANTON MANDARIN PUNCH BOWL,CIRCA 1825,........................1,100.00
CANTON MUG,BLUE & WHITE,ENTWINED BRANCH HANDLE,3 IN. HIGH...      125.00
CANTON OBLONG VEGETABLE DISH,CUT CORNERS & COVERED..........       55.00
CANTON OVAL LEAF SHAPED DISH,WHITE & BLUE.......................   15.00
CANTON PAIR CANDLESTICKS,11 IN..................................  195.00
CANTON PLATE,TEA-HOUSE MOTIF,6 IN...............................    5.00
CANTON PLATE,TEA-HOUSE MOTIF,8 IN...............................    8.00
CANTON PLATTER,17 IN............................................   60.00
CANTON PLATTER,17 X 14 IN.......................................   66.00
CANTON PLATTER,BLUE OCTAGONAL...................................   45.00
CANTON POSSET CUP & SAUCER,COVER & WISHBONE HANDLE..........       55.00
CANTON ROSE BOWL................................................   50.00
CANTON,ROSE SAKI CUP............................................    7.75
CANTON TEA POT,TEA-HOUSE MOTIF..................................   35.00
CANTON VASE,CONE-SHAPED WALL....................................   11.00
```

CAPO DI MONTE PORCELAIN was first made in Naples, Italy, from 1743 to 1759. The factory moved near Madrid, Spain, and reopened in 1771 and worked to 1834. Since that time the Doccia factory of Italy acquired the molds and designs and is producing Capo Di Monte wares. Other factories in Europe have copied the Capo Di Monte style, even using the N and crown mark which was made famous by the factory.

CAPO-DI-MONTE BOX,BLUE CROWN,FRANCE,CHERUBS,GOLD HINGED RIMS	22.00
CAPO-DI-MONTE FEMALE STATUE,MARKED,8 IN. HIGH,GOLD & WHITE..	150.00
CAPO-DI-MONTE FIGURINE MARKED,GENTLEMAN WITH BONNET.........	45.00
CAPO-DI-MONTE FIGURINE,TAILOR IN COURT DRESS RIDING A GOAT..	250.00
CAPO-DI-MONTE PITCHER WITH HANDLE..............................	65.00
CAPO-DI-MONTE STATUE,FEMALE,GOLD & WHITE......................	125.00
CAPO-DI-MONTE VASE,SIGNED,8 IN.................................	35.00

CARAMEL OR CHOCOLATE GLASS was made by the Indiana Tumbler and Goblet Company of Greentown, Indiana, from November, 1900, to June, 1903. It is a brown-colored slaglike glass.

CARAMEL SLAG, SEE SLAG..................................	
CARDS,PLAYING,GOLDWATER-MILLER.........................	2.00
CARDS,PLAYING,KENNEDY..................................	2.50
CARD,PLAYING,SET ORIENTAL..............................	6.00
CARD,PLAYING,SOUVENIR DECK 1902 OREGON.................	6.00
CARDS,PLAYING,WORLD WAR I FREEDOM......................	4.00

CARLSBAD, GERMANY is a mark found on china made by several factories in Germany. Most of the pieces available today were made after 1891.

CARLSBAD CHINA AUSTRIA EGG CUPS........................	3.50
CARLSBAD SERVICE FOR 4,BLUE,GREEN LEAVES,GOLD & RIPPLED EDGE	45.00
CARNIVAL GLASS, SEE BOTH LISTINGS FIRST BY COLOUR, SECOND BY ITEM,..................................	
OR PATTERN SEE ALSO ABC. NORTHWOOD, ETC..............	

CARNIVAL OR TAFFETA GLASS was an inexpensive, pressed, iridescent glass made about 1900 to 1920 (Carnival glass is currently being reproduced). Over 200 different patterns are known.

CARNIVAL GLASS AMBER & GREEN BURR PATTERN HANDLED SUGAR BOWL	35.00
CARNIVAL GLASS AMBER COSMOS CENTER,LEAVES 10 IN. BOWL.......	15.00
CARNIVAL GLASS AMBER FLORAL & GRAPE WATER PITCHER...........	28.00
CARNIVAL GLASS AMBER-TO PURPLE RIM BASE HOLLY BOWL,8 IN.....	22.50
CARNIVAL GLASS AMBER WILD FLOWER SQUARE PLATE...............	5.50
CARNIVAL GLASS AMETHYST BASKETWEAVE OUTSIDE,GRAPE INSIDE 6 IN. BOWL...	18.00
CARNIVAL GLASS AMETHYST COLONIAL CARNIVAL PATTERN PAIR CANDLESTICKS...	35.00
CARNIVAL GLASS AMETHYST GRAPE CABLE SWEET MEAT..............	85.00
CARNIVAL GLASS AMETHYST GREEK KEY & PONY PATTERN RUFFLED BOWL..	34.50
CARNIVAL GLASS AMETHYST HOLLY SHALLOW BOWL.................	15.00
CARNIVAL GLASS AMETHYST PANSY PATTERN OVAL BOWL............	24.50
CARNIVAL GLASS AMETHYST PEACOCKS ON THE FENCE 9 IN. FLUTED BOWL..	37.50
CARNIVAL GLASS AMETHYST POPPY SCROLL 7 IN. BOWL............	15.00
CARNIVAL GLASS AMYTHEST RASPBERRY TUMBLER..................	12.00
CARNIVAL GLASS AMETHYST SILVER SWEET PEA VASE,SCALLOPED EDGE	55.00
CARNIVAL GLASS AMETHYST STIPPLED RAYS DOUBLE-HANDLED BONBON.	22.00
CARNIVAL GLASS AMETHYST WITH BLUE PEACOCK AT URN JELLY COMPOTE..	25.00
CARNIVAL GLASS BLUE 3 FRUITS BOWL ON SPATULA FEET..........	29.00
CARNIVAL GLASS BLUE & GREEN & RED HORSEHEAD BOWL,3 IN......	48.75
CARNIVAL GLASS BLUE BASKETWEAVE DISH,RUFFLED & PERFORATED RIM...	9.00
CARNIVAL GLASS BLUE BIRDS & CHERRIES HANDLED NAPPY.........	25.00
CARNIVAL GLASS BLUE BIRDS ON A BOW JELLY COMPOTE...........	20.00
CARNIVAL GLASS BLUE BUTTERFLY 2 HANDLED CANDY..............	17.50
CARNIVAL GLASS BLUE CAPTIVE ROSE BOWL.....................	20.00
CARNIVAL GLASS BLUE CONCAVE DIAMONDS TUMBLER 20.00 TO...	22.00
CARNIVAL GLASS BLUE COPPER LUSTER HEN.....................	30.00

```
CARNIVAL GLASS BLUE DRAGON & LOTUS 9 IN. BOWL.............. 20.00
CARNIVAL GLASS BLUE DRAPERY TRI-CORNERED.................. 39.00
CARNIVAL GLASS BLUE FLOWER PATTERN AT EDGE BOWL........... 8.50
CARNIVAL GLASS BLUE FOOTED DISH MARKED N.................. 65.00
CARNIVAL GLASS BLUE GRAPE & GOTHIC ARCHES PITCHER,4 TUMBLERS 90.00
CARNIVAL GLASS BLUE,GREEN & PURPLE RUFFLED VASE........... 6.00
CARNIVAL GLASS BLUE HEARTS & FLOWERS FOOTED COMPOTE....... 40.00
CARNIVAL GLASS BLUE HEART & VINE BOWL..................... 22.00
CARNIVAL GLASS BLUE HERRINGBONE VASE...................... 17.00
CARNIVAL GLASS BLUE HOLLY & BERRY BOWL.................... 14.00
CARNIVAL GLASS BLUE IRIDESCENT BLACK BERRY PATTERN HAT VASE. 18.50
CARNIVAL GLASS BLUE-LEAVES ROSE BOWL,BEADS,BRANCH FEET..... 35.00
CARNIVAL GLASS BLUE OCTAGON SHAPE BUSHEL BASKET........... 45.00
CARNIVAL GLASS BLUE ORANGE TREE 14 PIECE PUNCH SET........ 165.00
CARNIVAL GLASS BLUE ORANGE TREE BOWL..................... 20.00
CARNIVAL GLASS BLUE PANSY TWIG 5 IN. VASE................ 25.00
CARNIVAL GLASS BLUE PERSIAN MEDALLION BONBON............. 18.00
CARNIVAL GLASS BLUE PERSIAN MEDALLION,GRAPE & CABLE FOOTED
  BOWL................................................... 85.00
CARNIVAL GLASS BLUE-PURPLE 9 IN. BOWL,DRAGON & LOTUS...... 20.00
CARNIVAL GLASS BLUE SINGING BIRD SET OF 6 MARKED TUMBLERS... 52.00
CARNIVAL GLASS BLUE STORK & RUSHES WATER SET............. 225.00
CARNIVAL GLASS BLUE VASE................................ 30.00
CARNIVAL GLASS BLUE WINDFLOWER BOWL...................... 23.00
CARNIVAL GLASS BRONZE COBALT PERSIAN MEDALLION COMPOTE...... 25.00
CARNIVAL GLASS BRONZE FINE RIBBED VASE.................. 7.50
CARNIVAL GLASS BRONZE OPALINE CHERRIES 9 IN. FLARED BOWL.... 19.50
CARNIVAL GLASS BRONZE PAIR GAS SHADES.................... 20.00
CARNIVAL GLASS CLEAR WATER PITCHER,RED CHERRY & GOLD LEAVES. 49.50
CARNIVAL GLASS COBALT BLUE BLACKBERRY COMPOTE,MINIATURE..... 17.50
CARNIVAL GLASS COBALT BLUE HOLLY BOWL.................... 22.50
CARNIVAL GLASS COBALT BLUE IMPERIAL GRAPE PATTERN PUNCH CUP. 6.50
CARNIVAL GLASS COBALT BLUE IRIDESCENT STORK IN RUSHES....... 15.00
CARNIVAL GLASS COBALT BLUE NORTHWOOD WATER SET........... 125.00
CARNIVAL GLASS COBALT BLUE OPEN ROSE BOWL,3 FOOTED WITH
  FLUTED EDGE............................................. 48.50
CARNIVAL GLASS COBALT BLUE ORANGE TREE PATTERN PUNCH CUP.... 6.50
CARNIVAL GLASS COBALT BLUE PANELLED DANDELION WATER PITCHER. 30.00
CARNIVAL GLASS COBALT BLUE STAG & HOLLY FOOTED BOWL......... 48.00
CARNIVAL GLASS COBALT BLUE STORK & RUSHES PATTERN TUMBLER... 92.00
CARNIVAL GLASS COBALT EYECUP............................ 3.75
CARNIVAL GLASS FROSTED SHELL & JEWEL WATER PITCHER......... 10.00
CARNIVAL GLASS FROSTY WHITE IRIDESCENT LEAF RAYS NAPPY...... 35.00
CARNIVAL GLASS GOLD BLUE DOUBLE LOOP CHALICE............. 40.00
CARNIVAL GLASS GOLD CHRYSANTHEMUM SPRIG SPOONER........... 37.00
CARNIVAL GLASS GOLDEN WEDDING BOTTLE..................... 10.00
CARNIVAL GLASS GOLDEN WEDDING MINIATURE BOTTLE........... 5.00
CARNIVAL GLASS GOLD GINGER ALE BOTTLE................... 9.00
CARNIVAL GLASS GOLD STAG & HOLLY FOOTED BOWL............. 35.00
CARNIVAL GLASS GOLD WITH PURPLE IRIDESCENT 9 IN. BOWL....... 20.00
CARNIVAL GLASS GREEN & BRONZE IRIDESCENT PLATE,3 FRUIT...... 30.00
CARNIVAL GLASS GREEN ACORN & MAPLE LEAVES BOWL........... 16.00
CARNIVAL GLASS GREEN ACORN BURRS SPOONER................. 32.00
CARNIVAL GLASS GREEN BEADED & FLUTED FOOTED BERRY BOWL..... 15.00
CARNIVAL GLASS GREEN BEADED CABLE PATTERN FOOTED ROSE BOWL.. 23.00
CARNIVAL GLASS GREEN BLACKBERRY COMPOTE.................. 27.00
CARNIVAL GLASS GREEN,BLUE & GOLD DIAMOND LACE TUMBLER...... 18.00
CARNIVAL GLASS GREEN BRONZE IRIDESCENT,FOOTED CANDY DISH.... 22.00
CARNIVAL GLASS GREEN BUSHEL BASKET...................... 35.00
CARNIVAL GLASS GREEN BUTTERFLY & BERRY WATER PITCHER....... 65.00
CARNIVAL GLASS GREEN BUTTERFLY & FERN TUMBLER............ 17.00
CARNIVAL GLASS GREEN BUTTERFLIES DOUBLE-HANDLED BONBON...... 22.00
CARNIVAL GLASS GREEN COIN SPOT 9 IN. BOWL............... 14.00
CARNIVAL GLASS GREEN CORN VASE
  85.00  TO.............................................. 95.00
```

```
CARNIVAL GLASS GREEN CUSPIDOR........................   12.50
CARNIVAL GLASS GREEN DIAMOND POINT SIGNED NORTHWOOD SUGAR
  BOWL...............................................   18.00
CARNIVAL GLASS GREEN FINE RIB 8 IN. VASE.............   17.50
CARNIVAL GLASS GREEN FINE RIB VASE...................    9.00
CARNIVAL GLASS GREEN GRAPE & CABLE BOWL..............   20.00
CARNIVAL GLASS GREEN GRAPE & CABLE COLOGNE BOTTLE....   62.00
CARNIVAL GLASS GREEN GRAPE & CABLE COVERED SUGAR.....   48.00
CARNIVAL GLASS GREEN GRAPE & CABLE HATPIN HOLDER.....   50.00
CARNIVAL GLASS GREEN GRAPE & CABLE PITCHER & 6 TUMBLERS..... 225.00
CARNIVAL GLASS GREEN GRAPE & CABLE THUMBPRINT SAUCE DISH,6..   45.00
CARNIVAL GLASS GREEN GRAPE WITH CABLE COVERED SUGAR..........   45.00
CARNIVAL GLASS GREEN GRAPE WITH GOTHIC ARCH WATER PITCHER...  125.00
CARNIVAL GLASS GREEN GREEK KEY FRUIT
  BOWL,BASKETWEAVE,SCALLOPED EDGE.....................   50.00
CARNIVAL GLASS GREEN HOLLY 9 IN. NAPPY...............   18.50
CARNIVAL GLASS GREEN HOLLY & BERRY BOWL..............   17.50
CARNIVAL GLASS GREEN IMPERIAL GRAPE STEMMED WINE.....   12.00
CARNIVAL GLASS GREEN IMPERIAL GRAPE WATER PITCHER....   65.00
CARNIVAL GLASS GREEN IMPERIAL GRAPE WATER PITCHER & 4
  TUMBLERS..........................................   69.00
CARNIVAL GLASS GREEN LUSTER ROSE PATTERN 6 IN. BOWL..........   12.75
CARNIVAL GLASS GREEN NESTING SWAN WATER PITCHER..............  225.00
CARNIVAL GLASS GREEN NORTHWOOD BASE FOR PUNCH BOWL...........   12.00
CARNIVAL GLASS GREEN NORTHWOOD CHERRY WATER PITCHER..........  145.00
CARNIVAL GLASS GREEN NORTHWOOD,LOOPED PETALS FINGER BOWL....   29.00
CARNIVAL GLASS GREEN NORTHWOOD PEACH TUMBLER.................    9.95
CARNIVAL GLASS GREEN OPEN ROSE RUFFLED 8 IN. BOWL...........   20.00
CARNIVAL GLASS GREEN PANSY BOWL,SILVER IRIDESCENCE..........   22.00
CARNIVAL GLASS GREEN PEACOCK TAILS ADVERTISING ,FLARED HAT
  SHAPE.............................................   40.00
CARNIVAL GLASS GREEN PEACOCK TAIL BOWL...............   16.00
CARNIVAL GLASS GREEN PEACOCK TAIL HAT-SHAPED DISH............   12.00
CARNIVAL GLASS GREEN PEDESTAL COMPOTE,RUFFLE EDGE,3-MOLD....   24.00
CARNIVAL GLASS GREEN PLATE BASKET,STRAWBERRY OUTSIDE........   30.00
CARNIVAL GLASS GREEN RASPBERRY WITH BASKETWEAVE WATER
  PITCHER...........................................   65.00
CARNIVAL GLASS GREEN RIBBED 10 IN. VASE..............   20.00
CARNIVAL GLASS GREEN ROSES,3 SCROLL FEET,BOWL.......   14.00
CARNIVAL GLASS GREEN SHELL & ROSES 6 IN. FOOTED BOWL........   10.00
CARNIVAL GLASS GREEN SIGNED WATER PITCHER & 4 TUMBLERS......  175.00
CARNIVAL GLASS GREEN SINGING BIRD TUMBLER............   17.50
CARNIVAL GLASS GREEN STIPPLED RAYS RUFFLED CANDY DISH.......   23.00
CARNIVAL GLASS GREEN STRAWBERRY SIGNED 9 IN. BOWL,SATIN
  FINISH............................................   22.50
CARNIVAL GLASS GREEN SWAN............................   14.00
CARNIVAL GLASS GREEN THREADED 5 IN. COMPOTE..........   14.00
CARNIVAL GLASS GREEN WILD ROSE NORTHWOOD CANDY BOWL.........   23.00
CARNIVAL GLASS GREEN WINDROSE & OPEN HEART BOWL..............   17.00
CARNIVAL GLASS HONEY TO TURQUOISE HEARTS & FLOWERS COMPOTE..   50.00
CARNIVAL GLASS ICE BLUE BEADED CABLE ROSE BOWL..............   42.00
CARNIVAL GLASS ICE BLUE FINE CUT & ROSES FOOTED CANDY DISH..   30.00
CARNIVAL GLASS ICE BLUE FINE CUT & ROSES ROSE BOWL..........   39.00
CARNIVAL GLASS ICE BLUE GRAPE & CABLE FOOTED CENTER PIECE...   25.00
CARNIVAL GLASS ICE GREEN BUSHEL BASKET...............    9.00
CARNIVAL GLASS ICE GREEN DIAMOND POINT VASE..........   15.00
CARNIVAL GLASS ICE GREEN DRAPERY 8 IN. VASE..........   15.00
CARNIVAL GLASS ICE GREEN HEARTS & FLOWERS BOWL..............   42.00
CARNIVAL GLASS ICE GREEN IMPERIAL GRAPE BOWL,SCALLOPED EDGE.   12.00
CARNIVAL GLASS MARIGOLD 2-HANDLED COMPOTE,5 IN.......   12.50
CARNIVAL GLASS MARIGOLD 7 PIECE WATER SET,PITCHER & 6
  TUMBLERS..........................................   90.00
CARNIVAL GLASS MARIGOLD 8 IN. BERRY BOWL.............   20.00
CARNIVAL GLASS MARIGOLD 9 IN. BOWL...................   10.00
CARNIVAL GLASS MARIGOLD 9 IN. FLUTED COINSPOT BOWL..........   12.00
```

```
CARNIVAL GLASS MARIGOLD 9 IN. GRAPE BOWL...................    12.50
CARNIVAL GLASS MARIGOLD 9 IN. RUFFLED BOWL.................    22.50
CARNIVAL GLASS MARIGOLD 11 IN. DIVIDED PLATE,BOUQUET &
  LATTICE.................................................     2.00
CARNIVAL GLASS MARIGOLD ASH TRAY..........................     2.00
CARNIVAL GLASS MARIGOLD ADVERTISING BASKET................    18.50
CARNIVAL GLASS,MARIGOLD BANANA BOWL,CHERRIES ON BOTH SIDES..   50.00
CARNIVAL GLASS MARIGOLD BEADED CIRCLES FOOTED BOWL.........     7.00
CARNIVAL GLASS MARIGOLD BEADED 2 HANDLED BASKET...........    12.50
CARNIVAL GLASS MARIGOLD BOUQUET-LATTICE LOW PEDESTAL SAUCE,6    9.00
CARNIVAL GLASS MARIGOLD BOWL..............................     3.00
CARNIVAL GLASS MARIGOLD BOWL,3 FRUITS.....................    14.00
CARNIVAL GLASS MARIGOLD BUTTERFLY & BERRY FRUIT DISH.......    20.00
CARNIVAL GLASS MARIGOLD BUTTERFLY & BERRY PATTERN 3-FOOTED
  FRUIT BOWL..............................................    45.00
CARNIVAL GLASS MARIGOLD BUTTERFLY & BERRY TUMBLER.........    10.00
CARNIVAL GLASS MARIGOLD BUTTERFLY & BERRY WATER SET.......    80.00
CARNIVAL GLASS MARIGOLD CAKE PLATE,TWIG HANDLE............    20.00
CARNIVAL GLASS MARIGOLD CANDY COMPOTE WITH DOMED
  COVER,CRACKLE PATTERN...................................     4.75
CARNIVAL GLASS MARIGOLD CHECKERBOARD PATTERN BOWL.........    12.00
CARNIVAL GLASS MARIGOLD CHERRY SPRAY ICE CREAM DISH,10 IN...   26.00
CARNIVAL GLASS MARIGOLD CHRYSANTHEMUM FOOTED BOWL.........    37.50
CARNIVAL GLASS MARIGOLD CLOVER SHAPED DISH
  1.50  TO...............................................      2.50
CARNIVAL GLASS MARIGOLD COCKATOO & GRAPES WHISK BROOM HOLDER   16.00
CARNIVAL GLASS MARIGOLD COMPOTE,5 IN. TALL................     7.00
CARNIVAL GLASS MARIGOLD CORN BOTTLE......................     85.00
CARNIVAL GLASS MARIGOLD COVERED DUCK,6 IN.,PAINTED
  BILL,IRIDESCENCE........................................    10.00
CARNIVAL GLASS MARIGOLD CUP...............................     1.00
CARNIVAL GLASS MARIGOLD CUSPIDOR..........................    25.00
CARNIVAL GLASS MARIGOLD DAISY & LOTUS 3-FOOTED DISH,RUFFLED.    6.50
CARNIVAL GLASS MARIGOLD DAISY CHAIN LAMP SHADE............     8.50
CARNIVAL GLASS MARIGOLD DAISY PINWHEEL & CABLE 7 IN. PLATE..   15.00
CARNIVAL GLASS MARIGOLD DAISY PIN WHEELS & CABLE BOWL.......   13.00
CARNIVAL GLASS MARIGOLD DIAMOND LACE BERRY SET............    42.50
CARNIVAL GLASS MARIGOLD DISH,PEACOCK TAIL PATTERN.........     7.50
CARNIVAL GLASS MARIGOLD DIVIDED PLATE.....................     2.50
CARNIVAL GLASS MARIGOLD DRAGON & LOTUS DISH...............    17.50
CARNIVAL GLASS MARIGOLD DRAGON & LOTUS PATTERN PLATE.......   12.00
CARNIVAL GLASS MARIGOLD FAN VASE,8 IN. TALL...............     7.50
CARNIVAL GLASS MARIGOLD,FENTONS GRAPE BOWL................    12.00
CARNIVAL GLASS MARIGOLD FENTONS HEAVY GRAPE BERRY SET.......   75.00
CARNIVAL GLASS MARIGOLD FENTONS WILD DAISY & LOTUS FRUIT
  DISH...................................................     20.00
CARNIVAL GLASS MARIGOLD FLORAL & GRAPE TUMBLER............     4.00
CARNIVAL GLASS MARIGOLD FLORAL & GRAPE WATER PITCHER......    27.50
CARNIVAL GLASS MARIGOLD FLOWER FROG......................      3.00
CARNIVAL GLASS MARIGOLD FOOTED HAT PIN HOLDER,GRAPE & CABLE,  37.00
CARNIVAL GLASS MARIGOLD FOOTED HAT PIN HOLDER,ORANGE TREE...  37.00
CARNIVAL GLASS MARIGOLD FRUIT LUSTER TUMBLER..............     5.50
CARNIVAL GLASS MARIGOLD GAS SHADE........................     20.00
CARNIVAL GLASS MARIGOLD GOOD LUCK ROSE BOWL...............    35.00
CARNIVAL GLASS MARIGOLD GRAPE & CABLE BOWL................    14.00
CARNIVAL GLASS MARIGOLD GRAPE & CABLE DISH,...............     9.50
CARNIVAL GLASS MARIGOLD GRAPE & GOTHIC ARCHES COVERED SUGAR.  14.00
CARNIVAL GLASS MARIGOLD GRAPE & GOTHIC ARCH PITCHER & 5
  TUMBLERS...............................................     95.00
CARNIVAL GLASS MARIGOLD GRAPE & GOTHIC ARCHES SPOONER.......   9.00
CARNIVAL GLASS MARIGOLD GRAPE & LEAVES 9 IN. BOWL MARKED N..  16.50
CARNIVAL GLASS MARIGOLD GRAPE & LEAF FOOTED HATPIN HOLDER...  26.00
CARNIVAL GLASS MARIGOLD GRAPE & LEAF PITCHER WITH 7 TUMBLERS  40.00
CARNIVAL GLASS MARIGOLD GRAPE COVERED POWDER BOX..........    15.00
CARNIVAL GLASS MARIGOLD GRAPE FRUIT DISH..................     9.50
```

```
CARNIVAL GLASS MARIGOLD GRAPE LEAVES PITCHER & 5 TUMBLERS...   30.00
CARNIVAL GLASS MARIGOLD GRAPE WITH FLUTED RIM 7 IN. MARKED
  DISH..................................................   19.50
CARNIVAL GLASS MARIGOLD HANDLED NAPPY....................   15.00
CARNIVAL GLASS MARIGOLD HAT PIN HOLDER...................   42.50
CARNIVAL GLASS MARIGOLD HAT PIN HOLDER,GRAPE & CABLE.....   16.50
CARNIVAL GLASS MARIGOLD HAT VASE,3 IN. CRIMPED
  EDGE,BLACKBERRY PATTERN................................   12.50
CARNIVAL GLASS MARIGOLD HEART & VINE ADVERTISING PLATE...   77.00
CARNIVAL GLASS MARIGOLD HERRINGBONE & IRIS COVERED SUGAR &
  CREAMER...............................................    7.50
CARNIVAL GLASS MARIGOLD HERRINGBONE & IRIS WATER PITCHER & 8
  TUMBLERS..............................................   30.00
CARNIVAL GLASS MARIGOLD HOBNAIL SWIRL ROSE BOWL..........   35.00
CARNIVAL GLASS MARIGOLD HOLLY BOWL,9 IN..................   15.00
CARNIVAL GLASS MARIGOLD HOLLY BOWL.......................    8.00
CARNIVAL GLASS MARIGOLD HORSES HEADS MEDALLION 7 IN. PLATE..   28.00
CARNIVAL GLASS MARIGOLD IMPERIAL GRAPE TUMBLER...........    6.00
CARNIVAL GLASS MARIGOLD INDIAN HEAD MATCH HOLDER.........   15.00
CARNIVAL GLASS MARIGOLD INDIAN HEAD TOOTHPICK,INDIAN FACE...   10.00
CARNIVAL GLASS MARIGOLD IRIS & HERRINGBONE 11 IN. BOWL...    3.50
CARNIVAL GLASS MARIGOLD IRIS & HERRINGBONE PITCHER.......   13.00
CARNIVAL GLASS MARIGOLD IRISH LACE CREAM & SUGAR.........    5.00
CARNIVAL GLASS MARIGOLD JACK IN PULPIT VASE..............   15.00
CARNIVAL GLASS MARIGOLD KITTENS BOWL,4 SIDES TURNED UP...   30.00
CARNIVAL GLASS MARIGOLD LACY PATTERN BOWL................    7.00
CARNIVAL GLASS MARIGOLD LAMP SHADE.......................   25.00
CARNIVAL GLASS MARIGOLD LATTICE & GRAPE FRUIT DISH.......   22.00
CARNIVAL GLASS MARIGOLD LATTICE EDGE BOWL,ADVERTISING
  FURNITURE CO..........................................   27.00
CARNIVAL GLASS MARIGOLD LEAF & BEADS FRUIT DISH..........   10.00
CARNIVAL GLASS MARIGOLD LIGHT SHADE,SCENES...............    3.50
CARNIVAL GLASS MARIGOLD LOUSIA BERRY BOWL ,SQUARE BASE...    5.00
CARNIVAL GLASS MARIGOLD LOUSIA BERRY DISH................    1.00
CARNIVAL GLASS MARIGOLD LOUSIA CREAMER & OPEN SUGAR......    3.00
CARNIVAL GLASS MARIGOLD LOUSIA COVERED CANDY DISH........    5.00
CARNIVAL GLASS MARIGOLD LOUSIA DOME BUTTER COVER.........    1.00
CARNIVAL GLASS MARIGOLD LOUSIA SQUARE DINNER PLATE.......    2.00
CARNIVAL GLASS MARIGOLD LOUSIA WATER SET,6 GLASSES.......   12.00
CARNIVAL GLASS MARIGOLD LUSTRE ROSE WATER PITCHER & 10
  TUMBLERS..............................................   90.00
CARNIVAL GLASS,MARIGOLD MAPLE LEAF CREAMER,HEAVY DEEP COLOUR   15.00
CARNIVAL GLASS MARIGOLD MAPLE LEAF TUMBLER...............    8.50
CARNIVAL GLASS MARIGOLD MATCHED PAIR RUSTIC VASES,RIBBED
  BODY..................................................   22.00
CARNIVAL GLASS MARIGOLD MELINDA 7 IN. FRUIT DISH.........   12.00
CARNIVAL GLASS MARIGOLD OPEN ROSE PATTERN BOWL...........   13.50
CARNIVAL GLASS MARIGOLD OPEN ROSE PATTERN 6 PIECE TABLE SET.   50.00
CARNIVAL GLASS MARIGOLD ORANGE TREE PAIR MUGS............   15.00
CARNIVAL GLASS MARIGOLD PAIR AUTO VASES..................   12.00
CARNIVAL GLASS MARIGOLD PANTHER SAUCE....................   11.50
CARNIVAL GLASS MARIGOLD PANSY BOWL.......................   12.00
CARNIVAL GLASS MARIGOLD PANSY SPRAY RIPPLE BOWL..........   15.00
CARNIVAL GLASS MARIGOLD PEACH AND PEAR WATER PITCHER.....   45.00
CARNIVAL GLASS MARIGOLD PEACH OPALESCENCE DISH,MOTHER OF
  PEARL FINISH..........................................   22.50
CARNIVAL GLASS MARIGOLD PEACOCK AT FOUNTAIN PUNCH BOWL...   65.00
CARNIVAL GLASS MARIGOLD PEACOCK WITH URN PLATE...........   29.50
CARNIVAL GLASS MARIGOLD PERSIAN MEDALLION VASE,APPLIED
  HANDLES...............................................    8.50
CARNIVAL GLASS MARIGOLD PIGGY BANK.......................    5.00
CARNIVAL GLASS MARIGOLD PINE CONE SAUCER.................    5.00
CARNIVAL GLASS MARIGOLD ,POINSETTIA PATTERN MILK PITCHER....   14.00
CARNIVAL GLASS MARIGOLD POWDER JAR,SCOTTIE...............    4.50
CARNIVAL GLASS MARIGOLD PUNCH BOWL & 5 CUPS,FLUTED TOP...   85.00
```

```
CARNIVAL GLASS MARIGOLD PUNCH CUP,STORK & RUSHES PATTERN....    3.95
CARNIVAL GLASS MARIGOLD PUNCH BOWL WITH STAND & 4 CUPS......   60.00
CARNIVAL GLASS MARIGOLD RAISED GRAPE 9 IN. BOTTLE...........   19.50
CARNIVAL GLASS MARIGOLD RIPPLE BOWL IN PANSY SPRAY..........   15.00
CARNIVAL GLASS MARIGOLD RIPPLE PATTERN VASE.................   12.00
CARNIVAL GLASS MARIGOLD ROBIN MUG...........................   17.50
CARNIVAL GLASS MARIGOLD ROSE & RUFFLES 9 IN. PLATE..........   10.00
CARNIVAL GLASS MARIGOLD ROSE,BARK,7 IN. BOTTLE..............    3.00
CARNIVAL GLASS MARIGOLD ROSE BOWL,ORANGE TREE,3 TWIG FEET...   25.00
CARNIVAL GLASS MARIGOLD ROSES & LOOP DOME VASE..............    8.00
CARNIVAL GLASS MARIGOLD ROSES BOWL ON LEGS..................   25.01-
CARNIVAL GLASS MARIGOLD ROSES BUTTER DISH...................   32.50
CARNIVAL GLASS MARIGOLD ROSE WATER SET,6 TUMBLERS & PITCHER.   65.00
CARNIVAL GLASS MARIGOLD RUFFLED DISH,WINDFLOWER.............   15.00
CARNIVAL GLASS MARIGOLD SAUCE COMPOTE SIGNED N..............   50.00
CARNIVAL GLASS MARIGOLD SCOTTIE POWDER JAR..................    4.50
CARNIVAL GLASS MARIGOLD SPITTOON,STIPPLED DOT,7 X 4 IN......   35.00
CARNIVAL GLASS MARIGOLD STAG & HOLLY BOWL...................   28.00
CARNIVAL GLASS MARIGOLD STAG AND HOLLY FOOTED BOWL..........   25.00
CARNIVAL GLASS MARIGOLD STAG AND HOLLY TRI FOOTED BOWL......   35.00
CARNIVAL GLASS MARIGOLD STAR & FILE TUMBLER.................   11.50
CARNIVAL GLASS MARIGOLD STEMMED WINE........................   10.00
CARNIVAL GLASS MARIGOLD SUGAR BOWL,BOUQUET & LATTICE PATTERN    1.50
CARNIVAL GLASS MARIGOLD SUNBURST FRUIT BOWL AND STAND.......   65.00
CARNIVAL GLASS MARIGOLD SWAN COVERED DISH...................   35.00
CARNIVAL GLASS MARIGOLD TREE OF LIFE OUTSIDE,PEACOCK TAIL
  IN,COMPOTE................................................   20.00
CARNIVAL GLASS MARIGOLD TREE OF LIFE PATTERN BERRY BOWL & 6
  SAUCES...................................................   12.00
CARNIVAL GLASS MARIGOLD TREE ORCHARD TUMBLER................   12.00
CARNIVAL GLASS MARIGOLD TUMBLER.............................    6.00
CARNIVAL GLASS MARIGOLD TUMBLER,OCTAGON.....................    8.50
CARNIVAL GLASS MARIGOLD TWIG FOOTED LEAF & BEAD PATTERN ROSE
  BOWL.....................................................   18.00
CARNIVAL GLASS MARIGOLD TWIN 2-PIECE FRUIT BOWL.............   30.00
CARNIVAL GLASS MARIGOLD VASE,14 IN. TALL,RIBBED.............    9.00
CARNIVAL GLASS MARIGOLD VINEYARD WATER PITCHER & 6 TUMBLERS.   65.00
CARNIVAL GLASS MARIGOLD VINTAGE GRAPE SET OF 6 TUMBLERS.....   45.00
CARNIVAL GLASS MARIGOLD VINTAGE PATTERN THREADED STEM WINE..    8.00
CARNIVAL GLASS MARIGOLD VINTAGE RUFFLED DISH................   14.00
CARNIVAL GLASS MARIGOLD WAFFLE BLOCK FRUIT BOWL.............   18.50
CARNIVAL GLASS MARIGOLD WALL FLOWER CONTAINER IN WICKER
  HOLDER...................................................   12.00
CARNIVAL GLASS MARIGOLD WATER PITCHER......................   25.00
CARNIVAL GLASS MARIGOLD WINDFLOWER 7 IN. HANDLED DISH.......    8.00
CARNIVAL GLASS MARIGOLD WINDFLOWER BOWL.....................    8.00
CARNIVAL GLASS,MARIGOLD WINDFLOWER BOWL,8IN. SIZE...........   10.50
CARNIVAL GLASS MARIGOLD WINDFLOWER CRIMPED 8 IN. BOWL.......    9.50
CARNIVAL GLASS MARIGOLD WINDMILL TUMBLER...................    7.50
CARNIVAL GLASS OPALESCENT PANELLED HOLLY WATER SET.........  115.00
CARNIVAL GLASS ORANGE 2 PART FRUIT BOWL....................   35.00
CARNIVAL GLASS ORANGE 2 PIECE PUNCH BOWL...................   35.00
CARNIVAL GLASS ORANGE & FAINT GREEN HOLLY & BERRIES 9 IN.
  BOWL.....................................................   18.50
CARNIVAL GLASS ORANGE BULLSEYE 12 IN. VASE.................   25.00
CARNIVAL GLASS ORANGE CAR VASE.............................    8.50
CARNIVAL GLASS ORANGE CRACKLE NUT DISH ON STEM WITH POINTED
  LID......................................................    5.00
CARNIVAL GLASS ORANGE GRAPE BOWL,8 IN.....................    5.00
CARNIVAL GLASS ORANGE GRAPE WINE..........................    6.50
CARNIVAL GLASS ORANGE HANDLED NAPPY.......................   15.00
CARNIVAL GLASS ORANGE INDIANHEAD TOOTHPICK HOLDER.........   10.00
CARNIVAL GLASS ORANGE PUNCH BOWL,BASE & 5 CUPS,FLUTED TOP...   85.00
CARNIVAL GLASS ORANGE ROUND FERN DISH,3 FEET..............   12.00
CARNIVAL GLASS ORANGE RUFFLE EDGE 3 FOOTED BOWL,VINTAGE
```

```
PATTERN...................................................  7.50
CARNIVAL GLASS ORANGE SECTIONED PLATE,LATTICE & BANQUET
  PATTERN.................................................  8.50
CARNIVAL GLASS ORANGE STIPPLE RAY CANDY DISH,SQUARE.......  9.50
CARNIVAL GLASS ORANGE TO CLEAR VASE......................  8.00
CARNIVAL GLASS ORANGE TREE OF LIFE WATER PITCHER......... 12.00
CARNIVAL GLASS ORANGE VASE,SLENDER WITH FLUTED OPENING... 25.00
CARNIVAL GLASS ORANGE WINE,THREADED STEM,VINTAGE PATTERN..  8.00
CARNIVAL GLASS PEACH OPALINE CORINTH VASE................ 23.00
CARNIVAL GLASS PEACOCK AT FOUNTAIN TUMBLER............... 25.00
CARNIVAL GLASS PUNCH BOWL & BASE,BLUE,ORANGE TREE........ 90.00
CARNIVAL GLASS PUNCH CUPS ,GREEN,ACORN & BERRIES......... 12.50
CARNIVAL GLASS PUNCH SET,MARIGOLD,PEACOCK AT FOUNTAIN....150.00
CARNIVAL GLASS PURPLE 1/2 IN. BUTTON.....................  1.00
CARNIVAL GLASS PURPLE 2 HANDLE ADVERTISING BUTTERFLIES
  BON-BON................................................ 37.50
CARNIVAL GLASS PURPLE 3 LEG BOWL,RUFFLE EDGE,ROSE PATTERN
  OUTSIDE................................................ 14.00
CARNIVAL GLASS PURPLE ACORN BURRS SPOONER................ 35.00
CARNIVAL GLASS PURPLE BANANA BOAT,GRAPE AND CABLE,FOOTED. 79.00
CARNIVAL GLASS PURPLE ,BLUE,GREEN,BRONZE,BOWL,CANE & STARS.. 16.50
CARNIVAL GLASS PURPLE BOWL,FLUTED & CRIMPED.............. 18.00
CARNIVAL GLASS PURPLE BOWL,LA BELLE ELAINE.............. 20.00
CARNIVAL GLASS PURPLE BOWL,PATTERN IN & OUT.............. 46.00
CARNIVAL GLASS PURPLE BOWL SCALLOPED PANELED RAYS........ 18.00
CARNIVAL GLASS PURPLE PUNCH BOWL STAND,PEACOCK AT FOUNTAIN,RED..... 18.00
CARNIVAL GLASS PURPLE BOWL STAR IN BASE.................  7.50
CARNIVAL GLASS PURPLE BRONZE BEADED CABLE ROSE BOWL,3 FOOTED 31.50
CARNIVAL GLASS PURPLE BUTTON............................  1.00
CARNIVAL GLASS PURPLE CHERRY PATTERN CREAM PITCHER....... 18.00
CARNIVAL GLASS PURPLE COPPER IRIDESCENCE HEART & VINE 8 IN.
  BOWL................................................... 20.00
CARNIVAL GLASS PURPLE COVERED STRUTTING PEACOCK CREAMER.. 22.50
CARNIVAL GLASS PURPLE DIAMOND LACE WATER PITCHER......... 75.00
CARNIVAL GLASS PURPLE DISH MARKED IMPERIAL.............. 15.00
CARNIVAL GLASS PURPLE DOME BASE DISH.................... 20.00
CARNIVAL GLASS PURPLE FINE RIB VASE..................... 15.00
CARNIVAL GLASS PURPLE FISHERMANS MUG.................... 34.00
CARNIVAL GLASS,PURPLE FLUTED GRAPE BOWL................. 27.50
CARNIVAL GLASS PURPLE FOOTED FRUIT BOWL................. 31.00
CARNIVAL GLASS PURPLE FRUIT 9 IN. FLUTED BOWL,CHERRY CENTER. 22.00
CARNIVAL GLASS PURPLE G/C COVERED BUTTER DISH........... 65.00
CARNIVAL GLASS PURPLE,GOOD LUCK BOWL, 8 IN.............. 45.00
CARNIVAL GLASS PURPLE GRAPE & CABLE 8 IN. 3 FOOTED BOWL.. 25.00
CARNIVAL GLASS PURPLE GRAPE & CABLE ORANGE BOWL......... 80.00
CARNIVAL GLASS PURPLE GRAPE & CABLE POWDER JAR &
  COVER,NORTHWOOD........................................ 30.00
CARNIVAL GLASS PURPLE GRAPE & CABLE PUNCH CUP........... 12.50
CARNIVAL GLASS PURPLE GRAPE & CABLE THUMBPRINT BASE BERRY
  BOWL................................................... 57.00
CARNIVAL GLASS PURPLE GRAPE & CABLE TUMBLER
  12.00  TO............................................. 20.00
CARNIVAL GLASS PURPLE GRAPE HAT PIN HOLDER.............. 45.00
CARNIVAL GLASS PURPLE GRAPE PUNCH CUP...................  8.00
CARNIVAL GLASS PURPLE GRAPEVINE LATTICE TUMBLER......... 15.00
CARNIVAL GLASS PURPLE GREEK KEY 8 SIDED FOOTED BOWL..... 25.00
CARNIVAL GLASS PURPLE HOLLY BOWL....................... 20.00
CARNIVAL GLASS PURPLE IMPERIAL ARCS BOWL............... 16.00
CARNIVAL GLASS PURPLE IMPERIAL GRAPE WATER GOBLET...... 42.50
CARNIVAL GLASS PURPLE IRIDESCENCE CHERRY PATTERN CREAM
  PITCHER............................................... 18.00
CARNIVAL GLASS PURPLE IRIDESCENT BUTTON,1/2 IN..........  1.00
CARNIVAL GLASS PURPLE IRIDESCENT PUNCH BOWL,GRAPE WITH CABLE 28.75
CARNIVAL GLASS PURPLE LEAF & BEADS ROSE BOWL........... 35.00
CARNIVAL GLASS PURPLE ,NORTHWOOD CHERRY COMPOTE,7X7IN... 65.00
```

```
CARNIVAL GLASS PURPLE,ORANGE TREE LOVING CUP.................  65.00
CARNIVAL GLASS PURPLE,ORANGE TREE PUNCH BOWL,11 IN..........  45.00
CARNIVAL GLASS PURPLE,ORANGE TREE ROSE BOWL.................  40.00
CARNIVAL GLASS PURPLE PANELLED DIAMOND & BOWS VASE..........  22.00
CARNIVAL GLASS PURPLE PANSY SPRAY 9 IN. BOWL...............  24.00
CARNIVAL GLASS PURPLE PEACOCK & URN SAUCE BOWL.............  18.00
CARNIVAL GLASS PURPLE,PEACOCKS ON FENCE BOWL, 8 IN.........  50.00
CARNIVAL GLASS PURPLE PLATE,9 IN...........................  36.00
CARNIVAL GLASS PURPLE RIBBED 10 IN. VASE,SCALLOP TOP.......  14.50
CARNIVAL GLASS PURPLE RIBBED 10 IN. VASE SIGNED............  17.50
CARNIVAL GLASS PURPLE SAUCE................................   7.50
CARNIVAL GLASS PURPLE SPATULA FOOTED BOWL..................  25.00
CARNIVAL GLASS PURPLE STRAWBERRY BOWL......................  24.00
CARNIVAL GLASS PURPLE STRAWBERRY HAND-GRIP PLATE...........  34.00
CARNIVAL GLASS PURPLE TO RED PEACOCK AT URN ICE CREAM DISH..  22.00
CARNIVAL GLASS PURPLE TOOTHPICK
  35.00   TO................................................  55.00
CARNIVAL GLASS PURPLE VASE,DIAMOND & RIBBED PATTERN,GOLD
  IRIDESCENT................................................  20.00
CARNIVAL GLASS PURPLE VASE,GOLD IRIDESCENCE,DIAMOND & RIB
  PATTERN...................................................  15.00
CARNIVAL GLASS PURPLE WINE,VINTAGE PATTERN.................  17.00
CARNIVAL GLASS RED 9 IN. VASE..............................  55.00
CARNIVAL GLASS RED BOWL,ACORN AND LEAVES,7 IN. DIAMETER....  85.00
CARNIVAL GLASS RED FLAT PLATE,14 ROUND FLUTES ON BORDER,...  43.00
CARNIVAL GLASS RED,GOLD & GREEN ACORN BURR FRUIT BOWL,9 IN..  80.00
CARNIVAL GLASS RUBY GOLD WINDMILL PATTERN BOWL.............  16.00
CARNIVAL GLASS SINGING BIRD TUMBLER........................  15.00
CARNIVAL GLASS SMOKY SANDWICH TRAY,VINTAGE PATTERN.........  37.50
CARNIVAL GLASS TURQUOISE OPALESCENT BOWL...................  55.00
CARNIVAL GLASS WHITE BATTENBERG LACE VASE..................  40.00
CARNIVAL GLASS WHITE BEADED SCROLL PATTERN COMPOTE.........  48.50
CARNIVAL GLASS WHITE CHRYSANTHEMUM PATTERN TUMBLER.........  35.00
CARNIVAL GLASS WHITE COMPOET,RUFFLED,RIBBED IRIDESCENT
  TOP,CLEAR STEM............................................  25.00
CARNIVAL GLASS WHITE FLARED-SHAPED BASKET..................  50.00
CARNIVAL GLASS WHITE FOOD CONTAINER........................   6.00
CARNIVAL GLASS WHITE GAS SHADE,PAIR........................  30.00
CARNIVAL GLASS WHITE GRAPE DELIGHT ROSE BOWL...............  42.50
CARNIVAL GLASS WHITE GRAPES & VINES FOOTED 5 IN. ROSE BOWL..  38.00
CARNIVAL GLASS WHITE GRAPEVINE LATTICE PLATE...............  24.00
CARNIVAL GLASS WHITE HEARTS & FLOWERS 8 IN. DISH...........  33.00
CARNIVAL GLASS WHITE HEINZ BOTTLE..........................  15.00
CARNIVAL GLASS WHITE HOLLY BAND SINCLAIR TOOTHPICK.........   7.50
CARNIVAL GLASS WHITE HOLLYBERRY PATTERN 9 IN. DISH.........  47.50
CARNIVAL GLASS WHITE HOLLY VINE PATTERN TOOTHPICK..........  12.50
CARNIVAL GLASS WHITE ICE CREAM BOWL,PERSIAN GARDEN.........  65.00
CARNIVAL GLASS WHITE INDIAN HEAD SINCLAIR TOOTHPICK........   7.50
CARNIVAL GLASS WHITE INDIAN HEAD TOOTHPICK.................  12.50
CARNIVAL GLASS WHITE IRIDESCENT INDIANHEAD TOOTHPICK.......  12.50
CARNIVAL GLASS WHITE LEAF CHAIN BOWL.......................  35.00
CARNIVAL GLASS WHITE ,NORTHWOOD,PLUM PATTERN CELERY,.......  48.50
CARNIVAL GLASS WHITE PANELLED DRAPE DISH...................  30.00
CARNIVAL GLASS WHITE PANELLED JELLY COMPOTE................  20.00
CARNIVAL GLASS WHITE PEACOCK & FENCE PLATE.................  60.00
CARNIVAL GLASS WHITE PERSIAN GARDEN ICE CREAM BOWL.........  60.00
CARNIVAL GLASS WHITE PERSIAN MEDALLION 4 IN. ROSE BOWL.....  45.00
CARNIVAL GLASS WHITE PLATE,PEACOCK ON FENCE,9 IN...........  63.50
CARNIVAL GLASS WHITE ROSE DELIGHT PATTERN FOOTED ROSE BOWL..  60.01-
CARNIVAL GLASS WHITE TREE PLATE,9 IN.,BEADED BERRY EXTERIOR.  36.00
CARNIVAL GLASS WHITE VINTAGE ROSE BOWL.....................  28.00
    CARNIVAL GLASS, SEE ALSO LISTING BY COLOUR.............
CARNIVAL GLASS 4 STAGS BOWL,FOOTED.........................  28.00
CARNIVAL GLASS ACORN BURR BERRY SET,MARKED,IRIDESCENCE.....  145.00
CARNIVAL GLASS ACORN BURR PUNCH CUP........................  14.00
```

```
CARNIVAL GLASS APPLE BLOSSOM BOWL.........................    13.00
CARNIVAL GLASS APPLE BLOSSOM TWIGS BOWL...................    23.00
CARNIVAL GLASS AURORA ROSE BOWL..........................    27.50
CARNIVAL GLASS BEADED ELLIPSE WATER PITCHER..............     9.00
CARNIVAL GLASS BLOCK & FAN CELERY HOLDER.................     6.50
CARNIVAL GLASS CHRYSANTHEMUM SPRIG COVERED SUGAR SIGNED
  NORTHWOOD..............................................    50.00
CARNIVAL GLASS COTTAGE PATTERN CELERY HOLDER.............     7.50
CARNIVAL GLASS DIAMOND QUILTED IMPERIAL PANSY 8 IN. DISH....   7.00
CARNIVAL GLASS FARMYARD..................................   650.00
CARNIVAL GLASS FINE RIB VASE.............................    13.50
CARNIVAL GLASS GRAPE & CABLE 2 HANDLED SQUARE COMPOTE ON
  PEDESTAL BASE..........................................    32.50
CARNIVAL GLASS GRAPE & CABLE 7 IN. RUFFLED BOWL ON 3 FEET...  35.00
CARNIVAL GLASS GRAPE AND CABLE 9 IN. BOWL................    27.00
CARNIVAL GLASS GRAPE & CABLE COMPOTE,SWEET MEAT..........    98.00
CARNIVAL GLASS GRAPE & CABLE TUMBLER.....................    16.00
CARNIVAL GLASS GRAPE & LEAF PUNCH BOWL WITH STAND & 10 CUPS.  150.00
CARNIVAL GLASS GRAPE & THUMBPRINT WATER PITCHER WITH 6
  TUMBLERS..............................................    150.00
CARNIVAL GLASS GRAPE CABLE THUMBPRINT CRACKER JAR........    25.00
CARNIVAL GLASS GRAPES OVAL BERRY BOWL....................    85.00
CARNIVAL GLASS HOLLY STAR FOOTED BONBON..................    12.00
CARNIVAL GLASS HONEYCOMB SPOONER.........................     4.00
CARNIVAL GLASS HORSE HEAD BOTTOM FLUTED BOWL.............    25.00
CARNIVAL GLASS IMPERIAL GRAPE BOWL.......................     8.00
CARNIVAL GLASS IMPERIAL GRAPE CUP & SAUCER...............    19.00
CARNIVAL GLASS IMPERIAL GRAPE WATER PITCHER & 5 GLASSES..    50.00
CARNIVAL GLASS INDIANHEAD IRIDESCENT TOOTHPICK...........    10.00
CARNIVAL GLASS INSULATOR,ORANGE,3 IN.....................    14.50
CARNIVAL GLASS MINIATURE BOWL,4 IN. WIDE RUFFLES.........    55.00
CARNIVAL GLASS NAPPY 2 HANDLED BIRDS ON A BOW,MARIGOLD...    17.00
CARNIVAL GLASS NORTHWOOD FLUTED PURPLE BOWL,EMBOSSED GRAPES
  & LEAVES..............................................    25.00
CARNIVAL GLASS NORTHWOOD ROSETTE ON 3 CURLED FEET........    18.50
CARNIVAL GLASS NU ART ORANGE GAS SHADE...................     5.00
CARNIVAL GLASS OPEN ROSE PATTERN COVERED BUTTER
  DISH,MARIGOLD.........................................    50.00
CARNIVAL GLASS OPEN ROSE PLATE MARIGOLD..................    20.00
CARNIVAL GLASS ORIENTAL POPPY WATER PITCHER..............   100.00
CARNIVAL GLASS,PR. 9 IN. TALL MARIGOLD VASES WITH IRIS
  FLOWER................................................    25.00
CARNIVAL GLASS PAIR CARAMEL STEMMED NUT DISHES...........    11.00
CARNIVAL GLASS PEACOCK & URN ICECREAM SET................   160.00
CARNIVAL GLASS PEACOCK AT FOUNTAIN ROUND BERRY BOWL SET WITH
  6 SAUCES..............................................   125.00
CARNIVAL GLASS PEACOCK AT FOUNTAIN ROUND FOOTED FRUIT BOWL..  100.00
CARNIVAL GLASS PEACOCK AT FOUNTAIN FRUIT BOWL,9 IN.......    80.00
CARNIVAL GLASS PEDESTAL CANDY DISH,DIAMOND QUILT,PEACH
  COLOUR................................................    16.50
CARNIVAL GLASS PERSIAN MEDALLION PEACH MINT DISH.........    12.00
CARNIVAL GLASS PIG BANK.................................     2.00
CARNIVAL GLASS PLATE,GRAPE AND CABLE PURPLE,SPATULA FEET....  33.00
CARNIVAL GLASS PLATE MARKED IG,10 I5.....................     5.25
CARNIVAL GLASS PLATE,ICE GREEN GREEK KEY & MUMS..........    65.00
CARNIVAL GLASS PLATE,OPEN ROSE PATTERN,GREEN.............    35.00
CARNIVAL GLASS PLATE,WHITE PEACOCK ON FENCE,9 IN.........    60.00
CARNIVAL GLASS POWDER JAR,GREEN,GRAPE & CABLE,SIGNED N...    75.00
CARNIVAL GLASS RIBBED RED AMBER BERRY SET................    17.50
CARNIVAL GLASS RIBBED VASE...............................    12.00
CARNIVAL GLASS ROSE BOWL,BLUE,PERSIAN MEDALLION..........    29.00
CARNIVAL GLASS ROSE BOWL,DAISY & PLUME PATTERN,GREEN &
  COPPER,MARKED.........................................    25.00
CARNIVAL GLASS ROSE BOWL,MARIGOLD.......................    50.00
CARNIVAL GLASS ROSE BOWL,WHITE LEAF & BEADS.............    50.00
```

CARNIVAL GLASS RUFFLED EDGE BOWL,VINTAGE
  PATTERN,AMETHYST,SIGNED... 24.50
CARNIVAL GLASS RUFFLE EDGE COMPOTE,GRAPE PATTERN,COBALT BLUE
  STEM... 18.00
CARNIVAL GREEN,RUFFLED RIB,9 IN. BY 2 IN...................... 7.00
CARNIVAL GLASS SAILING SHIP PLATE AMBER...................... 18.50
CARNIVAL GLASS SAUCE,BLUE,PINE CONE.......................... 12.00
CARNIVAL GLASS SETTING HEN COVERED BUTTER DISH.............. 55.00
CARNIVAL GLASS SIGNED BERRY BOWL,BLUE-GREEN,GRAPE & CABLE... 12.50
CARNIVAL GLASS SIGNED PURPLE FINE RIB VASE................... 15.00
CARNIVAL GLASS SPITTOON,SWIRLED HOBNAIL PATTERN,MARIGOLD.... 59.00
CARNIVAL GLASS SPOONHOLDER,GRAPE WITH THUMBPRINT............. 18.00
CARNIVAL GLASS STAG & HOLLY 7 IN. BOWL...................... 24.00
CARNIVAL GLASS STAR MEDALLION MILK PITCHER,MARIGOLD......... 15.00
CARNIVAL GLASS STAR OF DAVID BOWL,.......................... 20.00
CARNIVAL GLASS STIPPLED RAYS 10 IN. BOWL.................... 20.00
CARNIVAL GLASS STIPPLED RAYS BOWL........................... 13.00
CARNIVAL GLASS STIPPLED RAYS BOWL,AMETHYST................... 15.00
CARNIVAL GLASS STIPPLED RAYS BOWL,PURPLE.................... 14.00
CARNIVAL GLASS STIPPLED RAYS CREAMER & SUGAR................ 25.00
CARNIVAL GLASS STORK A B C FEEDING DISH,MARIGOLD............ 27.00
CARNIVAL GLASS SWAN MASTER SALT,SAPPHIRE BLUE............... 21.00
CARNIVAL GLASS SWAN,PASTEL GREEN............................ 9.75
CARNIVAL GLASS THUMBPRINT & SPEAR STAR BASE CREAMER......... 13.00
CARNIVAL GLASS TIGER LILY WATER PITCHER..................... 89.00
CARNIVAL GLASS TOOTH PICK HOLDER,MARIGOLD,FLUTE............. 35.00
CARNIVAL GLASS TREE OF LIFE FOOTED CANDY JAR,COVERED........ 9.00
CARNIVAL GLASS VASE,MARIGOLD,NORTHWOOD MARKED,DIAMOND POINT. 7.00
CARNIVAL GLASS VASES,PAIR,TREE BARK PATTERN................. 8.00
CARNIVAL GLASS VASE SIGNED NORTHWOOD,REEDED PATTERN,HONEY TO
  AMETHYST... 15.00
CARNIVAL GLASS VASE,WHITE CORN.............................. 83.00
CARNIVAL GLASS WHITE DRAPERY NORTHWOOD CANDY BOWL........... 27.00
CARNIVAL GLASS WREATHED CHERRY WATER PITCHER................ 15.00
CAROUSEL HORSE,116 YRS. OLD, BEAUTIFULLY RESTORED........... 200.00

  CASED GLASS is made with one thin layer of glass over another layer or layers of
  colored glass. Many types of art glass were "cased." Cased glass is usually a
  well-made piece by a reputable factory.
CASED GLASS BASKET WITH AMBER HANDLE,BLUE & WHITE........... 22.50
CASH REGISTER,BRASS,NATIONAL,REGISTERS TO $1.90............. 75.00
CASH REGISTER,BRASS,NATIONAL,WORKING COND................... 27.50
CASH REGISTER,NATIONAL,1896 MODEL........................... 200.00
CASH REGISTER,NATIONAL SER. NO. 143-E,PATENT 1898........... 150.00
CASH REGISTER,PREMIER....................................... 20.00

  CASTLEFORD POTTERY of Castleford, Yorkshire, England, was made by the
  David Dunderdale & Co. from 1790 to 1820.
CASTLEFORD PITCHER,WHITE WITH BLUE TRIM,RAISED FIGURES,CIRCA
  1790... 85.00
CASTOR,5 BOTTLE,REVOLVING,3 FOOTED.......................... 45.00
CASTOR, 5 BOTTLE REVOLVING, ETCHED MATCHING BOTTLES......... 37.00
CASTOR,AMBER.. 20.00
CASTOR,BLUE PICKLE IN FRAME................................. 35.00
CASTOR,FOOTED PICKLE.. 37.50
CASTOR,PICKLE,7 TONGS,SILVER,AMBER SWIRL GLASS INSERT....... 48.00
CASTOR,PICKLE,AMBER IN SILVER HOLDER,COVER & TONGS.......... 65.00
CASTOR,PICKLE,BEADED BAND IN FRAME WITH TONGS............... 18.50
CASTOR,PICKLE,BLUE CANE,SILVER PLATE FRAME.................. 55.00
CASTOR,PICKLE,BLUE SWIRL ,HOLDER............................ 68.00
CASTOR,PICKLE,CASED BLUE SATIN GLASS,SILVER HOLDER ON
  FEET,TONGS... 159.00
CASTOR,PICKLE,CLEAR GLASS,BARLEY PATTERN,SILVER PLATE FRAME
  & TONGS.. 24.50

CASTOR,PICKLE,CLEAR GLASS,CANE,SILVER PLATE FRAME............   25.00
CASTOR,PICKLE,CLEAR PATTERNED GLASS JAR WITH SILVER PLATE
  HOLDER...   18.50
CASTOR,PICKLE,CRANBERRY ,CANDLESTICK FRAME,RING HANDLE &
  FORK..   135.00
CASTOR,PICKLE,CRANBERRY INVERTED THUMBPRINT INSERT,SILVER
  PLATE TOP...   50.00
CASTOR,PICKLE,DIAMOND QUILTED CLEAR TO CRANBERRY,SILVER
  PLATE FRAME...   110.00
CASTOR,PICKLE,DOME BASE,BAND BOTTOM,........................   24.00
CASTOR,PICKLE,DOUBLE,2 GLASS CONTAINERS IN SILVER BEADED
  HOLDER..   39.50
CASTOR,PICKLE,FOOTED,SILVER FRAME...........................   26.00
CASTOR,PICKLE,FRAME WITH HAND INSERT........................   35.00
CASTOR,PICKLE,SILVER PLATE WITH TONGS,AMBER INVERTED
  THUMBPRINT INSERT...   45.00
CASTOR,PICKLE,TONGS,CRYSTAL INSERT..........................   33.50
CASTOR,PICKLE,TONGS,WESTMORELAND INSERT.....................   16.50
CASTOR,PICKLE,WEBSTER SILVER EMBOSSED BAND,PRISMATIC INSERT.   27.50
CASTOR,PICKLE WITH TONGS,BLUE BABY THUMBPRINT...............   45.00
CASTOR,PICKLE WITH TONGS,BROKEN COLUMN INSERT...............   30.00
CASTOR,PICKLE,WITH TONGS,GLASS INSERTS,DOME BASE,..........   24.00
CASTOR,PICKLE WITH TONGS,SILVER PLATE FRAME ,CUBE DESIGN
  GLASS INSERT..   19.00

*CASTOR SETS have been known as early as 1705. Most of those that have been
found today date from the Victorian times. A castor set usually consists of a
silver-plated frame that holds three to seven condiment bottles. The pickle
castor was a single glass jar about six inches high and held in a silver frame. A
cover and tongs were kept with the jar. They were popular from 1890 to 1900.*

CASTOR SET,3-BOTTLE,ETCHED,MERIDEN HOLDER...................   16.00
CASTOR SET,4 BOTTLE,CLEAR PRESSED...........................   37.50
CASTOR SET,4 BOTTLE,SILVER FOOTED FRAME WITH HANDLE,SILVER
  SPOON...   19.00
CASTOR SET,4 BOTTLES,PIERCED SILVER GALLERY STAND..........   47.50
CASTOR SET,4 BOTTLE,PRESSED GLASS...........................   15.00
CASTOR SET,4 BOTTLES,SILVER PLATE GEORGIAN FRAME,CUT GLASS..   95.00
CASTOR SET,4 BOTTLES,SILVER PLATE HOLDER....................   34.50
CASTOR SET,5 BOTTLE
  28.50 TO...   46.00
CASTOR SET,5 BOTTLES,MIDDLETOWN TRIPLE PLATE................   35.00
CASTOR SET,5 BOTTLES,SILVER PLATED BASE.....................   25.00
CASTOR SET,5 BOTTLES,SILVER PLATE FRAME.....................   40.00
CASTOR SET,5 BOTTLES,SILVER PLATE FRAME.....................   42.50
CASTOR SET,5 ETCHED BOTTLES & SILVER HOLDER.................   32.50
CASTOR SET,5 FEDERAL BOTTLES IN PEWTER FRAME................   45.00
CASTOR SET,6 BOTTLE LAZY SUSAN,CUT BOTTLES & STOPPER,SILVER
  FRAME...   65.00
CASTOR SET,6 BOTTLE,SILVER CARRIER..........................   35.00
CASTOR SET 6 BOTTLES..   30.00
CASTOR SET,6 BOTTLES & FRAME................................   45.00
CASTOR SET,6 BOTTLES ON SQUARE TILE.........................   52.50
CASTOR SET,6 ETCHED BOTTLES & MERIDEN SILVER HOLDER DATED...   40.00
CASTOR SET,ENGLISH,6 BOTTLES,CUT FLOWERS....................   65.00
CASTOR SET,ETCHED PATTERN...................................   22.00
CASTOR SET IN SILVER FRAME,4 CUT BOTTLES....................   28.00
CASTOR SET,KINGS CROWN......................................   12.50
CASTOR SET ,MT.WASHINGTON IN SILVER PLATE HOLDER ON 4
  FEET,HANDLE...   95.00
CASTOR SET,PICKLE WITH TONGS................................   18.75
CASTOR SET,REVOLVES,SILVER PLATE FRAME,CRANBERRY WATERFORD
  CUT BOTTLES...   75.00
CASTOR SET,RUBENA 3 BOTTLE,SILVER PLATE HEART SHAPED HOLDER.   50.00
CASTOR SET,SHEFFIELD HOLDER,4 ROUND BALL FEET,CUT GLASS
  BOTTLES...   62.00

```
CASTOR SET,SILVER PLATE MERIDEN 5 PIECE ,ETCHED
   BOTTLES,SWING CUPID..........................................   30.00
CASTOR SET,SILVER PLATE,BELL AT TOP............................   95.00
CASTOR SET,SILVER PLATE,5 BOTTLES,RELIEF 2 IN. OWL ON HANDLE   95.00
CASTOR SET,SILVER PLATE,5 BOTTLE..............................   55.00
CASTOR SET,SILVER PLATED BOTTLES..............................   29.50
CASTOR SET,TORPEDO,SILVER PLATED HOLDER.......................   32.00
CASTOR SET,TRASK,10 BOTTLES...................................   45.00
CASTOR,WITH TONGS,CRANBERRY THUMBPRINT........................   45.00
CATALOG,SEARS 1928............................................    9.00
CATALOGS,SEARS................................................   10.00
CATHEDRAL GLASS CUP & SAUCER,RED,CHARTREUSE & GREEN..........   35.00
```

CAULDON is an English pottery factory working after 1905.
```
CAULDON,ENGLAND CROWN,DEMI-TASSE CUP & SAUCER,BLUE FORGET ME
   NOTS.......................................................    4.50
C.D.KENNY CO.FRENCH POODLE FIGURINE...........................    8.50
```

CELADON is a Chinese porcelain having a velvet-textured green-gray glaze. Japanese and Korean factories also made a celadon colored glaze.
```
CELADON 10 IN. VASE,.........................................   78.00
CELADON BOTTLE WITH OPEN SHOULDER HANDLES,CARVED TEAK STAND.   85.00
CELADON CHINESE TEAPOT & COVERED SUGAR,BLUE WITH PINK &
   YELLOW ROSES..............................................   20.00
CELADON COVERED SUGAR........................................   10.00
CELADON GREEN CHINESE BOWL,TREE OF WHITE FLOWERS.............    7.50
CELADON GREEN MATCH HOLDER FOR WALL,FLOWERS.................    7.50
CELADON HANGING MATCH HOLDER................................   15.00
CELADON JARDINIERE,GREEN WITH PINK & BLUE EMBOSSED FLOWERS..   65.00
CELADON PLATE,8 IN..........................................   24.00
CELADON PLATE WITH BIRDS,10 IN..............................   40.00
CELADON TWO-HANDLED COVERED SUGAR AND CREAMER...............   55.00
CELADON VASE................................................   22.50
CERTIFICATE, BOOK OF 10 DEWEY-WARREN DOLLAR.................    6.00
CERTIFICATE, LOAN,CITY OF PHILA,1862........................    5.00
CERTIFICATE, SHARE FROM GREAT WESTERN MINING CO. 1863.......    5.00
CHALK DOG DRESSED IN COAT SITTING BESIDE BUCKET,TOOTHPICK OR
   MATCH.....................................................   35.00
CHALK PAINTED TURKEY ON NEST................................    7.50
CHALK PAIR MEN..............................................   10.00
CHALK PAIR PIGEONS ON OVAL STANDS...........................   95.00
CHALK STANDING DOG..........................................   55.00
```

CHALKWARE is really plaster of Paris decorated with watercolors. The pieces were molded from known Staffordshire and other porcelain models and painted and sold as inexpensive decorations. Most of this type of chalkware was made from about 1820 to 1870.
```
CHALKWARE STATUE,DUTCH BOY & DOG.............................   18.00
```

CHALLINOR TAYLOR COMPANY of Tarentum, Pennsylvania, worked in the 1870's and 1880's making pressed glass, purple slag, and other types of glass.
```
CHALLINOR DORA HANDLELESS CUP & SAUCER.......................   18.50
CHALLINORS MUFFINEER,FLORAL PATTERN,GREEN,CIRCA 1880.........   47.50
CHALLINORS MUFFINEER,WHITE,CIRCA 1880........................   47.50
CHAMBER SET 8 PIECE WHITE-GOLD TRIM..........................  100.00
CHECK PROTECTOR DATED 1915...................................    5.50
```

CHELSEA PORCELAIN was made in the Chelsea area of London from about 1745 to 1784. Recent copies of this work have been made from the original molds.
```
CHELSEA COVERED SUGAR,LUSTERED BERRIES.......................   35.00
CHELSEA CUP & SAUCER.........................................    8.50
CHELSEA CUP & SAUCER,ROSE THISTLE PATTERN....................   12.00
CHELSEA CUP & SAUCER,VINTAGE WITH LUSTER.....................   12.50
```

```
CHELSEA FIGURE................................................. 250.00
     CHELSEA GRAPE, SEE ALSO IRONSTONE........................
CHELSEA GRAPE CUP & SAUCER,....................................  14.00
CHELSEA GRAPE CUP & SAUCER,SET OF 4,BLUE.......................  50.00
CHELSEA GRAPE PLATE,7 IN.......................................   6.00
CHELSEA GRAPE PLATE,8 IN.......................................   8.00
CHELSEA GRAPE PLATE,COPPER LUSTER..............................   4.00
CHELSEA GRAPE PLATE,PURPLE WITH LUSTRE,9 IN....................   7.50
CHELSEA GRAPE PLATE,SPRIGGED EARTHENWARE,IMPRESSED ANCHOR
MARK..........................................................  12.00
CHELSEA TEAPOT................................................  45.00
CHESS SET,IVORY,CARVED........................................ 124.00
CHESS SET,IVORY,OLD...........................................  95.00
     CHINESE EXPORT, SEE ALSO CANTON,NANKING..................
CHINESE EXPORT,47 PIECES SERVICE,CIRCA 1780,BLUE,WHITE.......8,000.00
CHINESE EXPORT,ARMORIAL CREAM JUG,WALSH CREST WITH
GREEN,CIRCA 1750.............................................. 250.00
CHINESE EXPORT BLUE & WHITE PLATE,FLORAL DECOR,BROWN TRIM...   38.00
CHINESE EXPORT BOWL,ARMORIAL.................................. 400.00
CHINESE EXPORT BOWL,MILLEFIORI DECORATION,FAMILLE NOIRE
INSIDE....................................................... 220.00
CHINESE EXPORT BOWL CIRCA 1840,SIGNED.........................  38.00
CHINESE EXPORT BOWL ON TEAK STAND,27 FIGURES IN DECORATION.. 485.00
CHINESE EXPORT CANDLESTICK,PAIR BLUE & WHITE,10 IN. TALL.... 300.00
CHINESE EXPORT CUP...........................................  10.00
CHINESE EXPORT CUP & SAUCER,HANDLELESS.......................  30.00
CHINESE EXPORT CUP & SAUCER,HANDLELESS,GOLD DESIGN...........  37.50
CHINESE EXPORT CUP & SAUCER,ORANGE PEEL,3RD QUARTER 18TH
CENTURY,.....................................................  25.00
CHINESE EXPORT FITZHUGH BLUE TUREEN.......................... 190.00
CHINESE EXPORT GARNITURE,5 PIECE,CIRCA 1820................. 950.00
CHINESE EXPORT HOT WATER PLATE,PURPLE BORDER,CIRCA 1790..... 110.00
CHINESE EXPORT OBLONG TRAY,UNDERGLAZE BLUE DECORATED
LANDSCAPE....................................................  75.00
CHINESE EXPORT PAIR BOUGH POTS WITH COVERS.................. 650.00
CHINESE EXPORT PAIR VASES,CIRCA 1775......................2,500.00
CHINESE EXPORT PITCHER,HELMET................................  70.00
CHINESE EXPORT PLATE,13 X 11 IN.,BLACK,PURPLE,GREEN & GOLD.. 125.00
CHINESE EXPORT PLATTER, BLUE AND WHITE, LATE 18 CENTURY, 10
IN. LONG.....................................................  75.00
CHINESE EXPORT PLATTER,PARTRIDGE,PAIR,CIRCA 1750,FAMILLE
ROSE......................................................... 285.00
CHINESE EXPORT SET OF 12 PLATES,BLUE BORDERS,CIRCA 1790..... 975.00
CHINESE EXPORT SET OF 5 FAMILLE ROSE MANDARIN VASES 1775....2,750.00
CHINESE ENAMEL SPOON,PIERCED BOWL,APPLIED FLORAL ON HANDLE..  15.00
CHINESE EXPORT CUP & SAUCER
25.00  TO....................................................  30.00
CHINESE EXPORT TEAPOT........................................ 295.00
CHINESE EXPORT TEA POT,ARMORIAL,WALSH CREST.................. 300.00
CHINESE EXPORT TEAPOT CIRCA 1760,FIGURES & FLORAL DECORATION  85.00
CHINESE EXPORT TEASET,26 PIECES,ORANGE FLORAL...............1,285.00
CHINESE EXPORT TEA SET,2 LOVE BIRDS & CYPHERS,CIRCA 1800.... 375.00
CHOCOLATE EGLANTINE POT,ROSEBUD FINIAL,GOLD TRIM,ORNATE
HANDLE,GREEN.................................................  22.00
CHOCOLATE HANDPAINTED POT WITH 6 CUPS,ROSE BAND ON BLUE &
GOLD STRIPES.................................................  18.00
CHOCOLATE POT,8 IN.,SHADED GRAY TONES,FRUITED IN RELIEF,MATT
GLAZE........................................................  50.00
CHOCOLATE SET,IVORY,PASTEL WILD ROSES........................  85.00
CHOCOLATE SET,LEUCHTENBURG,PITCHER & 5 CUPS..................  45.00
CHRISTMAS LIGHT,MILK GLASS AMBER.............................   5.50
CHRISTMAS LIGHT,MILK GLASS BLUE..............................   5.50
CHRISTMAS LIGHT,MILK GLASS GREEN.............................   5.50
CHRISTMAS LIGHT,MILK GLASS WHITE.............................   5.50
CHRISTMAS LIGHT,TOLEWARE WITH PAINTED GLASS PANELS..........   7.50
```

CHRISTMAS TREE LIGHT,MILK GLASS SANTA....................... 1.00

CHRISTMAS PLATES were made by several firms. The most famous were made by the Bing and Grohndahl factory of Denmark, after 1895, and the Royal Copenhagen factory, after 1908. Each plate has a blue-and-white glaze with a scene in the center, the date, and the word "Jule"

CHRISTMAS PLATES 1965 JUBILEE PLATES........................ 37.50
CHRISTMAS PLATE,BING & GRONDAHL 1901......................... 110.00
CHRISTMAS PLATE,BING & GRONDAHL 1904......................... 55.00
CHRISTMAS PLATE,BING & GRONDAHL 1905......................... 84.50
CHRISTMAS PLATE,BING & GRONDAHL 1906......................... 67.50
CHRISTMAS PLATE,BING & GRONDAHL 1907......................... 50.00
CHRISTMAS PLATE,BING & GRONDAHL 1908......................... 54.50
CHRISTMAS PLATE,BING & GRONDAHL 1909......................... 69.50
CHRISTMAS PLATE,BING & GRONDAHL 1910......................... 54.75
CHRISTMAS PLATE,BING & GRONDAHL 1911......................... 54.75
CHRISTMAS PLATE,BING & GRONDAHL 1912......................... 54.75
CHRISTMAS PLATE,BING & GRONDAHL 1913
  38.00 TO.. 54.75
CHRISTMAS PLATE,BING & GRONDAHL 1914......................... 54.75
CHRISTMAS PLATE,BING & GRONDAHL 1915
  48.00 TO.. 54.75
CHRISTMAS PLATE,BING & GRONDAHL 1916......................... 54.75
CHRISTMAS PLATE,BING & GRONDAHL 1917......................... 54.75
CHRISTMAS PLATE,BING & GRONDAHL 1918
  38.00 TO.. 54.75
CHRISTMAS PLATE,BING & GRONDAHL 1919......................... 54.75
CHRISTMAS PLATE,BING & GRONDAHL 1920
  45.00 TO.. 54.75
CHRISTMAS PLATE,BING & GRONDAHL 1921......................... 45.75
CHRISTMAS PLATE,BING & GRONDAHL 1922......................... 54.75
CHRISTMAS PLATE,BING & GRONDAHL 1923
  45.00 TO.. 54.75
CHRISTMAS PLATE,BING & GRONDAHL 1924......................... 54.75
CHRISTMAS PLATE,BING & GRONDAHL 1925
  45.00 TO.. 54.75
CHRISTMAS PLATE,BING & GRONDAHL 1926......................... 54.75
CHRISTMAS PLATE,BING & GRONDAHL 1927......................... 54.75
CHRISTMAS PLATE,BING & GRONDAHL 1928......................... 54.75
CHRISTMAS PLATE,BING & GRONDAHL 1929
  50.00 TO.. 54.75
CHRISTMAS PLATE,BING & GRONDAHL 1930......................... 54.75
CHRISTMAS PLATE,BING & GRONDAHL 1931......................... 54.75
CHRISTMAS PLATE,BING & GRONDAHL 1932......................... 54.75
CHRISTMAS PLATE,BING & GRONDAHL 1934......................... 54.75
CHRISTMAS PLATE,BING & GRONDAHL 1935......................... 54.75
CHRISTMAS PLATE,BING & GRONDAHL 1936......................... 54.75
CHRISTMAS PLATE,BING & GRONDAHL 1937......................... 54.75
CHRISTMAS PLATE,BING & GRONDAHL 1940
  60.00 TO.. 92.75
CHRISTMAS PLATE,BING & GRONDAHL 1941
  60.00 TO.. 122.50
CHRISTMAS PLATE,BING & GRONDAHL 1942
  60.00 TO.. 89.75
CHRISTMAS PLATE,BING & GRONDAHL 1943
  60.00 TO.. 89.75
CHRISTMAS PLATE,BING & GRONDAHL 1944......................... 89.75
CHRISTMAS PLATE,BING & GRONDAHL 1945......................... 89.75
CHRISTMAS PLATE,BING & GRONDAHL 1947
  37.50 TO.. 59.75
CHRISTMAS PLATE,BING & GRONDAHL 1948
  37.50 TO.. 59.75
CHRISTMAS PLATE,BING & GRONDAHL 1949
  37.50 TO.. 59.75
CHRISTMAS PLATE,BING & GRONDAHL 1950

```
   37.50  TO............................................    59.75
CHRISTMAS PLATE,BING & GRONDAHL 1951
   37.50  TO............................................    59.75
CHRISTMAS PLATE,BING & GRONDAHL 1952.....................    59.75
CHRISTMAS PLATE,BING & GRONDAHL 1953.....................    59.75
CHRISTMAS PLATE,BING & GRONDAHL 1954
   45.00  TO............................................    59.75
CHRISTMAS PLATE,BING & GRONDAHL 1955.....................    79.75
CHRISTMAS PLATE,BING & GRONDAHL 1956
   40.00  TO............................................    79.75
CHRISTMAS PLATE,BING & GRONDAHI 1957.....................    79.75
CHRISTMAS PLATE,BING & GRONDAHL 1958.....................    79.75
CHRISTMAS PLATE,BING & GRONDAHL 1959.....................    79.75
CHRISTMAS PLATE,BING & GRONDAHL 1960.....................    59.75
CHRISTMAS PLATE,BING & GRONDAHL 1961.....................    43.75
CHRISTMAS PLATE,BING & GRONDAHL 1962
   29.50  TO............................................    31.50
CHRISTMAS PLATE,BING & GRONDAHL 1963
   29.75  TO............................................    31.50
CHRISTMAS PLATE,BING & GRONDAHL 1964
   15.00  TO............................................    24.75
CHRISTMAS PLATE,BING & GRONDAHL 1965.....................    24.75
CHRISTMAS PLATE,BING & GRONDAHL 1966
   11.00  TO............................................    16.50
CHRISTMAS PLATE,BING & GRONDAHL 1967
    9.50  TO............................................    10.75
CHRISTMAS PLATE,ROYAL COPENHAGEN 1908....................   500.00
CHRISTMAS PLATE,ROYAL COPENHAGEN 1910,GIRL WITH CHRISTMAS
   TREE.................................................    48.00
CHRISTMAS PLATE,ROYAL COPENHAGEN 1912....................    70.00
CHRISTMAS PLATE,ROYAL COPENHAGEN 1915....................    74.50
CHRISTMAS PLATE,ROYAL COPENHAGEN 1916....................    64.75
CHRISTMAS PLATE,ROYAL COPENHAGEN 1917
   37.50  TO............................................    64.75
CHRISTMAS PLATE,ROYAL COPENHAGEN 1918....................    64.75
CHRISTMAS PLATE,ROYAL COPENHAGEN 1919
   45.00  TO............................................    64.75
CHRISTMAS PLATE,ROYAL COPENHAGEN 1920....................    53.75
CHRISTMAS PLATE,ROYAL COPENHAGEN 1921....................    45.00
CHRISTMAS PLATE,ROYAL COPENHAGEN 1922....................    54.00
CHRISTMAS PLATE,ROYAL COPENHAGEN 1923
   40.00  TO............................................    64.75
CHRISTMAS PLATE,ROYAL COPENHAGEN 1925....................    45.00
CHRISTMAS PLATE,ROYAL COPENHAGEN 1926....................    53.75
CHRISTMAS PLATE,ROYAL COPENHAGEN 1927
   40.00  TO............................................    64.75
CHRISTMAS PLATE,ROYAL COPENHAGEN 1929
   40.00  TO............................................    64.75
CHRISTMAS PLATE,ROYAL COPENHAGEN 1930
   40.00  TO............................................    64.75
CHRISTMAS PLATE,ROYAL COPENHAGEN 1931....................    64.75
CHRISTMAS PLATE,ROYAL COPENHAGEN 1932....................    64.75
CHRISTMAS PLATE,ROYAL COPENHAGEN 1933....................    64.75
CHRISTMAS PLATE,ROYAL COPENHAGEN 1934....................    80.00
CHRISTMAS PLATE,ROYAL COPENHAGEN 1944
  112.00  TO............................................   240.00
CHRISTMAS PLATE,ROYAL COPENHAGEN 1945
  200.00  TO............................................   250.00
CHRISTMAS PLATE,ROYAL COPENHAGEN 1946
   45.00  TO............................................    59.75
CHRISTMAS PLATE,ROYAL COPENHAGEN 1947....................   100.00
CHRISTMAS PLATE,ROYAL COPENHAGEN 1951
  191.00  TO............................................   250.00
CHRISTMAS PLATE,ROYAL COPENHAGEN 1952....................    80.00
CHRISTMAS PLATE,ROYAL COPENHAGEN 1953
```

```
    64.75  TO.................................................    90.00
CHRISTMAS  PLATE,ROYAL  COPENHAGEN  1954.....................    69.75
CHRISTMAS  PLATE,ROYAL  COPENHAGEN  1955.....................   125.00
CHRISTMAS  PLATE,ROYAL  COPENHAGEN  1956.....................   105.00
CHRISTMAS  PLATE,ROYAL  COPENHAGEN  1957
    50.00  TO.................................................    54.75
CHRISTMAS  PLATE,ROYAL  COPENHAGEN  1958
    50.00  TO.................................................    72.75
CHRISTMAS  PLATE,ROYAL  COPENHAGEN  1959
    48.00  TO.................................................   100.00
CHRISTMAS  PLATE,ROYAL  COPENHAGEN  1960
    33.00  TO.................................................    45.00
CHRISTMAS  PLATE,ROYAL  COPENHAGEN  1961.....................    40.00
CHRISTMAS  PLATE,ROYAL  COPENHAGEN  1962
    50.00  TO.................................................    85.00
CHRISTMAS  PLATE,ROYAL  COPENHAGEN  1963
    25.00  TO.................................................    33.00
CHRISTMAS  PLATE,ROYAL  COPENHAGEN  1964
    18.00  TO.................................................    28.00
CHRISTMAS  PLATE,ROYAL  COPENHAGEN  1965
    15.00  TO.................................................    24.75
CHRISTMAS  PLATE,ROYAL  COPENHAGEN  1966
    14.75  TO.................................................    27.00
CHRISTMAS  PLATE,ROYAL  COPENHAGEN  1967.....................    11.75
CHRISTMAS  VASE,1916,BLUE  &  WHITE.........................   150.00
CIGAR  BANDS,APPROX.  175  MOUNTED  IN  OLD  BOOK...........    10.00
CIGAR  BAND  DISH  4  IN.  DIA..............................     3.00
CIGAR  STORE  INDIAN,HAND  CARVED  FROM  SOLID  HARDWOOD,LIFE  SIZE   275.00
```

CINNABAR is a vermilion or red lacquer. Some pieces are made with hundreds of thicknesses of the lacquer that are later carved.

```
CINNABAR  RED  TEAPOT,CARVED................................    30.00
CINNABAR  SNUFF  BOTTLE,CARVED  IN  3  LAYERS,LANDSCAPE  WITH
    FIGURES...................................................   165.00
CIRCUS  BROADSIDE  WITH  ILLUSTRATIONS......................     3.50
```

CIVIL WAR MEMENTOS are important collectors' items. Most of the pieces are military items used from 1861 to 1865.

```
CIVIL  WAR  5  IN.  WOOD  CANTEEN,RED  EAGLE.................    55.00
CIVIL  WAR  CANTEEN.........................................     7.50
CIVIL  WAR  CARTRIDGE  BUCKLE,MASS..........................    12.00
CIVIL  WAR  CENTENNIAL  PLATE,GENERAL  DE  FOREST...........     3.00
CIVIL  WAR  COMMENDATION  ,NEW  JERSEY,FRAMED...............    16.00
CIVIL  WAR  COURIER  CASE  DATED  DEC.  24,1861.............    25.00
CIVIL  WAR  DAGUERROTYPE  CASE,INCLUDING  PICTURE  OF  2  SOLDIERS.     6.75
CIVIL  WAR  DRUM............................................   100.00
CIVIL  WAR  FLUTE  MARKED  WITH  EAGLE  &  C................     8.50
CIVIL  WAR  IRON  LEAD  BULLET  POURER......................    18.00
CIVIL  WAR  LEATHER  CARTRIDGE  BOX  WITH  TIN  INSERTS.....    18.00
CIVIL  WAR  MAP,150  MILES  AROUND  RICHMOND,PORTRAITS  OF  6  UNION
    GENERALS..................................................    50.00
CIVIL  WAR  MINIEBALL,VICKSBURG  SIEGE  1863................     1.50
CIVIL  WAR  MUSKET  MARKED  TRENTON  1864  US,WALNUT  STOCK.   100.00
CIVIL  WAR  NON-COMMISSIONED  OFFICERS  SWORD  &  SCABBARD..    32.00
CIVIL  WAR  PAIR  HANDCUFFS  WITH  BRASS  KEY...............    25.00
CIVIL  WAR  PAIR  SILVER  COLOURED  OFFICERS  EPAULETS......    22.00
CIVIL  WAR  PAIR  SILVER  SHOE  BUCKLES.....................    16.00
CIVIL  WAR  PISTOL  CARTRIDGE  BOX,BLACK  LEATHER...........    30.00
CIVIL  WAR  PISTOL  CARTRIDGE  CASES........................     4.00
CIVIL  WAR  SHRAPNEL  FROM  VICKSBURG  SIEGE  OF  1863......     7.50
CIVIL  WAR  STARR  PERCUSSION  PISTOL,WORKS.................   145.00
CIVIL  WAR  SWORD,NON-COMMISSIONED  OFFICER.................    65.00
CIVIL  WAR,U.S.,  LEAD  BACK  OVAL  BELT  BUCKLE............     6.50
```

CLAMBROTH GLASS, popular in the Victorian era, is a grayish color and is semi-opaque like the soup.

CLAMBROTH BOWL,CHERRY CHAIN VARIANT,ORANGE TREE	22.50
CLAMBROTH CANDLESTICK	22.50
CLAMBROTH CANDY DISH,MARKED,4 APPLIED SHELL FEET	12.50
CLAMBROTH CARNATION BOWL,FROSTED BLOCK USA	8.00
CLAMBROTH JAR,COVERED,SQUARE PEDESTAL BASE,RIBBED PATTERN	32.00
CLAMBROTH MUG,HANDLED,BIRDS AT FOUNTAIN	11.50

CLEWS POTTERY was made by George Clews & Co. of Brownhills Pottery, Tunstall, England from 1906 to 1961.

CLEWS BLUE DR.SYNTAX PLATTER,DEATH OF PUNCH	45.00
CLEWS BLUE HANDLELESS CUP & SAUCER,SUMMER ROSES	28.00
CLOCK,2-SPIRE STEEPLE BY GILBERT	45.00
CLOCK,3 STEEPLE	150.00
CLOCK,7 IN. GERMAN CHINA,PINK & YELLOW ROSES	17.50
CLOCK,8 DAY BANJO TIME & STRIKE ,19 IN. TO TOP OF EAGLE FINIAL	35.00
CLOCK,8-DAY SETH THOMAS MANTEL,PAINTED GLASS PANELS	125.00
CLOCK,8 DAY SETH THOMAS,PORCELAIN FACE,WALNUT CASE,BELL STRIKE	37.50
CLOCK,8 DAY WEIGHT,STRAP MOVEMENT,35 IN. HIGH,RUNS	80.00
CLOCK,11 IN. HIGH,MAHOGANY	15.00
CLOCK,14 IN. HIGH,DATED 1901	18.50
CLOCK,17TH CENTURY GREEN LACQUER GRANDFATHER,GILT CHINOISERIE,LONDON	1,023.00
CLOCK,30 IN. OGEE WITH JEROME LABEL	25.00
CLOCK,NO.70 HOWARD JEWELERY REGULATOR,	200.00
CLOCK,400 DAY,17 IN. TO TOP OF DOME	65.00
CLOCK,1925 WESTCLOCK BEN HUR	5.00
CLOCK,A.STOWELL & CO.BOSTON BLACK MARBLE,SIDE COLUMNS	25.00
CLOCK,AMBER D&B GLASS,BRASS WORKS,RUNNING,14X6 IN.ABOUT 1885	100.00
CLOCK,ANGELICA KAUFFMANN SIGNED CHINA,FACE 3 LADIES & MAN	125.00
CLOCK,ANNIVERSARY ,UNDER GLASS DOME,BRASS WITH GERMAN WORKS.	59.50
CLOCK,ANSONIA 8 DAY,PORCELAIN CASE	75.00
CLOCK,ANSONIA 30-HOUR MAHOGANY CASE,DOOR FRAME MARBELIZED,GOLD LINER	16.50
CLOCK,ANSONIA,BLACK ENAMEL METAL CASE TRIMMED IN BRASS,STRIKES	45.00
CLOCK,ANSONIA CHINA,8 DAY,STRIKES	25.00
CLOCK,ANSONIA OUTSIDE ESCAPEMENT CAST IRON BLACK BASE,SHAKESPEARE	75.00
CLOCK,ANSONIA SCHOOL HOUSE,ROSEWOOD,STRIKES	65.00
CLOCK,ATKINS SCHOOLHOUSE 11 IN. DIAL SHORT DROP,ROSEWOOD CASE	80.00
CLOCK,BANJO,BLACK WALNUT BURL PALEN FRONT,GILBERT	50.00
CLOCK,BANJO,BRASS SIDE RAILS	65.00
CLOCK,BANJO BY THE NEW HAVEN CLOCK CO	60.00
CLOCK,BANJO,CHERRY CASE,WEIGHT DRIVEN,FROSTED & ETCHED GLASS	165.00
CLOCK,BANJO IN MAHOGANY CASE,BRASS EAGLE ON TOP,RUNS,WALTHAM	88.00
CLOCK,BANJO,INGRAHAM,39 IN. HIGH	58.00
CLOCK,BANJO ,INGRAM,SPRING WOUND	110.00
CLOCK,BANJO,INLAYED DESIGN,STRIKES	55.00
CLOCK,BANJO,SIDE RAILS,INGRAHAM	65.00
CLOCK,BANJO,STRIKES	50.00
CLOCK,BANJO,WALTHAM WEIGHT PRESENTATION	225.00
CLOCK,BANJO,WILLIAM B LORTON NEW YORK	250.00
CLOCK,B.B.LEWIS PATENT PERPETUAL CALENDAR,ROSEWOOD CASE	150.00
CLOCK,BAVARIAN,VIENNA REGULATOR	40.00
CLOCK,BEE HIVE,NEW HAVEN,MAHOGANY CASE,STRIKES,FROSTED GLASS DOOR	65.00
CLOCK,BEEHIVE,PAINTING ON BOTTOM DOOR	22.00
CLOCK,BISQUE FRENCH 15 DAY ON MARBLE BASE,DATED 1855	190.00
CLOCK,BLACK FOREST FARMERS	60.00
CLOCK,BLUE & COLOURFUL FLORAL CHINA	60.00

CLOCK,BLUE & WHITE KITCHEN,WINDMILLS........................ 18.00
CLOCK,BLUE DELFT TYPE BY VILLEROY & BOCH,METTLACH WORKS BY
  SETH THOMAS.. 95.00
CLOCK,BLUE WINDMILL WALL.................................... 23.50
CLOCK,BOSTON CLOCK CO.,WORKS................................ 125.00
CLOCK,BRASS 8 DAY MARINE WITH SHIPS BELL STRIKE............. 39.00
CLOCK,BRASS ANNIVERSARY,RUNS................................ 31.00
CLOCK,BRASS CASED ANSONIA ALARM WITH PORCELAIN DIAL......... 15.00
CLOCK,BRASS MANTLE,DOGS & REINDEER,DUKE & CO................ 125.00
CLOCK,BRASS NOVELTY,RUNS,DUTCH BOY & GIRL................... 12.50
CLOCK,BRASS SHIP,SETH THOMAS FROM SHIP CRUSADE.............. 60.00
CLOCK,BRASS WATERBURY REPEATER,RUNS,STRIKES................. 35.00
CLOCK,BRASS WORKS O.G.WEIGHT BY FORESTVILLE MFG.CO.,RUNS.... 48.00
CLOCK,BRONZE WITH ENAMEL DIAL,MATCHING
  CANDLESTICKS,CORINTHIAN COLUMNS.......................... 125.00
CLOCK,CALENDAR,ITHACA,WALNUT,MANTEL........................ 150.00
CLOCK,CALENDAR OR SCHOOL,OAK,OCTAGON,....................... 39.50
CLOCK,CALENDAR WITH GLASS FRONT WITH PENDULUM............... 85.00
CLOCK,CARRIAGE MINIATURE 3IN. H.,NEW HAVEN CLOCK CO......... 90.00
CLOCK,CAST IRON ANSONIA MANTLE,RUNNING...................... 30.00
CLOCK,CHINA,11 IN. HIGH,APPLE BLOSSOMS,GREEN,GOLD & WHITE... 52.00
CLOCK,CHINA 13 IN.,RUNS,RAISED GOLD SCROLLS,RAMS HEAD....... 27.50
CLOCK,CHINA 16 IN. HIGH,ROSES DECORATION................... 50.00
CLOCK,CHINA,BLUE DECOR WITH PINK LILIES,RUNS............... 42.00
CLOCK,CHINA BOUDOIR,2 SEMI-NUDE WOMEN SIGNED F.BOUCHER...... 35.00
CLOCK,CHINA CASE MARKED STRASBURG WARE,PAINTED SCENE ON
  FRONT... 75.00
CLOCK,CHINA,GILBERT MOVEMENT,MARKED DOLPHIN ON BACK......... 75.00
CLOCK,CHINA,MARKED ROYAL BONN GERMANY,4 BALL FEET........... 85.00
CLOCK,CHINA,PINK,GOLD & TULIPS CLUSTER,SPRAYS OF FLOWERS.... 25.00
CLOCK,CHINA,PINK & GREEN FLOWERS,ANSONIA,WORKS.............. 125.00
CLOCK,CHINA,SET 3 PIECE,2 MATCHING VASES,RUNS,FRENCH
  MOVEMENT.. 135.00
CLOCK,CHINA,WATERBURY 8 DAY,FANCY DIAL,RUNS................. 71.00
CLOCK,COBALT BLUE CHINA,KAUFFMANN SCENE,SHELL SCROLL FEET... 145.00
CLOCK,COKE REGULATOR....................................... 39.00
CLOCK, COPPER COACH.. 11.50
CLOCK,CUCKOO
  17.00 TO... 25.00
CLOCK,CUCKOO,30-HOUR....................................... 55.00
CLOCK,CUCKOO,AMERICAN CLOCK CO.,PHILADELPHIA,PA.,1900....... 25.00
CLOCK,DANIEL PRATT WEIGHT DRIVEN BANJO..................... 225.00
CLOCK,DANISH BY URBAN JORGENSEN & SONNER,K OBENHAVN......... 75.00
CLOCK,DORIC SHELF,ROSEWOOD CASE,........................... 40.00
CLOCK,DOUBLE TONE SIREN ALARM ,BRASS...................... 55.00
CLOCK,DUTCH HOOD WALL,STRIKE & ALARM,WEIGHT DRIVEN-........ 290.00
CLOCK,E.HOWARD REGULATER,12 IN. DIAL....................... 135.00
CLOCK,E.HOWARD REGULATER,14 IN. DIAL....................... 165.02
CLOCK,E.HOWARD MODEL 75,MAHOGANY CASE...................... 265.00
CLOCK,E.INGRAHAM CO. MANTLE,STRIKES....................... 15.00
CLOCK,ENGLISH MAHOGANY GEORGIAN MANTLE,BRASS WORKS,CIRCA
  1790.. 375.00
CLOCK,FREE-SWINGER,PENDULUM OUTSIDE........................ 70.00
CLOCK,FRENCH BRASS MANTLE,FIGURE ON TOP,RUNS............... 225.00
CLOCK,FRENCH CARRIAGE,BRASS WITH GLASS PANELS.............. 40.00
CLOCK,FRENCH CARRIAGE,CHIMES,GOLD PLATED CASE.............. 140.00
CLOCK,FRENCH CARRIAGE,REPEATER............................ 165.00
CLOCK,FRENCH DORE BRONZE MANTLE,RITTER CIRCA 1840,PORCELAIN
  FACE.. 250.00
CLOCK,FRENCH SET,BRASS,PORCELAIN FACE,2 SIDE PIECES FOR
  CANDLES... 285.00
CLOCK,FRENCH WAG ON WALL,WOODEN CASE,PENDULUM & WEIGHTS..... 37.00
CLOCK,FRENCH WALL,WESTMINSTER CHIME,BEVELED GLASS.......... 125.00
CLOCK,GINGERBREAD,KITCHEN,................................. 18.50
CLOCK,GINGERBREAD IN WALNUT WITH STRIKE & ALARM............ 25.00

```
CLOCK,GRANDFATHER.............................................   100.00
CLOCK,GRANDFATHER BY GIL.BANNERMAN-BANFF,SCOTLAND,CIRCA
  1760-80..................................................   325.00
CLOCK,GRANDFATHER ENGLISH 18TH CENTURY BY RUSSELL FALKIRK...1,000.00
CLOCK,GRANDFATHER,ENGLAND,CIRCA 1790,MAHOGANY...............   895.00
CLOCK,GRANDFATHERS WITH BRASS SPOOLS IN FRONT OF CASE.......   370.00
CLOCK,GRANDFATHERS WITH HAND-CARVED CASE,WESTMINSTER CHIMES.   480.00
CLOCK,GRANDFATHERS WITH WESTMINSTER CHIMES,OAK HAND CARVED
  CASE.....................................................   450.00
CLOCK,GRANDFATHER,WOODEN WORKS IN COUNTRY PINE CASE CIRCA
  1815.....................................................   275.00
CLOCK,GREEN JASPER KEWPIE,SIGNED ROSE O NEILL..............    80.00
CLOCK,HANGING,STRIKES......................................   135.00
CLOCK,HANGING WOODEN,8 IN. OWL FORM,WEIGHT ON CHAIN & PULLEY    8.00
CLOCK,HENRY C.SMITH WOODEN WORKS...........................    45.00
CLOCK,HORSE...............................................     7.00
CLOCK,INGRAHAM ADMIRAL DEWEY OAK CASE......................    57.50
CLOCK,INGRAHAM BANJO.......................................    65.00
CLOCK,INGRAHAM WALL........................................    55.00
CLOCK,IRON,LIKE BUILDING,15 BY 11 IN.,GREEN PILLARS,ANSONIA.   24.00
CLOCK,JEROME & CO SHELF,ROSEWOOD CASE WITH GUTTA PERCHA
  INSERT IN DOOR...........................................    55.00
CLOCK,JONATHAN BURR WEIGHT DRIVEN WOODEN...................    70.00
CLOCK,JOSLINS ECLIPSE TIME STAMP DATED 1920................    10.00
CLOCK,KITCHEN,13 IN. HIGH,ROSEWOOD,NEW HAVEN CLOCK CO......    15.00
CLOCK,KITCHEN MANTLE,OAK,INGRAHAM..........................    27.00
CLOCK,KITCHEN SHELF,BUTTERNUT FINISH,STRIKES,RUNS..........    40.00
CLOCK,MADE IN GERMANY,ROSEWOOD-PORCELAIN FACE,WORKS........    85.00
CLOCK,MAHOGANY BANJO BAROMETER CIRCA 1795..................   100.00
CLOCK,MAHOGANY BEEHIVE WITH ALARM..........................    46.00
CLOCK,MAHOGANY WALL BY BENNETT OF GREENWICH CIRCA 1770......   500.00
CLOCK,MANTLE 16 IN. WROUGHT IRON MATCHING CANDELABRA DATED
  1886.....................................................   165.00
CLOCK,MANTEL ABOUT 150 YEARS OLD,CHIMES EACH QUARTER ,WOODEN
  CASE.....................................................   185.00
CLOCK,MARBLE SET,BRASS CLOCK,PAIR 3 BRANCH
  CANDLEABRUM,ENGLISH......................................   195.00
CLOCK,MARBLE UNDER GLASS DOME,FRENCH,BRASS PENDULUM........   149.00
CLOCK,METAL,ROCOCO TRIM,PORCELAIN
  FRONT,FOOTED,GOLD,ELECTRIFIED............................    25.00
CLOCK,MILLER 8-DAY CHINA PLATE,RUNS........................    12.00
CLOCK,MINIATURE SETH THOMAS MANTLE,STRIKES ON HALF
  HOUR,RUNS,13 X 7 IN......................................    24.50
CLOCK,MINIATURE SCHOOL HOUSE...............................    75.00
CLOCK,MINIATURE WATERBURY SCHOOLHOUSE......................    55.00
CLOCK,MISSION GRANDFATHER,BRASS WEIGHT DRIVEN STRIKING
  MOVEMENT.................................................    65.00
CLOCK,MUSICAL CUCKOO.......................................    18.00
CLOCK,OAK FRONT KITCHEN....................................    35.00
CLOCK,OAK GINGERBREAD INGRAHAM 8 DAY,STRIKES...............    25.00
CLOCK,OAK MANTLE SESSIONS..................................    18.00
CLOCK,OAK SHELF 8-DAY,STRIKE ,GILBERT MOVEMENT.............    25.00
CLOCK,OCTAGON,9 IN.,ROSEWOOD BY ANSONIA CLOCK CO...........    15.00
CLOCK,OCTAGON DEEP DROP WALL REGULATOR.....................    55.00
CLOCK,OCTAGON REGULATOR SCHOOL HOUSE.......................    75.00
CLOCK,OGEE................................................     22.00
CLOCK,ORNATE GREEN CHINA CASE MANTEL,ANSONIA,PORCELAIN
  FACE,8-DAY...............................................    60.00
CLOCK,PORCELAIN 12 IN. HIGH,PATENTED 1889 AND 1890........    37.50
CLOCK,PORCELAIN,BLUE & GOLD,VIOLETS FRONT & SIDES,ANSONIA
  GONG STRIKE..............................................    75.00
CLOCK,PORCELAIN,2 MATCHING VASES,ELK SCENES................    50.00
CLOCK,PORCELAIN,WHITE WITH DRESDEN ROSES,NEW HAVEN WORKS....   38.00
CLOCK,REGULATOR,DARK WOOD,WALL,OCTAGON.....................    39.00
CLOCK,REGULATOR IN WALNUT,BRASS WORKS & PENDULUM...........    58.00
```

```
CLOCK,REGULATOR WALL  8 DAY,GOLD LEGEND ON DOOR,WALNUT.......     49.00
CLOCK,ROSEWOOD ANSONIA,24 IN. HIGH,BRASS BEZEL..............     65.00
CLOCK,ROSEWOOD CASED,SETH THOMAS,RUNS,CALENDAR..............    120.00
CLOCK,ROUND BRASS NICKEL PLATED  PAT.1886,CHEW FRIENDSHIP
  CUT PLUG................................................     18.00
CLOCK,SCHOOL HOUSE,WALNUT CASE,BRASS PENDULUM...............     55.00
CLOCK,SESSIONS 33 IN. WALNUT 8 DAY STRIKES,NAUTICAL DESIGN..     65.00
CLOCK,SESSIONS MANTLE,MARBELIZED,3 PILLARS EACH SIDE........     45.00
CLOCK,SESSIONS,WALNUT......................................      8.50
CLOCK, SESSIONS MANTEL,WALNUT CASE.........................     18.00
CLOCK,SESSIONS SCHOOLHOUSE,REGULATOR,WALL TYPE,RUNS,39 X 17
  IN....................................................     42.50
CLOCK,SETH THOMAS 1/2 OCTAGON MANTLE,SNOWBALL SCENE ON
  BOTTOM.................................................     75.00
CLOCK,SETH THOMAS 8 DAY,WEIGHT DRIVEN WOOD MOVEMENT SHELF,..    165.00
CLOCK,SETH THOMAS 12 IN. DIAL,PENDULUM INSIDE,8 DAY.........     45.00
CLOCK,SETH THOMAS 30 HOUR WEIGHT DRIVEN ,HALF COLUMNS WALNUT
  CASE...................................................     55.00
CLOCK,SETH THOMAS ARCH TOP MANTEL,STRIKES AT HALF & FULL....     19.00
CLOCK,SETH THOMAS BRONZE,DIANA,11 IN.......................     60.00
CLOCK,SETH THOMAS GOTHIC STEEPLE,25 IN. TALL,RUNS...........     50.00
CLOCK,SETH THOMAS OGEE WEIGHT DRIVEN,STRIKES...............     75.00
CLOCK,SETH THOMAS PILLAR & SCROLL MANTEL,PRISTINE..........    650.00
CLOCK,SETH THOMAS PLYMOUTH HOLLOW SHELF,STRIKER............     55.00
CLOCK,SETH THOMAS REGULATOR ROUND FACE,OAK CASE,BRASS WEIGHT    95.00
CLOCK,SETH THOMAS SHIPS,BRASS,STRIKES......................    100.00
CLOCK,SETH THOMAS WEIGHT DRIVEN REGULATOR,OAK CASE.........     65.00
CLOCK,SETH THOMAS WALL,5 FEET LONG,OPEN GLASS FRONT,BRASS
  PENDULUM BALL..........................................    125.00
CLOCK,SETH THOMAS,WALNUT CASE,8 DAY,ALARM,DATED 1906.......     12.00
CLOCK,SEVRES   CIRCA 1820,FRENCH 15 DAY STRIKING,NUDE FIGURE
  POINTS TIME............................................    300.00
CLOCK,SHAVING MIRROR WITH ANSONIA CLOCK ABOVE,WOOD FRAME....     16.00
CLOCK,SHIPS STRIKING SETH THOMAS,BRASS FACE................     50.00
CLOCK,SOLID,ORIGINAL......................................     45.00
CLOCK,SQUARE GLASS ENCLOSED 400-DAY.......................     25.00
CLOCK,SQUARE IRON MANTLE,BLACK............................     18.00
CLOCK,SQUARE TYPE REVERSE PAINTING ON GLASS IN FRONT,SETH
  THOMAS.................................................     25.00
CLOCK,STEEPLE,HAND RUBBED PINE CASE,STRIKES...............     65.00
CLOCK,STEEPLE,MAHOGANY,8 DAY,STRIKES,PAINTING SCENE.........     65.00
CLOCK,SWING ARM,METAL STATUE,26 IN. TALL...................    375.00
CLOCK,TAMBOUR SHAPE QUARTER HOUR WESTMINISTER CHIMES........     45.00
CLOCK,TIME,CINCINNATI TIME RECORDER CO.....................     45.00
CLOCK,TRIPLEX ELECTRIC TIME SWITCH,WALTHAM.................     15.00
CLOCK,VICTORIAN EMBOSSED OAK CASE KITCHEN HANGING,8 DAY.....     35.00
CLOCK,VICTORIAN WALNUT TEAR DROP,GOLD FLOWER DECORATION ON
  GLASS,8-DAY............................................     32.00
CLOCK,VIENNA REGULATOR,1 WEIGHT..........................     35.00
CLOCK,VIENNA REGULATOR,2 WEIGHTS.........................     45.00
CLOCK,VIENNA REGULATOR,3 WEIGHTS.........................     55.00
CLOCK,VIENNA REGULATOR,CARVED............................     35.00
CLOCK,VIENNA REGULATOR,RUNS,WALNUT CASED WITH PORCELAIN
  DIALS.................................................    165.00
CLOCK,VIENNA REGULATOR,SPRINGS...........................     25.00
CLOCK,VIENNA REGULATOR WALL IN WALNUT CASE,BRASS PENDULUM,8
  DAY...................................................     42.50
CLOCK,VIENNA REGULATOR,WALNUT CARVED CASE WITH SECOND HAND..    165.00
CLOCK,VIENNA REGULATOR WITH 2 WEIGHTS AND SECOND HAND.......    145.00
CLOCK,VIENNA WALL,2 WEIGHTS...............................    160.00
CLOCK,VIENNA WALL,ONE WEIGHT..............................     80.00
CLOCK,VIENNA WALL WITH 3 WEIGHTS..........................    280.00
CLOCK,W.GOODWIN WEIGHT DRIVEN BANJO.......................    225.00
CLOCK,WAG ON WALL,MISSION STYLE IN DARK OAK,BRASS
  NUMERALS,HANDS.........................................     25.00
```

CLOCK,WALL,HANGS FROM BRASS CHAIN,FRENCH PORCELAIN
NUMERALS,WORKS... 250.00
CLOCK,WALL,WESTMINSTER CHIMES............................. 115.00
CLOCK,WALNUT GINGERBREAD BY INGRAHAM...................... 15.00
CLOCK,WALNUT KITCHEN,SETH THOMAS 8-DAY BRASS,RUNS......... 34.50
CLOCK,WALNUT ORNATE 8-DAY................................. 35.00
CLOCK,WALNUT SHELF.. 7.50
CLOCK,WALNUT WALL,8 DAY BRASS WATERBURY CLOCK CO.,APPLIED
ROSETTES... 75.00
CLOCK,WATERBURY CARRIAGE,RUNS............................. 50.00
CLOCK,WATERBURY IN RUNNING CONDITION,BRASS TOP & FEET...... 65.00
CLOCK,WATERBURY MANTLE.................................... 45.00
CLOCK,WATERBURY MIDGET SCHOOL HOUSE,13 IN.,5 IN. DIAL...... 65.00
CLOCK,WATERBURY MINIATURE ,30 HOUR SPRING DRIVEN.......... 16.50
CLOCK,WATERBURY OGEE WEIGHT DRIVEN,STRIKES................ 65.00
CLOCK,WATERBURY SCHOOL HOUSE,OCTAGONAL TOP,RUNS,MAHOGANY
FINISH... 65.00
CLOCK,WATERBURY STEEPLE,19 IN.,.......................... 65.00
CLOCK,WATERBURY WALNUT 8 DAY STRIKING..................... 35.00
CLOCK,WATERBURY WALNUT CASE CALENDAR CLOCK,BRASS PENDULUM... 47.50
CLOCK,WALNUT SHELF BY F KROEBER,PENDULUM,30 HOUR
RUNNING,STRIKES.. 25.00
CLOCK,WILLIAM BEACH 1830,CARVED EAGLE FINIAL.............. 125.00
CLOCK,WOODEN KITCHEN..................................... 25.00

CLOISONNE ENAMEL was developed during the nineteenth century. A glass
enamel was applied between small ribbon-like pieces of metal on a metal base.
Most cloisonné is Japanese.

CLOISONNE 3-LEGGED ROUND COVERED JAR,GOLDSTONE............. 10.00
CLOISONNE 4 IN. COVERED JAR,GOLD AVENTURINE & BROWN WITH
BLUE,BLACK... 25.00
CLOISONNE 5 IN. VASE,FLORAL ON WHITE ,COPPER TRIM,MARKED
CHINA.. 7.00
CLOISONNE 6 IN. PLATE,PHOENIX BIRD,FLORALS,GOLD STONE...... 22.00
CLOISONNE 7 IN. PLATE,ROSE BACKGROUND,IMPERIAL DRAGON MOTIF
CIRCA 1800... 48.00
CLOISONNE 12 IN. PLATE,BLUE BACKGROUND,PHEASANT & ORANGE
LILIES.. 82.50
CLOISONNE BLACK MATCH BOX,DRAGON & FLORAL TRIM............ 3.00
CLOISONNE BLUE ASH TRAY GOLD & FLORALS................... 5.00
CLOISONNE BLUE & WHITE FLOWERS VASE...................... 12.50
CLOISONNE BOWL 5 IN. DIAMETER AND 2 IN. HIGH............. 25.00
CLOISONNE BOWL,BLACK AND DECORATED INSIDE & OUT,8 IN.
DIAMETER.. 95.00
CLOISONNE BOWL,BLUE & BLACK WITH YELLOW DRAGON........... 125.00
CLOISONNE BOWL,MULTICOLOUR FLORALS ON RED................ 12.50
CLOISONNE BRICK RED TRAY,INITIALS VR IN CENTER........... 30.00
CLOISONNE BUTTER PAT.................................... 4.00
CLOISONNE CARD TRAY,BLACK & WHITE WITH GOLD FLORAL DECOR.... 22.50
CLOISONNE CHINESE VASE.................................. 29.00
CLOISONNE CHINESE VASE,WHITE & TURQUOISE DRAGON,RED
BACKGROUND.. 20.00
CLOISONNE COVERED BOWL,GOLD WITH BLUE LINING............. 22.00
CLOISONNE COVERED BOX,BLACK CHINESE DRAGON.............. 18.50
CLOISONNE COVERED JAR,PINK & WHITE FLOWERS ON BLUE
GROUND,WOOD BASE.. 40.00
CLOISONNE COVERED VASE,BLACK BACKGROUND WITH RED ,PINK &
YELLOW.. 45.00
CLOISONNE CUP PLATE..................................... 5.00
CLOISONNE FISHSCALE VASE & WOOD STAND................... 20.00
CLOISONNE FLORAL SCROLL BLUE COVERED JAR................ 12.00
CLOISONNE HEART-SHAPED NAPKIN RING...................... 7.00
CLOISONNE IN HAWTHORNE PATTERN,2 VASES,COVERED BOX....... 35.00
CLOISONNE LAMP BASE ON TEAKWOOD STAND................... 45.00
CLOISONNE LAMP ,RED WITH FLOWER DECORATION.............. 35.00

CLOISONNE LAMP,TEAK BASE,PAIR................................... 60.00
CLOISONNE LIFT LID BOX,BRASS FOO DOG FINIAL,GREEN,RED
  FLOWERS... 20.00
CLOISONNE MELON-RIBBED CHINESE VASE,BLACK & GREEN WITH BIRDS   50.00
CLOISONNE MULTI-COLOUR FLORAL BOWL............................. 10.00
CLOISONNE MULTI-COLOUR FLORAL ROUND BOX....................... 12.00
CLOISONNE NAPKIN RING.. 4.25
CLOISONNE NAPKIN RING,5.. 20.00
CLOISONNE NAPKIN RING,FLORAL SIGNED........................... 9.50
CLOISONNE NUT BOWL,TURQUOISE ON YELLOW........................ 14.00
CLOISONNE ON POTTERY VASES,PAIR,FLORAL & BUTTERFLY DESIGN...   50.00
CLOISONNE OPEN SALT & MATCHING SALT SHAKER.................... 5.00
CLOISONNE OPEN SALT & PEPPER,BEIGE WITH BLUE FLOWERS......... 13.00
CLOISONNE OPEN SALT & PEPPER,BLUE WITH RED FLOWERS........... 13.00
CLOISONNE OPEN SALT DISH WITH MATCHING PEPPER,BLUE,RED......   13.00
CLOISONNE PAIR CHINESE VASES WITH STANDS...................... 17.00
CLOISONNE PAIR ORIENTAL VASES,BLUE WITH DRAGONS.............. 55.00
CLOISONNE PAIR TURQUOISE VASES,CHINESE........................ 60.00
CLOISONNE PAIR VASES,BLACK WITH DRAGONS....................... 47.00
CLOISONNE PAIR VASES ON BRASS,BLACK WITH PURPLE & BLUE IRIS
  & GREEN.. 38.50
CLOISONNE PAIR VASES,FLOWERS WORKED IN SILVER WIRE,WOOD
  STANDS.. 135.00
CLOISONNE ROSE PETAL JAR,13 IN................................ 15.00
CLOISONNE ROUND BOX... 13.75
CLOISONNE ROUND BOX,WHITE EDGED IN GREEN,PINK & YELLOW
  FLOWERS,SIGNED.. 40.00
CLOISONNE SALT & PEPPER,RED WITH FLOWERS...................... 9.50
CLOISONNE STAMP BOX,BIRDS,BRANCHES & FLOWER,MARKED CHINA....   3.75
CLOISONNE STERLING PIN.. 6.00
CLOISONNE TABLE TYPE MATCH HOLDER ON STAND................... 8.00
CLOISONNE TEA CADDY,RED & BLUE PRUNUS DECOR INCISED CHINA...   25.00
CLOISONNE URN SHAPED VASE,BLACK & GREEN BACKGROUND.......... 14.00
CLOISONNE VASE,7 IN. HIGH,URN SHAPED,BIRD ON FLOWERING
  TREE,BLUE.. 37.50
CLOISONNE VASE,BLACK WITH PINK & YELLOW CHRYSANTHEMUM.......   40.00
CLOISONNE VASE,BLUE SHELL BACKGROUND......................... 200.00
CLOISONNE VASE,HENNA COLOUR,FISH SCALE PATTERN..............   30.00
CLOISONNE VASE MARKED CHINA,BLACK WITH MULTI-COLOURED
  FLOWERS... 33.00
CLOISONNE VASE,MULTI-COLOR & GOLDSTONE FLOWERS & BUTTERFLIES
  ON GREEN.. 17.50
CLOISONNE VASE,PAIR... 47.00
CLOISONNE YELLOW COVERED BOX.................................. 30.00
CLOTHING,CIRCA 1910 SIZE 18 LADYS BLACK WOOL SUIT...........   7.50
CLOTHING,LAP ROBE,BLACK,RED,BROWN & GREEN,ST.BERNARD DOG....   50.00
CLOTHING,LONG CHRISTENING DRESS.............................. 10.00
CLOTHING,MACK SENNETT TYPE BATHING SUIT,BLACK,SIZE 44.......   5.00
CLOTHING,PAIR BLACK LEATHER HIGH BUTTON SHOES,..............   15.00
CLOTHING,PAIR HIGH BUTTON SHOES.............................. 4.00
CLOTHING,PAISLEY SHAWL,72 IN. SQUARE,BLACK................... 15.00
CLOTHING,PAISLEY SHAWL,BLACK CENTER,3 YARDS LONG............ 22.50
CLOTHING,SHAKER BERGUNDY WOOL HOODED CAPE................... 45.00
CLOTHING,SPANISH SHAWL,BLACK SILK,FROM SPAIN,HAND
  EMBROIDERED,FRINGE.. 59.50
CLOTHING,SPANISH SILK SHAWL,MELON COLOUR,44 IN. SQUARE......   18.50
CLOTHING,STOVEPIPE HAT IN LEATHER CASE....................... 15.00
CLOTHING,TAN PONGEE PARASOL,GREEN BORDER.................... 7.50

*CLUTHRA GLASS is a two layered-glass with small air pockets that form white
spots. The Steuben Glass Works of Corning, New York, made it after 1903,
Kimball Glass Company of Vineland, New Jersey, made Cluthra from about 1925.*
CLUTHRA,BLACK TOP,WHITE BODY,8 IN. HG. SIGNED STEUBEN....... 354.00
CLUTHRA KIMBALL SIGNED BULBOUS BODIED VASE,4 IN.
  HIGH,MOTTLED TURQUOISE...................................... 200.00

CLUTHRA SIGNED VASE,10 IN.,PEDESTAL,TEAR DROP BODY,YELLOW
  IRIDESCENCE.. 175.00
CLUTHRA VASE SIGNED SCHNEIDER............................... 450.00

COALPORT WARE has been made by the Coalport Porcelain Works of England
from 1795 to the present time.
COALPORT BLUE,YELLOW & GOLD PAIR OBLONG DISHES CIRCA 1820... 135.00
COALPORT CUP & SAUCER,CIRCA 1881,DEMITASSE SIZE,YELLOW &
  GOLD... 26.50
COALPORT DEMI-TASSE WINE WITH GOLD FLORAL,GOLD LINING....... 5.50
COALPORT TEAPOT,WHITE PORCELAIN IN GOLD WITH LOBSTER SHADE.. 62.50
  COBALT, SEE ALSO PRESSED GLASS..........................
COBALT 4 IN. VASE.. 2.00
COBALT 7 IN. FLUTED TOP VASE............................... 4.00

COBALT BLUE GLASS was made using oxide of cobalt. The characteristic bright
dark blue identifies it for the collector. Most cobalt glass found today was made
after the Civil War.
COBALT 21 IN. TALL VASE.................................... 75.00
COBALT BLUE 5 IN. FLARED VASE.............................. 8.00
COBALT BLUE 8 IN. SATIN VASE............................... 7.00
COBALT BLUE 8 SIDED PYRAMID SHAPED SALT SHAKER............. 3.00
COBALT BLUE BOWL & PAIR OF CANDLESTICKS.................... 69.00
COBALT BLUE BLOWN GLASS ROLLING PIN,17 IN. LONG............ 24.00
COBALT BLUE BLOWN MID-VICTORIAN RUFFLED TOP VASE,ENAMELED
  FLOWER... 16.50
COBALT BLUE DECANTER,RIBBED WITH CLEAR APPLIED HANDLE &
  STOPPER.. 27.50
COBALT BLUE DECANTER WITH CLEAR STOPPER.................... 24.00
COBALT BLUE DOUBLE SALTS IN OPENWORK METAL HOLDER,PAIR..... 25.00
COBALT BLUE FOOTED ROSE BOWL............................... 2.50
COBALT BLUE FISH SHAPE ASH TRAY............................ 1.00
COBALT BLUE FRUIT BOWL & CANDLESTICKS...................... 32.00
COBALT BLUE GLASS 11 IN. DIVIDED RELISH.................... 12.50
COBALT BLUE GLASS BALL,USED FOR SHOOTING TARGET............ 6.00
COBALT BLUE GLASS CANDLESTICK WITH SILVER DECOR............ 20.00
COBALT BLUE GLASS DEMI-TASSE CUP & SAUCER,GOLD GRAPES DECOR. 12.50
COBALT BLUE GLASS EYE CUP,BRITISH MARKED................... 2.00
COBALT BLUE GLASS HINGED JEWEL BOX,ENAMEL DECORATION....... 48.00
COBALT BLUE GLASS SEINE BALL 5IN. DIAM..................... 5.00
COBALT BLUE GLASS TOP HAT
  4.75 TO.. 6.00
COBALT BLUE GLASS VASE,SILVER BANDS,11 IN. TALL............ 45.00
COBALT BLUE GOBLET,12..................................... 50.00
COBALT BLUE HAND BLOWN COMPOTE,PEDESTAL BASE............... 3.00
COBALT BLUE HAT... 5.00
COBALT BLUE MAPLE LEAF SHAPED DISHES, 7 IN. DIA., 6 FOR.... 5.00
COBALT BLUE OPEN SUGAR BOWL,SILVER PLATE HOLDER,MADE IN
  ENGLAND.. 25.00
COBALT BLUE OVERLAY GLASS OPEN SALT,PAIR,COMPOTE STYLE..... 125.00
COBALT BLUE PAIR FRENCH POODLES........................... 28.50
COBALT BLUE,PAIR LOW CANDLESTICKS,3 IN.................... 3.00
COBALT BLUE PAIR PEDESTAL BOWL,CLOSED HANDLES............. 3.00
COBALT BLUE , PAIR VASES.................................. 8.00
COBALT BLUE PLATES, SCALLOPED EDGE 2 FOR.................. 1.50
COBALT BLUE PLATTER,GOLD SCALLOPED EDGE,PORTRAIT CENTER,SHIP 15.00
COBALT BLUE SALT & PEPPER,PEWTER TOP...................... 5.50
COBALT BLUE SET OF 6 INDIVIDUAL SALTS IN STERLING HOLDERS,6
  SPOONS... 85.00
COBALT BLUE SHERBETS,.................................... 3.50
COBALT BLUE TOP HAT ASH TRAY.............................. 2.00
COBALT BLUE TUMBLER,PRESSED DIAMOND DESIGN BLUE........... 14.00
COBALT BLUE VASE 10 IN. HIGH.............................. 12.00
COBALT BLUE VASE,GOLD FLOWERS............................. 26.00
COBALT BLUE VICTORIAN VASE,8 IN.,GOLD DECOR............... 11.00

COBALT BLUE WINE DECANTER & 5 GOBLETS...................... 20.00
COBALT BUTTERFLY & BERRY SUGAR............................ 13.50
COBALT GLASS BUD VASE,ETCHED,10 IN. H..................... 7.00
COBALT GLASS TOOTHPICK.................................... 8.00
COBALT JEWEL BOX,WHITE ENAMELLED DAISIES,GREEN LEAVES,BRASS
  COLLAR.. 29.50
COBALT LOW CANDLEHOLDER................................... 6.00
COBALT PLATE,8 IN.,RIBBED EDGE............................ 1.50
COBALT ROUND BOX,GOLD TRIM,FRENCH LADY & MAN.............. 27.50
COBALT SCALLOPED OPEN EDGE CANDY BOWL,CANE PATTERN........ 2.95
COBALT SHIRLEY TEMPLE DISHES,12 PIECES.................... 15.00
COBALT SHOE.. 10.50

COCA-COLA advertising items have become a special field for collectors.
COCA-COLA 1923 BOTTLE..................................... 2.00
COCA-COLA AMBER BOTTLE
  8.00   TO.. 10.00
COCA-COLA BOTTLE,BROWN.................................... 12.50
COCA-COLA BOTTLE,KEY WEST,SCA............................. 7.50
COCA-COLA BOTTLE,SMALL AQUA............................... 5.00
COCA-COLA CHEWING GUM JAR WITH TRADEMARK EMBOSSED......... 25.00
COCA-COLA GLASSES IN METAL INSERTS....................... 5.00
COCA-COLA GREEN BOTTLE,INDIAN HEAD,CASCO BOTTLING CO. 1925.. 6.50
COCA-COLA METAL TRAY,9 X 12 IN........................... 15.00
COCA-COLA SIPHON BOTTLE,GREEN DECAGON,MARKED,WITH PEWTER
  HEAD... 7.50
COCA-COLA TRAY,10 IN. BY 13 IN.,CIRCA 1930............... 7.50
COCA-COLA TRAY 1930
  5.00   TO.. 7.00
COCA-COLA TRAY 1937...................................... 6.00
COCA-COLA TRAY 1938...................................... 5.00
COCA-COLA TRAY 1941...................................... 5.00
COCA-COLA TRAY,GIRL WITH HAT............................. 6.00
COCA-COLA TRAY,PICTURE OF LADY HOLDING COKE,1935......... 7.50

COFFEE GRINDERS (home size) were first made about 1894. They lost favor by the 1930's.
COFFEE GRINDER,2 WHEEL,CAST IRON,13 IN. HIGH,22K GOLD PLATED
  EAGLE.. 75.00
COFFEE GRINDER,2 WHEEL COUNTER,FRARY & CLARK,26 IN. HIGH.... 85.00
COFFEE GRINDER,ARCADE CRYSTAL............................ 9.50
COFFEE GRINDER,ARCADE CRYSTAL WALL HUNG.................. 7.75
COFFEE GRINDER,CAST IRON,2 WHEEL,RED PAINT,WOODRUFF &
  EDWARDS.. 145.00
COFFEE GRINDER,COUNTER TOP,MARKED NEW BRITAIN ,CONN....... 65.00
COFFEE GRINDER,DOVETAILED................................ 12.50
COFFEE GRINDER,DOVETAILED WOOD,DRAWER.................... 17.00
COFFEE GRINDER,FRENCH,7 BRASS LION HEADS IN RELIEF....... 22.50
COFFEE GRINDER,HANGING,WOODEN CONTAINER & GRASS FRONT.... 18.00
COFFEE GRINDER,PORCELAIN LINED BOWL,GERMAN............... 16.00
COFFEE GRINDER,ROSEWOOD,BRASS HANDLE..................... 25.00
COFFEE GRINDER,WALL,CHINA................................ 12.50
COFFEE GRINDER,WALL,IRON,GLASS CONTAINER................. 7.00
COFFEE GRINDER,WALL TYPE,CAST IRON....................... 12.00
COFFEE GRINDER,WALNUT.................................... 12.50
COFFEE GRINDER,WALNUT,IRON CRANK HANDLE,DATED 1882....... 15.00
COFFEE GRINDER,WOODEN HANDLE,IRON CUP,DOVETAILED BOX &
  DRAWER... 15.00
COFFEE GRINDER,WOODEN TABLE,1 DRAWER WITH IRON TOP & CRANK.. 16.00
COFFEE MILL,FRENCH,BRASS BOWL & WOOD FRAME............... 12.50
COFFEE MILL,WOODEN WITH IRON TOP CRANK HANDLE,DRAWER..... 12.00

COIN SILVER was made in America before 1860. Coin silver was made from melted currency and usually has a silver content of about 800 or 900 parts silver. Sterling silver is 925 parts silver with 75 parts copper. Most coin silver spoons are thin, handmade pieces.

COIN SILVER BEAKER,HALLMARK MC DANNOLD........................	160.00
COIN SILVER BEAKER HALLMARK B MEAD...........................	147.50
COIN SILVER COFFEE POT,COVERED SUGAR & CREAMER,BOSTON 1820..	500.00
COIN SILVER CRANBERRY SPOON IN KINGS PATTERN,2..............	7.95
COIN SILVER CREAMER,OVAL,FOOTED,HALLMARKED CIRCA 1802.......	145.00
COIN SILVER CREAMER,WARD & JONES,BOSTON CIRCA 1815.........	145.00
COIN SILVER CUP,DRINKING,NEW YORK CIRCA 1810...............	75.00
COIN SILVER CUP,HANDLED,LINCOLN & REED....................	75.00
COIN SILVER DESSERT SPOON,FORSYTH,GEORGE	
H.LOUISVILLE,KY.,1843-48..................................	6.00
COIN SILVER DESSERT SPOON.................................	4.00
COIN SILVER FORK,BABY,LOWS,BALL & CO.,BOSTON,CIRCA 1840.....	4.75
COIN SILVER GRAVY LADLE INITIALS I.J.R....................	6.00
COIN SILVER KNIFE,FLAT HANDLE,BY BIGELOW BROS., &	
KENNARD,BOSTON 1845.......................................	5.75
COIN SILVER LADLE CIRCA 1835,J E CALDWELL.................	85.00
COIN SILVER LADLE,FIDDLEBACK,PARTRIDGE ON FRONT...........	15.00
COIN SILVER LADLE,SOUP,ETCHED WHEAT,GOLD WASHED ETCHED BOWL.	49.50
COIN SILVER MUG BY LEWIS & SMITH CIRCA 1800...............	250.00
COIN SILVER MUG,SINGLE HANDLE,CIRCA 1837..................	50.00
COIN SILVER MUSTARD SPOON.................................	5.00
COIN SILVER NAPKIN RINGS,PAIR,PLAIN OVALS.................	3.75
COIN SILVER SALT,MASTER,JONES,C.1913......................	4.00
COIN SILVER SALT,MASTER,PITMAN,FOSTER.....................	4.00
COIN SILVER SALT SHELL,GLASS INSERT WITH SALT SPOON.......	3.95
COIN SILVER SALVER,BEADED EDGE,3 REPOUSSE FEET,CIRCA 1805...	87.50
COIN SILVER SPOON,5 INITIALED A.B.........................	22.50
COIN SILVER SPOON INITIALED F.P.L.........................	2.75
COIN SILVER SPOON,MASTER SALT,MARKED,FIDDLE SHAPED,PAIR.....	12.50
COIN SILVER SPOON,MASTER SALT,OVAL SHELL BOWLS,PAIR.........	9.00
COIN SILVER SPOON,MOURNING,DATE COT.,1825.................	10.00
COIN SILVER SPOON,SALT,PAIR,FIDDLEBACK,BY R & W	
WILSON,PHILADELPHIA.......................................	15.00
COIN SILVER SPOON,SERVING,BY J.CARY.......................	5.00
COIN SILVER SPOON,SERVING,SET,MARYLAND....................	50.00
COIN SILVER SPOON,SERVING,SMITH & CHAMBERLAIN.............	5.00
COIN SILVER SPOON,SOUP,SET OF 6,FIDDLE BACK...............	26.50
COIN SILVER SPOONS,SALT,BAILEY & CO.,PHILA 1850...........	6.00
COIN SILVER SUGAR SHELL BY C F STONE 1840.................	6.95
COIN SILVER SUGAR SHELL BY PAGE BROS. CIRCA 1820..........	6.95
COIN SILVER SUGAR SHELL,CIRCA 1840........................	10.00
COIN SILVER SUGAR TONGS...................................	8.00
COIN SILVER SUGAR TONGS BY C.BREWER,N.Y.CIRCA 1824,ENGRAVED	
MOTHER 1784...	19.75
COIN SILVER SUGAR TONGS,PITMAN C.1810.....................	17.00
COIN SILVER TABLE SPOON...................................	6.50
COIN SILVER TABLESPOON,2,FARRINGTON & HUNNEWEL CIRCA 1835...	11.50
COIN SILVER TABLESPOON BY C.A.BATCHELDER,BOSTON,CIRCA 1850..	5.75
COIN SILVER TABLESPOON BY FARRINGTON &	
HUNNEWELL,BOSTON,CIRCA 1835...............................	5.75
COIN SILVER TABLESPOON,BY FARRINGTON &	
HUNNEWELL,MONOGRAMMED,PAIR................................	9.00
COIN SILVER TABLESPOON BY H.PITTS,BERKLEY,MASS.,MARKED......	5.75
COIN SILVER TABLESPOON BY HOTCHKISS & SCHREUDER CIRCA 1850..	5.75
COIN SILVER TABLESPOON BY HOVEY PARKER CO.,..............	6.95
COIN SILVER TABLESPOON,CIRCA 1840.........................	4.00
COIN SILVER TABLESPOON MARKED,1785........................	30.00
COIN SILVER TABLESPOON,PAIR,18TH CENTURY,MARKED C BIXLER....	45.00
COIN SILVER TABLESPOON,POINTED END,R W ON FRONT...........	13.00
COIN SILVER TABLESPOON,S.MUMFORS ,RHODE ISLAND CIRCA 1820...	6.50
COIN SILVER TABLESPOON,TIBAULT BROS.,C.1810...............	9.50
COIN SILVER TABLESPOONS,2,W.TENNY,C.1840..................	7.50
COIN SILVER TABLESPOONS,6,FIDDLE HANDLES,INITIALED MJJ	

```
MARKED...................................................  47.50
COIN SILVER TEASPOON
   3.00  TO..............................................   4.00
COIN SILVER TEASPOON,2,BY E & J KELLEY,NANTUCKET,MASS.......   6.00
COIN SILVER TEASPOON,2,BY E.E. & S.C. BAILEY CIRCA 1825-50..   5.75
COIN SILVER TEASPOON,5,BY N.HARDING,BOSTON,CIRCA 1820.......  16.75
COIN SILVER TEASPOON,6,BY J./.HOLDEN CIRCA 1840-50,MARKED...  18.75
COIN SILVER TEASPOON,6,FIDDLEBACK,BY CURRIER & TROTT........  30.00
COIN SILVER TEASPOON BY B.GODDARD..........................   3.00
COIN SILVER TEASPOON BY B & M.M.SWAN,CIRCA 1830,INITALS
   H.M.T..................................................   3.00
COIN SILVER TEASPOON BY D.GODDARD,WORCESTER,MASS.,CIRCA
   1840...................................................   3.00
COIN SILVER TEASPOON BY JONES GELSTON & PORTER BOSTON 1810..   2.95
COIN SILVER TEASPOON,CIRCA 1840............................   3.00
COIN SILVER TEASPOON,DAY,HALE,LEATER,INITIALS A.R. ON FRONT
   HANDLE.................................................   6.00
COIN SILVER TEASPOON,FIDDLEBACK,CIRCA 1810.................   3.00
COIN SILVER TEASPOON MARKED ENGLISH........................   4.50
COIN SILVER TEASPOON MARKED HALLSEL........................   5.00
COIN SILVER,TEASPOON,N.GEFFROY,C.1800......................   5.50
COIN SILVER TEASPOON,R.N.WILSON,C.1825.....................   4.75
COIN SILVER TEASPOON,ROUND END,5...........................  45.00
COIN SILVER TEASPOON,SET OF 3,BY GRIFFEN,MONOGRAMMED.......  12.00
COIN SILVER TEASPOON,SET OF 6 MARKED G.S.& G.L.ROGERS......  20.00
COIN SILVER TEASPOON,SET OF 6,MARKED J.S.LOMBARD...........  20.00
COIN SILVER TEASPOON,SET OF 10.............................  30.00
COIN SILVER TEASPOON SIGNED SETH E.BROWN...................   3.00
COIN SILVER TEASPOON,SQUIRE BROS.C.1846....................   3.75
COIN SILVER TEASPOON WITH MARK OF B.GODDARD................   3.00
COIN SILVER TEASPOONS,4 MATCHED AMERICAN,FIDDLE SHAPED
   HANDLES................................................  15.00
COIN SILVER TEASPOONS,5,INITIALED NG MARKED................  15.00
COIN SILVER TEASPOONS,6,W.MOULTON,C.1772...................  32.50
COIN SILVER TEASPOONS,MONOGRAMMED..........................   4.00
COIN SILVER TEASPOONS,SET OF 7,BY GEORGE B. APPLETON,SALEM
   MASS.,1852.............................................  22.75
COIN SILVER TEASPOONS,SET OF 12............................   5.00
```

COMMEMORATION ITEMS have been produced to honor a new or deceased member of a royal family. Coronation cups and plates are part of this category, and they have been made since the 1800's. Some souvenir spoons and plates are included in this category.

```
COMMEMORATION PITCHER,DEWEY,CLEAR..........................  27.00
COMMEMORATION PITCHER,RUBY & CLEAR THUMBPRINT,ETCHED WORLDS
   FAIR 1893..............................................  11.00
     COMMEMORATION PLATE, SEE ALSO SOUVENIR PLATE...........
COMMEMORATION PLATE,1939 NEW YORK WORLDS FAIR,GEORGE
   WASHINGTON.............................................  16.00
COMMEMORATION PLATE,BELGIAN,KING LEOPOLD-QUEEN MARIE 1831...  17.50
COMMEMORATION PLATE,BLUE,OLD ST.DAVIDS RADNOR..............   7.00
COMMEMORATION PLATE,LONGFELLOWS EARLY HOME,10 IN.,ROLLED
   BORDER.................................................  10.00
COMMEMORATION PLATE,TORONTO,BLUE IMPRESSED BRITISH ANCHOR...   9.00
     COOKIE CUTTER, SEE TIN, CUTTER.........................
```

W. T. COPELAND & SONS, LTD. ran the Spode works in Staffordshire, England, from 1847 to the present. Copeland & Garret was the firm name from 1833 to 1847.

```
     COPELAND, SEE ALSO SPODE...............................
COPELAND 10 IN. B IMPRESSED PLATE,CASTLE CENTER SCENE.......  10.00
COPELAND COMPORT SHADED IN GREY,WHITE,BLACK,IMPRESSED......   3.00
COPELAND DEMI-TASSE CUP & SAUCER,GOLD ON GREEN.............   5.50
COPELAND & GARRETT ROUND COVERED CHEESE,GOLD TRIM,FLOWERS &
   BIRDS..................................................  18.50
```

COPELAND IMPRESSED PLATTER,BLUE GRAY FLOWERS & FOLIAGE,19 X 15 IN..	7.50
COPELAND MARKED JASPERWARE PITCHER,TAN HUNTING SCENE SIGNED.	20.00

COPELAND SPODE. See SPODE.

COPELAND SPODE BLUE CANDY JAR,COVERED,REED HANDLE............	18.00
COPELAND SPODE CHINA DECORATED WITH CHRISTMAS TREES 10 IN. PLATE...	4.00
COPELAND SPODE CHINA DECORATED WITH CHRISTMAS TREES CUP & SAUCER...	5.00
COPELAND SPODE CRESCENT DISH,BIRD,FLOWERS,BUTTERFLY.........	8.00
COPELAND-SPODE MARKED ENGLAND PAIR BLUE JASPERWARE TUMBLERS,CLASSICAL......................................	45.00
COPELAND SPODE PINK MANDARIN PATTERN CELERY DISH............	8.50
COPELAND SPODE PLATE,FOX CHASE SCENE,GREEN BACKGROUND.......	8.00
COPELAND SPODE ROSE BRIAR PATTERN 4-CUP POT,COVERED SUGAR,& CREAMER...	18.00
COPELAND-SPODE SQUARE BOWL,BLUE WITH WHITE.................	27.00
COPELAND-SPODE TEA SET,11 PIECES,CHINESE DESIGN.............	135.00
COPELAND SPODE TOWER PLATE.................................	7.00
COPPER, SEE ALSO KITCHEN, STORE, TOOLS.................	
COPPER 18TH CENTURY BEDWARMER,WOOD HANDLE..................	65.00
COPPER 18TH CENTURY BEDWARMING PAN,ENGRAVED DECORATION,WOOD HANDLE...	65.00
COPPER,AEROPLANE WEATHERVANE,..............................	98.00
COPPER & BRASS CHAFING DISH................................	15.00
COPPER & BRASS CHAFING DISH,NO BURNER......................	22.50
COPPER & BRASS CHAFING DISH WITH BURNER....................	15.00
COPPER & BRASS & DELFT COAL HOD............................	69.50
COPPER & BRASS ICE CREAM SCOOP.............................	8.50
COPPER & BRASS JAPANESE TEAKETTLE,HINGED SPOUT,DOUBLE HANDLE	30.00
COPPER BALANCE SCALES......................................	29.00
COPPER BED-WARMER..	45.00
COPPER BED WARMER,LID CUT OUTS DESIGN......................	45.00
COPPER BED WARMER OVAL.....................................	45.00
COPPER BED WARMER,WOOD HANDLE..............................	45.00
COPPER BOILER..	13.50
COPPER BOOTS,MOLDS FOR CHILDRENS RUBBERS...................	15.00
COPPER CAN WITH APPLIED BRASS HANDLES MARKED GERALD & ALLEN KENDALLS...	16.50
COPPER CHAFING DISH,10 IN. DIAMETER,STAND,WATER PAN & BURNER,DATE 1895.......................................	15.00
COPPER CHAFING DISH,ROCHESTER,DATED 1904...................	18.50
COPPER COFFEE POT..	20.00
COPPER COFFEE POT,SMALL....................................	6.00
COPPER COFFEE POT WITH WOODEN HANDLE.......................	12.50
COPPER COFFEE URN & TRAY,4-FOOTED PEDESTAL,WHITE PORCELAIN,BRASS SPIGOT.................................	80.00
COPPER COFFEE URN WITH ALCOHOL BURNER ON CURVED FEET........	35.00
COPPER COFFEE URN WITH SPIGOT ON STAND WITH ALCOHOL BURNER..	30.00
COPPER COW FOR WEATHERVANE.................................	35.00
COPPER CUP,BRASS HANDLE....................................	4.00
COPPER,DUTCH CANDLESTICKS,PAIR,ROUND BASE,9 IN. HIGH........	35.00
COPPER ETCHED WARMING PAN,HANDLE...........................	38.00
COPPER FULL-MOLDED FISH SIGN,TACKLE STORE..................	75.00
COPPER FUNNEL WITH HANDLE & SHUT OFF.......................	8.50
COPPER GOOSENECK TEA KETTLE................................	30.00
COPPER HAND HAMMERED ROUND TRAY............................	8.50
COPPER HAND HAMMERED TRAY,OPEN HANDLES.....................	8.00
COPPER HANDHAMMERED EGG WHITE BOWL.........................	32.50
COPPER HANDLED PAIL..	12.00
COPPER HAND MADE COPPER LADLE..............................	15.00
COPPER HANDMADE FLOWER POT,ENAMEL INLAID...................	135.00
COPPER IRISH TEA KETTLE....................................	35.00
COPPER,IRISH WHISKEY MEASURES WITH HANDLE & POURING SPOUT	

CIRCA 1830...	32.00
COPPER IRON HANDLED POT,9 IN. WIDE........................	37.50
COPPER KETTLE	
8.50 TO...	12.00
COPPER KETTLE,6 QUART SIZE,HALLMARKED BY MAKER,COPPER HANDLE	25.00
COPPER KETTLE,15 GALLON...................................	15.00
COPPER LUSTER, SEE LUSTER.................................	
COPPER MOLD,SCALLOPED EDGE ,SWIRL DESIGN,BRASS HOOK FOR	
HANGING...	2.00
COPPER MUG..	25.00
COPPER MUG,SILVER PLATE INSIDE,...........................	4.00
COPPER MUG,WORLDS FAIR 1933...............................	4.25
COPPER PAN,RING FOR HANGING...............................	22.00
COPPER PITCHER..	25.00
COPPER PITCHER,PEWTER SPOUT & HANDLE,7 IN.................	18.00
COPPER PITCHER USED FOR OIL...............................	12.00
COPPER POWDER FLASK,BRASS DISPENSER,RAISED SHELL DESIGN.....	22.00
COPPER POWDER FLASK,CROSSED WEAPONS.......................	25.00
COPPER POWDER FLASK,HUNTER MAKING LOVE TO GIRL.............	25.00
COPPER POWDER FLASK,VINE AND RIBBED,MARKED................	25.00
COPPER POWDER FLASK,WITH CHARGER,MARKED PAT,GREEN TASSEL	
CORD..	15.00
COPPER ,ROUND BASKET,6 IN. MOVABLE HANDLE.................	8.00
COPPER SUGAR SCOOP,13 IN..................................	27.50
COPPER TANKARD 1 HALF PINT,HANDLED........................	7.50
COPPER TEAKETTLE	
5.00 TO...	50.00
COPPER TEAKETTLE,12 IN....................................	28.50
COPPER TEAKETTLE,BRASS TRIM,GOOSE NECK....................	38.50
COPPER TEAKETTLE,HAND WROUGHT & SOLDERED WITH BRASS........	65.00
COPPER TEAKETTLE,LACQUERED................................	15.00
COPPER TEAKETTLE MADE IN ENGLAND..........................	14.50
COPPER TEAKETTLE ON STAND,OPALESCENT GLASS HANDLES.........	30.00
COPPER TEAPOT...	20.00
COPPER TEAPOT,PEWTER SPOUT,6 CUP SIZE.....................	18.50
COPPER TRAY,30 X 18 IN....................................	80.00
COPPER,TURTLE SPITTOON,GREEN & BLACK ENAMEL...............	55.00
COPPER VASE,CHURCH,RIBBED,MARKED CHARD,PAIR...............	8.00
COPPER WASH BOILER..	6.50
COPPER WASH BOILER 22 IN. BY 13 IN. BY 12 IN. ,COVER.......	10.00
COPPER WATERING CAN,MARKED................................	4.50

CORALENE GLASS was made by firing many small colored beads on the outside of glassware. It was made in many patterns in the United States and Europe.

CORALENE GOLD ON WEBB PEACHBLOW 9 IN. VASE,IVORY LINING.....	225.00
CORALENE VASE,BLUE BEADS ON PINK-WHITE SATIN,5 IN. HIGH,2	
IN. DIAMETER...	95.00
CORALENE VASE,CHARTREUSE WITH GOLD FERN PATTERN,7 IN. HIGH..	225.00
CORALENE VASE,SATIN GLASS,WHITE,YELLOW BEADING.............	140.00
CORALENE VASE,SATIN PINK-MAUVE TO WHITE,SEAWEED PATTERN,GOLD	
RIM..	175.00

CORONATION CUPS have been made since the 1800's. Pieces of pottery or glass with a picture of the monarch and the date have been made as souvenirs for many coronations.

CORONATION BASKET,CLEAR STIPPLED GLASS,GEORGE VI 1937.......	17.50
CORONATION BEAKERS,RUSSIAN,1886 CZAR NICHOLAS II...........	20.00
CORONATION CREAMER,KING EDWARD 1937.......................	6.00
CORONATION CUP & SAUCER OF KING GEORGE & QUEEN ELIZABETH	
1937..	10.00
CORONATION CUP,KING GEORGE & MARY 1937....................	5.00
CORONATION MUG,EDWARD VIII................................	7.00
CORONATION MUG,GEORGE 5TH & MARY..........................	4.00
CORONATION MUG,KING EDWARD 1937...........................	6.00
CORONATION MUG KING EDWARD VIII 1937......................	6.75

```
CORONATION MUG KING GEORGE VI & QUEEN ELIZABETH 1937........     5.95
CORONATION MUG,WOODS IVORY WARE,KING EDWARD VII MAY 1937....    12.50
CORONATION PLATE KING EDWARD VIII 1936......................     5.75
CORONATION PLATE QUEEN ELIZABETH II 1953....................     4.75
CORONATION QUEEN VICTORIA OCTAGONAL SHAPED JUBILEE PLATE....     7.50
CORONATION SCUTTLE MUG,KING GEORGE & ELIZABETH 1937.........    10.00
CORONET GAME PLATE.SIGNED L.LOUDERT,2 TURKEYS & FOLIAGE.....    38.00
```

COSMOS PATTERN GLASS is a pattern of pressed milk glass with colored
flowers.

```
COSMOS APPLE BLOSSOM BUTTER DISH............................    72.00
COSMOS BASE MINIATURE LAMP..................................    15.00
COSMOS BUTTER DISH,PINK BAND
   47.50  TO...............................................    60.00
COSMOS CASTOR SET...........................................    60.00
COSMOS COVERED BUTTER DISH..................................    65.00
COSMOS GLASS COVERED BUTTER.................................    65.00
COSMOS GLASS COVERED SUGAR..................................    45.00
COSMOS GLASS COVERED SUGAR,PINK BAND........................    42.50
COSMOS GLASS CREAMER........................................    35.00
COSMOS GLASS LAMP...........................................    85.00
COSMOS LAMP BASE,MINIATURE
   10.00  TO...............................................    32.50
COSMOS LAMP BASE,PINK BAND..................................    32.50
COSMOS LAMP BASE WITH CHIMNEY,MINIATURE.....................    30.00
COSMOS MILK GLASS COVERED SUGAR.............................    42.00
COSMOS MILK GLASS MINIATURE LAMP,7IN. TALL..................    75.00
COSMOS MINIATURE BLUE BAND LAMP.............................    85.00
COSMOS PATTERN WHITE OPAQUE GLASS LAMP......................    75.00
COSMOS PINK BAND OPEN SUGAR.................................    25.00
COSMOS PINK BAND SALT & PEPPER..............................    48.00
COSMOS PINK BAND WATER PITCHER..............................    90.00
COSMOS PINK MINIATURE CONDIMENT SET,,SILVER PLATED MUSTARD
   SPOON & TRAY............................................    85.00
COSMOS TUMBLER,BLUE BAND....................................    20.00
COSMOS TUMBLER,PINK BAND....................................    25.00
COSMOS TYPE WARE PITCHER & 6 TUMBLERS.......................   150.00
   COUNTRY STORE,  SEE STORE...............................
```

CRACKLE GLASS was originally made by the Venetians but most of the ware
found today dates from the 1800's. The glass was heated, cooled, and refired
so that many small lines appeared inside the glass. It was made in many factories
in the United States and Europe.

```
RACKLE GLASS CELERY,FOOTED, TULIP TOP.......................    18.00
RACKLE GLASS COVERED WATER PITCHER & 4 HANDLED TUMBLERS,....    50.00
CRACKLE GLASS PERFUME TRAY,FREE FORM........................    12.00
CRACKLE GLASS PITCHER,5 IN.,BULBOUS,CLEAR REEDED APPLIED
   HANDLE..................................................    20.00
CRACKLE GLASS PITCHER,CRANBERRY.............................    80.00
CRACKLE GLASS SNUFF BOTTLE,GLAZE,MAN SNARING RABBIT,FOX.....    60.00
CRACKLE GLASS VASE,AMETHYST,BLOWN,7 IN. HIGH,RIPPLED TURNED
   DOWN TOP................................................     8.00
CRACKLE GLASS VASE,BLUE,SIGNED DEGUE BALL...................    52.00
CRACKLE GLASS WATER PITCHER,COVERED.........................    15.00
```

CRANBERRY GLASS is an almost transparent yellow-red glass. It resembles the
color of cranberry juice.

```
CRANBERRY GLASS BABY THUMBPRINT FINGER BOWL.................    15.00
CRANBERRY GLASS BABY THUMBPRINT PICKLE CASTOR WITH
   TONGS,ENAMEL FLOWERS....................................    95.00
CRANBERRY GLASS BABY THUMBPRINT TOOTHPICK HOLDER............    25.00
CRANBERRY GLASS BASE,PAIR,CRYSTAL,CAMEO CUT FLOWERS.........    45.00
CRANBERRY GLASS BASKET,3 IN. HIGH,RUFFLED EDGE,CLEAR APPLIED
   HANDLE..................................................    36.00
CRANBERRY GLASS BASKET,6 IN.,CLEAR RUFFLED EDGE,APPLIED
```

THORN HANDLE... 65.00
CRANBERRY GLASS BELL,................................... 35.00
CRANBERRY GLASS BELL,CORSET SHAPE,4 IN. TALL,CRYSTAL SPEAR
HANDLE... 15.00
CRANBERRY GLASS BOTTLE,COLOGNE,GOLD,PORCELAIN PORTRAIT...... 65.00
CRANBERRY GLASS BOTTLE,PERFUME,LACY DECORATED CORAL FLOWERS. 32.50
CRANBERRY GLASS BOWL,4 IN. DEEP,BELLTONE.................... 22.50
CRANBERRY GLASS BOWL,BRIDES,SWIRLED,METAL FRAME............. 33.00
CRANBERRY GLASS BOWL,COVERED,RIGAREE DECORATION IN CLEAR
AROUND MIDDLE.. 35.00
CRANBERRY GLASS BOWL,MILK,CLEAR FLINT FEET,WIDE LIP.......... 45.00
CRANBERRY GLASS BOWL,SILVER LID & SPOON.................... 23.50
CRANBERRY GLASS BOWL,TO OPALESCENT,SCALLOPED,WHEELING....... 22.50
CRANBERRY GLASS BOWL WITH FOOTED STAND,RUFFLED TOP,SILVER
PLATE STAND... 45.00
CRANBERRY GLASS BOX,CANDY,COVERED......................... 27.00
CRANBERRY GLASS BOX,COVERED,6 IN. BY 3 IN.................. 38.00
CRANBERRY GLASS BOX,COVERED,DECORATED WHITE ENAMELLED
FLOWERS & SCROLLS....................................... 25.00
CRANBERRY GLASS BOX,FOOTED,ENAMELLED...................... 85.00
CRANBERRY GLASS BOX,HINGED,DECORATED,3 APPLIED CLEAR SCROLL
FEET.. 50.00
CRANBERRY GLASS BOX,POWDER,HINGE TOP,MOTIF OF WHITE CUPIDS.. 85.00
CRANBERRY GLASS BOX,WHITE ENAMEL HINGED................... 35.00
CRANBERRY GLASS BRIDES BASKET,TO WHITE CENTER,SWIRLED
RUPPLED & FLUTED.. 45.00
CRANBERRY GLASS BUD VASE,ENAMEL DECOR,5 IN. HIGH........... 12.00
CRANBERRY GLASS BUD VASE,ENAMEL DECOR,BULBOUS SHAPE,5 IN.
HIGH.. 15.00
CRANBERRY GLASS BULLS EYE WATER PITCHER,RED................ 85.00
CRANBERRY GLASS BUTTER DISH,4 IN. HIGH.................... 35.00
CRANBERRY GLASS CANDY DISH,5 IN. TALL ON CRYSTAL PEDESTAL
BASE.. 14.00
CRANBERRY GLASS CASTOR SET,3 PIECE,SILVER FLAT IRON SHAPED
HOLDER.. 70.00
CRANBERRY GLASS CELERY,RUFFLED & FOOTED,7 IN. TALL.......... 22.50
CRANBERRY GLASS CHIMNEY.................................. 12.00
CRANBERRY GLASS CLEAR BLOCK SUGAR SHAKER.................. 40.00
CRANBERRY GLASS COMPOTE,CRACKLE TO CLEAR,METAL HOLDER....... 40.00
CRANBERRY GLASS COMPOTE,JELLY,CLEAR BASE,5 IN. DIAMETER..... 19.00
CRANBERRY GLASS COMPOTE,OVERSHOT RUFFLED SANDWICH........... 27.50
CRANBERRY GLASS COMPOTE,SATIN,10 IN. DIAMETER AT RUFFLED
TOP,HANDPAINT... 45.00
CRANBERRY GLASS CREAM & SUGAR,APPLIED CLEAR GLASS RIGAREE
FEET.. 45.00
CRANBERRY GLASS CREAM PITCHER,4 IN. TALL,APPLIED HANDLE..... 16.00
CRANBERRY GLASS CREAMER.................................. 30.00
CRANBERRY GLASS CREAMER,CLEAR HANDLE,SHELL FEET............ 17.50
CRANBERRY GLASS CREAMER,ROUGH PONTIL,CLEAR HANDLE & BASE,4
IN. TALL.. 25.00
CRANBERRY GLASS CREAMER,WHITE THREADED,8 CRIMPED
FEET,APPLIED HANDLE..................................... 18.75
CRANBERRY GLASS CRUET................................... 43.00
CRANBERRY GLASS CRUET,FLARED TOP,REEDED CLEAR APPLIED HANDLE 27.50
CRANBERRY GLASS DECANTER,12 IN.,GOLD FLOWER & MEDALLIONS.... 65.00
CRANBERRY GLASS DECANTER,BLOWN,GOLD DECORATED,MELON RIBBED.. 95.00
CRANBERRY GLASS DECANTER,BULBOUS,CLEAR APPLIED HANDLE....... 40.00
CRANBERRY GLASS DECANTER,CLEAR APPLIED SCALLOPED
HANDLE,RIBBED BODY...................................... 40.00
CRANBERRY GLASS DECANTER,CORDIAL,MARKED AUSTRIA,9 IN........ 37.00
CRANBERRY GLASS DECANTER,OVERLAY,FLUTED CUTTING............ 60.00
CRANBERRY GLASS DECANTER,PAIR............................ 150.00
CRANBERRY GLASS DECANTER,PAIR,MELON RIBBED,7 IN. HIGH....... 40.00
CRANBERRY GLASS DELAWARE BERRY BOWL,OVAL,BRIGHT GOLD........ 18.00
CRANBERRY GLASS DELAWARE BOWL,8 IN. ROUND,GOLD............. 40.00

CRANBERRY GLASS DELAWARE BOWL,CENTER,ROUND.................. 29.00
CRANBERRY GLASS DELAWARE BOWL IN SILVER BASKET.............. 35.00
CRANBERRY GLASS DELAWARE SAUCE DISH........................ 20.00
CRANBERRY GLASS DELAWARE SAUCE,ROUND,GOLD.................. 15.00
CRANBERRY GLASS DELAWARE TOOTHPICK HOLDER.................. 35.00
CRANBERRY GLASS DIAGONAL DESIGN SYRUP,BULBOUS,CLEAR SPPLIED
HANDLE... 36.50
CRANBERRY GLASS DIAMOND PATTERN TOOTHPICK HOLDER,OVERLAY.... 12.00
CRANBERRY GLASS DIAMOND QUILTED ROSE BOWL,OPALESCENT........ 26.50
CRANBERRY GLASS DIAMOND QUILTED WATER PITCHER,BULBOUS WITH
SQUARE MOUTH.. 65.00
CRANBERRY GLASS DISH,CANDY,CLEAR PEDESTAL.................. 23.00
CRANBERRY GLASS DRAPE PATTERN ROSE BOWL,VASELINE APPLIED
PETALS.. 25.00
CRANBERRY GLASS DRESSER TRAY,DECORATED ENAMELLED
FLORALS,GOLD TRIM... 27.50
CRANBERRY GLASS EPERGNE,3 LILIES,CLEAR GLASS TRIM........... 155.00
CRANBERRY GLASS EPERGNE,CLEAR TO WHITE TO CRANBERRY,BRASS
FITTINGS.. 165.00
CRANBERRY GLASS EPERGNE,CRIMPED TOP & LOWER BOWL,3 LILIES... 110.00
CRANBERRY GLASS EPERGNE,OPALESCENT,3 TRUMPET VASES PLUS
CENTER.. 165.00
CRANBERRY GLASS EPERGNE,PEWTER 3 GRIFFIN HOLDER............. 37.50
CRANBERRY GLASS EPERGNE,THREADED,3 FLOWER HOLDERS........... 65.00
CRANBERRY GLASS EPERGNE,THREE LILY,FLUTED EDGES,SWIRLED &
DECORATED... 115.00
CRANBERRY GLASS EPERGNE,WHITE OVERLAY,RUFFLED.............. 65.00
CRANBERRY GLASS FINGER BOWL,BELLTONE...................... 14.00
CRANBERRY GLASS FINGER BOWL ON PLATE...................... 50.00
CRANBERRY GLASS FRUIT
BOWL,OVERLAY,PEDESTAL,CANDLESTICKS,TEARDROP,PAIR........... 32.50
CRANBERRY GLASS GAS SHADE................................. 25.00
CRANBERRY GLASS GAS SHADE,OPALESCENT STRIPES.............. 10.00
CRANBERRY GLASS GLASS,JUICE,ROUND BOTTOM.................. 7.00
CRANBERRY GLASS GLASS,WINE
10.00 TO... 15.00
CRANBERRY GLASS HOBNAIL BASKET,CLEAR APPLIED HANDLE......... 49.50
CRANBERRY GLASS HOBNAIL HANGING LAMP,BRASS FONT............. 285.00
CRANBERRY GLASS HOBNAIL PITCHER,BLOWN,5 IN................. 32.00
CRANBERRY GLASS HOBNAIL PITCHER,MINIATURE,OPALESCENT........ 95.00
CRANBERRY GLASS HOBNAIL WITH OPALESCENCE ROSE BOWL & FLOWER
BASKET.. 40.00
CRANBERRY GLASS HONEYCOMB DISH,CHEESE,COVERED,CLEAR KNOB.... 125.00
CRANBERRY GLASS INKWELL,HINGED BRASS PETAL SHAPE COVER...... 25.00
CRANBERRY GLASS INSERT PICKLE CASTOR...................... 65.00
CRANBERRY GLASS INVERTED BULLS EYE FLOWER BOWL,RUFFLED TOP.. 25.00
CRANBERRY GLASS INVERTED MELON RIBS SUGAR SHAKER........... 51.00
CRANBERRY GLASS INVERTED THUMBPRINT BOTTLE,BARBER,SATIN
FINISH.. 24.00
CRANBERRY GLASS INVERTED THUMBPRINT COMPOTE,COVERED,OVERLAY. 35.00
CRANBERRY GLASS INVERTED THUMBPRINT CREAMER............... 55.00
CRANBERRY GLASS INVERTED THUMBPRINT FINGER BOWL........... 16.50
CRANBERRY GLASS INVERTED THUMBPRINT NAPPY,6 IN............ 12.00
CRANBERRY GLASS INVERTED THUMBPRINT PICKLE CASTOR.......... 60.00
CRANBERRY GLASS INVERTED THUMBPRINT PICKLE CASTOR,ENAMELED
FLOWERS... 70.00
CRANBERRY GLASS INVERTED THUMBPRINT PITCHER,CLEAR APPLIED
HANDLE 72.50
CRANBERRY GLASS INVERTED THUMBPRINT SUGAR BOWL WITH STAND
AND COVER... 35.00
CRANBERRY GLASS INVERTED THUMBPRINT SUGAR IN SILVER PLATE
FOOTED HOLDER... 95.00
CRANBERRY GLASS INVERTED THUMBPRINT SUGAR SHAKER........... 22.50
CRANBERRY GLASS INVERTED THUMBPRINT TUMBLER
15.00 TO... 20.00

```
CRANBERRY GLASS INVERTED THUMBPRINT TUMBLER,2...............    13.00
CRANBERRY GLASS INVERTED THUMBPRINT VASE,10 IN. HIGH.........    55.00
CRANBERRY GLASS INVERTED THUMBPRINT VASE,WHITE,ROUND,4 IN...    18.00
CRANBERRY GLASS INVERTED THUMBPRINT WATER PITCHER,AMBER
 APPLIED HANDLE.............................................    85.00
CRANBERRY GLASS INVERTED THUMBPRINT WATER PITCHER,BULBOUS...    40.00
CRANBERRY GLASS JAM JAR,APPLE SHAPE WITH SILVER PLATED COVER    15.00
CRANBERRY GLASS JAR,CANDY,CLEAR APPLIED KNOB ON LID,PAIR....    40.00
CRANBERRY GLASS JAR,PICKLE,EMBOSSED LEAF,PANELLED
 BODY,SILVER LID...........................................    50.00
CRANBERRY GLASS LIGHT SHADE,MATCHING PAIR,FROSTED FLOWERS...    15.00
CRANBERRY GLASS MASTER SALT,3 FOOTED.......................    18.50
CRANBERRY GLASS MILK PITCHER,TANKARD SHAPE,CLEAR APPLIED
 HANDLE....................................................    30.00
CRANBERRY GLASS MUFFINEER..................................    23.00
CRANBERRY GLASS MUFFINEER,LACY TOP.........................    25.00
CRANBERRY GLASS MUFFINEER,OPAL SWIRL.......................    45.00
CRANBERRY GLASS MUFFINEER,PANELED..........................    38.00
CRANBERRY GLASS MUFFINEER,PANELED CUT......................    27.50
CRANBERRY GLASS MUFFINEER,PANELED,SILVER TOP...............    20.00
CRANBERRY GLASS MUFFINEER,SILVER TOP.......................    32.00
CRANBERRY GLASS MUFFINEER,RIBBED,OPALESCENT................    29.50
CRANBERRY GLASS MUG,FOOTED,HANDLED.........................    14.00
CRANBERRY GLASS MUG,GOLD DECORATION TOP & BASE CLEAT HANDLE.    52.00
CRANBERRY GLASS MUSTARD POT,PANELLED,SILVER LID............    18.00
CRANBERRY GLASS NAILSEA BOWL,FOOTED,WHITE VERRE MOIRE,3
 CAMPHOR FEET..............................................    97.50
CRANBERRY GLASS NAILSEA ROLLING PIN........................    58.00
CRANBERRY GLASS OPAL STRIPE TOOTHPICK HOLDER...............    15.00
CRANBERRY GLASS OPALESCENT SWIRL WITH COIN DOT SUGAR SHAKER.    27.50
CRANBERRY GLASS PATCH BOX,DECORATED IN ENAMEL..............    23.00
CRANBERRY GLASS PEG LAMP FONT,GOLD FLORAL DECOR............    20.00
CRANBERRY GLASS PICKLE CASTOR,APPLIED FINIAL...............    42.00
CRANBERRY GLASS PICKLE CASTOR INSERT,HAND ENAMELED FLOWERS &
 LEAVES....................................................    28.00
CRANBERRY GLASS PITCHER & 4 TUMBLERS.......................    60.00
CRANBERRY GLASS PITCHER,3 IN. HIGH,CLEAR GLASS HANDLE......    16.00
CRANBERRY GLASS PITCHER,5 IN.,ROSE-AMBER,ENAMEL STORKS &
 LEAVES....................................................    85.00
CRANBERRY GLASS PITCHER,11 IN. TALL,ENAMEL DECORATED.......    45.00
CRANBERRY GLASS PITCHER,CLEAR REEDED HANDLE
 25.00   TO...............................................    50.00
CRANBERRY GLASS PITCHER,FLUTED RIM.........................    19.00
CRANBERRY GLASS PITCHER,GOLD DECORATION....................    29.50
CRANBERRY GLASS PITCHER,REEDED APPLIED HANDLE,PONTIL RIBBED.    30.00
CRANBERRY GLASS PITCHER,WATER,BULBOUS SHAPE,CLEAR APPLIED
 HANDLE....................................................    42.50
CRANBERRY GLASS PITCHER,WATER,CLEAR APPLIED HANDLE,FLUTED
 TOP.......................................................    47.50
CRANBERRY GLASS PITCHER,WATER,TO CLEAR,OPALESCENT SMOKEY
 SWIRLS....................................................    32.50
CRANBERRY GLASS PITCHER,WATER WITH 3 TUMBLERS,ENAMELED
 FLOWERS...................................................    70.00
CRANBERRY GLASS POINTED HOBNAIL FAIRY LAMP.................    30.00
CRANBERRY GLASS PUNCH BOWL,COVERED,SPACE FOR LADLE,GILDED &
 ENAMELED,.................................................   175.00
CRANBERRY GLASS ROSE BOWL..................................    42.00
CRANBERRY GLASS ROSE BOWL,3 IN.............................    22.50
CRANBERRY GLASS ROSE BOWL ON 3 CLEAR GLASS FEET............    18.50
CRANBERRY GLASS ROYAL IVY FROSTED TOOTHPICK................    40.00
CRANBERRY GLASS ROYAL IVY SAUCE,FLAT.......................    12.50
CRANBERRY GLASS ROYAL IVY SUGAR SHAKER.....................    32.50
CRANBERRY GLASS SALT & PEPPER,ENAMEL DECOR.................    15.00
CRANBERRY GLASS SALT & PEPPER SHAKERS,ENAMEL FLOWERS.......    39.50
CRANBERRY GLASS SALT CUP,FLASHED GOLD,APPLIED BISQUE PANSIES    16.00
```

```
CRANBERRY GLASS SALT,OPEN,2 APPLIED PETAL BANDS,SILVER FRAME    36.00
CRANBERRY GLASS SALT,OPEN,4 CRYSTAL FEET,SILVER RIM.........    18.50
CRANBERRY GLASS SALT,ROUND.................................     6.00
CRANBERRY GLASS SALT SHAKER,STERLING TOP
  14.50  TO................................................    30.00
CRANBERRY GLASS SET,MUSTARD POT,SALT,PAPPER & SILVER SPOON..    45.00
CRANBERRY GLASS SHADE,MINIATURE,SWIRLED,CUFF ON TOP.........    15.00
CRANBERRY GLASS SPANISH LACE TUMBLER.......................     9.50
CRANBERRY GLASS SUGAR SET ON LACY SILVER HOLDER............    22.50
CRANBERRY GLASS SUGAR SHAKER...............................    30.00
CRANBERRY GLASS SUGAR SHAKER,6 IN. HIGH....................    35.00
CRANBERRY GLASS SUGAR SHAKER,BEVELED CUT PANELS............    39.50
CRANBERRY GLASS SUGAR SHAKER,CUT GLASS,SILVER PLATED TOP,5
  IN. TALL.................................................    22.50
CRANBERRY GLASS SUGAR SHAKER,EXPANDED DIAMOND QUILTED......    38.50
CRANBERRY GLASS SUGAR SHAKER,PANELED,SILVER DOME...........    19.00
CRANBERRY GLASS SUGAR SHAKER,SILVER DOMED TOP..............    22.50
CRANBERRY GLASS SUGAR SHAKER,TO CLEAR......................    30.00
CRANBERRY GLASS SWEETMEAT DISH,2 PIECE,CLEAR GLASS KNOB ON
  TOP.....................................................     22.50
CRANBERRY GLASS SWIRLED PATTERN,COMPOTE ON LOW CLEAR
  STANDARDS................................................    30.00
CRANBERRY GLASS THUMBPRINT BOWL,ENAMEL DECORATIONS,9 IN.....   48.00
CRANBERRY GLASS THUMBPRINT CASTOR SET,5 BOTTLES IN PEWTER
  FRAME....................................................    50.00
CRANBERRY GLASS THUMBPRINT PICKLE CASTOR,SILVER FRAME.......   65.00
CRANBERRY GLASS THUMBPRINT SYRUP PITCHER,PEWTER COVER.......   35.00
CRANBERRY GLASS THUMBPRINT TUMBLER,SET OF 8.................   64.00
CRANBERRY GLASS TUMBLE-UP..................................    25.00
CRANBERRY GLASS TUMBLER,3 IN. TALL,COIN GOLD DECORATION OF
  TULIPS...................................................     9.00
CRANBERRY GLASS TUMBLER,DECORATED GOLD ENCRUSTED FLOWERS....   32.50
CRANBERRY GLASS TUMBLER,ENAMEL DECORATED...................     8.50
CRANBERRY GLASS TUMBLER,ENAMEL FLOWER DECOR.................   22.00
CRANBERRY GLASS TUMBLER,FRUIT JUICE........................     7.50
CRANBERRY GLASS TUMBLER,GOLD DECORATION....................    12.50
CRANBERRY GLASS TUMBLER,OPAQUE SWIRL.......................     9.50
CRANBERRY GLASS TUMBLER,SET OF 6,OPALESCENT COIN SPOT.......   60.00
CRANBERRY GLASS TUMBLER,STERLING CAPPED TRIM...............    17.00
CRANBERRY GLASS VASE,6 IN.,CLIMBING ELVES & FOLIAGE IN
  WHITE,PAIR...............................................    65.00
CRANBERRY GLASS VASE,8 IN..................................    25.00
CRANBERRY GLASS VASE,10 IN.,SPIRAL OF CLEAR GLASS
  ENCIRCLING,5 FEET........................................    25.00
CRANBERRY GLASS VASE,11 IN.,GOLD ENAMELLED PLOWERS & BERRIES   27.50
CRANBERRY GLASS VASE,16 IN.................................    60.00
CRANBERRY GLASS VASE,BLUE,ENAMELLED APPLE BLOSSOMS &
  STEMS,SIGNED.............................................    46.00
CRANBERRY GLASS VASE,CLEAR SHELL FEET,PAIR.................    45.00
CRANBERRY GLASS VASE,ENAMEL................................    25.00
CRANBERRY GLASS VASE,FLORAL PATTERN IN YELLOW ENAMEL........   23.00
CRANBERRY GLASS VASE,FLUTED................................    35.00
CRANBERRY GLASS VASE,GOLD FLOWERS,LEAVES,VINES,PEDESTAL BASE   75.00
CRANBERRY GLASS VASE,GOLD LEAVES,DOTS,OVAL PORCELAIN
  PORTRAITS,PAIR..........................................    185.00
CRANBERRY GLASS VASE,GOLD TRIM.............................    42.00
CRANBERRY GLASS VASE,JACK-IN-PULPIT........................    45.00
CRANBERRY GLASS VASE,JACK-IN-PULPIT,8 IN. TALL,CRYSTAL BASE.   23.00
CRANBERRY GLASS VASE,JACK-IN-PULPIT,10 IN. HIGH,APPLIED
  CRYSTAL RIBBON...........................................    25.00
CRANBERRY GLASS VASE,JACK-IN-PULPIT,10 IN. TALL,CRIMPED
  RUFFLED TOP..............................................    25.00
CRANBERRY GLASS VASE,JACK-IN-PULPIT,13 IN. TALL............    35.00
CRANBERRY GLASS VASE,JACK-IN-PULPIT,CLEAR AT BASE TO
  CRANBERRY AT TOP,2.......................................    48.00
```

CRANBERRY GLASS VASE,JACK-IN-PULPIT,CLEAR FOOT WITH APPLIED
TRIM... 17.50
CRANBERRY GLASS VASE,JACK-IN-PULPIT,RIPPLED TOP,PAIR........ 35.00
CRANBERRY GLASS VASE,PANELED GLASS,ENAMELED SPRAY OF
FLOWERS,WHITE,BLUE..................................... 50.00
CRANBERRY GLASS VASE,RUFFLED,FLARED TOP WITH ENAMELED
FLOWERS... 16.00
CRANBERRY GLASS VASE WITH APPLIED CLEAR TRIM,9 IN9......... 18.50
CRANBERRY GLASS VASES,PAIR,DECORATED WHITE ENAMELLED
FLORAL,PEDESTAL....................................... 67.50
CRANBERRY GLASS WATER PITCHER,ENAMEL FLOWERS............... 70.00
CRANBERRY GLASS WATER PITCHER,PANELED,APPLIED CLEAR RIBBED
HANDLE.. 70.00
CRANBERRY GLASS WATER SET,TANKARD PITCHER,ENAMEL DECOR..... 115.00
CRANBERRY GLASS WINE BOTTLE WITH STOPPER,SLICK GROUND PONTIL 23.50
CRANBERRY GLASS WINE CRUET,CLEAR HANDLE & STOPPER.......... 38.00
CRANBERRY GLASS WINE DECANTER WITH HANDLE,MARY GREGORY
DECORATION.. 47.50
CRANBERRY GLASS WINE GLASS,SET OF 6,CLEAR STEMS............ 60.00
CRANBERRY GLASS WINES,8,ON CRANBERRY TRAY................. 190.00

*CREAMWARE OR QUEENSWARE was developed by Josiah Wedgwood about
1765. It is a cream-colored earthenware that has been copied by many factories.*
CREAMWARE JUG,RIBBED BODY,2 RIBBED , STRAP HANDLES.......... 55.00
CREAMWARE SET OF 4 PLATES,ROSE & LEAF
SPRAYS,LUSTER,BASKETWEAVE............................... 90.00

*CROESUS GLASS is a special pattern of pressed glass made about 1897. It was
made in clear glass, emerald green, or amethyst. Each piece was decorated
with gold.*
CROESUS GREEN 4 PIECE TABLE SET.............................. 220.00
CROESUS GREEN 5 PIECE BERRY SET............................. 135.00
CROESUS GREEN BOWL & 4 SAUCES,ROUND,8 IN.................... 150.00
CROESUS GREEN BOWL,FOOTED,WITH 2 FOOTED BERRY BOWLS......... 60.00
CROESUS GREEN BUTTER DISH................................... 57.50
CROESUS GREEN BUTTERDISH,SCALLOPED.......................... 35.00
CROESUS GREEN BUTTER,SUGAR,CREAMER & SPOONER................ 217.00
CROESUS GREEN CREAMER....................................... 45.00
CROESUS GREEN CRUET WITH STOPPER............................ 77.00
CROESUS GREEN PICKLE.. 15.00
CROESUS GREEN SAUCE... 25.00
CROESUS GREEN SPOONER....................................... 30.00
CROESUS GREEN SUGAR BOWL,COVERED............................ 60.01-
CROESUS GREEN TANKARD PITCHER,12 IN. HIGH................... 110.00
CROESUS GREEN TOOTHPICK..................................... 49.00
CROESUS GREEN TOOTHPICK,GOLD................................ 38.50
CROESUS GREEN TUMBLER
22.00 TO... 35.00
CROESUS GREEN TUMBLER,GOLD.................................. 35.00
CROESUS GREEN TUMBLERS,PAIR................................. 57.50
CROESUS GREEN WATER PITCHER................................. 100.00
CROESUS GREEN WATER SET WITH 4 TUMBLERS..................... 150.00
CROESUS PLATE,EMERALD GREEN ON 3 FEET....................... 17.50
CROESUS PURPLE BERRY BOWL................................... 20.00
CROESUS PURPLE BERRY SET,BOWL & 4 DISHES.................... 85.00
CROESUS PURPLE JELLY COMPOTE................................ 75.00
CROESUS PURPLE SAUCE.. 30.00
CROESUS PURPLE SPOONER...................................... 47.50
CROESUS,PURPLE,SPOONER,GOLD................................. 75.00
CROESUS,PURPLE SPOONER WITH GOLD,FOOTED..................... 90.00
CROESUS PURPLE TOOTHPICK HOLDER............................. 45.00
CROESUS,PURPLE,VINEGAR CRUET,SALT & PEPPERS................. 140.00
CROESUS SPOONER,GREEN & GOLD................................ 28.00
CROESUS SUGAR,GOLD.. 62.00

CROWN DERBY is the nickname given to the works of the Royal Crown Derby factory, which began working in England in 1859. An earlier and more famous English Derby factory existed from 1750 to 1848. The two factories were not related. Most of the porcelain found today with Derby mark is the work of the later Derby factory.

```
CROWN DERBY, SEE ALSO ROYAL CROWN DERBY.................
CROWN DERBY CHOCOLATE CUP.......................................   14.50
CROWN DERBY DESSERT PLATE.......................................   12.50
CROWN DERBY SET OF 3 URNS CIRCA 1780,ENGLISH,.................1,250.00
```

CROWN MILANO GLASS was made by Frederick Shirley about 1890. It had a plain biscuit color with a satin finish. It was decorated with flowers, and often had large gold scrolls.

```
CROWN MILANO COOKIE JAR,LID & SILVER RIM,SIGNED..............   325.00
CROWN MILANO DECORATED CRACKER JAR..........................   350.00
CROWN MILANO JARDINIERE,BEIGE BACKGROUND,SIGNED,OAK LEAVES..   210.00
CROWN MILANO MELON RIBBED PITCHER,FLOWER & LEAF IN GOLD.....   245.00
CROWN MILANO PAIR VASES,GOLD LEAVES & FLOWERS...............   390.00
CROWN MILANO RIBBED BURMESE COLOUR SALT SHAKER..............    18.00
CROWN MILANO SALT SHAKER,TOMATO TYPE,MELON RIB,PEWTER TOP...    22.50
CROWN MILANO SIGNED & NUMBERED ROUND SCALLOPED EDGE
  VASE,FLOWERS..............................................   500.00
CROWN MILANO SIGNED TRI-CORNERED BRIDES BASKET,CORN FLOWER
  DECOR....................................................   345.00
CROWN MILANO VASE,6 IN. H.,6 IN. ACROSS....................   345.00
  CRUET, SEE ALSO OTHER SECTIONS, AMBER, PRESSED GLASS,
  ETC....................................................
```

CRUETS of glass or porcelain were made to hold vinegar or oil. They were especially popular during Victorian times.

```
CRUET 1 QUARTER PINT VINEGAR,SWIRL & LOOP PATTERN...........    5.50
CRUET,4-PIECE HICKMAN MINIATURE SET.........................   18.00
CRUET,10 IN. CRANBERRY BULBOUS,STAR CUT BASE................   48.00
CRUET,AMBER DEWEY
  28.00 TO................................................   32.00
CRUET,AMBER GLASS,8 IN. TALL,APPLIED AMBER HANDLE...........   20.00
CRUET,AMBER GLASS PANELLED SQUARE BODY......................   22.00
CRUET,AMBER WITH CLEAR CUT GLASS............................   45.00
CRUET,AMETHYST WITH SILVER TEA POT STYLE....................    8.50
CRUET,APPLE GREEN BLOWN VINEGAR.............................    5.00
CRUET,ART GLASS IN MILLEFIORE,COLORED CANDY CANES...........   65.00
CRUET,BAVARIA CHINA,GREEN WITH PINK ROSES...................   21.50
CRUET,BEADED GRAPE.........................................   12.50
CRUET,BLOCK PATTERN........................................    6.00
CRUET,BLOWN MOLDED CLEAR THOUSAND EYE WITH STOPPER.........   50.00
CRUET,BLOWN PITTSBURGH 16 RIB VINEGAR......................   50.00
CRUET,BLUE GLASS..........................................   40.00
CRUET,BLUE WITH FERN PATTERN,CLEAR STOPPER.................   28.50
CRUET,BLUE PANEL & STAR,2 SHAKERS & TRAY...................   69.50
CRUET,BOHEMIAN RUBY GLASS,DEER,CASTLE......................   20.00
CRUET,BROKEN COLUMN.......................................   25.00
CRUET,BUCKINGHAM PATTERN..................................    6.75
CRUET,CANARY DEWEY.......................................   32.00
CRUET,CHAMPAGNE-COLOURED SATIN WITH OVERLAY ENAMEL DECOR....   45.00
CRUET,CHECKERBOARD VINEGAR.................................   15.00
CRUET,CHINA,RED ROSES.....................................   15.00
CRUET,CLEAR CUBE WITH FAN PATTERN,TULIP SHAPED STOPPER.....   10.00
CRUET,CLEAR DAISY & BUTTON.................................   20.00
CRUET,CLEAR GLASS.........................................    8.00
CRUET,CLEAR GLASS HOBNAIL..................................    6.00
CRUET,CLEAR GLASS RIBBED PATTERN,APPLIED HANDLE.............    7.50
CRUET,CLEAR PANELED DAISY & BUTTON.........................   13.00
CRUET,CLEAR TO PEARL OPALESCENT,HOBNAIL....................   10.00
CRUET,CRANBERRY,6 IN. TALL,BLOWN STOPPER...................   30.00
```

```
CRUET,CRANBERRY INVERTED THUMBPRINT,CLEAR HANDLE............    45.00
CRUET,CRANBERRY WITH BLUE,WHITE & YELLOW ENAMELING..........    38.50
CRUET,CRYSTAL,CUT & ETCHED FLOWERS,APPLIED HANDLES,PAIR.....    47.00
CRUET,CUSTARD GLASS........................................    36.50
CRUET,CUSTARD GLASS,FLOWER PATTERN.........................    45.00
CRUET,CUT GLASS............................................    16.00
CRUET,CUT GLASS,DIAMOND POINT & FAN........................    15.00
CRUET,CUT GLASS,DIAMOND POINT..............................    13.00
CRUET,CUT GLASS,PINWHEELS..................................    15.00
CRUET,CUT GLASS SIGNED HOARE,7 IN. TALL....................    27.50
CRUET,CUT IN FLASHED PATTERN WITH FANS.....................    35.00
CRUET,CUT LOG,MATCHING STOPPER.............................    19.50
CRUET DATED 1891,RUBY BOHEMIAN GLASS EGGERMAN PATTERN,DEER &
  CASTLE...................................................    17.50
CRUET,DECORATED CRANBERRY,CLEAR REEDED APPLIED HANDLE.......    50.00
CRUET,ELECTRIC BLUE,OPAQUE BASE & TOP OF HANDLE,FLEUR DE LIS    25.00
CRUET,EMERALD GREEN GLASS,MATCHING STOPPER,LOUIS XV,GOLD ON
  FLOWERS..................................................    40.00
CRUET,END OF DAY,BLUE BLOWN STOPPER........................    38.00
CRUET,FACETED STOPPER,VIRGINIA,GALLOWAY....................     8.50
CRUET,FLUTED SCROLLS OF JACKSON............................    30.00
CRUET,FOSTORIA VINEGAR ETCHED..............................    13.75
CRUET,FROSTED BAND WITH PINK FLOWERS.......................    18.00
CRUET,FROSTED CIRCLE VINEGAR...............................    15.00
CRUET,FROSTED OIL..........................................     1.25
CRUET,GLASS HEISEY.........................................     3.50
CRUET,GREEN GLASS,SILVER OVERLAY,MATCHING STOPPER...........    30.00
CRUET,GREEN PRESSED BLOWN,CLEAR STOPPER,PAIR,,8 SIDED.......    25.00
CRUET,GREEN,TEAPOT SHAPE,SILVER............................    16.50
CRUET,HANDPAINTED,GOLD GLAZED ON WHITE,SIGNED JOSEPHINE
  ROYER....................................................    15.00
CRUET,HEART WITH THUMBPRINT................................    24.50
CRUET,HOBNAIL..............................................     9.50
CRUET,INTERLOCKING HEARTS,STERLING SILVER OVERLAY...........    25.00
CRUET,INVERTED PANEL,6 IN.,CLEAR...........................     5.50
CRUET,IVORINA VERDE,GOLD,CLEAR.............................    48.00
CRUET,MILLEFIORI VINEGAR,DECORATED CAMPHOR STOPPER,DATED
  1848.....................................................   165.00
CRUET,OLIVE AMBER VINEGAR,CLEAR TWISTED HANDLE.............    32.50
CRUET,OLIVE GREEN,4 SIDES,SWIRL PATTERN,REEDED
  HANDLE,MATCHING STOPPER...................................    40.00
CRUET,OPALINE,APPLIED LEAVES & FLOWERS.....................    42.00
CRUET,PAIR CRANBERRY,10 IN. TALL,..........................    70.00
CRUET,PAIR DIAMOND & SUNBURST..............................    18.00
CRUET,PAIR IN ORNATE FOOTED STAND WITH HANDLE,.............     7.00
CRUET,PANELED THISTLE......................................     9.00
CRUET,PATTERN GLASS,BUTTERFLIES,APPLIED HANDLE.............     3.50
CRUET,PATTERN GLASS,CLEAR,CROSS BAR........................    13.50
CRUET,PEACOCK FEATHER
  6.50   TO.................................................    15.00
CRUET,PEARLIZED AMERICAN CRANBERRY VINEGAR,GOLD FLORAL,ART
  NOUVEAU...................................................    47.50
CRUET,PINK DIAMOND QUILTED MOTHER OF PEARL,CAMPHOR HANDLE...    55.00
CRUET,PRESSED GLASS WITH STOPPER...........................     8.00
CRUET,RIBBON GLASS PINK....................................    28.50
CRUET,ROYAL BLUE WITH AMBER HANDLE.........................    18.00
CRUET,RUBY BOHEMIAN GLASS..................................    20.00
CRUET,SAPPHIRE BLUE GLASS,AMBER CUT & FACETED STOPPER.......    23.00
CRUET SET,BOHEMIAN GLASS,3 CAVALIER MENS HEADS ON FRAME &
  HANDLE...................................................   175.00
CRUET SIGNED E GALLE NANCY,HANDPAINTED,FLORALS,OVOID SHAPE..   110.00
CRUET,SILVER DEPOSIT WITH STOPPER..........................    10.50
CRUET,TEAPOT,SAPPHIRE BLUE WITH SILVER DEPOSIT DECOR........    42.50
CRUET,THISTLE PATTERN......................................     8.50
CRUET,VASELINE GLASS VINEGAR...............................    10.00
```

CRUET,VICTORIAN GIRANDOLE WITH HAND CUT PRISMS............... 42.50
CRUET,VINEGAR,2-MOLD-BLOWN,SQUARE............................ 7.00
CRUET,VINEGAR,AMBER,BLUE ROPE-TWIST HANDLE................... 27.50
CRUET,VINEGAR,AMBER,WITH ENAMEL FLOWERS,SAPPHIRE BLUE HANDLE 27.50
CRUET,VINEGAR,AQUA-BLUE,AMBER HANDLE......................... 24.00
CRUET,VINEGAR,GOLDEN AMBER WITH ENAMEL FLOWERS,RIBBED HANDLE 27.50
CRUET,VINEGAR,RUBY BOHEMAIN GLASS,INTAGLIO CUT & FROSTED
   FLORAL... 37.50
CRUET,WINE.TURQUOISE & OVAL SHAPE,AMBER FACET CUT STOPPER... 37.50

CUP PLATES are small glass or china plates that held the cup while a gentleman
of the mid-nineteenth century drank his coffee or tea from the saucer. The most
famous cup plates were made of glass at the Boston and Sandwich factory
located in Massachusetts.
CUP PLATE EAGLE... 65.00
CUP PLATE,HISTORICAL,BLUE.................................. 65.00
CUP PLATE,IMPRESSED ANDREW JACKSON,SEPIA................... 135.00

CURRIER AND IVES made the famous American lithographs marked with their
name from 1857 to 1907.
CURRIER & IVES PLATE,PORCELAIN,LITHOGRAPH.................. 10.00
   CURRIER AND IVES PRESSED GLASS PATTERN, SEE PRESSED
GLASS...
CURRIER & IVES PRINT,2 LITTLE FRAID CATS.................. 18.00
CURRIER & IVES PRINT,1874 ROCK OF AGES,FRAMED............. 5.00
CURRIER & IVES PRINT,BLACK & WHITE LITTLE NELLIE.......... 15.00
CURRIER & IVES PRINT,BYRON IN HIGHLANDS................... 15.00
CURRIER & IVES PRINT,COLOURED OF BOSTON PUBLIC GARDEN 1869.. 12.00
CURRIER & IVES PRINT,COMIC MINSTREL,HORSE-RACE............. 250.00
CURRIER & IVES PRINT,EASTERN BEAUTY,COLOURED,FRAMED........ 20.00
CURRIER & IVES PRINT,HOMEWARD BOUND....................... 30.00
CURRIER & IVES PRINT LITTLE GIRL ,FRAMED................. 9.50
CURRIER & IVES PRINT,LITTLE MANLY,FRAMED.................. 16.50
CURRIER & IVES PRINT,MARYS LITTLE LAMB................... 15.00
CURRIER & IVES PRINT,MISCHIEVOUS LITTLE KITTIE,FRAMED..... 39.50
CURRIER & IVES PRINT,MORNING IN THE WOODS................. 295.00
CURRIER & IVES PRINT,MY PONY & DOG....................... 20.00
CURRIER & IVES PRINT,NOAHS ARK,COLOURED,FRAMED........... 42.00
CURRIER & IVES PRINT,NORTHERN BEAUTY,COLOURED,FRAMED...... 20.00
CURRIER & IVES PRINT,ON THE COAST OF CALIFORNIA,FRAMED.... 27.50
CURRIER & IVES PRINT,PLACID LAKE,ADIRONDACKS.............. 38.00
CURRIER & IVES PRINT,PLAYFUL FAMILY,DOG.................. 10.00
CURRIER & IVES PRINT,SIGNED FRAMED GENERAL TOM THUMB
   PORTRAIT,COLOURED....................................... 18.00
CURRIER & IVES PRINT,STEAMER RHODE ISLAND,FOLIO.......... 165.00
CURRIER & IVES PRINT,ST.PATRICK.......................... 15.00
CURRIER & IVES PRINT,THE BATTLE OF THE
   WILDERNESS,COLOURED,FRAMED.............................. 42.00
CURRIER & IVES PRINT,THE FAVOURITE HORSE................. 20.00
CURRIER & IVES PRINT,THE GERMAN BEAUTY,UNDER GLASS IN FRAME. 25.00
CURRIER & IVES PRINT,THE LITTLE BROTHER,FRAMED........... 15.00
CURRIER & IVES PRINT,THE TROTTING QUEEN MAUD S
   RECORD,COLOURED,FRAMED.................................. 50.00
CURRIER & IVES PRINT,TREE OF LIFE,CHRISTMAS.............. 15.00
CURRIER & IVES PRINT,WOODCOCK SHOOTING................... 145.00

CUSTARD GLASS is an opaque glass sometimes known as buttermilk glass. It
was first made after 1886 at the La Belle Glass Works, Bridgeport, Ohio.
CUSTARD GLASS ALBA MUSTARD............................... 15.00
CUSTARD GLASS ALBA SALT & PEPPER........................ 30.00
CUSTARD GLASS ARGONAUT SHELL BERRY,OVAL................. 135.00
CUSTARD GLASS ARGONAUT SHELL COVERED SUGAR.............. 100.00
CUSTARD GLASS ARGONAUT SHELL CREAMER
   27.50 TO.. 85.00
CUSTARD GLASS ARGONAUT SHELL JELLY COMPOTE WITH SEAWEED..... 80.00

```
CUSTARD GLASS ARGONAUT SHELL OVAL BERRY BOWL..............    135.00
CUSTARD GLASS ARGONAUT SHELL SAUCE........................     35.00
CUSTARD GLASS ARGONAUT SHELL SIGNED NORTHWOOD OVAL
   FRUIT,FOOTED..........................................    132.00
CUSTARD GLASS ARGONAUT SHELL SUGAR........................     85.00
CUSTARD GLASS ARGONAUT SHELL SPOONER,WITH GOLD............     36.00
CUSTARD GLASS ARGONAUT SHELL TUMBLER......................     15.00
CUSTARD GLASS ARGONAUT SPOONER............................     65.00
CUSTARD GLASS BABY THUMBPRINT CUP WITH BEADING............      5.00
CUSTARD GLASS BASKET WITH LOOP HANDLE,HONEYCOMB & DAISY...     48.00
CUSTARD GLASS BEADED CABLE ROSE BOWL......................     45.00
CUSTARD GLASS BEADED CIRCLE BUTTER DISH...................     50.00
CUSTARD GLASS BEADED CIRCLE PATTERN SPOONER...............     22.00
CUSTARD GLASS BELL,ENAMEL FLORALS,RED
   SCRIPT,1871-1911,CHANANIAH LODGE.......................     40.00
CUSTARD GLASS BELL,SMOKE..................................      4.00
CUSTARD GLASS BERRY SET,& 6 SAUCES,GOLD,IVORINA VERDE
   PATTERN...............................................    135.00
CUSTARD GLASS BERRY SET,7 PIECE...........................    143.00
CUSTARD GLASS BERRY SET,IVORINA VERDE,WINGED SCROLL,7 PIECES  175.00
CUSTARD GLASS BLUE CHRYSANTHEMUM SPRIG BUTTER SIGNED
   NORTHWOOD.............................................    150.00
CUSTARD GLASS BLUE CHRYSANTHEMUM SPRIG SPOONER............    112.00
CUSTARD GLASS BLUE OPAL ARGONAUT CREAMER..................     50.00
CUSTARD GLASS BLUE OPAQUE CHRYSANTHEMUM SPRIG COVERED
   SUGAR,GOLD............................................    155.00
CUSTARD GLASS BLUE OPAQUE CHRYSANTHEMUM SPRIG CREAMER,GOLD..  135.00
CUSTARD GLASS BLUE OPAQUE CHRYSANTHEMUM SPRIG JELLY
   COMPOTE,GOLD..........................................    145.00
CUSTARD GLASS BLUE OPAQUE CHRYSANTHEMUM SPRIG SPOONER,GOLD..   95.00
CUSTARD GLASS BOAT SHAPED PEDESTAL FOOTED SAUCE...........     24.50
CUSTARD GLASS BOWL,4 IN...................................      6.50
CUSTARD GLASS BOWL,PEDESTAL...............................     35.00
CUSTARD GLASS BROWN GRAPE TUMBLER.........................     16.00
CUSTARD GLASS BUTTER DISH,IVORINA VERDE,GOLD..............     47.50
CUSTARD GLASS BUTTER DISH,WINGED SCROLL WITH GOLD
   FLOWER,FOOTED.........................................     50.00
CUSTARD GLASS CANDLESTICKS,FLUTED.........................     18.00
CUSTARD GLASS CANDLESTICKS,PAIR...........................    125.00
CUSTARD GLASS CANDLESTICKS,PAIR,LEAF DESIGN,OVAL BASES.....     8.50
CUSTARD GLASS CASED & BLOWN SWEETMEAT BASKET,WHITE........     29.50
CUSTARD GLASS CELERY VASE,LIBBEY COLOUR MAIZE-ART GLASS....     49.00
CUSTARD GLASS CENTER HANDLE 10 IN. CAKE PLATE.............     10.75
CUSTARD GLASS CHOCOLATE SHUTTLE CREAMER...................     30.00
CUSTARD GLASS CHRYSANTHEMUM SPRIG 4 PIECE TABLE SET.......    215.00
CUSTARD GLASS CHRYSANTHEMUM SPRIG BUTTER DISH.............     95.00
CUSTARD GLASS CHRYSANTHEMUM SPRIG BY NORTHWOOD GOLD CREAMER.   72.50
CUSTARD GLASS CHRYSANTHEMUM SPRIG BY NORTHWOOD GOLD COVERED
   BUTTER...............................................    115.00
CUSTARD GLASS CHRYSANTHEMUM SPRIG BY NORTHWOOD GOLD COVERED
   SUGAR................................................     92.50
CUSTARD GLASS CHRYSANTHEMUM SPRIG BY NORTHWOOD GOLD SPOONER.   40.00
CUSTARD GLASS CHRYSANTHEMUM SPRIG COMPOTE,6 IN............     48.00
CUSTARD GLASS CHRYSANTHEMUM SPRIG COMPOTE,GREEN,PINK & GOLD.   26.50
CUSTARD GLASS CHRYSANTHEMUM SPRIG COVERED BUTTER DISH.....     98.00
CUSTARD GLASS CHRYSANTHUMUM SPRIG COVERED BUTTER DISH,SIGNED
   NORTHWOOD.............................................    125.00
CUSTARD GLASS CHRYSANTHEMUM SPRIG COVERED SUGAR...........     75.00
CUSTARD GLASS CHRYSANTHEMUM SPRIG CREAM PITCHER...........     65.00
CUSTARD GLASS CHRYSANTHEMUM SPRIG CREAMER & SUGAR,MARKED....   70.00
CUSTARD GLASS CHRYSANTHEMUM SPRIG CREAMER.................     50.00
CUSTARD GLASS CHRYSANTHEMUM SPRIG CREAMER,NORTHWOOD SPELLED
   IN GOLD..............................................     45.00
CUSTARD GLASS CHRYSANTHEMUM SPRIG CRUET
   30.00  TO............................................     45.00
```

```
CUSTARD GLASS CHRYSANTHEMUM SPRIG CRUET,GOLD AND COLOURING..    75.00
CUSTARD GLASS CHRYSANTHEMUM SPRIG CRUET WITH STOPPER........   100.00
CUSTARD GLASS CHRYSANTHEMUM SPRIG JELLY COMPOTE
  35.00  TO...................................................    42.50
CUSTARD GLASS CHRYSANTHEMUM SPRIG OVAL BOWL..................   125.00
CUSTARD GLASS CHRYSANTHEMUM SPRIG PINK & GOLD CONDIMENT SET.   180.00
CUSTARD GLASS CHRYSANTHEMUM SPRIG SAUCE......................    33.00
CUSTARD GLASS CHRYSANTHEMUM SPRIG SAUCE DISH IN BLUE.........    65.00
CUSTARD GLASS CHRYSANTHEMUM SPRIG SPOONER
  25.00  TO...................................................    45.00
CUSTARD GLASS CHRYSANTHEMUM SPRIG TUMBLER....................    12.00
CUSTARD GLASS,CLEAR PEDESTAL MUG,CUT.........................     7.50
CUSTARD GLASS COMPOTE,FOOTED BASE,3 BRANCH STEM..............    75.00
CUSTARD GLASS CONE SHAPED VASE WITH PINK FLOWERS.............    15.00
CUSTARD GLASS CORN PATTERN SALT & PEPPER,PAIR...............    18.00
CUSTARD GLASS COVERED BUTTER,CREAMER & SPOONER,CHRYSANTHEMUM
  SPRIG......................................................   150.00
CUSTARD GLASS COVERED BUTTER DISH,BEADED CIRCLE PATTERN.....    45.00
CUSTARD GLASS COVERED BUTTER,WINGED SCROLL..................    55.00
CUSTARD GLASS COVERED JAR,DATED 1894........................    29.50
CUSTARD GLASS COVERED SUGAR,BLUE CHYRSANTHMUM...............   140.00
CUSTARD GLASS COVERED SUGAR,CREAMER, SPOONER ON GOLD
  FEET,SPRIG PATTERN.........................................    65.00
CUSTARD GLASS CRACKER JAR,GRAPE & THUMBPRINT................    25.00
CUSTARD GLASS CREAM PITCHER SIGNED NORTHWOOD,ARGONAUT
  SHELL,GREEN,GOLD...........................................    40.00
CUSTARD GLASS CREAMER,ALLENTOWN,PA..........................    10.00
CUSTARD GLASS CREAMER,COLOUR PHOTO HIGH SCHOOL,EDGAR
  NEBRASKA...................................................    15.00
CUSTARD GLASS CREAMER,HAVERHILL,MASS........................    10.00
CUSTARD GLASS CREAMER,IONA,MICH.............................    12.00
CUSTARD GLASS CREAMER,NORTH TROY,VT.........................    12.00
CUSTARD GLASS CREAMER,WAUSAU,WIS............................    12.00
CUSTARD GLASS CREAMER,WINGED SCROLL.........................    22.50
CUSTARD GLASS CUP SHAPE COMMEMORATION TOOTHPICK.............     6.00
CUSTARD GLASS DECANTER DATED 1886 & 6 STEMMED LIQUOR GLASSES    45.00
CUSTARD GLASS DELAWARE GREEN TRIM CREAM PITCHER.............    20.00
CUSTARD GLASS DELAWARE PATTERN SAUCE,GREEN PAINTING........    14.00
CUSTARD GLASS DELAWARE PATTERN SAUCE,ROSE PAINTING.........    14.00
CUSTARD GLASS DIAMOND AND PEG PATTERN MILK PITCHER,........    20.00
CUSTARD GLASS DISH,BASKETWEAVE,7 IN.........................    12.00
CUSTARD GLASS DISH,NAUTILUS SHELL,CREAM TO MILKY
  WHITE,SIGNED NORTHWOOD.....................................    65.00
CUSTARD GLASS,DOME LIGHT SHADE,ENAMEL DECOR.,SIGNED.........    15.00
CUSTARD GLASS FLARED HAT,APPLE BLOSSOM PATTERN IN BLUE......    15.00
CUSTARD GLASS FLUTED SCROLLS OR JACKSON FOOTED CREAMER......    20.00
CUSTARD GLASS FOOTED BANANA BOAT,LOUIS XV,GOLD.............    75.00
CUSTARD GLASS FOOTED BERRY SET,INTAGLIO PATTERN,BOWL & 6
  SAUCES....................................................   150.00
CUSTARD GLASS FOOTED LOUIS XV SAUCE DISH,GOLD..............    22.00
CUSTARD GLASS FRUIT BOWL,HOLLY BAND,11 IN.,SIGNED MC KEE....    20.00
CUSTARD GLASS GEM BUTTER DISH..............................    52.00
CUSTARD GLASS GENEVA GOLD DECOR 4-PIECE TABLE SET..........   175.00
CUSTARD GLASS GENEVA PATTERN FOOTED SAUCE DISH.............    14.00
CUSTARD GLASS GENEVA RED & GREEN FOOTED SPOONER...........    27.50
CUSTARD GLASS GENEVA RED & GREEN OPEN SUGAR...............    32.50
CUSTARD GLASS GOBLET,BEADED SWAG...........................    18.00
CUSTARD GLASS GRAPE & ARCHES GOBLET........................    35.00
CUSTARD GLASS GRAPE & CABLE BREAKFAST SUGAR BOWL...........    29.00
CUSTARD GLASS GRAPE & CABLE,BROWN STAIN FOOTED ICE CREAM
  DISH......................................................    17.50
CUSTARD GLASS GRAPE & CABLE SUGAR & CREAMER................    55.00
CUSTARD GLASS GRAPE & GOTHIC ARCH STEMMED GOBLET...........    21.00
CUSTARD GLASS GRAPE & GOTHIC ARCHES BUTTER DISH............    50.00
CUSTARD GLASS GRAPE & GOTHIC ARCHES GOBLET,SEPIA TRIM.......    21.00
```

```
CUSTARD GLASS GREEN FOOTED SUGAR & CREAMER,MERRY CHRISTMAS
   IN RED...........................................................    32.00
CUSTARD GLASS HAT,5 IN. DIAMETER,EMBOSSED LEAF & BERRY WITH
   GOLD............................................................    20.00
CUSTARD GLASS HAT ,BRIM IN BLACKBERRY DESIGN.................    14.00
CUSTARD GLASS HEISEY RING BAND COVERED BUTTER,GOLD DOTS,RED
   ROSES...........................................................    65.00
CUSTARD GLASS HOBSTAR MUG,BLUE,2.............................    25.00
CUSTARD GLASS HOLLY-BERRY PATTERN CHEESE DISH................    16.00
CUSTARD GLASS HOLLY PATTERN CREAMER..........................     8.00
CUSTARD GLASS ICE CREAM DISH,PEACOCK AT URN..................    75.00
CUSTARD GLASS INDIVIDUAL CREAMER,SOUVENIR....................     7.00
CUSTARD GLASS INDIVIDUAL FRUIT DISH,DIAMOND PEG PATTERN......    13.00
CUSTARD GLASS INTAGLIO GREEN 9 IN. COMPOTE...................    75.00
CUSTARD GLASS INTAGLIO FOOTED SAUCE DISH,GOLD FLOWERS &
   TRIM,GREEN......................................................    22.50
CUSTARD GLASS INTAGLIO GREEN & GOLD BERRY BOWL & 4 SAUCES...   150.00
CUSTARD GLASS INTAGLIO GREEN & GOLD SALT & PEPPER...........    65.00
CUSTARD GLASS INTAGLIO OPEN COMPOTE..........................    82.50
CUSTARD GLASS INTAGLIO SPOONER,GOLD WITH GREEN TRIM.........    27.50
CUSTARD GLASS INVERTED FAN SPOONER...........................    45.00
CUSTARD GLASS IRIS PATTERN TUMBLER...........................    25.00
CUSTARD GLASS IRIS PATTERN WATER PITCHER.....................    65.00
CUSTARD GLASS IVORINA VERDE 3 CORNERED RELISH................    20.00
CUSTARD GLASS IVORINA VERDE BUTTER DISH......................    50.00
CUSTARD GLASS IVORINA VERDE,CHRYSANTHEMUM SPRIG TANKARD & 5
   TUMBLERS........................................................   200.00
CUSTARD GLASS,IVORINA VERDE DRESSER TRAY,PIN TRAY,POWDER BOX
   & RING TREE.....................................................    85.00
CUSTARD GLASS IVORINA VERDE SAUCE............................     7.50
CUSTARD GLASS IVORINA VERDE SPOONER,GOLD TRIM................    10.00
CUSTARD GLASS IVORINA VERDE TOOTHPICK,GOLD...................    18.00
CUSTARD GLASS IVORINA VERDE TOOTHPICK HOLDER.................    38.00
CUSTARD GLASS IVORINA VERDE TUMBLER,GOLD.....................    14.00
CUSTARD GLASS IVORINA VERDE WATER PITCHER....................    65.00
CUSTARD GLASS JACKSONS OPEN SUGAR,GOLD.......................    18.00
CUSTARD GLASS JADE GREEN TUMBLER.............................    10.00
CUSTARD GLASS JELLY COMPOTE,STEMMED,CHRYSANTHEMUM SPRIG.....    16.00
CUSTARD GLASS JELLY,LITTLE GEM SQUATTY.......................    15.00
CUSTARD GLASS LOUIS XV BANANA BOAT...........................    75.00
CUSTARD GLASS LOUIS XV BERRY DISH............................    23.00
CUSTARD GLASS LOUIS XV BERRY DISH,OVAL.......................    80.00
CUSTARD GLASS LOUIS XV BUTTER,COVERED
   44.50  TO.......................................................    69.00
CUSTARD GLASS LOUIS XV BUTTER DISH,COVERED,GOLD ON FLOWERS..    70.00
CUSTARD GLASS LOUIS XV COVERED SUGAR,GOLD WEAR...............    30.00
CUSTARD GLASS LOUIS XV CREAMER...............................    40.00
CUSTARD GLASS LOUIS XV FOOTED OVAL BANANA DISH & 4
   SAUCES,GOLD.....................................................   218.00
CUSTARD GLASS LOUIS XV FOOTED OVAL CENTER BOWL...............    98.00
CUSTARD GLASS LOUIS XV GOLD WEAR CREAMER.....................    25.00
CUSTARD GLASS LOUIS XV GOLD WEAR SPOONER.....................    20.00
CUSTARD GLASS LOUIS XV OVAL BERRY BOWL ON 4 CURLED FEET.....    65.00
CUSTARD GLASS LOUIS XV SAUCE.................................    35.00
CUSTARD GLASS LOUIS XV SPOONER
   25.00  TO.......................................................    39.00
CUSTARD GLASS LOUIS XV SUGAR,COVERED
   40.00  TO.......................................................    49.00
CUSTARD GLASS LOUIS XV TUMBLER...............................    20.00
CUSTARD GLASS MAPLE LEAF BUTTER DISH.........................    75.00
CUSTARD GLASS MAPLE LEAF CREAMER.............................    45.00
CUSTARD GLASS MAPLE LEAF SPOONER,GREEN & GOLD,3 HANDLES.....    25.00
CUSTARD GLASS MAPLE LEAF SUGAR BOWL,3 HANDLES...............    22.00
CUSTARD GLASS MARKED HEISEY RING BAND PATTERN COVERED SUGAR
   & SPOONER.......................................................    60.00
```

```
CUSTARD GLASS MATCHING PAIR CANDLESTICKS...................    60.00
CUSTARD GLASS MINIATURE CREAMER,PAINTED ROSES,SOUVENIR CONEY
  ISLAND........................................................    12.00
CUSTARD GLASS MINIATURE HEN..................................     2.00
CUSTARD GLASS MUG,BABY THUMBPRINT...........................    12.00
CUSTARD GLASS MUG,MINIATURE,SOUVENIR........................     7.50
CUSTARD GLASS MUG WITH TOM & JERRY IN BLACK,SIGNED..........     3.75
CUSTARD GLASS NORTHWOOD FAN WATER PITCHER & 6 TUMBLERS......   150.00
CUSTARD GLASS NORTHWOOD MAPLE LEAF COVERED BUTTER...........    75.00
CUSTARD GLASS NORTHWOOD MAPLE LEAF CREAMER..................    40.00
CUSTARD GLASS NORTHWOOD MAPLE LEAF CREAM PITCHER,GREEN,GOLD
  TRIM.........................................................    25.00
CUSTARD GLASS NORTHWOOD MAPLE LEAF WATER PITCHER............   110.00
CUSTARD GLASS OPEN HANDLE 10 IN. CAKE PLATE.................    12.50
CUSTARD GLASS OVAL BERRY BOWL,CHRYSANTHEMUM SPRIG
  PATTERN,SIGNED...............................................    90.00
CUSTARD GLASS OVAL FOOTED LOUIS XV BERRY BOWL,GOLD..........    75.00
CUSTARD GLASS PAIR 7 IN. 6 SIDED CANDLESTICKS IN BLUE.......    35.00
CUSTARD GLASS PAIR CANDLESTICKS,BERRY,LEAF BORDER,4 IN......    10.00
CUSTARD GLASS PEACOCK AT URN 9 IN. BOWL.....................    45.00
CUSTARD GLASS PEACOCK AT URN 10 IN. LOW BOWL................    65.00
CUSTARD GLASS PEDESTAL BERRY BOWL,INTAGLIO PATTERN..........    85.00
CUSTARD GLASS PERSIAN MEDALLION ROSE BOWL,BROWN STAIN.......    35.00
CUSTARD GLASS PINEAPPLE & FAN SOUVENIR SAULT STE.MARIE
  CREAMER......................................................    14.50
CUSTARD GLASS PITCHER,ARGONAUT SHELL........................   175.00
CUSTARD GLASS PLATE,7 IN.,FENTON HORSE MEDALLION WITH PINK
  CORDOVAN.....................................................    48.50
CUSTARD GLASS PLATE,7 IN.,RAISED SCROLLS SILVERED...........     7.50
CUSTARD GLASS PRAYER RUG PATTERN 2 HANDLED NAPPY............     9.50
CUSTARD GLASS PUDDING MOLD IN FRENCH VANILLA................    18.50
CUSTARD GLASS PUNCH SET,TANKARD PITCHER,6 TUMBLERS,GOLD.....   225.00
CUSTARD GLASS RIBBED DRAPE RED ROSE DECOR BOWL,8 IN.........    60.00
CUSTARD GLASS RIBBED DRAPE RED ROSE DECOR SPOONER...........    35.00
CUSTARD GLASS RIBBED DRAPE RED ROSE DECOR TUMBLER,2.........    35.00
CUSTARD GLASS RIBBED THUMBPRINT TANKARD SHAPE CREAMER,......    17.50
CUSTARD GLASS SALT & PEPPER SHAKERS MARKED HEISEY,PUNTY BAND   14.00
CUSTARD GLASS SHERBET.......................................     6.00
CUSTARD GLASS SIGNED HEISEY COVERED BUTTER..................    60.00
CUSTARD GLASS SIGNED HEISEY COVERED SUGAR...................    45.00
CUSTARD GLASS SIGNED HEISEY TABLE SET,RING BAND PATTERN.....   235.00
CUSTARD GLASS SIGNED MC KEE HANDLED FRUIT JUICER DISH.......     5.00
CUSTARD GLASS SIGNED MC KEE HOLLY BAND OVAL SERVING DISH....    15.00
CUSTARD GLASS SIGNED NORTHWOOD ARGONAUT SHELL SAUCE
  DISH,GOLD....................................................    30.00
CUSTARD GLASS SIGNED NORTHWOOD CHRYSANTHEMUM SPRIG BUTTER
  DISH........................................................    98.00
CUSTARD GLASS SIGNED NORTHWOOD CHRYSANTHEMUM SPRIG CREAMER..    55.00
CUSTARD GLASS SIGNED NORTHWOOD CHRYSANTHEMUM SPRIG SPOONER..    55.00
CUSTARD GLASS SINGING BIRD MUG..............................    20.00
CUSTARD GLASS SOUVENIR CUP..................................    15.00
CUSTARD GLASS SOUVENIR GOBLET,6 IN. HIGH,BULBOUS SHAPE......    14.50
CUSTARD GLASS SOUVENIR GOBLET,HEXAGONAL BASE,RED ROSE.......    17.50
CUSTARD GLASS SOUVENIR PITCHER,2 IN.........................     5.50
CUSTARD GLASS SOUVENIR TOOTHPICK,PLYMOUTH MASS..............    12.50
CUSTARD GLASS SOUVENIR TOOTHPICK,RING BAND
  PATTERN,LANCASTER,N.H........................................     8.50
CUSTARD GLASS SOUVENIR TUMBLER
  12.00  TO...................................................    15.00
CUSTARD GLASS SOUVENIR TUMBLER,COURT HOUSE ROCK COUNTY
  BASSETT,NEB..................................................    14.00
CUSTARD GLASS SOUVENIR WINE.................................    10.00
CUSTARD GLASS SOWERBY BREAKFAST SET,ENGLISH MEADOW,REGISTRY-
  MARK........................................................    36.50
CUSTARD GLASS SPOONER,BLUE CHRYSANTHMUM.....................   120.00
```

CUSTARD GLASS SPOONER,CHRYSANTHEMUM PATTERN,MARKED NORTHWOOD	35.00
CUSTARD GLASS SPOONER,CHRYSANTHEMUM SPRIG	50.00
CUSTARD GLASS SPOONER,LOUIS XV,FOOTED,GOLD TRIM	30.00
CUSTARD GLASS SPOONER SIGNED NORTHWOOD,CHRYSANTHEMUM SPRIG,GREEN,PINK	45.00
CUSTARD GLASS SPOONER,WINGED SCROLL WITH GOLD FLOWER,FOOTED.	30.00
CUSTARD GLASS SUGAR BOWL & COVER,LOUIS XV FINIAL,GOLD	15.00
CUSTARD GLASS SUGAR,COVERED,LOUIS XV,FOOTED,GOLD TRIM	45.00
CUSTARD GLASS SUGAR,WINGED SCROLL	22.50
CUSTARD GLASS TABLE CENTER SET SIGNED HEISEY,RING BAND	235.00
CUSTARD GLASS TEA CUP,BLUE FLOWER,PAINTED SPRAY	10.00
CUSTARD GLASS TIE BACKS,10 PETAL FLOWER,PAIR	28.00
CUSTARD GLASS,TOM & JERRY MUGS SIGNED MC K	3.25
CUSTARD GLASS TOOTHPICK 10.00 TO	11.50
CUSTARD GLASS TOOTHPICK BANDED PORTLAND,SOUVENIR ST.ALBANS MAINE,RED	12.50
CUSTARD GLASS TOOTHPICK,DIAMOND WITH PEG,SIGNED KRYS-TOL	13.50
CUSTARD GLASS TOOTHPICK,GOLD RIM	18.00
CUSTARD GLASS TOOTHPICK,HEISEY,BABY THUMBPRINT	12.50
CUSTARD GLASS TOOTHPICK HOLDER,3 FEET,GOLD BEADING,SOUVENIR OF HOULTON	14.00
CUSTARD GLASS TOOTHPICK,RIBBED THUMBPRINT	20.00
CUSTARD GLASS TOOTHPICK HOLDER,RIBBED THUMBPRINT,PAINTED SPRAY	22.50
CUSTARD GLASS TOOTHPICK HOLDER,TURNED UP LEAVES FORM FEET	15.00
CUSTARD GLASS TOOTHPICK,IVORINA VERDE,BULBOUS SHAPE,NO GOLD.	30.00
CUSTARD GLASS TUMBLER,BENTON,PA.,FLOWERS,GOLD RIM	14.00
CUSTARD GLASS TUMBLER,GENEVA PATTERN 22.00 TO	25.00
CUSTARD GLASS TUMBLER,HANDPAINTED ROSE	8.50
CUSTARD GLASS TUMBLER,WINGED SCROLL	12.00
CUSTARD GLASS VASE,3 IN.,CRIMPED TOP,BLACKBERRIES	10.50
CUSTARD GLASS VASE,6 IN. HIGH,PICTURE OF PIONEER DEPT. STORE	15.00
CUSTARD GLASS VASE,7 IN.,DRAPERY,BROWN TRIM	20.00
CUSTARD GLASS VINEGAR,WINGED SCROLL,CLEAR STOPPER	25.00
CUSTARD GLASS WATER PITCHER & 6 TUMBLERS,RING BAND PATTERN,.	130.00
CUSTARD GLASS WATER PITCHER,ROSE WITH GREEN LEAVES,GOLD VEINED	90.00
CUSTARD GLASS WATER PITCHER,WINGED SCROLL,YELLOW,TANKARD TYPE	65.00
CUSTARD GLASS WATER SET,SIGNED NORTHWOOD,GRAPE & GOTHIC ARCH	132.50
CUSTARD GLASS WINGED SCROLL JAM JAR,4 GOLD SCROLL FEET	30.00

CUT GLASS has been made since ancient times, but the large majority of the pieces now for sale date from the "Brilliant" period of glass design (1880 to 1905). These pieces had elaborate geometric designs cut with a deep miter cut.

CUT GLASS & CRANBERRY PEDESTALED WINE GOBLET	20.00
CUT GLASS & ETCHED SUGAR & CREAMER,BUTTERFLY DESIGN	27.50
CUT GLASS & SILVER OVERLAY CREAMER & SUGAR	15.00
CUT GLASS ATOMIZER,CLEAR BASE,AMETHYST TOP	18.00
CUT GLASS ATOMIZER,SIGNED,CRANBERRY TO CLEAR,FANS,STARS,DIAMONDS	75.00
CUT GLASS ATOMIZER,SQUARE	8.50
CUT GLASS AUTO VASE,PAGE,WITH BRACKET	15.00
CUT GLASS BANANA BOAT,HOBSTARS,CANE,HOBNAIL	39.00
CUT GLASS BASKET	59.00
CUT GLASS BASKET,11 X 8 IN.,RADIAL CUT FLOWERS,HARVARD BORDER	50.00
CUT GLASS BASKET,12 IN.,CRYSTAL,RIBBING & ETCHED FLOWERS	18.00
CUT GLASS BASKET,FROSTED FLORAL	12.50
CUT GLASS BASKET,HOBSTAR PATTERN,6 BY 4 IN	42.50
CUT GLASS BEER MUG,9 IN. GERMAN,PEWTER LID,DRAGON HANDLE,GERMAN WRITING	37.50
CUT GLASS BELL	6.50

```
CUT GLASS BELL,DINNER,4 IN.,HOBSTARS,STRAWBERRY,FANS........     50.00
CUT GLASS BELL,4 IN. TALL,HOBSTAR..............................  36.00
CUT GLASS BELL,7 IN. HIGH......................................  12.50
CUT GLASS BELL,8 IN............................................  17.50
CUT GLASS BELL,HARVARD & FLOWER & LEAF.........................  45.00
CUT GLASS BELL,SILVER METAL CLAPPER ON CHAIN..................   32.00
CUT GLASS BERRY BOWL,8 SIDED,SHALLOW,HOBSTARS.................    27.00
CUT GLASS BOTTLE,11 IN. HIGH...................................   5.50
CUT GLASS BOTTLE,FACETED HOLLOW BLOWN STOPPER.................   29.50
CUT GLASS BOTTLE,PANELLED,7 IN. TALL,METAL TOP...............     2.00
CUT GLASS BOTTLE WITH HINGED METAL COVER INKWELL............    10.00
CUT GLASS BOUDOIR LAMP,SILVER RIM FOR SHADE..................    87.50
CUT GLASS BOWL,7 IN. ROUND SHALLOW...........................    14.51-
CUT GLASS BOWL,8 IN.
  29.50  TO...................................................   38.50
CUT GLASS BOWL,8 IN.,FROSTED FLORAL..........................    12.00
CUT GLASS BOWL,8 IN. DIA.,HOB STAR,FAN & FLORAL..............    26.75
CUT GLASS BOWL,8 IN.,8 HOBSTARS,SCALLOPED RIM...............     22.00
CUT GLASS BOWL,8 IN. ,KIMBERLY PATTERN.......................    85.00
CUT GLASS BOWL,8 IN.,3 STARS,3 PINWHEELS,SCALLOPED RIM......     20.00
CUT GLASS BOWL,8 IN. ROUND,SIGNED EGGINTON,BIRD IN CAGE
  PATTERN....................................................    65.00
CUT GLASS BOWL,9 IN...........................................   60.00
CUT GLASS BOWL,13 FANS FORM EDGE,DIAMOND CUT.................    52.00
CUT GLASS BOWL,AMERICAN,SCALLOPED RIM,24-POINT HOBSTARS.....     38.00
CUT GLASS BOWL,BLUE OVERLAY IN RUSSIAN PATTERN,GOLD TRIM....    145.00
CUT GLASS BOWL,BUZZ PATTERN...................................   22.00
CUT GLASS BOWL,CANE PATTERN...................................   60.00
CUT GLASS BOWL,DOUBLE HANDLED,FAN CUT BORDER,DIAMOND POINT
  CUT BODY...................................................    40.00
CUT GLASS BOWL,FINE CUT HEART PRIMROSE.......................    20.00
CUT GLASS BOWL,FOOTED,FLOWER DESIGN..........................    31.00
CUT GLASS BOWL,HANDCUT,RAYED BASE,ETCHED STARS...............     6.50
CUT GLASS BOWL,HOBSTAR BASE,PINWHEELS,GEOMETRICS.............    25.00
CUT GLASS BOWL,INVERTED STRAWBERRY,MARKED,CLEAR..............    16.00
CUT GLASS BOWL,LACY,TRELLIS RUFFLE-------------------------     17.50
CUT GLASS BOWL,OVAL,FLOWERS & LEAVES.........................    28.00
CUT GLASS BOWL,OVAL,INTAGLIO CUT FLOWER IN EACH PANEL........    20.00
CUT GLASS BOWL,PINWHEEL,HOBSTAR,7 IN.........................     7.50
CUT GLASS BOWL,PRISMATIC & CUT BASE..........................    26.00
CUT GLASS BOWL,STRAWBERRY DIAMOND & FAN DESIGN...............    25.00
CUT GLASS BOWL,3 PINWHEELS DIVIDED BY ENGLISH HOBNAIL.......     24.50
CUT GLASS BOWL WITH 3 FEET,HARVARD VARIANT BAND..............    18.00
CUT GLASS BOWL WITH GEOMETRICS & FAN & DIAMOND...............    12.00
CUT GLASS BOWL WITH LADLE,IRIS PATTERN,SIGNED HAWKES........     25.00
CUT GLASS BOWL WITH STERLING RIM.............................    90.00
CUT GLASS BOX,4 X 11 IN.,HINGED,GLOVE,CORNFLOWERS...........     95.00
CUT GLASS BOX,7 IN. SQUARE,HINGED,HANDKERCHIEF,POINSETTIA
  FLOWERS....................................................    95.00
CUT GLASS BOX,COVERED,PANELLED SIDES,WAFFLE CUT TOP..........     8.00
CUT GLASS BOX,ROUND COVERED..................................    45.00
CUT GLASS BOX,ROUND COVERED,STERLING SILVER RIMS & HINGE....    110.00
CUT GLASS BOX,ROUND HINGED,LEAVES & DIAMOND PATTERN.........     85.00
CUT GLASS BUD VASE ON SCALLOPED PEDESTAL BASE...............     18.00
CUT GLASS BUD VASE,NARROW STEM,FLARE TO TOP,FLORAL CUT......     15.00
CUT GLASS BUTTER,COVERED.....................................    57.00
CUT GLASS BUTTER,COVERED,8 IN.,48 SERRATES,FACET KNOB CUT
  DOME......................................................     47.00
CUT GLASS BUTTER PAT
  3.00  TO...................................................    5.00
CUT GLASS BUTTER PAT,3 IN. DIAMETER..........................     8.00
CUT GLASS CAKE PLATE WITH INTAGLIO FLOWERS AND BUTTERFLIES..     35.00
CUT GLASS CANDLEHOLDERS,PAIR.................................    16.00
CUT GLASS CANDLESTICK,CASED,PURPLE TO CLEAR,CANE WITH FAN
  ,ENGLISH,.................................................     90.00
```

```
CUT GLASS CANDLESTICK,PAIR.....................................  18.00
CUT GLASS CANDLESTICK,PURPLE TO CLEAR,ENGLISH,CANE & FAN
  PATTERN......................................................  90.00
CUT GLASS CANDLESTICKS,PAIR,ENGRAVED...........................  22.50
CUT GLASS CANDLESTICKS,PAIR,7 IN.,HEX BASES & STEMS...........  28.00
CUT GLASS CANDLESTICKS,8 IN....................................  22.00
CUT GLASS CANDLESTICKS,PAIR 12 IN. AMERICAN TAPERED......... 150.00
CUT GLASS CANDY COMPOTE........................................  45.00
CUT GLASS CANDY COMPOTE,6 IN. TALL,SLENDER STEM...............  10.00
CUT GLASS CANDY COMPOTE,HOBSTARS...............................  22.50
CUT GLASS CANDY DISH
  10.00  TO...................................................  22.00
CUT GLASS CANDY DISH,5 IN. SQUARE,ETCHED ROSES................  10.00
CUT GLASS CANDY DISH,6 IN. ROUND...............................   7.50
CUT GLASS CANDY DISH WITH TOP,9 IN. TALL,CLEAR................   8.50
CUT GLASS CANDY DISHES,PAIR....................................   5.00
CUT GLASS CANDY DISH,FOOTED,ETCHED COSMOS.....................  13.00
CUT GLASS CANDY DISH,ROUND.....................................   8.50
CUT GLASS CAKE STAND,BLUE FINE CUT.............................  18.00
CUT GLASS CAKE STAND,GREEN FAN & DIAMOND.......................  15.00
CUT GLASS CANOE................................................  15.00
CUT GLASS CARAFE,8 IN. HIGH....................................  20.00
CUT GLASS CARAFE,ALTERNATING DIAMONDS OF STARS & HOBSTARS...  27.50
CUT GLASS CARAFE,CIRCA 1885,STRAWBERRY & DIAMOND............  32.50
CUT GLASS CARAFE,HOBSTARS & ALTERNATING SECTIONS OF NOTCHED
  PRISM.......................................................  28.00
CUT GLASS CARAFES,PAIR.........................................  45.00
CUT GLASS CARAFE,8 IN.,PRISM CUT...............................  22.00
CUT GLASS CARAFES,PAIR RUSSIAN,STARRED BUTTON,32 POINT STAR
  BOTTOM...................................................... 160.00
CUT GLASS CASTOR BOTTLE,DIAMOND & HONEYCOMB...................   7.00
CUT GLASS CASTER SET,4 BOTTLE..................................  28.00
CUT GLASS CASTOR SET,4 PIECE,FOOTED SILVER HOLDER............  36.00
CUT GLASS CELERY DISH
  20.00  TO...................................................  25.00
CUT GLASS CELERY DISH,10 IN....................................  20.00
CUT GLASS CELERY DISH,10 IN. LONG..............................  14.50
CUT GLASS CELERY DISH,11 IN....................................  25.00
CUT GLASS CELERY DISH,11 IN.,HOBSTAR & PALM LEAF.............  22.00
CUT GLASS CELERY,12 IN.,BUTTERFLY..............................  22.50
CUT GLASS CELERY DISH,DIAMOND POINT & FAN,MALTESE CROSS IN
  BASE........................................................  18.00
CUT GLASS CELERY DISH,HOBSTARS & FAN...........................  22.00
CUT GLASS CELERY DISH MARKED J.HOARE & CO. 1853 CORNING.....  37.50
CUT GLASS CELERY,HOBSTAR & FAN.................................  16.50
CUT GLASS CELERY,HOBSTARS DIAMOND POINT & FAN................  24.00
CUT GLASS CELERY,INTAGLIO 11 IN.,FLORAL PATTERN.............  15.00
CUT GLASS CELERY TRAY,4 FLORAL SPRAYS,4 HOBSTARS,SCALLOPED
  NOTCHED RIM.................................................  10.50
CUT GLASS CELERY TRAY,HOBSTARS & CROSSHATCH...................  35.00
CUT GLASS CELERY TRAY,SCALLOPED NOTCHED RIM,STAR IN
  CENTER,THISTLE ENDS.........................................  15.00
CUT GLASS CELERY VASE,CUT LOG..................................  10.00
CUT GLASS CENTER DISH,9 IN.,HOBSTAR FLOWERS...................  58.00
CUT GLASS CENTERPIECE SET,10 IN. UNDERPLATE WITH
  BOWL,HARVARD,FLORALS........................................  75.00
CUT GLASS CHAMPAGNE,BIGLER.....................................  12.00
CUT GLASS CHAMPAGNE BUCKET.....................................  42.50
CUT GLASS CHAMPAGNE GOBLET,PEAR SHAPED STEM...................  12.75
CUT GLASS CHAMPAGNE,SET OF 6 STEMMED,CANE PATTERN,HONEYCOMB
  STEMS.......................................................  90.00
CUT GLASS CHAMPAGNE,SET OF 8,HARVARD,INTAGLIO FLOWERS &
  LEAVES...................................................... 135.00
CUT GLASS CHAMPAGNE,SET OF 8 HOLLOW STEM,SIGNED JULIAN
  STREET......................................................  37.50
```

CUT GLASS CHEESE & CRACKER DISH,DAISIES,TULIPS & BUTTERFLY..	42.50
CUT GLASS CHEESE,COVERED,BIG PLATE & DOME...................	99.00
CUT GLASS CHEESE DISH,6 X 9 IN...............................	150.00
CUT GLASS CHEESE DISH,LATTICE,FAN & THUMBPRINT DESIGN.......	23.00
CUT GLASS CHEESE DISH WITH THUMBPRINT,LATTICE & FAN.........	23.00
CUT GLASS CHEESE DOME.......................................	57.00
CUT GLASS CLARET,DOUBLE TRAPPED-AIR STEMS,ELONGATED ALMONDS.	12.50
CUT GLASS COASTER WITH 16 POINT STAR CENTER,GORHAM STERLING RIM...	35.00
CUT GLASS COLOGNE...	18.00
CUT GLASS COLOGNE BOTTLE,5 IN. TALL.........................	18.00
CUT GLASS COLOGNE BOTTLE,DIAMOND CUT,MATCHING STOPPER.......	20.00
CUT GLASS COLOGNE BOTTLES,PAIR,FITTED LEATHER CASE,GOLD TOPS	75.00
CUT GLASS COLOGNE,FACETED STOPPER...........................	35.00
CUT GLASS COLOGNE,FRENCH,RECTANGULAR BASE,STERLING STOPPER..	35.00
CUT GLASS COMPOTE,5 IN.,DAHLIA CANE.........................	7.00
CUT GLASS COMPOTE,7 IN. HIGH,HOB STAR,FLARING STEM WITH FINE CUTS...	65.00
CUT GLASS COMPOTE,8 IN.,FROSTED FLORAL......................	12.00
CUT GLASS COMPOTE,10 IN. HIGH,PINWHEEL CUTTING WITH HOBSTARS	85.00
CUT GLASS COMPOTE,BELGIAN...................................	40.00
CUT GLASS COMPOTE,FLORAL SPRAY..............................	22.50
CUT GLASS COMPOTE,HARVARD PATTERN,8 IN. ON 10 IN. STANDARD..	50.00
CUT GLASS COMPOTE,HOBSTAR & FAN.............................	68.50
CUT GLASS COMPOTE,HOBSTARS,FANS,MITRES SAWTOOTH.............	22.50
CUT GLASS COMPOTES,PAIR INTAGLIO CUT,CLEAR STEMS,FLORAL.....	45.10
CUT GLASS COMPOTE,PEDESTALED,PINWHEEL,CANE & HOBSTAR........	42.00
CUT GLASS COMPOTE,PEDESTAL STEM,8 IN........................	39.00
CUT GLASS COMPOTE,PEDESTAL STEM,NUT.........................	27.50
CUT GLASS COMPOTE,STARRED BASE,BEVEL STEM CUT EDGED.........	55.00
CUT GLASS COMPOTE,STEMMED,AMBER.............................	17.50
CUT GLASS COMPOTE,STRAWBERRY,DIAMOND,FAN WITH BEADED LINE,..	18.50
CUT GLASS CONDIMENT SET,4 BOTTLES IN SILVER HOLDER..........	38.00
CUT GLASS CONDIMENT SET IN SILVER FOOTED FRAME WITH HANDLE..	19.00
CUT GLASS COOKIE JAR,COBALT BLUE CUT TO CLEAR PANELS........	29.50
CUT GLASS COOKIE JAR,SILVER PLATE COVER,HOBSTAR.............	65.00
CUT GLASS COOKIE JAR WITH LID,SIGNED J.HOARE & CO.,PINEAPPLE & DIAMOND...	175.00
CUT GLASS COOKIE JAR WITH SILVER COLLAR,BALE HANDLE & ENGRAVED LID..	29.00
CUT GLASS CRACKER & DIP PLATE WITH STERLING SILVER,FLORAL DESIGN...	45.00
CUT GLASS CRACKER JAR,SILVER LID & TOP,ENGLISH REGISTRY MARKED...	38.00
CUT GLASS CREAM & SUGAR,HOBSTAR DIAMOND POINT & FAN,NOTCHED RIMS..	40.00
CUT GLASS CREAM & SUGAR,SAW TOOTH EDGE......................	17.00
CUT GLASS CREAM & SUGAR,STALKS & STARS......................	67.50
CUT GLASS CREAM & SUGAR,SUNBURST PATTERN....................	55.00
CUT GLASS,CREAM PITCHER,SCUTTLE SHAPED,AMERICAN.............	15.00
CUT GLASS CREAMER & 2 HANDLED SUGAR.........................	36.00
CUT GLASS CREAMER & 2 HANDLED SUGAR,SERRATED TOPS,HOBSTAR ROSETTE..	21.00
CUT GLASS CREAMER & 2 HANDLED SUGAR SET.....................	38.50
CUT GLASS CREAMER & SUGAR 19.50 TO..	45.00
CUT GLASS CREAMER & SUGAR ON PEDESTAL BASES,FRY⌀S RASPBERRY.	75.00
CUT GLASS CREAMER & SUGAR,PEDESTAL BASE,VARIATION OF STALKS & STARS..	67.50
CUT GLASS CREAMER & SUGAR,SCROLL CUT,BUZZ SAW PATTERN.......	18.00
CUT GLASS CREAMER & SUGAR SIGNED LIBBY......................	42.50
CUT GLASS CREAMER,BREAKFAST,CUT HANDLE......................	15.00
CUT GLASS CREAMER,DIAMOND MEDALLION.........................	9.50
CUT GLASS CREAMER,FLYING BIRDS WITH STRAWS IN BEAK,STEMMED,FEET...	32.50

CUT GLASS CREAMER,HOBS & FAN.................................... 12.00
CUT GLASS CREAMER,HOBSTAR ROSETTE.............................. 13.00
CUT GLASS CREAMER,PINWHEEL..................................... 13.00
CUT GLASS CRUET,3 WAY POUR..................................... 28.00
CUT GLASS CRUET,6 IN. HIGH,.................................... 17.00
CUT GLASS CRUET,7 IN.,BULBOUS,CUT STOPPER..................... 13.00
CUT GLASS CRUET,7 IN.,STRAWBERRY,DIAMOND & FAN STAR.......... 15.00
CUT GLASS CRUET,APPLIED HANDLE,STOPPER....................... 20.00
CUT GLASS CRUET,BELL SHAPE,CUT HANDLE NECK AND STOPPER....... 18.50
CUT GLASS CRUET,BUZZ PATTERN.................................. 22.00
CUT GLASS CRUET,DIAMOND POINT................................. 13.00
CUT GLASS CRUET,DIAMOND POINT WITH FACETED STOPPER........... 15.00
CUT GLASS CRUET,FANS & DIAMONDS WITH PANEL NECK.............. 21.75
CUT GLASS CRUET,FAN & STRAWBERRY.............................. 10.00
CUT GLASS CRUET,HARVARD CUT,.................................. 22.50
CUT GLASS CRUETS,PAIR,ON GOLD TRAY,THUMBPRINT BASE & TOPS... 36.50
CUT GLASS CRUET,SIGNED.. 28.00
CUT GLASS CRUET TYPE DECANTER,SQUATTY BASE................... 35.00
CUT GLASS CRUET WITH CUT GLASS STOPPER,THUMBPRINT............ 25.00
CUT GLASS CRUET WITH STOPPER.................................. 25.00
CUT GLASS DECANTER.. 15.00
CUT GLASS DECANTER,3 ROWS OF THUMBPRINT PATTERN,1 QUART..... 20.00
CUT GLASS DECANTER,10 IN.,5 ROWS OF THUMBPRINTS,MULTIFACETED
  STOPPER... 17.00
CUT GLASS DECANTER 10 IN. BELL SHAPE.......................... 13.50
CUT GLASS DECANTER,10 IN.,FLORAL,DELVAUX,18 RUE ROYALE...... 40.00
CUT GLASS DECANTER,10 IN. TALL,CHAIR BOTTOM DESIGN,RAYED
  BASE.. 32.00
CUT GLASS DECANTER,12 IN. HIGH................................ 30.00
CUT GLASS DECANTER,13 IN.,HANDLED,HARVARD & FLORAL.......... 125.00
CUT GLASS DECANTER 13 IN. SIGNED ST.LOUIS FRANCE............. 40.00
CUT GLASS DECANTER,BALL BODY.................................. 33.00
CUT GLASS DECANTER,CRANBERRY OVERLAY.......................... 65.00
CUT GLASS DECANTER,CURVED FLUTES WITH THUMBPRINT............. 38.00
CUT GLASS DECANTER,FERN & FERN & FLUTE,WHITE SULPHIDE....... 375.00
CUT GLASS DECANTER,HANDLED,STAR CUT PEDESTAL
  BASE,HOBSTAR,PRISM,FANS..................................... 60.00
CUT GLASS DECANTER IN APRICOT AMBER TO CLEAR,16 IN. HIGH.... 85.00
CUT GLASS DECANTER,LOOP & BLOCK,RUBY & CLEAR................. 22.50
CUT GLASS DECANTER,MITER CUT WITH THUMBPRINT,STAR BASE...... 28.00
CUT GLASS DECANTER,NOTCHED HANDLE............................. 69.50
CUT GLASS DECANTER,OVERLAY,COBALT TO OPAQUE WITHE,GOLD BAND. 95.00
CUT GLASS DECANTER,QUART,CIRCA 1840,2 TUNE SWISS MUSIC BOX.. 85.00
CUT GLASS DECANTER,QUART,DIAMOND & PANEL,STOPPER............ 35.00
CUT GLASS DECANTER SIGNED LIBBY,STAR WITH PINEAPPLE &
  STRAWBERRY.. 58.00
CUT GLASS DECANTER,SQUARE BOTTLE OVER ALL CUT IN CANE....... 32.00
CUT GLASS DECANTER,TRUMPET SHAPE,OVERLAY,BLUE TO CLEAR...... 75.00
CUT GLASS DECANTER,WATER,BULBOUS,STAR BASE,CUT RIBS ON
  NECK,FANS... 22.00
CUT GLASS DECANTER WITH CURVED CUT HANDLE.................... 65.00
CUT GLASS DECANTERS,PAIR,CANE PATTERN,10 IN. TALL........... 58.00
CUT GLASS DECANTERS,PAIR,ETCHED,CONTINENTAL SILVER BASES &
  STOPPERS.. 200.00
CUT GLASS DECANTERS,PAIR MATCHING,WATERFORD TYPE............ 65.00
CUT GLASS DECANTERS,PAIR PEDESTAL WITH CUT STOPPERS,12 IN.
  HIGH.. 150.00
CUT GLASS DESK SET,SAPPHIRE BLUE,BRASS HOLDER............... 65.00
CUT GLASS DESSERT BOWL & LINER,SET OF 10 FROSTED FLOWER
  SUPREMES,FOOTED... 250.00
CUT GLASS DESSERT,DIAMOND POINT BORDER & STAR............... 6.50
CUT GLASS DISH,5 IN.,HOBSTARS................................. 4.50
CUT GLASS DISH,8 IN. OVAL..................................... 8.00
CUT GLASS DISH,10 IN.,FLAT EXTENDING HANDLES,HOBSTARS....... 135.00
CUT GLASS DISH SIGNED EGGINTON,6 HOBSTARS AROUND 6-POINT

```
  STAR.................................................  55.00
CUT GLASS DISH,SIGNED LIBBEY,,11 IN. X 5 IN..........  47.00
CUT GLASS DISH,STEMMED...............................  22.00
CUT GLASS DISH WITH MATCHING CUBE CANDLEHOLDERS......   5.50
CUT GLASS DRESSER BOTTLE WITH SILVER TOP.............  15.00
CUT GLASS DRESSER BOX,SILVER RIM,HINGED LID,HEART
  SHAPED,THISTLES...................................  75.00
CUT GLASS DRESSER JAR,PINWHEELS.....................  37.50
CUT GLASS DRESSER SET..............................  60.00
CUT GLASS DRESSER TRAY, 12 IN. BY 7IN..............  43.00
CUT GLASS FERN BOWL ON FEET,GEOMETRIC CUTTING......  22.00
CUT GLASS FERN DISH,6 IN. FOOTED,HOBSTARS..........  19.50
CUT GLASS FERN DISH,7 IN.,HOBSTAR & FERNS..........  65.00
CUT GLASS FERN DISH,FLORAL PATTERN WITH HARVARD....  19.00
CUT GLASS FERN DISH ON LEGS........................  15.00
CUT GLASS FERN DISH,PINWHEEL.......................  22.00
CUT GLASS FERNERY,3 FOOTED,ALTERNATE PANELS OF DIAMOND POINT
  & FAN............................................  19.00
CUT GLASS FERNERY,7 IN.,3 FOOTED...................  24.00
CUT GLASS FERNERY ON 3 FEET,PINWHEELS & FANS.......  25.00
CUT GLASS FIGURINES,PAIR GOOSE GIRL................  14.50
CUT GLASS FINGER BOWL,DIAMOND & FAN PATTERN........  14.50
CUT GLASS FINGER BOWL,HOBNAIL PATTERN..............  22.00
CUT GLASS FINGER BOWL,HOBSTAR & FAN................  18.50
CUT GLASS FINGER BOWL,PINWHEEL.....................  15.00
CUT GLASS FINGER BOWL,PINWHEEL STAR & FAN..........  15.00
CUT GLASS FLOWER BOWL..............................   7.50
CUT GLASS FRUIT BOWL,8 IN. DIAMETER................  35.00
CUT GLASS FRUIT BOWL,8 IN. SERRATED EDGE PINWHEEL..  30.00
CUT GLASS FRUIT BOWL,10 IN.........................  75.00
CUT GLASS FRUIT BOWL,DIAMOND & FAN.................  45.00
CUT GLASS FRUIT BOWL,HOBSTAR.......................  35.00
CUT GLASS FRUIT BOWL ON STANDARD...................  75.00
CUT GLASS FRUIT BOWL,ROUND.........................  25.00
CUT GLASS FRUIT BOWL,SIGNED HAWKES,SUNBURST CENTER.  95.00
CUT GLASS GOBLET...................................  15.00
CUT GLASS GOBLET,5 POINTED HOBNAIL CLEAR...........   9.00
CUT GLASS GOBLET,BAR & DIAMOND.....................   8.50
CUT GLASS GOBLET,DOUBLE TEARDROP OR HOURGLASS STEM.  25.00
CUT GLASS GOBLET,GREEN,CLEAR STEM & BASE...........  20.00
CUT GLASS GOBLET,INTAGLIO,PANELLED STEM............  15.00
CUT GLASS GOBLET,INTAGLIO ROSES,CUT STEM,RAYED BASE  14.00
CUT GLASS GOBLET,KNOB STEM.........................  10.00
CUT GLASS GOBLET,POINTED STEM......................   9.50
CUT GLASS GOBLET,RUBY,CLEAR STEM & BASE............  20.00
CUT GLASS GOBLET,STRAWBERRY DIAMOND PATTERN........  17.50
CUT GLASS GOBLET,STEMMED,PINWHEEL CUT..............   3.00
CUT GLASS GOBLET,TOASTING,HARVARD PATTERN,DATED 1887  33.00
CUT GLASS GOBLETS,SET OF 12 AMETHYST,WHITE STEM....  82.00
CUT GLASS GOLD FISH BOWL,CUT & ETCHED WITH 3 FISH & FOLIAGE.  22.00
CUT GLASS HAIR RECEIVER,COSMOS DESIGN..............  35.00
CUT GLASS HAIR RECEIVER,FLOWERS....................  18.00
CUT GLASS HAIR RECEIVER,FROSTED FLORAL.............   6.00
CUT GLASS HAIR RECEIVER,HARVARD....................  27.50
CUT GLASS HAIR RECEIVER WITH SILVER TOP,INITIALS EMB  17.00
CUT GLASS HAWKES MARK ON 6 IN. DIA. HINGED COVERED ROUND BOX  150.00
CUT GLASS HAWKES OIL & VINEGAR BOTTLES.............  25.00
CUT GLASS HUMIDOR,HARVARD PATTERN..................  22.50
CUT GLASS ICE BUCKET...............................  28.50
CUT GLASS ICE BUCKET,5 IN..........................  50.00
CUT GLASS ICE BUCKET,6 IN. HIGH,HOBSTAR,VESCAS & CHAIN  55.00
CUT GLASS ICE CREAM DISH,HARVARD PATTERN...........  29.50
CUT GLASS ICE CREAM TRAY...........................  85.00
CUT GLASS ICE CREAM TRAY,HOBSTARS,DIAMOND POINT & FAN  42.50
CUT GLASS ICE TUB..................................  65.00
```

CUT GLASS ICE TUB,4 HOBSTARS WITH HOBSTAR BASE & DIAMOND
  POINT & FAN.. 55.00
CUT GLASS INKWELL.. 3.00
CUT GLASS INKWELL,SQUARE WITH STERLING MUSHROOM SHAPED
  HINGED LID... 95.00
CUT GLASS INKWELL WITH SILVER PLATE HOLDER.................... 20.00
CUT GLASS JELLY 3 FOOTED BASE................................ 45.00
CUT GLASS JELLY DISH,ETCHED BUTTERFLIES & COSMOS............. 15.00
CUT GLASS JUG,10 IN.,AMERICAN............................... 30.00
CUT GLASS JUICE GLASS,SET OF 11,DIAMOND CUT HALF WAY UP..... 75.00
CUT GLASS JUICE GLASS,STRAWBERRY,DIAMOND & FAN.............. 5.00
CUT GLASS JUICE TUMBLER,SET OF 10........................... 75.00
CUT GLASS KNIFE REST
  7.00   TO.. 18.00
CUT GLASS KNIFE REST,3 IN................................... 12.50
CUT GLASS KNIFE REST,4 IN. LONG............................. 12.00
CUT GLASS KNIFE REST,4 IN. LONG,SCALLOPED CENTER BAR........ 4.50
CUT GLASS KNIFE REST,4 IN.,NOTCHED PRISMS................... 15.00
CUT GLASS KNIFE REST,5 IN................................... 14.00
CUT GLASS KNIFE REST,BALL ENDS
  9.00   TO.. 10.50
CUT GLASS KNIFE REST,BALL ENDS,NOTCHED PRISMS............... 15.00
CUT GLASS KNIFE REST,BALL ENDS,RIB CUT CENTER.............. 12.00
CUT GLASS KNIFE REST,BEVELED EDGES,DIAMOND POINT & FAN...... 6.00
CUT GLASS KNIFE REST,CLEAR.................................. 8.50
CUT GLASS KNIFE REST,CLOVER SHAPE ENDS,3 SECTIONAL PRISM
  SIGNED.. 10.00
CUT GLASS KNIFE REST,CUT BALL ENDS.......................... 12.50
CUT GLASS KNIFE REST,CUT PANEL HOB-STAR BALLS WITH ROUNDS AT
  ENDS.. 15.00
CUT GLASS KNIFE REST,DAISY PATTERN.......................... 10.00
CUT GLASS KNIFE REST,DIAMOND FACETED........................ 16.00
CUT GLASS KNIFE REST,DIAMOND POINT & STAR................... 9.50
CUT GLASS KNIFE-REST,DUMB-BELL SHAPE........................ 14.00
CUT GLASS KNIFE REST,FACETED BALLS WITH 8-POINT STAR IN
  HEXAGON... 16.50
CUT GLASS KNIFE REST,FACETED BALLS WITH FACETED STARS....... 16.50
CUT GLASS KNIFE REST FOR CARVING KNIFE...................... 20.00
CUT GLASS KNIFE REST,HEXAGON SHAPED ENDS & CUT.............. 17.50
CUT GLASS KNIFE REST IN FLORAL & LEAF DESIGN................ 18.00
CUT GLASS KNIFE REST,INTAGLIO CUT FRUIT,TRIANGLE SHAPE...... 12.00
CUT GLASS KNIFE REST,LAPIDARY CUT,BALL SHAPED ENDS.......... 15.00
CUT GLASS KNIFE REST,LARGE PRISM CUT KNOBS,POINTED ENDS..... 12.50
CUT GLASS KNIFE REST,PAIR................................... 14.00
CUT GLASS KNIFE REST,PAIR,4 IN. LONG........................ 10.00
CUT GLASS KNIFE REST,PINEAPPLE END......................... 3.50
CUT GLASS KNIFE REST,SET OF 13,12 INDIVIDUAL & 1 MASTER..... 100.00
CUT GLASS LAMP,13 IN. HIGH,MUSHROOM SHADE,30 PRISMS........ 110.00
CUT GLASS LAMP,16 IN. HIGH,PEWTER RIM & FITTINGS,ELECTRIFIED 250.00
CUT GLASS LAMP WITH PRISMS,CANE CUT BORDER,& ROSE CUT,22 IN.
  HIGH.. 225.00
CUT GLASS LEMONADE,HANDLED,4 IN............................. 10.00
CUT GLASS LEMONADE PITCHER.................................. 4.50
CUT GLASS LIBBEY TUMBLER,CUT BLADE.......................... 15.00
CUT GLASS LIQUOR BOTTLE,11 IN. TALL,PINWHEELS & FANS........ 40.00
CUT GLASS MASTER SALT,HOBSTARS & NOTCHED PRISMS............. 12.50
CUT GLASS MAYONNAISE BASE & UNDERPLATE...................... 21.00
CUT GLASS MAYONNAISE SET,HOBSTAR,DIAMOND POINT & NOTCHED
  PRISM... 30.00
CUT GLASS MILK PITCHER,CHAIRBOTTOM.......................... 59.00
CUT GLASS MINIATURE MUG,2 IN. ,IRISH....................... 14.00
CUT GLASS MINIATURE ROSEBOWL,FANS,STRAWBERRY DIAMOND........ 20.00
CUT GLASS MINIATURE ROSE BOWL SHAPED SALTS,HOBSTAR.......... 75.00
CUT GLASS MUFFINEER,PANELED CLEAR,EMBOSSED STERLING TOP..... 14.50
CUT GLASS MUFFINEER,SILVER PLATED TOP....................... 18.00

```
CUT GLASS MUG,6 IN. TALL................................   55.00
CUT GLASS MUG,DIAMOND & CUT LEAF........................   12.00
CUT GLASS MUSTARD,HANDLED,HINGED SILVER LID.............   20.00
CUT GLASS MUSTARD JAR,COVERED,HOBSTAR...................   12.00
CUT GLASS MUSTARD JAR,DIAMOND POINT,....................    9.00
CUT GLASS MUSTARD JAR,DIAMOND POINT WITH STAR BOTTOM....    9.00
CUT GLASS MUSTARD ON SILVER TRAY........................   16.50
CUT GLASS NAPKIN RING HOLDER & KNIFE REST COMBINED,.....   10.00
CUT GLASS NAPKIN RING HOLDER,TRIANGLE SHAPE,CROSS STAR &
  DIAMOND...............................................   14.00
CUT GLASS NAPKIN RING,HORSESHOE SHAPE...................    8.50
CUT GLASS NAPKIN RINGS,PAIR.............................   24.00
CUT GLASS NAPPY.........................................   13.00
CUT GLASS NAPPY,2 HANDLED
  10.00  TO.............................................   27.00
CUT GLASS NAPPY,5 IN. HANDLED...........................    9.50
CUT GLASS NAPPY,5 IN.,HANDLED,CANE & FLORAL.............    5.50
CUT GLASS NAPPY,5 IN.,HOBSTAR...........................   18.50
CUT GLASS NAPPY,6 IN.,4 HOBSTARS & FANS.................    7.00
CUT GLASS NAPPY,6 IN.,HANDLED,CANE & FLORAL.............    6.00
CUT GLASS NAPPY,6 IN. HOBSTARS WITH DIAMOND POINT & FAN.   12.00
CUT GLASS NAPPY,6 IN.,RING HANDLE PINWHEELS & HOBSTARS..    8.50
CUT GLASS NAPPY,6 IN.,SIGNED HAWKES.....................   19.00
CUT GLASS NAPPY BUTTON AND DAISY........................   10.50
CUT GLASS NAPPY,FAN HOBNAIL.............................    8.50
CUT GLASS NAPPY,SALESMANS SAMPLE,DOUBLE HANDLED.........   22.50
CUT GLASS NAPPY,STRAWBERRY & FAN........................   20.00
CUT GLASS NUT BOWL,HOBSTARS,CANE........................   45.00
CUT GLASS PAPERWEIGHT,CONE..............................   15.00
CUT GLASS PAPERWEIGHT,HOBSTAR,SCALLOPED EDGE............   23.00
CUT GLASS PASTE JAR,VERTICAL ROWS OF NOTCHED PRISM,PYRAMIDAL
  STAR..................................................   22.50
CUT GLASS PATCH BOX,HINGED..............................    8.50
CUT GLASS PERFUME
  12.50  TO.............................................   18.00
CUT GLASS PERFUME BOTTLE,5 IN.,PINWHEEL & STAR..........   25.00
CUT GLASS PERFUME BOTTLE,10 IN. RECLINING...............   18.00
CUT GLASS PERFUME BOTTLE,19TH CENTURY,OXFORD LAVENDER,8.   30.00
CUT GLASS PERFUME BOTTLE,FLORAL PATTERN,INTAGLIO........   25.00
CUT GLASS PERFUME BOTTLES,CUT STOPPERS,PAIR.............    6.50
CUT GLASS PERFUME BOTTLES,PAIR..........................   69.50
CUT GLASS PERFUME BOTTLE,SAWTOOTH PATTERN...............    4.75
CUT GLASS PERFUME BOTTLE,STERLING TOP...................   22.50
CUT GLASS PERFUME,CZECH MARKED,LADY DANCING & PLAYING FLUTE.  10.50
CUT GLASS PERFUME,DIAMOND WITH STARS WITH FANS..........   32.00
CUT GLASS PERFUME,INTAGLIO,PETTICOAT SHAPE,CRANBERRY STOPPER  18.00
CUT GLASS PERFUMES,PAIR LAY DOWN,STERLING TOPS..........   16.00
CUT GLASS PERFUME,2 SIDED LAY-DOWN,STERLING SILVER CAP..   28.00
CUT GLASS PERFUME VIAL..................................    8.00
CUT GLASS PERFUME WITH CUT STOPPER,BULBOUS..............   15.00
CUT GLASS PERFUME WITH STERLING LID,CRANBERRY PANELED CUT...  24.50
CUT GLASS PERFUME WITH STERLING TOP,LAYDOWN.............    6.50
CUT GLASS PICTURE FRAMES,PAIR,CANE PATTERN WITH MITER LEAVES  35.00
CUT GLASS PILL VIAL,STERLING HINGED LID.................   22.00
CUT GLASS PIPE HOLDER,HEXAGONAL BUTTON & CROSS CUT......   22.00
CUT GLASS PITCHER,9 IN. TALL,DIAMOND PANELS & FANS......   30.00
CUT GLASS PITCHER,10 IN. TALL,2 FLORAL PANELS,DIAMONDS &
  FANS..................................................   27.50
CUT GLASS PITCHER,11 IN. HIGH,NARROW NECK...............   50.00
CUT GLASS PITCHER,11 IN. TALL,PINWHEELS & STARS,V PANELS.  32.00
CUT GLASS PITCHER & 4 TUMBLERS,TANKARD-TYPE.............   50.00
CUT GLASS PITCHER,HARVARD...............................   85.00
CUT GLASS PITCHER,HOBBS DIAMOND & SUNBURST..............    5.00
CUT GLASS PITCHER SIGNED LIBBY..........................   60.00
CUT GLASS PITCHER,TANKARD...............................   37.50
```

```
CUT GLASS PITCHER SIGNED HAWKES...............................   85.00
CUT GLASS PLATE,4 IN.,FROSTED STAR BOTTOM....................    2.50
CUT GLASS PLATE,7 IN.,FLORAL CENTER,STARS ON BORDER.........    7.00
CUT GLASS PLATE,7 IN. STARFISH..............................   11.00
CUT GLASS PLATE,9 IN.,HOBSTAR CENTER........................   22.00
CUT GLASS PLATE,10 IN. HEAVY CUT,6 RUFFLES..................   47.00
CUT GLASS PLATE,BARRED OVAL SQUARE..........................    4.00
CUT GLASS PLATE,DIAMOND MEDALLION...........................    8.50
CUT GLASS PLATE,HOBSTAR & DIAMOND...........................   22.00
CUT GLASS PLATES,PAIR 7 IN.,DIAMETER,HOBSTAR................   33.00
CUT GLASS PLATE,ROUND,11 IN.,HOBSTARS,NOTCHED RIM...........   28.00
CUT GLASS PLATES,SET OF 6 STRAWBERRY DIAMOND & FAN FLAT.....   60.00
CUT GLASS PLATE,SET OF 10 CRYSTAL IRIDESCENT 6 IN...........   16.00
CUT GLASS PLATTER,POINTED HOBNAIL & FAN.....................   12.00
CUT GLASS POWDER BOX,EMBOSSED SILVER COLLAR & HINGE.........   37.50
CUT GLASS POWDER BOX,HINGED COVER,HARVARD PATTERN...........   28.00
CUT GLASS POWDER BOXES,PAIR 5 IN. DIAMETER COVERED..........   60.00
CUT GLASS POWDER BOX WITH ART NOUVEAU TYPE LID..............   14.00
CUT GLASS POWDER JAR,COVERED................................   65.00
CUT GLASS POWDER JAR,NOTCHED CUT,STERLING TOP,FLORAL
 ENGRAVED...................................................    8.00
CUT GLASS POWDER JAR,PINWHEEL PATTERN.......................   16.00
CUT GLASS POWDER JAR,PRISM CUT,SILVER PLATE COVER...........   12.50
CUT GLASS POWDER JAR,STARS & PRISMS,STERLING COVER..........   16.00
CUT GLASS POWDER JAR WITH STERLING TOP,INITIALED...........    13.00
CUT GLASS PUNCH BOWL,2 PIECE,HOBSTARS,FANS,CANES,STARS......   90.00
CUT GLASS PUNCH BOWL,2 PIECE,HOBSTARS,GEOMETRICS,CUT COLLAR
 AT TOP....................................................   125.00
CUT GLASS PUNCH BOWL,3-IN-1,16 IN. TALL,COMPOTE BASE........  250.00
CUT GLASS PUNCH BOWL,9 IN. TALL,...........................    60.00
CUT GLASS PUNCH BOWL,12 IN.,2 PARTS,HOBSTARS...............   225.00
CUT GLASS PUNCH BOWL,14 IN.,24 POINT HOBSTAR...............   200.00
CUT GLASS PUNCH BOWL,14 IN. DIAMETER,15 IN. HIGH,HOBSTARS...  400.00
CUT GLASS PUNCH BOWL CIRCA 1810,2 PARTS....................   285.00
CUT GLASS PUNCH BOWL,FORBES SILVER SHELL LADLE WITH GLASS
 HANDLE....................................................   325.00
CUT GLASS PUNCH BOWL,HANDCUT...............................    60.00
CUT GLASS PUNCH BOWL,HANDCUT CRYSTAL WITH SILVERPLATED
 HORNS,PEWTER LID..........................................    94.00
CUT GLASS PUNCH BOWL,PEDESTALED............................   135.00
CUT GLASS PUNCH BOWL WITH COVER & 11 CUPS,THREE
 FOOTED,SAWTOOTH & STAR....................................   110.00
CUT GLASS PUNCH CUP,10,5 GEOMETRICS,FANS & 5 STRAWBERRY
 DIAMOND & FAN.............................................    60.00
CUT GLASS PUNCH CUP,CLUB STARS IN PANELS,CUT HANDLES,RAYED
 BASE.....................................................     5.00
CUT GLASS PUNCH CUPS,SET OF 9,CIRCA 1810...................   150.00
CUT GLASS PUNCH CUP,SET OF 11..............................    80.00
CUT GLASS PUNCH CUPS,SET OF 12.............................    87.00
CUT GLASS PUNCH CUP,STARS,FANS,STRAWBERRY DIAMOND,CROSS CUT.   12.00
CUT GLASS RELISH,OVAL,SHARP SCALLOPED EDGE.................    18.00
CUT GLASS RELISH ROWBOAT,BLUE,11 IN. LONG..................    24.50
CUT GLASS RHINE WINE GOBLET,COBALT BLUE BLOCK DESIGN.......    28.50
CUT GLASS RHINE WINES,SET OF 6,RUBY,BLUE,PURPLE,CRANBERRY...   36.00
CUT GLASS ROSE BOWL,2 PIECE FOOTED.........................    89.50
CUT GLASS ROSE BOWL,FOOTED,BROWN TRIM,FINECUT ROSES........    35.00
CUT GLASS ROSE VASE........................................    26.00
CUT GLASS SALT AND PEPPER,3 IN.,GLASS TOPS.................     8.50
CUT GLASS SALT AND PEPPER,4 IN.,SILVER TOPS................     9.00
CUT GLASS SALT & PEPPER,PAIR CORNUCOPIA SHAPED LYING DOWN...   25.00
CUT GLASS SALT & PEPPER,SCROLLED STERLING SILVER TOPS.......   20.00
CUT GLASS SALT & PEPPER SET,PAIR,NOTCHED PRISM,DIAMOND POINT
 & FAN....................................................    12.00
CUT GLASS SALT AND PEPPER SHAKERS SIGNED HAWKES,STERLING
 TOPS.....................................................    20.00
```

```
CUT GLASS SALT & PEPPER,SILVER TOP,DIAMOND..................      9.50
CUT GLASS SALT & PEPPER WITH STERLING TOPS
  4.00  TO.......................................................     12.00
CUT GLASS SALT,8-SIDED INDIVIDUAL OPEN......................      1.25
CUT GLASS SALT CELLARS,PAIR ENGLISH WITH SILVER
  RIMS,HALLMARKED............................................     15.00
CUT GLASS SALT DIP..........................................      2.15
CUT GLASS SALT DIP,6........................................     13.75
CUT GLASS SALT DIP,FLOWER,4
  10.00  TO..................................................     10.75
CUT GLASS SALT DIPS 1 IN. DIAMETER..........................      2.10
CUT GLASS SALT DIP,FERN PATTERN.............................      4.00
CUT GLASS SALT DIP,PEDESTAL,GREEN...........................      1.50
CUT GLASS SALT DIP,ZIPPER PATTERN...........................      2.15
CUT GLASS SALT DIP,ZIPPER & FACET,SET OF 6..................     14.00
CUT GLASS SALT DIPS,12......................................     42.00
CUT GLASS SALT,FOOTED,SET OF 10,PANELLED
  STEMS,SCALLOPED,CROSS HATCHED.............................     95.00
CUT GLASS SALT,INDIVIDUAL,6 PANEL WITH STAR CUT.............      4.00
CUT GLASS SALT,INDIVIDUAL,HEART SHAPE.......................      1.50
CUT GLASS SALT,INDIVIDUAL,NOTCHED RIM,STAR BOTTOM...........      2.50
CUT GLASS SALT,MASTER,2 HANDLED,PINWHEEL DESIGN.............      6.50
CUT GLASS SALT,OBLONG.......................................     20.00
CUT GLASS SALT,OPEN,BLOCK PATTERN...........................      7.50
CUT GLASS SALT,SET OF 6 INDIVIDUAL,HOBSTAR,DIAMOND & FAN....     20.00
CUT GLASS SALT,SET OF 6 RIB ROUND OPEN......................     16.50
CUT GLASS SALT,ROUND........................................      2.25
CUT GLASS SAUCE,DIAMOND SUNBURST FLAT.......................      2.50
CUT GLASS SERVING DISH,TREEE SHAPED.........................     25.00
CUT GLASS SHERBET,DIAMOND & FAN,CUT GLASS BANDS AROUND BOWL.      8.00
CUT GLASS SHERBET,FOOTED,STRAWBERRY DIAMOND & FAN,SET OF 3..     12.00
CUT GLASS SHERRY GLASSES,SET OF 4,PANELLED BOWL,DOUBLE KNOBS     26.00
CUT GLASS SHERRY GLASSES,SET OF 4,PANELLED BOWL,PRISM CUT
  STEM......................................................     26.00
CUT GLASS SHOT GLASSES,SET OF 6,PEDESTALED..................     21.00
CUT GLASS SIGNED BRIERLEY COMPOTE,AMETHYST BOWL,CLEAR STEM..     24.50
CUT GLASS SIGNED CLARK BOWL.................................     65.00
CUT GLASS SIGNED CLARK PITCHER,HOBSTARS.....................     85.00
CUT GLASS SIGNED GINTON TUMBLER,...........................     16.50
CUT GLASS SIGNED GRAVIC PUNCH BOWL ON STAND WITH
  LADLE,FLORAL DESIGN.......................................  1,500.00
CUT GLASS SIGNED HAWKES 2 LIPPED OIL & VINEGAR CRUET,GOLD &
  BLACK.....................................................     18.00
CUT GLASS SIGNED HAWKES 3 IN. BOWL,VICTORIA PATTERN.........     45.00
CUT GLASS SIGNED HAWKES 4 IN. VASE..........................     18.00
CUT GLASS SIGNED HAWKES 4 TUMBLERS..........................     60.00
CUT GLASS SIGNED HAWKES 5 HOLLOW STEM CHAMPAGNE GLASSES.....     25.00
CUT GLASS SIGNED HAWKES 6 IN. BOWL,COLONIAL PATTERN.........     14.50
CUT GLASS SIGNED HAWKES 7 IN. PLATE.........................     23.00
CUT GLASS SIGNED HAWKES 8 IN. BOWL,FAN TOP..................     50.00
CUT GLASS SIGNED HAWKES 8 TUMBLERS,FLYING GEESE,ENGRAVED....     32.50
CUT GLASS SIGNED HAWKES 9 IN. PERFUME,ENGRAVED BIRDS ON
  BRANCHES..................................................     28.00
CUT GLASS SIGNED HAWKES 9 IN. VASE,ENGRAVED DESIGN OF
  FLOWERS...................................................     42.50
CUT GLASS SIGNED HAWKES 12 IN COCKTAIL  SHAKER..............     30.00
CUT GLASS SIGNED HAWKES,14 IN.,TRUMPET VASE
  55.00  TO..................................................     65.00
CUT GLASS SIGNED HAWKES 14 IN. VASE,FACETED KNOB NEAR FOOT..    135.00
CUT GLASS SIGNED HAWKES BITTERS BOTTLE,STERLING TOP.........     22.00
CUT GLASS SIGNED HAWKES,BOTTLES, IN SILVER CONTAINER,LOCK &
  KEY,PAIR...................................................    175.00
CUT GLASS SIGNED HAWKES BOWL,HOBSTARS.......................     47.50
CUT GLASS SIGNED HAWKES BOWL,WREATH & FLOWER PATTERN........     68.00
CUT GLASS SIGNED HAWKES BUD VASE,ACID ETCHED................     17.00
```

CUT GLASS SIGNED HAWKES BULBOUS SCALLOPED RIM VASE.......... 35.00
CUT GLASS SIGNED HAWKES CANDLESTICK,GREEN COLOUR............ 29.50
CUT GLASS SIGNED HAWKES CIGARETTE BOX,CLASSIC PATTERN....... 40.00
CUT GLASS SIGNED HAWKES CIGARETTE BOX,COVER CUT & AMBER
  OVERLAY... 30.00
CUT GLASS SIGNED HAWKES CLEAR VASE,ETCHING,11 IN. TALL...... 45.00
CUT GLASS SIGNED HAWKES COCKTAIL SHAKER,RAISED DIAMONDS..... 48.00
CUT GLASS SIGNED HAWKES COMPOTE............................ 45.00
CUT GLASS SIGNED HAWKES COMPOTE,CLASSIC PATTERN,STAR CUT
  BASE... 110.00
CUT GLASS SIGNED HAWKES CREAMER,INTERMITTENT STAR WITHIN
  STAR... 16.50
CUT GLASS SIGNED HAWKES,ENGRAVED STEUBEN VERRE DE SOIE ICE
  TEA TUMBLER.. 65.00
CUT GLASS SIGNED HAWKES FRENCH DRESSING BOTTLE,STERLING
  DATED STOPPER.. 24.50
CUT GLASS SIGNED HAWKES GRAPHIC COMPOTE,IRIS PATTERN....... 85.00
CUT GLASS SIGNED HAWKES HANDLED NAPPY,ABERDEEN PATTERN..... 30.00
CUT GLASS SIGNED HAWKES HARVARD & FAN BOWL................. 38.00
CUT GLASS SIGNED HAWKES INTAGLIO OIL & VINEGAR BOTTLE,..... 27.50
CUT GLASS SIGNED HAWKES LOUIS XIV PATTERN SET OF 8 7 IN.
  PLATES... 30.00
CUT GLASS SIGNED HAWKES LUMP SUGAR TRAY.................... 15.00
CUT GLASS SIGNED HAWKES MAYONNAISE BOWL & DISH,CROSS DIAMOND 55.00
CUT GLASS SIGNED HAWKES MILLICENT PATTERN LETTER HOLDER..... 40.00
CUT GLASS SIGNED HAWKES OIL & VINEGAR BOTTLE............... 20.00
CUT GLASS SIGNED HAWKES ORANGE BOAT SHAPED BOWL,INTAGLIO
  MEDALLION.. 150.00
CUT GLASS SIGNED HAWKES OVAL PICTURE FRAME,HOBSTARS......... 125.00
CUT GLASS SIGNED HAWKES PEDESTAL FOOT VASE,QUEENS PATTERN... 70.00
CUT GLASS SIGNED HAWKES PEDESTAL NUT DISH WITH SILVER
  OVERLAY RIM.. 12.50
CUT GLASS SIGNED HAWKES PERFUME BOTTLE..................... 28.00
CUT GLASS SIGNED HAWKES PLATE............................. 28.00
CUT GLASS SIGNED HAWKES PLATE WITH SILVER TRIM............. 17.50
CUT GLASS SIGNED HAWKES ROCK CRYSTAL ICED TEA GLASS &
  UNDERPLATE... 40.00
CUT GLASS SIGNED HAWKES ROUND BOWL,3 PANELS OF HOBSTARS,3
  INTAGLIO... 137.50
CUT GLASS SIGNED HAWKES SALT,CLEAR,RAISED EXTENDED ENDS..... 5.00
CUT GLASS SIGNED HAWKES SALT,GOLD BAND.................... 6.00
CUT GLASS SIGNED HAWKES STEMMED FRUIT BOWLS WITH STEMMED
  INSERTS.. 20.00
CUT GLASS SIGNED HAWKES SET OF 4 STEMMED WINES,ROCK CRYSTAL
  PATTERN.. 80.00
CUT GLASS SIGNED HAWKES SET OF 8 CHAMPAGNES,INITALED D B D.. 50.00
CUT GLASS SIGNED HAWKES SUGAR & CREAMER WITH GOLD BAND &
  BLUE DOTS.. 22.50
CUT GLASS SIGNED HAWKES TANTALUS SET,2 LIQUOR BOTTLES,SILVER
  HOLDER,.. 250.00
CUT GLASS SIGNED HAWKES TUMBLER,SET OF 4................... 11.00
CUT GLASS SIGNED HAWKES VASE,9 IN. HIGH................... 125.00
CUT GLASS SIGNED HAWKES VASE,HONEYCOMB & STAR,............. 65.00
CUT GLASS SIGNED HAWKES VASE,RIBBON & STAR................. 25.00
CUT GLASS SIGNED HAWKES VINEGAR & OIL BOTTLE WITH SILVER
  STOPPER.. 14.50
CUT GLASS SIGNED HAWKES VINTAGE PATTERN COBALT BLUE MUSTARD
  JAR.. 45.00
CUT GLASS SIGNED HAWKES WATER PITCHER & 6 TUMBLERS,CANES &
  HOBSTARS... 85.00
CUT GLASS SIGNED HAWKES WATER PITCHER,BULBOUS BASE,FLARED
  TOP.. 48.50
CUT GLASS SIGNED HAWKES WINE,CUT STARS.................... 15.00
CUT GLASS SIGNED HEISEY BASKET,8 PANEL BOWL SECTION,FLOWER
  WITH HOBSTAR... 75.00

```
CUT GLASS SIGNED HOARE CELERY TRAY.........................    37.00
CUT GLASS SIGNED HOARE,FLOWER CENTER,HOBSTARS,FANS,CANE,STEP
  CUTTING.................................................      75.00
CUT GLASS SIGNED HUNT BOWL,LACE PATTERN....................    37.50
CUT GLASS SIGNED LIBBEY 11 IN. PLATE,OVER 6 POUNDS.........   130.00
CUT GLASS SIGNED LIBBEY 11 IN. VASE.......................     40.00
CUT GLASS SIGNED LIBBEY BOWL..............................     65.00
CUT GLASS SIGNED LIBBEY BOWL,9 IN.........................     85.00
CUT GLASS SIGNED LIBBEY BOWL,SCALLOPED EDGE,FLORAL INTAGLIO
  CUT MOTIF...............................................    250.00
CUT GLASS SIGNED LIBBEY,BUD VASE,CHRYSANTHEMUM PATTERN.....    37.50
CUT GLASS SIGNED LIBBEY CANDY DISH,INTAGLIO LEAVES & BERRIES  35.00
CUT GLASS SIGNED LIBBEY CELERY TRAY,FLAT..................     25.00
CUT GLASS SIGNED LIBBEY CREAMER...........................     14.00
CUT GLASS SIGNED LIBBEY CRUET.............................     30.00
CUT GLASS SIGNED LIBBEY,ENGRAVED CHAMPAGNE................     10.00
CUT GLASS SIGNED LIBBEY FERNERY ON 3 FEET.................     65.00
CUT GLASS SIGNED LIBBEY FOOTED VASE,MUSHROOM TOP,ENGRAVED
  LEAVES..................................................     48.00
CUT GLASS SIGNED LIBBEY HANDLED NAPPY.....................     32.00
CUT GLASS SIGNED LIBBEY,NAPPY WITH HANDLE.................     29.00
CUT GLASS SIGNED LIBBEY SALT,SET OF 6 PEDESTAL,CUT WITH
  LEAVES..................................................     42.00
CUT GLASS SIGNED LIBBEY SET OF 10 PUNCH CUPS,HOBSTAR......    185.00
CUT GLASS SIGNED LIBBEY,TUMBLERS,SET OF 4,HOBSTARS........     55.00
CUT GLASS SIGNED LIBBEY,VASES,MATCHED PAIR,11 IN. TALL....    125.00
CUT GLASS SIGNED LIBBEY WINE,TEAR-DROP STEMS,HOBSTARS,FAN &
  CROSS...................................................     25.00
CUT GLASS SIGNED LIZZIE LIE DOWN PERFUME,STERLING TOP.....     15.00
CUT GLASS SIGNED NEWARK CELERY DISH.......................     35.00
CUT GLASS SIGNED PAIRPOINT FORK & SPOON DATED 1880........    150.00
CUT GLASS SIGNED SEVRES KNIFE REST,SWIRLED CENTER POSTS...      6.00
CUT GLASS SIGNED SINCLAIRE,DECANTER,GREEK KEY & LAUREL,10
  IN. TRAY................................................     55.00
CUT GLASS SIGNED SINCLAIRE OVAL SHALLOW BOWL,BIRD IN CAGE
  PATTERN.................................................     69.50
CUT GLASS SIGNED SINCLAIRE,TUMBLER........................     10.00
CUT GLASS SIGNED SINCLAIRE TUMBLER,HONEYCOMB PATTERN......      7.00
CUT GLASS SIGNED SINCLAIRE,VASE,AMBER.....................     30.00
CUT GLASS SIGNED STEUBEN 6 PRONG VASE.....................    175.00
CUT GLASS SIGNED TUTHILL COMPOTE,PRIMROSE PATTERN.........    155.00
CUT GLASS SIGNED TUTHILL HANDLED DECANTER.................    165.00
CUT GLASS SIGNED UNGER BROS. BOWL.........................     42.00
CUT GLASS SIGNED WEBB,ENGLAND,6 WINES.....................    125.00
CUT GLASS SNUFF BOTTLE,SILVER PLATED TOP WITH ATTACHED SPOON  16.00
CUT GLASS SPOONER,DIAMOND MEDALLION.......................      7.50
CUT GLASS SPOONER,FROSTED WEDDING.........................     12.00
CUT GLASS SPOONHOLDER.....................................     28.00
CUT GLASS STEIGEL TYPE TOASTING GLASS,ETCHED FLORALS ON
  YELLOW..................................................     20.00
CUT GLASS STEIN,6 IN.,AMBER,6 KNOB FEET,RIBBED PATTERN....     55.00
CUT GLASS SUGAR & CREAMER
  19.50  TO...............................................     42.50
CUT GLASS SUGAR & CREAMER,DIAMOND POINT ON ROUND BASE.....     38.00
CUT GLASS SUGAR AND CREAMER,FROSTED ENGRAVED ROSES........     14.00
CUT GLASS SUGAR AND CREAMER,HOBSTAR.......................     45.00
CUT GLASS SUGAR & CREAMER,HOBSTAR PATTERN.................     25.00
CUT GLASS SUGAR & CREAMER,HOBSTARS,DIAMOND POINT,& FAN....     40.00
CUT GLASS SUGAR & CREAMER,INTAGLIO OF THISTLES...........      38.00
CUT GLASS SUGAR & CREAMER ON PEDESTAL,HOBSTAR CUT........      60.00
CUT GLASS SUGAR & CREAMER,PINWHEEL........................     18.00
CUT GLASS SUGAR & CREAMER,RUSSIAN PATTERN,SCORED BUTTONS..     45.00
CUT GLASS SUGAR,2 HANDLED OPEN,WHIRLING STAR PATTERN......     12.00
CUT GLASS SUGAR BOWL SIGNED HAWKES........................      9.50
CUT GLASS SUGAR,CHAIR BOTTOM AND DAISY....................     15.00
```

```
CUT GLASS SUGAR-CINNAMON SHAKER,BRASS TOP...................  15.00
CUT GLASS SUGAR,CLEAR,FLORAL CUT,FOOTED.....................   2.50
CUT GLASS SUGAR,DIAMOND MEDALLION...........................   7.50
CUT GLASS SUGAR DISH,CUBE...................................   7.00
CUT GLASS SUGAR HOLDER,CUBE,TUDOR PLATE TONGS...............  14.00
CUT GLASS SUGAR LOAF TRAY,HEXAGONAL BUTTON & CROSS CUT......  18.00
CUT GLASS SUGAR,NOTCHED HANDLES.............................   9.50
CUT GLASS SUGAR SHAKER IN SULTAN PATTERN,EGG SHAPED.........  50.00
CUT GLASS SUGAR SHAKER,INTAGLIO ,STERLING TOP...............  12.00
CUT GLASS SUGAR SHAKER,RUBY BLOCK,OVERLAY,RUSSIAN PATTERN...  64.00
CUT GLASS SUGAR SHAKER,STERLING SILVER TOP..................  40.00
CUT GLASS SUGAR SIFTER,OPALESCENT SWIRL TO CLEAR WHITE......  18.00
CUT GLASS SWEETMEAT JAR SIGNED HAWKES,SILVER FLIP TOP WITH
  SPOON.....................................................  45.00
CUT GLASS SWEET MEAT DISH...................................  10.50
CUT GLASS SYRUP JUG WITH GORHAM SILVER PLATED LID,5 IN. HIGH  25.00
CUT GLASS SYRUP,METAL TOP,FLORAL CUT........................  15.00
CUT GLASS SYRUP,SILVER TOP..................................  28.00
CUT GLASS TANKARD,HARVARD PATTERN,12 IN.....................  75.00
CUT GLASS TOBACCO JAR,PANEL,SILVER LID......................  12.00
CUT GLASS TOBACCO JAR,SILVER PLATE LID,STAR CUT BASE........   3.00
CUT GLASS TOOTHPICK,DIAMOND & FAN,WEIGHTED BASE.............  15.00
CUT GLASS TOOTHPICK HOLDER
  7.50  TO.................................................. 13.50
CUT GLASS TOOTHPICK HOLDER,DIAMOND STRAWBERRY & FAN.........   9.50
CUT GLASS TOOTHPICK HOLDERS,PAIR............................  11.00
CUT GLASS TOOTHPICK HOLDERS,PAIR,BARREL SHAPED,PAPERWEIGHT
  BASE.....................................................  15.00
CUT GLASS TOOTHPICK HOLDERS,PAIR SQUARE.....................  20.00
CUT GLASS TOOTHPICK HOLDER WITH ENAMELED
  FLOWERS,BLUE,SAWTOOTH EDGE................................   8.00
CUT GLASS TOOTHPICK,PAIR ETCHED CRYSTAL,SWEDISH
  BIRDS,FLOWERS,OVAL.......................................  11.00
CUT GLASS TOOTHPICK,PAPERWEIGHT BASE........................  12.50
CUT GLASS TOOTHPICK,SQUARE CUT..............................  10.00
CUT GLASS TOOTHPICK WITH CUT BASE...........................  22.50
CUT GLASS TRAY,EGG & SAND...................................  10.00
CUT GLASS TROPHY,STERLING SILVER RIMMED,SILVER ENGRAVED.....  85.00
CUT GLASS TUB & TRAY........................................  85.00
CUT GLASS TUMBLER
  5.00  TO.................................................. 11.50
CUT GLASS TUMBLER,12,...................................... 100.00
CUT GLASS TUMBLER,BUZZ PATTERN,.............................   7.50
CUT GLASS TUMBLER,BUZZ SAW..................................  22.00
CUT GLASS,TUMBLER,BUZZ SAW PINWHEELS & FAN..................   5.50
CUT GLASS TUMBLER,CORNFLOWER & LEAF DESIGN..................   6.50
CUT GLASS TUMBLER,COSMOS....................................   5.50
CUT GLASS TUMBLER,DIAMOND & FAN.............................   5.50
CUT GLASS TUMBLER,FAN AND PINWHEELS,PAIR....................  10.00
CUT GLASS TUMBLER,HARVARD WITH STARRED BUTTONS..............  13.50
CUT GLASS TUMBLER,HEAVY CRYSTAL & DEEP CUT..................  10.00
CUT GLASS TUMBLER,HOBSTAR & FAN.............................   8.50
CUT GLASS TUMBLER,MULTI-CUT.................................   9.00
CUT GLASS TUMBLER,PINWHEEL & SUNBURST.......................   4.25
CUT GLASS TUMBLER,PINWHEEL PATTERN..........................   3.50
CUT GLASS TUMBLER,SET OF 4,.................................   7.50
CUT GLASS TUMBLER,SET OF 6
  25.00  TO................................................. 60.00
CUT GLASS TUMBLER,SET OF 6,PINWHEEL,ENGLISH STRAWBERRY
  DIAMOND & FAN............................................  47.50
CUT GLASS TUMBLER,SET OF 12,PRISM CUT WITH HOBSTAR & FAN.... 180.01-
CUT GLASS TUMBLER,STRAWBERRY & DIAMOND PATTERN..............   7.00
CUT GLASS TUMBLER,SWIRL & FAN...............................   5.50
CUT GLASS TUMBLER,ZIPPER STAR...............................   5.50
CUT GLASS TUMBLE-UP,STRAWBERRY,DIAMOND & FAN................  35.00
```

```
CUT GLASS VASE,5 IN...............................................   14.00
CUT GLASS VASE,6 IN...............................................    7.00
CUT GLASS VASE,7 IN...............................................   13.00
CUT GLASS VASE,8 IN. HIGH
   10.00  TO...................................................     12.00
CUT GLASS VASE,8 IN. OVOID,GREEN WITH CUT BACK GEOMETRIC
   DESIGN,SIGNED..............................................    100.00
CUT GLASS VASE,8 IN. TALL,AMERICAN,HOUR GLASS SHAPE,PINWHEEL      18.00
CUT GLASS VASE,9 IN. GROTESQUE...............................      19.00
CUT GLASS VASE,9 IN. HIGN
   20.00  TO...................................................     27.00
CUT GLASS VASE,10 IN. FLARED..................................      14.50
CUT GLASS VASE,10 IN.,HARVARD WITH COSMOS....................      23.00
CUT GLASS VASE,10 IN. SIGNED HAWKES..........................     110.00
CUT GLASS VASE,10 IN. WEBB & CORBETT.........................      35.00
CUT GLASS VASE,1J IN.,HARVARD PATTERN HALF WAY DOWN..........      28.00
CUT GLASS VASE,11 IN. HIGH,INTAGLIO OF 2 BIRDS,BERRY BUSHES
   & FLOWERS...................................................    295.00
CUT GLASS VASE,12 IN.,.........................................     50.00
CUT GLASS VASE,12 IN.,DIVIDED INTO 4 PANELS WITH 4 STARS AT
   TOP........................................................      30.00
CUT GLASS VASE,12 IN.,ETCHED FLOWERS.........................      50.00
CUT GLASS VASE,12 IN.,PEDESTAL,4 VERTICAL PANELS WITH 12
   HOBSTARS....................................................     30.00
CUT GLASS VASE,12 IN. TALL,ETCHED WITH FLOWERS...............      50.00
CUT GLASS VASE,14 IN.,ZIPPER..................................     28.50
CUT GLASS VASE, 16IN. HIGH....................................     65.00
CUT GLASS VASE,17 IN..........................................    225.00
CUT GLASS VASE,17 IN. TALL....................................    225.00
CUT GLASS VASE,18 IN. TALL....................................     95.00
CUT GLASS VASE,22IN. H........................................    225.00
CUT GLASS VASE,ARCADIA PATTERN,12 IN. TALL,FLARED BOTTOM....      79.00
CUT GLASS VASE,AZURE BLUE VELVET DIAMOND QUILTED,BULBOUS
   BODY.......................................................      75.00
CUT GLASS VASE,CLEAR,FLORAL & ETCHED PEACOCK.................      18.50
CUT GLASS VASE,COLOURED,CLEAR PANELED ......................      40.00
CUT GLASS VASE,COSMOS,10 IN..................................      18.00
CUT GLASS VASE,CYLINDER,FLOWER & LEAF,RAYED BASE............      35.00
CUT GLASS VASE,CYLINDER SHAPE,10 IN. HIGH,INTAGLIO CUT
   FLOWERS....................................................      19.00
CUT GLASS VASE,DIAMOND POINT PAIR............................      52.50
CUT GLASS VASE,FACETED BAND ON BASE,ETCHED GRAPES ON YELLOW.      25.00
CUT GLASS VASE,HARVARD PATTERN...............................      30.00
CUT GLASS VASE,OGONTZ PATTERN,GEORGE DRAKE CO...............      32.00
CUT GLASS VASE ON DISK FOOT,ST.LOUIS DIAMOND & NOTCHED PRISM      37.50
CUT GLASS VASE,QUEENS PATTERN ON PEDESTAL,10 IN. TALL.......     125.00
CUT GLASS VASE,TRUMPET,HOBSTAR WITH FAN.....................      26.00
CUT GLASS VASE,TRUMPET SHAPED,CRANBERRY TO CLEAR,MERIDEN
   SILVER HOLDER..............................................      35.00
CUT GLASS VASE,TRUMPET,STRAWBERRY DIAMOND,FANS AT TOP,RAYED
   BASE.......................................................      15.00
CUT GLASS VASE,VELVET BLUE,DIAMOND QUILTED,6 IN. HIGH,BALL
   SHAPED BODY................................................      95.00
CUT GLASS VASE,WATERFORD TYPE................................      50.00
CUT GLASS VASE WITH PURPLE OVERLAY,FOOTED...................      65.00
CUT GLASS VASES,PAIR OVERLAY,COBALT BLUE TO CLEAR,OCTAGON
   SHAPED.....................................................      65.00
CUT GLASS VINEGAR CRUET,PRISM & BULLSEYE....................      16.50
CUT GLASS VINEGAR CRUET WITH GOLD BIRD AND FLORAL DECOR.....      20.00
CUT GLASS WASTE BOWL,DIAMOND POINT..........................       8.50
CUT GLASS WATER BOTTLE
   17.50  TO..................................................      27.00
CUT GLASS WATER BOTTLE,PRISMATIC NECK,PINWHEEL & HOBSTAR....      21.00
CUT GLASS WATER CARAFE
   15.00  TO..................................................      29.50
```

```
CUT GLASS WATER CARAFE,HOBSTAR,DIAMOND POINT & FAN.......... 25.00
CUT GLASS WATER CARAFE,LOUIS XIV........................... 50.00
CUT GLASS WATER CARAFE,NOTCHED & PANELED THROAT,BULLSEYES... 20.00
CUT GLASS WATER CARAFE SIGNED HAWKES,MIDDLESEX PATTERN...... 37.00
CUT GLASS WATER CARAFE,STRAWBERRY DIAMOND & FAN PATTERN..... 20.00
CUT GLASS WATER PITCHER
22.00   TO................................................ 65.00
CUT GLASS WATER PITCHER,9 IN. HIGH......................... 28.00
CUT GLASS WATER PITCHER,10 IN. TANKARD TYPE,BUZZ SAW
PINWHEELS & FAN............................................ 32.50
CUT GLASS WATER PITCHER,10 IN. WITH 6 TUMBLERS,COSMOS WITH
HARVARD................................................... 65.00
CUT GLASS WATER PITCHER & 4 GLASSES,PINWHEEL............... 45.00
CUT GLASS WATER PITCHER,BULBOUS............................ 60.00
CUT GLASS WATER PITCHER,EARLY AMERICAN..................... 39.00
CUT GLASS WATER PITCHER,HOBSTAR............................ 30.00
CUT GLASS WATER PITCHER,HOBSTAR ,11 IN. TALL............... 42.50
CUT GLASS WATER PITCHER,NOTCHED PRISM,HOBSTARS,RAYED BASE... 37.50
CUT GLASS WATER PITCHER,MARKED............................. 38.00
CUT GLASS WATER PITCHER,PINWHEEL........................... 35.00
CUT GLASS WATER PITCHER,PINWHEELS,APPLIED HANDLES.......... 28.00
CUT GLASS WATER PITCHER,RUBY,PINWHEEL,HOBSTARS &
CROSS-HATCHING............................................ 50.00
CUT GLASS WATER SET,& 4 TUMBLERS........................... 135.00
CUT GLASS WATER SET, INTAGLIO,FROSTED GRAPE-LEAVES & VINE
PATTERN................................................... 150.00
CUT GLASS WATER SET SIGNED,PITCHER & 6
TUMBLERS,HOBSTAR,DIAMOND.................................. 165.00
CUT GLASS WATER SET,6 TUMBLERS,PINWHEEL & HOB STAR......... 110.00
CUT GLASS WATER PITCHER,SUNBURST PATTERN................... 35.00
CUT GLASS WATER TUMBLER.................................... 7.50
CUT GLASS WATER TUMBLER,FLOWER PATTERN..................... 4.50
CUT GLASS WEDDING COMPOTE WITH COVER....................... 15.00
CUT GLASS WHISKEY SET,SMOKEY COLOR,CUT PANELS.............. 22.50
CUT GLASS WINE,9 IN.,AMETHYST & CLEAR,HOBSTARS,FANS & PRISMS 40.00
CUT GLASS WINE,BLUE FINECUT & PANEL........................ 15.00
CUT GLASS WINE COOLER WITH STERLING RIM.................... 65.00
CUT GLASS WINE DECANTER,13 IN.............................. 30.00
CUT GLASS WINE DECANTER,PAIR,RUSSIAN PATTERN,10 IN. HIGH... 185.00
CUT GLASS WINE GOBLET,FLUTE................................ 6.00
CUT GLASS WINE MARKED STUART ENGLAND....................... 4.00
CUT GLASS WINE,PAIR,CRANBERRY,BLUE & OLIVE................. 25.00
CUT GLASS WINE,PINWHEEL,SERRATED STEM...................... 18.00
CUT GLASS WINE,SCOTCH THISTLE.............................. 12.00
CUT GLASS WINE,SET OF 4,ENGRAVED WITH BUTTERFLIES & FLOWERS. 10.00
CUT GLASS WINES,SET OF 6,HEXAGONAL CUT STEMS,DIAMOND POINT
BAND...................................................... 60.00
CUT GLASS WINE,STEMMED,DIAMOND & FAN PATTERN,PAIR.......... 15.00
CUT GLASS WINE,STRAWBERRY & FAN............................ 10.00
CUT GLASS WHISKEY GLASS.................................... 6.50
```

CUT VELVET is a special type of art glass made with two layers of blown glass which shows a raised pattern. It usually had an acid finish or velvet-like texture. It was made by many glass factories during the late Victorian years.

```
CUT VELVET VASES,PAIR,SWIRL,FRILLY TURNED DOWN TOP......... 285.00
CUT VELVET VASE,WISTERIA PURPLE COLOUR,DIAMOND QUILTED..... 250.00
```

D'ARGENTAL was a French cameo glass maker of the late Victorian period.

```
D ARGENTAL FRENCH CAMEO ROUND COVERED BOX,CARVED FLOWERS &
LEAVES.................................................... 137.50
D ARGENTAL, SIGNED VASE, RED CAMES OVER CHARTREUSE......... 168.00
D ARGENTAL VASE,4 IN. TALL,RED ON CARAMEL................. 75.00
D ARGENTAL VASE,5 IN. TALL,COBALT BLUE ON TAN............. 75.00
     DAGUERROTYPE, SEE ALBUM, PHOTOGRAPHY...................
     DANISH CHRISTMAS PLATES, SEE CHRISTMAS PLATES..........
```

DAUM, NANCY, is the mark used by Auguste and Antonin Daum on pieces of French cameo glass made after 1875.

DAUM NANCY BOWL,3 IN.,PEDESTAL BASE,SCENIC LAKE,BROWN & YELLOW,SIGNED...	85.00
DAUM NANCY BOWL,8 IN.,FOLDER RIM,SATIN FINISH,CINTRA ORANGE.	30.00
DAUM NANCY BOWL,CAMEO,AUTUMN LEAVES,BLACKBERRIES ON GREEN,SIGNED..	165.00
DAUM NANCY BOWL,CABINET SIZED,PASTEL CAMEO,BLUE-GREEN-LAVENDER..................................	47.50
DAUM NANCY BOWL,CROSS OF LORAINE,3 FOOTED,BLUISH PURPLE,SIGNED...	50.00
DAUM NANCY BOWL,CROSS OF LORRAINE,BLUE & YELLOW,SIGNED......	48.00
DAUM NANCY BOWL,CROSS OF LORAINE ETCHED,SIGNED...............	40.00
DAUM NANCY BOWL,CUT & ENAMELED BLUE & WHITE BELL FLOWERS,SIGNED...	70.00
DAUM NANCY BOWL,ENAMELED,QUATERFOIL TOP WITH GOLD,SIGNED....	75.00
DAUM NANCY BOWL,OVERLAY,CRIMPED TOP,VINE DESIGN..............	125.00
DAUM NANCY BOWL,SCALLOPED,GREENISH AMBER,CARVED THISTLE BORDER...	125.00
DAUM NANCY BOX,COVERED,IRIDESCENT LAVENDER FLOWERS & LEAVES.	75.00
DAUM NANCY CUT POLISHED FLOWERS ON ACID BACKGROUND,SIGNED...	125.00
DAUM NANCY DECANTER,SMOKE COLOUR,ACID CUT BACK STRIPES,SIGNED...	85.00
DAUM NANCY FIELD MOUSE IN CABBAGE PATCH,PATE DE VERRE SIGNED	375.00
DAUM NANCY GOBLET,6 IN. TALL,APRICOT COLOURED IRIS & BUDS & GREEN...	85.00
DAUM NANCY JAR,COVERED,ENAMELED & CAMEO-CUT BLUE CORN FLOWERS,SIGNED..	145.00
DAUM NANCY LAMP,SCENIC,CAMEO,LAKE SCENE,BROWN,ORANGE & YELLOW,SIGNED..	250.00
DAUM NANCY LAMP,SCENIC,PASTEL COLOURING,SIGNED..............	225.00
DAUM NANCY LIQUOR SET,ORIENTAL STYLE CARVING,TRAY,BOTTLE & 10 GLASSES..	575.00
DAUM NANCY OPALESCENT,ENAMELED DUTCH HARBOUR SCENE,SIGNED...	75.00
DAUM NANCY PERFUME,ORANGE TO FROSTED WITH RAISED GOLD FLORAL DESIGN...	120.00
DAUM NANCY PLATE,5 IN. SQUARE,CUT BLUE BERRIES,GREEN & RUST ON ORANGE...	75.00
DAUM NANCY POMADE JAR,CUT PURPLE,GREEN & WHITE FLOWERS IN GOLD...	65.00
DAUM NANCY ROSE BOWL,3 IN.,MOTTLED PINK,YELLOW & BROWN,SIGNED..	35.00
DAUM NANCY ROSE BOWL,3 IN. TALL,IRIS,LAVENDER,YELLOW,SIGNED FRANCE...	110.00
DAUM NANCY ROSE BOWL,GREEN & BLACK,MOTTLED,SIGNED...........	48.00
DAUM NANCY ROSE BOWL,SCALLOPED,CAMEO,WINTER SUNSET WITH TREES,SIGNED...	137.50
DAUM NANCY ROSE BOWL,WOODLAND SCENE........................	75.00
DAUM NANCY TOOTHPICK,CAMEO & ENAMELED FLORAL ON GREEN.......	39.50
DAUM NANCY TUMBLER,CAMEO,YELLOW BERRY FLOWERS & GREEN,SIGNED	98.00
DAUM NANCY TUMBLER,SCENIC CAMEO,SIGNED.....................	135.00
DAUM NANCY VASE,3 IN.,ORANGE BASE WITH GREEN MOTTLING,PURPLE,SIGNED......................................	60.00
DAUM NANCY VASE,4 IN.,CAMEO,PURPLE BERRIES,AUTUMN LEAVES....	115.00
DAUM NANCY VASE,4 IN.,CAMEO,THISTLE,SIGNED.................	100.00
DAUM NANCY VASE,4 IN.,CONICAL FOOTED,CAMPHOR BASE,GREEN,SIGNED..	95.00
DAUM NANCY VASE,5 IN.,CLEAR WITH BLUE TINT,CAMEO LEAF & VINE,SIGNED...	145.00
DAUM NANCY VASE,5 IN.,PATE DE VERRE TECHNIQUE,SIGNED........	135.00
DAUM NANCY VASE,6 IN.,BULBOUS,CAMEO RIVER SCENE,SINGED......	135.00
DAUM NANCY VASE,11 IN. TALL,BROWN & RED ON MOTTLED YELLOW...	125.00
DAUM NANCY VASE,12 IN. TALL,BROWN & RED ON YELLOW,SCULPTURED BLOSSOMS...	125.00
DAUM NANCY VASE,14 IN.,CLUTHRA ORANGE,SIGNED...............	80.00

DAUM NANCY VASE,15 IN. TALL,ACID CUT-BACK,ENAMELED COLUMBINE	125.00
DAUM NANCY VASE,19 IN. TALL,COCKSCOMB CAMEO DESIGN,BROWN ON ORANGE...	175.00
DAUM NANCY VASE,19 IN. TALL,SCENIC,GREEN ON MOTTLED REDDISH.	225.00
DAUM NANCY VASE,20 IN.,CAMEO,TREES,LAKE & FISHING BOAT,SIGNED...	275.00
DAUM NANCY VASE,23 IN. TALL,CUT-BACK FLORAL DESIGN,ENAMEL...	175.00
DAUM NANCY VASE,23 IN. TALL,GREEN ON STREAKED BLUE,APPLIED GLASS BUDS..	190.00
DAUM NANCY VASE,23 IN. TALL,STREAKED YELLOW & BROWN WITH GREEN,..	175.00
DAUM NANCY VASE,CAMEO & ENAMELLED,FAN SHAPED,THISTLE FLOWERS,SIGNED...	87.50
DAUM NANCY VASE,CAMEO,SIGNED,3 IN. TALL,2 IN. DIAMETER......	67.50
DAUM NANCY VASE,CAMEO,SQUATTY,CARVING OF FLOWERS & LEAVES IN RUST..	98.50
DAUM NANCY VASE,CUT & ENAMELLED SUNFLOWERS,SIGNED...........	80.00
DAUM NANCY VASE,FROSTED,LEAF DESIGN WITH GOLD,PURPLE CROCUS & GREEN..	115.00
DAUM NANCY VASE,HAND DECORATED,BLUISH BACKGROUND WITH FLORAL	80.00
DAUM NANCY VASE,LEMON,ORANGE,GREEN,SIGNED....................	135.00
DAUM NANCY VASE,PRIMROSES DECORATED WITH GOLD IN ACID,SIGNED	75.00
DAUM NANCY VASE,SCENIC,CUT FOREST SCENE,SIGNED..............	160.00
DAUM NANCY VASE,SEASONS,FROSTY & YELLOW BACKGROUND,SIGNED...	115.00
DAUM NANCY VASE,YELLOW & BLUE SPONGED ON CAMPHOR-LIKE GLASS,SIGNED..	87.50
DAUM NANCY VASE,YELLOW,ORANGE MORNING GLORY FLOWERS,MARKED..	135.00

DAVENPORT POTTERY and porcelain was made at the Davenport factory in Longport, Staffordshire, England, from 1793 to 1887. Earthenwares, cream-wares, porcelains, ironstone wares and other products were made. Most of the pieces are marked with a form of the word "Davenport."

DAVENPORT SET OF 6 DINNER PLATES,MARKED,SCENIC,TRANSFER IN BLUE..	60.00

DECOYS are carved or turned wooden copies of birds. The decoy was placed in the water to lure flying birds to the pond for the hunters.

DECOY,BLACK DUCK...	40.00
DECOY,CANVAS MALLARD HEN.......................................	45.00
DECOY,CANADIAN GOOSE...	45.00
DECOY,CORK DUCK,GLASS EYES.....................................	8.00
DECOY,DUCK 12.50 TO...	15.00
DECOY,DUCK,GLASS EYE,PAIR......................................	25.00
DECOY,DUCK,WHITE CEDAR,BLUEBILL................................	3.75
DECOY,DUCK,WHITE CEDAR,MALLARD.................................	3.75
DECOY,DUCK,WHITE CEDAR,TEAL....................................	3.75
DECOY,DUCK WITH EYES...	18.00
DECOY,GOOSE,18 IN..	25.00
DECOY,HAND MADE DUCK,BLACK & WHITE.............................	7.50
DECOY,MALLARD,EVANS..	36.00
DECOY,PAINTED DUCK...	4.75
DECOY,SWIVEL-HEAD GLASS-EYED MALLARD...........................	7.00
DECOY,TIN SHORE BIRD...	22.50
DECOY,VERMONT CARVED WOODEN DUCK...............................	8.00
DECOY,WOODEN...	6.00
DECOY,WOODEN PINE FINISH.......................................	7.50

THE DEDHAM POTTERY COMPANY of Dedham, Massachusetts, started making pottery in 1866. It was reorganized as the Chelsea Pottery Company in 1891, and became the Dedham Pottery Company in 1895. The factory was famous for its crackleware dishes, which pictured blue outlines of animals, flowers, and other natural motifs.

DEDHAM POTTERY BOWL,RABBITS,BLUE RABBIT MARK & INCISED DP...	35.00
DEDHAM POTTERY CELERY DISH,FOOTED OVAL......................	55.00

```
DEDHAM POTTERY CREAMER,MORNING & NIGHT,RAISED ROOSTER & OWL.   175.00
DEDHAM POTTERY CREAMER,RABBIT DESIGN.........................   18.50
DEDHAM POTTERY CUP,RABBIT....................................   13.50
DEDHAM POTTERY DINNER PLATE,MUSHROOMS,10 IN...................   38.00
DEDHAM POTTERY DINNER PLATE,RABBIT,10 IN......................   38.00
DEDHAM POTTERY PLATE,5-SIDED.................................   50.00
DEDHAM POTTERY PLATE,GRAPE PATTERN,8 IN.......................   15.00
DEDHAM POTTERY PLATE WITH RABBIT RIM.........................   23.00
DEDHAM POTTERY SHERBET,PAIR,RABBIT PATTERN...................  170.00
DEDHAM POTTERY TILE,RABBIT DESIGN............................   68.00
DE GUE SIGNED ACID CUT BACK VASE,WISTERIA BACKGROUND.........  135.00
     DELDARE, SEE BUFFALO POTTERY............................
```

DELFT is a tin glazed pottery that has been made since the seventeenth century.
It is decorated with blue on white or with colored decorations. Most of the pieces
sold today were made after 1891, and the name "Holland" appears with the
Delft factory marks.

```
DELFT 15 IN. CHOP PLATE,MILL SCENES,PAIR.....................   37.50
DELFT BLUE & WHITE COW CREAMER,WINDMILL TREES................   15.00
DELFT BLUE & WHITE FIREPLACE TILES,6,SCENES..................   35.00
DELFT BLUE & WHITE PLATE,WINDMILL............................   16.00
DELFT,BLUE,GERMANY,8 IN. PLATE...............................   25.00
DELFT,BLUE,GERMANY,12 X 8 IN. PLATTER........................   40.00
DELFT,BLUE,GERMANY,14 X 9 IN. PLATTER........................   45.00
DELFT,BLUE,GERMANY,CELERY DISH...............................   40.00
DELFT,BLUE,GERMANY,CREAMER & SUGAR SET.......................   55.00
DELFT,BLUE,GERMANY,CUP & COUPED SAUCER.......................   50.00
DELFT,BLUE,GERMANY,OATMEAL DISH..............................   15.00
DELFT,BLUE,GERMANY,RELISH TRAY...............................   25.00
DELFT,BLUE,GERMANY,SAUCE DISH................................   11.00
DELFT,BLUE,GERMANY,TEAPOT....................................   55.00
DELFT BOWL,ENGLISH CIRCA 1750................................  280.00
DELFT CHINA WINDMILL INCENSE COVER,STARLING HALLMARKED,VANES
  TURN.......................................................   12.50
DELFT CHOP PLATE,WHITE HORSE.................................   17.50
DELFT COW...................................................   27.50
DELFT COW PITCHER,7 IN......................................   12.50
DELFT COW WITH HORNS,BASE ATTACHED...........................   12.00
DELFT DUTCH BOY & GIRL PAIR SALT & PEPPER....................    5.00
DELFT ENGLISH PAIR CHARGERS..................................  200.00
DELFT HANGING PLATE,BLUE & WHITE WITH WINDMILL,BOATS &
  TREES,HOLLAND..............................................   11.00
DELFT HANGING PLATE,MARK HOLLAND,HOUSE ,TREES,BOAT...........   17.50
DELFT HOLLAND SALT AND PEPPER,PEWTER LIDS....................   10.50
DELFT JUG...................................................   10.00
DELFT MARKED BLUE & WHITE WALL PLAQUE,MAN & WOMAN IN HORSE
  DRAWN SLED.................................................   20.00
DELFT MARKED BLUE & WHITE WALL PLAQUE,PEOPLE IN CANOE,COWS
  IN PASTURE.................................................   20.00
DELFT PAIR FIGURINES,2 BOYS,2 GIRLS,DUTCH
  COSTUMES,MARKED,BLUE.......................................   25.00
DELFT PAIR FIGURINES IN BLUE SIGNED,BOY & GIRL STANDING.....   42.50
DELFT PAIR OF COVERED URNS,GRAY,GREEN BACKGROUNDS,FLORAL &
  BIRD.......................................................  175.00
DELFT PITCHER,3 IN. HANDLE,FACE OF PUNCH SIGNED..............   12.00
DELFT PLAQUE,9 IN.,BOAT IN CANAL,HOUSE & TREES...............   22.00
DELFT PLAQUE,WINDMILLS,SAILBOATS,OAK FRAME...................   32.50
DELFT PLATE, BLUE, 16 IN. W., SIGNED NAAR ARTZ..............   50.00
DELFT PLATE CIRCA 1780,LIVERPOOL 9 IN. POLYCHROME...........  110.00
DELFT PLATE,MARKED DELFT,GERMANY.............................   16.00
DELFT PORCELAIN COW CREAMER STANDING,GREYISH BLUE WITH
  SCENES....................................................   22.00
DELFT SIGNED BUST OF NAPOLEON,SQUARE BASE....................   35.00
DELFT SIGNED BUST OF NELSON,SQUARE BASE......................   35.00
DELFT SIGNED VASE,BLUE AND WHITE,WINDMILL....................    8.50
```

```
DELFT TILE,5 IN.,LAVENDER FLOWERS IN VASE...................    6.00
DELFT WHEEL BARROW TOOTHPICK...............................   10.00
DELFT WINDMILL BOTTLE......................................   10.00
```

DE VEZ is a name that appears on French art nouveau cameo glass.

```
DE VEZ BOWL,3 IN. TALL,RED ON FROSTED CREAM...............  100.00
DE VILBISS ATOMIZER,7 IN.,CASED ORANGE,STIPPLED GOLD FOOT...  57.50
DE VILBISS ATOMIZER,BLACK,GOLD DECOR......................    9.00
DE VILBISS ATOMIZER,MERCURY CRACKLE,HAND BLOWN............    4.50
DE VILBISS ATOMIZER,PINK FROSTY GLASS WITH GOLD OVERLAY,GOLD
   STEM....................................................    7.50
DE VILBISS PERFUME,ACID CUT BACK CRANBERRY................   35.00
DE VILBISS PERFUME,ORANGE IRIDESCENT,GOLD FITTINGS,SIGNED...  18.00
DOCTORS INSTRUMENTS IN BOX,INCLUDING 2 BLEEDERS...........   10.00
DOCTORS WOOD BOX WITH 60 PILL BOTTLES.....................   15.00
   DOLL, SEE ALSO SHIRLEY TEMPLE...........................
DOLL,A & M DREAM BABY.....................................   24.00
DOLL,ALEXANDER,DRESSED,14 IN. TALL........................   35.00
DOLL,ALEXANDER QUINTS,DRESSED.............................  110.00
DOLL,ALEXANDER SONYA HEINE,DRESSED,21 IN. TALL............   50.00
DOLL,ALEXANDER,WIGLESS....................................   27.00
DOLL,ALEXIS SMITH,20 IN. TALL.............................   27.50
DOLL,AM BLUE EYES LITTLE GIRL.............................   85.00
DOLL,A.M.GERMANY DREAM BABY,ORIGINAL BODY.................   65.00
DOLL,AM ROCKABYE DREAM BABY,BLUE EYES.....................   85.00
DOLL,AMOS ANDRA RUBBER COLOURED BABY......................    3.00
DOLL,ARMAND MARSEILLE,16IN.M.,BISQUE FACE,SLEEPING
   EYES,ORIGINAL HAIR.....................................   65.00
DOLL,ARMAND MARSEILLE,25 IN.,DRESSED......................   39.00
DOLL,ARMAND MARSEILLE BISQUE HEAD,COMPOSITION JOINTED
   BODY,16 IN. TALL.......................................   22.50
DOLL,ARMAND MARSEILLE,CHARACTER BABY,BLUE EYES............   85.00
DOLL,ARMAND MARSEILLE,KID BODY,DRESSED IN SCOTTISH,12 IN.
   TALL..................................................   27.50
DOLL,ARMAND MARSEILLE MARKED DRESSED DUTCH GIRL,BISQUE
   HEAD,10 IN. TALL......................................   35.00
DOLL,ARMY DRESSED,WAAC...................................   17.50
DOLL,BABYETTE,COMPOSITION,9 IN. TALL.....................    7.50
DOLL,BIEDERMEIER CHINA BALD HEAD,BROWN WIG,DRESSED,13 IN.
   TALL..................................................  165.00
DOLL,BISQUE 3 IN. KEWPIE CARRYING SUITCASE,& UMBRELLA,SIGNED
   O NEILL................................................   35.00
DOLL,BISQUE 4 IN. KEWPIE.................................   15.00
DOLL,BISQUE,A & M GERMANY,DRESSED,BLONDE HUMAN HAIR WIG,24
   IN. TALL..............................................   50.00
DOLL,BISQUE BABY,MARKED A.M.GERMANY,OPEN MOUTH,9 IN. TALL...  28.00
DOLL,BISQUE BABY WITH MOLDED ON JUMPER SUIT,JOINTED BODY,8
   IN. TALL..............................................   85.00
DOLL,BISQUE BLONDE,3 IN. TALL............................    7.00
DOLL,BISQUE,BONNET DOLL,ARMS MOVE,.......................    7.50
DOLL,BISQUE BONNET HEAD,BLONDE HAIR,DRESSED,BLUE EYES,11 IN.
   TALL..................................................   52.00
DOLL,BISQUE,BONNET,UNDRESSED,15 IN. TALL.................   17.00
DOLL,BISQUE BOY 5 IN. TALL FOLDED ARMS,HAT WITH CAPTAIN KIDD   7.50
DOLL,BISQUE CHILD GERMAN,BLUE EYES.......................   40.00
DOLL,BISQUE CLOSED MOUTH BLUE SLEEP EYES,FRENCH,27 IN. TALL.  215.00
DOLL,BISQUE,CLOSED MOUTH,SHOULDER HEAD,15 IN. TALL.........   75.00
DOLL,BISQUE COLOURED GIRL MARKED,DRESSED,15 IN. TALL......   75.00
DOLL,BISQUE DOME HEAD BABY,BLUE SLEEP EYES,DRESSED,8 IN.
   TALL..................................................   28.00
DOLL,BISQUE DOME HEAD,BOY,BLUE INVERTED EYES,.............   65.00
DOLL,BISQUE DOME HEAD,MOLDED HAIR,BROWN PAINTED EYES,17 IN.
   TALL..................................................   95.00
DOLL,BISQUE DRESSED AMBERG BABY,7 IN. TALL...............   45.00
DOLL,BISQUE FACE,GERMANY,BALL JOINT BODY,EYES OPEN &
```

CLOSE,23 IN. TALL.. 65.00
DOLL,BISQUE FRENCH BOY,DRESSED,GLASS EYES,3 IN. TALL........ 22.50
DOLL,BISQUE,FRENCH DOLL HOUSE TYPE,GIRL,DRESSED,GLASS EYES,3
IN. TALL.. 22.50
DOLL,BISQUE,FROZEN CHARLOTTE,4 IN. TALL..................... 15.00
DOLL,BISQUE FROZEN CHARLOTTE JAPAN,2 IN.,................... 3.50
DOLL,BISQUE FROZEN CHARLOTTE,JAPAN,5 IN. TALL............... 5.00
DOLL,BISQUE ,GERMAN,HUMAN HAIR WIG,WORLD WAR I WARDROBE,12
IN. TALL.. 29.00
DOLL,BISQUE GIRL,4 IN. TALL................................. 6.00
DOLL,BISQUE GIRL 4 IN. TALL,PAINTED BLONDE HAIR & CLOTHES... 3.50
DOLL,BISQUE GIRL & BOY,HINGED ARMS,PAINTED SOCKS & SHOES,7
IN. TALL.. 15.00
DOLL,BISQUE GIRL,DRESSED,DOLL HOUSE TYPE,BLOND WIG,4 IN.
TALL.. 15.00
DOLL,BISQUE HEAD,14 IN...................................... 16.00
DOLL,BISQUE HEAD & ARMS,DRESSED,KID BODY,18 IN. TALL........ 42.50
DOLL,BISQUE HEAD BABY,BLUE GLASS STATIONARY EYES,10 IN. TALL 55.00
DOLL,BISQUE HEAD BABY,J.D.K.,BROWN GLASS EYES,DRESSED,13 IN.
TALL.. 49.50
DOLL,BISQUE HEAD BABY,MARKED 199 GERMANY,COMPOSITION BODY,9
IN. TALL.. 27.00
DOLL,BISQUE HEAD BALD BABY,PAPIER MACHE BODY,12 IN. TALL.... 38.00
DOLL,BISQUE HEAD BLOND HAIR BABY,21 IN. TALL WOODEN
HIGHCHAIR... 15.00
DOLL,BISQUE HEAD BLONDIE SIGNED A M GERMANY,DRESSED,12 IN.
TALL.. 24.00
DOLL,BISQUE HEAD BOY,DUTCH,MARKED S & H,DRESSED,8 IN. TALL.. 25.00
DOLL,BISQUE HEAD CHILD,CLOTH BODY,15 IN. TALL............... 75.00
DOLL,BISQUE HEAD,COLOURED BABY,MARKED SIMON,NAMED HILDA,6
IN. TALL.. 12.00
DOLL,BISQUE HEAD,COMPOSITION BODY,DRESSED,GERMAN,7 IN. TALL. 24.50
DOLL,BISQUE HEAD,COMPOSITION HANDS,GERMANY,12 IN. TALL...... 45.00
DOLL,BISQUE HEAD DATED 1884,19 IN. TALL..................... 45.00
DOLL,BISQUE HEAD,DRESSED,10 IN. TALL........................ 60.00
DOLL,BISQUE HEAD,DRESSED,BABY,BLONDE HAIR,SLEEPING BLUE
EYES,6 IN. TALL... 17.50
DOLL,BISQUE HEAD,DRESSED,BELTON,BROWN PAPERWEIGHT EYES,11
IN. TALL.. 150.00
DOLL,BISQUE HEAD,DRESSED,BLOND MOLDED HAIRDO,16 IN. TALL.... 125.00
DOLL,BISQUE HEAD,DRESSED,FRENCH S F B J ,LITTLE GIRL,9 IN.
TALL.. 85.00
DOLL,BISQUE HEAD,DRESSED,FRENCH S.F.B.J.,LITTLE GIRL,11 IN.
TALL.. 95.00
DOLL,BISQUE HEAD,DRESSED,MARKED D-S,BROWN HUMAN HAIR WIG,23
IN. TALL.. 115.00
DOLL,BISQUE HEAD GIRL,BROWN GLASS EYES,DRESSED,9 IN. TALL... 15.00
DOLL,BISQUE HEAD GIRL MARKED GERMANY,DRESSED,KID BODY,15 IN.
TALL.. 49.00
DOLL,BISQUE HEAD IMPRESSED G BR GERMANY,23 IN. TALL......... 65.00
DOLL,BISQUE HEAD INDIAN,DRESSED,BROWN STATIONARY EYES,18 IN.
TALL.. 155.00
DOLL,BISQUE HEAD,J D K BABY,OPEN-CLOSED MOUTH,DRESSED....... 60.00
DOLL,BISQUE HEAD,JOINTED COMPOSITION BODY,DRESSED,9 IN. TALL 12.50
DOLL,BISQUE HEAD,KID BODY,CELLULOID ARMS,DRESSED,16 IN. TALL 50.00
DOLL,BISQUE HEAD LITTLE GIRL,FRENCH,DRESSED,18 IN. TALL..... 250.00
DOLL,BISQUE HEAD MARKED A M,DRESSED,BLUE SLEEP EYES,9 IN.
TALL.. 20.00
DOLL,BISQUE HEAD MARKED A.M.,DRESSED,SOLID DOME,CLOSED
MOUTH,12 IN... 48.00
DOLL,BISQUE HEAD MARKED A M D E P ,DATED 1894,DRESSED,9 IN.
TALL.. 21.00
DOLL,BISQUE HEAD,MARKED A.N.GERMANY,GOOGLY,BLUE GLASS EYES,7
IN. TALL.. 105.00
DOLL,BISQUE HEAD MARKED,BROWN SLEEP EYES,OPEN MOUTH,11 IN.

TALL..	35.00
DOLL,BISQUE HEAD MARKED D R G M,DRESSED,22 IN. TALL..........	35.00
DOLL,BISQUE HEAD,MARKED,DATED 1894,A M D E P, COLOURED,9 IN.	
TALL..	65.00
DOLL,BISQUE HEAD MARKED,DRESSED,BLUE SLEEP EYES,10 IN. TALL.	45.00
DOLL,BISQUE HEAD MARKED GERMANY,DRESSED,CLOSED MOUTH,18 IN.	
TALL..	85.00
DOLL,BISQUE HEAD MARKED GERMANY,DRESSED,GIRL,22 IN. TALL....	47.50
DOLL,BISQUE HEAD MARKED GERMANY,MY GIRLIE,DARK	
HAIR,DRESSED,25 IN. TALL....................................	45.00
DOLL,BISQUE HEAD MARKED MADE IN GERMANY,DRESSED,9 IN. TALL..	22.00
DOLL,BISQUE HEAD,MARKED M F,CIRCULAR CLOSED MOUTH,4 IN. TALL	18.00
DOLL,BISQUE HEAD MARKED R-A,DATED 1907,DRESSED,11 IN. TALL..	19.50
DOLL,BISQUE HEAD MARKED S.F.B.J.PARIS,FRENCH,OPEN MOUTH,16	
IN. TALL..	50.00
DOLL,BISQUE HEAD,PAPIER MACHE JOINTED BODY,SLEEPING EYES....	8.50
DOLL,BISQUE HEAD,SIGNED GERMANY,KID BODY....................	50.00
DOLL,BISQUE HEAD,SLEEP EYES,REAL HAIR WIG,GERMANY,22 IN.	
TALL..	39.50
DOLL,BISQUE HEAD SOLID DOME,MARKED NIPPON,DRESSED,6 IN. TALL	8.00
DOLL,BISQUE HEAD WITH BEAU BRUMMEL OUTFIT,WALKING,25 IN.	
TALL..	175.00
DOLL,BISQUE HEAD WITH BLOND WIG,ARMAND MARSEILLE,GERMANY....	69.50
DOLL,BISQUE HEADED LADY,DRESSED,MOLDED BLOND HAIR,19 IN.	
TALL..	135.00
DOLL,BISQUE,HINGED ARMS,4 IN. TALL..........................	7.00
DOLL,BISQUE,HINGED ARMS & LEGS,BLONDE HAIR,BLUE	
EYES,DRESSED,4 IN. TALL.....................................	17.00
DOLL,BISQUE,JAPAN,BLONDE,BLUE EYES,8 IN. TALL...............	4.25
DOLL,BISQUE JOINTED,PALE,16 IN. TALL........................	40.00
DOLL,BISQUE LADY,BROWN EYES,23 IN...........................	37.50
DOLL,BISQUE MARKED C 8,GERMAN,DRESSED,3 FACES,13 IN. TALL...	350.00
DOLL,BISQUE MARKED NIPPON,6 IN. TALL........................	8.50
DOLL,BISQUE MOLDED HAIR,BLUE MOLDED BOW,DRESSED,4 IN. TALL..	10.00
DOLL,BISQUE,MOLDED HAIR,MARKED MADE IN GERMANY,6 IN. TALL...	4.00
DOLL,BISQUE NEGRO,DRESSED...................................	25.00
DOLL,BISQUE OPEN MOUTH DRESSED BOY,14 IN. TALL..............	14.50
DOLL,BISQUE PIXIE,JOINTED ARMS,BIG TUMMY,BLONDE HAIR........	10.00
DOLL,BISQUE,RED CROSS UNIFORM,2 IN. TALL....................	10.00
DOLL,BISQUE,SEATED,1 IN. TALL...............................	4.00
DOLL,BISQUE SEEBY-SHEEBY,DRESSED,MADE IN JAPAN,6 IN. TALL...	24.00
DOLL,BISQUE SHOULDER HEAD MARKED 639,SOLID DOME,17 IN. TALL.	145.00
DOLL,BISQUE SHOULDER HEAD MARKED HCH,DRESSED,BROWN EYES,19	
IN. TALL..	42.00
DOLL,BISQUE SHOULDER HEAD MARKED GERMANY,DRESSED IN RED	
VELVET,17 IN..	85.00
DOLL,BISQUE SHOULDER HEAD MARKED NIPPON,DRESSED,9 IN. TALL..	18.00
DOLL,BISQUE SHOULDER HEAD MARKED S I P,DRESSED,19 IN. TALL..	45.00
DOLL,BISQUE SHOULDER HEAD,SOLID DOME,DRESSED,11 IN. TALL....	185.00
DOLL,BISQUE SHOULDER TYPE HEAD,GERMANY,RUTH,3 IN. TALL......	10.00
DOLL,BISQUE SIGNED ROSE O NEAL CUPIE,5 IN. TALL.............	30.00
DOLL,BISQUE SOLID DOME HEAD,DRESSED,MARKED GERMANY 162,6 IN.	
TALL..	15.00
DOLL,BISQUE SOLID HEAD MARKED 235,DRESSED,PORTRAIT,13 IN.	
TALL..	95.00
DOLL,BISQUE TURNED HEAD,DRESSED,CLOSED MOUTH,BROWN EYES,16	
IN. TALL..	79.00
DOLL,BLACK HAIR CHINA,21 IN. TALL,DRESSED...................	75.00
DOLL,BLACK HAIR CHINA BOY,DRESSED...........................	45.00
DOLL,BLACK HAIR,CHINA,DRESSED,17 IN. TALL...................	27.50
DOLL,BLONDE BLUE EYED GERMAN BISQUE MABEL,22 IN. LONG,......	45.00
DOLL,BLONDE CHINA HANDS & FEET,17 IN.......................	28.00
DOLL,BLONDE CHINA HEAD,22 IN. TALL,BLUE EYES,DRESSED........	65.00
DOLL,BLONDE CHINA,ORIGINAL BODY.............................	32.50
DOLL,BLONDE HAIR,BROWN EYES,OPEN MOUTH,DRESSED,15 IN. TALL..	125.00

DOLL,BLUE BOY 24 IN. CHINA BLONDE MOLDED HAIR,DRESSED,,CHINA HEAD..	60.00
DOLL,BONNET 15 IN.,DRESSED,BLONDE MOLDED HAIR,PAINTED BLUE EYES...	50.00
DOLL,BOY 10 IN. TALL,CELLULOID ,PORTUGAL COSTUME............	7.50
DOLL,BOY BABY,BISQUE,11 IN.,................................	45.00
DOLL,BOY BABY GERMANY BISQUE HEAD...........................	25.00
DOLL,BOY DRESSED LIKE LITTLE LORD FAUNTLEROY,BISQUE.........	40.00
DOLL,BOY,SAILOR SUIT,LAMBS WOOL WIG,14 IN. TALL.............	48.00
DOLL,BUBBLES,22 IN. TALL....................................	20.00
DOLL,BUDDY LEE 12 IN. COMPOSITION,DRESSED...................	85.00
DOLL,BUDDY LEE COMPOSITION,12 IN.,DRESSED...................	15.00
DOLL,BYE-LO 13 IN. BISQUE HEAD..............................	115.00
DOLL,BYE-LO 13 IN. ,CLOTH BODY,DRESSED......................	90.00
DOLL,BYE-LO BABY COP R.C.S. PUTNAM,BROWN SLEEP EYES,10 IN...	70.00
DOLL,BYE-LO BABY ,SIGNED,BROWN EYES,DRESSED,9 IN. TALL......	125.00
DOLL,BYE-LO,BISQUE HEAD MARKED GRACE S.PUTNAM,DRESSED,10 IN. TALL..	105.00
DOLL,BYE-LO COMPOSITION BABY,1930,20 IN. TALL...............	32.00
DOLL,BYE-LO,COMPOSITION MARKED,16 IN.,SLEEP EYES,DRESSED....	39.75
DOLL,BYE-LO,SGINED GRACE S.PUTNAM,12 IN. TALL...............	135.00
DOLL,CAMPBELL KID,6 IN. VINLY IDEAL.........................	7.50
DOLL,CAMPBELL KID,DRESSED GIRL..............................	2.25
DOLL,CAMPBELL KID,PLASTIC,DRESSED,SIGNED,6 IN. TALL.........	5.00
DOLL,CAMPBELL KID,RUBBER,8 IN. TALL.........................	5.00
DOLL,CAMPBELL SOUP ,DRESSED.................................	10.00
DOLL,CELLULOID,2 IN..	1.25
DOLL,CELLULOID BABY,8 IN. TALL.............................	2.00
DOLL,CELLULOID BABY,DRESSED,2 IN. TALL.....................	5.00
DOLL,CELLULOID BABY MARKED STORK,JACKSON & PARSONS,11 IN. TALL..	40.00
DOLL,CELLULOID,BETTY BOOP,7 IN.............................	5.00
DOLL,CELLULOID BOY,DRESSED,19 IN. TALL.....................	35.00
DOLL,CELLULOID BOY,TURTLE MARK,PAINTED HAIR,EYES,11 IN. TALL	12.00
DOLL,CELLULOID DRESSED SWEDISH BOY,MARKED TURTLE,MOLDED HAIR,10 IN..	14.50
DOLL,CELLULOID FACE,DRESSED,BED,27 IN. TALL................	7.00
DOLL,CELULOID GOOGLY EYE TYPE EYES,6 IN. TALL..............	6.00
DOLL,CELLULOID HEAD,KID BODY,DRESSED.......................	28.00
DOLL,CELLULOID MARKED GERMANY,BLUE PAINTED EYES,3 IN. TALL..	6.00
DOLL,CELLULOID MARKED MOODER,7 IN. TALL....................	8.50
DOLL,CELLULOID,MOLDED HAIR,6 IN. TALL......................	5.00
DOLL,CELLULOID ,MOVEABLE PARTS.............................	1.25
DOLL,CHALK KEWPIE..	2.00
DOLL,CHARLIE MC CARTHY,DRESSED,28 IN. TALL.................	28.00
DOLL,CHASE STOCKINET BABY,22 IN............................	65.00
DOLL,CHASE STOCKINET BABY,MOLDED BLONDE HAIR,17 IN. TALL....	48.50
DOLL CHINA BABY & BATH TUB,3 IN. HIGH......................	8.50
DOLL,CHINA BLOND WITH BANGS,CHINA ARMS & LEGS,12 IN. TALL...	90.00
DOLL,CHINA DRESSED,EARS SHOWING,15 IN. TALL................	89.00
DOLL,CHINA,DRESSED,KID ARMS & HANDS,BLACK HAIR,25 IN. TALL..	75.00
DOLL,CHINA FLAT HEAD,11 IN. TALL...........................	22.00
DOLL,CHINA FLAT NOSE,HALF DRESSED,16 IN. TALL..............	49.00
DOLL,CHINA FLAT TOP,BLACK HAIR,19 IN. TALL.................	35.00
DOLL,CHINA FLAT TOP,CLOTH BODY,9 IN. TALL..................	22.50
DOLL,CHINA FLAT TOP,DRESSED,BLACK HAIR,16 IN. TALL.........	40.00
DOLL,CHINA FLAT TOP HEAD,BLACK,DRESSED,CENTER PART,16 IN. TALL..	45.00
DOLL,CHINA FLAT TOP HEAD,BLUE EYES,DRESSED,12 IN. TALL......	50.00
DOLL,CHINA FROZEN CHARLOTTE 4 IN. TALL.....................	6.00
DOLL,CHINA HEAD,3 HOLE,BLACK HAIR,DRESSED,20 IN. TALL.......	89.50
DOLL,CHINA HEAD,ARMS & FEET,DRESSED,15 IN. TALL............	55.00
DOLL,CHINA HEAD,ARMS & LEGS,CLOTH BODY,BLACK,7 IN. TALL.....	12.00
DOLL,CHINA HEAD,ARMS & LEGS,DRESSED,20 IN. TALL............	39.50
DOLL,CHINA HEAD,ARMS,HANDS,COLOUR ALPHABET,DRESSED,7 IN.	

```
TALL...................................................     30.00
DOLL,CHINA HEAD,BLACK HAIR,DRESSED,12 IN. TALL..............    25.00
DOLL,CHINA HEAD,BLACK WAVES,ORIGINAL BODY,DRESSED,9 IN. TALL    28.00
DOLL,CHINA HEAD,BLUE EYES,19 IN. TALL.......................    35.00
DOLL,CHINA HEAD BRUNETTE,BLUE EYES,DRESSED,23 IN. TALL......    68.00
DOLL,CHINA HEAD,DRESSED.....................................    30.00
DOLL,CHINA HEAD,DRESSED,CLOTH BODY,18 IN. TALL..............    35.00
DOLL,CHINA HEAD MARKED GERMANY,DRESSED,8 IN. TALL...........    16.00
DOLL,CHINA HEAD,KID BODY,BLONDE,DRESSED,26 IN. TALL.........    85.00
DOLL,CHINA HEAD MARY TODD 33 IN. TALL,DRESSED...............   100.00
DOLL,CHINA JOINTED KEWPIE-LIKE ,PAINTED HAIR & EYES,5 IN.
   TALL....................................................    10.00
DOLL,CHINA MARKED DOROTHY,LUSTER CHEST,11 IN. TALL..........    19.50
DOLL,CHINA PINCUSHION,13 IN. TALL..........................     2.50
DOLL,CIRCA 1859 PAPER,MISS FLORENCE,3 DRESSES,4 IN. TALL....    37.50
DOLL,CLOSED MOUTH,BLUE PAPERWEIGHT ON-SLEEP EYES,17 IN. TALL   125.00
DOLL,CLOTH BODY,LEATHER ARMS,24 IN. TALL...................     90.00
DOLL,COMPOSITION BODY BABY MARKED GERMANY,DRESSED,12 IN.
   TALL....................................................    35.00
DOLL,COMPOSITION BOY & GIRL,DRESSED,5 IN. TALL..............     8.50
DOLL,COMPOSITION COLOURED BOY,11 IN. TALL..................      6.00
DOLL,COMPOSITION FATTY,PAINTED EYES,PAINTED CLOTHES,5 IN.
   TALL....................................................     3.00
DOLL,COMPOSITION HEAD & ARMS,CLOTH BODY,DRESSED,COLOURED,12
   IN. TALL................................................    24.50
DOLL,COMPOSITION OF THE 1930S,DRESSED,14 IN. TALL...........    10.50
DOLL,COMPOSITION,ORIENTAL,8 IN. TALL.......................     24.00
DOLL,COMPOSITION,ORIGINAL WIG & CLOTHING...................      6.00
DOLL,COMPOSITION TODDLER OF 1930S,DRESSED,14 IN. TALL.......     8.50
DOLL,CRECHE,17 IN. TALL,MAN,DRESSED........................     35.00
DOLL,CRECHE CIRCA 18TH CENTURY,8 IN. TALL..................     25.00
DOLL,CRECHES PEASANT MAN,1700 ORIGINAL COSTUME,GLASS EYES,11
   IN. TALL................................................    60.00
DOLL,DEANNA DURBIN,20 IN. TALL.............................     27.50
DOLL,DEANNA DURBIN,DRESSED,16 IN. TALL.....................     50.00
DOLL,DECALCO PAPER,C.1920,UNCUT SHEET......................       .75
DOLL,DIONNE QUINT TODDLER,13 IN.,COMPOSITION,DRESSED.......     25.00
DOLL DISHES,CHINA SOUVENIR HERMITAGE.......................      3.00
DOLL,DOLLY MADISON,CHINA HEAD,DRESSED,22 IN. TALL..........    125.00
DOLL,DOLLY MADISON CHINA HEAD,DRESSED,BLACK MOLDED HAIR,23
   IN. TALL................................................   185.00
DOLL,DOTTER,BLONDE MOLDED HAIR,PAINTED BLUE EYES,KID BODY,15
   IN. TALL................................................    85.00
DOLL,DRESDEN CHINA,HANGING,DRESSED,7 IN. TALL..............     15.00
DOLL,DRESSED,31 IN. HIGH,BISQUE HEAD,SLEEPING EYES,LONG
   BLONDE CURLS............................................    85.00
DOLL,DRESSED,A & M BISQUE FLORADORA,KID BODY,BISQUE HANDS...    40.00
DOLL,DRESSED BISQUE HEAD GERMAN MARKED,23 IN. TALL,BROWN
   EYES...................................................     75.00
DOLL,DRESSED EFFANBEE COMPOSITION BABY BOY,RED CARACUL WIG..    28.00
DOLL,DRESSED,K & R SIMON HALBIG BLONDE HAIR CLOSED MOUTH
   BABY...................................................    150.00
DOLL,DRESSED,KIDDIE TOY GERMANY,BABY MOUNTED ON PILLOW......    35.00
DOLL,DRESSED,MARKED 370 0/1,GERMAN BISQUE,A & M,SLEEPING
   EYES...................................................     45.00
DOLL,DRESSED MC GUFFEY ANNA,DARK BRAIDS,FRECKLES,COMPOSITION    28.00
DOLL,DRESSED RUBBER IDEAL BABY BOY MARKED L.B..............     20.00
DOLL,DUTCH GIRL NODDING HEAD,11 IN. TALL...................     17.50
DOLL,EFFANBEE BABY,CLOTH BODY,COMPOSITION ARMS & LEGS.......    17.00
DOLL,EFFANBEE DIMPLED THUMB SUCKER,DRESSED,COMPOSITION,16
   IN. TALL................................................    25.00
DOLL,EFFANBEE PATSY,14 IN. TALL............................     26.00
DOLL,EMMA CLEAR 47 GIBSON GIRL,PARIAN HEAD,BLONDE,DRESSED,18
   IN. TALL................................................    85.00
DOLL,ENGLISH WAX FASHION OR COURT CIRCA 1750-1780..........   175.00
```

DOLL,ETHEL CHINA HEAD,16 IN. TALL............................	58.00
DOLL,FLORA DORA DRESSED,BISQUE HEAD,STATIONARY BROWN EYES,11	
IN. TALL..	45.00
DOLL,FLORADORA GERMAN BISQUE BROWN EYES,KID BODY............	27.50
DOLL,FRENCH BISQUE,20 IN. TALL,MARKED DEP,DRESSED...........	125.00
DOLL,FRENCH BOY MARKED PARIS,SOLDIER CLOTHES,12 IN. TALL....	45.00
DOLL,FRENCH FASHION,14 IN. TALL.............................	175.00
DOLL,FRENCH MARKED DEP,LASHES,OPEN MOUTH,DRESSED,HUMAN	
HAIR,14 IN. TALL...	80.00
DOLL,FRENCH S F B J LITTLE GIRL,DRESSED,17 IN. TALL.........	125.00
DOLL,FROZEN CHARLOTTE......................................	5.00
DOLL,FROZEN CHARLOTTE,1 IN. TALL...........................	1.50
DOLL,FROZEN CHARLOTTE,2 IN.................................	6.00
DOLL,FROZEN CHARLOTTE,BLOND HAIR,PINK LUSTER HEAD,14 IN.	
TALL...	175.00
DOLL,FROZEN CHARLOTTE,BLACK HAIR,PINK LUSTER HEAD,15 IN.	
TALL...	100.00
DOLL,FROZEN CHARLOTTE,CHINA,4 IN. TALL......................	12.00
DOLL,FROZEN CHARLOTTE,CHINA,5 IN. TALL......................	15.00
DOLL,FROZEN CHARLOTTE,COLOURED,4 IN. TALL..................	18.00
DOLL,GEBRUDER-HEUBACH GIRL,15 IN. TALL,HUMAN HAIR..........	50.00
DOLL,GENERAL DOUGLAS MAC ARTHUR COMPOSITION,DRESSED IN FULL	
UNIFORM..	30.00
DOLL,GERBER RUBBER BOY MARKED,GLASS EYES,11 IN. TALL........	8.50
DOLL,GERMAN,1875...	6.50
DOLL,GERMAN,1890...	6.50
DOLL,GERMAN BABY,12 IN. TALL,DRESSED,HEUBACH CHARACTER-FACED	75.00
DOLL,GERMAN BABY MARKED A O M,DRESSED,BLUE EYES,13 IN. TALL.	45.00
DOLL,GERMAN BISQUE CHILD,BROWN HAIR & EYES,24 IN...........	26.00
DOLL,GERMAN BISQUE HEAD 16 IN. TALL,AM FLORADORA,PAPIER	
MACHE BODY...	35.00
DOLL,GERMAN BROWN EYES,HEUBACK KOPPELSDORF.................	85.00
DOLL,GERMAN,BROWN EYES,OPEN MOUTH..........................	85.00
DOLL,GERMAN CHARACTER BABY SHOFFMAN-HOFFMISTER.............	100.00
DOLL,GERMAN CHINA PIN CUSHION ,SPANISH LADY................	4.00
DOLL,GERMAN MARKED 151,BROWN SLEEP EYES,SOLID DOME,12 IN.	
TALL...	50.00
DOLL,GERMAN MARKED SIMON HALBIG,BLUE EYES..................	90.00
DOLL,GERMAN MARKED SH,FASHION,KID BODY,PIERCED EARS,14 IN.	
TALL...	70.00
DOLL,GERMANY PIN CUSHION BLONDE............................	3.50
DOLL,GERMAN PORCELAIN PIN CUSHION,3 IN. TALL...............	5.50
DOL6,GERMAN PORCELAIN PINCUSHION ,DRESSED,.................	10.00
DOLL,GERMAN TIN BABY,II IN. TALL...........................	20.00
DOLL,GOOGLIE EYE,COMPOSITION BODY,JOINTED..................	15.00
DOLL,GRACE KELLY,MONACO,19 IN. TALL........................	27.50
DOLL,GREINER DRESSED 1958 LABEL,23 IN. TALL................	125.00
DOLL,GREINER SIGNED,21 IN. TALL............................	98.00
DOLL,HARD RUBBER 12 IN. 1958 MR.MAGOO......................	10.00
DOLL,HEUBACH COMPOSITION GIRL,3 IN. TALL...................	28.00
DOLL,HEUBACK KOPPELSDORF...................................	85.00
DOLL,HEUBACH MARKED IN SQUARE,DRESSED,DOME HEAD,11 IN. TALL.	65.00
DOLL,HEUBACH SIGNED BISQUE HEAD BRUNETTE,BLUE EYES,8 IN.	
TALL...	25.00
DOLL,HIGHLAND MARY,BISQUE HEAD,DRESSED,17 IN. TALL..........	135.00
DOLL,HIGHLAND MARY,BLOND MOLDED HAIR,DRESSED,PAINTED BLUE	
EYES,16 IN...	105.00
DOLL,HIGHLAND MARY,CHINA,DRESSED,BLOND MOLDED HAIR,16 IN.	
TALL...	95.00
DOLL,ITALIAN 9 IN. TALL,STORE TAG ON DRESS FLORENCE ITALY...	15.00
DOLL,J.D.KESTNER BABY ,....................................	25.00
DOLL,JACKSON & PARSON BABY,HEAD & BODY MARKED,DIAPER........	30.00
DOLL,JOINTED 7 IN. UNIS FRANCE.............................	30.00
DOLL,JOINTED ,10 IN. FRENCH CLOSED MOUTH...................	65.00
DOLL,JOINTED ,12 IN..	40.00

```
DOLL,JOINTED 13 IN. MARKED G.H.............................. 35.00
DOLL,JOINTED 16 IN. FULPER,KID BODY......................... 70.00
DOLL,JOINTED 18 IN. CLOSED MOUTH............................ 125.00
DOLL,JOINTED 19 IN. MARKED SANTA............................ 40.00
DOLL,JOINTED,BROWN SLEEP EYES,RED HAIR,23 IN. TALL.......... 40.00
DOLL,JOINTED COMPOSITION,DRESSED,MARKED S H 1079-9 GERMANY.. 65.00
DOLL,JUDY GARLAND,DRESSED,HUMAN HAIR WIG,21 IN. TALL........ 48.00
DOLL,JUMEAU SIGNED,BLUE EYES,32 IN.......................... 340.00
DOLL,JUNO ENGLAND CROWN MARK TIN HEAD,CLOTHES,19 IN......... 24.00
DOLL,KAISER BABY MARKED K STAR R,DRESSED,10 IN.............. 125.00
DOLL,KELLY CLOWN,WHITTLED,10 IN. TALL....................... 10.00
DOLL,KESTNER BABY,BLONDE BISQUE HEAD,CLOTH BODY,DRESSED..... 35.00
DOLL,KESTNER BISQUE SHOULDER HEAD MARKED B GERMANY 154 D E
  P,18 IN.................................................... 40.00
DOLL,KESTNER,DRESSED,5 IN. TALL............................. 25.00
DOLL,KESTNER FLIRTY EYE,DRESSED,18 IN. TALL................. 65.00
DOLL,KESTNER GIRL,HUMAN HAIR,24 IN. TALL.................... 50.00
DOLL,KESTNER MARKED A-MADE GERMANY,DRESSED,17 IN. TALL...... 45.00
DOLL,KESTNER MARKED B MADE IN GERMANY,UNDRESSED,OPEN
  MOUTH,16 IN. TALL......................................... 33.00
DOLL,KESTNER MARKED K 14,25 IN. TALL........................ 60.00
DOLL,KEWPIE................................................. 12.50
DOLL,KEWPIE,ROSE O NEILL,MINIATURE BIDQUE WITH UMBRELLA &
  DOG....................................................... 19.50
DOLL,KEWPIE TYPE,JOINTED,BISQUE............................. 23.00
DOLL,KID BODY,FRENCH CLOSED MOUTH,15 IN. TALL,BISQUE HEAD,.. 165.00
DOLL,KID BODY,FRENCH CLOSED MOUTH,15 IN. TALL,DRESSED....... 165.00
DOLL,KID BODY,SET IN EYES,DRESSED........................... 40.00
DOLL,KUDDLE KEWPIE MARKED ROSE O NEILL...................... 10.00
DOLL,LADY,DRESSED,11 IN. TALL............................... 42.00
DOLL,LADY MARKED GERMANY 1290, BLONDE MOHAIR WIG,DRESSED,25
  IN. TALL.................................................. 75.00
DOLL,LENCI BOY & GIRL WITH STANDS & LABEL,11 IN. TALL....... 45.00
DOLL,LENCI FELT,BROWN EYES,CLOSED MOUTH,BLONDE
  WIG,DRESSED,22 IN. TALL................................... 45.00
DOLL,LENCI,HUMAN HAIR WIG,COLOURFUL COSTUME,17 IN. TALL..... 50.00
DOLL,LITTLE ANNIE ROONEY,DRESSED............................ 6.00
DOLL,MADAM ALEX. BALLERINA DOLL IN PINK..................... 15.00
DOLL,MADAME ALEXANDER FLIRTY EYE LITTLE GIRL,DRESSED,BROWN
  EYES ,.................................................... 60.00
DOLL,MADAME ALEXANDER,SKATING BABE,ORIG.COSTUME............. 18.00
DOLL,MAGGIE & JIGGS,CARVED WOOD,13 IN. TALL................. 20.00
DOLL,MARKED 390 G,DRESSED,BLONDE HAIR,BLUE EYES,22 IN. TALL. 40.00
DOLL,MARKED AM DEP 1890,DRESSED,18 IN. TALL................. 45.00
DOLL,MARKED B4,DRESSED,OPEN MOUTH,BROWN EYES,REDDISH HAIR
  WIG,23 IN................................................. 40.00
DOLL,MARKED GERMANY PORCELAIN PINCUSHION,SPANISH
  GIRL,DRESSED.............................................. 8.50
DOLL,MARKED LILLY 3/0 GERMANY,DRESSED,GERMAN BISQUE......... 45.00
DOLL,MARKED QUEEN LOUISE GERMANY,22 IN. TALL,1890,DRESSED... 47.50
DOLL,MARKED R KAISER CHARACTER BABY,DRESSED................. 125.00
DOLL,MARKED SKOOKUM,INDIAN,BOY & GIRL PAIR.................. 6.50
DOLL,MC GUFFY BABY,17 IN. TALL.............................. 17.00
DOLL,MECHANICAL,DRESSED,BISQUE HEAD,WALKS,TALKS,MOVES ARMS &
  HEAD...................................................... 300.00
DOLL,MECHANICAL TALKING BOY,6 RECORDS,UNIVERSAL TALKING TOY
  CO........................................................ 128.00
DOLL,MECHANICAL WIND-UP WALKER,MARKED GERMANY X,DRESSED,9
  IN. TALL.................................................. 48.00
DOLL,MICKEY MOUSE RUBBER.................................... 5.00
DOLL,MILLINERS MODEL,22 IN. TALL............................ 225.00
DOLL,MINERVA SIGNED,GLASS EYES,MOLDED HAIR,22 IN. TALL...... 38.00
DOLL,MINERVA TIN HEAD 16 IN. TALL,DRESSED................... 18.00
DOLL,NEGRO 10 IN. TALL COMPOSITION BABY,DRESSED,STATIONARY
  HEAD...................................................... 10.00
```

DOLL,NEGRO GIRL,9 IN. TALL,COMPOSITION BABY,STATIONARY
  HEAD,DRESSED..   12.50
DOLL,NEGRO GIRL,12 IN. TALL,COMPOSITION BABY,SWIVELED HEAD..   15.00
DOLL,OLD FASHIONED GOWN OF CALICO...........................   3.50
DOLL,O NEILL PRINTED,COMPOSITION HEAD & HANDS,DRESSED,11 IN.
  TALL..   12.50
DOLL,PAIR 3 IN. BISQUE JAPAN DOLLS..........................   3.00
DOLL,PAIR 6 IN. BISQUE PIANO BABIES.........................   55.00
DOLL,PAIR 15 IN. GRANDPA & GRANDMA WAX IN WOODEN
  CHAIRS,DRESSED..   30.00
DOLL,PAIR HEDWIG,SUSANNE & ELIN,14 IN.......................   80.00
DOLL,PAPER FORBES LADY IN BICYCLING OUTFIT..................   4.00
DOLL,PAPER,JEANETTE,1895,WITH WARDROBE B/W..................   .75
DOLL,PAPER JEANETTE 1895,HAND COLOURED......................   2.00
DOLL,PAPER JEANETTE WITH WARDROBE,1815......................   .75
DOLL,PAPER,RAPHAEL TUCK SWEET ABIGAIL,FOLDER & 2 DRESSES....   20.00
DOLL,PAPER WATERCOLORED.....................................   2.00
DOLL,PAPER,WORCESTER SAL AND A DRESS........................   3.50
DOLL,PAPIER MACHE,BLACK HAIR,BLUE EYES,DRESSED,20 IN. TALL..   37.00
DOLL,PAPIER MACHE,BLOWN BROWN GLASS EYES,DRESSED,16 IN. TALL   38.00
DOLL,PAPIER MACHE,BOUDOIR,DRESSED...........................   12.00
DOLL,PAPIER MACHE BOUDOIR USED AS LAMP SHADE................   17.00
DOLL,PAPIER MACHE,BOY,9 IN. TALL,ORIGINAL CLOTHES...........   60.00
DOLL,PAPIER MACHE BOY,AMUSO,GERMANY,DRESSED,28 IN. TALL.....   55.00
DOLL,PAPIER MACHE BOY,JOINTED BODY,DRESSED..................   22.50
DOLL,PAPIER MACHE,BROWN PAPERWEIGHT EYES,16 IN. TALL........   33.00
DOLL,PAPIER MACHE,DRESSED,EARS SHOWING,20 IN. TALL..........   149.00
DOLL,PAPIER MACHE FLAT TOP,CURLS AROUND HEAD,DRESSED,18 IN.
  TALL..   89.00
DOLL,PAPIER MACHE HEAD,CLOTH BODY,28 IN. TALL...............   45.00
DOLL,PAPIER MACHE HEAD,JOINTED ARMS & LEGS,20 IN. TALL......   16.00
DOLL,PAPIER MACHE,LADY,10 IN. TALL,ORIGINAL CLOTHES.........   50.00
DOLL,PAPIER MACHE PIN CUSHION,3 IN. TALL,HANDS ON HIPS......   4.00
DOLL,PAPIER MACHE PIN CUSHION WITH WIG,⅓ IN. TALL,PAINTED
  FACE..   3.00
DOLL,PAPIER MACHE PIN CUSHION WITH WIG,4 IN. TALL,HANDS ON
  HIPS..   4.50
DOLL,PAPEIR MACHE PIN CUSHION,6 IN. TALL,HANDS ON HIPS......   5.50
DOLL,PAPIER MACHE PIN CUSHION,8 IN. TALL,BISQUE ARMS........   11.50
DOLL,PAPIER MACHE SHOULDER HEAD,GLASS BULGE EYES,DRESSED,11
  IN. TALL..   18.00
DOLL,PARIAN CONTEMPORARY BY HAROLD,DRESSED,BLACK HAIR,16 IN.
  TALL..   40.00
DOLL,PARIAN COUNTESS DAGMAR,UNDRESSED,BLUE PAINTED EYES,19
  IN. TALL..   175.00
DOLL,PARIAN DRESSED BLOND,BLACK BAND ON HAIR,14 IN. TALL....   95.00
DOLL,PARIAN,DRESSED,BLONDE,GLASS EYES,TURNED HEAD,22 IN.
  TALL..   395.00
DOLL,PARIAN GIBSON GIRL 23 IN. BLONDE,PAINTED BLUE
  EYES,DRESSED..   55.00
DOLL,PARIAN SIGNED MANN,DRESSED,BLOND MOLDED HAIR,16 IN.
  TALL..   55.00
DOLL,PATSY LOU SIGNED & DRESSED,20 IN. TALL.................   32.00
DOLL,PATSYETTE,SLEEP EYES...................................   15.00
DOLL,PENNY,1 HALF IN. HI. PAINTED...........................   2.00
DOLL,PENNY,ARMS STRUNG ON CORD,PAINTED FACE & SHOES.........   2.00
DOLL,PENNY WOODEN HANDCARVED HANDPAINTED,11 IN. TALL........   2.50
DOLL,PETITE SALLY BLONDE HAIR TODDLER MARKED 1920,20 IN.
  TALL..   12.50
DOLL,PIN CUSHION,GREY HAIR ,GERMANY
  4.75 TO..   5.75
DOLL,PIN CUSHION HEAD,BLONDE CURLY HAIR,JAPAN...............   4.00
DOLL,PIN CUSHION HEAD,DRESSED,BLOND MOLDED HAIR,6 IN........   18.00
DOLL,PIN CUSHION HEAD,MARKED BLUE QUESTION MARK,CHINA,5 IN.
  TALL..   12.00

```
DOLL,PIN CUSHION HEAD,MOLDED HIGH HAIRDO,PAINTED BLUE EYES,4
   IN. TALL..............................................    4.00
DOLL,PIN CUSHION,WHITE CHINA LADY..........................    8.50
DOLL,PIN CUSHION WITH HAT..................................    4.50
DOLL,PINK LUSTER BLACK HAIR CHINA ,DRESSED.................   65.00
DOLL,PORCELAIN PIN CUSHION,GERMAN..........................    7.00
DOLL,POUTY 19 IN. BLONDE BLUE BLOWN GLASS
   EYES,DRESSED,BISQUE HEAD................................   75.00
DOLL,POUTY BROWN HAIR & BROWN EYES,DRESSED,19 IN. TALL......   80.00
DOLL,PRE GREINER,BLACK HAIR,16 IN. TALL....................   45.00
DOLL,PRINCESS ELIZABETH,14 IN. TALL........................   18.00
DOLL,PRINCESS ELIZABETH,19 IN. TALL........................   20.00
DOLL,PRINCESS ELIZABETH,20 IN. TALL........................   27.50
DOLL,PUTNAM BYE-LO 10 IN. CLOTH BODY,DRESSED...............   88.50
DOLL,PUTNAM MARKED,DRESSED,WICKER STROLLER,4 IN. TALL.......  125.00
DOLL,QUEEN ELIZABETH,DRESSED,CHINA HEAD,KID BODY...........   25.00
DOLL,QUEEN LOUISE,BROWN HAIR WIG,BROWN EYES,DRESSED,21 IN.
   TALL...................................................   60.00
DOLL,RAG,1900 ART FABRIC MILLS.............................   10.00
DOLL,RAG,AUNT JEMINA AND UNCLE MOSE........................    4.50
DOLL,RAG,DRESSED,PAINTED EYES,NOSE & MOUTH,15 IN. TALL......   15.00
DOLL,RAG RED RIDING HOOD...................................    2.00
DOLL,RAG WITH PRINTED FACE,25 IN. TALL,DRESSED.............   10.00
DOLL,RAGGEDY ANDY 18 IN. CLOTH.............................    7.50
DOLL,RAGGEDY ANN,BLACK HAIR................................    2.50
DOLL,RED CROSS NURSE FROM WORLD WAR 1......................    7.00
DOLL,ROSE MARIE,DRESSED,19 IN. TALL........................   17.00
DOLL,ROSE O NEILL LABELED 5 IN. CELLULOID KEWPIE,BLUE DRESS.   11.50
DOLL,RUBBER 3 FACE,22 IN. TALL.............................   10.00
DOLL,RUBBER HEAD,2 HEADED,CLOTH BODY,13 IN. TALL...........   10.00
DOLL,RUBBER HEAD,MARKED K STAR R 835,PAINTED EYES,11 IN.
   TALL...................................................   48.50
DOLL,SAMURAI WARRIOR SEATED,15 IN. TALL,CIRCA 1880,BROCADE &
   SEMI-ARMOR.............................................   75.00
DOLL,SAUCY WALKER BRIDE 22 IN. COMPOSITION,DRESSED.........   22.50
DOLL,SCARLETT O HARA,COMPOSITION,DRESSED,15 IN. TALL.......   35.00
DOLL,SCHOENHUT 1911 MARK,15 IN. TALL.......................   39.50
DOLL,SCHOENHUT BOY,SAILOR COSTUME,16 IN. TALL..............   60.00
DOLL,SCHOENHUT,BROWN HAIR & EYES,21 IN. TALL...............   30.00
DOLL,SCHOENHUT SMILING GIRL,DRESSED,16 IN. TALL............   65.00
DOLL,SCHOENHUT WOODEN,BLUE PAINTED EYES,CLOSED MOUTH,17 IN.
   TALL...................................................   65.00
DOLL,SCHOENHUT WOODEN DRESSED RING MASTER,8 IN. TALL.......   22.00
DOLL,SCHOENHUT WOODEN GIRL,DRESSED,16 IN. TALL.............   95.00
DOLL,SHIRLEY TEMPLE 13 IN. UNDRESSED......................   15.00
DOLL,SHIRLEY TEMPLES FAITHFUL LUCIFER,DRESSED,14 IN. TALL...   35.00
DOLL,SHOFFMAN-HOFFMISTER...................................   85.00
DOLL,SHOFFMAN-HOFFMISTER,BLUE EYES,OPEN MOUTH..............  100.00
DOLL,SIGNED ARMAND MARSEILLE,16 IN. TALL,.................   65.00
DOLL,SIGNED GRACE S.PUTNAM,DRESSED,BYE-LO BABY DOLL,10 IN.
   TALL...................................................   58.00
DOLL,SIGNED HORSMAN MAMA ,COMPOSITION HEAD,DRESSED.........   10.00
DOLL,SIGNED ROSE O NEILL COMPOSITION KEWPIE...............   25.00
DOLL,SIMON & HALBIG MARKED BISQUE COLOURED HEAD,18 IN. TALL.  150.00
DOLL,SIMON & HALBIG MARKED BISQUE HEAD,DRESSED,22 IN. TALL..   50.00
DOLL,SIMON HALBIG,DRESSED,JOINTED BODY,SLEEP EYES,29 IN.
   TALL...................................................   75.00
DOLL,SITTING ACTION KEWPIE................................   25.00
DOLL,SMALL NEGRO CELLULOID.................................    2.00
DOLL,SONJA HENIE,14 IN. TALL...............................   20.00
DOLL,SONJA HENIE,20 IN. TALL...............................   27.50
DOLL,STANDING BISQUE BABY GIRL,YELLOW DRESS................   37.50
DOLL,STEINER COMPOSITION HEAD..............................   18.00
DOLL,STONE BISQUE BOY 4 IN. TALL,PAINTED CLOTHES...........    2.00
DOLL,TERRY LEE,DRESSED,DARK WIG,WALKS,1/ IN. TALL..........   14.00
```

```
DOLL,TERRY LEE HARD PLASTIC GIRL,DRESSED,15 IN. TALL........     16.00
DOLL,THE BREATHING DOLL MARKED S & H,DRESSED,22 IN. TALL....     50.00
DOLL,TIN HEAD,18 IN. TALL,GERMANY,BROWN EYES,HAIR,KID
  BODY,DRESSED.................................................     75.00
DOLL,TODDLER,BROWN SLEEP EYES,AUBURN WIG,17 IN. TALL.........     65.00
DOLL,TOPSY,COMPOSITION,4 IN. TALL.............................      5.00
DOLL TRUNK,CAMEL BACK TOP,REFINISHED.........................     28.00
DOLL,TULPER,BROWN HAIR & EYES................................     47.00
DOLL,TWIRLING JESTER MUSIC BOX...............................     50.00
DOLL,UNCLE SAM,DRESSED,WORLD WAR I,BLUE SLEEP EYES,24 IN.
  TALL.......................................................     55.00
DOLL,UNIS FRANCE B.J.PALE BISQUE,DRESSED,17 IN. TALL.........     80.00
DOLL,UNIS FRANCE B.J.BISQUE,19 IN. TALL......................     80.00
DOLL,WALKURE GERMAN BISQUE,24 IN.............................     35.00
DOLL,WALT E.DISNEY MICKEY MOUSE..............................      3.00
DOLL,WALT E.DISNEY MINNIE MOUSE..............................      3.00
DOLL,WALT E. DISNEY PLUTO....................................      5.00
DOLL,WARRIOR,SEATED, DRESSED IN COURT ROBES,WOOD HEAD &
  HANDS,JAPANESE.............................................     95.00
DOLL,WAX BOY BLUE GLASS EYES,22 IN.,DRESSED IN TUXEDO.......     38.00
DOLL,WAX GERMAN CHILD,DRESSED, 17 IN. TALL...................      4.00
DOLL,WAX FACE,BROWN PAPERWEIGHT EYES,DRESSED,15 IN. TALL....     36.00
DOLL,WAX HEAD,DRESSED,21 IN. TALL,SET BLUE EYES..............     85.00
DOLL,WAX OVER PAPIER MACHE POMPADOUR HEAD....................     25.00
DOLL,WAX OVER PAPIER MACHE SHOULDER HEAD,DRESSED,CLOTH
  BODY,18 IN. TALL..........................................     65.00
DOLL,WAX POURED HEAD,ARMS & LEGS,MUSLIN BODY,24 IN. TALL....    110.00
DOLL,WAX POURED HEAD,DRESSED,SLEEP EYES,BLONDE WIG,19 IN.
  TALL.......................................................    125.00
DOLL,WAX POURED SHOULDER HEAD,DRESSED,SLEEP BLUE EYES,23 IN.
  TALL.......................................................    135.00
DOLL,WHIMSIE ,21 IN. ,3 FACE RUBBER..........................     10.00
DOLL,WINDUP,SEATED,7 IN. TALL................................      3.00
DOLL,WOOD CARVED,DRESSED,2 IN. TALL..........................      1.50
DOLL,WOOD FIGURINE OF NUN,IVORY FACE,HANDS & FEET,BROWN
  HABIT......................................................     90.00
DOLL,WOOD NEGRO WITH PAPIER MACHE HEAD.......................     10.00
DOLL,WOODEN HAND CARVED,DRESSED,PAINTED EYES,10 IN. TALL....     10.00
DOLL,WOODEN MILLINERS MODEL,9 IN. TALL,PAPIER MACHE
  HEAD,DRESSED...............................................     85.00
DOORKNOBS,PAIR GLASS WITH SILVER FLORAL INSET...............      8.00
DOORKNOBS,WOODEN.............................................      2.50
```

DOORSTOPS have been made in all types of materials. The vast majority of doorstops sold today are cast iron and were made from about 1890 to 1930. Most of them are shaped like people, animals, flowers, or ships.
```
DOORSTOP, SEE IRON, DOORSTOP................................
```

DOUGHTY BIRDS were made by Dorothy Doughty for the Royal Worcester Porce- lain Company of England from 1936 to 1962. They have become very collectible.
```
DOROTHY DOUGHTY LAZULI BUNTINGS COCK & HEN,ORIENTAL CASE....3,000.00
DOROTHY DOUGHTY MOUNTAIN BLUEBIRDS,PAIR FIGURINES...........   950.00
DOROTHY DOUGHTY PAIR KINGLETS...............................3,500.00
  DOULTON, SEE ALSO ROYAL DOULTON...........................
```

DOULTON POTTERY and porcelain were made by Doulton and Co. of Burslem, England after 1882. The name "Royal Doulton" appeared on their wares after 1902.
```
DOULTON 10 IN. PLATE,ROBERT BURNS...........................     18.00
DOULTON 10 IN. PLATE,THE BOOKWORM...........................     17.00
DOULTON 10 IN. PLATE,THE MAYOR..............................     17.00
DOULTON ARTIST SIGNED 7 IN. PITCHER,MOTTLED GREEN & FLORAL..     30.00
DOULTON-BURSLEM 10 IN. DINNER PLATE,8.......................    100.00
DOULTON-BURSLEM CRACKER JAR,SILVER TOP......................     22.50
```

```
DOULTON-BURSLEM ENGLAND BLUE CRACKER JAR,SILVER BAIL & COVER      25.00
DOULTON-BURSLEM ENGLAND CRACKER JAR,PORTRAIT OF GIRL IN
  GARDEN...............................................         25.00
DOULTON BURSLEM ENGLAND MARKED QUEEN VICTORIA PORCELAIN
  TUMBLER,1897..........................................         15.00
DOULTON-BURSLEM-ENGLAND MARKED WASSAIL BOWL,GREEN HOLLY WITH
  RED..................................................         55.00
DOULTON EWER TYPE VASE,BURNT ORANGE & GREEN TOP &
  HANDLE,GOLD,FLOWERS...................................         40.00
DOULTON FLOW BLUE PLATE.................................         15.00
DOULTON LAMBETH IMPRESSED STONEWARE PITCHER,BROWN &
  TAN,DATED 1856-1864...................................         40.00
DOULTON-LAMBETH MARKED CONDIMENT SET,SILVER TOPS & RIMS....      28.50
DOULTON LAMBETH MARK ENGLAND COMMEMORATIVE PITCHER,COLUMBIAN
  1893.................................................          38.00
DOULTON LAMBETH OVAL PLAQUE OF GEORGE WASHINGTON CIRCA
  1869,GREEN...........................................         15.00
DOULTON LAMBETH PITCHER,RAISED BLUE FLOWER DECORATION ON
  GRAY.................................................         42.00
DOULTON LAMBETH QUEEN VICTORIA TANKARD ANNIVERSARY PITCHER,.     52.50
DOULTON MARKED BARLOW PITCHER,ARTIST SIGNED,MOTTLED
  BROWN,BLUE...........................................         90.00
DOULTON PAIR BLUE & WHITE MADRAS PATTERN 8 IN. PLATES.......     19.00
DOULTON SIGNED HANNAH BARLOW 7 IN. VASE,BUFF & BROWN........     40.00
DOULTON WHITE JAM JAR..................................         10.50
    DRESDEN. SEE ALSO MEISSEN..........................
```

DRESDEN CHINA is any china made in the town of Dresden, Germany. The most famous factory in Dresden is the Meissen factory.

```
DRESDEN,1 DOZEN CUPS & SAUCERS.........................         85.00
DRESDEN 8 IN. PLATE,GOLD PANELED,BORDER & SCROLL WORK.......      7.95
DRESDEN 8 IN. PLATE,GREEN WITH 3 FLORAL GROUPINGS ON BORDER.     18.00
DRESDEN 23 IN. GERMANY NUT BASKET,GREEN GLAZE..............       2.25
DRESDEN BLUE & GOLD HEART SHAPE PORTRAIT TRINKET BOX SIGNED.     14.00
DRESDEN BOTTLE,5 IN. HIGH..............................         12.00
DRESDEN CABINET PIECES,LITTLE TABLE WITH HIGH BACK
  CHAIR,PINK ROSES.....................................         40.00
DRESDEN CANDLE STAND...................................         25.00
DRESDEN CANDELABRA,4 CANDLES,PAIR,EACH....................      225.00
DRESDEN CHINA 1914 CALENDAR PLATE,BOY IN RAGGED CLOTHES.....     11.75
DRESDEN CHINA MUG,PURPLE GRAPES........................         12.00
DRESDEN CHINA PITCHER,WHITE............................          6.00
DRESDEN DOUBLE FIGURINE,MAN STANDING,WOMAN SITTING IN CHAIR.     65.00
DRESDEN DRESSER TRAY...................................         21.00
DRESDEN DRESSER TRAY DECORATED WITH CHERUBS............         37.50
DRESDEN FIGURINE,GENT IN COLONIAL PINK SUIT,7 IN. TALL......     41.50
DRESDEN FOOTED EGG SHAPED BOX,PINK & PURPLE,HINGED OPEN WORK
  LID.................................................         175.00
DRESDEN HANDLED FRUIT KNIFE............................          2.50
DRESDEN HEXAGON SHAPED SCALLOPED BOWL,FLOWERS AGAINST WHITE
  BACKGROUND...........................................         75.00
DRESDEN LAMP BASE,PINK,BLUE,APPLIED FLOWERS............         65.00
DRESDEN MARKED BOWL,ROSES & GOLD.......................         20.00
DRESDEN MARKED CUP & SAUCER,GREEN,GOLD ROSES IN MEDALLIONS..     18.00
DRESDEN MARKED DEMI-TASSE CUP & SAUCER,HANDPAINTED FLOWERS..     12.00
DRESDEN MARKED FRUIT BOWL,FLOWERED,SCROLLED EDGE & OPEN
  ENDS,GOLD............................................         47.50
DRESDEN PAIR ANGEL CANDLESTICKS,WHITE..................         25.00
DRESDEN PAIR CANDELABRA,4 CANDLES EACH.................        225.00
DRESDEN PAIR PEASANT MAN & LADY,9 IN. TALL,LATTICE PEDESTAL.    137.50
DRESDEN PERFUME BOTTLE.................................         16.50
DRESDEN PLATE,10 IN.,ROSES.............................         10.50
DRESDEN PORTRAIT CALENDAR PLATE 1909,.................          12.50
DRESDEN PORTRAIT COVERED BOX,CUPIDS,LADIES,FLORALS.........      30.00
DRESDEN ROUND FOOTED BOX,HINGED OPEN WORK LID & FLORAL MOTIF    150.00
```

DRESDEN SIGNED MONKEY......................................	95.00
DRESDEN STEMMED 7 IN. COMPOTE..............................	22.00
DRESDEN TEA CADDY,FLORAL MOTIF,CYLINDER SHAPED,4 IN. HIGH...	45.00
DRESDEN TEA CADDY,FLORAL MOTIF,ROUND & SCALLOPED,6 IN. HIGH.	50.00
DRESDEN TYPE FIGURE,MAN,WOMAN,DOG ON CIRCULAR BASE..........	42.50
DRESDEN WITH RK MARK COOKIE JAR WITH LID,GOLD HANDLES.......	28.00
DRESDEN WITH RK MARK MUSTARD JAR WITH LID & CHINA SPOON.....	15.00
DRESDEN WITH RK MARK TEA CADDY WITH LID....................	28.00
DR.SYNTAX READING HIS TOUR 9 IN. PLATE.....................	65.00

DURAND GLASS was made by Victor Durand from 1879 to 1935 at several factories. Most of the iridescent Durand glass was made by Victor Durand, Jr., from 1912 to 1924 at the Durand Art Glass Works in Vineland, New Jersey.

DURAND AMETHYST RIBBED VASE,PEDESTAL BASE SIGNED...........	250.00
DURAND BOWL,GREEN WITH IRIDESCENT VERTICAL PANELS & SWIRLS..	125.00
DURAND CANDLE HOLDER.......................................	135.00
DURAND EMERALD GREEN WATER BOTTLE,BEEHIVE HORIZONTAL RIDGING	12.00
DURAND FINGER BOWL,FUCHSIA WITH WHITE RIM..................	27.50
DURAND LARSON FEATHER PATTERN CENTERPIECE BOWL,GREEN & WHITE	275.00
DURAND OIL LUSTRE MUSHROOM ENGRAVED CANDLESTICK............	75.00
DURAND PAIR VASES,GREEN UNEVEN LINES,FLOWERS,GOLD BAND AT TOP...	195.00
DURAND RED FEATHERED SHERBET,CANERY FOOT,CUT BORDER........	150.00
DURAND SIGNED GREEN KING TUT PATTERN VASE WITH GOLD LINER...	400.00
DURAND SIGNED GOLD IRIDESCENT WITH RED HIGHLIGHTS BLUE SHEEN VASE...	139.00
DURAND SIGNED PAIR VASES,FOOTED BASES,....................	475.00
DURAND VASE,BLUE WITH WHITE LEAF & VINE DECOR,SIGNED.......	500.00
EARTHENWARE T & R BOOTE 16 IN. TURKEY PLATTER..............	6.00

EGERMANN OR EGGERMAN GLASS was made by Friedrich Egermann in Bohemia about 1830. His glass was made to resemble polished stone and has often been mistaken for carved polished agate. The glass is called lithyalin.

EGGERMAN RUBY CANDLE STICKS,PAIR,DEER & CASTLE.............	28.00
EGLANTINE CHOCOLATE POT,SCALLOPED BASE,ORNATE HANDLE,GREEN WITH GOLD...	22.00
ELITE L FRANCE CUP & SAUCER & CAKE PLATE,WHITE & GOLD.......	10.00
ELITE L FRANCE GRAVY BOAT,GOLD DESIGN & BEADING,...........	10.00
ELITE L FRANCE SET OF 6 PLATES,RAISED GOLD BEADING ON 8 SCALLOPS..	20.00
ENAMEL,RUSSIAN BOWTIE PIN,2 IN. BY 1 IN.,SIGNED............	140.00
ENAMEL,RUSSIAN,DRINKING CUP,88,GRACHEV,3IN. L..............	225.00
ENAMEL RUSSIAN LETTER OPENER...............................	90.00
ENAMEL,RUSSIAN,NAPKIN RING,OVAL,1 IN. HIGH,SIGNED 84 M 3 PR.	200.00
ENAMEL,RUSSIAN,SALT,2IN.DIA.SIGNED 88 SAZYKOV..............	150.00
ENAMEL,RUSSIAN,SALT DIPS,1IN.DIA.BY 1IN.H.,SIGNED FR 88,SILVER GILT,EA...	175.00
ENAMEL,RUSSIAN,SALTS WITH SPOONS,MARKED 84,PR.............	225.00
ENAMEL,RUSSIAN ST.SILVER EGG,MARKED,ONE HALF IN. LONG......	100.00
ENAMEL,RUSSIAN SILVER TROIKA PIN,2IN.L....................	250.00
ENAMELED TRANSPARENT SPOON,GOLD PLATED....................	62.50

END OF DAY GLASS is now an out-of-fashion name for spattered glass. The glass was made of many bits and pieces of colored glass. Traditionally, the glass was made by workmen from the odds and ends left from the glass used during the day. Actually it was a deliberately manufactured product popular about 1880 to 1900, and some of it is still being made.

END OF DAY BASKET,8 IN.,CLEAR GLASS SPLASHED WITH BLUE.....	28.00
END OF DAY BASKET,THORN HANDLE,RED,YELLOW,AMETHYST.........	60.00
END OF DAY BASKET,WINE,RED,YELLOW,RUFFLED TOP,CLEAR HANDLE..	35.00
END OF DAY FRUIT BOWL,8 IN.,PINK & BLUE....................	20.00
END OF DAY GLASS MARBLE....................................	8.00
END OF DAY PITCHER,BULBOUS,CLEAR APPLIED HANDLE,RUBY........	50.00
END OF DAY ROSE BOWL,GREEN & WHITE........................	23.00

```
END OF DAY SALT SHAKER,YELLOW..................................    6.50
END OF DAY SOCK DARNER,MULTI-COLOURED,BLOWN & CASED.........   20.00
END OF DAY STICK VASE,SPATTER,OVERLAY,REDDISH PINK..........   17.50
END OF DAY STOCKING DARNER.................................   35.00
END OF DAY SUGAR SHAKER,BULBOUS SHAPE......................   22.50
END OF DAY SUGAR SHAKER,PINK & WHITE ON CLEAR..............   21.00
END OF DAY SUGAR SHAKER,YELLOW,PINK & WHITE................   18.00
END OF DAY TUMBLER,PINK,WHITE & YELLOW SPATTERS............   20.00
END OF DAY VASE............................................    4.95
END OF DAY VASE,8 IN.,FLUTED TOP,PINK,WHITE & BLACK........   22.50
END OF DAY VASE,8 IN.,RUFFLED EDGE,PINK & GREEN CENTER ROPE
  BAND....................................................   15.00
END OF DAY VASE,11 IN. TALL,MAROON BASE TO ORANGE TOP......   18.00
END OF DAY VASE,12 IN......................................   18.00
END OF DAY VASE,BULBOUS,BLOW MOLD,RUFFLED TOP,PINK & YELLOW.  16.50
END OF DAY VASE,CZECHOSLOVAKIA,GREEN,BLUE & GOLD GREEN......   22.00
END OF DAY VASE,IRIDESCENT CZECH...........................   25.00
END OF DAY VASE,ORANGE COLOURING WITH OVERLAY,APPLIED
  HANDLES.................................................   25.00
END OF DAY VASE,PINCHED SIDE,FLUTE TOP,YELLOW,WHITE & PINK..   35.00
END OF DAY VASE,PINK & WHITE...............................   15.00
END OF DAY VASE,PINK & YELLOW,6 IN. TALL,BULBOUS
  SHAPE,RUFFLED TOP.......................................   17.00
END OF DAY VASE,PINK & YELLOW,7 IN. TALL,BULBOUS BODY.......   18.50
END OF DAY VASE,RUFFLED RIM,CLEAR,BOHEMIAN & BEIGE..........   40.00
END OF DAY VASE,SATIN,ORANGE,YELLOW & BLUE.................   25.00
END OF DAY VASE,SIGNED DE LATTE NANCY,YELLOW,BLUE,BROWN.....   19.00
END OF DAY VASE,YELLOW.....................................   38.00
END OF DAY VASE,YELLOW & PINK,RUFFLED TOP,PAIR.............   26.00
END OF DAY WATER PITCHER,7 IN.,RUBY,BULBOUS,APPLIED CLEAR
  HANDLE..................................................   45.00
END OF DAY WATER PITCHER,PINK,GREEN & WHITE,APPLIED IVY
  LEAVES..................................................   65.00
```

*FABERGE (Carl Gustavovich) was a goldsmith and jeweler to the Russian Im-
perial Court from about 1870 to 1914.*

```
FABERGE EGGS,ONE DOZEN....................................1,100.00
FABERGE MARKED SILVER FILAGREE FLOWER-FORM,WINE WITH CHINA
  INSERT..................................................  350.00
FABERGE SIGNED SET OF 6 SPOONS,MATTE RUSSIAN ENAMEL ON
  SILVER.................................................1,200.00
```

*FAIRINGS are small souvenir china boxes sold at county fairs during the nine-
teenth century.*

```
FAIRING OR GONE TO BED,WHEN A MAN MARRIES HIS TROUBLES BEGIN   40.00
      FAIRY LAMP, SEE LAMP.................................
FAMILLE ROSE PORCELAIN DISH,18TH CENTURY...................  210.00
FAN,13 IN. BLACK SATIN,CARVED IVORY.......................    3.25
FAN,BLACK SILK,7 IN. HIGH,13 IN. OPEN.....................    3.50
FAN,BLACK SILK,OPEN SPRAYS OF FLOWERS PAINTED.............    6.00
FAN,BLUE SATIN HANDPAINTED,IVORY RIBS.....................    7.00
FAN,CALENDAR,GERMANY,CARDBOARD,HOLLY & WINTER SCENES.......    6.00
FAN,CARVED BAMBOO & VELLUM,PAINTING ORIENTAL SIGNED........   12.50
FAN,CARVED IVORY STICKS,HANDPAINTED FLORAL ON CREAM,SILK
  WITH LACE...............................................   25.00
FAN,DIONNE QUINT HAND.....................................    1.00
FAN,GREY SILK AND SEQUIN..................................   10.00
FAN,HAND,5 IN. BRASS CASE,SCREEN OVER BLADES,SPRING HANDLES.  15.00
FAN,HANDPAINTED WITH IVORY RIBS...........................   18.00
FAN,IVORY,20 STICKS,CARVED IVORY LACE DESIGN..............   15.00
FAN,MOURNING,BLACK LACQUER STICKS.........................    3.00
FAN,PAINTED CHINESE SILK..................................    7.00
FAN,PAINTED FRONT & BACK,DORE BRONZE BLADES...............   40.00
FAN,RED STAIN,CARVED IVORY................................   10.00
FAN,TORTOISE SHELL........................................   12.00
```

```
FAN,VICTORIAN,3 WHITE OSTRICH PLUMES,MOTHER OF PEARL
  HANDLE,RIBBON BOW.......................................    4.50
FAN,WHITE,EMBROIDERY ON FABRIC,CARVED IVORY FRAME,BLACK
  LACQUERED BOX..........................................   11.00
FAN,WHITE SATIN,OPEN   24 IN.,SMALL SPRAY OF FLOWERS.......    6.00
FAN,WHITE SATIN,OPEN SPRAYS OF FLOWERS.....................    7.00
FAN,WHITE SILK,OPEN FIGURES OF MAN AND WOMAN IN COLOURS....    4.00
FAN,WOOD STICKS CHILDREN PAINTED ON PAPER..................   11.50
FIELD GLASSES IN CASE.....................................    8.00
FILM,16 IN. BUCK ROGERS ON JUPITER,100 FT.,1930...........   21.00
FINDLAY CREAMER,SILVER INLAY..............................  125.00
```

FINDLAY OR ONYX GLASS was made using three layers of glass. It was manufactured by the Dalzell Gilmore Leighton Company about 1889 in Findlay, Ohio.
The silver, ruby, or black pattern was molded into the glass. The glass came in
several colors, but was usually white or ruby.

```
FINDLAY,MUFFINEER,ONYX,5IN.H.,PLATINUM LUSTRE ON RAISED
  DAISY..................................................  165.00
FINDLAY ONYX PITCHER,SILVER INLAY.........................  125.00
FINDLAY ONYX SUGAR SHAKER.................................  200.00
FINDLAY ONYX SYRUP,TIN TOP................................  265.00
FINDLAY ONYX TOOTHPICK HOLDER.............................  150.00
FINDLAY WHITE ONYX CELERY.................................  195.00
FIRE BUCKET..............................................   25.00
FIRE BUCKET,LEATHER......................................   60.00
FIRE CHIEFS HELMET,WHITE,CIRCA 1905,SILVER METAL SHIELD...   30.00
FIRE EXTINGUISHER,RED PEAR SHAPED GLASS IN BRASS FRAME....   12.50
```

FIREGLOW GLASS resembles English Bristol glass. But a reddish-brown color
can be seen when the piece is held to the light. It is a form of art glass made by
the Boston and Sandwich Glass Co. of Massachussets, and others.

```
FIREGLOW, PINK VASE, 8 IN................................  127.50
FIREGLOW VASE,9 IN. TALL,PINK GOLD COLOUR,GREEN,BROWN LEAVES
  & WHITE................................................   48.00
FIRE GRENADE AMBER GLASS HARDENS 1884.....................    7.50
FIRE MARK,HYDRANT HOSE....................................   25.00
FIRE WAGON,TWO WHEEL,WOODEN SPOKES,HAND PULLED............  150.00
FIREMAN,STEEL FIRE TRUCK LADDER,TURNER TOY................   17.50
FIREMANS BELGIAN HELMET WITH CROSSED AXES,BADGE & RED
  COCKADE................................................   35.00
FIREMANS ENGLISH LEATHER HELMET WITH BRASS FITTINGS & BADGE. 25.00
FIREMANS HELMET..........................................    7.50
FIREMANS HELMET BRASS TRIM...............................   22.50
FIREMANS HELMET,T.D.F.,TRUMPET FINIAL....................   55.00
FIREMANS LEATHER PARADE BELT,LETTERS PHOENIX CIRCA 1900...    7.50
FIREMANS RIPPER,ROOF,HANDWROUGHT.........................   25.00
```

FISCHER of Hungary is a fine chinaware (see HEREND).

```
FISCHER,J.BUDAPEST SIGNED WITH COAT OF ARMS PIERCED
  VASE,GOLD,BLUE.........................................   75.00
FISH PLATTER,11 IN.......................................   10.00
```

FISH SETS were popular during the late Victorian period. A large platter with at
least a dozen plates made a set. Each piece of the pottery or porcelain was
usually decorated with a different type of fish.

```
FISH SET,VICTORIA,CARLSBAD,AUSTRIA,11 PLATES,14 PIECES,...  175.00
FLAG,CONFEDERATE,12 BY 18 IN.............................    1.50
FLARE,RAILROAD...........................................    5.00
```

FLINT GLASS was made from flint or lead with the glass mixture. It is colorless
and has a brilliance.

```
FLINT 18TH CENTURY BLOWN 1 HALF POST CASE BOTTLE.........   35.00
FLINT,18TH CENTURY STIEGEL TYPE FLIP,6 IN. HIGH,TULIP
  ENGRAVING..............................................   60.00
FLIP GLASS RUSSIAN ENAMEL DATED 1896.....................  125.00
```

FLOW BLUE or flo blue was made in England about 1830 to 1900. The plates were printed with designs using a cobalt blue coloring. The color flowed from the design to the white plate so the finished plate had a smeared blue design. The plates were usually made of ironstone china.

FLOW BLUE 3 PIECES SCINDE PATTERN..............................	32.50
FLOW BLUE 72 PIECES,PROGRESS..................................	400.00
FLOW BLUE 81 PIECES..	150.00
FLOW BLUE BONE DISH,ARGYLE...................................	6.50
FLOW BLUE BOWL,8 IN.,WALDORF PATTERN.........................	9.50
FLOW BLUE BOWL,9 IN.,WALDORF PATTERN.........................	12.00
FLOW BLUE BOWL,CEREAL,6 IN.,GOLD,HENRY ALCOCK................	3.50
FLOW BLUE BOWL,CONWAY..	9.00
FLOW BLUE BOWL,HERON PATTERN,IMPROVED STONE CHINA CIRCA 1840	15.00
FLOW BLUE BOWL,LABELLE.......................................	22.50
FLOW BLUE BOWL ON 4 FEET DATED XMAS 1898,GOLD	
DECORATED,LABELLE,OVAL.......................................	35.00
FLOW BLUE BOWL,ROUND,TRILEY NEW WHARF POTTERY ENGLAND........	12.75
FLOW BLUE BOWL,TEMPLE..	8.75
FLOW BLUE BOWL,WALDORF SEMI-PORCELAIN,ENGLAND,FLORAL,8 IN.	
DIAMETER...	7.50
FLOW BLUE BREAD & BUTTER PLATE,ARGYLE	
PATTERN,GRINDLEY,ENGLAND.....................................	3.25
FLOW BLUE BUTTER DISH,HADDEN BY GRINDLEY.....................	17.50
FLOW BLUE BUTTER DISH,MARTHA PATTERN.........................	12.50
FLOW BLUE BUTTER PAT...	2.50
FLOW BLUE BUTTER PAT,3.......................................	7.50
FLOW BLUE BUTTER PAT,ENGLAND.................................	4.00
FLOW BLUE BUTTER PAT,SET OF 6................................	17.00
FLOW BLUE BUTTER PAT,VINE PATTERN,VINRANKA SWEDEN............	2.25
FLOW BLUE CAKE PLATE,GLENMORE,GRINDLEY CO.,6 IN..............	4.00
FLOW BLUE CAKE PLATE,SCALLOPED,SWISS ROYAL BONN GERMANY.....	4.75
FLOW BLUE CASSEROLE,OPEN.....................................	16.50
FLOW BLUE CELERY TRAY,WARWICK................................	8.00
FLOW BLUE COMMEMORATION PLATE,CONCORD MASS. MARKED MADE IN	
ENGLAND..	8.00
FLOW BLUE CORONATION PLATE,ALEXANDRA 1902....................	15.00
FLOW BLUE CRACKER JAR,FLORAL DESIGN ACCENTED IN GOLD.........	27.00
FLOW BLUE CRACKER JAR,IVY LEAF DESIGN........................	46.00
FLOW BLUE CRACKER JAR SIGNED INSIDE TAYLORS WITNESS,IVY	
LEAVES...	45.00
FLOW BLUE CREAMER,3 IN.,RAISED FORGET-ME-NOTS,GOLD DECOR....	9.00
FLOW BLUE CREAMER & SUGAR....................................	22.00
FLOW BLUE CREAMER,FAIRY VILLAS...............................	18.50
FLOW BLUE CREAMER,TOURAINE...................................	15.00
FLOW BLUE CUP & SAUCER,ALLERTONS,ENGLAND.....................	4.50
FLOW BLUE CUP & SAUCER,GLENMORE,GRINDLEY CO..................	5.00
FLOW BLUE CUP & SAUCER,HANDLELESS............................	24.00
FLOW BLUE CUP & SAUCER,LIBERATAS,PRUSSIA,ALBANY	
PATTERN,GRINDLEY...	4.25
FLOW BLUE CUP & SAUCER,NORMANDY..............................	10.50
FLOW BLUE CUP & SAUCER,SHANGHAI..............................	6.00
FLOW BLUE CUP & SAUCER,TOURAINE..............................	10.00
FLOW BLUE CUP & SAUCER,WATTEAU...............................	2.75
FLOW BLUE CUP PLATE	
11.00 TO...	15.00
FLOW BLUE CUP PLATE,IRONSTONE,A CLEMENSON....................	7.75
FLOW BLUE CUP PLATE,SCINDE...................................	15.00
FLOW BLUE CUP,WHITE WITH CLUSTERS OF 3 LEAVES & SPRAYS OF	
FLOWERS..	4.50
FLOW BLUE FRUIT PLATE,.......................................	6.00
FLOW BLUE GRAVY BOAT,ALLERTON,SIGNED.........................	19.00
FLOW BLUE GRAVY BOAT,CAMBRIDGE...............................	9.50
FLOW BLUE GRAVY BOAT,SIGNED,SEPARATE PLATE,GOLD,ORNATE	
HANDLES..	17.00
FLOW BLUE GRAVY BOAT,VIRGINIA,RUFFLED EDGE,GOLD TRIM........	15.00

```
FLOW BLUE HANDLELESS CUP & SAUCER,EXCELSIOR PATTERN.........        20.00
FLOW BLUE LUNCHEON PLATE.....................................        4.75
FLOW BLUE LUNCHEON PLATE,GLENMORE,GRINDLEY,9 IN..............        5.00
FLOW BLUE MILK PITCHER,CRUMBLIN PATTERN......................        8.00
FLOW BLUE MILK PITCHER,ENAMEL DECOR,BLUE K & G,LUNEVILLE
  FRANCE.....................................................       11.00
FLOW BLUE MILK PITCHER,NON PARIEL............................       25.00
FLOW BLUE MILK PITCHER,TULIP DESIGN,8 IN. TALL...............       12.00
FLOW BLUE PITCHER...........................................       75.00
FLOW BLUE PITCHER,IVY LEAVES IN BLUE,GOLD ENHANCED..........       14.00
FLOW BLUE PLACE SETTING FOR 12,75 PIECES,TOURAINE...........      650.00
FLOW BLUE PLACE SETTING,WALDORF.............................       46.50
FLOW BLUE PLATE , 9 IN......................................        7.50
FLOW BLUE PLATE,ADVERTISING,COMPLIMENTS JOHN HEDDIN CO. MASS       10.00
FLOW BLUE PLATE,ARGYLE,6 IN.................................        5.00
FLOW BLUE PLATE,ARGYLE PATTERN,10 IN........................        8.50
FLOW BLUE PLATE BAMBOO PATTERN,10 IN........................        6.50
FLOW BLUE PLATE,BLUE DESIGNS OF FLOWERS & LEAF & BIRDS,10
  IN........................................................        4.75
FLOW BLUE PLATE,CAPITOL BUILDING,SPRINGFIELD,ILLINOIS,9 IN..       15.00
FLOW BLUE PLATE,CASTLE ENGLAND..............................       10.50
FLOW BLUE PLATE,CHISWICK PATTERN,RIDGEWAY,ENGLAND,8 IN......        2.25
FLOW BLUE PLATE,CHUSAN,9 IN.................................       12.00
FLOW BLUE PLATE,CONWAY......................................        4.50
FLOW BLUE PLATE,COUNTRY SCENES,7 IN.........................        4.00
FLOW BLUE PLATE,CROWN & CHAIN MARK,5 IN.....................        3.50
FLOW BLUE PLATE,EDWARD VII CORONATION.......................       15.00
FLOW BLUE PLATE,FAIRY VILLA,STONE CHINA,9 IN................        7.50
FLOW BLUE PLATE,FAIRY VILLAS,7 IN...........................        8.00
FLOW BLUE FAIRY VILLAS PATTERN,9 IN.........................       12.00
FLOW BLUE PLATE,FLINSBURG...................................        3.75
FLOW BLUE PLATE,GRECIAN SCROLL,9 IN.........................       10.00
FLOW BLUE PLATE,HONG KONG,9 IN..............................       11.50
FLOW BLUE PLATE,INDIAN FESTOON,ONE 9 IN. & ONE 17 IN........       27.00
FLOW BLUE PLATE,INDIAN JAR,9 IN.............................       12.00
FLOW BLUE PLATE,IVANHOE SERIES,8 IN.........................       15.00
FLOW BLUE PLATE,JEANETTE,8 IN...............................        6.00
FLOW BLUE PLATE,KIN SHAN,9 IN...............................       12.00
FLOW BLUE PLATE,LANCASTER PATTERN,BLUE FLOWERS,SCALLOPED
  EDGE,9 IN.................................................       10.00
FLOW BLUE PLATE,LIVERTAS,PRUSSIA,9 IN.......................        1.00
FLOW BLUE PLATE,LORAINE PATTERN,RIDGEWAY,ENGLAND,9 IN.......        3.75
FLOW BLUE PLATE,LUNEVILLE,FRANCE,8 IN.,VIOLET-GOLD ANCHOR...       50.00
FLOW BLUE PLATE,MANILLA.....................................       12.50
FLOW BLUE PLATE,MANILLA,8 IN................................        7.50
FLOW BLUE PLATE,MANILLA,9 IN................................       12.00
FLOW BLUE PLATE,MANILLA PATTERN,9 IN........................       10.00
FLOW BLUE PLATE,MARIE PATTERN,6 IN..........................        5.00
FLOW BLUE PLATE,NARROW BLUE WITH GOLD BAND,6 IN.............        1.50
FLOW BLUE PLATE,NON PAREIL..................................
FLOW BLUE PLATE,OREGON PATTERN..............................        6.00
FLOW BLUE PLATE,PAIR 10 IN.,W.ADAMS KYBER...................       38.00
FLOW BLUE PLATE,PEACH PATTERN,9 IN..........................        8.00
FLOW BLUE PLATE,PELEW.......................................       15.00
FLOW BLUE PLATE,PELEW,9 IN..................................       12.00
FLOW BLUE PLATE,PORTRAIT,8 IN.,URFRIED RELATING TO CEDRIC...       32.00
FLOW BLUE PLATE,PORTRAIT,REBECCA REPELLING THE TEMPLAR......       35.00
FLOW BLUE PLATE,REGINA PATTERN,10 IN.,DARK BLUE.............        7.00
FLOW BLUE PLATE,SCALLOPED EDGE,NEW WHARF PATTERN,ENGLAND,8
  IN........................................................        3.75
FLOW BLUE PLATE,SCHAPOO,7 IN................................       12.00
FLOW BLUE PLATE,SCHAPOO,8 IN................................       12.00
FLOW BLUE PLATE,SCINDE,7 IN.................................       10.50
FLOW BLUE PLATE,SCINDE,8 IN.................................       12.50
FLOW BLUE PLATE,SCINDE,9 IN.
```

```
     12.75  TO............................................................  15.00
FLOW  BLUE  PLATE,SCINDE,10 IN..........................................  18.00
FLOW  BLUE  PLATE,SCINDE,ALCOCK,7 IN....................................  16.00
FLOW  BLUE  PLATE,STATES,9 IN...........................................   5.75
FLOW  BLUE  PLATE,TOURAINE,8 IN.........................................   6.75
FLOW  BLUE  PLATE,TOURAINE,9 IN.........................................   8.75
FLOW  BLUE  PLATE,VERONA PATTERN,SCALLOPED
     EDGE,MEAKIN,ENGLAND,6 IN...........................................   2.25
FLOW  BLUE  PLATE,WALDORF,10 IN.........................................  12.00
FLOW  BLUE  PLATE,WATTEAU PATTERN,9 IN..................................  12.50
FLOW  BLUE  PLATE,WILLOW PATTERN,ANCHOR MARK,8 IN.......................   9.00
FLOW  BLUE  PLATTER,13 IN.,ROUND,2 HANDLED..............................  25.00
FLOW  BLUE  PLATTER,13 X 15 IN..........................................  14.50
FLOW  BLUE  PLATTER,17 X 13 IN..........................................  16.00
FLOW  BLUE  PLATTER,ARGYLE ENGLAND,18 X 14 IN...........................  26.00
FLOW  BLUE  PLATTER,ARGYLE PATTERN,GRINDLEY,15 X 10 IN...................  16.00
FLOW  BLUE  PLATTER,BLUE DESIGN,CLASSIC DECORATION......................  12.00
FLOW  BLUE  PLATTER,CONWAY..............................................  10.00
FLOW  BLUE  PLATTER,DEEP,BLACK,FLOWERS WITH GARLANDS....................  18.00
FLOW  BLUE  PLATTER,GEORGIA,10 IN.......................................   9.00
FLOW  BLUE  PLATTER,IRIS ROYAL ENGLAND,13 X 9 IN........................  18.00
FLOW  BLUE  PLATTER,MANILLA PATTERN.....................................  25.00
FLOW  BLUE  PLATTER,MARACHAL............................................   7.50
FLOW  BLUE  PLATTER,MAREGNAL NEIL,ENGLAND,14 X 10 IN....................  14.00
FLOW  BLUE  PLATTER,OREGON CHINESE,15 IN................................  22.50
FLOW  BLUE  PLATTER,SAXEN CHINA,BLUE BORDER WITH GOLD...................   4.75
FLOW  BLUE  PLATTER,TOURAINE,HENRY ALCOCK & CO.,ENGLAND.................   8.50
FLOW  BLUE  PLATTER,WALDORF,9 X 11 IN...................................  13.50
FLOW  BLUE  PLATTER,WALDORF,11 IN.......................................  12.50
FLOW  BLUE  PLATTER,WALDORF PATTERN.....................................  10.00
FLOW  BLUE  PLATTER,WELL & TREE,SCINDE..................................  65.00
FLOW  BLUE  PLATTER,WILD ROSE PATTERN,14 X 11 IN........................  18.00
FLOW  BLUE  RELISH DISH,OVAL,HADDEN,W.G.GRINDLEY........................   4.75
FLOW  BLUE  SAUCE,ALASKA,W H GRINDLEY,ENGLAND...........................   2.00
FLOW  BLUE  SAUCE DISH..................................................   2.75
FLOW  BLUE  SAUCE DISH,BLUE DESIGNS OF FLOWERS,LEAF & BIRDS.............   2.75
FLOW  BLUE  SAUCE DISH,CHISWICK PATTERN,RIDGWAY,ENGLAND.................   2.50
FLOW  BLUE  SAUCE DISH,GLENMORE,GRINDLEY CO.,5 IN.......................   3.50
FLOW  BLUE  SAUCE DISH,HADDEN,W.H.GRINDLEY..............................   2.75
FLOW  BLUE  SAUCE,KNOX..................................................   4.00
FLOW  BLUE  SAUCER......................................................   1.00
FLOW  BLUE  SAUCER,GLENMORE,GRINDLEY CO.................................   2.50
FLOW  BLUE  SAUCER,LANCASTER NEW WHARF POTTERY ENGLAND..................   2.50
FLOW  BLUE  SAUCER,LOIS PATTERN,ENGLAND.................................   1.25
FLOW  BLUE  SAUCER,TOGO PATTERN,COLONIAL POTTERY STOKE,ENGLAND          3.75
FLOW  BLUE  SOUP BOWL,10 IN.,ATHENS SCENE,FLOWERED BORDER...............   8.50
FLOW  BLUE  SOUP PLATE,10 IN. ACROSS,SCINDE PATTERN.....................  18.00
FLOW  BLUE  SOUP PLATE,CLYDE,NEW WHARF
     POTTERY,ENGLAND,SCALLOPED EDGE.....................................   3.75
FLOW  BLUE  SOUP PLATE,GIRONDE PATTERN,W.H.GRINDLEY.....................   4.75
FLOW  BLUE  SOUP PLATE,NEW WHARF........................................   8.50
FLOW  BLUE  SOUP PLATE,WALDORF PATTERN..................................   8.50
FLOW  BLUE  SOUP TUREEN,WATTEAU PATTERN,DOULTON.........................  50.00
FLOW  BLUE  TEAPOT,MANHATTAN PATTERN,GOLD TRIM,WHITE SCROLLS,8
     IN. TALL...........................................................  28.50
FLOW  BLUE  TEAPOT,SUGAR,CREAMER & WASTE BOWL...........................  85.00
FLOW  BLUE  TOILET WASH BASIN,AMOY DAVENPORT............................  48.00
FLOW  BLUE  TOILET WASH BASIN,SCINDE,SCALLOPED RIM......................  40.00
FLOW  BLUE  TRAY WITH APPLIED HANDLES,13 IN. DIAMETER...................  15.00
FLOW  BLUE  TUREEN,WATTEAU,COVERED......................................  25.00
FLOW  BLUE  TUREEN WITH BUDS............................................  16.00
FLOW  BLUE  VEGETABLE BOWL,FAIRY VILLAS,10 IN...........................  15.00
FLOW  BLUE  VEGETABLE BOWL,JEANETTE PATTERN.............................   9.00
FLOW  BLUE  VEGETABLE BOWL,OVAL,TOURAINE,9 IN...........................  10.00
FLOW  BLUE  VEGETABLE BOWL,SET OF 2,FAIRY VILLAS,10 IN..................  30.00
```

FLOW BLUE VEGETABLE DISH..	9.30
FLOW BLUE VEGETABLE DISH,9 X 6 IN.,COVERED,ENGLAND CHAN NEIL	22.00
FLOW BLUE VEGETABLE DISH,ARGYLE,HEXAGON SHAPED,GRINDLEY CO..	18.50
FLOW BLUE VEGETABLE DISH,COVERED,OCTAGON....................	35.00
FLOW BLUE VEGETABLE DISH,COVERED,OVAL,MONARCH,SEMI-PORCELAIN	30.00
FLOW BLUE VEGETABLE DISH,COVERED,PELEW......................	50.00
FLOW BLUE VEGETABLE DISH,ROUND,GOLD RIM.....................	12.50
FLOW BLUE VEGETABLE DISH WITH	
HANDLES,COVERED,TOURAINE,STANLEY............................	18.50
FLOW BLUE VEGETABLE TUREEN,BALTIC PATTERN...................	20.00
FLOW BLUE VEGETABLE TUREEN,COVERED,BALTIC PATTERN...........	15.00
FLOW BLUE WATER PITCHER,INDIAN JAR PATTERN..................	55.00
FLOW BLUE WASH PITCHER,TONQUIN HEATH........................	32.00
FOLDING DRINKING CUP,LEATHER INCASED ,ENGLISH COIN ON	
TOP,DATED 1887...	4.00

FOO DOGS are mythical Chinese figures, part dog and part lion. They were made of pottery, porcelain, carved stone, and wood.

FOO DOGS,TOURQUOISE TEMPLE,10 IN. H. - 3 IN. W..............	157.00

FOSTORIA GLASS, made in Fostoria, Ohio, is a twentieth-century product.

FOSTORIA GREEN ETCHED WATER PITCHER,6 GLASSES...............	45.00
FOVAL, SEE FRY...	
FRAME, SEE FURNITURE, FRAME................................	
FRANCISWARE BOWL...	10.00
FRANCISWARE BUTTER DISH....................................	38.00
FRANCISWARE CREAM PITCHER..................................	35.00
FRANCISWARE CREAMER & SUGAR................................	47.50
FRANCISWARE ICE CREAM DISH.................................	16.00
FRANCISWARE OVAL BOWL......................................	33.00
FRANCISWARE SAUCE..	15.00
FRANCISWARE SAUCE DISH.....................................	12.00
FRANCISWARE SAUCE DISH,SQUARE RIM..........................	12.50
FRANCISWARE TUMBLER WITH AMBER GLASS TOP,FROSTED HOBNAIL....	10.00

FRY GLASS was made by the famous H. C. Fry Glass Company of Rochester, Pennsylvania. It includes cut glass, but the famous Fry glass today is the Foval or pearl art glass. This is an opal ware decorated with colored trim. It was made from 1922 to 1933.

FRY ALL PEARL TUMBLER......................................	12.00
FRY BLOWN SAUCER...	6.00
FRY CUT GLASS NAPPY..	18.50
FRY DIVIDED BAKEWARE PLATE MARKED..........................	8.50
FRY FOVAL DE VILBISS PERFUME WITH ETCHED DESIGN,BLUE BASE...	27.00
FRY FOVAL DEMI-TASSE CUPS & SAUCERS........................	37.50
FRY FOVAL GLASS CREAMER & SUGAR,BLUE OPALESCENT............	65.00
FRY FOVAL HANDLED & FOOTED SUGAR BOWL,DELFT TRIM...........	40.00
FRY FOVAL JADE GREEN SWAG WATER PITCHER,9 IN. HIGH,MATCHING	
COVER..	275.00
FRY FOVAL LEMONADE SET,PITCHER & 4 GLASSES,YELLOW IRIDESCENT	210.00
FRY FOVAL SHERBET & UNDERPLATE,GREEN FOOT BASE.............	65.00
FRY FOVAL SUGAR & CREAMER,APPLIED GREEN HANDLES,GREEN BASES.	120.00
FRY FOVAL SUGAR & CREAMER WITH APPLIED GREEN HANDLES.......	120.00
FRY FOVAL SUGAR & CREAMER WITH DELFT BLUE HANDLES..........	135.00
FRY GLASS OVENWARE SIGNED,2 DISHES.........................	15.00
FRY JACK-IN-THE-PULPIT EPERGNE.............................	75.00
FRY MARKED CREAMER & SUGAR,INTAGLIO CUTTINGS...............	65.00
FRY OPALESCENT 8 IN. CASSEROLE WITH COVER..................	10.00
FRY OPALESCENT OVEN WARE COVERED RECTANGULAR DISH,MARKED....	22.50
FRY OVEN WARE SIGNED,6 IN.,PUDDING DISH....................	4.25
FRY OVENWARE CASSEROLE.....................................	4.00
FRY PEARLWARE PITCHER,WHITE WITH OLIVE APPLIED HANDLE......	80.00
FRY SIGNED 9 IN. PIE PLATE.................................	8.50
FRY SIGNED CUT GLASS BOWL,FLOWER BASKET PATTERN WITH PRISM &	
FLUTE..	55.00

```
FRY SIGNED CUT GLASS CELERY TRAY.............................     22.50
FRY SIGNED CUT GLASS VASE,10 IN. HIGH,HOBSTAR & SUNBURST....     47.50
FRY SIGNED SET OF 4 OVENWARE CUSTARDS.......................     12.00
FRY STRIPPED PASTEL PITCHER,COBALT HANDLE...................     25.00
```

FULPER is the mark used by the American Pottery Company of Flemington, New Jersey.

```
FULPER FLOWER BOWL SUPPORTED BY 3 PELICANS..................     12.50
FULPER VASE,MARKED,5 IN.,BROWN & TAN GLAZE..................      9.50
FULPER VASE,MARKED,8 IN.,BROWN & BLUE GLAZE.................     12.50
FULPER VASE,MARKED,11 IN.,BLUE GLAZE
  7.50   TO................................................     14.50
FURNITURE,APOTHECARY CASE INLAID WITH MOTHER OF
  PEARL,ENGLISH MAHOGANY....................................    175.00
FURNITURE,APOTHECARY CHEST,CHERRY,20 DRAWERS,GOLD LEAF-BACK.    500.00
FURNITURE,APOTHECARY CHEST IN SHAPE OF TEA
  CADDY,ENGLISH,MAHOGANY....................................    350.00
FURNITURE,APOTHECARY CHEST WITH BLOWN BOTTLES,SCALES,ENGLISH
  MAHOGANY..................................................    175.00
FURNITURE,APOTHECARY WALL CHEST,42 DRAWERS,................    265.00
FURNITURE,ARMCHAIR,AMERICAN WALNUT FLEMISH SCROLL..........    375.00
FURNITURE,ARMCHAIR,PAIR CIRCA 1810,BLACK REGENCY...........    785.00
FURNITURE,ARMCHAIR CIRCA 1810,IRISH MAHOGANY...............    495.00
FURNITURE,ARMCHAIR CIRCA 1820,BLACK REGENCY................    450.00
FURNITURE,ARMCHAIR CIRCA 1830,BIEDERMEIER..................    375.00
FURNITURE,ARMCHAIR,GENERAL LEE,WALNUT......................    175.00
FURNITURE,ARMCHAIR,PAIR WINDSOR,CRINOLINE
  UNDER-STRETCHER,CIRCA 1780...............................    485.00
FURNITURE,ARMCHAIR,WALNUT CHIPPENDALE......................    750.00
FURNITURE,ARMCHAIR,WEAVERS,RUSH SEAT,LADDER BACK...........     85.00
FURNITURE,ARMCHAIR,WINDSOR,BRACE BACK......................    265.00
FURNITURE,BAR,BARBERS BACK,GLASS DOORS,BRASS HARDWARE.......    125.00
FURNITURE,BAR IN CHERRY,20 FT. LONG,SCROLL WORK............5,000.00
FURNITURE,BED,AMERICAN EMPIRE DOUBLE SIZE ROPE,MAPLE,CIRCA
  1820......................................................    210.00
FURNITURE,BED,BLACK OAK HALF-CANOPY........................    500.00
FURNITURE,BED,BRASS DECORATED TOP IRON,ADMIRAL DEWEY HEADS..    150.00
FURNITURE,BED,HEPPLEWHITE HIGH POST........................    375.00
FURNITURE,BED,IRON,GILDED..................................     18.00
FURNITURE,BED,LACY IRON,FULL SIZE,BRASS TRIM,PAINTED.......     32.00
FURNITURE,BED,MAPLE TRUNDLE................................     18.00
FURNITURE,BED,PAIR MAPLE CONVERTED TO TWIN.................    185.00
FURNITURE,BED,PINE FOLDING.................................    100.00
FURNITURE,BED POSTS,4 CANNON BALL,PLAIN MAPLE..............     65.00
FURNITURE,BED POST,SET OF 4 CURLY MAPLE,CANNON BALL........    125.00
FURNITURE,BED,SPOOL,MAPLE..................................     12.50
FURNITURE,BED STEPS,WOODEN.................................     17.50
FURNITURE,BED,STEVEDORE....................................     25.00
FURNITURE,BED,TRUNDLE LESS RAILS...........................     20.00
FURNITURE,BED,VICTORIAN DOLLS,25 X 13 IN.,HARD & SOFT WOODS
  STAINED...................................................     16.00
FURNITURE,BED,VICTORIAN WALNUT.............................     45.00
FURNITURE,BEDROOM SET,2 PIECE VICTORIAN WALNUT,BED & MARBLE
  TOP DRESSER...............................................    125.00
FURNITURE,BEDROOM SET,MAHOGANY,HANDMADE & HAND CARVED,5
  PIECES...................................................1,500.00
FURNITURE,BENCH,IRON,FIGURAL HEADS,UPHOLSTERED SEAT........     32.50
FURNITURE,BENCH,PINE,PLANK SEAT............................     18.00
FURNITURE,BENCH,WALNUT VICTORIAN,22 X 18 X 22 IN...........     95.00
FURNITURE,BIBLE BOX IN OAK WITH CARVED FRONT...............    250.00
FURNITURE,BLANKET CHEST,1 DRAWER PINE,CUT OUT ENDS TOP.....     75.00
FURNITURE,BLANKET CHEST,2 DRAWER,1800......................    145.00
FURNITURE,BLANKET CHEST,18TH CENTURY PINE,NEW ENGLAND......    250.00
FURNITURE,BLANKET CHEST,BUTTERNUT,BLUE BUTTERMILK PAINT.....     65.00
FURNITURE,BLANKET CHEST,MINIATURE,DOVETAILED...............     47.50
```

```
FURNITURE,BLANKET CHEST,OAK,RAISED PANELS...................    350.00
FURNITURE,BLANKET CHEST ON TURNED LEGS.....................     39.00
FURNITURE,BLANKET CHEST,PINE,CIRCA 1820,SIMULATED MAHOGANY
    FINISH.................................................     35.00
FURNITURE,BLANKET CHEST,PINE...............................     40.00
FURNITURE,BLANKET CHEST,PINE,DOVETAILED,LOCK & KEY..........    65.00
FURNITURE,BLANKET CHEST,PINE,PAINTED,1 DRAWER...............    85.00
FURNITURE,BOOKCASE CIRCA 1750,GREEN GLAZED FINISH,LOUIS XV..1,200.00
FURNITURE,BOOKCASE CIRCA 1780,HEPPLEWHITE MAHOGANY..........1,095.00
FURNITURE,BOOKCASE CIRCA 1790,SHERATON.....................2,100.00
FURNITURE,BOOKCASE,LOUIS XVI PAINTED OFF WHITE,GILT
    TRIM,CIRCA 1790........................................1,110.00
FURNITURE,BOOK CASE,REVOLVING,SHERATON MAHOGANY,SATINWOOD
    INLAY..................................................   185.00
FURNITURE,BOOK RACK,WALNUT,HAND CARVED LEAVES,ACRON &
    HORSESHOE..............................................     9.50
FURNITURE,BRACKET FOR MIRROR,HANDCARVED FRAME WITH GOLDLEAF.    45.00
FURNITURE,BREAKFRONT CIRCA 1780,ENGLISH CHIPPENDALE.........2,850.00
FURNITURE,BRIDES BOX,DOMED,RED & BLACK GRAIN,LOCK...........    18.50
FURNITURE,BUFFET,REGENCY,2 PEDESTAL,CIRCA 1810.............1,795.00
FURNITURE,BUGGY SEAT,SPINDLE BACK..........................     25.00
FURNITURE,BUREAU BOOKCASE,BROWN MAHOGANY,CIRCA 1770,ENGLAND.2,850.00
FURNITURE,BUREAU BOOKCASE,QUEEN ANNE DOUBLE
    DOME,ROSEWOOD,CIRCA 1710...............................4,800.00
FURNITURE,BUREAU BOOKCASE,MAHOGANY CIRCA 1790..............1,250.00
FURNITURE,BUREAU,GEORGIAN MAHOGANY,CIRCA 1790,42 X 40 X 21
    IN.....................................................   875.00
FURNITURE,BUREAU,MAHOGANY,INLAID BOW-FRONT,INITALED EAGLE
    BRASSES................................................   450.00
FURNITURE,BUREAU WITH 2 UPPER & 2 LOWER DRAWERS,MAHOGANY
    ROPE-FRONT.............................................     90.00
FURNITURE,CABINET,14 IN. TALL..............................     40.00
FURNITURE,CABINET,CARVED CHINESE TEAKWOOD OPEN CURIO,5 FEET
    HIGH...................................................   495.00
FURNITURE,CABINET CIRCA 1740,AMERICAN PINE SHELL TOP CORNER.1,650.00
FURNITURE,CABINET CIRCA 1790,SHERATON MAHOGANY CORNER.......   750.00
FURNITURE,CABINET,COMBINATION OAK COUNTER CLOCK &
    SPOOL,BRASS PULLS......................................     32.00
FURNITURE,CABINET FOR THREAD,CHESTNUT,2 DRAWERS AT TOP,18
    IN. TALL...............................................     39.50
FURNITURE,CABINET,FRENCH,LOUIS XVI,MAHOGANY WITH BRONZE.....   275.00
FURNITURE,CABINET,HARDWARE,6 FOOT,PINE.....................    350.00
FURNITURE,CABINET,HEPPLEWHITE MAHOGANY BONNET TOP INLAID
    CORNER.................................................   220.00
FURNITURE,CABINET,OAK,HANDCARVED CIRCA 1700,3 DOORS.........1,650.00
FURNITURE,CABINET ON PLINTH,MAHOGANY,CIRCA 1810............    785.00
FURNITURE,CABINETS,PAIR MARBLE TOP,18TH CENTURY............6,000.00
FURNITURE,CABINETS,PAIR OAK BARBER SHOP....................     58.00
FURNITURE,CABINET,ROSEWOOD REGENCY CIRCA 1810.............1,395.00
FURNITURE,CABINET WITH SHELF CIRCA 1840,MAHOGANY...........   550.00
FURNITURE,CANDLE BOX,RED SOFTWOOD HANGING ,HANDMADE DOVETAIL
    CORNERS................................................     42.50
FURNITURE,CANDLESTAND,HEPPLEWHITE,MAHOGANY,OCTAGONAL TOP....   110.00
FURNITURE,CANDLESTAND IN CHERRY............................     82.00
FURNITURE,CANDLESTAND IN MAPLE,SHAKER......................    150.00
FURNITURE,CANDLESTAND,MAPLE TILT TOP.......................    145.00
FURNITURE,CANDLESTAND,VICTORIAN,WALNUT,RECTANGULAR.........     12.50
FURNITURE,CAPTAINS CHEST,6 BOARD,.........................     95.00
FURNITURE,CAPTAINS CHEST,19TH CENTURY,MAHOGANY WITH BRASS
    MOUNTS.................................................   750.00
FURNITURE,CARD & SEWING TABLE COMBINATION,EMPIRE MAHOGANY...    90.00
FURNITURE,CARD TABLE,EMPIRE................................     45.00
FURNITURE,CARD TABLE,QUEEN ANNE............................    275.00
FURNITURE,CASE FOR LIQUOR BOTTLES,18TH CENTURY PINE,STRAP
    HINGES.................................................     45.00
```

```
FURNITURE,CASE WITH SET OF MUSICAL GLASSES,MAHOGANY,ENGLISH
  CIRCA 1810..............................................  425.00
FURNITURE,CHAIR,18TH CENTURY MAHOGANY......................  600.00
FURNITURE,CHAIR,BENTWOOD
  12.00  TO...............................................   27.50
FURNITURE,CHAIR,BLACK FINISHED WINDSOR THUMBBACK...........   35.00
FURNITURE,CHAIR,BLACK REGENCY CANE,SET OF 10,CIRCA 1810.....1,995.00
FURNITURE,CHAIR,CARVED ROSEWOOD HALL,RED DAMASK UPHOLSTERY..  32.50
FURNITURE,CHAIR,CHILDS ICE CREAM,BLACK.....................   20.00
FURNITURE,CHAIR,CHIPPENDALE CORNER,OAK ,RUSH SEAT..........  225.00
FURNITURE,CHAIR,CHIPPENDALE MAHOGANY ROUNDABOUT............  265.00
FURNITURE,CHAIR CIRCA 1710,QUEEN ANNE ENGLISH WALNUT
  ROUNDABOUT.............................................1,250.00
FURNITURE,CHAIR CIRCA 1750,FRUITWOOD GROTTO................  395.00
FURNITURE,CHAIR CIRCA 1760,30 IN. TALL....................  400.00
FURNITURE,CHAIR,CIRCA 1790,GEORGE III,FRUITWOOD,CORNER.....  450.00
FURNITURE,CHAIR CIRCA 1790,HARTFORD URN BACK MAHOGANY SIDE..  350.00
FURNITURE,CHAIR,CZECH.LONGBACKED,CARVED....................   30.00

FURNITURE,CHAIR,DUCK-BILL,ROD-BACK,WINDSOR,BAMBOO-TURNINGS   40.00
FURNITURE,CHAIR,ENGLISH CIRCA 1785,CARVED..................  750.00
FURNITURE,CHAIR,FRUIT CARVED WALNUT LADIES,SERPENTINE FRONT.  65.00
FURNITURE,CHAIR,GILT BALLROOM.............................   35.00
FURNITURE,CHAIR,HEART ICE CREAM...........................   10.00
FURNITURE,CHAIR,HORN MADE FROM STEER HORNS,UPHOLSTERED SEAT.  32.00
FURNITURE,CHAIR,ICE CREAM,STRAIGHT LOOP BACK,PAINTED
  WHITE,SET OF 4.........................................   95.00
FURNITURE,CHAIR,LACY WICKER SIDE,CANE SEAT.................   18.50
FURNITURE,CHAIR,LADDER BACK...............................   15.00
FURNITURE,CHAIR,LADYS VICTORIAN,WALNUT FRAME,GREEN
  UPHOLSTERY.............................................  150.00
FURNITURE,CHAIR,LOOP ICE CREAM............................    7.50
FURNITURE,CHAIR,MAPLE 3 SLAT-BACK ,SIDE...................   48.00
FURNITURE,CHAIR,MAPLE COUNTRY QUEEN ANNE,14 IN. HIGH.......   75.00
FURNITURE,CHAIR,PAIR BELTER SIDE........................1,200.00
FURNITURE,CHAIR,PAIR CHIPPENDALE,MAHOGANY,GOLD VELVET
  UPHOLSTERY.............................................  300.00
FURNITURE,CHAIR,PAIR COTTAGE ROD-BACK BAMBOO WINDSOR CIRCA
  1850...................................................   45.00
FURNITURE,CHAIR,PAIR FIRESIDE VICTORIAN...................  190.00
FURNITURE,CHAIR,PAIR HEPPLEWHITE SIDE CIRCA 1780..........  450.00
FURNITURE,CHAIR,PAIR IRISH MAHOGANY SIDE..................  550.00
FURNITURE,CHAIR,PAIR PAINTED DIRECTOIRE CIRCA 1810,GREENISH
  BLUE...................................................  900.00
FURNITURE,CHAIRS,PAIR PLANK SEAT HITCHCOCK................   55.00
FURNITURE,CHAIR,PAIR QUEEN ANNE SIDE,WALNUT,CIRCA 1725-1750. 875.00
FURNITURE,CHAIR,PAIR REGENCY WALNUT SIDE,CANE SEATS........   50.00
FURNITURE,CHAIR,PAIR SHERATON.............................  300.00
FURNITURE,CHAIR,PAIR VICTORIAN WALNUT SIDE,CUSHION SEAT &
  BACK...................................................   18.00
FURNITURE,CHAIR,PAIR WALNUT ENGLISH QUEEN ANNE TRANSITIONAL
  CIRCA 1750.............................................  750.00
FURNITURE,CHAIR,QUEEN ANNE SIDE,CIRCA 1720................  375.00
FURNITURE,CHAIR,REGENCY FRUITWOOD CIRCA 1815..............  495.00
FURNITURE,CHAIR,ROSEWOOD GOTHIC,UPHOLSTERED IN RED VELVET...  95.00
FURNITURE,CHAIR,SET OF 4 ARROW BACK THUMB BACK PLANT
  SEAT,YELLOW............................................  175.00
FURNITURE,CHAIR,SET OF 4 BOW BACK WITH CANE SEATS.........   90.00
FURNITURE,CHAIR,SET OF 4 CARVED OAK DINING CIRCA 1790....1,800.00
FURNITURE,CHAIR,SET OF 4 CIRCA 1780,HEPPLEWHITE ELBOW....1,495.00
FURNITURE,CHAIR,SET OF 4 HALF-SPINDLE PLANT SEAT,PAINTED....  100.00
FURNITURE,CHAIR,SET OF 4,HEPPLEWHITE SIDE,CIRCA 1780.....1,095.00
FURNITURE,CHAIR,SET OF 4 ICE CREAM........................   50.00
FURNITURE,CHAIR,SET OF 4 MAHOGANY SIDE,CARVED...........2,750.00
FURNITURE,CHAIR,SET OF 4 PLANK SEAT HITCHCOCK.............  110.00
```

```
FURNITURE,CHAIR,SET OF 4 QUEEN ANNE SIDE....................4,000.00
FURNITURE,CHAIR,SET OF 4 SHERATON,RUSH SEATS WITH CUT OUT
  CORNERS...................................................  125.00
FURNITURE,CHAIR,SET OF 4 WITH NEEDLEPOINT SEATS.............   89.00
FURNITURE,CHAIR,SET OF 5 BENTWOOD DINING,N IN CIRCLE TOPPED
  WITH CROWN...............................................   85.00
FURNITURE,CHAIR,SET OF 5 ENGLISH MAHOGANY,CARVED,CIRCA 1780.2,100.00
FURNITURE,CHAIR,SET OF 6 BRACE-BACK WINDSOR.................2,300.00
FURNITURE,CHAIR,SET OF 6 CURLY MAPLE LADDER BACK...........  175.00
FURNITURE,CHAIR,SET OF 6 ENGLISH CHIPPENDALE
  SIDE,MAHOGANY,CIRCA 1760.................................1,950.00
FURNITURE,CHAIR,SET OF 6 ENGLISH LOOPBACK COTTAGE,YEW.......  240.00
FURNITURE,CHAIR,SET OF 6 MAHOGANY QUEEN ANNE SIDE CIRCA 17303,850.00
FURNITURE,CHAIR,SET OF 6 MAHOGANY SIDE,CABRIOLE FRONT LEGS..  150.00
FURNITURE,CHAIR,SET OF 6 PLANKED SEAT HITCHCOCK,PINE & MAPLE  300.00
FURNITURE,CHAIR,SET OF 6 WINDSOR ARROWBACK SIDE............  375.00
FURNITURE,CHAIR,SET OF 7 MAHOGANY QUEEN ANNE PROVINCIAL
  DINING ROOM.............................................3,650.00
FURNITURE,CHAIR,SET OF 8 HEPPLEWHITE MAHOGANY..............3,000.00
FURNITURE,CHAIR,SET OF 8 QUEEN ANNE DINING ROOM,WALNUT
  PATINA..................................................3,850.00
FURNITURE,CHAIR,SET OF 10 LIBRARY ,RED LEATHER SEATS,CIRCA
  1800....................................................1,995.00
FURNITURE,CHAIR,SET OF 10 REGENCY ROSEWOOD BALLROOM CIRCA
  1810....................................................1,200.00
FURNITURE,CHAIR,SET OF 12 CHIPPENDALE RIBBON-BACK,LEATHER
  SEATS...................................................3,000.00
FURNITURE,CHAIR,SIDE,PILGRIM..............................  185.00
FURNITURE,CHAIR,SLAT BACK,RED PAINT,RUSH SEAT.............   28.00
FURNITURE,CHAIR,THUMB BACK LADDER BACK....................   28.00
FURNITURE,CHAIR,TIGER MAPLE FIDDLE BACK SIDE,CANE SEAT.....   30.00
FURNITURE,CHAIR,WALNUT QUEEN ANNE SIDE,SALEM ORIGIN........  750.00
FURNITURE,CHAIR,WICKER CORNER,GREEN MATTE..................   48.00
FURNITURE,CHAIR,VICTORIAN CORSET BACK CLOSED ARM GENTLEMANS.   95.00
FURNITURE,CHAIR,VICTORIAN,FOLDING,CARPET SEAT & BACK........   12.50
FURNITURE,CHAIR,VICTORIAN WALNUT ROSE CARVED,CABRIOLE LEGS..  150.00
FURNITURE,CHAIR,WINDSOR,ARM...............................  350.00
FURNITURE,CHAIR,WINDSOR,FAN BACK..........................  185.00
FURNITURE,CHAIR WITH CANE BACK,BENTWOOD...................   32.50
FURNITURE,CHAIR,WRITING ARM WINDSOR.......................  750.00
FURNITURE,CHEST,4 DRAWER PINE,CUT OUT BRACKET BASE,WOODEN
  KNOB PULLS..............................................  185.00
FURNITURE,CHEST,BACHELORS,CHIPPENDALE,WALNUT,18 X 28 X 30
  IN......................................................  200.00
FURNITURE,CHEST CIRCA 1810,MAHOGANY 4 DRAWER..............  350.00
FURNITURE,CHEST,CURLY MAPLE 4 DRAWER,SANDWICH GLASS KNOBS...  250.00
FURNITURE,CHEST-DESK,ELM,CIRCA 1810.......................1,095.00
FURNITURE,CHEST,EARLY AMERICAN BIRDSEYE MAPLE BOW-FRONT
  LADYS VANITY............................................  110.00
FURNITURE,CHEST,EMPIRE,4 DRAWERS,CHERRY WITH INLAID MAHOGANY  135.00
FURNITURE,CHEST,GERMAN LIFT LID WITH HIGH
  BACK,OAK,HANDCARVED.....................................  850.00
FURNITURE,CHEST,HEPPLEWHITE,4 DRAWER,MAPLE & BIRCH.........  325.00
FURNITURE,CHEST,MAHOGANY BOW FRONT CIRCA 1800.............  350.00
FURNITURE,CHEST,MAHOGANY,WRITING BED & PULL OUT
  MIRRORS,CIRCA 1790......................................1,650.00
FURNITURE,CHEST,MULBERRY & PERSIMMON WOOD,12 IN. TALL,18 IN.
  LONG....................................................   45.00
FURNITURE,CHEST OF 15 DRAWERS,MAHOGANY & BIRCH,DOVETAILED...   75.00
FURNITURE,CHEST OF DRAWERS................................  135.00
FURNITURE,CHEST OF DRAWERS,AMERICAN CURLY MAPLE,PINE
  TOP,CIRCA 1775..........................................  950.00
FURNITURE,CHEST OF DRAWERS,CHERRY,4 DRAWERS...............  185.00
FURNITURE,CHEST OF DRAWERS,CHIPPENDALE CIRCA 1760,5 DRAWERS.  425.00
FURNITURE,CHEST OF DRAWERS CIRCA 1775,MAHOGANY............  882.00
```

```
FURNITURE,CHEST OF DRAWERS CIRCA 1800,HEPPLEWHITE MAHOGANY..    398.00
FURNITURE,CHEST OF DRAWERS,EMPIRE,MAHOGANY,4 LONG DRAWERS &
  2 SMALL...................................................     45.00
FURNITURE,CHEST OF DRAWERS,ENGLISH ELM CHIPPENDALE..........    175.00
FURNITURE,CHEST OF DRAWERS,HEPPLEWHITE SWELL FRONT
  40.00  TO................................................    750.00
FURNITURE,CHEST OF DRAWERS,MAHOGANY,NEW ENGLAND CIRCA 1785..    485.00
FURNITURE,CHEST OF DRAWERS,PINE,BRACKET BASE,RED PAINT......    395.00
FURNITURE,CHEST ON CHEST,18TH CENTURY
  CHIPPENDALE,MAHOGANY,CIRCA 1770.........................1,110.00
FURNITURE,CHEST ON CHEST,QUEEN ANNE LOW,CIRCA 1710,JAPAN
  BLACK & GOLD.............................................1,950.00
FURNITURE,CHEST,PAINTED GREEN,1854.........................     32.00
FURNITURE,CHEST,PINE 3 DRAWER,SOLID ENDS,BACKSPLASH.........     73.00
FURNITURE,CHEST,PINE,CARVED ABOUT 1850,BROWN STAINED........    275.00
FURNITURE,CHEST,QUEEN ANNE 5 DRAWER,WALNUT,21 IN. HIGH......    185.00
FURNITURE,CHEST,QUEEN ANNE ON FRAME,WALNUT,DRAKE FOOT
  CABRIOLE LEGS...........................................3,000.00
FURNITURE,CHEST,RED LACQUER WOOD WITH 5 DRAWERS,11 IN. HIGH.     40.00
FURNITURE,CHEST,SCOTCH MULE,MAHOGANY,CIRCA 1780.............    750.00
FURNITURE,CHEST,SHERATON,20 X 40 X 34 IN...................1,000.00
FURNITURE,CHEST,WALNUT BLANKET.............................     32.00
FURNITURE,CHEST WITH 2 COMPARTMENTS ON TOP,MINIATURE EMPIRE
  4 DRAWER.................................................     62.50
FURNITURE,CHEST WITH DITTY BOX,PINE,DOWRY..................     50.00
FURNITURE,CHEST WITH DRESSING SLIDE,CHIPPENDALE,34
  IN.,WALNUT,4 DRAWER......................................    575.00
FURNITURE,CHURCH ARMREST CIRCA 1840........................     48.00
FURNITURE,CLOCK SHELF,BLACK WALNUT,SCALLOPED...............     22.50
FURNITURE,CLOCK SHELF,WALNUT...............................     15.00
FURNITURE,COAL BOX,MAHOGANY,BRASS HARDWARE,SLANT FRONT......     45.00
FURNITURE,COAT RACK........................................     15.00
FURNITURE,COBBLERS BENCH WITH DRAWER,20 X 54 IN............    135.00
FURNITURE,COFFER,18TH CENTURY OAK..........................    383.00
FURNITURE,COMB RACK WITH MIRROR,WALNUT,HANGING.............      5.00
FURNITURE,COMMODE,DECORATED................................     49.00
FURNITURE,COMMODE,MARBLE TOP
  40.00  TO................................................     85.00
FURNITURE,COMMODE,OAK WITH MARBLE TOP & SPLASH BACK WITH
  CANDLE SHELVES...........................................     70.00
FURNITURE,COMMODE,PINE,DRAWER AT TOP,2 DOORS IN BASE........     18.50
FURNITURE,COMMODE,PINE ,LIFT TOP...........................     88.00
FURNITURE,COMMODE WITH 4 DRAWERS,1 DOOR,MARBLE TOP..........     80.00
FURNITURE,COMMODE WITH SERPENTINE FRONT,LIFT TOP,WHITE WITH
  GOLD.....................................................     55.00
FURNITURE,CONSOLE SIGNED A H DAVENPORT,AMERICAN-EAGLE,22 X
  40 X 31 IN...............................................1,850.00
FURNITURE,CRADLE,BENT SLAT,HAMMOCK BASE....................    125.00
FURNITURE,CRADLE,MAPLE VICTORIAN SWINGING..................     55.00
FURNITURE,CRADLE,OLD PENDULUM..............................     35.00
FURNITURE,CRADLE,PINE......................................     95.00
FURNITURE,CRADLE,SWING ON STAND............................     95.00
FURNITURE,CRADLE,VICTORIAN.................................     35.00
FURNITURE,CRADLE,WICKER....................................     50.00
FURNITURE,CRADLE WITH HOOD CIRCA 1780......................     55.00
FURNITURE,CREDENZA,SPANISH,INLAID ORMOLU...................    550.00
FURNITURE,CREWEL SCREEN SIGNED & DATED....................1,200.00
FURNITURE,CUPBOARD,2 PART WALL,PANELED DOORS,BIRCH & PINE...    165.00
FURNITURE,CUPBOARD,BIEDERMEIER,BLACK TRIM CIRCA 1830........    795.00
FURNITURE,CUPBOARD,CHERRY,GLASS DOORS,2 SMALL DRAWERS,2
  DOORS....................................................    200.00
FURNITURE,CUPBOARD,CHESTNUT CORNER,2 GLASS DOORS AT TOP,2 IN
  BASE.....................................................    110.00
FURNITURE,CUPBOARD,CHINA & LINEN,SPANISH,MAHOGANY & ROSEWOOD1,450.00
FURNITURE,CUPBOARD CIRCA 1800,VERMONT......................    485.00
```

```
FURNITURE,CUPBOARD CIRCA 1825,BIEDERMEIER FRUITWOOD.........   895.00
FURNITURE,CUPBOARD,DRINK,CIRCA 1790,HEPPLEWHITE.............   295.00
FURNITURE,CUPBOARD,HINGING,PINE,1 DRAWER FRONT..............    22.50
FURNITURE,CUPBOARD,HUTCH...................................    69.00
FURNITURE,CUPBOARD,MAPLE,KITCHEN,13 DRAWERS,3 DOORS.........    87.50
FURNITURE,CUPBOARD ON CUPBOARD,BONNET TOP CORNER,CHERRY
  CIRCA 1795..............................................1,250.00
FURNITURE,CUPBOARD,PENNSYLVANIA DUTCH,2 PART GLASS
  DOORS,POPLAR.............................................   525.00
FURNITURE,CUPBOARD,PENNSYLVANIA DUTCH 2 PIECE,INTERIOR SPOON
  RACK...................................................   385.00
FURNITURE,CUPBOARD,PIE,SAFE,PUNCHED TIN,WALNUT,41 X 56 IN...    22.50
FURNITURE,CUPBOARD,PINE,2-PART CORNER......................   500.00
FURNITURE,CUPBOARD,PINE CORNER,BARREL BACK,OGEE,CUT OUT WORK   750.00
FURNITURE,CUPBOARD,PINE HANGING,4 6 IN. DEEP SHELVES........    65.00
FURNITURE,CUPBOARD,PINE PEWTER,BONNET TOP..................   350.00
FURNITURE,CUPBOARD,VICTORIAN WALNUT,4 DRAWERS IN BASE.......    85.00
FURNITURE,CUPBOARD,WALL....................................    20.00
FURNITURE,DAVENPORT,ENGLISH REGENCY,ROSEWOOD,LEATHER
  TOP,CIRCA 1840..........................................   625.00
FURNITURE,DAYBED,CHIPPENDALE,MAHOGANY,CIRCA 1760...........1,095.00
FURNITURE,DAYBED CIRCA 1750,GEORGIAN MAHOGANY,YELLOW SILK
  DAMASK.................................................2,300.00
FURNITURE,DAYBED,CIRCA 1815,BIEDERMEIER....................   895.00
FURNITURE,DAYBED,PAIR,ADAM ROSEWOOD,CIRCA 1800.............   895.00
FURNITURE,DEACONS BENCH....................................   165.00
FURNITURE,DEACONS BENCH,6 FEET LONG........................    55.00
FURNITURE,DESK & BOOKCASE,AMERICAN MAHOGANY................8,500.00
FURNITURE,DESK & CHAIR,CHILDS SCHOOLHOUSE,IRON & OAK........    30.00
FURNITURE,DESK & CHEST,CHIPPENDALE,MAHOGNAY,CIRCA 1760......   785.00
FURNITURE,DESK & MATCHING CHAIR,SCHOOL.....................    30.00
FURNITURE,DESK,BURLED WALNUT REGENCY PARTNERS..............2,225.00
FURNITURE,DESK,BUTLERS,MAHOGANY,ARCHED PIGEON HOLES.........   415.00
FURNITURE,DESK,CHERRY ROLL TOP.............................   365.00
FURNITURE,DESK CHEST,CURLY MAPLE...........................   525.00
FURNITURE,DESK,CHILDS OAK ROLL TOP & OAK CHAIR.............    37.50
FURNITURE,DESK CIRCA 1730,SHAPED FRONT,BURL WALNUT.........1,850.00
FURNITURE,DESK CIRCA 1760-1780,AMERICAN SERPENTINE-FRONT
  MAHOGANY...............................................3,950.00
FURNITURE,DESK CIRCA 1760,IRISH MAHOGANY KNEEHOLE..........2,400.00
FURNITURE,DESK CIRCA 1780,CONNECTICUT CHERRY...............1,600.00
FURNITURE,DESK CIRCA 1780,GEORGIAN MAHOGANY SLANT FRONT.....   850.00
FURNITURE,DESK CIRCA 1785,HEPPLEWHITE CHERRY SLANT TOP......   800.00
FURNITURE,DESK CIRCA 1800,GEORGIAN TABLE...................   650.00
FURNITURE,DESK CIRCA 1800,HEPPLEWHITE CHERRY & MAPLE SLANT
  FRONT..................................................   450.00
FURNITURE,DESK CIRCA 1830,FRENCH EMPIRE DROP FRONT.........1,295.00
FURNITURE,DESK,ENGLISH MAHOGANY KNEEHOLE,43 X 22 X 39 IN....1,250.00
FURNITURE,DESK,FLEMISH FINISHED OAK FALL FRONT,GOTHIC CARVED  325.00
FURNITURE,DESK FRAME,VICTORIAN GILDED,FLORAL ..............    10.00
FURNITURE,DESK,HEPPLEWHITE SLANT-TOP ,AMERICAN MAHOGANY
  CIRCA 1790.............................................   775.00
FURNITURE,DESK IN MAHOGANY,TAMBOUR HEPPLEWHITE.............1,250.00
FURNITURE,DESK IN MULBERRY WOOD WITH EBONY INLAY,QUEEN ANNE
  KNEEHOLE...............................................1,850.00
FURNITURE,DESK,LADYS,MAPLE.................................    75.00
FURNITURE,DESK,LARKIN OAK FALL FRONT,MIRROR & CORNER
  BRACKETS...............................................    25.00
FURNITURE,DESK,LORD CARLTON HOUSE CIRCA 1810,MAHOGANY,39 X
  47 X 22 IN.............................................3,200.00
FURNITURE,DESK MADE IN IRELAND CIRCA 1770,18TH CENTURY
  MAHOGANY...............................................   985.00
FURNITURE,DESK,PINE SCHOOL.................................    20.00
FURNITURE,DESK,MAHOGANY SLANT FRONT,CIRCA 1780.............   825.00
FURNITURE,DESK,PINE SLANT LID BOX,20 IN. WIDE BY 19 IN. DEEP   28.00
```

```
FURNITURE,DESK,SECRETARY,CHERRY,CONNECTICUT CIRCA 1780,BALL
 & CLAW FEET...................................................3,300.00
FURNITURE,DESK,SHIPS,MAHOGANY,SLANT TOP,DRAWERS ON ONE SIDE.    225.00
FURNITURE,DESK,SPOOL CABINET,4 DRAWERS & METAL IN WELL......     45.00
FURNITURE,DESK,VENETIAN BOMBE OLIVE WOOD,BLACK...............1,500.00
FURNITURE,DESK,WALNUT DROP-LID,69 IN. TALL,BRASS RING PULLS
 ON 3.......................................................     75.00
FURNITURE,DESK,WALNUT SECRETARY SLANT TOP...................    850.00
FURNITURE,DICTIONARY STAND,IRON,WOODEN BOOK WINGS & SHELF...     25.00
FURNITURE,DOUGH BOX.........................................     25.00
FURNITURE,DOUGH BOX,PENNSYLVANIA ,TURNED LEGS,POPLAR WOOD...    130.00
FURNITURE,DOUGH BOX,PINE,1 BOARD HINGED TOP WITH BREAD BOARD
 ENDS.......................................................     18.00
FURNITURE,DOUGH BOX WITH HANDLES,PENNSYLVANIA...............     65.00
FURNITURE,DOUGH TRAY,LIDDED DOVETAILED,26 IN...............      45.00
FURNITURE,DRESSER,17TH CENTURY WELSH,OAK,CIRCA 1690,3
 PANELED DRAWERS...........................................1,250.00
FURNITURE,DRESSER,18TH CENTURY OAK WELSH...................     850.00
FURNITURE,DRESSER,BRASS FRAME WITH EASLE & MIRROR..........      13.50
FURNITURE,DRESSER,BURL WALNUT,MARBLE TOP,POST FOR MIRROR,4
 DRAWERS....................................................    200.00
FURNITURE,DRESSER,ENGLISH PINE,GRAINED LIKE WALNUT,CIRCA
 1770......................................................1,165.00
FURNITURE,DRESSING GLASS,ENGLISH SERPENTINE FRONT,MAHOGANY
 CIRCA 1790................................................     325.00
FURNITURE,DRESSER,PINE & POPLAR,CIRCA 1820-40,52 IN. HIGH...    110.00
FURNITURE,DRESSER,VICTORIAN WALNUT,MARBLE TOP,FRUIT
 PULLS,MIRROR..............................................      85.00
FURNITURE,DRY SINK.........................................      50.00
FURNITURE,DRY SINK,42 IN. LONG.............................     125.00
FURNITURE,DRY SINK OF PINE,PAINT-GRAINED TO APPEAR WALNUT
 AND MAPLE.................................................      58.00
FURNITURE,DRY SINK,PINE,TOP OVERLAPS BASE..................      42.00
FURNITURE,DRY SINK ,PINE WITH COPPER LINED WELL,2 DRAWERS...    185.00
FURNITURE,DUMB-WAITER,GEORGIAN,2 TIER,CIRCA 1800...........     595.00
FURNITURE,EASEL WITH BRASS FINIALS,BAMBOO..................      19.50
FURNITURE,FIREPLACE SCREEN,VICTORIAN,PORTRAIT IN MIDDLE.....    195.00
FURNITURE,FIRE REFLECTOR SCREEN,24 X 34 IN.,TIFFANY TYPE
 LEADED GLASS..............................................     110.00
FURNITURE,FOOTSTOOL,MARKED SHAKER,SLANTED..................      50.00
FURNITURE,FOOTSTOOL,NEEDLEPOINT,BLUE BACKGROUND,WALNUT FRAME     18.00
FURNITURE,FOOTSTOOL,PINE...................................      15.00
FURNITURE,FOOTSTOOL,PINE & MAPLE,OVAL SHAPED TOP...........       8.50
FURNITURE,FOOTSTOOL,PINE,BOOTJACK ENDS,SKIRTED SIDES.......       8.00
FURNITURE,FOOTSTOOL,WALNUT OVAL,CARVING,TAPESTRY COVERING...     14.00
FURNITURE,FRAME,20 IN. WALNUT..............................      24.00
FURNITURE,FRAMES,OVAL PAIR CONVEX GLASS,ROSEWOOD FINISH.....     23.50
FURNITURE,FRAME,PAIR OVAL GOLD LEAF,14 X 12 IN.............      45.00
FURNITURE,FRAME,PAIR WALNUT,GOLD LINING....................       6.00
FURNITURE,FRAME,WALNUT.....................................       7.50
FURNITURE,FRAME WITH FLORAL TOP FINIAL,OVAL................       5.00
FURNITURE,GLOBE WITH COMPASS SHOWING ROUTES OF HISTORIC
 VOYAGES...................................................     650.00
FURNITURE,HALL RACK WITH SWANS & SPOOL UNBRELLA
 STAND,WALNUT,MIRROR.......................................      42.50
FURNITURE,HAMPER WITH DOMED LID,WICKER.....................      15.00
FURNITURE HARNESS BENCH,PRIMITIVE..........................      27.50
FURNITURE,HAT HOOK,BARBERS.................................       2.50
FURNITURE,HAT RACK,10 PEG FOLDING..........................       5.00
FURNITURE,HAT RACK,WALNUT FOLDING,10 KNOBS.................      14.50
FURNITURE,HAT RACK,WOOD WITH 4 LACY IRON BRACES............       6.00
FURNITURE,HIGHBOY,CHIPPENDALE,CIRCA 1820...................2,200.00
FURNITURE,HIGHBOY IN MAPLE,QUEEN ANNE,BRASS TRIMMINGS.......2,750.00
FURNITURE,HIGHBOY,QUEEN ANNE,BURL WALNUT,CABRIOLE LEGS,WEB
 FOOT.....................................................2,800.00
```

```
FURNITURE,HIGHBOY,QUEEN ANNE,MAPLE,CIRCA 1750,2
   FANS,SCALLOPED APRON.....................................2,600.00
FURNITURE,HIGHBOY,WILLIAM & MARY.............................1,800.00
FURNITURE,HIGH CHAIR.........................................  18.00
FURNITURE,HIGH CHAIR,AMERICAN 17TH CENTURY CHILDS,CARVER
   TYPE.....................................................  275.00
FURNITURE,HIGH CHAIR,CANADIAN CHILDS,RAW HIDE SNOWSHOE-WEAVE
   SEAT.....................................................  125.00
FURNITURE,HIGH CHAIR DATED 1874,CHILDS WALNUT................   50.00
FURNITURE,ICE CREAM SET,5 PIECES.............................   65.00
FURNITURE,ICE CREAM SET,ROUND MILK GLASS TOP,4 WIRE CHAIRS..  110.00
FURNITURE,ICE CREAM SET,TABLE & 2 CHAIRS,OAK TOP.............   78.00
FURNITURE,KNIFE BOX,PAIR 18TH CENTURY ENGLISH SHERATON
   MAHOGANY.................................................  375.00
FURNITURE,KNIFE BOX,PAIR MAHOGANY SHERATON,FLAME
   FINIAL,CIRCA 1790........................................  485.00
FURNITURE,LAP DESK,9 X 12 X 3 IN.............................   13.00
FURNITURE,LAP DESK,11 IN. X 8 IN.............................    4.75
FURNITURE,LAP DESK ,INLAY MAHOGNAY,LOCK & KEY,12 X 9 IN.....   15.00
FURNITURE,LAP DESK,MAHOGANY & VENEER,PAINTED BLACK & GOLD
   STRIPES..................................................   14.50
FURNITURE,LAP DESK,ROSEWOOD,HANDPAINTED FLOWER CLUSTERS.....   35.00
FURNITURE,LAP DESK,WALNUT,BLACK BAND & GOLD.................   10.00
FURNITURE,LAP DESK,WALNUT FINISH,4 COMPARTMENTS.............    7.00
FURNITURE,LAP DESK,WALNUT,VELVET LINED......................    7.50
FURNITURE,LAP DESK WITH INK WELL............................   14.50
FURNITURE,LIBRARY STEPS,OAK REGENCY CIRCA 1800..............  795.00
FURNITURE,LOOKING GLASS WITH VAUXHALL MIRROR CIRCA
   1710,QUEEN ANNE,GILT.....................................1,750.00
FURNITURE,LOVE SEAT,HEPPLEWHITE,SERPENTINE FRONT & BACK
   RAIL,CIRCA 1760..........................................1,675.00
FURNITURE,LOVE SEAT,VICTORIAN,2 SIDE CHAIRS & ROCKER,RED
   VELVET...................................................  325.00
FURNITURE,LOVE SEAT,VICTORIAN,BLACK WALNUT WITH OVAL MIRROR.  500.00
FURNITURE,LOVE SEAT,VICTORIAN MEDALLION BACK FINGER
   CARVED,RED VELVET........................................  125.00
FURNITURE,LOWBOY,CHERRY CABRIOLE LEG,SHELL CARVING,33 IN.
   HIGH.....................................................1,600.00
FURNITURE,LOWBOY CIRCA 1690,QUEEN ANNE WALNUT,29 X 18 X 27
   IN.......................................................1,500.00
FURNITURE,LOWBOY,CIRCA 1710,QUEEN ANNE......................  695.00
FURNITURE,LOWBOY,ENGLISH OAK QUEEN ANNE.....................  850.00
FURNITURE,LOWBOY ,QUEEN ANNE,CIRCA 1740,CONNECTICUT CHERRY..5,500.00
FURNITURE,LOWBOY,QUEEN ANNE,OAK CROSS-BANDED INLAY..........  600.00
FURNITURE,LOWBOY,QUEEN ANNE,WALNUT,CABRIOLE LEGS,DRAKE FOOT.2,600.00
FURNITURE,MANTEL,PINE,CIRCA 1830,60 IN. WIDE,47 IN. HIGH....   20.00
FURNITURE,MANTEL WITH MIRROR,WALNUT.........................   26.00
FURNITURE,MEDICINE CABINET,WALNUT...........................   21.00
FURNITURE,MELODEON CASE.....................................   33.00
FURNITURE,MIRROR,3 WAY,VICTORIAN DRESSER....................   25.00
FURNITURE,MIRROR,10 IN. PLATEAU.............................   27.50
FURNITURE,MIRROR,12 IN. SCROLL TYPE DRESSER.................    7.50
FURNITURE,MIRROR,12 IN. WALNUT OVAL TYPE WALL...............    7.50
FURNITURE,MIRROR,16 IN. BY 24 IN. ROUNDED CORNERS,MAHOGANY
   AND METAL................................................   12.00
FURNITURE,MIRROR,BAROQUE,HANDCARVED FRAME WITH GOLDLEAF.....   72.00
FURNITURE,MIRROR,CHIPPENDALE................................  375.00
FURNITURE,MIRROR,CHIPPENDALE,CARVED PHOENIX.................  425.00
FURNITURE,MIRROR CIRCA 1810,REGENCY CHEVAL..................  350.00
FURNITURE,MIRROR,EASEL,GERMAN SILVER OVER WALNUT,ROCOCO
   FRAME,17X14 IN...........................................   20.00
FURNITURE,MIRROR,GEORGIAN...................................  850.00
FURNITURE,MIRROR,HALL,MARBLE SHELF,8 FEET X 26 IN...........1,000.00
FURNITURE,MIRROR,LOUIS XVI CARVED,FRANCE,CIRCA 1790.........  500.00
FURNITURE,MIRROR,MAHOGANY CHEVAL SHERATON CIRCA 1790........  300.00
```

```
FURNITURE,MIRROR,MAHOGANY,CHIPPENDALE FRET WORK..............   195.00
FURNITURE,MIRROR ON TRAY IN SILVER FRAME,ROUND,DRESSER......    16.00
FURNITURE,MIRROR,QUEEN ANNE.................................   395.00
FURNITURE,MIRROR,PHILADELPHIA SHERATON MAHOGANY.............   250.00
FURNITURE,MIRROR,PLATEAU ROUND FOR TABLE,SILVER FRAME ON
  FEET......................................................    22.00
FURNITURE,MIRROR,REVERSE PAINTING...........................    58.00
FURNITURE,MIRROR REVERSE PAINTING ON TOP....................    42.50
FURNITURE,MIRROR,ROUND,PLATEAU,SILVER SCROLL EDGE...........    12.00
FURNITURE,MIRROR,SHAVING,MAHOGANY,1 DRAWER,13 IN. HIGH......    30.00
FURNITURE,MIRROR,SWEDISH EMPIRE CIRCA 1810..................   895.00
FURNITURE,MIRROR WITH BIRD,SCROLLED,CIRCA 1760..............   440.00
FURNITURE,MIRROR WITH EAGLE,GILT CONVEX.....................   575.00
FURNITURE,MIRROR,WOODEN FRAMED..............................    12.50
FURNITURE,MUSIC STAND.......................................    30.00
FURNITURE,NIGHT STAND,CURLY MAPLE SHERATON 2 DRAWER,BRASS
  CASTORS...................................................    95.00
FURNITURE,NIGHT STAND,MARBLE TOP............................    17.50
FURNITURE,NIGHT STAND WITH INLAYS,HEPPLEWHITE SATINWOOD.....   275.00
FURNITURE,NIGHT STAND WITH MAHOGANY BASED FRONT,MAPLE.......    25.00
FURNITURE,NIGHT TABLE WITH DRAWER,HEPPLEWHITE,MAPLE.........    70.00
FURNITURE,NIGHT TABLE WITH DRAWER,HEPPLEWHITE,CHERRY........    70.00
FURNITURE,ORGAN STOOL,4 CARVED IRON LEGS....................    18.00
FURNITURE,ORGAN STOOL,BOX TYPE WITH PETIT POINT TOP.........    12.50
FURNITURE,ORGAN STOOL,ELEVATING ROUND.......................     9.00
FURNITURE,OX-CART WAGON SEAT,3 SLAT BACK....................   225.00
FURNITURE,PANEL IN CARVED TEAKWOOD FRAME,CHINESE RED
  CINNABAR,1800.............................................   465.00
FURNITURE,PANEL,PAIR 18TH CENTURY CREWEL WORK,TREE OF
  LIFE,WOOL.................................................   550.00
FURNITURE,PANTRY,STENCILLED TOLEWARE WITH CLOCK &
  COMPARTMENTS..............................................    95.00
FURNITURE,PARLOR SET,7 PIECE,CARVED ROSEWOOD SOFA..........5,200.00
FURNITURE,PEDESTAL WITH FLUTED COLUMNS & SATINWOOD
  URN,MAHOGANY.............................................1,160.00
FURNITURE,PIANO BENCH,2-PASSENGER,LIFT TOP..................    18.00
FURNITURE,PIANO STOOL & BACK................................    25.00
FURNITURE,PIANO STOOL,ELEVATING.............................    15.00
FURNITURE,PIANO STOOL,TWISTED WIRE & OAK....................    35.00
FURNITURE,PIANO STOOL WITH ADJUSTABLE SEAT..................    12.50
FURNITURE,PIANO STOOL WITH BACK,ADJUSTABLE SEAT,MAHOGANY
  FINISH....................................................    25.00
FURNITURE,POTTY CHAIR,CHERRY OVER PINK......................    25.00
FURNITURE,RACK,ANTLER.......................................    10.00
FURNITURE,ROCKER,4 SLAT LADDER BACK ARM.....................    48.00
FURNITURE,ROCKER,18TH CENTURY MAPLE & HICKORY LADDERBACK....    69.50
FURNITURE,ROCKER,ARM,MAHOGANY WITH CARYATID FACES...........    40.00
FURNITURE,ROCKER,ARROW BACK.................................    60.00
FURNITURE,ROCKER,BOSTON,PLANK SEAT..........................    18.50
FURNITURE,ROCKER,BOWBACK WINDSOR,BLACK PAINTED..............   156.00
FURNITURE,ROCKER,BOSTON
  30.00  TO.................................................    75.00
FURNITURE,ROCKER,CHILDS BOSTON,CANE SEAT....................    28.00
FURNITURE,ROCKER,CHILDS LINCOLN.............................    20.00
FURNITURE,ROCKER,CHILDS MAPLE...............................    27.50
FURNITURE,ROCKER,CHILDS WINDSOR.............................    28.50
FURNITURE,ROCKER,COMBBACK,STEPDOWN WINDSOR..................   195.00
FURNITURE,ROCKER,COTTAGE PLATFORM,RED CARPETING ON SEAT &
  BACK......................................................    12.50
FURNITURE,ROCKER,FINGER CARVED..............................    29.00
FURNITURE,ROCKER,HIGH BACK WITH TAPESTRY SEAT...............    27.50
FURNITURE,ROCKER,LADYS,WALNUT,ROSE CARVED,CABRIOLE LEGS.....    47.50
FURNITURE,ROCKER,MAPLE PLATFORM,CANE SEAT & BACK...........    37.50
FURNITURE,ROCKER,PLATFORM WITH ADJUSTABLE HEAD-REST,FOOT
  REST......................................................    29.50
```

```
FURNITURE,ROCKER,SIGNED SHAKER,SHAG SEAT...................... 135.00
FURNITURE,ROCKER,THUMB BACK,PLANK SEAT,STENCILING...........   25.00
FURNITURE,ROCKER,VICTORIAN LINCOLN...........................  27.50
FURNITURE,ROCKER,VICTORIAN PLATFORM,GOLD ILLUMINATED LINE
  CARVINGS...................................................  27.50
FURNITURE,ROCKER,VICTORIAN PLATFORM,TAPESTRY UPHOLSTERED....  18.50
FURNITURE,ROCKER,WALNUT PLATFORM.............................  15.00
FURNITURE,ROCKER,WICKER PLATFORM,CANE SEAT...................  12.50
FURNITURE,ROCKER,WINDSOR..................................... 135.00
FURNITURE,ROCKER,WINDSOR TYPE,CHEESE CUTTER ROCKERS,BLACK
  PAINT & GOLD............................................... 110.00
FURNITURE,ROCKER,YOUTHS WINDSOR,RED PAINT....................  30.00
FURNITURE,ROCKING CHAIR,CHILDS...............................  27.50
FURNITURE,ROCKING CHAIR,MAPLE,BIRDS EYE MAPLE BACK..........  20.00
FURNITURE,RUSHLIGHT STAND & CANDLEHOLDER,IRON ON WOOD....... 385.00
FURNITURE,SCONCE,PAIR MIRRORED CIRCA 1840................... 185.00
FURNITURE,SCREEN,4 PANEL ORIENTAL,IVORY BIRDS.............. 135.00
FURNITURE,SCREEN,CHERRY FRAME 3 PART,22 X 58 IN.,CENTER
  PAINTINGS................................................. 125.00
FURNITURE,SCREEN,COROMANDEL,JADE,IVORY,CARNELIAN,BLACK
  PAINTED BIRDS............................................2,500.00
FURNITURE,SCREEN,NEW YORK POLE CIRCA 1790................... 800.00
FURNITURE,SEA CHEST,18TH CENTURY............................  25.00
FURNITURE,SEA CHEST,PINE,ROPE HANDLES,DOVETAILED,RED PAINT..  38.00
FURNITURE,SECRETAIRE CHEST CIRCA 1750,CHIPPENDALE MAHOGANY..1,250.00
FURNITURE,SECRETAIRE CHEST,GEORGE III,MAHOGANY WITH BRASS
  HANDLES................................................... 550.00
FURNITURE,SECRETARY CIRCA 1770,CHIPPENDALE MAHOGANY,LEATHER
  INTERIOR................................................2,250.00
FURNITURE,SECRETARY CIRCA 1780,GILT TOOLED,ENGLAND
  HEPPLEWHITE.............................................3,950.00
FURNITURE,SECRETARY CIRCA 1790,GEOGRIAN,MAHOGANY...........1,095.00
FURNITURE,SECRETARY,1820-1840 NEW BRUNSWICK MAHOGANY
  SHERATON.................................................. 900.00
FURNITURE,SECRETARY DESK,SHERATON BIRCH & PINE,30 IN.
  WRITING HEIGHT............................................ 375.00
FURNITURE,SECRETARY,MAHOGANY EMPIRE,3 DRAWERS IN BASE.......  95.00
FURNITURE,SECRETARY,QUEEN ANNE,WALNUT....................... 495.00
FURNITURE,SETTEE,7-FOOT LONG MAPLE,SPINDLE BACK,SPOOL LEGS.. 165.00
FURNITURE,SETTEE CIRCA 1800,QUEEN ANNE WALNUT..............1,350.00
FURNITURE,SETTEE,CONNECTICUT SHERATON,MAPLE,RUSH SEAT....... 775.00
FURNITURE,SETTEE,HALF-ARROW,6 FOOT,BLACK PAINT.............. 300.00
FURNITURE,SETTEE,MAHOGANY,ARCHED CREST RAIL................2,200.00
FURNITURE,SETTEE,QUEEN ANNE,MAHOGANY,OYSTER DAMASK UPHOLSTRY 295.00
FURNITURE,SETTEE,PENNSYLVANIA DUTCH WIDE PLANK SEAT......... 200.00
FURNITURE,SETTEE,SHERATON,CREAM DAMASK UPHOLSTERY..........1,150.00
FURNITURE,SETTEE,SPANISH,18TH CENTURY,SOUTH
  AMERICA,CARVED,VELVET..................................... 450.00
FURNITURE,SEWING BOX,WALNUT,MEDALLION,LIFT OUT TRAY.........   7.50
FURNITURE,SEWING BOX WITH BONE TOOLS,CHINESE DECOR..........  65.00
FURNITURE,SEWING TABLE......................................  40.00
FURNITURE,SEWING TABLE & DESK,ENGLISH HEPPLEWHITE,BIRDS EYE
  MAPLE..................................................... 495.00
FURNITURE,SHADOW BOX FRAME,GOLD LINER,WALNUT...............   15.00
FURNITURE,SHAVING STAND WITH SANDWICH GLASS
  PULLS,CHERRY,18TH CENTURY................................. 150.00
FURNITURE,SHELF,CLOCK,OAK CARVED............................  15.00
FURNITURE,SHELF,CORNER,HAND CARVED DEER HEAD...............   22.50
FURNITURE,SHELF,VICTORIAN WALNUT KNICK KNACK,CUT OUT DESIGN
  ON BACK...................................................   3.95
FURNITURE,SHRINE IN LACQUERED CABINET WITH GOLD
  INTERIOR,18TH CENTURY..................................... 100.00
FURNITURE,SIDEBOARD,AMERICAN HEPPLEWHITE,SERPENTINE
  FRONT,MAHOGANY.........................................4,500.00
FURNITURE,SIDEBOARD,BOW FRONT MAHOGANY WITH TULIPWOOD INLAYS 395.00
```

```
FURNITURE,SIDEBOARD,CHERRY & BIRDS EYE MAPLE,DRAWER & 2
   DOORS.............................................................. 225.00
FURNITURE,SIDEBOARD CIRCA 1780,ENGLISH HEPPLEWHITE
   SERPENTINE.....................................................1,000.00
FURNITURE,SIDEBOARD CIRCA 1790,ENGLISH,34 IN. HIGH..........  950.00
FURNITURE,SIDEBOARD CIRCA 1790,ENGLISH INLAID SERPENTINE
   MAHOGANY.......................................................2,800.00
FURNITURE,SIDEBOARD CIRCA 1790,ENGLISH........................  950.00
FURNITURE,SIDEBOARD CIRCA 1810,REGENCY........................1,095.00
FURNITURE,SIDEBOARD,ENGLISH,BROWN MAHOGANY WITH SATIN WOOD
   INLAY..........................................................1,400.00
FURNITURE,SIDEBOARD,ENGLISH SHERATON,7 FEET X 32 IN. X 36
   IN.............................................................2,850.00
FURNITURE,SIDEBOARD FROM SAILING SHIP,MAHOGANY & PINE,3
   DRAWERS.......................................................  850.00
FURNITURE,SIDEBOARD,ORNATE VICTORIAN..........................  160.00
FURNITURE,SIDEBOARD,PINE,CIRCA 1820-40,DOVETAILED DRAWERS &
   DOORS.........................................................   99.00
FURNITURE,SIDEBOARD,SHERATON MAHOGANY,6 FEET,SATINWOOD INLAY  950.00
FURNITURE,SIDEBOARD,TIGER-VENEERED MAPLE
   BREAKFRONT,MASSACHUSETTS......................................1,725.00
FURNITURE,SIDEBOARD WITH WINE DRAWERS,MAHOGANY INLAID
   BOW-FRONT.....................................................2,500.00
FURNITURE,SINK,HIGH...........................................  145.00
FURNITURE,SINK,HIGH BACK
   125.00   TO...................................................  149.00
FURNITURE,SODA FOUNTAIN BACK BAR,LEADED STAIN
   GLASS,MIRROR,LAMPS...........................................1,500.00
FURNITURE,SOFA,2 1815 ENGLISH,BUTTONED GOLD LEATHER..........4,200.00
FURNITURE,SOFA,AMERICAN CHIPPENDALE CIRCA 1750-1780..........1,800.00
FURNITURE,SOFA,CHINESE CARVED TEAKWOOD,DRAGON ARMS...........  850.00
FURNITURE,SOFA,EMPIRE,HANDCARVING,ROSEWOOD INLAYS...........  300.00
FURNITURE,SOFA,EMPIRE MAHOGANY................................   65.00
FURNITURE,SOFA,GEORGE III,CIRCA 1810..........................  550.00
FURNITURE,SOFA,ORNATE,MOTHER OF PEARL INLAY,GOLD PAINTED
   DECOR.........................................................  150.00
FURNITURE,SOFA,VENETIAN UPHOLSTERED,18TH CENTURY.............2,500.00
FURNITURE,SOFA,WALNUT FINGER CARVED MEDALLION BACK...........  110.00
FURNITURE,SOFA,WALNUT,VICTORIAN,FINGER CARVED BACK,TAPESTRY.   65.00
FURNITURE,SPICE CHEST,8 DRAWER,...............................   15.00
FURNITURE,SPICE CHEST,QUEEN ANNE,MAHOGANY,CIRCA 1740........2,000.00
FURNITURE,SPICE CABINET,8 DRAWER,WHITE PORCELAIN KNOBS.......   28.50
FURNITURE,SPICE CABINET,MAPLE,8 DRAWERS,PORCELAIN KNOBS.....   29.00
FURNITURE,SPICE CABINET,PINE,8 DRAWER.........................   30.00
FURNITURE,SPICE CABINET,WOODEN,8 DRAWERS.....................   23.50
FURNITURE.SPICE CHEST,LIFT TOP WITH 3 COMPARTMENTS,PORCELAIN
   KNOBS.........................................................   42.00
FURNITURE,SPINNING WHEEL......................................   75.00
FURNITURE,SPOOL CABINET,2 DRAWERS.............................   29.50
FURNITURE,SPOOL CABINET,2-2 DRAWERS,BLACK WALNUT.............   17.00
FURNITURE,SPOOL CABINET,2 DRAWER,OAK,BRASS HANDLES...........   18.00
FURNITURE,SPOOL CABINET,6 DRAWER,CHESTNUT,WHITE PORCELAIN
   KNOBS.........................................................   45.00
FURNITURE,SPOOL CABINET,WALNUT,2 DRAWERS.....................   18.00
FURNITURE,SPOOL CABINET,WALNUT,4 DRAWERS,BRASS PULLS.........   58.00
FURNITURE,SPOOL CHEST,5 DRAWER,25 X 19 X 17 IN...............   22.00
FURNITURE,SPOON RACK,18TH CENTURY ENGLISH WALNUT & CHERRY...  285.00
FURNITURE,STAND,1 DRAWER MAPLE,MAHOGANY VENEER DRAWER FRONT.   32.00
FURNITURE,STAND,2 DRAWER DROP LEAF............................   49.00
FURNITURE,STAND,CHERRY HEPPLEWHITE 1-DRAWER,27 IN. HIGH.....   45.00
FURNITURE,STAND,MARBLE TOP,OVAL,WALNUT........................   69.00
FURNITURE,STAND ON PEDESTAL BASE,2 DRAWER EMPIRE.............   98.00
FURNITURE,STAND,PARLOR,OAK,BALL CLAW FEET....................   13.00
FURNITURE,STAND,TILT-TOP......................................  135.00
FURNITURE,STOOL,FIREPLACE,CHERRYWOOD,SABRE LEGS,OVERSTUFFED
```

```
TOP........................................................   30.00
FURNITURE,STOOL,MILK,4 LEGGED...............................    8.00
FURNITURE,STOOL,OVAL TRIPOD,MAHOGANY........................  295.00
FURNITURE,STOOL,PAIR REGENCY ROSEWOOD,CIRCA 1820............  495.00
FURNITURE,STOOL,WINDSOR.....................................   85.00
FURNITURE,STOVE,DEPOT.......................................   50.00
FURNITURE,STOVE,FOOT,WOOD WITH BAIL,SLIDING DOOR............   35.00
FURNITURE,STOVE,FRANKLIN TYPE,SLIDING DOORS IN FRONT,PATENT
 1860.......................................................   22.50
FURNITURE,STOVE,FRANKLIN MARKED CINDERELLA FIREPLACE,CAST
 IRON.......................................................  125.00
FURNITURE,STOVE,LIONEL......................................   27.50
FURNITURE,STOVE,POT BELLIED,27 IN. HIGH,BELLY FLANGE CANOPY.   39.00
FURNITURE,STOVE,POT BELLY,3 LEGGED,MARKED DAISY.............   50.00
FURNITURE,SWING,WALNUT......................................   35.00
FURNITURE,TABLE,5 LEG.......................................   85.00
FURNITURE,TABLE,17TH CENTURY WALNUT LIBRARY,TURNED REEDED
 LEGS.....................................................1,500.00
FURNITURE,TABLE,18TH CENTURY AMERICAN OVAL TOP MAPLE QUEEN
 ANNE TAVERN................................................  750.00
FURNITURE,TABLE,18TH CENTURY SHERATON PEMBROKE,MAHOGANY.....1,250.00
FURNITURE,TABLE,25 IN. WALNUT TOP ICE CREAM.................   25.00
FURNITURE,TABLE,BANQUET,ENGLAND CIRCA 1800,MAHOGANY.........1,395.00
FURNITURE,TABLE,BIRD CAGE TILT TOP CIRCA 1790,MAPLE & CHERRY  385.00
FURNITURE,TABLE,BLACK WALNUT DROP LEAF......................   55.00
FURNITURE,TABLE,BURNT WOOD,ROUND,30 IN. DIAMETER............   27.50
FURNITURE,TABLE,CARD,MAHOGANY LYRE BASE,29 X 17 X 36 IN.....   40.00
FURNITURE,TABLE,CHERRY DROP LEAF WITH ORIGINAL CASTERS......   45.00
FURNITURE,TABLE,CHERRY KITCHEN..............................   45.00
FURNITURE,TABLE,CHERRY SHERATON AMERICAN DROP-LEAF..........  250.00
FURNITURE,TABLE,CHINESE ROSEWOOD MINIATURE,INLAID MOTHER OF
 PEARL......................................................  125.00
FURNITURE,TABLE,CHIPPENDALE TIP ,WALNUT.....................  225.00
FURNITURE,TABLE CIRCA 1700,HEPPLEWHITE CHERRY DROP LEAF.....  250.00
FURNITURE,TABLE CIRCA 1730,DUTCH LIBRARY...................1,350.00
FURNITURE,TABLE CIRCA 1740,CHIPPENDALE GAME................1,095.00
FURNITURE,TABLE CIRCA 1740,QUEEN ANNE HANDKERCHIEF,ENGLISH
 WALNUT.....................................................  875.00
FURNITURE,TABLE CIRCA 1750,MAHOGANY ENGLISH DROP LEAF.......  525.00
FURNITURE,TABLE CIRCA 1765,TILT TOP TRIPOD MAHOGANY.........  325.00
FURNITURE,TABLE CIRCA 1780,MAHOGANY BREAKFAST..............   498.00
FURNITURE,TABLE CIRCA 1785,HEPPLEWHITE SERVING-WRITING......  695.00
FURNITURE,TABLE CIRCA 1790,COUNTRY DROP-LEAF ,PINE TOP......   98.00
FURNITURE,TABLE CIRCA 1800,GEORGIAN ARCHITECTS.............1,995.00
FURNITURE,TABLE CIRCA 1800,MAHOGANY,AMERICAN HEPPLEWHITE
 PEMBROKE...................................................   65.00
FURNITURE,TABLE CIRCA 1820,ENGLISH MAHOGANY BREAKFAST.......  425.00
FURNITURE,TABLE CIRCA 1825,BIEDERMEIER GRIFFIN CONSOLE......  895.00
FURNITURE,TABLE CIRCA 1830,FLIP TOP DINING.................   575.00
FURNITURE,TABLE,COFFEE,MAHOGANY DROP LEAF,6 LEG,INLAID WITH
 SATIN WOOD.................................................  125.00
FURNITURE,TABLE-DESK,LIBRARY,MAHOGANY CIRCA 1790,LEATHER TOP  675.00
FURNITURE,TABLE,DISHTOP,1835,CARVED PEDESTAL................  600.00
FURNITURE,TABLE,DROP LEAF,MAPLE............................   245.00
FURNITURE,TABLE,ENGLISH BREAKFAST,MAHOGANY COLOUR CIRCA 1780  900.00
FURNITURE,TABLE,ENGLISH MAHOGANY DRUM,GREEN LEATHER
 TOP,CIRCA 1810...........................................1,125.00
FURNITURE,TABLE,GEORGIAN TILT TOP,MAHOGANY.................   195.00
FURNITURE,TABLE,HANDCARVED,COMES FROM A CASTLE,CIRCA 1700...  340.00
FURNITURE,TABLE,HEPPLEWHITE CHERRY 6 LEG DROP LEAF.........   225.00
FURNITURE,TABLE,HEPPLEWHITE TIP-TOP OCTAGONAL,CHERRY.......   110.00
FURNITURE,TABLE,HUNT,MAHOGANY,7 FEET LONG.................1,450.00
FURNITURE,TABLE,ICE CREAM..................................   23.00
FURNITURE,TABLE,IRISH BACKGAMMON OF SPANISH MAHOGANY CIRCA
 1730.....................................................2,750.00
```

```
FURNITURE,TABLE,MAHOGANY 4 LEG CHIPPENDALE CIRCA 1760-80....      75.00
FURNITURE,TABLE,MAHOGANY DROP LEAF CIRCA 1780................     650.00
FURNITURE,TABLE,MAHOGANY DROP LEAF,CLUB FOOT,CIRCA 1770.....      595.00
FURNITURE,TABLE,MAHOGANY PEMBROKE,SHAPED TOP & APRON,PIERCED
  STRETCHER...................................................1,500.00
FURNITURE,TABLE,MAHOGANY,ROPE LEG SWING LEG ,29 IN. HIGH....      185.00
FURNITURE,TABLE,MAHOGANY STAINED BIRCH TOP..................       70.00
FURNITURE,TABLE,MAPLE TAPERED LEG DROP LEAF.................       40.00
FURNITURE,TABLE,MARBLE TOP
  17.50  TO.................................................      110.00
FURNITURE,TABLE,MARBLE TOP,BLACK WALNUT.....................       46.50
FURNITURE,TABLE,MARBLE TOP,CARVED ROSE,PAIR VICTORIAN CHAIRS       75.00
FURNITURE,TABLE,OCTAGONAL AUSTRIAN DINING CIRCA 1830........      750.00
FURNITURE,TABLE,OCTAGONAL TILT TOP,MAHOGANY,CIRCA 1850......      550.00
FURNITURE,TABLE,OVAL MAHOGANY PEMBROKE CIRCA 1800...........      495.00
FURNITURE,TABLE,OVAL MARBLE TOP,WALNUT BASE,3 KNOB TRIMS....       52.00
FURNITURE,TABLE,PEMBROKE,BROWN MAHOGANY.....................      250.00
FURNITURE,TABLE,PEMBROKE,MAHOGANY,CIRCA 1790,SCROLLED TOP...      400.00
FURNITURE,TABLE,PEMBROKE TYPE BIRCH DROP LEAF...............       48.00
FURNITURE,TABLE,PINE,5-FOOT HARVEST.........................      250.00
FURNITURE,TABLE,PINE DROP LEAF..............................       45.00
FURNITURE,TABLE,PINE HARVEST,48 IN. LONG....................       38.00
FURNITURE,TABLE,QUEEN ANNE DROP LEAF,MAHOGANY...............      600.00
FURNITURE,TABLE,RECTANGULAR MARBLE TOP WALNUT,ROUNDED
  CORNERS...................................................       55.00
FURNITURE,TABLE,REFECTORY,CENTER STRETCHED 3 3 DRAWERS......      750.00
FURNITURE,TABLE,REGENCY ARTISTS CIRCA 1810..................      695.00
FURNITURE,TABLE,REGENCY MAPLEWOOD LIBRARY CIRCA 1820........      995.00
FURNITURE,TABLE,REGENCY SABER LEG TEA CIRCA 1810............      650.00
FURNITURE,TABLE,REGENCY SIDE IN MAHOGANY,2 DRAWERS,53 X 24 X
  36 IN....................................................      550.00
FURNITURE,TABLE,ROUND BIEDERMEIER CIRCA 1825................      295.00
FURNITURE,TABLE,ROUND MAHOGANY TILT TOP.....................      250.00
FURNITURE,TABLE SCREEN,2 PANELS,HINGED,ORIENTAL BLACK,......       12.50
FURNITURE,TABLE,SERVING,MAHOGANY,CIRCA 1820.................      450.00
FURNITURE,TABLE,SHERATON 3 PART BANQUET,AMERICAN
  MAHOGANY,1810-15..........................................      800.00
FURNITURE,TABLE,SHERATON CHERRY BANQUET,3-PART,SPIRAL CARVED
  LEGS.....................................................2,250.00
FURNITURE,TABLE,SHERATON COMMODE CIRCA 1780.................      795.00
FURNITURE,TABLE,SHERATON MAPLE LAMP,1 DRAWER................       75.00
FURNITURE,TABLE,SIDE,CIRCA 1790,GEORGIAN WALNUT.............      495.00
FURNITURE,TABLE,SOFA,MAHOGANY,CIRCA 1810....................      795.00
FURNITURE,TABLE STANDS,PAIR CINNABAR CARVED LACQUER & WOOD..      650.00
FURNITURE,TABLE,SUPPER,MAHOGANY,CIRCA 1810..................      695.00
FURNITURE,TABLE,TAVERN,18TH CENTURY,27 IN. HIGH,1 DRAWER....      150.00
FURNITURE,TABLE,TAVERN,STRETCHER BASE.......................      500.00
FURNITURE,TABLE,TEA,CIRCA 1850,PHILADELPHIA.................      695.00
FURNITURE,TABLE,TEAKWOOD,5-SIDED,CARVED,9 IN. TOP...........       75.00
FURNITURE,TABLE,TEAKWOOD ROUND,19 IN. HIGH,CARVED,SMALL
  SHELF....................................................       55.00
FURNITURE,TABLE,TILT TOP....................................      135.00
FURNITURE,TABLE,VICTORIAN TURTLE TOP,BURLED WALNUT VENEER...       47.50
FURNITURE,TABLE,VICTORIAN WALNUT DROP LEAF EXTENSION........       32.00
FURNITURE,TABLE,VICTORIAN WALNUT MARBLE TOP.................       62.50
FURNITURE,TABLE,VICTORIAN WALNUT OVAL WHITE MARBLE-TOP
  CENTER PEDESTAL...........................................       75.00
FURNITURE,TABLE,WALNUT STRETCHER............................      350.00
FURNITURE,TABLE,WALNUT,CHERRY FINISH BARBERS,41 IN. HIGH....      195.00
FURNITURE,TABLE WITH 1 DRAWER,VICTORIAN FELT TOP
  WALNUT,29X33X20 IN........................................       48.00
FURNITURE,TABLE WITH CABRIOLE LEGS,MARBLE,VICTORIAN WALNUT
  TURTLE-TOP................................................       85.00
FURNITURE,TABLE WITH OCTAGON TOP,TILT TOP,MAPLE,CIRCA U780..      465.00
FURNITURE,TABLE WITH PEDESTAL BASE,EMPIRE MAHOGANY DROP LEAF       45.00
```

```
FURNITURE,TOOL CHEST,PINE,DOVETAILED,INSIDE STRAP
  HINGES,IRON HANDLES.....................................    18.50
FURNITURE,TOWEL RACK,WALNUT SPOOL,FLOOR TYPE...............    12.50
FURNITURE,TOWEL RACK WITH 3 ARMS,WALL.....................     4.00
FURNITURE,TOWEL ROLLER WITH SHELF ON TOP,SCROLLED EDGE.....    12.50
FURNITURE,TRIPOD,18TH CENTURY AMERICAN MAHOGANY...........    350.00
FURNITURE,TRUNK,DOME TOP..................................     13.00
FURNITURE,TRUNK,LEATHER COVERED FLAT TOPPED,BRASS STUDS,BAIL
  HANDLE..................................................    15.00
FURNITURE,TRUNK,PINE......................................    22.00
FURNITURE,TRUNK WITH BRASS LOCK & BINDING,PINE............    10.00
FURNITURE,UMBRELLA & HAT RACK,PINE........................    15.00
FURNITURE,WAGON SEAT,35 IN. LONG..........................    25.00
FURNITURE,WAGON SPRING SEAT...............................    25.00
FURNITURE,WASH STAND,CORNER...............................    65.00
FURNITURE,WASH STAND,MARBLE TOP,CHILDS,MAHOGANY,WOOD SPLASH
  BOARD...................................................    30.00
FURNITURE,WASH STAND,OAK,DRAWER,SHELF & TOWEL BAR..........    40.00
FURNITURE,WHATNOT,CHERRY FINISH,2 SHELF...................     5.00
FURNITURE,WHATNOT SEWING BOX FOR WALL,WALNUT,5 SHELVES DOWN
  EACH SIDE...............................................    15.00
FURNITURE,WHATNOT,VICTORIAN WALNUT CORNER,4 FEET HIGH.......    40.00
FURNITURE,WHATNOT,WALNUT,CARVED & FOR CORNER..............    25.00
FURNITURE,WHATNOT,WALNUT CORNER,5 SHELVES.................    42.00
FURNITURE,WHATNOT,WALNUT CORNER,58 IN. TALL ON FEET,5
  SHELVES.................................................    59.00
FURNITURE,WHATNOT WITH READING STAND CIRCA 1820,REGENCY.....   595.00
FURNITURE,WIG STAND,MAHOGANY..............................   165.00
FURNITURE,WIG STAND,WALNUT................................    75.00
FURNITURE,WINDOW SEAT CIRCA 1765,CHIPPENDALE..............   450.00
FURNITURE,WINE CABINET,OAK,HANDCARVED,2 DRAWERS,LEAD GLASS..   680.00
FURNITURE,WINE COOLER CIRCA 1820,ENGLISH HEXAGONAL BRASS
  BOUND MAHOGANY..........................................   700.00
FURNITURE,WINE COOLER,18TH CENTURY ENGLISH MAHOGANY,BLOWN
  DECANTER................................................   950.00
FURNITURE,WINE COOLER CIRCA 1810,REGENCY..................   475.00
FURNITURE,WINE COOLER,PAIR MAHOGANY,14 X 12 IN..........1,250.00
FURNITURE,WING CHAIR......................................   425.00
FURNITURE,WING CHAIR,SHERATON.............................   585.00
FURNITURE,WOOL WINDER,4 ARM AMPLE.........................     8.50
FURNITURE,WRITING BOX,SHAKER,SIDE DRAWER & INK DRAWER.......   100.00
FURNITURE,WRITING BOX,SHIP CAPTAINS PORTABLE..............    20.00
FURNITURE,WRITING TABLE,18TH CENTURY CHINESE
  CHIPPENDALE,BRASS INLAID................................   800.00
FURNITURE,WRITING TABLE,MAHOGANY,BLACK LEATHER TOP,54 X 42 X
  32 IN.................................................1,250.00
```

GALLÉ GLASS was made by the Gallé factory founded by Emile Gallé of France.
The firm made cameo glass, furniture, and other art nouveau items from 1879
to 1905.

```
GALLE 4 IN. SIGNED VASE,VIOLETS & BUDS OF PURPLE..........    85.00
GALLE 5 IN. CAMEO VASE,MOSS GREEN CUT TO AVACADO,LEAF DESIGN  120.00
GALLE 7 IN. STEMMED WINE,GREEN RIBBED,SIGNED..............    50.00
GALLE 8 IN. CAMEO VASE,SCENIC,BROWN,GREEN,PINK & BLUE.......   175.00
GALLE  10 IN. FLUTED VASE,MORNING GLORY BLOOMS.............   265.00
GALLE AMBER COVERED JAR,6 IN. TO TOP OF BLUE FINIAL,.......    25.00
GALLE BOWL,CUT BROWN PINE CONES & LEAVES ON BLUE SATINY
  BACKGROUND..............................................   110.00
GALLE BOWL,2 X 4 IN. ,RED ON FROSTED PINKISH-TAN..........    90.00
GALLE CABINET VASE,AUTUMN LEAVES,WISTERIA,PINE CONES.......    95.00
GALLE CAMEO CANDY DISH 6IN.DIA.,HONEY COLOURED............   145.00
GALLE CAMEO SIGNED VASE,FLOWER & LEAF DESIGN ON WINE COLOUR.   125.00
GALLE CARMINE CAMEO 3 IN. VASE...........................   130.00
GALLE FLORAL GREEN & PINK VASE...........................   145.00
GALLE SCENIC VASE,6 IN. TALL,4 ACID
```

```
CUTTINGS,BROWN,GREEN,BLUE................................   140.00
GALLE SCENIC VASE,PANELS PRODUCED BY TREES INCORPORATED INTO
  DESIGN.................................................   240.00
GALLE SIGNED 4 COLOUR VASE................................   225.00
GALLE SIGNED 5 IN. VASE,FOAMY WHITE OVOID WITH CARVED LEAVES   145.00
GALLE SIGNED 6 IN. VASE,CUT PURPLE FLOWERS ON
  LAVENDER,LEAVES & STEMS................................    85.00
GALLE SIGNED 8 IN. SWIRLED CYLINDER VASE ON WAFER
  BASE,ENAMELED..........................................   125.00
GALLE SIGNED 12 IN.  VASE,BLUE BACKGROUND,THISTLE SEEDS &
  BUDS..................................................   185.00
GALLE SIGNED 12 IN. RED & CLEAR CAMEO CUT OAK LEAVES VASE...   140.00
GALLE SIGNED BOWL,MULTI-COLOUR GACKGROUND,CAMEO BLUE MORNING
  GLORIES...............................................    90.00
GALLE SIGNED CAMEO CUT 7 IN. HIGH CONE SHAPED VASE..........   115.00
GALLE SIGNED CAMEO CUT TOOTHPICK HOLDER....................    75.00
GALLE SIGNED CAMEO GLASS VASE.............................    62.00
GALLE SIGNED CAMEO GLASS PAIR VASE,FROSTY WHITE WITH GOLD
  PINE CONES............................................   175.00
GALLE SIGNED CAMEO MOUNTAIN SCENIC VASE,7 IN. HIGH..........   175.00
GALLE SIGNED CAMEO PERFUME,SCENIC DESIGN IN BROWN ON ROSE...   100.00
GALLE SIGNED CAMEO SCENIC,5 IN. HIGH,4 COLOURS.............   160.00
GALLE SIGNED CAMEO VASE,5 IN. HIGH,TORTOISE SHELL WITH
  LEAVES,FLOWERS........................................   175.00
GALLE SIGNED CAMEO VASE,6 IN. TALL STICK WITH FLAT
  BASE,GREEN & PURPLE....................................    80.00
GALLE SIGNED CAMEO VASE,FRONDS OF FERNS OPENING,CARVED IN
  RED & GREEN...........................................   195.00
GALLE SIGNED CAMEO VASE,BLUE & PURPLE LEAVES ON YELLOW......   165.00
GALLE SIGNED CAMEO VASE,ORANGE-BROWN MUMS ON LIGHT ORANGE...   175.00
GALLE SIGNED CAMEO VASE,RED ON WHITE,TREES,CACTUS & BIRDS...   245.00
GALLE SIGNED CAMEO VASE,SCENIC POND,PURPLE
  FLOWERS,BLUE-GREEN WATER...............................   165.00
GALLE SIGNED COVERED POTTERY DISH.........................   250.00
GALLE SIGNED CUP & SAUCER,ENAMEL ON CRYSTAL................   120.00
GALLE SIGNED DEEP CUT ORANGE LILY PADS VASE,2 IN.
  TALL,LEAVES & STEMS....................................    65.00
GALLE SIGNED ENAMELLED VASE,15 IN. HIGH,THISTLES...........   280.00
GALLE SIGNED HANGING SHADE,CARVED,LEMON BACKGROUND.........   275.00
GALLE SIGNED INTAGLIO TOOTHPICK,COLUMBINE & LILY OF THE
  VALLEY IN GOLD........................................    85.00
GALLE SIGNED MINIATURE CAMEO VASE,ORANGE TO CLEAR,FLOWERS &
  LEAVES................................................   115.00
GALLE SIGNED MINIATURE CAMEO VASE,PURPLISH TO CLEAR,FLOWERS
  & LEAVES...............................................   115.00
GALLE SIGNED MINIATURE CAMEO VASE,PURPLE TO CLEAR,GRAPES &
  VINES.................................................   115.00
GALLE SIGNED MINIATURE PINK SATIN GROUND WITH OLIVE GREEN
  NASTURTIUMS...........................................    90.00
GALLE SIGNED PEDESTALED CAMEO VASE,CRANBERRY & MAROON LEAVES
  ON FROST..............................................   175.00
GALLE SIGNED PERFUME WITH ATOMIZER........................    85.00
GALLE SIGNED POTTERY VASE,8 IN. TALL,WHITE WITH BLUE & GOLD.   145.00
GALLE SIGNED RHINE WINE GLASS,4 IN. TALL,ENAMELED
  GLASS,GREEN...........................................    65.00
GALLE SIGNED SCENIC CAMEO COVERED PEDESTAL VASE,EGG SHAPED..   225.00
GALLE SIGNED VASE,4 COLOURS..............................   225.00
GALLE SIGNED VASE,19 IN. HIGH,PURPLE WITH WHITE
  OVERLAY,GREEN.........................................   450.00
GALLE SIGNED VASE,AMETHYST ON PINK ACID...................    85.00
GALLE SIGNED VASE,CORAL FLOWERS ON YELLOW ACID.............    75.00
GALLE SIGNED VASE,CUT GREEN ON PINK,ACID..................    70.00
GALLE SIGNED VASE,GREEN ON BLUE,PLUM COLOR FLORAL PATTERN...   102.00
GALLE SIGNED VASE,GREEN ON PINK,ACID.....................    65.00
GALLE SIGNED VASE,GREEN VINE & FLOWERS ON FROSTED PINK......   125.00
```

GALLE SIGNED VASE,GREENS WITH YELLOW IRIS...................	450.00
GALLE SIGNED VASE,PINK GROUND GREEN NASTURTIUMS.............	105.00
GALLE SIGNED VASE,POLISHED AMETHYST ON YELLOW ACID..........	80.00
GALLE SIGNED VASE,PURPLE FLOWERS............................	67.50
GALLE SIGNED VASE,RED BERRIES & LEAVES ON ORANGE ACID.......	95.00
GALLE SIGNED VASE,ROSE,AMBER & WHITE,CHERRIES & LEAVES......	95.00
GALLE SIGNED WITH STAR CAMEO VASE,13 IN. HIGH,FERNS,SHINY & DULL FINISH...	195.00
GALLE STICK VASE,13 IN. TALL,BROWN CASING ON FROSTED WHITE & YELLOW...	150.00
GALLE STICK VASE,13 IN. TALL,REDDISH-BROWN ON PINK..........	150.00
GALLE STICK VASE,18 IN. TALL,PURPLE CASING ON YELLOW........	190.00
GALLE STICK VASE,23 IN. TALL,BROWN ON GREEN,FROSTED WHITE...	225.00
GALLE VASE,5 IN. TALL,PURPLE WITH WATERLILIES & 2 BUTTERFLIES IN CAMEO.....................................	110.00
GALLE VASE,8 IN. TALL,PURPLE WITH PLANTS & GRASSHOPPER IN CAMEO..	115.00
GALLE VASE,9 IN. TALL,FUCHSIA CAMEO DESIGN,PURPLE ON FROSTED YELLOW...	125.00
GALLE VASE,10 IN. TALL,SIGNED WITH STAR,APRICOT COLOR WITH GREEN..	145.00
GALLE VASE,12 IN. TALL,ORANGE CASING ON BLUE,WATER LILIES & DRAGONFLY..	190.00
GALLE VASE,STICK NECK,GREEN & PINK FLOWERS ON SATINY BACKGROUND...	85.00

GAME PLATES are any type of plate decorated with pictures of birds, animals, or fish. The game plates usually came in sets consisting of twelve dishes and a serving platter. These game plates were most popular during the 1880's.

GAME,AMERICAN HISTORY,PARKER BROS.,......................	3.00
GAME,AUTHORS,MC LOUGHLIN.................................	1.00
GAME,BOX OF WHIST,16 TRAY SET...........................	8.00
GAME,CARD,1895,NATIONAL FINANCE.........................	12.51-
GAME,CHAUTAUQUA WORD....................................	1.00
GAME,CIGARETTE GAME,WALNUT..............................	75.00
GAME,COLUMBIAS PRESIDENTS,GRANTS PICTURE ON TOP.........	5.00
GAME,DOMINO SET MARKED 1919.............................	3.50
GAME,FLINCH DECK OF PLAYING CARDS,150,TRUNK BOX,CIRCA 1901-1913...	3.50
GAME,GEOGRAPHICAL,PARKER BROS.,SALEM....................	2.00
GAME,HAMILTON POKER.....................................	65.00
GAME,INLAID CHECKERBOARD................................	7.50
GAME PLATE, 8 IN. DIA.,2 DUCKS IN FLIGHT................	12.75
GAME PLATE ,8 IN.,WHITE WITH YELLOW,GROUSE..............	6.50
GAME PLATE,11 IN.,SCALLOPED GOLD RIM,LONG BILLED BIRD.......	30.00
GAME PLATE,BAVARIA 13 IN. DIAMETER,GOLD SCALLOPED BORDER....	35.00
GAME PLATE,BIRD,SCALLOP GOLD EDGE,CENTER STANDING BIRD......	11.00
GAME PLATE,BIRD,9 IN.,HANDPAINTED,PARROT & FLOWERS,PEACH BORDER...	12.50
GAME PLATE,BLUE,WHITE,STAG ON EDGE OF CLIFF.................	15.00
GAME PLATE,DOE WATERING,BUCK STANDING WATCH,HANDPAINTED.....	33.00
GAME PLATE,DOG HEAD PORTRAIT PLATE,9 IN....................	11.00
GAME PLATE HANGING,10 IN.,PAIR PARTRIDGE,GOLD ROCOCO EDGE...	35.00
GAME PLATE MARKED GERMANY,PAIR PHEASANTS,GREEN WITH GOLD BORDER...	12.50
GAME PLATE SIGNED R K BECK,SHORE BIRDS.....................	8.00
GAME PLATE SIGNED R K BECK,DUCK IN FLIGHT..................	8.00
GAME PLATES,SIGNED WM.BIRBECK,ONE DOZEN....................	450.00
GAME PLATTER,BIRD,HANDPAINTED & ARTIST SIGNED,DUCK IN FLIGHT	37.50
GAME,ROUND DECK OF CARDS IN BOX,DICCUS.....................	18.00
GAME,SET OF 20 JAPANESE PLAYING CARDS SHOWING FIGURES & POEMS..	5.00
GAME,SET OF DOMINOES....................................	15.00
GAS SHADE,GREEN PAINTED SCENE,PAIR,ART GLASS............	25.00
GAS SHADE,PAINTED SCENE,PAIR,ART GLASS..................	25.00

GAS SHADE,WINTER SCENE,ART GLASS,4...........................	60.00
GAUDY DUTCH CUP,OYSTER PATTERN...............................	30.00
GAUDY DUTCH MILK PITCHER.....................................	30.00
GAUDY IRONSTONE DOG MOUTH CREAMER............................	55.00
GAUDY IRONSTONE PITCHER,4 IN. TALL...........................	52.00
GAUDY IRONSTONE PITCHER,BLUE,ORANGE,GREEN MARKED MASONS IRONSTONE...	42.50
GAUDY IRONSTONE PITCHER,HELMET-SHAPED,ORIENTAL FIGURES & FOLIGAE,MARKED..	17.50
GAUDY IRONSTONE PLATE..	25.00
GAUDY IRONSTONE PLATE,ASHWORTH,10 IN.........................	7.50
GAUDY IRONSTONE PLATE,CORELLA,9 IN...........................	22.00
GAUDY IRONSTONE PLATE,FLOWERS & SCROLLS IN BLUE & ORANGE....	28.50
GAUDY IRONSTONE PLATE,MARKED MASONS PATENT IRONSTONE CHINA,ENAMEL...	7.00
GAUDY IRONSTONE PLATE,MASONS.................................	10.00
GAUDY IRONSTONE PLATE,ROSETTA,9 IN...........................	22.00
GAUDY IRONSTONE PLATE,URN PATTERN,7 IN.......................	22.50
GAUDY IRONSTONE PLATTER,EXCELSIOR,GREEN......................	38.00
GAUDY IRONSTONE PLATTER,LUSTER,CUT CORNERS...................	85.00
GAUDY IRONSTONE PLATTER,MARKED MASONS PATENT IRONSTONE CHINA,ENAMEL...	10.00
GAUDY IRONSTONE PLATTER,MORNING GLORY,GOLD,BLUE..............	75.00
GAUDY IRONSTONE SOUP PLATE MARKED MASONS,PERSIANA PATTERN...	30.00
GAUDY IRONSTONE SOUP PLATE,MASONS,8 IN. DIAMETER.............	30.00
GAUDY IRONSTONE WARMING PLATE,ROUND HOLLOW,OPENING FOR HOT WATER..	50.00
GAUDY LUSTER CREAMER...	35.00
GAUDY LUSTER STRAWBERRY PLATE,12 SIDES.......................	50.00
GAUDY LUSTER WAGON WHEEL DESIGN TEA POT......................	25.00
GAUDY MASONS IRONSTONE SIGNED OVAL CHOP PLATE................	29.00
GAUDY MASONS IRONSTONE SIGNED SAUCE BOAT.....................	29.00

GAUDY WELSH is an Imari decorated earthenware with red, blue, green, and gold decorations. It was made after 1820.

GAUDY WELSH 3 IN. PITCHER,OYSTER PATTERN.....................	28.00
GAUDY WELSH 5 IN. BOWL,OYSTER PATTERN........................	45.00
GAUDY WELSH 5 IN. CREAMER,COPPER LUSTRE TRIM.................	35.00
GAUDY WELSH 8 IN. PLATE......................................	14.00
GAUDY WELSH 10 IN. PLATE,BLACKBERRIES........................	20.00
GAUDY WELSH CUP & SAUCER.....................................	15.00
GAUDY WELSH CUP & SAUCER,SHANGHAI............................	30.00
GAUDY WELSH CUP & SAUCER,SPRIG PATTERN.......................	25.00
GAUDY WELSH CUP & SAUCER,TULIP PATTERN.......................	35.00
GAUDY WELSH DAISY & CHAIN CUP & SAUCER.......................	14.50
GAUDY WELSH GOLDEN WEDDING RING TEA SET......................	100.00
GAUDY WELSH MILK PITCHER,OYSTER PATTERN......................	28.00
GAUDY WELSH MINIATURE MUG....................................	15.00
GAUDY WELSH MUG..	7.50
GAUDY WELSH PITCHER 4 IN.,...................................	32.00
GAUDY WELSH PLATE,IRONSTONE..................................	10.00
GAUDY WELSH SOFT PASTE 2 IN. MUG,GRAPE PATTERN...............	17.50
GAUDY WELSH TEA SET,20 PIECES................................	225.00
GAUDY WELSH TULIP CUP & SAUCER...............................	22.50

GIBSON GIRL PLATES were made in the early 1900's by the Royal Doulton Pottery at Lambeth, England. There are twenty-four different plates featuring a picture of the Gibson girl by the artist Charles Dana Gibson.

GIBSON GIRL PLATE,MR.WADDLES ARRIVES LATE & FINDS HER CARD FILLED...	30.00
GIBSON GIRL,SERIES A ARTISTS PROOF,DRAWINGS..................	25.00

GILLINDER GLASS was made by the firms founded by James Gillinder and his sons in 1860. The original firm was The Franklin Flint Glass Co., then came

Gillinder and Bennet, and finally Gillinder and Sons. The firms made many patterns of pressed and cut glass until the 1930's.

GILLINDER SIGNED LADIES SHOE,FROSTED........................   10.00

GINGER JARS have wide mouths and a rounded body. It is believed that the jar originally held candied fruits and ginger and was given to friends on the Chinese New Year.

GINGER JAR,BLUE & WHITE HAWTHORNE,6 IN. HIGH.................	36.00
GIRONDELLES BRASS SET,3 PIECES,MARBLE BASE FIGURE OF WOMAN..	115.00
GLASS DOORSTOP,INDIANA CIRCA 1900,INSCRIBED ON WHITE OVER RED..	25.00
GLASS LEADED PANEL,12X20 IN...................................	12.00
GLASS ROLLING PIN,15 IN.BLUE.................................	25.00
GLASSES,GRANNY,GOLD FRAMES...................................	3.50
GOLD, SEE ALSO JEWELRY...................................	
GOLD 14K THIMBLE CARVED.....................................	17.50
GOLD,18K LADIES THIN PENCIL.................................	10.00
GOLD,18K MANS POCKET KNIFE.................................	10.00
GOLD DORE HOLDER LIQUEUR SET,7 IN. TURQUOISE BOTTLE & 6 2 IN. GLASSES...	65.00
GOLD EMBOSSED HINGED TRINKET BOX............................	8.50
GOLD ENGRAVED LADIES PEN IN CASE............................	5.00
GOLD MECHANICAL PENCIL......................................	5.50
GOLD PLATED CRUCIFIX,13 IN. HIGH............................	22.50
GOLD ROSARY BEADS,20 IN. LONG WITH GOLD CRUCIFIX............	200.00
GOLD THIMBLE 8.00 TO.....................................	17.50
GOLD VICTORIAN PENCIL,SCREW OUT.............................	8.50
GOOFUS GLASS COVERED POWDER BOWL,HIGH RELIEF,ROSES..........	10.50

GRANITEWARE is an enameled tinware that has been used in the kitchen from the late nineteenth century to the present. Earlier graniteware was green or turquoise blue, with white spatters. The later ware was gray with white spatters. Reproductions are being made in all colors.

GRANITE,BLUE COFFEE POT....................................	4.00
GRANITE BLUE SPITTOON.......................................	12.00
GRANITE COFFEE POT,11 IN. TALL,GRAY........................	3.50
GRANITE COFFEE POT,BLUE....................................	3.50
GRANITE COFFEE POT,GREY....................................	2.50
GRANITE COLLANDER,BLUE & WHITE.............................	5.00
GRANITE DOUBLE BOILER,BLUE & WHITE.........................	4.50
GRANITE GREY COFFEE POT....................................	2.50
GRANITE LADLE,GREY ON WHITE................................	3.50
GRANITE LOAF PAN,9 IN. LONG,BLUE & WHITE...................	4.50
GRANITE MOTTLED GRAY TEA STRAINER..........................	4.75
GREENTOWN, SEE ALSO PRESSED GLASS....................	
GREENTOWN AMBER CAT ON HAMPER..............................	32.50
GREENTOWN AMBER DOME RABBIT................................	36.00
GREENTOWN AUSTRIAN CLEAR MUG...............................	3.50
GREENTOWN AUSTRIAN COVERED CREAMER.........................	18.00
GREENTOWN AUSTRIAN COVERED SUGAR...........................	8.00
GREENTOWN AUSTRIAN CREAMER.................................	4.00
GREENTOWN CORD DRAPERY SALT SHAKER.........................	8.50
GREENTOWN DAISY & BUTTON HAND MITTED BOWL..................	16.50
GREENTOWN GLASS AUSTRIAN FOOTED SAUCE DISH.................	8.50
GREENTOWN GLASS DEWEY FLOWER FLANGE AMBER FRAPPE GLASS WITH LID...	30.00
GREENTOWN GLASS SQUIRREL PATTERN CLEAR WATER PITCHER.......	30.00
GREENTOWN HAIR BRUSH TRAY..................................	18.00
GREENTOWN MUG,BLUE SLAG....................................	15.00
GREENTOWN MUG,WHITE 5 IN. EMBOSSED FIGURES & GERMAN WRITING.	15.00
GREENTOWN PICKLE DISH,CORD DRAPERY.........................	7.50
GREENTOWN WINE...	4.50
GUN, SEE WEAPON.......................................	

GUNDERSEN GLASS was made at the Gundersen Pairpont Works of New Bedford, Massachusetts, from 1952 to 1957. Gundersen peachblow is especially famous.

GUNDERSON PAIRPOINT AMETHYST COMPOTE............................	20.00
GUNDERSON PEACHBLOW CANDLESTICKS,HALLMARKED,PAIR,RUFFLED TOP	160.00
GUNDERSON PEACHBLOW GOBLET,DULL FINISH.......................	150.00
GUNDERSON PEACHBLOW ROUND FOOTED BOWL,BELLTONE,RASPBERRY....	145.00
GUNDERSON PEACHBLOW VASE,FROSTED HANDLE ON EACH SIDE........	125.00
GUTTA PERCHA, SEE ALBUM, PHOTOGRAPHY...................	
HAIR ORNAMENT,GOLD LEAF OVAL SHADOW BOX......................	15.00
HAIR WREATH IN SHADOW BOX WITH WALNUT FRAME.................	30.00
HANDCUFFS MARKED PEERLESS,SPRINGFIELD DATED FEB. 12,1912....	10.00
HANDCUFFS,STEEL PAIR,PEERLESS MARKED........................	10.00
HANDCUFFS USN & P.N.P. NO KEY...............................	17.50
HAND PAINTED CYLINDER VASE DATED 1910,12 IN.................	12.00

HAND PAINTED CHINA is a category that refers to china decorated at home by housewives. Before this became a fad, factories had artists paint decorations freehand. The earlier pieces are usually not included in the classification "hand painted." The craze for china decorated at home was from 1885 to 1915. Sometimes the designs can give an indication of age—for example, roses were in vogue for several years before violets, etc.

HAND PAINTED PLATE,BAVARIAN, 9 IN. LIGHT GREEN,LARGE PANSIES	10.00
HAND PAINTED PLATE MARKED GREEN & CLAY,ENGLAND..............	6.50
HAND PAINTED PLATE SAILBOAT & LIGHTHOUSE...................	6.00

HANDEL (Philip) worked in Meriden, Connecticut, about 1885 and in New York City from about 1900 to the 1930's. His firm made art glass and other types of lamps.

HANDEL LAMP,SIGNED SHADE & BASE,14 IN.,TABLE,BRONZED BASE...	75.00
HANDEL LAMP,SIGNED,YELLOW,GLASS SHADE WITH BAND OF ORANGE,BRONZE BASE..	95.00
HANDEL SCENIC VASE SIGNED BY ARTIST J.BAILEY,MOONLIGHT SCENE	37.50
HARNESS,SINGLE DRIVING.....................................	35.00
HAT PIN HOLDER...	5.00

HATPIN HOLDERS were popular only during the period of the large hat held by the equally large hatpin. The hatpins were about three inches in length. Most of the holders date from the period from 1880 to 1910.

HATPIN HOLDER,PORCELAIN,PAINTED.............................	12.00
HAVILAND, SEE ALSO LIMOGES.................................	

HAVILAND CHINA has been made in Limoges, France, since 1846. The factory was started by the Haviland brothers of New York City. Other factories worked in the town of Limoges making a similar chinaware.

HAVILAND 46 PIECES GOLD BAND...............................	160.00
HAVILAND,50 PIECES...	100.00
HAVILAND BONE DISH...	3.50
HAVILAND BONE DISH,APPLE BLOSSOM...........................	8.50
HAVILAND BONE DISH,FLORAL..................................	3.25
HAVILAND BONE DISH,RANSOM..................................	4.00
HAVILAND BOUILLON CUP......................................	5.00
HAVILAND BOULLION CUP & SAUCER,CEYLON PATTERN,THEO.........	5.50
HAVILAND BOUILLON CUP & SAUCER,CREAM COLOUR WITH GOLD TRIM..	5.00
HAVILAND BOUILLON CUP & SAUCER,GREEN BORDER & MAROON OUTLINE	5.00
HAVILAND BOUILLON CUP & SAUCER,STAR BLANK,PINK & BLUE DECOR.	6.00
HAVILAND BOWL,CLOVER PATTERN,9 IN..........................	17.00
HAVILAND BOWL,LIMOGES,HANDPAINTED ROSES ON BLUE & WHITE,GOLD TRIM..	12.00
HAVILAND BOWL ON LOW FOOT,OCTAGON..........................	8.50
HAVILAND BOWL SIGNED ON BOTTOM TRIPLE PATE A FUE,OPEN.......	12.00
HAVILAND BOX,JEWEL,WHITE,GOLD,BALL FEET....................	5.00
HAVILAND BREAD & BUTTER PLATE,RANSOM PATTERN...............	2.50
HAVILAND BUTTER CHIPS,FLORAL...............................	2.00

```
HAVILAND BUTTER DISH,PRINCESS ,COVERED.....................    25.00
HAVILAND BUTTER PAT,4....................................     7.00
HAVILAND BUTTER PAT,FRENCH...............................     1.50
HAVILAND BUTTER PAT,SET OF 10,PORCELAIN,LIMOGES..........    18.00
HAVILAND BUTTER PAT,WHITE RANSOM.........................     2.50
HAVILAND BUTTER WITH PORCELAIN INSERT,COVERED,GOLD TRIM.....    15.00
HAVILAND CAKE PLATE,MOSS ROSE,PINK BORDER,RIBBON INSET
  HANDLES...............................................     3.75
HAVILAND CAKE PLATTER & 4 PLATES,ROSE GARLANDS,GOLD
  TRIM,THEO.............................................    12.00
HAVILAND CANDLESTICK,RANSOM PATTERN,HANDPAINTED VIOLETS.....    12.50
HAVILAND CELERY TRAY,SQUARE ENDS........................     9.00
HAVILAND CHOCOLATE CUP & SAUCER,GREEN & PINK MOTIF,GOLD.....    10.50
HAVILAND CHOCOLATE POT,CLOVER PATTERN...................    18.50
HAVILAND CHOCOLATE POT,FLOWERED.........................    20.00
HAVILAND CHOCOLATE POT WITH 5 CUPS & SAUCERS............    35.00
HAVILAND CHOCOLATE SET,HANDPAINTED,PITCHER & 4 CUPS &
  SAUCERS..............................................    75.00
HAVILAND CHOP PLATE,12 IN...............................    12.00
HAVILAND CHOP PLATE & BOWL,PORCELAIN OVEN WARE LINER,ORCHID
  & YELLOW..............................................    40.00
HAVILAND COFFEE CUP & SAUCER,GOLD.......................     7.50
HAVILAND COFFEE POT,LONG STEMMED BLUE FLOWERS,WHITE,GOLD....    45.00
HAVILAND COMPOTE IN WHITE PORCELAIN MARKED,BLUE BORDER......    25.00
HAVILAND COOKIE TRAY,FRENCH,OPEN HANDLES,GREEN & MAIZE
  FLOWERS..............................................    12.50
HAVILAND CREAM & SUGAR SET,AUTUMN LEAF..................     8.00
HAVILAND CREAMER.......................................     8.00
HAVILAND CUP & SAUCER..................................     5.00
HAVILAND CUP & SAUCER & CAKE PLATE,....................    10.00
HAVILAND CUP & SAUCER & CAKE PLATE,LIMOGES,CLUNY PATTERN....     7.00
HAVILAND CUP & SAUCER,BLUE FLOWERS.....................     8.50
HAVILAND CUP & SAUCER,FRENCH...........................     7.50
HAVILAND CUP & SAUCER,HANDPAINTED FLORAL,SET OF 10..........    75.00
HAVILAND CUP & SAUCER,LIMOGES,BLUE FLOWERS,GREEN LEAVES.....     5.00
HAVILAND CUP & SAUCER,MARKED,PRINCESS PATTERN..............    12.00
HAVILAND CUP & SAUCER,MONOCO PATTERN...................     6.50
HAVILAND CUP & SAUCER,PINK FLOWERS.....................     7.50
HAVILAND CUP & SAUCER,SET OF 4,GREEN WITH DUBONNET..........     9.50
HAVILAND CUP & SAUCER,SET OF 4,RANSOM EDGE & GOLD..........    32.50
HAVILAND CUP & SAUCER,SET OF 6,HANDPAINTED BLUE FOR GET ME
  NOTS,GOLD............................................    48.00
HAVILAND CUP,GOLD EDGE & HANDLE,GREEN BORDER WITH RED........     1.50
HAVILAND DEMI TASSE CUP & SAUCER.......................     3.00
HAVILAND DEMI-TASSE CUP & SAUCER,LIMOGES,WHITE & GOLD &
  GREEN & PINK.........................................    10.00
HAVILAND DEMI-TASSE CUP & SAUCER,SET OF 3..............    13.00
HAVILAND DEMI-TASSE CUP & SAUCER,WHITE RANSOM..........     7.50
HAVILAND DESSERT DISH,LIMOGES..........................     1.50
HAVILAND DINNER PLATE,10 IN.,FRENCH....................     4.50
HAVILAND DINNER PLATE,SET OF 8 9 IN....................    40.00
HAVILAND DINNER PLATE,GREEN BORDER & MAROON OUTLINE........     4.00
HAVILAND DINNER PLATE,GREEN WITH DUBONNET..............     5.00
HAVILAND DINNER SET OF 71 PIECES,LIMOGES...............   200.00
HAVILAND DRESSER SET,MARKED,HANDPAINTED ROSES..............    25.00
HAVILAND FRUIT DISH,FOOTED,PINK FLOWERS................    20.00
HAVILAND GAME PLATE,10 IN.,TURQUOISE GOLD BORDER...........    15.00
HAVILAND GRAVY BOAT,GREEN WITH DUBONNET................    15.00
HAVILAND GRAVY BOAT ON ATTACHED TRAY,GREEN BORDER & MAROON
  OUTLINES.............................................     7.50
HAVILAND GRAVY BOAT ON PLATTER,WHITE...................    12.00
HAVILAND GRAVY BOAT WITH ATTACHED TRAY,RANSOM PATTERN.......    12.00
HAVILAND GRAVY WITH ATTACHED TRAY,SCALLOPED EDGE...........    12.50
HAVILAND GRAVY WITH SEPARATE PLATE,GOLD ON HANDLE..........    14.00
HAVILAND HAIR RECEIVER,GOLD & WHITE....................     9.00
```

```
HAVILAND LUNCHEON PLATE,GREEN BORDER & MAROON OUTLINE.......     3.50
HAVILAND MAYONNAISE BOWL & 5 PLATES,LIMOGES 1800, MAPLE-LEAF
  SHAPE....................................................    18.50
HAVILAND MUG,OWL,FRENCH...................................     5.00
HAVILAND OYSTER PLATE,FORGET-ME-NOT PATTERN,GOLD............    12.00
HAVILAND OYSTER PLATE,PINK HONEYSUCKLE WITH GREEN
  LEAVES,MARK.............................................     6.75
HAVILAND OYSTER PLATE,UNDERSEA PLANT LIFE,FISH.............     6.00
HAVILAND PIN DISH.........................................     4.50
HAVILAND PLATE,6 IN.,OPEN SINGLE FLOEER,GREEN BLUE WITH
  BROWN CENTER............................................     1.50
HAVILAND PLATE,7 IN.,GOLD,FRANCE..........................     1.75
HAVILAND PLATE,7 IN.,LIMOGES FRANCE,PARADISE PATTERN.......     3.75
HAVILAND PLATE,7 IN.,MONOCO PATTERN.......................     3.50
HAVILAND PLATE,8 IN.,BLANK,PINK ROSE TINTED,GREEN LEAVES....     2.25
HAVILAND PLATE,8 IN.,BLUE FORGET ME NOT AROUND WITH PINK
  ROSES...................................................     6.50
HAVILAND PLATE,8 IN.,LIMOGES,SILVER PATTERN...............     3.50
HAVILAND PLATE,8 IN.,RED BORDER,SET OF 8..................    50.00
HAVILAND PLATE,8 IN.,SCALLOPED RIM,HANDPAINTED BIRD CENTER..    18.50
HAVILAND PLATE,8 IN.,SCROLL IN GOLD,YELLOW,WHITE,PINK
  FLOWERS.................................................     3.75
HAVILAND PLATE,9 IN.,BLACK,BORDER OF GREEN & ROSE FLOWERS...     1.00
HAVILAND PLATE,9 IN.,CHRYSANTHEMUM........................     5.50
HAVILAND PLATE,9 IN.,ROSE GROUPS GREEN....................     5.75
HAVILAND PLATE,10 IN......................................     4.00
HAVILAND PLATE,10 IN.,OPEN HANDLE,BLUE DESIGN,ROSE CENTER...     6.25
HAVILAND PLATE,10 IN.,ROSE DESIGN.........................     6.25
HAVILAND PLATE,BLANK,INITIAL M,HANDPAINTED STOFFER.........     3.00
HAVILAND PLATE,BREAD & BUTTER SIZE,RAMSOM.................     1.25
HAVILAND PLATE,CAKE,GREEN WITH PINK EDGE..................     7.50
HAVILAND PLATE,CEYLON PATTERN,6 IN.,THEO..................     3.00
HAVILAND PLATE,CEYLON PATTERN,7 IN.,THEO..................     3.50
HAVILAND PLATE,CEYLON PATTERN,9 IN.,THEO..................     5.00
HAVILAND PLATE,HANDPAINTED FLORAL & GOLD..................    15.00
HAVILAND PLATE,HANDPAINTED GRAPE..........................    17.50
HAVILAND PLATE,HANDPAINTED HOLLY BERRIES ON DARK BACKGROUND.     8.00
HAVILAND PLATE,HANDPAINTED LEAVES ON AQUA,MERRY CHRISTMAS
  1887...................................................     5.00
HAVILAND PLATE,HANDPAINTED VIOLETS........................     5.50
HAVILAND PLATE,OYSTER,WHITE,BLUE & RED FLOWERS.............    10.00
HAVILAND PLATE,PINK CLOVER,8 IN...........................     5.00
HAVILAND PLATE,RANSOM PATTERN,7 IN........................     3.00
HAVILAND PLATE,RANSOM PATTERN,10 IN.......................     5.00
HAVILAND PLATE,SET OF 6,7 IN.,WHITE.......................    10.00
HAVILAND PLATE,SET OF 6 7 IN.,SILVER......................    22.50
HAVILAND PLATE,SET OF 6 7 IN.,SILVER WEDDING..............    25.00
HAVILAND PLATE,SET OF 6,8 IN., & 1 13 IN. PLATE,PINK & WHITE
  ROSES...................................................    30.00
HAVILAND PLATE,SET OF 6 CHEVERNY..........................    15.00
HAVILAND PLATE,SET OF 10..................................    33.00
HAVILAND PLATE,SET OF 10 8 IN.............................    35.00
HAVILAND PLATE,SIGNED,13 IN.,GOLD SCALLOPED BANDED
  RIM,PINK,GREEN..........................................    35.00
HAVILAND PLATE,SIGNED LE ROY,10 IN.,ROSE,PINK & YELLOW......    12.50
HAVILAND PLATE,SPRAY OF PINK OPEN ROSES,WHITE,GREEN.........     2.50
HAVILAND PLATE WITH FLAT UNDERSIDE,9 IN.,CEYLON
  PATTERN,THEO............................................     2.00
HAVILAND PLATE,WHITE,FRENCH...............................     4.50
HAVILAND PLATTER,2,LIMOGES................................    15.00
HAVILAND PLATTER,8 X 11 IN.,GREEN BORDER & MAROON OUTLINES..     7.50
HAVILAND PLATTER,12 IN....................................    10.00
HAVILAND PLATTER,12 X 15 IN.,GREEN BORDER & MAROON OUTLINES.    12.50
HAVILAND PLATTER,14 IN.,FRANCE............................     7.50
HAVILAND PLATTER,14 X 9 IN................................     4.75
```

```
HAVILAND PLATTER,16 X 12 IN.,BLANK,RED LINE BORDER,.........     5.75
HAVILAND PLATTER 1850 PERIOD,WHITE,OCTAGON SHAPE,HANDPAINTED    25.00
HAVILAND PLATTER,BACON SIZE,GREEN WITH DUBONNET.............    10.00
HAVILAND PLATTER,CELERY SIZE,GREEN WITH DUBONNET............    12.50
HAVILAND PLATTER,OVAL,GOLD ON HANDLES......................    12.00
HAVILAND PLATTER,OVAL WHITE................................     1.00
HAVILAND PLATTER,RANSOM PATTERN,11 IN......................     7.50
HAVILAND PLATTER,RANSOM PATTERN,16 IN......................    12.50
HAVILAND PLATTER,TURKEY,18 IN. LONG,PURPLE FLOWERS & GREEN
   LEAVES,GOLD.............................................    18.00
HAVILAND PLATTER,WHITE WITH GOLD EDGE......................     3.75
HAVILAND PORTRAIT PLATE,PAIR HANDPAINTED,COLONIAL COUPLE
   DANCING................................................    65.00
HAVILAND RAMEKIN,SET OF 6,& SAUCER WITH HOLLY
   GARLANDS,LIMOGES.......................................    30.00
HAVILAND RAMEKINS WITH LINERS,5,ROSES,4 IN. DIAMETER.......    22.50
HAVILAND SANDWICH PLATTER,LIMOGES,HANDPAINTED PEONIES & GOLD   35.00
HAVILAND SAUCE DISH,GOLD BAND..............................     1.75
HAVILAND SAUCE DISH,GREEN BORDER & MAROON OUTLINE..........     2.00
HAVILAND SAUCE DISH,SET OF 6,PINK FLOWERS & GREEN LEAVES....   14.00
HAVILAND SAUCE,LIMOGES,BLUE,TAN,GREEN WITH GOLD BAND.......     2.00
HAVILAND SAUCE,RANSOM PATTERN..............................     2.50
HAVILAND SAUCE,SET OF 6,FRANCE.............................     5.00
HAVILAND SAUCE,SET OF 8....................................    25.00
HAVILAND SAUCER............................................     1.50
HAVILAND SAUCER,WHITE BLANK................................     1.50
HAVILAND SAUCER,WHITE,RAISED SCROLL DESIGN.................     1.50
HAVILAND SAUCER,WHITE,RANSOM EDGE..........................     1.50
HAVILAND SET OF 22 PIECES,LIMOGES FRANCE...................    35.00
HAVILAND SET OF 44 PIECES,RANSOM PATTERN...................   280.00
HAVILAND SET OF 50 PIECES,CORONET..........................   105.00
HAVILAND SET OF 89 PIECES,PINK ROSES & GREEN LEAVES........   250.00
HAVILAND SOUP BOWL.........................................     2.50
HAVILAND SOUP,GREEN BORDER & MAROON OUTLINE................     3.50
HAVILAND SOUP,RANSOM.......................................     3.50
HAVILAND SOUP,RANSOM PATTERN,7 IN..........................     3.00
HAVILAND SOUP,SET OF 8.....................................    35.00
HAVILAND SOUP TUREEN,FOOTED,COVER,PLACE FOR LADLE..........    24.50
HAVILAND SUGAR & CREAMER,AUTUMN LEAF.......................    25.00
HAVILAND TEACUP & SAUCER...................................     8.00
HAVILAND TEACUP & SAUCER,WHITE,FRANCH......................     7.50
HAVILAND TEAPOT & COVERED SUGAR,GOLDEN WEDDING.............    35.00
HAVILAND TEAPOT,SUGAR & CREAMER,LIMOGES,FLOWERS & WHEAT
   SPRAYS.................................................    18.00
HAVILAND TEAPOT,WHITE,9 IN.,DRAPED CABLE,GOLD TRIM.........    20.00
HAVILAND TOBACCO JAR,BROWN.................................    47.50
HAVILAND TUREEN & 2 COVERED VEGETABLE DISHES,MOSS ROSE.....    55.00
HAVILAND TUREEN,COVERED,HOLE IN COVER FOR LADLE............    35.00
HAVILAND TUREEN,PAIR COVERED OCTAGON SHAPED ON INTEGRAL
   PLATTER................................................    20.00
HAVILAND TURKEY PLATTER,18 IN.,FRANCE......................    11.50
HAVILAND VEGETABLE DISH,2,LIMOGES..........................    15.00
HAVILAND VEGETABLE DISH,COVERED,GOLD ON HANDLES &
   TRIM,SCALLOPED BOTTOM...................................    20.00
HAVILAND VEGETALBE DISH,COVERED,PRINCESS...................    14.50
HAVILAND VEGETABLE DISH,OVAL OPEN..........................     9.00
HAVILAND VEGETABLE DISH,ROUND COVERED,10 IN................    20.00
HAVILAND WATER PITCHER,FRONTENAC,SCALLOPED FOOT............    18.50
HAVILAND WATER PITCHER,ST.LAZARE...........................    20.00
```

HEISEY GLASS was made from 1895 to 1958 in Newark, Ohio, by A. H. Heisey and Co. Inc.

```
HEISEY & STERLING SILVER CANDY DISH,COVERED................     8.00
HEISEY ALE GLASS,COLONIAL PATTERN..........................     2.00
HEISEY BASKET..............................................    12.50
```

```
HEISEY BASKET,BUTTERFLY & FLOWERS CUT........................    28.50
HEISEY BASKET SIGNED PATENT DATE 8/17/15.....................    22.00
HEISEY BASKET,SIGNED,PINK,OCTAGON SHAPE,APPLIED HANDLE.......    12.50
HEISEY BASKET,SIGNED ,SCALLOPED TOP,CUT DAISIES.............     28.50
HEISEY BERRY BOWL,COARSE RIB.................................    10.00
HEISEY BERRY SET,COLONIAL...................................     16.00
HEISEY BERRY DISH,MARKED.....................................     1.00
HEISEY BONE DISH,MASTER,SIGNED,GREEN.........................     8.50
HEISEY BOWL,2 HANDLED OVAL...................................     6.50
HEISEY BOWL,9 IN.,FLORAL ETCHING............................     10.00
HEISEY BOWL,COLONIAL,MARKED.................................     15.00
HEISEY BOWL,CONVEX RIB,RAYED BASE............................     3.50
HEISEY BOWL,FOOTED PINK,FLUTED..............................      7.50
HEISEY BOWL,ROSE,CEREAL TYPE,MARKED.........................      4.50
HEISEY BOWL,SIGNED,8 IN.,CUT  & FLORAL & LEAVES,RAYED STAR
  BASE.......................................................    15.00
HEISEY BOWL,SIGNED,FINE RIB,12 IN.,CLEAR....................     10.00
HEISEY BOWL,SIGNED,FLARED....................................     8.50
HEISEY BOWL,SIGNED,YELLOW,DIAMOND QUILTED...................     18.00
HEISEY BREAD & BUTTER PLATE,15..............................     25.00
HEISEY BREAD TRAY,ROMAN KEY PATTERN.........................     12.00
HEISEY BUFFET SET,3 PIECE,CUT PRISMS........................     40.00
HEISEY BUTTER,MARKED,FLUTE PATTERN,COVERED..................     15.00
HEISEY BUTTER PAT,PAIR,MARKED...............................      4.75
HEISEY CAKE PLATE,15 IN.,CLEAR,MOLDED LIKE FLOWER DESIGN IN
  GLASS......................................................    13.50
HEISEY CAKE STAND,COTTAGE PATTERN...........................     10.00
HEISEY CANDLE HOLDER,SAUCER TYPE,RING HANDLE,SIGNED.........      6.50
HEISEY CANDLES,PAIR,SIGNED,CORNUCOPIA.......................      7.50
HEISEY CANDLESTAND,LOCKET ON CHAIN..........................     22.50
HEISEY CANDLESTICK FOR 2 CANDLES,SIGNED,HARP SHAPE..........     14.00
HEISEY CANDLESTICKS,PAIR,SIGNED, 9 IN. HIGH,6-SIDED BASE.....    18.00
HEISEY CANDLESTICK,PAIR,SIGNED,HEXAGON BASE.................     20.00
HEISEY CANDY COMPOTE,COVERED,SIGNED,GOLD & ENAMELED DECOR...    18.50
HEISEY CANDY COMPOTE,MARKED,7 IN.,PEDESTAL,PINK WITH PINE
  CONE.......................................................    30.00
HEISEY CANDY COMPOTE,SIGNED,COVERED,ETCHED..................     13.50
HEISEY CANDY DISH,COARSE RIB................................      6.00
HEISEY CANDY DISH ON STAND..................................      6.00
HEISEY CANDY DISH,RIBBED PATTERN,COVERED,3 SECTIONED,7 IN.
  DIAMETER...................................................     15.00
HEISEY CANDY DISH,SIGNED,GREEN,RIBBED & ETCHED,OPEN HANDLES.     7.50
HEISEY CANDY DISH,SIGNED,COVERED............................     12.00
HEISEY CELERY,LOCKET ON CHAIN...............................     11.50
HEISEY CELERY,SIGNED,COLONIAL PATTERN.......................      7.00
HEISEY CELERY,SIGNED,PANELLED BEVELED BLOCK.................      7.00
HEISEY CHAMPAGNE,SET OF 4,SIGNED,FLUTE PATTERN..............      9.00
HEISEY CHEESE & CRACKER DISH,SIGNED,PANELLED,GOLD BORDER....     15.00
HEISEY CHEESE & CRACKER SET WITH GOLD BAND,SIGNED,FLAMINGO..     20.00
HEISEY CHILDS SET...........................................     10.00
HEISEY CIGARETTE SET,SIGNED,TUBE HOLDER & 4 ASHTRAYS........     10.00
HEISEY COASTER,ROMAN KEY,SET OF 6...........................     10.00
HEISEY COMPOTE..............................................     10.00
HEISEY COMPOTE,BEADED BAND..................................     10.00
HEISEY COMPOTE,LOW,SIGNED,5 IN..............................      3.50
HEISEY COMPOTE,ORCHID,ETCHED................................     12.00
HEISEY COMPOTE,PAIR,SIGNED,ETCHED FLORALS...................     14.00
HEISEY COMPOTE,ROMAN KEY,OPEN...............................     12.50
HEISEY COMPOTE,SIGNED,6 IN. HIGH............................      8.00
HEISEY COMPOTE,SIGNED,PINK..................................     25.00
HEISEY CREAM PITCHER & SPOON HOLDER,CLEAR,MINIATURE,MARKED..     7.00
HEISEY CREAM PITCHER & SPOON HOLDER,GOLD ON CREAM,MARKED....    10.00
HEISEY CREAM PITCHER,SIGNED,RIBBED DESIGN WITH SILVER EDGE &
  BASE.......................................................     7.50
HEISEY CREAMER & SUGAR,.....................................      9.50
```

HEISEY CREAMER & SUGAR,GREEN...............................	10.00
HEISEY CREAMER & SUGAR IN FLUTED PATTERN,MARKED..............	8.00
HEISEY CREAMER,GREEN,EXPANDED DIAMOND PATTERN................	14.50
HEISEY CREAMER,GREEN,MARKED.................................	7.00
HEISEY CREAMER,MARKED......................................	6.50
HEISEY CREAMER,SIGNED,SQUARE SHAPED,YELLOW..................	7.00
HEISEY CREAMER & SUGAR,SIGNED..............................	22.50
HEISEY CREAMER,PEDESTAL,5 IN.,PLEATED PANELS...............	2.50
HEISEY CREAMER,SIGNED,CLEAR,8 PANELLED.....................	7.25
HEISEY CREAMER & SUGAR,SIGNED,ETCHED.......................	12.00
HEISEY CREAMER & SUGAR,SIGNED,HONEY COLOURED,THUMBPRINT WITH BAND...	20.00
HEISEY CRUET,CLEAR,8-SIDED,CUT EDGES,PYRAMID SHAPE..........	10.00
HEISEY CRUET,MARKED..	11.00
HEISEY CUP,SOUVENIR,CUSTARD GLASS,PLYMOUTH.................	10.00
HEISEY DESSERT DISH,SET OF 8,PANELLED,FOOTED...............	28.00
HEISEY DESSERT ON PEDESTAL,SET OF 2,MARKED,FLUTED..........	5.00
HEISEY DESSERT PLATE,MARKED,6 IN.,SET OF 6,PANELLED & SCALLOPED..	20.00
HEISEY DESSERT,STEMMED,COLONIAL PATTERN,SET OF 4...........	14.00
HEISEY DISH,DIVIDED,MARKED,STERLING SILVER BASE,LEAF ETCHED DESIGN...	12.00
HEISEY DISH,GREEN,6 IN.,2 HANDLED.........................	5.00
HEISEY DISH,OBLONG,MARKED.................................	7.50
HEISEY DISH,OVAL,AMBER,9 IN.,MARKED.......................	7.00
HEISEY DISH,OVAL,CLEAR GLASS..............................	5.50
HEISEY DISH,SILVER OVERLAY,7 IN.,LOOPED DESIGN.............	7.50
HEISEY FINGER BOWL,SET OF 14,MARKED.......................	35.00
HEISEY FRUIT DISH,COLONIAL PATTERN........................	3.00
HEISEY GLASS,SET OF 6,SIGNED..............................	25.00
HEISEY GOBLET,COLONIAL....................................	4.50
HEISEY GOBLET,FLUTE 5.50 TO......................................	7.00
HEISEY GOBLET,FLUTE,7 IN..................................	4.00
HEISEY GOBLET,HONEYCOMB...................................	5.00
HEISEY GOBLET,LADYS,5 IN..................................	2.00
HEISEY GOBLET,MARKED,COLONIAL.............................	3.00
HEISEY GOBLET,SIGNED,SET OF 12,WATER......................	36.00
HEISEY GRAVY BOAT,GREEN,MARKED,EXPANDED DIAMOND PATTERN.....	9.50
HEISEY HAIR RECEIVER & POWDER JAR,SIGNED,PRESSED CUT PINWHEEL PATTERN..	37.50
HEISEY HAIR RECEIVER,MARKED & DATED,MOTHER OF PEARL LID.....	16.50
HEISEY HAIR RECEIVER,SIGNED,SILVER TOP,STRAWBERRY,DIAMOND & FAN PATTERN..	9.50
HEISEY ICE BUCKET,FLAMINGO COLOURED,METAL HANDLE & TONGS....	10.00
HEISEY ICE BUCKET,MARKED,METAL HANDLE,FLUTED..............	10.00
HEISEY ICE BUCKET,RIBBED PATTERN,4 IN. HIGH...............	15.00
HEISEY ICE BUCKET,ROSE COLOURED,HAMMERED METAL HANDLE,SIGNED	20.00
HEISEY ICE CREAM BOAT,SMALL PEDESTAL TYPE.................	6.50
HEISEY INKWELL,SIGNED,SILVER,H INSERT,4 BALL FEET..........	8.50
HEISEY JAM JAR,COVERED,GLASS SPOON........................	15.00
HEISEY JAR,COVERED,PANELLED...............................	12.00
HEISEY JAR,COVERED,SILVER OVERLAY CUT,FOOTED..............	27.00
HEISEY JELLY,SIGNED,ALEXANDRITE,PEDESTALED................	18.00
HEISEY JUICE GLASS,PURPLE.................................	15.00
HEISEY LUNCHEON PLATE,FLAMINGO COLOURED,6 IN..............	25.00
HEISEY MAYONNAISE SET,3 PIECE,CUT & ETCHED................	8.00
HEISEY MILK PITCHER.......................................	12.00
HEISEY MUSTARD JAR,COVERED................................	8.00
HEISEY MUSTARD,PINK,LID,PLACE FOR SPOON...................	10.50
HEISEY NAPPY..	6.00
HEISEY NAPPY,SIGNED.......................................	4.50
HEISEY NUT BOWL,4 IN......................................	5.00
HEISEY NUT DISH,SIGNED....................................	6.50
HEISEY PAPERWEIGHT,PIGEON.................................	20.00

```
HEISEY PARFAIT GLASS...................................  5.50
HEISEY PERFUME BOTTLE,MARKED,BULBOUS...................  10.00
HEISEY PERFUME,PAIR....................................  5.00
HEISEY PICKLE DISH.....................................  5.00
HEISEY PICKLE DISH,SIGNED,CLEAR........................  6.50
HEISEY PITCHER.........................................  8.50
HEISEY PITCHER,COLONIAL................................  25.00
HEISEY PLATE,8 IN......................................  4.00
HEISEY PLATE,10 IN. DIAMETER,MARKED....................  10.00
HEISEY PLATE,10 I5.,ROUND,MARKED.......................  6.50
HEISEY PLATE,11 IN.....................................  22.00
HEISEY PLATE,DIAMOND MARKED,PEACH COLOURED GLASS.......  18.00
HEISEY PLATE,GREEN.....................................  2.00
HEISEY PLATE ON STANDARD,TIDBIT,MARKED,SILVER OVERLAY,9 IN..  12.00
HEISEY PLATE,MARKED,PINK GLASS,8 SIDED,9 IN. AT WIDEST POINT  4.75
HEISEY PLATE,MARKED,ROSE,SET OF 6......................  30.00
HEISEY PLATE,MARKED,RAISED BORDERS,GOLD EMBOSSED RIM....  9.50
HEISEY PLATE,MARKED,SAHARE.............................  3.50
HEISEY PLATE,PINK......................................  2.00
HEISEY PLATE,SET OF 6,ROSE-COLOURED,7 IN...............  20.00
HEISEY PLATE,SIGNED,7 IN.,RAYED BASE...................  3.25
HEISEY PLATE,SIGNED,COLONIAL PATTERN,9 IN.,............  6.50
HEISEY PLATE,SIGNED,PINK,SET OF 8......................  30.00
HEISEY PLATE,STAR-CUT,4 IN. DIAMETER...................  1.00
HEISEY PLATES,8, FLAMINGO PINK.........................  3.50
HEISEY POWDER JAR,SIGNED,JUMBO,6 IN.,DOMED COVER.......  14.00
HEISEY PUNCH BOWL & 8 CUPS.............................  37.50
HEISEY PUNCH BOWL & 18 CUPS,BLOCK PATTERN,SIGNED.......  85.00
HEISEY PUNCH BOWL & PEDESTAL,SIGNED,COLONIAL PATTERN...  55.00
HEISEY PUNCH BOWL ,2 PIECE WITH 16 CUPS &
  LADLE,SIGNED,COLONIAL................................ 125.00
HEISEY PUNCH BOWL ON BASE & 6 CUPS,SIGNED,CLEAR........  65.00
HEISEY PUNCH BOWL ON STANDARD,12 PUNCH CUPS MARKED.....  90.00
HEISEY PUNCH BOWL,SIGNED,COLONIAL PATTERN..............  35.00
HEISEY,PUNCH CUP,COLONIAL PATTERN,SIGNED,8.............  24.00
HEISEY PUNCH CUP,MARKED................................  2.25
HEISEY PUNCH CUP,SET OF 12,SIGNED,CLEAR,SUNBURST BOTTOMS...  35.00
HEISEY RELISH,12 IN.,OVAL,RIBBED SIDES.................  20.00
HEISEY RELISH DISH,FANCY LOOPS.........................  4.00
HEISEY RELISH DISH,TRIANGLE,RIBBED,CLEAR GLASS,3 OPEN
  HANDLES..............................................  6.50
HEISEY RELISH,SIGNED...................................  3.50
HEISEY RELISH,SIGNED,CLEAR,VEIN-RIBBED,13 IN.,LEAF FORM.....  8.00
HEISEY SALT & PEPPER,PANELLED,STERLING TOPS............  8.00
HEISEY SALT & PEPPER SUGAR SHELLS......................  2.50
HEISEY SALT DIP,MARKED,GREEN,8-SIDED...................  6.50
HEISEY SALT DIP,MARKED,PINK,FOOTED,COLONIAL,TUB SHAPE..  5.50
HEISEY SALT DIP,MARKED,PINK,RIDGED ,TUB SHAPE,STAR CUT
  BOTTOM...............................................  5.50
HEISEY SALT DIP,SET OF 6,ROUND SAWTOOTH................  14.50
HEISEY SALT,OPEN,CUT BASE..............................  15.00
HEISEY SAUCE,5 IN.,MARKED..............................  1.50
HEISEY SAUCE BOAT,MARKED,PINK,LATTICE & FLOWERS........  9.00
HEISEY SAUCE DISH ON PLATE,SIGNED,CLEAR,COMET PATTERN..  7.50
HEISEY SAUCE DISHES MARKED PAT,10,LOOPS & STAR IN BASE.  15.00
HEISEY SAUCE LADLE,SIGNED,CLEAR........................  4.00
HEISEY SAUCE,MOONGLEAM.................................  20.00
HEISEY SAUCE,SET OF 4,MARKED...........................  12.00
HEISEY SAUCES,SIGNED,SET OF 6,COLONIAL.................  20.00
HEISEY SET,23 PIECES,SIGNED............................  48.00
HEISEY SHERBET,FLUTE...................................  3.00
HEISEY SHERBET.........................................  3.50
HEISEY SHERBET,SIGNED,FOOTED,GREEK KEY.................  3.00
HEISEY SHERBERT,STEMMED,COLONIAL PATTERN...............  2.00
HEISEY SPOONER.........................................  8.00
```

HEISEY SPOONER,FANCY LOOPS.. 5.50
HEISEY SPOONER,MARKED,COLONIAL PATTERN,SCALLOPED TOP......... 8.00
HEISEY SPOONER,PANELLED,1908..................................... 10.00
HEISEY SUGAR,2 HANDLES,SIGNED.................................... 4.50
HEISEY SUGAR & CREAMER,HANDLED.................................. 4.00
HEISEY SUGAR & CREAMER,MARKED,4-SIDED WITH SQUARE HANDLES... 9.50
HEISEY SUGAR & CREAMER,MARKED,SILVER OVERLAY................ 12.00
HEISEY SUGAR & CREAMER,PINK..................................... 6.00
HEISEY SUGAR & CREAMER,SIGNED,CLEAR............................ 15.00
HEISEY SUGAR & CREAMER,SIGNED,CLEAR WITH SILVER OVERLAY..... 14.50
HEISEY SUGAR & CREAMER,SIGNED,GREEN............................ 22.00
HEISEY SUGAR & CREAMER,WAFFLE PATTERN,OPEN.................... 7.50
HEISEY SUGAR BOWL,CUSTARD,PINK ROSE DECOR..................... 42.50
HEISEY SUGAR HOLDER,CUBE.. 5.00
HEISEY SYRUP JUG,MARKED,METAL TOP.............................. 8.00
HEISEY SYRUP PITCHER,CLEAR GLASS,APPLIED HANDLE.............. 8.50
HEISEY TOOTHPICK.. 4.75
HEISEY TOOTHPICK HOLDER,MARKED.................................. 5.00
HEISEY TOOTHPICK HOLDER,MARKED,CUSTARD GLASS................. 12.00
HEISEY TOOTHPICK,SIGNED... 8.00
HEISEY TOOTHPICK,SIGNED,CUSTARD GLASS,SOUVENIR.............. 8.00
HEISEY TUMBLER,CLEAR,BLOCK PATTERN............................. 2.35
HEISEY TUMBLER,CUSTARD,DUBUQUE,LA. & LOUISE 1908............ 12.50
HEISEY TUMBLER,CUSTARD GLASS,RING BAND........................ 22.50
HEISEY TUMBLER,GOLD TOP... 3.00
HEISEY TUMBLER,HONEYCOMB.. 5.00
HEISEY TUMBLER,MARKED,PRINCE OF WALES PLUMES.................. 10.00
HEISEY TUMBLER,SET OF 4,ROMAN KEY.............................. 15.00
HEISEY TUMBLER,SIGNED,CUSTARD,ROSE DECORATION................ 16.00
HEISEY TUMBLER WITH GOLD TRIM................................... 4.00
HEISEY VASE,8 IN.. 8.50
HEISEY VASE 8IN. FLARED TOP..................................... 16.00
HEISEY VASE,PINK,MARKED... 8.50
HEISEY VASE,STARS & STRIPES,9 IN............................... 10.00
HEISEY WATER GLASS,SIGNED,COLONIAL PATTERN WITH ROUND BASE.. 3.00
HEISEY WATER PITCHER.. 10.00
HEISEY WATER PITCHER,COLONIAL................................... 16.00
HEISEY WATER PITCHER,MARKED,COLONIAL........................... 15.00
HEISEY WATER PITCHER,SIGNED..................................... 15.00
HEISEY WATER SET,7 PIECES,YELLOW,SANDWICH PATTERN,MARKED.... 75.00
HEISEY WINE GLASS,SIGNED,NARROW RIB............................ 3.00
HEISEY WINE,PANEL... 4.00
HEISEY WINE,SET OF 8... 20.00

HEREND, HUNGARY, had a porcelain factory that was founded in 1839, and it has continued working into the twentieth century. The firm was directed by Moritz Fischer, and the wares are sometimes called Fischer china.
HEREND HUNGARY PRESERVE DISH WITH APPLIED HANDLE............ 30.00

HIGBEE GLASS was made by the J. B. Higbee Company of Bridgeville, Pennsylvania, about 1900.
HIGBEE MARKED FOOTED COMPOTE,TURNING AMETHYST............... 6.00
HIGBEE PAIR CRYSTAL CANDLESTICKS............................. 12.50
HIGBEE SIGNED WITH BEE CAKE PLATE WITH 2 HANDLES............ 8.50

HOBNAIL GLASS is a pattern of pressed glass with "bumps" in an allover pattern. Dozens of hobnail patterns and variants have been made. Reproductions of many types of hobnail glass can be found.
HOBNAIL BARBER BOTTLE,BLUE,7 IN.,RINGED NECK,BLOWN.......... 19.00
HOBNAIL BARBER BOTTLE WITH MILK GLASS STOPPER,BLUISH
  WHITE,IRIDESCENT... 5.00
HOBNAIL BARBER BOTTLES,PAIR,BLUE............................. 35.00
HOBNAIL BASKET,CLEAR APPLIED THORN HANDLE................... 49.50
HOBNAIL BASKET,RUBY OPALESCENT,7 IN.,CLEAR HANDLE.......... 9.00
HOBNAIL BERRY BOWL,POINTED TOP.............................. 15.00

```
HOBNAIL  BOWL,8  IN.,POINTED  EDGE.............................    15.00
HOBNAIL  BOWL  &  2  PLATTERS.................................    32.00
HOBNAIL  BUTTER  &  SPOONER,FROSTED,RUFFLED  EDGE,COVERED.......    25.00
HOBNAIL  CELERY,OPALESCENT....................................    20.00
HOBNAIL  CELERY  VASE,FAN  TOP................................    15.00
HOBNAIL  CREAMER,BLUE.........................................    16.00
HOBNAIL  CREAMER,CLEAR  GLASS.................................     7.00
HOBNAIL  CRUET,CLEAR,PRESSED  GLASS...........................    17.50
HOBNAIL  JUICE  GLASS.........................................     1.00
HOBNAIL  LAMP,OIL.............................................     3.00
HOBNAIL  MUG
  5.50   TO....................................................     7.50
HOBNAIL  MUG  WITH  HANDLE,BLUE...............................    12.50
HOBNAIL  MUG  WITH  ROPE  HANDLE,GREEN........................    16.00
HOBNAIL  MUSTARD  POT,BLUE,PIERCED  LID.......................    10.00
HOBNAIL  PLATE,BLUE,6  IN.....................................    12.50
HOBNAIL  PLATE,ENGLISH,THUMBPRINT,7  IN.......................     7.50
HOBNAIL  PLATE,ENGLISH,THUMBPRINT,9  IN.......................     7.50
HOBNAIL  ROSE  BOWL,SWIRL.....................................    35.00
HOBNAIL  SALT  &  PEPPER,PAIR,CLEAR
  6.00   TO....................................................    10.00
HOBNAIL  SALT  &  PEPPER  SHAKERS  IN  GLASS  HOLDER,POINTED,CLEAR.  16.50
HOBNAIL  SALT  &  PEPPER  SHAKERS,PAIR,OPALESCENT,BRASS  TOPS....    12.50
HOBNAIL  SALT  DISH,SET  OF  6,PEDESTALED,ENGLISH.............    12.00
HOBNAIL  SALT,MASTER,BABY  CARRIAGE,VASELINE  GLASS...........    12.00
HOBNAIL  SAUCE  DISH,BLUE  FROSTED,SQUARE.....................     8.50
HOBNAIL  SAUCE  DISH,FAN  TOP.................................     5.00
HOBNAIL  SAUCE,POINTED  TOP...................................     6.00
HOBNAIL  SHOE,YELLOW  OPALESCENT..............................     6.00
HOBNAIL  SPITTOON,SODA  GOLD  MARIGOLD........................    22.00
HOBNAIL  SPOONER,5  SIDED  RIM................................   135.00
HOBNAIL  SPOONER,BLUE  OPALESCENT,SQUARE,FOOTED...............    20.00
HOBNAIL  SPOONER,HAT,GREEN  OPALESCENT........................    15.00
HOBNAIL  SYRUP  WITH  PATENT  DATED  TOP,SMOKEY  OPALESCENT.......    37.50
HOBNAIL  TOOTHPICK,CLEAR,AMBER  BAND..........................    21.00
HOBNAIL  TOOTHPICK,OPALESCENT,FOOTED..........................     9.75
HOBNAIL  TRAY,FLATTENED,11  IN.  DIAMETER.....................    10.00
HOBNAIL  TUMBLER,BLUE  OPALESCENT,POLISHED  PONTIL............    40.00
HOBNAIL  TUMBLER,BLUE,POINTED.................................    10.00
HOBNAIL  TUMBLER,BLUE  OPALESCENT.............................    17.50
HOBNAIL  TUMBLER,OPALESCENT
 12.00   TO....................................................    20.00
HOBNAIL  VASES,PAIR,LAVENDER..................................    17.50
HOBNAIL  WASTE  BOWL..........................................     8.50
HOBNAIL  WATER  PITCHER  &  6  TUMBLERS,BLUE,FROSTED..........    65.00
HOBNAIL  WATER  PITCHER.......................................    15.00
HOBNAIL  WATER  PITCHER,BAND  PATTERN.........................    14.00
HOBNAIL  WATER  PITCHERS,PAIR,YELLOW,ENGLISH..................    17.50
HOBNAIL  WATER  SET  WITH  TRAY,BLUE  POINTED,THUMBPRINT  BASE....    95.00
HOBNAIL  WATER  TRAY,AMBER,ROUND..............................    18.00
```

HOLLY AMBER or golden agate glass was made by the Indiana Tumbler and Goblet Company from January 1, 1903, to June 13, 1903. It is a pressed glass pattern featuring holly leaves in the amber shaded glass.

```
HOLLY  AMBER  BERRY  BOWL.....................................    30.00
HOLLY  AMBER  PATTERN  TOOTHPICK  HOLDER......................    35.00
HOLLY  AMBER  RELISH  DISH....................................   150.00
HOLLY  AMBER  SAUCE..........................................   115.00
HOLLY  AMBER  TOOTHPICK......................................   325.00
HOLLY  AMBER  TUMBLER........................................   175.00
HORSE  COLLAR  LEATHER........................................     4.50
HORSE  DRAWN  WAGON  BY  STUDEBAKER,DEPOT  TO  HOTEL  WAGON,GOOD
  ORIG.  COND.............................................1,500.00
HULL  POTTERY,CORNUCOPIA,PINK/BLUE  FLORAL  CREAM,7IN.  H........     6.00
HULL  POTTERY  DOUBLE  CORNUCOPIA  PINK  &  BLUE.................     5.75
```

HULL POTTERY HANGING PLANTER,SIGNED USA,GLAZED	
,PINK,IVORY,GREEN HANDLE......................................	8.50
HULL POTTERY VASE & CREAMER...................................	6.50
HULL POTTERY VASE,ART,6 IN.,PINK & BLUE WITH YELLOW FLOWERS.	3.00
HULL POTTERY VASE,MARKED,7 IN.................................	3.75
HULL POTTERY VASE,PAIR ART,PINK WITH GREEN & YELLOW FLOWERS.	8.00
ICE CREAM MOLD, SEE PEWTER................................	
ICE SKATES, CLAMP-ON...	3.00

IMARI PATTERNS are named for the Japanese ware decorated with orange and blue stylized flowers. The design on the Japanese ware became so characteristic that the name Imari has come to mean any pattern of this type. It was copied by the European factories of the eighteenth and early nineteenth centuries.

IMARI BOWL,FOOTED,WHITE BACKGROUND WITH BIRDS,TREES &	
ROCKS,BLUE...	12.50
IMARI BOWL ON LOW BASE,GOLD TRIM..............................	50.00
IMARI BOWL,POLYCHROME,CIRCA 1840..............................	32.00
IMARI BOWL,POLYCHROME COLOUR & FLORAL,CIRCA 1840........	48.00
IMARI BOWL,RUFFLED TOP,BLUE & ORANGE PANELED,POT OF FLOWERS	
CENTER...	25.00
IMARI BRUSH HOLDER,BLUE & WHITE...............................	12.00
IMARI BRUSH HOLDER IN BLUE & WHITE CHINA......................	12.00
IMARI CHARGER PLATE,POLYCHROME DECOR BASKET CENTER...........	42.00
IMARI COVERED DISH, 4IN. DIA..................................	32.00
IMARI COVERED VEGETABLE DISH,MARKED...........................	25.00
IMARI COVERED RICE BOWL.......................................	10.00
IMARI DISH,OVAL,COLOUR WITH MYTHOLOGICAL BIRDS...............	34.00
IMARI INK WELL, PORCELAIN INSERT AND HINGED COVER.............	22.00
IMARI OIL JAR,BLUE & WHITE,WOOD STAND.........................	28.00
IMARI PLATE,8 IN..	8.00
IMARI PLATE,14 IN...	27.50
IMARI PLATE,BLUE & WHITE WITH BIRDS AT WATERS EDGE CIRCA	
1830...	40.00
IMARI PLATE,BLUE & WHITE WITH CARP IN CENTER,BROWN TRIM.....	9.00
IMARI PLATE,BLUE BASKET,RED FLOWERS CENTER,8 IN..............	15.00
IMARI PLATE,BLUE BORDER,DESIGN OF PHOENIX BIRD,TREES,........	48.00
IMARI PLATE,BLUE,PEONIES,CHERRY BLOSSOMS & BIRDS,12 IN......	20.00
IMARI PLATE,ROUND,SCALLOPED EDGE,19 IN. ACROSS,6 IN.	
DEEP,RED BORDER..	97.00
IMARI PLATE,RUST,BLUE & GREEN.................................	9.00
IMARI PLATE,SCALLOPED,BLUE SCROLLS,8 IN.......................	8.50
IMARI PLATE,SCENIC WITH FUJI,BLUE BACKGROUND,8 IN............	22.00
IMARI PLATE WITH 6 IN. BOWL SET,DOVES,8 IN...................	30.00
IMARI PLATTER,9 X 7 IN..	20.00
IMARI PLATTER,OCTAGONAL.......................................	22.50
IMARI PLATTER,OPEN EDGE.......................................	40.00
IMARI ROSE JAR & CARVED TEAK STAND............................	22.00
IMARI SALT DIP,BLUE & WHITE,STAR SHAPED WITH BLUE MUMS IN	
BOWL...	4.50
INCENSE BURNER MARKED MING DYNASTY............................	24.50

INDIAN TREE is a china pattern that was popular during the last half of the nineteenth century. It was copied from earlier patterns of English china that were very similar. The pattern includes a crooked branch of a tree and a partial land-scape with exotic flowers and leaves. It is colored green, blue, pink, and orange.

INDIAN TREE BREAD & BUTTER,COALPORT...........................	3.50
INDIAN TREE CHINA,30 PIECES...................................	85.00
INDIAN TREE CHINA JOHN MADDOCK & SONS SUGAR BOWL &	
CREAMER,BLUE...	15.00
INDIAN TREE PATTERN WOOD & SON BURSLEM SIGNED CUP............	1.00
INDIAN TREE PATTERN WOOD & SON BURSLEM SIGNED PLATE,10 IN...	4.00
INDIAN TREE PATTERN WOOD & SON BURSLEM SIGNED SAUCE DISH....	2.00
INDIAN TREE PLATES,JOHNSON BROS..............................	4.50
INDIAN TREE,PORCELAIN MARKED ENGLISH 1790 D.W.P.&	

CO.,VEGETABLE DISH.. 55.00
INKWELL AMBER CARTERS DATED 1897............................. 18.00
INKWELL,BLOWN GLASS,GROUND PONTIL MARK ON BASE,HINGED PEWTER
LID... 6.75
INKWELL,CAMEL 9 IN. SEATED WITH MAN ON BACK.................. 22.50
INKWELL,METAL CAMEL.. 9.00
INKWELL,METAL,DEMON HEAD,PEN SLOT IN EARS,FOOTED............. 15.00
INKWELL,OLIVE AMBER,COVENTRY 3-MOLD.......................... 40.00
INKWELL,PEACOCK,10 IN. LONG,MARK GDP......................... 47.50
INKWELL,PORCELAIN COVERED,TOP HAS WOMAN & CHILD,6
IN.,AUSTRIAN... 22.00
INKWELL,RESTING CAMEL IN COLOUR METAL........................ 18.00
INKWELL,UMBRELLA TYPE,AQUA................................... 12.00
INKWELL,WHITE METAL ELEPHANT HEAD,MONKEY FINIAL.............. 35.00

INSULATORS of glass or pottery have been made for use on telegraph or tele-
phone poles since 1844.
INSULATORS, A.T. & T. GREEN
.50.. 3.50
INSULATOR,AMERICAN TELEPHONE & TELEGRAPH AQUA................ 1.75
INSULATOR,AQUA GLASS TELEPHONE,HEMINGRAY..................... 1.00
INSULATOR,BENNINGTON TYPE,ELECTRIC LINE,BROWN................ 3.50
INSULATOR,BENNINGTON TYPE.................................... 4.00
INSULATOR,BLUE-GREEN,3 IN. HIGH,............................. 6.00
INSULATORS, BROOKFIELD NO. 16 GREEN.......................... 1.50
INSULATORS, CALIF.. 4.50
INSULATORS, CLEAR.. 1.50
INSULATORS, DEEP PURPLE...................................... 3.00
INSULATORS,GLASS DATED 1893,EACH............................. .50
INSULATORS, GLASS HEMINGRAY # 40 BLUE DRIPS.................. 2.50
INSULATORS, GLASS HEMINGRAY , PONY BLUE, DATED 1893.......... 2.50
INSULATORS, GLASS, WHITALL TATUM NO. 1 BABY BLUE............. 3.50
INSULATORS, GOLDEN AMBER..................................... 5.50
INSULATORS, HEMINGRAY NO. 16 MARINE BLUE..................... 3.00
INSULATOR,HEMINGRAY.. 3.00
INSULATOR,HEMINGRAY GRAY PONY................................ .50
INSULATOR,HEMINGRAY GREEN.................................... .35
INSULATOR,HEMINGRAY,PONY,BLUE DROPS DATED 1893............... 2.50
INSULATOR,HEMINGRAY SPIRAL GROOVE............................ 15.00
INSULATOR,SPIRAL GROOVE PAT.OCT.8 1907....................... 19.50
INSULATOR,STAR AQUA.. 2.50
INSULATORS, STAR GREEN OR BLUE............................... 2.00
INSULATOR,TELEPHONE GLASS AMBER.............................. 1.00
INSULATOR,TELEPHONE GLASS BLUE............................... 1.00
INSULATOR,TELEPHONE GLASS BLUE-GREEN......................... 1.00
INSULATOR,TELEPHONE GLASS CLEAR.............................. 1.00
INSULATOR,TELEPHONE,HEMINGRAY NO. 9,3........................ 1.00
INSULATOR,W.BROOKFIELD AQUA.................................. 7.50
INSULATOR,W.BROOKFIELD BLUE.................................. 10.00
INSULATOR,WGM CO.,AMETHYST................................... 7.50
INSULATOR,WHITALL TATUM NO.5................................. 2.00
INSULATORS, GREEN
.50 TO.. 2.00
INSULATORS,GLASS W.G.M.CO.,AMETHYST M
6.50 TO.. 7.50
INSULATORS, MCLAUGHLIN NO. 16 LIGHT COBALT BLUE............. 4.50
INSULATORS, NO.9... 1.50
INSULATORS, NO. 9 ASSORTED.................................. 2.00
INSULATORS, NO. 9 PONY GREEN................................ 2.50
INSULATORS, NO. 19 BLUE..................................... 3.50
INSULATORS, NO. 20 BLUE..................................... 3.00
INSULATORS, NO. 20 GREEN.................................... 2.50
INSULATORS, NO. 42 GREEN.................................... 1.75
INSULATOR,ONE STAR GREEN.................................... 4.50
INSULATORS, PINK.. 5.00

INSULATORS, S.F. PONY GREEN............................... 3.50

INVALID FEEDERS were made during the eighteenth and nineteenth centuries. The feeder is a dish having a spout or beak that made it easier for a sick person to be fed.

INVALID FEEDER,WHITE CHINA,LOW BOWL,HANDLE................... 6.00
IRON & GLASS INKWELL,LETTER RACK & PEN RACK FOR 3 PENS...... 8.75
IRON & TIN BANK SHAPE SAFE,4 IN. HIGH,COMBINATION LOCK...... 4.95
IRON,ACTRESS FIGURINE,26 IN. TALL,BOLTED PLATFORM
  STAGE,MARKED... 25.00
IRON ADJUSTABLE CHIMNEY TRAMMEL HOOK,KNOB CATCH.............. 17.50
IRON AIREDALE... 5.00
IRON ANDIRONS,CAST PAIR,FULL GARGOYLE FIGURE................ 48.00
IRON ANDIRONS,DOLPHINS...................................... 55.00
IRON ANDIRONS,GEORGE WASHINGTON ,WEIGHT 34 POUNDS........... 65.00
IRON ANDIRON,SET OF 2 FIREPLACE,CAST,CANNON BALL FINIALS.... 39.00
IRON ANDIRONS,TWO LADIES.................................... 35.00
IRON APPLE CORER & PEELER PAT 1882,CLAMPS ON TABLE.......... 6.50
IRON,APPLE PARER,1856,TURN TABLE........................... 6.00
IRON APPLE PARER,BLACK..................................... 4.50
IRON,APPLE PARER,WOOD BASED................................ 12.00
IRON,APPLE PEELER,1872-78.................................. 12.00
IRON,APPLE PEELER,1898 GOODELL............................. 7.95
IRON APPLE PEELER,CAST..................................... 10.00
IRON,APPLE PEELER,GOODELL WHITE MOUNTAIN................... 5.95
IRON APPLE PEELER,HUDSON PARER CO. 1882.................... 7.00
IRON APPLE PEELER,MECHANICAL,SARGENT & FOSTER DATED 1853.... 15.00
IRON APPLE PEELER,TABLE MODEL.............................. 4.50
IRON APPLE PEELER,TABLE MODEL DATED 1863................... 6.50
IRON ART NOUVEAU WALL PLAQUE 13 IN. ,LADY SURROUNDED BY
  FLOWERS... 17.50
IRON ASHTRAY,CAST,FRY PAN.................................. 2.00
IRON BABBIT LADLE,18 IN.................................... 12.00
IRON BEAN POTS,SET OF 6.................................... 22.00
IRON BEAR TRAP... 35.00
IRON BEAR TRAP,HAND FORGED................................. 45.00
IRON BEEHIVE STRINGHOLDER PAT.1861......................... 9.50
IRON BEEHIVE STRING HOLDER,STORE COUNTER TYPE.............. 10.00
IRON BEETLE BOOT JACK...................................... 10.00
IRON BILLIKEN BAND,CAST,WORDS GOOD LUCK BILLIKEN........... 25.00
IRON,BLACK BEETLE BOOT JACK................................ 8.00
IRON,BLACKSMITHS HAND WROUGHT 18 IN. TRIPOD HORSE SHOEING
  STAND... 12.00
IRON BLACKSMITH MADE CRADLE................................ 35.00
IRON,BLACKSMITH MADE FIRE SHOVEL........................... 2.50
IRON BLACKSMITH TONGS...................................... 5.00
IRON BOOKENDS,CAST,OLD FASHIONED GIRL REACHING UP TO DRINK.. 4.00
IRON BOOKENDS,PAIR,SHIP WITH SAILS......................... 9.50
IRON BOOKENDS WITH BUST OF COOLIDGE INSCRIBED,PAIR......... 5.75
IRON BOOTJACK,12 IN. LONG,LACY SCROLL DESIGN............... 6.75
IRON BOOTJACK,CAST,20 IN. LONG,FOR SHOES & BOOTS.......... 18.00
IRON BOOTJACK,CAST,CRICKET SHAPE.......................... 2.50
IRON BOOT JACK,NAUGHTY NELLIE
  2.00 TO... 6.00
IRON BOOTJACK OPENWORK PATTERN............................. 5.75
IRON BOOTJACK,TRY IT...................................... 9.50
IRON BOOTJACK,TRY ME...................................... 9.50
IRON BOOT SCRAPERS WITH SCROLLED EARS,18TH CENTURY,WROUGHT.. 36.00
IRON BOTTLE OPENER SHAPE OF NUDE WOMAN..................... 3.00
IRON BRACKET,CAST,4 ARM FLOWER............................. 12.50
IRON,BRANDING ,A J,SOCKET END............................. 12.50
IRON,BRANDING,B... 4.00
IRON,BRANDING,HAND-FORGED,SOCKET END OR RING END TYPE HANDLE 4.00
IRON BRANDING ,HAND FORGED,RING END TYPE HANDLE........... 4.00
IRON BRANDING,HAND FORGED,SOCKET END

```
4.00  TO...................................................  37.50
IRON,BRANDING IRON,WY LETTERS...............................  19.50
IRON BRAZIER STAND,WROUGHT..................................  75.00
IRON,BRASS & WOOD CANDELABRA,3 LIGHT........................   8.50
IRON,BRASS COLOUR SPOOL TREE,3 TIERS WITH 6 SPINDLES,4
  TURTLE FEET...............................................   8.00
IRON,BRONZED,13 X 10 IN. EMBOSSED PICTURE OF TEDDY ROOSEVELT  18.00
IRON,BULBOUS CAST TEA-KETTLE,RECESSED BASE,EMBOSSED ON
  HINGED LID................................................  18.00
IRON BULLET MOLD,DIXIE UNION CITY TENN BRAND................   7.50
IRON BULLET OR SHELL MOLD...................................   4.50
IRON BUTTONHOLE CUTTER ON WALNUT BASE.......................  12.50
IRON CABINET PIECE,SADIRON SHAPE WITH HANDLE................  20.00
IRON CAKE PAN,LAMB,CAST.....................................  12.00
IRON CAKE PAN,SPONGE,CAST,FLUTED............................   7.00
IRON CAMEL LAMP,BRASS SHADE & FRINGE, ORIG. BLACK PAINT.....   6.50
IRON CANDLE HOLDER,HAND FORGED,STICKING TOMMY,USED ON
  GLOUCESTER...............................................    7.75
IRON CANDLE SNUFFER.........................................   6.00
IRON CANDLE SNUFFERS,PAIR...................................   8.00
IRON CANDLE STICK 8 IN. HIGH,TRIPOD LEGS....................  12.00
IRON CAP FOR TOP OF HITCHING POST WITH MOVABLE RING.........  18.00
IRON CAP PISTOL,SCOUT,6 IN..................................   8.00
IRON CAP PISTOL,6 IN. 50 SHOT 1914 INVINCIBLE...............   9.00
IRON CAP PISTOL,9 IN.,BIG HORN,REPAINTED,NO GRIP INSERTS....   7.00
IRON CEILING HOOK...........................................   4.50
IRON CHAIN TYPE TRAMMEL HOOK,...............................  22.50
IRON CHARCOAL DATED 1852....................................   5.50
IRON CHARCOAL IRON..........................................  15.00
IRON CHARCOAL IRON,ITALIAN..................................  16.50
IRON CHARCOAL SMOKE STACK...................................  10.00
IRON,CHARCOAL WITH FLUTING ATTACHED,PAT.1888................   9.00
IRON,CHARCOAL WITH SIDE FLUTER PLATE MARKED ECLIPSE 1903....  12.50
IRON CHEESEMAKERS CURD CUTTER,38 IN. LONG...................  17.50
IRON CHERRY PITTER..........................................   3.50
IRON,CHERRY PITTER,DOUBLE...................................   6.50
IRON CHERRY PITTER,MT. JOY, PENNSYLVANIA,USA................   5.95
IRON,CHERRY PITTER ON LEGS,GALVANIZED,PATENT 11/7/1863......  10.00
IRON,CHERRY PITTER,SPIDER LEG...............................  25.00
IRON,CHERRY PITTER,SPIDER LEGS,DATED MAY 15, 1866...........  18.00
IRON CHILDS BANDED WOODEN WASH TUB,CLAMP ON RUBBER ROLLER
  WRINGER...................................................  20.00
IRON ,CHILDS BLACK STOVE,MARKED RIVAL,1 FRYING PAN..........  28.50
IRON CHILDS SHOE LAST,6 IN. HIGH MOUNTED ON FIGURE OF PONY..   6.50
IRON CHILDS TOY,DOUBLE POINTED SADIRON MARKED GIRDS.........   3.75
IRON CHILDS TOY TRIVET,OVAL SHAPE, SCROLL DESIGN............   3.75
IRON CIGAR 4 IN. LONG.......................................   2.75
IRON CIGAR CLIPPER,CAST,GET THE OCHO HABIT..................    .10
IRON COAL SCOOP,WOOD HANDLE,................................   5.00
IRON,COLONIAL PERIOD PRONG TYPE LONG HANDLED TRIPOD STAND...  35.00
IRON COMBINATION SAFE BANK..................................  12.50
IRON CORD BALL HOLDER,OPEN CUP HANDLE.......................   6.50
IRON CORN HUSKER WITH LEATHER...............................   3.00
IRON CORNSTICK..............................................  12.50
IRON CORNSTICK MOLD,7 STICKS,KERNELS MARKED KRUSTY KORN KOB.   5.01-
IRON CORNSTICK PAN..........................................   5.00
IRON CREAM WHIPPER ON QT.GLASS..............................   8.50
IRON CUPPED HANDS,PAINT.....................................  15.00
IRON,CURLING................................................   3.75
IRON CURTAIN TIEBACKS DATED 1871,SET OF 8,LACY ,COPPER
  PLATED...................................................   15.00
IRON DOG,FULL FIGURE OF BOSTON TERRIER,10 IN. LONG..........  11.75
IRON DOG MATCH SAFE MARKED..................................  10.00
IRON DOG,SHEPHERD,GERMAN....................................   5.00
IRON DOLLS BED..............................................  20.00
```

IRON DOOR KNOCKER....................................	10.00
IRON DOOR KNOCKER,LYRE SHAPED SIGNED KENDRICK..........	42.00
IRON DOOR LATCH,CAST,HAND FORGED,LEAF SHAPE,12 IN.,1800.....	14.00
IRON DOOR LATCH,CAST,HAND FORGED,ROUND 10 IN.,1800...........	14.00
IRON DOOR LATCH,LIMA BEAN.............................	12.50
IRON DOOR LOCK CIRCA 1800,KEY.........................	40.00
IRON DOORSTOP,BASKET OF FLOWERS.......................	6.00
IRON DOORSTOP,BROWN & WHITE BULL DOG..................	14.00
IRON DOORSTOP,BULL DOG,8 IN. LONG.....................	12.00
IRON DOORSTOP,ENGLISH SETTER,16 IN. LONG..............	12.00
IRON DOORSTOP,FROG...................................	8.50
IRON DOORSTOP FULL FIGURE OF BOSTON TERRIER,9 IN. LONG......	9.95
IRON DOORSTOP,PAIR OF SCOTTIE DOGS....................	12.50
IRON DOORSTOP,PRAIRIE SCHOONER.......................	15.00
IRON DOORSTOP,PUSSYCAT...............................	12.00
IRON DOORSTOP SHAPE FULL RIGGED CLIPPER SHIP,12 IN. LONG....	7.95
IRON DOORSTOP SHAPE LIGHTHOUSE WITH COTTAGE...........	5.75
IRON DOORSTOP,SHAPE OF HOUSE,PAINTED..................	4.50
IRON DOORSTOP,SHAPE OLD FASHION GIRL WEARING BONNET..........	3.95
IRON DOORSTOP SHAPE OLD FASHION GIRL WITH HAT & BOUQUET.....	4.95
IRON DOORSTOP SHAPE PARROT ON STUMP...................	4.95
IRON DOORSTOP,SHIP,10 X 10 IN.........................	4.50
IRON DOUBLE URN WITH OPEN WORK IN BACK MATCH HOLDER.........	12.75
IRON DRAFTING PEN INKER HOLDER WITH HIGGINS BOTTLE..........	8.00
IRON EAGLE DOOR PLAQUE...............................	135.00
IRON EAGLE FROM WHITE EAGLE OIL CO.,CAST,33 IN. HIGH........	350.00
IRON EASEL FRAME,OPENWORK SCROLL & LEAF PATTERN.............	4.75
IRON FIGURE OF LOBSTER FISHERMAN,CAST.................	12.00
IRON FILIGREE WALL MATCH SAFE........................	7.00
IRON FIREDOGS,CAST,17TH CENTURY......................	200.00
IRON FIRE ENGINE,PUMPER TYPE WITH BOILER,3 HORSES...........	35.00
IRON FIRE FRONT,MOTIF,WOMAN & ANGEL...................	45.00
IRON FIREPLACE CRANE.................................	15.00
IRON FIREPLACE CRANE,WROUGHT,15 IN. ARM..............	12.50
IRON FIREPLACE TRIVET................................	32.00
IRON FLAT BOTTOMED KETTLE,LIFT RING ON SIDE...........	9.50
IRON FLAT IRON.......................................	7.50
IRON FLATIRON,HANDMADE,OVAL HANDLE...................	6.00
IRON FLUTER,ROCKING TYPE,GENEVA BRAND 1866............	12.50
IRON ,FLUTING BRASS ROLLERS..........................	17.50
IRON FLUTING IRON,BRASS ROLLERS,CROWN,1875............	9.50
IRON FLUTING IRON WITH BASE..........................	12.00
IRON FLUTING IRON WITH IRON TONGS....................	35.00
IRON FLY,CAST,4 IN. LONG,TOP HALF HINGED FOR LIFTING,DESK	
PIECE...	2.50
IRON FOOD CHOPPER PAT.1899 SARGENT & CO...............	5.00
IRON FOOT REST,HORSE SHOE,CAST,REST YOUR FEET HERE INSCRIBED	19.50
IRON FOOT SCRAPER	
8.00 TO..	15.00
IRON FOOT SCRAPER,REMOVABLE TRAY.....................	27.50
IRON FORK,HAND WROUGHT,HEARTHSIDE,2 TINE..............	7.50
IRON FRAME EGGBEATER.................................	2.50
IRON FRAMES,PAIR,LACY................................	13.00
IRON FRYING PAN,LONG HANDLED,18TH CENTURY,RAT TAIL END	
HANDLE..	45.00
IRON GRIDDLE...	12.50
IRON GRILL,HAND WROUGHT,TWIRLING,18TH CENTURY NEW ENGLAND,3	
LEGS..	35.00
IRON,HAIR CURLING,9 IN...............................	3.25
IRON HANDCUFFS WITH CLOCKSTYLE KEY...................	15.00
IRON HANDLED ICE CREAM SCOOP.........................	5.00
IRON HAND PRINTING PRESS DATED 1888..................	16.50
IRON,HAND SCALES,WILL WEIGH 25 POUNDS................	3.50
IRON HANDLE IRON.....................................	2.50
IRON HANGING BALL STRING HOLDER......................	7.50

```
IRON HANGING FIREPLACE POT.....................................    5.00
IRON HANGING MATCH CONTAINER LIFT-UP COVER,STRIKER ON TOP...    7.75
IRON HANGING MATCH HOLDER......................................    7.75
IRON HANGING MATCH HOLDER,GARGOYLE HEAD.....................   18.00
IRON HANGING MATCH SAFE.......................................    4.75
IRON HARNESS HOOK.............................................    7.50
IRON HEARTH COOKING BAKING PAN,3 FEET.......................   10.00
IRON,HEARTH COOKING PAN,3 FEET & BAIL HANDLE................    7.50
IRON,HEARTH KETTLE STAND,4 FEET & 7 BARS....................    5.00
IRON HEARTH PEEL,18TH CENTURY,25 IN. LONG,HAND WROUGHT......   17.50
IRON HEARTH SKILLET...........................................   25.00
IRON HEARTH TOASTER,18TH CENTURY,HAND WROUGHT,WOOD HANDLE...   24.00
IRON HEARTH TONGS,18TH CENTURY,HAND WROUGHT,PENNY FEET,20
   IN. LONG....................................................   10.00
IRON HEARTH TYPE WAFER IRON...................................   45.00
IRON HIGH BUTTON SHOE,BLACK & GOLD PAINT....................   18.00
IRON HINGE,HAND WROUGHT,6 IN. TALL..........................    4.00
IRON HITCHING POST,2-MOLD,CAST,13 IN........................   65.00
IRON HITCHING POST,LOOP & TASSEL TO GO ON IRON PIPE.........   10.00
IRON HITCHING POST,TREE,4 FEET HIGH.........................  185.00
IRON HOG CATCHER..............................................    5.50
IRON HOG SCRAPER TYPE CANDLESTICK BY SHAW...................   12.50
IRON HOLDER FOR 2 SADIRONS,MARKED COLEBROOKDALE IRON
   CO.POTTSTOWN PA.............................................   12.75
IRON HORSE BIT,...............................................    3.00
IRON HORSE HEAD,CAST,PAINTED BLACK,15 POUNDS................    8.00
IRON ICE SCRAPER..............................................    2.50
IRON ICE TONG
   2.00    TO..................................................    5.00
IRON INKSTAND,2 GLASS SWIRL INKWELLS........................    8.00
IRON INKSTAND,2 SQUARE JARS,1 ROUND,PAULS SAFETY INK........   12.50
IRON INKWELL,4 FOOTED,ART NOUVEAU STAINED GLASS IN OPENINGS.   23.50
IRON INKWELL,CAST.............................................    6.00
IRON INKWELL,CRAB WITH NATURAL COLOUR & RUBY EYES,FACETED
   HINGED TOP..................................................   67.50
IRON INKWELL,PEN HOLDER TYPE,CAST,BLUE & GOLD...............   14.50
IRON KETTLE,10 QUART..........................................   12.00
IRON KETTLE WITH COVER,12 QUART.............................   10.00
IRON KETTLE WITH SPOUT,CAST.................................    5.00
IRON KEY,5 IN. LONG...........................................    9.50
IRON KEYS,6 IN.,2.............................................    5.00
IRON KEY,8 IN. LONG...........................................    9.00
IRON KEY,HANDMADE.............................................   12.00
IRON LACY SHELF BRACKETS,PAIR,7 X 5 IN......................    2.95
IRON LACY SHELF BRACKETS,PAIR,8 X 6 IN......................    2.95
IRON LACY SHELF BRACKETS,PAIR...............................    2.95
IRON LADY HOLDING 10 IN. ROUND FRAME MIRROR,CAST...........   10.50
IRON LAMB MOLD
   10.00    TO.................................................   18.00
IRON LAMB PUDDING MOLD........................................   22.50
IRON LAMP HOLDER,BAND WITH ORNATE BACK,BRASS COLOURED,CLEAR
   GLASS LAMP..................................................   12.00
IRON LANTERN..................................................    8.00
IRON LEAD MELTING POT,CAST,HAND FORGED HANDLE...............    8.00
IRON LEAD POURING LADLE,CAST,LONG HANDLE....................    6.00
IRON LEG IRONS,SLAVE,PAIR DATED 1863 WITH KEY...............   37.00
IRON LEGS,SET OF 4,CAST,15 IN...............................   14.00
IRON LEMON SQUEEZER...........................................    3.75
IRON LEMON SQUEEZER,WOOD BALL................................    2.00
IRON LETTER SLOT FOR FRONT DOOR HINGED COVER MARKED LETTERS.    3.75
IRON LOCK,ENTRANCE,CAST,PATENT 1852,RAISED HUNTING SCENE....   12.00
IRON MAIL BOX
   5.00    TO..................................................    9.50
IRON MAIL BOX PAPERHOLDER.....................................    8.50
IRON MARKED ASBESTOS WITH NICKEL HOLDER.....................    3.25
```

```
IRON MARKED MRS. POSTS SADIRON.............................   2.50
IRON MATCH HOLDER,CAST,7 IN. HIGH..........................   3.00
IRON MATCH HOLDER,CAST,FLEUR DE LIS DESIGN.................   2.50
IRON MATCH HOLDER SHAPE OF TURTLE MARKED RICHMOND STOVE CO..  8.75
IRON MATCH HOLDERS,HANGING,VINTAGE.........................   7.50
IRON MATCH STRIKER PIERCED TO HANG,CAST,NEGRO FACE.........  10.00
IRON MEAT HOOK WITH ROUND HANDLE...........................   3.00
IRON MEAT HOOK WITH WOOD...................................   4.00
IRON MEAT PRESS,MARCH 1884.................................   7.50
IRON MEAT PRESS,PAN WITH SCREW DOWN PRESSER,LABEL 1893.....  15.00
IRON MEDAL,GERMANY WORLD WAR 2 ,ENGLISH PROPAGANDA.........   5.00
IRON MORTAR & PESTLE,9 IN. TALL,5 IN. DIAMETER AT FLARING
   TOP....................................................  15.00
IRON MORTAR & PESTLE,17 POUNDS.............................  20.00
IRON MORTAR & PESTLE,CAST..................................  20.00
IRON MUD SCRAPER...........................................   6.00
IRON MUFFIN MOLD,CAST,12 HOLE,HANDLED......................   5.00
IRON MUFFIN PAN,CAST.......................................  12.50
IRON MUSKRAT TRAP..........................................   1.00
IRON NEEDLE & THREAD HOLDER,PIN CUSHION AT TOP,TURN TABLE...  21.00
IRON NORWEGIAN SUGAR-LOAF CUTTER...........................  13.50
IRON NUT CRACKER,CAST,CLAMP-ON.............................   3.00
IRON NUT CRACKER,CLAMP TYPE................................   3.00
IRON NUT CRACKER,DOGGIE,RAISE TAIL JAWS OPEN AND CRACKS NUT.  12.50
IRON NUT CRACKER,ELEPHANT SHAPED...........................  12.50
IRON NUT CRACKER MARKED THE MAY NUTCRACKER,SCREWS ON TABLE..   8.50
IRON NUT CRACKER WITH HANDLE ON WOOD BASE..................   5.00
IRON PANCAKE GRIDDLE WITH HANDLE...........................   3.75
IRON PAPERWEIGHT,FIGURE OF COLUMBUS,OBLONG BASE............  15.00
IRON PAPERWEIGHT,SETTER DOG LYING,OBLONG BASE..............  15.00
IRON PAPERWEIGHT SHAPE WORLD WAR 1 SAILORS HAT.............   4.75
IRON PAPERWEIGHT SHAPE WORLD WAR 1 SOLDIERS CAMPAIGN HAT....   4.75
IRON PEN RACK WITH GROOVES FOR 10 PENS.....................   3.75
IRON PENNY BANK,ELEPHANT ON TUB WITH STOOL.................  23.00
IRON PENNY BANK,SHAPE STANDING LION........................   9.75
IRON PICTURE FRAMES,PAIR,SQUARE,ORNATE.....................  14.00
IRON PICTURE OR MIRROR FRAME,COPPER PLATED,OVAL............  18.50
IRON PINKER,CAST,CHANDLER ROTARY,8 BLADES..................  28.00
IRON PLANT HOLDER W/BRACKET,ORIG.RED & GOLD................  14.50
IRON PLATTER,CAST,GIRL FEEDS HARNESSED HORSE BY BUILDINGS...  22.50
IRON PLUG TOBACCO CUTTER...................................   6.00
IRON PLUMBERS LADLE........................................   4.00
IRON POLICEMAN BANK........................................  17.50
IRON POP CORN SHELLER,MARKED...............................   3.95
IRON POPOVER ,BAKES 11.....................................  15.00
IRON,POT BELLIED BLACK STOVE,HAND DECORATED................  23.75
IRON POT,STEW,SIDE HANDLED,FOR HEARTH,2 QUART..............  12.50
IRON POT WITH HEART HASPED
   HANDLE,CAST,TRI-FOOTED,PENNSYLVANIA DUTCH...............  12.00
IRON POT WITH RAT TAIL HANDLE,TRI-FOOTED,CAST..............  12.00
IRON POTATO MASHER,CAST,FRAME..............................   2.00
IRON RAISIN SEEDER.........................................   6.00
IRON RAISIN SEEDER,ENTERPRISE MFG. 1895....................   6.50
IRON ROCKER,MINIATURE,CAST,OPEN SCROLL BACK,3 IN. HIGH.....   4.75
IRON RUSHLIGHT HOLDER,WROUGHT..............................  55.00
IRON S HOOK FASTENS POT TO CRANE...........................   4.00
IRON S HOOK,TWISTED SHAFT,RATTAILED........................  10.00
IRON,SADIRON...............................................   2.00
IRON SADIRON,HANDLE,ASBESTOS...............................   7.50
IRON SCISSOR CANDLE SNUFFER................................   4.00
IRON SEWING BIRD...........................................  35.00
IRON SHELF BRACKET,PAIR,CAST,5 X 7 IN......................   4.50
IRON SHELF BRACKET,PAIR CAST,1880 DESIGN OF BIRDS & LEAVES..   6.50
IRON SHELF BRACKETS........................................   3.00
IRON SHELF BRACKETS,PAIR,FANCY SCROLLS.....................   7.00
```

```
IRON SHELF BRACKETS,PAIR,FEATHER & 3 PETAL FLOWER DESIGN....      7.00
IRON SHELF BRACKETS,PAIR,PAINTED,GRAPE DESIGN...............      8.50
IRON SHOE LAST WITH 2 IRON SHOES...........................      3.00
IRON SHOE SOLE CUTTER......................................      7.50
IRON,SHOEMAKERS LAZY-SUSAN NAIL CUP........................      7.50
IRON SHOES FOR OXEN CLOVEN HOOF,PAIR.......................      2.50
IRON SITTING KITTEN........................................      4.50
IRON SKATES,PAIR...........................................      5.00
IRON SKILLET...............................................     12.50
IRON SKILLET,CAST,GOOD HEALTH..............................      2.50
IRON SLEEVE................................................      5.00
IRON SLEEVE,DETACHABLE HANDLE,MARKED GRAND UNION TEA
     CO.,PAT. 1897.........................................      3.75
IRON SLEEVE MARKED SENSIBLE,DETACHABLE HANDLE..............      2.95
IRON SNOW BIRD SHAPE OF EAGLE..............................      6.75
IRON SNOW EAGLES WITH BRACKETS,PAIR........................     20.00
IRON SOLDERING IRON,HANDMADE...............................      2.50
IRON,SPANISH AMERICAN BRANDING.............................     12.50
IRON,SPANISH HORSE RING BITS,12............................     24.00
IRON,SPANISH SPUR..........................................      1.25
IRON SPATULA,TWISTED END,WROUGHT...........................      7.50
IRON SPIDER,HAND WROUGHT,FIREPLACE.........................     25.00
IRON SPIKE CORN DRYERS.....................................      1.95
IRON SPOON,WROUGHT,ROUND BOWL,17 IN. LONG..................      6.50
IRON SPURS,PAIR HAND MADE,SPANISH..........................      8.00
IRON STAGE COACH WITH DRIVER AND TEAM OF HORSES............     30.00
IRON STATUE BIRD DOG POINTING,BROWN PAINT..................      5.00
IRON STIRRUP WITH STAR CIRCLE BASE.........................      3.00
IRON STOVE,CAST ,EAGLE,4 COVERS,PIPE 4IN...................     15.00
IRON STOVE,KITCHEN HEATER,CAST,2 LID,12 X 24 IN............     75.00
IRON STOVE LIFTER WITH COIL SPRING HANDLE,CAST.............      2.00
IRON STOVE LIFTER WITH STRAIGHT HANDLE,CAST................      1.00
IRON STOVE SHAKER & LIFTER.................................      3.50
IRON STRIKING IRON FOR FLINT,HAND WROUGHT,TWISTED..........     15.00
IRON,SWINGING CAST BRACKET WALL LAMP,MERCURY REFLECTOR......     29.00
IRON TEASPOON,5 IN.........................................     10.00
IRON TOBACCO CUTTER MARKED STAR............................     10.00
IRON TOBACCO CUTTER,SPEAR HEAD,STORE,THE F.J.SORS CO.......     11.00
IRON TOILET TISSUE HOLDER,CAST.............................      2.00
IRON TONG,LONG HANDLED BLACKSMITHS
     2.50   TO.............................................      5.50
IRON TOOTHPICK HOLDER,WOODPECKER...........................      6.00
IRON TRIVET,6 PAW FEET,STAR IN CENTER OF ROSES.............      5.50
IRON TRIVET,9 SQUARES,CIRCLE IN CENTER,16 FEET.............      1.50
IRON TRIVET,BUST OF HARRISON...............................     22.50
IRON TRIVET,CINCINNATI.....................................     12.50
IRON TRIVET,ENTERPRISE BAR.................................      2.95
IRON TRIVET,GRAPE SCROLL...................................     12.00
IRON TRIVET,HANDLED HEART WITH W...........................      3.95
IRON TRIVET,INITIAL C......................................      4.50
IRON TRIVET,HORSESHOE & EAGLE..............................     10.00
IRON TRIVET,IRREGULAR STRIPES..............................      3.00
IRON TRIVET,LETTER H.......................................      4.75
IRON TRIVET,LINCOLN DRAPE..................................     12.00
IRON TRIVET,OBLONG WAFFLE..................................      3.95
IRON TRIVET,ORDER CINCINNATI...............................     12.00
IRON TRIVET,MULE SHOE......................................      3.95
IRON TRIVET,SIMPLEX ON SLATE STAND.........................      2.95
IRON TRIVET,SPIDER WEB.....................................      2.50
IRON TRIVET,STREETER CROWN & MALTESE CROSS.................      3.75
IRON TRIVET,TREE OF LIFE...................................     12.50
IRON TRIVET,URN CENTER,....................................      6.00
IRON,TULIP WROUGHT SUFFOLK LATCH,14 IN.....................     30.00
IRON VETERINARIANS RETRACTOR...............................     17.50
IRON WAFFLE BAKER SET,CAST.................................      9.00
```

```
IRON WAFFLE IRON......................................... 15.00
IRON WAFFLE IRON,WROUGHT,HANDLED,FIREPLACE,CAST IRON BODY... 29.50
IRON WALL BILL CLIP,SPRING TYPE,PAT.1872................... 3.75
IRON WALL BRACKET FOR BIRD CAGES,LACY OPENWORK............. 2.50
IRON WALL BRACKET,SCREW IN TYPE FOR BIRD CAGES............. 2.50
IRON WALL MATCH CONTAINER,2 COMPARTMENTS.................. 8.75
IRON WALL MATCH CONTAINER,LIFT UP COVER,MARKED............. 8.75
IRON WALL MATCH CONTAINER SHAPE BARREL ON FENCE............ 7.95
IRON WALL MATCH SAFE..................................... 6.50
IRON WASH TUB WITH OLD HAND PUMP,PAINTED,4 IN. DIA......... 18.00
IRON WATER FOUNTAIN,CAST................................. 15.00
IRON,WELL PULLEY........................................ 3.00
IRON WHIP HOLDER WITH CHAIN FOR HANGING................... 6.00
IRON WIRE HAIRED TERRIER................................. 4.00
IRON WITH STAND,COLEMAN GASOLINE......................... 5.00
IRON WITH WOOD HANDLE.................................... 2.50
```

IRONSTONE CHINA was first made in 1813. It gained its greatest popularity during the mid-nineteenth century. The heavy, durable, off-white pottery was made in white or was colored with any of hundreds of patterns. Much flow blue pottery was made of ironstone. Some of the pieces had raised decorations.

```
IRONSTONE, SEE ALSO CHELSEA GRAPE.......................
IRONSTONE BONE DISH,PURPLE,VIOLET,GOLD RIM................ 1.50
IRONSTONE BONE DISH,SET OF 6,WHITE WITH PINK FLORAL....... 12.00
IRONSTONE BOWL,WHITE
 2.50 TO............................................... 4.75
IRONSTONE BOWL,WHITE,ROUND,JOHNSON BROTHERS............... 2.50
IRONSTONE BOX,MINIATURE,COVERED,WHITE.................... 5.00
IRONSTONE BUTTER CHIP,BLUE FORGETMENOT,RAISED FLORAL BORDER
 WITH GOLD............................................. 1.25
IRONSTONE BUTTER CHIP,BLUE WITH GOLD..................... 1.25
IRONSTONE BUTTER CHIP,PINK WITH GREEN FLORAL............. 3.00
IRONSTONE BUTTER PAT,ROUND,WHITE,JOHNSON BROS............ 1.00
IRONSTONE BUTTER PAT,SQUARE............................. 1.50
IRONSTONE BUTTER PAT,WHITE ROUND........................ .50
IRONSTONE BUTTER PAT,WHITE,ROUND,W.P. & CO............... .75
IRONSTONE CHAMBER & LID................................ 8.00
IRONSTONE CHAMBER POT,PINK BANDS,COVER.................. 5.00
IRONSTONE CHAMBER POT,RAISED WHITE FLORAL............... 4.00
IRONSTONE CHEESE DISH WITH PLATE,PINK & WHITE........... 9.50
IRONSTONE CHILDS PLATE,2 EMBOSSED KITTENS ON GREEN,BROWN
 EDGE................................................. 6.00
IRONSTONE CHILDS TEA SET,BUD FINALS..................... 20.00
IRONSTONE CHOCOLATE CUP,PAIR 5 SIDED.................... 6.75
IRONSTONE COMPOTE,MASONS,BROWN & CREAM,VISTA PATTERN..... 28.00
IRONSTONE COVERED VEGETABLE DISH,2 SQUARE HANDLES,J.EDWARDS
 & SONS............................................... 14.00
IRONSTONE CREAMER,COVERED SUGAR,2 CUPS &
 SAUCERS,INDEPENDENCE................................. 20.00
IRONSTONE CREAMER,MASONS,WHITE FLOWERS & DRAGONS ON RUST.... 17.50
IRONSTONE CUP & SAUCER................................. 14.50
IRONSTONE CUP & SAUCER,CHELSEA GRAPE LUSTERED,WISHBONE
 HANDLE............................................... 10.00
IRONSTONE CUP,HANDLELESS............................... 5.00
IRONSTONE CUP,HANDLELESS WITH COPPER LUSTER BAND IN & OUT... 6.75
IRONSTONE DINNER PLATE,J & G MEAKIN,WHITE,DATED......... 6.50
IRONSTONE DINNER PLATE,WHITE........................... 6.50
IRONSTONE DISH,OVAL,SIDE,WHITE,ALFRED MEAKIN........... 3.00
IRONSTONE DISH,SQUARE,COVERED,WHITE,MEAKIN............. 7.50
IRONSTONE DISH,VEGETABLE,COVERED,BLUE,COLUMBIA
 PATTERN,WEDGWOOD..................................... 35.00
IRONSTONE DISHES,DOLL HOUSE SIZE,54 PIECES.............. 12.00
IRONSTONE DRESSER BOX,MASONS,RED & WHITE,COVER HAS CASTLE
 PICTURE.............................................. 9.00
IRONSTONE GRAVY BOAT.................................. 4.00
```

```
IRONSTONE GRAVY BOAT,RECTANGULAR,LUSTRE TEA LEAF............   15.00
IRONSTONE GRAVY BOAT,WHITE WITH ANCHOR......................   15.00
IRONSTONE GRAVY BOAT WITH LION HEAD ON HANDLE...............    5.00
IRONSTONE GRAVY TUREEN,LADLE................................   22.00
IRONSTONE HAIR RECEIVER.....................................    3.00
IRONSTONE LADLE.............................................   18.00
IRONSTONE MILK PITCHER,LILY OF THE VALLEY...................   12.50
IRONSTONE MOLD,PINEAPPLE DESIGN,OBLONG,MARKED JOHN ALCOOK...    8.00
IRONSTONE MUSTARD POT,COVERED,MARKED GOODWIN & FLENTKE......    3.00
IRONSTONE MUSTARD,WHITE WITH GREEN..........................    2.75
IRONSTONE MUG,12-SIDED,EDWARDS DECORATED,LOOPS OF GOLD &
  GREEN.....................................................    8.50
IRONSTONE PITCHER,9 IN......................................   15.00
IRONSTONE PITCHER,9 IN. TALL,LEAVES & BERRIES ON HANDLE.....   17.00
IRONSTONE PITCHER & BOWL SET,WHITE,RIBBED...................   26.00
IRONSTONE PITCHER,JOHNSON,SHEAF OF WHEAT,WHITE..............   15.00
IRONSTONE PITCHER,MASONS,DECORATED,6 IN.,DOLPHIN
  HANDLE,CHINESE DECOR......................................   27.00
IRONSTONE PITCHER,MEAKIN,MOSS ROSE,SQUARE..................    10.00
IRONSTONE PITCHER WITH DOLPHIN HANDLE,CHINESE,MASONS
  PATENTED,6 IN.............................................   32.00
IRONSTONE PLATE,7 IN.,LAVENDER,COLOGNE......................    6.00
IRONSTONE PLATE,7 IN.,MARKED MASONS PATENT CHINA ENGLAND....    4.00
IRONSTONE PLATE,8 IN........................................    8.00
IRONSTONE PLATE,9 IN.,WOOLISCROFT OPAQUE CHINA CIRCA 1855...    6.00
IRONSTONE PLATE,10 SIDED,FIG PATTERN........................    7.00
IRONSTONE PLATE,COMMEMORATION,10 IN.,1939 KING & QUEEN VISIT    6.50
IRONSTONE PLATE,DINNER,BROWN ESSEX,MEAKIN...................    1.75
IRONSTONE PLATE,DINNER,MEAKIN,WHITE.........................    1.75
IRONSTONE PLATE,LUNCHEON,BLUE &
  WHITE,MARINA,G.PHILLIPS,LONGPORT..........................   22.00
IRONSTONE PLATE,MARKED JAMES CLEWS,9 IN.,BLUE WILLOW PATTERN   32.50
IRONSTONE PLATE MARKED MASONS PATENT IRONSTONE CHINA
  ENGLAND,10 IN.............................................    7.00
IRONSTONE PLATE,MASONS,10 IN.,ORCHID........................    4.00
IRONSTONE PLATE,MASONS,AMERICAN MARINE,PINK.................    2.00
IRONSTONE PLATE,MASONS,CHINESE LANDSCAPE,9 IN...............   25.00
IRONSTONE PLATE,MASONS GAUDY................................   10.00
IRONSTONE PLATE,MULBERRY,REGISTRY MARK 1894.................   18.00
IRONSTONE PLATE,OVAL,SIDE,WHITE.............................    2.25
IRONSTONE PLATE,PAIR,MADE IN ENGLAND 1882 BY
  GRINDLEY,DAFFODIL PATTERN.................................   17.00
IRONSTONE PLATE,PAIR SQUARE WHITE WITH BROWN FLORAL.........    5.00
IRONSTONE PLATE,WASHINGTON HEADQUARTERS,NEWBURG,NEW YORK
  1783-1883.................................................    3.00
IRONSTONE PLATES,WHITE......................................    2.00
IRONSTONE PLATE,WHITE,9 IN..................................    1.00
IRONSTONE PLATE,WHITE,9 IN.,J & G MEAKIN,HANLEY,ENGLAND
  2.75  TO..................................................    3.00
IRONSTONE PLATTER,BROWN & WHITE,OBLONG,SYRIA CASTLES ON
  WATER.....................................................   16.00
IRONSTONE PLATTER,CHAS.MEAKIN,PLAIN 14IN....................    4.00
IRONSTONE PLATTER,COPPER LUSTER BAND EDGE,OCTAGONAL.........    8.00
IRONSTONE PLATTER,JOHNSON MARKED,OBLONG.....................    6.00
IRONSTONE PLATTER,LUSTER TEA LEAF 14 IN.,OPAQUE STONE CHINA.   15.00
IRONSTONE PLATTER,NEST OF 3.................................   15.00
IRONSTONE PLATTER,OBLONG,WHITE,J & G MEAKIN,HANLEY,ENGLAND..   12.50
IRONSTONE PLATTER,OVAL 16 IN.,MARKED........................   12.00
IRONSTONE PLATTER,OVAL,WHITE,WEDGWOOD & CO..................    3.25
IRONSTONE PLATTER,PORCELAIN,ROYALE,ENG. GREEN FLORAL 10 IN..    4.50
IRONSTONE PLATTER,RECTANGULAR,FURNIVAL IMPRESSED,SPRAY
  PATTERN,BROWN.............................................   12.00
IRONSTONE PLATTER,SHAW DEEP WELL,WHITE 17IN.................    6.00
IRONSTONE PLATTER,STAFF,W & E CORN,RAISED GRAPES 14IN.......    6.00
IRONSTONE PLATTER,WHITE,CORN & WHEAT........................   74.00
```

```
IRONSTONE PLATTER,WHITE,DAVENPORT,WITH EMBOSSED GRAPE LEAVES
  & SCROLL.....................................................   10.00
IRONSTONE PLATTER,WHITE,OVAL.................................    2.75
IRONSTONE PLATTER,WHITE,OVAL,ALFRED MEAKIN,ENGLAND..........    2.75
IRONSTONE PLATTER,WHITE,OVAL,J & G MEAKIN,HANLEY,ENGLAND
  3.50 TO...................................................    5.00
IRONSTONE PLATTER,WHITE,OVAL,T.R.BEETE......................    3.75
IRONSTONE POTTY,MEAKIN,WHITE................................   20.00
IRONSTONE PUDDING MOLD,OVAL CROCKERY,SHEAF OF WHEAT PATTERN.    5.00
IRONSTONE SALVER,BLUE & WHITE,SCENIC........................   23.50
IRONSTONE SAUCE,SET OF 8,BROWN ESSEX,MEAKIN.................    5.00
IRONSTONE SAUCER,SET OF 4,DALEHALL..........................    4.00
IRONSTONE SCUTTLE MUG,FLOWERS...............................    4.50
IRONSTONE SERVICE FOR 8,GRAPE-LUSTER CIRCA 1850.............  650.00
IRONSTONE SERVICE OF 43 PIECES,COPPER LUSTER TEA LEAF.......  125.00
IRONSTONE SLOP JAR..........................................   12.00
IRONSTONE SOAP DISH WITH LINER,MASONS PATENT CHINA
  MARKED,BLUE DRAGON........................................   11.50
IRONSTONE SOUP BOWL,BLUE ROSES,PAIR.........................    4.25
IRONSTONE SOUP PLATE,BLUE & WHITE,MARINA,G.PHILLIPS,LONGPORT   22.50
IRONSTONE SOUP PLATE,WHITE,J & G MEAKIN
  1.75 TO...................................................    4.25
IRONSTONE SOUP TUREEN,JOHNSON BROS.,EAR OF CORN HANDLES.....   22.00
IRONSTONE SOUP TUREEN,MEAKIN,CRESWELL PATTERN,PINK,BROWN &
  GOLD......................................................   17.50
IRONSTONE SUGAR BOWL,COVERED,GRAPE FINIAL...................   15.00
IRONSTONE SUGAR WITH RING LID...............................   15.00
IRONSTONE,TEALEAF,BOWL,SOUP,FLAT............................    4.00
IRONSTONE,TEALEAF,BOWL,SQUARE,WEDGWOOD......................   10.00
IRONSTONE,TEALEAF,BUTTER CHIP...............................    3.00
IRONSTONE,TEALEAF,BUTTER DISH,POWELL & BISHOP,GOLD,MELON RIB   14.50
IRONSTONE,TEALEAF,BUTTER DISH WITH INSERT,GOLD..............   22.00
IRONSTONE,TEALEAF,BUTTER PAT,LUSTER,GOLD,SQUARE,POWELL &
  BISHOP....................................................    1.50
IRONSTONE,TEALEAF,CREAMER,LUSTER............................   15.00
IRONSTONE,TEALEAF,CREAMER,LUSTER & SPRIG,HANLEY,ENGLAND.....   15.00
IRONSTONE,TEALEAF,CUP & SAUCER
  6.00 TO...................................................   20.00
IRONSTONE,TEALEAF,CUP & SAUCER,CLEMENSON BROS.,RAISED WHEAT.   12.50
IRONSTONE,TEALEAF,CUP & SAUCER,COFFEE,LUSTER,GOLD,POWELL &
  BISHOP....................................................    7.00
IRONSTONE,TEALEAF,CUP & SAUCER,CUMBOW.......................    7.50
IRONSTONE,TEALEAF,CUP & SAUCER,MEAKIN.......................    5.00
IRONSTONE,TEALEAF,CUP & SAUCER,SET OF 6,GOLD LEAF...........   50.00
IRONSTONE,TEALEAF,DISH,BERRY,LUSTER,WHITE...................    5.00
IRONSTONE,TEALEAF,DISH,SOAP,3 PIECE.........................   18.00
IRONSTONE,TEALEAF,DISH,SOUP.................................   40.00
IRONSTONE,TEALEAF,DISH,VEGETABLE,COVERED,OBLONG,GOLD,POWELL
  & BISHOP..................................................   17.50
IRONSTONE,TEALEAF,DISH,VEGETABLE,SAUARE.....................    2.00
IRONSTONE,TEALEAF,DISH,VEGETABLE,SQUARE,LUSTER,RIBBED.......    9.50
IRONSTONE,TEALEAF,GRAVY BOAT
  9.00 TO...................................................   14.00
IRONSTONE,TEALEAF,GRAVY BOAT,COPPER,........................   15.00
IRONSTONE,TEALEAF,GRAVY BOAT,OPEN,MELLER & TAYLOR...........    9.25
IRONSTONE,TEALEAF,GRAVY LADLE,COPPER LUSTER BORDER..........    5.75
IRONSTONE,TEALEAF,GRAVY WITH LADLE,COVERED..................   27.50
IRONSTONE,TEALEAF,PLATE.....................................    8.50
IRONSTONE,TEALEAF,PLATE,6 IN.,MEAKIN........................    1.50
IRONSTONE,TEALEAF,PLATE,7 IN.,DAVENPORT.....................    7.50
IRONSTONE,TEALEAF,PLATE,7 IN.,WILKINSON & HUME..............    3.50
IRONSTONE,TEALEAF,PLATE,8 IN.,ALFRED MEAKIN.................    3.50
IRONSTONE,TEALEAF,PLATE,8 IN.,BURGESS.......................    3.50
IRONSTONE,TEALEAF,PLATE,8 IN.,GRINDLEY......................    7.50
IRONSTONE,TEALEAF,PLATE,8 IN.,J.EDWARDS.....................    3.50
```

```
IRONSTONE,TEALEAF,PLATE,8 IN.,MEAKIN.........................  2.00
IRONSTONE,TEALEAF,PLATE,8 IN.,SHAW...........................  3.50
IRONSTONE,TEALEAF,PLATE,8 IN.,WEDGWOOD & CO...................  3.50
IRONSTONE,TEALEAF,PLATE,8 IN.,WILKINSON.......................  4.75
IRONSTONE,TEALEAF,PLATE,9 IN.,CORN............................ 10.00
IRONSTONE,TEALEAF,PLATE,9 IN.,MEAKIN.......................... 10.00
IRONSTONE,TEALEAF,PLATE,9 IN.,SHAW............................  9.00
IRONSTONE,TEALEAF,PLATE,MEAKIN................................ 10.00
IRONSTONE,TEALEAF,PLATE,PAIR,LUSTER,SALAD SIZE................  8.00
IRONSTONE,TEALEAF,PLATTER..................................... 16.00
IRONSTONE,TEALEAF,PLATTER,10 X 9 IN........................... 16.00
IRONSTONE,TEALEAF,PLATTER,13 X 9 IN........................... 16.00
IRONSTONE,TEALEAF,PLATTER,14 X 10 IN.......................... 15.00
IRONSTONE,TEALEAF,PLATTER & 2 BUTTER PATS,MARKED.............. 19.00
IRONSTONE,TEALEAF,PLATTER & COVERED DISH,GOLD TRIM........... 35.00
IRONSTONE,TEALEAF,PLATTER,J.C.CLEMENTS CO..................... 15.00
IRONSTONE,TEALEAF,PLATTER,LUSTER,14 IN.,ENGLAND.............. 15.00
IRONSTONE,TEALEAF,PLATTER,MEAKIN............................. 18.00
IRONSTONE,TEALEAF,RELISH TRAY,GOLD LEAF,MARKED IRONSTONE
    CHINA.....................................................  3.75
IRONSTONE,TEALEAF,SAUCE,LUSTER,GOLD,POWELL & BISHOP.........  2.50
IRONSTONE,TEALEAF,SOUP LADLE,COPPER LUSTER BORDER...........  6.75
IRONSTONE,TEALEAF,SOUP PLATE,5,MEAKIN....................... 15.00
IRONSTONE,TEALEAF,SUGAR BOWL,GOLD........................... 18.00
IRONSTONE,TEALEAF,SUGAR BOWL,LUSTER......................... 21.50
IRONSTONE,TEALEAF,SUGAR,COVERED,GOLD........................ 16.00
IRONSTONE,TEALEAF,TEAPOT,MEAKIN............................. 26.50
IRONSTONE,TEALEAF,TOOTHBRUSH HOLDER......................... 14.00
IRONSTONE,TEALEAF,TOOTHBRUSH HOLDER,MEAKIN.................. 15.00
IRONSTONE,TEALEAF,TUREEN WITH TRAY & LADLE,ROYAL CLIFF...... 37.50
IRONSTONE TEAPOT BY E.PEARSON,7 CUP CAPACITY................ 17.50
IRONSTONE TEAPOT,EMBOSSED BELLFLOWER PATTERN,10 IN.,WEDGWOOD 24.00
IRONSTONE TUREEN,10 IN.,PARKHURST,STRAWBERRY KNOB ON COVER.. 19.50
IRONSTONE TUREEN,COVER & PLATTER,BLUE,ORANGE,& RED.......... 55.00
IRONSTONE TUREEN,COVERED,POWELL & BISHOP,FLUTED BOTTOM & LID 15.00
IRONSTONE TUREEN,MASONS PATENT 1813,RIDGWAY MARK,TURKISH
    DECOR.................................................... 40.00
IRONSTONE TUREEN,OVAL,LION HEAD HANDLES,JOHN EDWARDS
    IMPRESSED ROYAL......................................... 25.00
IRONSTONE TUREEN,SOUP,3 QUART,IVORY,BROWN FLOWERS,MEDALLIONS 25.00
IRONSTONE TUREEN,VEGETABLE,OVAL,COVERED,WHITE,J & G MEAKIN..  4.00
IRONSTONE VEGETABLE DISH,OVAL,OPEN,WHITE,STAFFORDSHIRE......  5.00
IRONSTONE WASHBOWL & PITCHER................................ 26.00
IRONSTONE WASH BOWL & PITCHER,DAVENPORT,CORN PATTERN........ 16.50
IRONSTONE WASH SET PITCHER,BONITA VP CO.,WHITE WITH GOLD
    BAND....................................................  4.50
IRONSTONE WASH SET,WHITE PITCHER,WEDGWOOD & CO.,ROYAL
    IRONSTONE...............................................  5.50
IRONSTONE WATER PITCHER,ROYAL CHINA,JOHNSON BROS.,ENGLAND... 15.00
IRONSTONE WELL & TREE PLATTER,WHITE
    BACKGROUND,ORANGE,BLUE,GREEN............................ 25.00
IRONSTONE,WHITE,4 IN. PLATE OR SHALLOW BOWL,G MEAKIN........  2.25
IRONSTONE,WHITE,6 IN. PLATE,COLUMBINE SHAPE & REGISTRY
    NUMBER..................................................   .50
IRONSTONE,WHITE,6 IN. PLATE,J & G MEAKIN....................  1.50
IRONSTONE,WHITE,6 IN. PLATE,J W PARKHURST &
    CO.,HANLEY,ENGLAND......................................  1.25
IRONSTONE,WHITE,6 IN. PLATE,WELLSVILLE CHINA U S A..........  1.00
IRONSTONE WHITE 7 IN. PLATE.................................  1.50
IRONSTONE,WHITE,7 IN. PLATE,J & G MEAKIN,HANLEY,ENGLAND.....  1.25
IRONSTONE,WHITE,8 IN. PLATE,IMPRESSED CONGRESS,JEAN EDWARDS.  3.00
IRONSTONE,WHITE,8 IN. PLATE,J & G MEAKIN,HANLEY,ENGLAND.....  1.50
IRONSTONE,WHITE,8 IN. PLATE,J W PARKHURST &
    CO.,HANLEY,ENGLAND......................................   .50
IRONSTONE WHITE 8 IN. PLATE,WHEAT BORDER....................  6.00
```

IRONSTONE,WHITE,8 IN. PLATE,W R GRINDLEY...................... 1.85
IRONSTONE,WHITE,9 IN. PLATE,ALFRED MEAKIN ROYAL IRONSTONE... 1.50
IRONSTONE,WHITE,9 IN. PLATE,CHARLES MEAKIN,ENGLAND........... 2.50
IRONSTONE,WHITE,9 IN. PLATE,D E MC NICHELS,CLARKSBURG,WEST
    VIRGINIA... .50
IRONSTONE,WHITE,9 IN. PLATE,J & G MEAKIN,HANLEY,ENGLAND
    2.75 TO... 3.00
IRONSTONE,WHITE,9 IN. PLATE,J & G MEAKIN,WHEAT PATTERN....... 3.50
IRONSTONE,WHITE,9 IN. PLATE,JOHNSON BROS..................... 2.00
IRONSTONE,WHITE,9 IN. PLATE,KNOWLES,TAYLOR & KNOWLES......... 3.50
IRONSTONE,WHITE,9 IN. PLATE,MARKED 2 LIONS & CROWN........... 2.00
IRONSTONE,WHITE,9 IN. PLATE,MELLER,TAYLOR & CO.,ENGLAND..... 2.75
IRONSTONE,WHITE,10 IN. PLATE,JOHNSON BROS.ENGLAND,ROYAL
    IRONSTONE... 3.00
IRONSTONE,WHITE,10 IN. PLATE,J W PARKHURT,HANLEY............. 3.25
IRONSTONE,WHITE,10 IN. PLATE,POWELL & BISHOP,ENGLAND........ 2.50
IRONSTONE,WHITE,BONE DISH,BRIDGEWILD & SON.................. 2.25
IRONSTONE WHITE BOWL & PITCHER,JOHNSON ENGLAND,RAISED SCROLL 25.00
IRONSTONE WHITE BOWL WITH PITCHER SET,JOHNSON BROS.ENGLAND.. 20.00
IRONSTONE,WHITE,BUTTER DISH,ALFRED MEAKIN.LTD.,ENGLAND...... 3.00
IRONSTONE,WHITE,BUTTER DISH COVERED,J & G MEAKIN............ 4.85
IRONSTONE,WHITE,BUTTER PAT,ALFRED MEAKIN,ENGLAND............ .75
IRONSTONE,WHITE,BUTTER PAT,JOHNSON,ENGLAND.................. .75
IRONSTONE WHITE CHAMBER JAR WITH COVER & BAIL HANDLE........ 7.50
IRONSTONE,WHITE,CUP & SAUCER,J & G
    MEAKIN,EASTWOOD,HANLEY,ENGLAND............................ 4.50
IRONSTONE WHITE COFFEE POT BY J & G MEAKIN,GRAPE PATTERN.... 19.75
IRONSTONE WHITE COVERED SUGAR BOWL IN CORN DESIGN........... 16.00
IRONSTONE WHITE COVERED GRAVY TUREEN,ROPE & BAR HANDLES &
    FINIAL.. 17.50
IRONSTONE WHITE CUP & SAUCER WITH ORANGE TRIM............... 12.50
IRONSTONE,WHITE,CUP PLATE,JOHNSON BROS...................... 3.75
IRONSTONE,WHITE,DIVIDED DISH................................ 12.75
IRONSTONE,WHITE,EGG CUP..................................... 3.00
IRONSTONE,WHITE,GRAVY,ALFRED MEAKIN,ENGLAND................. 4.00
IRONSTONE WHITE GRAVY BOAT & UNDER PLATTER,WHEAT DESIGN..... 12.00
IRONSTONE,WHITE,HANDLELESS CUP.............................. 3.50
IRONSTONE,WHITE,HANDLELESS CUP & SAUCER,ALFRED
    MEAKIN,ENGLAND.. 4.75
IRONSTONE WHITE HANDLELESS CUP & SAUCER,ANTHONY SHAW........ 3.00
IRONSTONE,WHITE,HANDLELESS CUP & SAUCER,J & G
    MEAKIN,HANLEY,ENGLAND..................................... 3.75
IRONSTONE,WHITE HANDLELESS CUP & SAUCER,MADDOCK CO.ENGLAND
    3.00 TO.. 4.75
IRONSTONE,WHITE,LAMP MADE OF PITCHER & WASH BOWL,WOODEN BASE 27.50
IRONSTONE WHITE MATCH HOLDER................................ 2.00
IRONSTONE,WHITE PLATE,ALFRED MEAKIN,ENGLAND................. 1.75
IRONSTONE,WHITE,PLATE,JOHNSON BROS ROYAL IRONSTONE.......... 2.25
IRONSTONE,WHITE,PLATTER,J & G MEAKIN,HANLEY,ENGLAND......... 3.75
IRONSTONE,WHITE,RELISH DISH,POWELL & BISHOP................. 3.00
IRONSTONE,WHITE,SAUCE DISH,ALFRED J MEAKIN.................. 2.25
IRONSTONE,WHITE,SAUCE DISH,GOODWIN BROTHERS................. 1.00
IRONSTONE,WHITE,SAUCER,BURGESS & GODDARD.................... 2.25
IRONSTONE,WHITE,SAUCER,JOHNSON BROS.,ENGLAND................ 1.50
IRONSTONE,WHITE,SET OF 6 ROUND BUTTER PATS,JOHNSON
    BROS.,ENGLAND... 5.75
IRONSTONE,WHITE,SIDE DISH MARKED HOTEL...................... 2.50
IRONSTONE WHITE SOAP DISH................................... 3.00
IRONSTONE,WHITE,SOAP DISH,ALFRED MEAKIN,ENGLAND............. 2.25
IRONSTONE WHITE SOUP LADLE.................................. 14.00
IRONSTONE,WHITE,SOUP PLATE,ENGLAND.......................... 2.75
IRONSTONE,WHITE,SOUP PLATE,J & G MEAKIN..................... 1.75
IRONSTONE,WHITE,SOUP PLATE,J W PARKHURST &
    CO.,HANLEY,ENGLAND.. 2.85
IRONSTONE,WHITE,SOUP PLATE,JOHNSON BROS,ENGLAND

```
2.00  TO..............................................    3.00
IRONSTONE,WHITE,SOUP PLATE,POWELL & BISHOP..............    1.25
IRONSTONE,WHITE,SOUP PLATE,WEDGWOOD.....................    6.00
IRONSTONE,WHITE,SOUP TUREEN LADLE.......................    5.75
IRONSTONE,WHITE,SOUP TUREEN,SCROLL DESIGN...............   14.75
IRONSTONE WHITE SUGAR BOWL..............................    4.50
IRONSTONE,WHITE,SUGAR BOWL,JOHNSON BROS.................    5.75
IRONSTONE,WHITE,TOAST RACK,GOLD.........................    8.25
IRONSTONE,WHITE,VEGETABLE DISH..........................    4.50
IRONSTONE,WHITE,VEGETABLE DISH,ALFRED MEAKIN,ENGLAND....    2.25
IRONSTONE,WHITE,VEGETABLE DISH,J & G MEAKIN,HANLEY,ENGLAND..    5.00
IRONSTONE,WHITE,VEGETABLE DISH,SQUARE,MELON RIBBED......    4.50
     IVORINA VERDE, SEE CUSTARD GLASS...................
IVORY ARTIST SIGNED 18TH CENTURY INDIA FIGURINE,GANESHA THE
  ELEPHANT..............................................   70.00
IVORY BRIDGE OF 5 RHINOCEROS,CHINESE,TEAKWOOD BASE,6 IN.
  LONG.................................................  100.00
IVORY,CARVED,7 IN. BY 6 IN. ANCIENT & 2 CHILDREN.......  137.50
IVORY CARVED BUDDHA,CARVED WOOD STAND,NATURAL FINISHED
  IVORY,7 IN...........................................   85.00
IVORY CARVED CANDLE SCREEN,FIGURE OF MAN & WOMAN ,20 IN.
  HIGH................................................  325.00
IVORY CARVED CARD CASE,GARDEN SCENES,HONEYCOMB LATTICE
  BACKGROUND..........................................   42.50
IVORY CARVED MUG,SIGNED BY A BARLOW,18TH CENTURY BOAR HUNT..  185.00
IVORY CARVED NAPKIN RING...............................    2.00
IVORY CARVED TUSK,20 IN.,MOUNTED ON BLACK BASE,CHINESE
  DESIGN..............................................  125.00
IVORY CARVINGS OF 7 JAPANESE GODS,4 IN. TALL..........  300.00
IVORY CHESS SET,CARVED CHINESE FIGURES,WHITE & RED....  155.00
IVORY CHESS SET,CHINESE RED & WHITE CIRCA 1830........  175.00
IVORY CHINESE CARD HOLDER,CARVED,11 BY 6 IN...........  100.00
IVORY CHINESE FIGURE 1 IN.,MOUNTED ON BLACK STAND.....    3.00
IVORY CHINESE FIGURINES,19 IN. HIGH,LADY & OLD MAN....   45.00
IVORY CHINESE FIGURINE,MAN IN BASE....................   40.00
IVORY CIGARETTE CASE SIGNED,ENGRAVED TWO MONKEYS AND A
  SPIDER..............................................   75.00
IVORY COVERED TOBACCO BOX,OVAL SHAPE,SIGNED...........  200.00
IVORY ELEPHANT MOUNTED ON WOODEN BASE.................    6.00
IVORY FIGURINE,GEISHA GIRL............................   20.00
IVORY FLOWER VASE,HANDCARVED WITH FLOWERS.............  160.00
IVORY,GERMAN CARVINGS,4 TROLLS ON WOOD STANDS.........  180.00
IVORY HAND CARVED FOO LION............................   14.00
IVORY HAND CARVED SHOE HORN,7 IN.,CHINESE FIGURES AT TOP....   17.00
IVORY HAND CARVED TURTLE..............................   14.00
IVORY MINIATURE HANDPAINTED LADY,BRASS FRAME & HANGER.......   28.00
IVORY OF LITTLE GIRL HANDPAINTED OVAL,BLACK WOOD FRAME......   40.00
IVORY PAINTED PORTRAIT SIGNED ,SATIN,MOTHER OF PEARL INLAID
  FRAME...............................................   75.00
IVORY PAINTING,3 X 2 IN.,COPY OF MONA LISA............   45.00
IVORY ROUND BOX,MOSAIC DESIGN OF GREEN,BLACK & WHITE..    6.50
IVORY SALT SPOON......................................    3.50
IVORY SEWING CLAMP,BIRDS..............................    7.50
IVORY SIGNED HANDPAINTED OVAL,BRASS FRAME,YOUNG WOMAN.......   45.00
IVORY SIGNED HANDPAINTED OVAL PORTRAIT OF WOMAN,BRASS FRAME.   45.00
IVORY SIGNED SNUFF BOTTLE,CARVED & DECORATED..........   95.00
IVORY SNUFF BOTTLE,CAMEL,STOPPER & LADLE..............   35.00
IVORY SNUFF BOTTLE WITH LONG LIFE FIGURE,DEER,ARTIST SIGNED.   65.00
IVORY UMBRELLA HANDLE,CARVED LIZARD...................    7.50
IVORY WHALE TOOTH,NAMES...............................    9.00

     JACK-IN-THE-PULPIT, SEE ALSO UNDER SPECIFIC ART GLASS
HEADINGS.............................................
```

JACKFIELD WARE was originally a black glazed pottery made in Jackfield, Eng-

land, since 1630. A yellow glazed ware has also been calleo Jackfield ware. Most of the pieces referred to as Jackfield are black pieces made during the Victorian era.

JACKFIELD BLACK COVERED HEN, ENAMELED WHITE SPOTS,GOLD.......	95.00
JACKFIELD COW CREAMER......................................	35.00
JACKFIELD COW CREAMER,RED POTTERY WITH BLACK GLAZE & GOLD DECORATION..	28.50
JACKFIELD DOGS,GLASS EYES,BLACK LUSTER,GOLD DECOR,PAIR......	65.00
JACKFIELD JUG MINIATURE,....................................	4.50
JACKFIELD PITCHER,CYLINDRICAL PANELED BODY..................	12.00

JACK-IN-THE-PULPIT VASES were named for their odd trumpet-like shape that resembles the wild plant called a jack-in-the-pulpit. The design originated in the late Victorian years.

JACK-IN-THE-PULPIT VASE,5 IN.,PINK SHADE....................	18.50
JACK-IN-THE-PULPIT VASE,CASED..............................	18.00
JACK-IN-THE-PULPIT VASE,VENETIAN,GOLD TRIM,PAIR............	32.50
JADE,BUNCH OF GRAPES,GREEN WITH DARK GREEN LEAVES..........	135.00
JADE CLAMBROTH OCTAGONAL BOX...............................	65.00
JADE GREEN BOTTLE,SILVER MOUNTED,CARVED TEAK STAND,CARVED...	170.00
JADE,GREEN ELEPHANT WITH CARVED ROSEWOOD STAND..............	95.00
JADE,MUTTONFAT,3 FIGURES & ORIENTAL WRITING.................	25.00
JADE SQUARE PANELED WHITE SILVER MOUNTED BOTTLE,ROSEWOOD STAND...	110.00
JADE WHITE BOTTLE,CARVED TEAK STAND,CORAL STOPPER,LEAVES & VINES...	110.00
JADE,WHITE DISC OF SCHOLAR,ROSEWOOD STAND,2 IN. HIGH........	25.00
JADE,WHITE MYTHOLOGICAL ANIMAL ON ROSEWOOD STAND,..........	45.00
JADE,WHITE,MUTTONFAT,MANDARIN BUTTON.......................	35.00
JADE,WHITE SWAN RESTING ON LOTUS PAN,ROSEWOOD STAND........	30.00
JADE,WHITE TRAY IN GILT METAL MOUNT WITH CARVED CARNELIAN FU LION...	35.00
JAR,TOBACCO,SIGNED HANDEL,OWL..............................	35.00
JASPER, SEE ALSO WEDGWOOD.................................	

JASPERWARE is a fine-grained pottery developed by Josiah Wedgwood in 1775. The jasper was made in many colors including the most famous, a light blue. It is still being made.

JASPERWARE BLACK WITH WHITE CLASSICAL FIGURES COVERED URN MARKED DUDSON...	125.00
JASPERWARE BLUE SUGAR SHAKER,WHITE CLASSICAL FIGURES........	35.00
JASPERWARE CLASSIC URN,IMPRESSED STAR CROWN MARK,3 CUPIDS,BROWN.......................................	32.50
JASPERWARE GREEN & WHITE HEART-SHAPED HAIR RECEIVER........	22.00
JASPERWARE GREEN & WHITE PITCHER...........................	16.00
JASPERWARE HAIR RECEIVER,GREEN,CUPIDS DANCING..............	16.50
JASPERWARE PLAQUE,GREEN,6 IN.,WHITE CUPID..................	20.00
JASPERWARE PLATE,GREEN.....................................	6.00
JASPERWARE PLATE,OCTAGONAL,BLUE & WHITE,WOMAN ON HORSE SIDESADDLE..	15.00
JASPERWARE PLAQUE,GRAY-GREEN & WHITE,HEAD & SHOULDERS OF CHILD CENTER...	19.50
JASPERWARE PLAQUE,ROUND BLUE & WHITE INDIAN CENTER SIGNED...	22.00
JASPERWARE PLAQUE,ROUND,GREEN & WHITE STORK CENTER.........	19.50
JASPERWARE SAGE GREEN OVAL PLAQUE,MEDIEVAL LADY............	21.00
JASPERWARE SYRUP PITCHER,BLUE,5 IN. HIGH,CLASSIC FIGURES....	38.50
JASPERWARE TEA SET,GERMAN,RAISED WHITE FIGURES.............	35.00
JASPERWARE WHITE PLAQUE,CASCADE GARDEN,WORLDS FAIR,ST.LOUIS 1904,GREEN...	8.50
JEWELRY,AMBER INCLUSION RING,28 K AMBER IN 19 FLEUR-DE-LIS PRONGS...	95.00
JEWELRY,BEADS,16 IN. STRAND YELLOW GLASS....................	3.00
JEWELRY,BEADS,30 IN. STRAND PURPLE CUT GLASS................	4.00
JEWELRY,BEADS,36 IN. STRAND OLD MOTHER OF PEARL.............	6.00
JEWELRY,BEADS,38 IN. STRING ELFIN AMBER....................	150.00

```
JEWELRY,BEADS & EARRINGS OF AGATE METAL.....................      8.00
JEWELRY,BEADS,BOHEMIAN GARNET,FACET CUT,95 PEA-SIXED STONES
   IN GARNETS.............................................       49.50
JEWELRY BEADS,FACETED JET BLACK..............................      5.00
JEWELRY,BEADS,FLAPPERS,BLUE LUSTRE...........................      9.00
JEWELRY,BEADS,FLAPPERS,BRONZE & GREEN LUSTER.................      6.00
JEWELRY,BEADS,FLAPPER TYPE GLASS,63 IN.,3 IN. TASSEL........      3.00
JEWELRY,BEADS,GLASS..........................................      1.00
JEWELRY,BEADS,GLASS,AMBER COLOUR.............................      5.00
JEWELRY,BEADS,GLASS,LONG,GREEN...............................      5.00
JEWELRY BRACELET,5 ROWS ROSE CUT GARNETS....................     60.00
JEWELRY,BRACELET,14K GOLD ,5 CHINESE JADES IN GREEN.........    125.00
JEWELRY,BRACELET,14K GOLD,5 WHITE JADES.....................    125.00
JEWELRY,BRACELET,14K GOLD,ANGEL SKIN CAMEOS,5 IN GOLD FRAME.    175.00
JEWELRY,BRACELET,15K GOLD MESH,TOP SQUARE,SLIDE OF PLATINUM
   & DIAMONDS.............................................     195.00
JEWELRY BRACELET,17 MINI JEWELED SLIDE,14K..................    225.00
JEWELRY,BRACELET & NECKLACE FROM CEYLON,MOONSTONE...........     16.00
JEWELRY,BRACELET,ETRUSCAN WRAP AROUND,GOLD OVER SILVER......     29.00
JEWELRY BRACELET,FLEXIBLE,9 KT.,7 GARNETS,8 SAPPHIRES.......     95.00
JEWELRY,BRACELET,FRENCH ENAMEL FLEXIBLE,GOLD & BLUE & WHITE
   ENAMEL.................................................     250.00
JEWERLY,BRACELET,GOLD 3 STRAND FLEXIBLE,DIAMOND IN CENTER...    165.00
JEWELRY,BRACELET,GOLD BANGLE,RAISED CENTER WITH PEARL INSET.     32.00
JEWELRY,BRACELET,GOLD FILLED,FLOWERS........................     25.00
JEWELRY,BRACELET,GOLD FILLED STRETCH,ROUND EMBLEM PLAQUE
   FRONT.................................................      16.00
JEWELRY,BRACELET,GOLD WITH ENGRAVING........................     45.00
JEWELRY,BRACELET,GREEN CARVED JADE,6 OVAL JADE SECTIONS.....    300.00
JEWELRY,BRACELET,MESH GOLD FILLED...........................     17.50
JEWELRY,BRACELET,PAIR WOVEN HAIR,CLASP WITH STONE DECORATION     35.00
JEWELRY,BRACELET,STERLING SILVER ENGRAVED BANGLE............     25.00
JEWELRY,BRACELET,TORTOISE SHELL.............................      5.00
JEWELRY,BRACELET WITH 5 EMERALD CUT SMOKY TOPAZES,14K YELLOW
   GOLD..................................................     125.00
JEWERLY,BRACELET WITH 8 OPAL STUDDED CHARMS,3 STRAND
   FLEXIBLE GOLD.........................................     235.00
JEWELRY,BRACELET,YELLOW GOLD FLEXIBLE LINKS,17 ENGRAVED
   SQUARES..............................................      25.00
JEWELRY,BROOCH,14K GOLD SPRAY,& 10 JEWELED STICK PIN........    225.00
JEWELRY,BROOCH,CARVED CORAL,RIBBON BOW AT TOP WITH CARVED
   SHELL PENDANT.........................................      28.00
JEWELRY,BROOCH,GOLD,ENAMEL SCENE CENTER,2 COURT LADIES......     95.00
JEWELRY,BROOCH,GOLD SUNBURST,OVAL FIRE OPAL IN CENTER WITH
   PEARLS...............................................     475.00
JEWELRY,BROOCH,HANDPAINTED BLUE FOR-GET-ME-NOTS ON CHINA....      6.50
JEWELRY,BROOCH,OVAL GOLD PLATED MEMORIAL,ENTWINED LOCKS OF
   BLOND HAIR...........................................      20.00
JEWELRY,BROOCH,PINK GLASS INTAGLIO..........................     26.00
JEWELRY,BROOCH,SHELL CAMEO,WOMANS HEAD WITH SET IN GOLD
   FRAME................................................      30.00
JEWELRY,BUTTON HOOK,GOLD PLATED HANDLE......................      2.75
JEWELRY,CHAIN,15 IN. LONG SLIDE FOR LADIES WATCH,2 OPALS IN
   SLIDE................................................      16.50
JEWELRY,CHAIN,26 IN. LONG SLIDE FOR LADIES WATCH,OPAL IN
   SLIDE................................................      18.50
JEWELRY,CHAIN,50 IN. WITH GOLD SLIDE,7 PEARLS & GARNET......     35.00
JEWELRY,CHAIN,GOLD FILLED SLIDE FOR LADIES WATCH,23 IN.
   LONG,3 PEARLS........................................      18.50
JEWELRY CHAIN,GOLD OVER SILVER,29 IN. LONG,SAPPHIRES
   INTERSPERSED.........................................      18.00
JEWELRY,CHAIN,LADYS GOLD SLIDE 23 IN.,BLUE FIRE OPAL,6
   PEARLS...............................................      26.50
JEWELRY,CHAIN,VICTORIAN OPAL & GOLD,41 IN.,10 BLUE OVAL
   OPALS................................................     129.00
```

```
JEWELRY,CHAIN WITH FOB,NECK,12K GOLD FILLED LADIES..........   12.00
JEWELRY,CHAIN WITH GOLD HEART SLIDE,48 IN.,ENGRAVED WITH
  OPAL.....................................................   35.00
JEWELRY,CHAIN WITH PLAIN SLIDE,GOLD.........................    5.00
JEWELRY,CHAIN WITH SLIDE,GOLD ROPE..........................   85.00
JEWELRY,CHARM,ELK TEETH.....................................    6.00
JEWELRY,CROSS,GOLD ENGRAVED.................................    8.00
JEWELRY,CROSS WITH PEARL & APPLIED GOLD DECOR,3 IN. LONG....   65.00
JEWELRY,CUFF LINKS,14K GOLD DOUBLE LINK,ENGRAVED............   18.00
JEWELRY,CUFF LINK,CHINA.....................................    8.00
JEWELRY CUFF LINKS,ORIENTAL HAND-CARVED JADE................   75.00
JEWELRY,EARRING,HONEY COLOURED AMBER,OVAL BEAD DROP ON 14K
  WIRE.....................................................    8.00
JEWELRY,EARRINGS,3-PIECE SET FOR PIERCED,GOLD FILLED WITH
  CORAL....................................................   20.00
JEWELRY,EARRINGS,AMBER CARVED,SILVER MOUNTS.................   15.00
JEWELRY,EARRINGS,CHINESE JADE,CARVED BAMBOO PLANT WITH
  DIAMOND..................................................  150.00
JEWELRY,EARRINGS,EMERALD STUD PIERCED POST,14K GOLD MOUNTING   79.00
JEWELRY,EARRINGS,FRENCH PIQUE ON TORTOISE SHELL,COLOURFUL
  PEARL INLAYS.............................................   24.00
JEWELRY,EARRINGS,GARNET TINY PIERCED POST 14K GOLD..........   15.00
JEWELRY,EARRINGS,GOLD 5 PETAL FLOWER,PEARL CENTER,PIERCED
  POST.....................................................   22.50
JEWELRY,EARRINGS,GOLD PIERCED,DROP STYLE....................   15.00
JEWELRY,EARRINGS,GOLD & WHITE CORAL BUTTON..................   20.00
JEWELRY,EARRINGS,PIERCED GOLD,1 IN. GOLD HOOP...............   13.00
JEWELRY,EARRINGS,PIERCED GOLD,3 QUARTER IN. HOOP............    8.50
JEWELRY EARRINGS,PIERCED GOLD,5 EIGHTH IN. HOOP.............    6.50
JEWELRY EARRINGS,PIERCED GOLD,GOLD FLOWER WITH BLACK ENAMEL.   11.00
JEWELRY,EARRINGS IN PLATINUM SQUARE MOUNTINGS,DIAMONDS......   75.00
JEWELRY,EARRINGS,MINIATURE MILLVILLE PAPERWEIGHT FOR PIERCED
  EARS.....................................................   30.00
JEWELRY,EARRINGS,PAIR BALL SHAPED LIGHT BLUE-WHITE
  WEDGWOOD,PIERCED.........................................   35.00
JEWELRY,EARRINGS,PAIR GARNET CLUSTER FOR PIERCED EARS.......   35.00
JEWELRY,EARRINGS,PAIR GARNET CLUSTER STAR SHAPED,GOLD
  WIRES,PIERCED............................................   20.00
JEWELRY,EARRINGS,PAIR GOLD LEAF MOTIF WITH CORAL ROSE
  CENTERS..................................................   65.00
JEWELRY,EARRINGS,PAIR WITH 1/2 CARAT GREEN OPAL IN ROSE
  SETTING..................................................   65.00
JEWELRY,EARRINGS,PIERCED,GOLD FILLED,WHITE SAPPHIRES SET IN
  PETALS...................................................    6.00
JEWELRY,EARRINGS,PIERCED GOLD,GOLD BALLS...................    3.75
JEWELRY,EARRINGS,PIERCED GOLD,GOLD FLOWER..................   10.00
JEWELRY,EARRINGS,PIERCED GOLD,GOLD FLOWER WITH OPAL CENTER..   10.00
JEWELRY,EARRINGS,PIERCED GOLD,GOLD FLOWER WITH PEARL CENTER.   10.00
JEWELRY,EARRINGS,PIERCED GOLD,HOOP,FLORENTINE FINISH........   12.50
JEWELRY,EARRINGS,PIERCED GOLD,LOVERS KNOT WITH OPAL CENTER..    9.00
JEWELRY,EARRINGS,PIERCED GOLD,LOVERS KNOT WITH PEARL CENTER.   15.00
JEWELRY,EARRINGS,PIERCED GOLD,PRONG MOUNTED OPAL............   14.00
JEWELRY,EARRINGS,PIERCED GOLD,TURQUOISE BALLS..............   11.00
JEWELRY,EARRINGS,PIERCED GOLD,WHITE PEARLS................   10.50
JEWELRY,EARRINGS,PIERCED,YELLOW & WHITE GOLD ENGRAVED DISCS.   15.00
JEWELRY,EARRINGS,TORTOISE SHELL,INLAID SILVER..............   10.00
JEWELRY,EARRINGS,VENETIAN GLASS RED........................    3.00
JEWELRY,EARRINGS WITH GOLD CROWN SHAPED TOPS,PAIR OVAL
  FACETED PERIDOT..........................................   45.00
JEWELRY,EARRINGS,WOVEN HAIR PIERCED,3 TUBULAR DROPS
  EACH,GOLD................................................   25.00
JEWELRY,FOB,MOSAIC 5 DROP GRADUATED,BLUE & PINK............   25.00
JEWELRY,FOB WITH LEATHER STRAP,MAGOBAR OIL WELL DRILLING....    4.50
JEWELRY,HATPIN,1 IN. CUBE,BLACK ONYX,JET RELIEFS...........    3.75
JEWELRY,HATPIN,AMBER ACORN IN FULL DETAIL..................    6.00
```

```
JEWELRY HATPIN,AMETHYST.................................     5.00
JEWELRY,HATPIN,AMETHYSTS CLUSTERED AROUND RHINESTONE......     3.50
JEWELRY,HATPIN,APPLE GREEN SQUARE FACETED CRYSTAL........     2.00
JEWELRY HATPIN,EMERALD JEWELED..........................     5.00
JEWELRY HATPIN,GOLD PLATED,CAMEO IN HEAD................    10.00
JEWELRY HATPIN,PAIR,IN VELVET LINED BOX,MOTHER OF PEARL
  CENTER STONES.........................................    10.00
JEWELRY HATPIN,POSEIDON RIDING THE WAVES WITH HORSE,SILVER..     6.00
JEWELRY,HATPIN,RHINESTONE STUDDED.......................     4.50
JEWELRY,LOCKET & CHAIN,ENGLISH SILVER,OVAL LOCKET.......   200.00
JEWELRY,LOCKET,CAMEO,BEIGE & WHITE......................    15.00
JEWELRY,LOCKET,GOLD FILLED,NAME HELEN...................     5.00
JEWELRY,LOCKET,OVAL,HAND-ENGRAVINGS,14 CARAT CHAIN......    45.00
JEWELRY,LOCKET PENDANT,GEORGIAN 18TH CENTURY,2 BAROQUE
  PEARLS...............................................    79.00
JEWELRY,LORGNETTE,NOUVEAU SILVER CLOSTE CASE............    29.00
JEWELRY,NECKLACE,14K GOLD CHAIN WITH 14 OVAL GOLD LACY
  MEDALLIONS...........................................    21.00
JEWELRY,NECKLACE,18 IN. AMBER FACETED GRADUATED........    25.00
JEWELRY,NECKLACE,20 IN. NATURAL CORAL,SHORT BRANCHES WITH
  DUMBBELL.............................................    10.00
JEWELRY,NECKLACE,AMBER INCLUSION,19 IN.,14K YELLOW GOLD
  CLASP................................................    68.00
JEWELRY,NECKLACE,CLOISONNE.............................    10.00
JEWELRY,NECKLACE,GOLD BEAD,14K BEADS,GOLD CHAIN,15 IN. LONG.    41.50
JEWELRY,NECKLACE,HAND CARVED DORY......................     6.50
JEWELRY,NECKLACE IN AMBER GARNET BLACK CULTURED PEARLS..     5.50
JEWELRY,NECKLACE,IVORY.................................     5.00
JEWELRY,NECKLACE,IVORY,OVAL SHAPED,2 ROSES CUT OUT & LEAVES.    20.00
JEWELRY,NECKLACE,RUBY AMBER............................    59.50
JEWELRY,NECKLACE,SCARAB,7 STONES,STERLING SETTING......    12.50
JEWELRY,PENDANT,3K LIGHTING RIDGE BLACK OPAL ,SEED
  PEARLS,CHAIN.........................................   150.00
JEWELRY,PENDANT,36 K AMBER INCLUSION,14K GOLD CHAIN.....    95.00
JEWELRY,PENDANT,ART NOUVEAU,4 BAROQUE PEARLS,GOLD & GREEN &
  PINK.................................................    95.00
JEWELRY,PENDANT,CARVED BURMA JADE......................    35.00
JEWELRY,PENDANT,FACETED HEART SHAPED WITH PEARL AT TOP..    20.00
JEWELRY,PENDANT,GOLD ART NOUVEAU WOMANS HEAD WITH SAPPHIRE
  IN HAIR..............................................    20.00
JEWELRY,PENDANT,GOLD & PEARL STUDDED CROWN.............    35.00
JEWELRY,PENDANT,GOLD & PRONG MOUNTED ROUND OPAL........    20.00
JEWELRY,PENDANT,GOLD FILIGREE,14K WITH DIAMOND & PEARL..    25.00
JEWELRY,PENDANT,GOLD,OPEN,PALE PINK CAMEO BUST,3 SEED PEARLS    18.00
JEWELRY,PENDANT,GOLD,PEARLS,OPALS & DIAMOND CROWN......    75.00
JEWELRY,PENDANT,HUNGARIAN 18TH CENTURY,BLUE & GREEN ENAMELED
  PEACOCK..............................................    95.00
JEWELRY,PENDANT LOCKET,DIAMOND,GOLD ENGRAVED,OPENS TO MANS
  TINTYPE..............................................    25.00
JEWELRY,PENDANT ON 14 CARAT CHAIN,38 CARATS............    95.00
JEWELRY,PENDANT,SILVER & EMERALD QUARTZ STUDDED,CHAIN,19 IN.
  LONG.................................................   300.00
JEWELRY,PIN,1 IN. PORCELAIN PAINTED PORTRAIT OF GIRL WITH
  FLOWERS..............................................    15.00
JEWELRY,PIN,2 IN. OVAL PAINTED FLORAL PORCELAIN........    12.00
JEWELRY,PIN,10K WHITE GOLD DIAMOND SHAPE FILAGREE......     9.00
JEWELRY,PIN,14K GOLD BAR,CORAL BALLS IN CENTER,PEARL AT ENDS    18.00
JEWELRY,PIN,14K GOLD TRUMPET BAR.......................    30.00
JEWELRY,PIN & DROP,FILIGREE WHITE GOLD BOW KNOT,30 DIAMONDS.   350.00
JEWELRY,PIN & EARRINGS,HANDPAINTED PORCELAIN,BLUE......    24.00
JEWELRY,PIN & PENDANT,MOSAIC,BLACK BACKGROUND WITH FLOWERS..   275.00
JEWELRY,PIN,ART NOUVEAU,GOLD BAR,DIAMOND & RUBY STUDDED.....   125.00
JEWELRY,PIN,BAROQUE PEARL BAR,9 PEARLS.................    25.00
JEWELRY,PIN,BAROQUE PEARL CRESCENT,BAROQUE PEARLS & GOLD....    45.00
JEWELRY,PIN,BOHEMIAN GARNET SET IN GOLD CRESCENT.......    35.00
```

```
JEWELRY,PIN,BOHEMIAN SUNBURST,STUDDED WITH GARNETS..........    39.50
JEWELRY,PIN,BUST PORTRAIT PAINTING ON PORCELAIN OVAL,14K
  GOLD FRAME.................................................    65.00
JEWELRY,PIN,BUTTERFLY,GOLD WITH SAPPHIRE IN BODY............    50.00
JEWELRY,PIN,CAMEO,GRAPES IN LADYS HAIR.....................    35.00
JEWELRY,PIN,CAMEO,STERLING FRAME...........................    15.00
JEWELRY,PIN,ENGLISH HAND MADE HANDPAINTED BONE CHINA,MISS
  CANADA ROSE...............................................     3.50
JEWLERY,PIN,FILIGREE WHEELBARROW...........................    17.00
JEWELRY,PIN,GOLD & ETCHED BLACK ENAMEL,GOLD TASSEL CIRCA
  1870....................................................   125.00
JEWELRY,PIN,GOLD BAR WITH BLUE SAPPHIRE....................    15.00
JEWELRY,PIN,GOLD CRESCENT WITH PLATINUM TIPS,PEARL STUDDED..    45.00
JEWELRY,PIN,GOLD LAPEL,3 ENAMELLED BLUE FORGET-ME-NOTS,PEARL
  CENTER...................................................    18.50
JEWELRY,PIN,GOLD OPEN WORK HEART,PRONG MOUNTED DIAMOND IN
  CENTER...................................................   150.00
JEWELRY,PIN,GOLD ROWBOAT,ENAMELED FLOWERS..................    50.00
JEWELRY,PIN,GOLD WASHED KEY WITH GARNET SET,CHAINS &
  ATTACHING PIN............................................    10.00
JEWELRY,PIN,GOLD WITH TOPAZ CENTER,PEARLS..................   300.00
JEWELRY,PIN,HAND MADE 14K GOLD BICYCLE,3 MOONSTONES IN
  WHEELS...................................................    65.00
JEWELRY,PIN,HANDPAINTED PORCELAIN,PINK FLORAL..............    18.00
JEWELRY,PIN,JADE,CARVED GREEN & WHITE JADE.................   150.00
JEWELRY PIN,LADIES LAPEL,SILVER GILT FILIGREE JEWEL........     5.00
JEWELRY,PIN,MALACHITE DOME SHAPED BAR,STERLING BACK GOLD
  LOOP CHAIN...............................................    75.00
JEWELRY,PIN,OVAL JADE,GOLD & CARVED GREEN JADE.............   125.00
JEWELRY,PIN,PINK CORAL BAR,PINK BALLS,GOLD FILLED..........     7.00
JEWELRY,PIN,PINK CORAL ROUND,7 CORAL BALLS,GOLD MOUNT......     8.00
JEWELRY,PIN,PINK SHELL,OPEN-WORK YELLOW GOLD FRAME.........    45.00
JEWELRY,PIN,PORCELAIN 2 IN. ROUND PAINTED PORTRAIT SIGNED
  LADY SOPHIA..............................................    50.00
JEWELRY,PIN,SAPPHIRE & DIAMOND,GOLD BAR WITH 4 DIAMONDS &
  SAPPHIRE.................................................   275.00
JEWELRY,PIN,SCOTCH DIRK SILVER & AGATE.....................    25.00
JEWELRY,PIN,SCOTCH SILVER & MULTI-COLOUR,ST.ANDREWS CROSS...   125.00
JEWELRY,PIN,STERLING SILVER MARKED GRASSHOPPER,END OF DAY
  GLASS BODY...............................................    15.00
JEWELRY,PIN,VICTORIAN MOON GARNET..........................    30.00
JEWELRY,PIN,WEDGWOOD,ROUND GOLD & PEARL FRAMED,BLACK & WHITE
  CENTER...................................................   125.00
JEWELRY,PIN,WHITE JADE,FLOWER MOTIF,14 K CLASP.............    26.00
JEWELRY,PIN,WINGED DRAGON,GOLD GRIFFIN WITH BLUE & WHITE
  ENAMEL,PEARL.............................................    45.00
JEWELRY,PIN WITH PEARL CENTER,GOLD 4 PETAL FLOWER..........    35.00
JEWELRY,RIDING CROP,DIAMOND,PLATINUM & DIAMOND STUDDED,49
  DIAMONDS.................................................   365.00
JEWELRY,RING,1/4 CARAT EMERALD WITH 1/4 CARAT DIAMOND......   125.00
JEWELRY,RING,2 OPALS SET IN 14K GOLD BOW...................   100.00
JEWELRY,RING,9K GOLD SNAKE,MANS,2 SNAKE HEADS,2 GARNETS & 4
  DIAMONDS.................................................    85.00
JEWELRY,RING,10 K GOLD,PINK ZIRCON.........................    12.00
JEWELRY,RING,14K GOLD ALMANDINE GARNET,8 PEARLS............    40.00
JEWELRY,RING,14 K GOLD,ANGEL SKIN CAMEO....................   125.00
JEWELRY,RING,14K GOLD & PLATINUM DINNER,1 DIAMOND & 4 RUBIES   125.00
JEWELRY,RING,14K GOLD SOLITAIRE OPAL,OVAL STONE IN WIDE BAND    35.00
JEWELRY,RING,14K MANS MASON,ENAMELLED DEGREE INSIGNIA......    35.00
JEWELRY,RING,14K GOLD WIDE WEDDING.........................    18.00
JEWELRY,RING,18 K GOLD CARVED MANS,2 LIONS FACING HOLDING
  RUBY....................................................   150.00
JEWELRY,RING,ALEXANDRITE SQUARE STONE......................    18.00
JEWELRY,RING,BABY,SIGNET WITH LEAF DESIGN..................    10.00
JEWELRY,RING,BLACK OPAL & 3 10-POINT CUT DIAMONDS,LADIES....   150.00
```

```
JEWELRY,RING,CAMEO SWIVEL,GOLD MOUNTING....................    45.00
JEWELRY,ROSE,CARVED IVORY.................................    18.00
JEWELRY,RING,CLUSTER,AMETHYST CENTER STONE WITH 13 SEED
   PEARLS................................................    20.00
JEWELRY,RING,EMERALD 5 ACROSS,ORNATE VICTORIAN YELLOW GOLD..  159.00
JEWELRY RING FACETED SIBERIAN AMETHYST WITH GREEN
   TOURMALINE,LADIES.....................................    68.00
JEWELRY,RING,GARNET CLUSTER...............................    38.00
JEWELRY,RING,GOLD,32ND DEGREE MASONIC WITH RED & BLACK
   ENAMEL................................................    25.00
JEWELRY,RING,GOLD & 3 OVAL FACETED SAPPHIRES IN A ROW RING,2
   DIAMONDS..............................................   150.00
JEWELRY,RING,GOLD & HEART SHAPED OPAL PRONG MOUNTED
   SOLITAIRE.............................................    30.00
JEWELRY,RING,GOLD & OVAL MEXICAN OPAL,PRONG MOUNTING......   150.00
JEWELRY,RING,GOLD & OVAL MOONSTONE.......................    40.00
JEWELRY,RING,GOLD & PEARL STUDDED PRINCESS,DIAMOND IN CENTER  50.00
JEWELRY,RING,GOLD & ROUND BROWN & WHITE WHELL CAMEO FOX HEAD  75.00
JEWELRY,RING,GOLD & ROUND FACETED AMETHYST SOLITAIRE IN
   PRONG MOUNTING........................................    30.00
JEWELRY RING,GOLD & ROUND FACETED SAPPHIRE SOLITAIRE,PRONG
   MOUNTING..............................................    22.00
JEWELRY,RING,GOLD BALL...................................    22.50
JEWELRY,RING,GOLD FLOWER,OPAL CENTER,2 TOPAZES & 3 AMETHYSTS  60.00
JEWELRY,RING,GOLD GYPSY WITH OVAL CATS EYE & 2 DIAMONDS.....  475.00
JEWELRY,RING,GOLD,LADIES,AMETHYST CENTER STONE.............  160.00
JEWELRY,RING,GOLD,MANS,SHIELD SHAPED BLOODSTONE CENTER......   50.00
JEWELRY,RING,GOLD,MANS,SIGNET WITH RECTANGULAR FIELD,GROOVED
   SHANK.................................................    22.00
JEWELRY,RING,GOLD,OPAL & DIAMOND,2 GOLD SNAKES AROUND OPAL..  125.00
JEWELRY,RING,GOLD,PLAIN SHANK WITH FACETED PRONG MOUNTED
   SAPPHIRE..............................................    22.00
JEWELRY,RING,GOLD,PLAIN SHANK WITH MOUNTED ORIENTAL PEARL...   45.00
JEWELRY,RING,GOLD,PLAIN SHANK WITH MOUNTED PEARL...........    20.00
JEWELRY,RING,GOLD,ROUND BLOODSTONE CENTER.................    16.50
JEWELRY,RING,GOLD,ROUND FACETED AMETHYST CENTER...........    30.00
JEWELRY,RING,GOLD,ROUND MOUNTED OPAL CENTER...............    20.00
JEWELRY,RING,GOLD ROUND OPAL & DIAMOND CLUSTER,14 DIAMONDS..  250.00
JEWELRY,RING,GOLD WITH 3 PEARLS..........................    15.00
JEWELRY,RING,HOOP WITH 4 AMETHYSTS & ROSE DIAMONDS BETWEEN..   75.00
JEWELRY,RING,LADIES 14K WHITE GOLD,2 PEARLS,ONYX INLAYS.....   35.00
JEWELRY,RING,LADIES,18K GOLD LACY SETTING OVAL BLACK ONYX...   18.01-
JEWELRY,RING,LADIES BLACK OPAL,3 PRONG SET DIAMONDS.........  150.00
JEWELRY,RING,LADIES,BLACK OPAL,6 DIAMONDS.................   175.00
JEWELRY,RING,LADIES,OPAL,3 OPALS IN 6 PRONGS..............   125.00
JEWELRY,RING,LADIES OPAL 14K GOLD,2 PRONG-SET DIAMONDS......  400.00
JEWELRY,RING,LADIES,OVAL WHITE SHELL CAMEO CARVING IN 10K
   GOLD..................................................    16.50
JEWELRY,RING,LADIES,YELLOW GOLD OPEN FACED MOUNTING,5 RUBIES   22.50
JEWELRY,RING,MANS 9K GOLD,2 HEADS OF SNAKES,GARNETS &
   DIAMONDS..............................................    85.00
JEWELRY,RING,MANS 10K,GOLD,R ON BLACK STONE...............    10.00
JEWELRY,RING,MARQUISE,1 MOSS AGATE,GOLD MOUNTING..........    49.00
JEWELRY,RING,OPAL IN BELCHER SETTING.....................    15.00
JEWELRY,RING,PINK SAPPHIRE...............................    16.50
JEWELRY,RING,ROSE DIAMOND CLUSTER,10 DIAMONDS,1 LARGE
   CENTER,14K GOLD.......................................   129.00
JEWELRY,RING,SAPPHIRE CLUSTER,HALF CARAT WITH 11 6 POINT
   DIAMONDS..............................................    75.00
JEWELRY,RING,SIGNET WITH DIAMOND OFF TO ONE SIDE.........    35.00
JEWELRY,RING,SMOKY TOPAZ IN TIFFANY SETTING..............    13.00
JEWELERY, RING,SOLID GOLD................................    27.00
JEWELRY,RING,SOLITAIRE DIAMOND,WHITE GOLD &
   PLATINUM,85-POINT STONE...............................   575.00
JEWELRY,RING,SWIRL-SET HAND ENGRAVED LADIES,14K GOLD,2
```

```
DIAMONDS..................................................  125.00
JEWELRY,RING,TOPAZ SCARAB WITH 5 SMALL DIAMONDS,14K GOLD....   95.00
JEWELRY,RING,WHITE GOLD & 5 PEARLS,PRONG MOUNTED IN A ROW...   25.00
JEWELRY,RING,WHITE GOLD HOOP WITH 5 DIAMONDS................   35.00
JEWELRY,RING WITH 8 DIAMONDS,GOLD & BROWN WHITE STONE CAMEO.  300.00
JEWELRY,RING,YELLOW CHINESE JADE LADIES,HAND MADE FILIGREE..  125.00
JEWELRY,SLIDE CHAIN,LADIES 22 IN.,WITH OPAL.................   35.00
JEWELRY,SLIDE,ENGRAVED HALF-MOON SET WITH 3 OPALS...........   16.00
JEWELRY,SLIDE,GOLD,6 PEARLS,PINK STONE,23 IN. LONG..........   26.75
JEWELRY,SLIDE WITH JEWELS,14K GOLD.........................   16.50
JEWELRY,STICKPIN,2 GOLD,SAFETY SLIDES,1 DIAMOND,1 RUBY......   15.00
JEWELRY,STICKPIN,4 LEAF CLOVER FILIGREED...................   20.00
JEWELRY,STICKPIN,14K,DOUBLE WISHBONE.......................    7.00
JEWELRY,STICKPIN,14K,ENGRAVED KNOT.........................    9.00
JEWELRY,STICKPIN,14K GOLD,15 DIAMONDS AROUND 1 CENTER GARNET  75.00
JEWELRY STICKPIN,14K GOLD DOOR KNOCKER.....................   18.00
JEWELRY STICKPIN,14K GOLD FRESH WATER BAROQUE PEARL WITH
  RUBY.....................................................   15.00
JEWELRY STICKPIN,14K GOLD HORSE SHOE.......................   20.00
JEWELRY,STICKPIN,1915......................................    2.50
JEWELRY STICKPIN,&-PETAL LEAF WITH 3 SEED PEARLS...........    3.50
JEWELRY STICKPIN,CARVED BOARS HEAD.........................   12.00
JEWELRY STICKPIN,ETRUSCAN,DIAMOND IN STAR SETTING..........   15.00
JEWELRY,STICKPIN,FANCY BEADED CROSS........................   20.00
JEWELRY STICKPIN,GOLD,AMETHYST QUARTZ,CARVED SETTER DOG.....  20.00
JEWELRY STICKPIN,GOLD CHAIN SLIDE,LYRE WITH PEARLS.........    8.50
JEWELRY STICKPIN,GOLD,ELK TOOTH............................    2.00
JEWELRY,STICKPIN,GOLD WITH OPAL............................    5.00
JEWELRY,STICKPIN,HALF PEARL IN PRONGS......................   10.00
JEWELRY,STICKPIN,LILAC AMETHYST IN PRONGS..................   22.00
JEWELRY STICKPIN,LOVERS KNOT,EMBOSSED......................   12.00
JEWELRY STICKPIN,OVAL GOLDSTONE,GREEN LEAF WITH 7 SEED
  PEARLS...................................................    3.50
JEWELRY STICKPIN WITH 1 QUARTER CARAT DIAMOND IN ROSE
  SETTING..................................................   38.00
JEWELRY STICKPIN WITH DIAMOND IN FILIGREE SETTING,10K GOLD..  25.00
JEWELRY,STICKPIN,SWORD WITH ENAMELED HANDLE................   25.00
JEWELRY,STICKPIN WITH AQUAMARINE STONE,14K GOLD............    4.75
JEWELRY STICKPIN,WITH FIGURE FOX RUNNING SET WITH DIAMONDS..  45.00
JEWELRY STICKPIN WITH ROSE QUARTZ CARVED CAMEO.............   25.00
JEWELRY STICKPIN WITH TINY PEARLS IN FLOWERS AND DIAMOND
  CENTER...................................................   30.00
JEWELRY,TIE BACK,SNAKE,DIAMOND.............................   25.00
JEWELRY,TIE CLIP WITH SAPPHIRE IN CENTER,OVAL GOLD.........   20.00
JEWELRY,TIE TAC,GOLD,CORAL ROSE............................    9.50
JEWELRY,TIE TAC,GOLD,ENAMEL OVAL MASONIC EMBLEM............    7.50
JEWELRY,TIE TAC,GOLD,GARNET CLUSTER........................   22.00
JEWELRY,TIE TAC,GOLD,JOCKEY CAP............................   33.00
JEWELRY,TIE TAC,GOLD,PRONG MOUNTED DIAMOND.................  110.00
JEWELRY,TOOTHPICK,14K GOLD IN 14K GOLD CASE................   29.00
JEWELRY,TOOTHPICK,GOLD.....................................    5.00
JEWELRY,UMBRELLA HANDLE,MOTHER OF PEARL & GOLD.............    4.50
JEWELRY VINAIGRETTE,SILVER SIGNED TIFFANY CO...............   50.00
JEWELRY,WATCH CHAIN,14K GOLD FOR MANS,15 IN. LONG,RING &
  SNAP.....................................................   25.00
JEWELRY,WATCH CHAIN & FOB,7 PICTURES OF NIAGARA FALLS......   12.00
JEWELRY,WATCH CHAIN,BRAIDED HAIR...........................    5.00
JEWELRY,WATCH CHAIN,HAIR...................................   35.00
JEWELRY,WATCH CHAIN,LADIES 14K GOLD........................   45.00
JEWELRY,WATCH CHAIN,LADIES,GOLD FILLED,SLIDE...............   24.50
JEWELRY,WATCH CHAIN,MANS GOLD FILLED.......................    7.50
JEWELRY,WATCH CHAIN,MANS GOLD VEST.........................   16.50
JEWELRY ,WATCH CHAIN,VEST,WITH GOLD KNIFE..................    6.50
JEWELRY,WATCH CHAIN WITH GOLD FOB,WOVEN HAIR...............   18.50
```

JOHN ROGERS STATUES were made from 1859 to 1892. The originals were bronze but the thousands of copies made by the Rogers factory were of painted plaster. Eighty different figures were made.

JOHN ROGERS GROUP,COMING TO THE PARSON,SIGNED & DATED....... 145.00

KATE GREENAWAY, who was a famous illustrator of children's books, drew pictures of children in high-waisted Empire dresses. She lived from 1846 to 1901. Her designs appear on china, glass, and other pieces.

KATE GREENAWAY ALMANAC DATED 1886,MINIATURE.................. 4.50
KATE GREENAWAY 3 PIECE CHILDS SET........................... 30.00
KATE GREENAWAY BISQUE BOY & GIRL ON SWING BOARD.............. 25.00
KATE GREENAWAY BOY & GIRL FIGURE,BISQUE,6 IN. TALL.......... 10.00
KATE GREENAWAY CUP,GLASS,CHILDS,3 GIRLS..................... 10.00
KATE GREENAWAY FIGURINE SALT & PEPPER SHAKER,PAIR........... 18.00
KATE GREENAWAY GIRL SALT SHAKER
  8.50 TO... 15.00
KATE GREENAWAY NAPKIN RING,CHILDREN PLAYING AT SEASHORE..... 14.00
KATE GREENAWAY PITCHER,CHILDREN,SQUIRREL IN RELIEF.......... 27.50
KATE GREENAWAY PORCELAIN SALT & PEPPER SHAKER DOLLS,4 IN.
  HIGH,PAIR... 50.00
KATE GREENAWAY SALT & PEPPER DOLLS,4 IN. TALL............... 50.00
KAUFFMANN CLASSIC VASE,PINK WITH SCENES.................... 30.00
KAUFFMANN SIGNED PORTRAIT PLATTER,14 IN. LONG,RUST & GOLD
  BORDER... 14.00
KAUFFMANN VASE,CYLINDER,WINTER SCENE IN ENAMEL,GOLD BANDS,8
  IN... 32.00
KAUFFMANN VASE,PAIR SIGNED,HANDLES,15 IN. HIGH.............. 60.00

KAZIUN GLASS has been made by Charles Kaziun since 1942. His paperweights have been gaining fame steadily. Most of his glass and all of the paperweights are signed with a K designed cane worked into the design. He makes buttons, earrings, perfume bottles, and paperweights.

KAZIUN MINIATURE PEDESTAL PAPERWEIGHT TILTED,RED &
  GOLDSTONE,SIGNED... 145.00
KAZIUN MINIATURE PEDESTAL WEIGHT,TURQUOISE & WHITE FLECKED
  BACKGROUND... 145.00
KAZIUN SIGNED 2 IN. PAPERWEIGHT,RED CHERRIES & GREEN LEAVES
  ON WHITE... 320.00

KELVA GLASSWARE was made by the C.F. Monroe Company of Meriden, Connecticut, about 1904. It is a pale pastel painted glass decorated with flowers, designs, or scenes.

KELVA CIGAR JAR,GREEN WITH ROSES,SIGNED.................... 75.00
KELVA SIGNED ROUND BOWL,GREEN,PINK,FLOWERS................. 48.00

KEW BLAS is the name used by the Union Glass Company of Somerville, Massachusetts. The name refers to an iridescent golden glass made from the 1890's to 1924.

KEW BLAS 8 IN. STEMMED BULBOUS SHAPED VASE................. 210.00
KEW BLAS SIGNED RIBBED COMPOTE,BLUE IRIDESCENCE ON
  TRANSPARENT GOLD... 350.00

KEWPIES were first pictured in the LADIES' HOME JOURNAL by Rose O'Neil. The pixie-like figures became an immediate success, and Kewpie dolls started appearing in 1911. Kewpie pictures and other items followed.

KEWPIE 4 IN. CREAMER SIGNED ROSE O NEILL,PRUSSIA........... 47.50
KEWPIE BABY DISH... 28.00
KEWPIE BISQUE DOLL,5 IN. TALL,MARKED...................... 37.00
KEWPIE,BISQUE IN BED...................................... 10.50
KEWPIE CANDY BOX,DECOR,COVERED,TIN........................ 15.00
KEWPIE CANDY CONTAINER,SIGNED............................. 15.00
KEWPIE CANDY CONTAINER SIGNED BORGFELDT................... 16.00
KEWPIE CHALK,THE THINKER,PAT.1913........................ 15.00
KEWPIE CHILDS SET,PORCELAIN,12 PIECES.................... 145.00
KEWPIE CHILDS SET,SIGNED ROSE O NEILL WILSON,BAVARIA,15

```
PIECES.........                ................................      185.00
KEWPIE CLOCK,BLUE,SIGNED ROSE O NEILL....................       55.00
KEWPIE CUP & SAUCER SIGNED ROSE O NEILL..................       15.00
KEWPIE DOLL,2 IN. CELLULOID.............................         4.00
KEWPIE DOLL,5 IN. TALL,CELLULOID,ROSE O NEILL LABEL.........     14.00
KEWPIE DOLL,13 IN.,COMPOSITION................................   17.50
KEWPIE DOLL,BISQUE,7 IN. TALL,RED LABELED,STAND.............     37.00
KEWPIE DOLL,BISQUE,O NEILL,5 IN. TALL.......................     25.00
KEWPIE DOLL,BOY,6 IN. TALL,SIGNED,IRWIN MADE IN U S A.......      8.50
KEWPIE DOLL,COMPOSITION,13 IN. TALL.........................     35.00
KEWPIE DOLL,COMPOSITION HEAD,CLOTH BODY,22 IN. TALL.........    100.00
KEWPIE DOLL,COMPOSITION,HEART LABEL,8 IN. TALL..............      6.00
KEWPIE DOLL MADE IN JAPAN DATED 1913,BISQUE,4 IN. TALL......     18.00
KEWPIE DOLL,O NEILL,COMPOSITION JOINTED,13 IN. TALL.........     20.00
KEWPIE DOLL,ROSE O NEILL,1 IN.,COMPOSITION.................      50.00
KEWPIE DOLL,ROSE O NEILL,GLASS EYES,RUBBER,11 IN. TALL......      8.50
KEWPIE DOLL,ROSE O NEILL RED LABEL,COMPOSITION..............     24.00
KEWPIE DOLL,SIGNED,11 IN.,COMPOSITION.......................     15.00
KEWPIE DOLL,SITTING,BLUE WINGS,RUBBER,MARKED ROSE O NEILL...     15.00
KEWPIE DOLL,STANDING,MARKED ROSE O NEILL,9 IN. TALL.........     15.00
KEWPIE GLASS TOOTHPICK......................................     12.75
KEWPIE ICE CREAM MOLD.......................................     22.00
KEWPIE ICE CREAM MOLD SIGNED................................     30.00
KEWPIE IRON PAPERWEIGHT.....................................     25.00
KEWPIE MARKED KEWPIE SHAPED SILVER PEPPER SHAKER............     10.00
KEWPIE MAYONNAISE LADLE.....................................     12.50
KEWPIE PEWTER ICE CREAM MOLD................................     22.00
KEWPIE PITCHER,ROSE O NEILL WILSON-KEWPIE,GERMANY...........     35.00
KEWPIE PLATE,SIGNED.........................................     10.00
KEWPIE PLATE,SIGNED O NEILL,ABC.............................     30.00
KEWPIE PLATE SIGNED ROSE O NEILL............................     15.00
KEWPIE,ROSE O NEILL PLATE & CREAMER.........................     18.00
KEWPIE SIGNED ROSE O NEILL ,GERMANY CREAMER.................     28.00
KEWPIE SIGNED ROSE O NEILL TRAVELER.........................     45.00
KEWPIE TRAY,ROSE O NEILL,ROUND,WITH 6 COASTERS..............     60.00
KEYS 9 ORNATE...............................................      7.00
KEY IRON,PALACE,1780........................................     10.00
KEYS,LARGE JAIL & RANCH,5IN.................................      1.25
```

KIMBALL GLASS COMPANY of Vineland, New Jersey, worked in the early 1900's.
The firm was managed by Colonel Ewan Kimball, who had worked with several
other glass firms, including the company of Kimball and Durand. His glass was
made through the 1930's.

```
KIMBALL SIGNED HORIZONTAL RIBBING VASE,BLUE CLUTHRA CASED
  WITH WHITE................................................    135.00
KIMBALL WHITE CLUTHRA VASE..................................    200.00
KINGS CROWN CIRCA 1850 GOBLET,GREEN THUMBPRINT..............     10.00
```

KING'S ROSE pattern of soft paste Staffordshire was made in England from
about 1820 to 1830. It was decorated in pink, red, yellow, and green. The pat-
tern featured a large roselike flower.

```
KINGS ROSE 6 IN. PLATE,LUSTER VINE BORDER..................    100.00
KINGS ROSE HANDLELESS CUP & SAUCER BY WOOD,IMPRESSED MARK...     65.00
  KITCHEN, SEE ALSO STORE, TOOL, WOODEN...................
KITCHEN,CORN POPPER,WIRE....................................      2.00
KITCHEN,CUTTER,SLAW
  3.50  TO..................................................      6.00
KITCHEN,EGG BEATER,GLASS,DATED 1884.........................      7.50
KITCHEN,EGG BEATER,SPIRAL,WOOD HANDLE.......................      2.50
KITCHEN,FORK,FIREPLACE TOASTING.............................     55.00
KITCHEN,FORK,MEAT,STEEL,18TH CENTURY........................     10.00
KITCHEN,FORK,POT,2 TINED....................................      2.50
KITCHEN,FORK,U STYLE,21 X 36................................      7.00
KITCHEN,GADGET TO LIFT EGGS,WIRE............................      2.00
KITCHEN,GRATER,KRAUT,10 IN.,CREAM CITY......................      1.50
```

```
KITCHEN,GRATER,NUTMEG,SWINGING GRATER WITH WOODEN KNOB
  NUTMEG HOLDER.............................................    4.50
KITCHEN,GRATER,NUTMEG,TIN,EDGAR 1891........................    7.50
KITCHEN,GRATER,SPANISH,HANDWROUGHT..........................   30.00
KITCHEN,GRILL,HAND FORGED,SPIDER LEGS.......................   43.00
KITCHEN,LEMON SQUEEZER,2 HANDLED,WOODEN.....................    4.75
KITCHEN,LEMON SQUEEZER,HINGED,WOODEN........................    7.50
KITCHEN,LEMON SQUEEZER,METAL................................    3.75
KITCHEN,MASHER,POTATO,PAINTED,10 IN.........................    2.50
KITCHEN,MASHER,POTATO,WOOD
  2.50  TO...................................................    4.00
KITCHEN,MOLD,PUDDING,TURKS HEAD.............................   16.50
KITCHEN,MOLD,SET OF 2 IRON PATTY IRONS WITH HANDLE..........    3.75
KITCHEN,PAN,BAKING,8 CUP....................................    5.00
KITCHEN,PAN,FRY,HANDLE,3 LEGGED.............................   25.00
KITCHEN,POT,STEW,TO COOK WITH ON HEARTH,SIDE HANDLED........   12.50
KITCHEN,ROASTER,COFFEE,HEARTH TYPE,REVOLVING POT............   25.00
KITCHEN,ROLLER,PASTRY,SWEDISH,12 IN. LONG,GROOVED...........    5.00
KITCHEN,ROLLING PIN,BLOWN SAPPHIRE BLUE GLASS...............   15.00
KITCHEN,ROLLING PIN,GLASS,SET OF 4..........................   10.00
KITCHEN,ROLLING PIN,GLASS...................................    6.00
KITCHEN,ROLLING PIN,WOOD....................................    3.50
KITCHEN,SCOOP,BUTTER,VERMONT MADE...........................    5.00
KITCHEN,SCOOP,CRANBERRY,CAPE COD............................   37.50
KITCHEN,SCOOP,GRAIN,OVAL,TIN,DUTCH..........................   15.00
KITCHEN,SCOOP,GRAIN,WOOD....................................    5.00
KITCHEN,SCOOP,GRAIN,WOOD HANDLE,TIN.........................    4.00
KITCHEN,SCOOP,TIN,ICE CREAM,CIRCA 1880......................    4.00
KITCHEN,SIFTER,FLOUR,TIN....................................    1.00
KITCHEN,SIFTER,FLOUR,WOODEN MARKED BLOODS PATENT 1861.......   20.00
KITCHEN,SPOON,ENAMEL........................................    5.00
KITCHEN,SQUEEZER,LARD,WOODEN................................    4.00
KITCHEN,SQUEEZER,LEMON,AMERICAN,BARREL FORM.................   25.00
KITCHEN,SQUEEZER,LEMON,METAL HINGE,WOODEN...................   10.00
KITCHEN,SQUEEZER,LEMON,WOODEN...............................    9.50
KITCHEN,STEAMER,POTATO......................................    5.00
KITCHEN,STRAINER,SPOON......................................   14.00
KITCHEN,STRAINER,TEA,FLORAL DECOR...........................    6.00
KLONDIKE CREAMER & SUGAR....................................  385.00
KLONDIKE VASE,8 IN. HIGH....................................  175.00
KNIFE BOX,PINE,HANDLED DIVIDER..............................    6.00
KNIFE,CIRCLE REMINGTON POCKET...............................   25.00
KNIFE,CURVED BLADE STAG HANDLED POCKET......................    6.00
KNIFE,DOUBLE BLADE MINCING,WOOD HANDLE......................    1.00
KNIFE,GOLD PEN,2 IN. ,WITH 2 BLADES,LOOP FOR CHAIN..........    6.50
KNIFE,JACK,WITH WIDE BLADE,CARVED HANDLE....................    5.50
KNIFE,POCKET,1 BLADE PLUS 2 IVORY TOOTHPICKS & 1 EAR SPOON..    4.50
KNIFE,POCKET,RUSSELL STANDARD BARLOW........................   25.00
KNIFE,THOMASTON KNIFE CO FOLDING POCKET.....................    3.00
KOCH PEACH PLATE,BLUE WATER BACKGROUND......................   12.50
KOCH PEDESTAL PLATE,GRAPES TINTED...........................   18.00
KOCH SIGNED 6 IN. PLATE,LOUISE BAVARIA
  BACKGROUND,GREEN,GRAPES...................................    8.50
KOCH SIGNED 12 IN. CHOP PLATE,APPLES HANGING OVER WATER.....   35.00
KOCH PLATE,SIGNED,APPLES....................................   15.00
KOCH SIGNED MARKED LOUISE BAVARIA 9 IN. GRAPE DESIGN PLATE..    9.00
KOCH SIGNED PLATE,APPLE,BROWN BACKGROUND....................   17.50
KOCH SIGNED PLATE,APPLES,GREEN BACKGROUND...................   18.00
```

*KPF is part of the mark used by the Meissen, Germany, factory about 1723
(Königlich Porzellan Fabrik). These letters also appear as the mark of several
late nineteenth-century German factories.*

```
KPF GERMANY MARKED BUTTER DISH WITH LINER,HANDPAINTED ROSE
  BORDERS...................................................   10.00
```

KPM is part of one of the marks used by the Meissen factory about 1723 (Königliche Porzellan Manufaktur). Other later firms using the letters include the Royal Manufactory of Berlin, Germany, that worked from 1832 to 1847. A factory in Scheibe, Germany, used the mark in 1928. The mark was also used in Waldenburg, Germany, and other German cities during the twentieth century.

KPM GERMANY BREAD & BUTTER PLATE...........................	.50
KPM GERMANY CREAMER & SUGAR..............................	7.50
KPM GERMANY CUP & SAUCER SET..............................	3.50
KPM GERMANY DINNER PLATE.................................	1.00
KPM GERMANY LUNCH PLATE..................................	1.00
KPM GERMANY SOUP.......................................	1.00
KPM GERMANY TUREEN,COVERED...............................	5.00

KUTANI WARE is a Japanese porcelain made after the mid-seventeenth century. Most of the pieces found today are nineteenth-century.

KUTANI 1000 FACED RED MARK 7 IN. PLATE....................	9.50
KUTANI 1000 FACED RED MARK 8 IN. PLATE....................	10.00
KUTANI FOOTED BOWL......................................	20.00
KUTANI FOOTED BOWL,PEOPLE IN GARDEN,SCALLOPED RIM,CIRCA 1860	20.00
KUTANI PAIR GREEN & YELLOW DOUBLE GOURD VASES IN WOOD BASES.	45.00
KUTANI PLATE,2 SAGES UNDER PINE TREE......................	6.00
KUTANI-WARE WINE JUG,BIRD,FAN & FLOWERS WITH GOLD..........	10.00

LALIQUE GLASS was made by René Lalique's factory in Paris, France, from 1860 to 1945. The glass was molded, pressed, and engraved. Many of the most familiar designs were clear or with a bluish-tinged glass molded into birds, animals, or foliage.

LALIQUE BOTTLE,OVERLAY CAMPHOR SATIN GLASS,SIGNED..........	40.00
LALIQUE BOTTLE WITH STOPPER,SIGNED........................	12.50
LALIQUE BOTTLE,PERFUME,8 IN.,OCTAGONAL,FROSTED &	
CLEAR,SIGNED...	60.00
LALIQUE BOWL,CLEAR,12 HERRING RAISED OUTSIDE,SIGNED........	35.00
LALIQUE BOWL,DAHLIAS & LEAVES,AMBER TINGED,SIGNED..........	65.00
LALIQUE BOWL,FROSTED BRANCHES & CLEAR FLOWERS..............	23.00
LALIQUE BOWL,IRIDESCENT SCULPTURED LEAVES & STEMS,SIGNED....	48.00
LALIQUE BOWL,OPALESCENT BIRDS,SIGNED EZAN FRANCE...........	32.00
LALIQUE CANDY DISH,CLEAR & FROSTED WITH BEADED HEARTS,SIGNED	
FRANCE..	49.00
LALIQUE GOBLET,SET OF 6 LOW FOOTED,EMBOSSED FRONDS,SIGNED...	48.00
LALIQUE KNIFE RESTS,PAIR.................................	15.00
LALIQUE NUDE RESTRAINING CHARGING GOAT,SIGNED CRISTOL	
LALIQUE FRANCE.......................................	67.50
LALIQUE NUDE SET ON BLACK MARBLE BASE,SATIN FROSTED,SIGNED	
FRANCE..	125.00
LALIQUE PERFUME,FROSTED,SCRIPT SIGNED,OVERLAPPING LEAVES....	15.00
LALIQUE PLACE CARD HOLDER,SIGNED & NUMBERED...............	22.50
LALIQUE PLATE,8 IN.,FROLICKING NUDES,FROSTED SATIN.........	20.00
LALIQUE PLATE,1966 ANNUAL................................	75.00
LALIQUE PLATE,ANNUAL,CRYSTAL,SIGNED.......................	25.00
LALIQUE PLATE,DANCING NUDES,8 IN..........................	40.00
LALIQUE PLATE,FROLICKING NUDES,UNDERSIDE SATIN FROSTED......	29.00
LALIQUE PLATE,NUDES,8 IN.,UNSIGNED........................	22.50
LALIQUE PLATTER,15 X 13 IN.,SIGNED........................	137.50
LALIQUE PLATTER SIGNED...................................	137.50
LALIQUE POWDER BOX,ROUND,COVERED,MADE FOR D ORSAY,SIGNED	
FRANCE..	22.00
LALIQUE PUNCH CUP IN AMBER GLASS,SIGNED...................	22.00
LALIQUE SPARROW,5 IN. LONG,SIGNED.........................	30.00
LALIQUE STATUETTE,LITTLE FROSTED DOE ON CRYSTAL CLEAR	
BASE,SIGNED..	25.00
LALIQUE VASE,7 IN. TALL,SIGNED...........................	75.00
LALIQUE VASE,BLUE,CUT SHINY FERNS,SIGNED..................	55.00
LALIQUE VASE,BLUE,FANTAIL FISH,SEAWEED DECOR..............	50.00
LALIQUE VASE,BULBOUS,LEAVES ON FOUR CORNERS,SIGNED.........	55.00
LALIQUE VASE,CLEAR NECK BASE & INNER CORE,CARVED	

```
BIRDS,SIGNED................................................   65.00
LALIQUE VASE,FROSTED CLEAR GLASS WITH RAISED FLOWERS,SIGNED.   55.00
LALIQUE VASE,FOOTED,OPALESCENT,6 IN. TALL,SIGNED............   75.00
LALIQUE VASE,FROSTED CUT LEAVES,8 IN.,SIGNED FRANCE.........   45.00
LALIQUE VASE,OVOID CLEAR,INTAGLIO CUTTING,ROSES,...........   35.00
LALIQUE VASE,PEDESTAL BASE,FROSTED BODY,ACANTHUS
  LEAVES,SIGNED.............................................   30.00
LALIQUE VASE,REDDISH AMBER,SHORT NECKED,SIGNED.............   87.50
LALIQUE VASE,TUMBLER TYPE,CLEAR GLASS WITH FROSTED
  LEAVES,SIGNED FRANCE......................................   32.50
LALIQUE VASE,WHITE,BLUE CENTERED FLOWERS,8 IN..............   63.50
      LAMP, SEE ALSO HANDLE, MILK GLASS, STEUBEN, TIFFANY,
  ETC......................................................
LAMP,ALADDIN...............................................    5.00
LAMP,ALLADIN BRACKET,GREEN MILK GLASS BASE.................   12.00
LAMP,ALADDIN BRACKET,PINK BRISTOL BASE.....................   12.00
LAMP,ALADDIN,CLEAR PATTERN GLASS,FROSTED & CLEAR SHADE......   15.65
LAMP,ALADDIN HANGING,GREEN MILK GLASS BASE.................   12.00
LAMP,ALADDIN HANGING,PINK BRISTOL BASE.....................   12.00
LAMP,ALADDIN,PINK MILK GLASS URN SHAPE,ELECTRIC,SIGNED......   20.00
LAMP,ALADDIN WITH BURNER,GLASS.............................   10.00
LAMP,AMBER-CLEAR CLARKE FAIRY..............................   30.00
LAMP,AMBER CHRISTMAS LIGHT,CHICAGO LAMP CANDLE CO...........    6.50
LAMP,AMBER COLOURED WHALE OIL..............................   35.00
LAMP,AMBER SATIN MOTHER OF PEARL MINIATURE.................   40.00
LAMP,AMBER WHALE OIL.......................................   45.00
LAMP,AMETHYST BLOWN BELL-SHAPE HANGING HALL,GLOBE 13 IN.....   60.00
LAMP,AMETHYST MINIATURE,BELL-SHAPED,BRASS HOLDER DATED 1873.   27.50
LAMP,AMERICAN COIN GLASS,50 CENT PIECES....................  145.00
LAMP,ANGLE,SINGLE,ORIGINAL GLASS...........................   35.00
LAMP,ANGLE ,SQ.TIN FONT,WALL HANG.ORIG.GLASS...............   45.00
LAMP,ARGY ROUSSEAU SIGNED PATE DE VERRE FAIRY ON BRONZE
  FOOTED BASE..............................................  175.00
LAMP,ART GLASS ELECTRIC OF THE 1920,SATIN FINISH...........   74.50
LAMP,ART GLASS,PAIR,GOLD WITH FEATHER DESIGN ,KNEELING
  EGYPTIAN BASE............................................   90.00
LAMP,ART GLASS TABLE.......................................   15.00
LAMP,ART NOUVEAU BASE,SPATTER SHADE,PINK,WIRED.............   95.01-
LAMP,ART NOUVEAU EBONIZED TABLE,TOP CARVED IN 8-LOBED
  STYLIZED LEAF............................................   95.00
LAMP,ART NOUVEAU,SATIN MUSHROOM SHADE EDGED IN GREEN,IRON
  BASE....................................................   65.00
LAMP,ART NOUVEAU TABLE,BRASS BASE WITH FIELD POPPIES.......   75.00
LAMP,ASTRAL,CRANBERRY,CLEAR PEDESTAL BASE..................   65.00
LAMP,ASTRAL,DOUBLE STEP MARBLE BASE,FROSTED GLOBE..........   90.00
LAMP,ASTRAL,ETCHED GLOBE,BRASS COLUMN & MARBLE BASE........  110.00
LAMP,ASTRAL WITH PRISMS....................................   65.00
LAMP,BANNER................................................    8.00
LAMP,BANQUET ,4 FOOTED BASE,HANDPAINTED FLOWER SHADE.......  110.00
LAMP,BANQUET 21 IN. TALL,BRASS FOUNT,.....................   25.00
LAMP,BANQUET,33 IN. TALL,BALL SHADE IN BLUE,GREEN &
  WHITE,BRASS FOUNT........................................   80.00
LAMP,BANQUET,FOUNT OF YELLOW TO ORANGE ,WHITE LINED,BRASS
  PEDESTAL.................................................   35.00
LAMP BASE 16IN. CUT GLASS..................................   45.00
LAMP,BASE & BURNER OF ALADDIN,BASE PINK OPALESCENT GLASS....   12.00
LAMP,BASKETWEAVE ,PRESSED GLASS FOUNT......................   12.00
LAMP,BEAUTY-NITE,MILK GLASS SHADE..........................   18.00
LAMP,BELLFLOWER ON MARBLE BASE.............................   40.00
LAMP,BETTY,BRASS,.........................................   48.00
LAMP,BETTY LAMP IRON.......................................   60.00
LAMP,BICYCLE OIL,RED & GREEN GLASS REFLECTORS..............   12.50
LAMP,BIGLER WHALE OIL BASE 9 IN............................   30.00
LAMP,BLOWN CLEAR GLASS FINE RIB,APPLIED HANDLE.............   18.00
LAMP,BLUE GLASS HAND.......................................   18.00
```

```
LAMP,BLUE MINIATURE SUN LIGHT,TIN BASE WITH RING HANDLE.....     27.50
LAMP,BLUE PATTERN GLASS...................................      7.50
LAMP,BLUE SATIN GLASS HANGING,5 IN. LONG,BRASS FITTINGS
   35.00  TO..............................................     40.00
LAMP,BLUE TWINKLE WITH STARS..............................     17.50
LAMP,BLUE WINDMILL,SQUARE FOUNT,BLOWN GLASS BALL SHADE......     65.00
LAMP,BOHEMIAN GLASS HAND,WHITE MILK GLASS BASE.............     25.00
LAMP,BRACKET..............................................     15.00
LAMP,BRASS 3 ARM HANGING,INDIAN FINIALS....................    100.00
LAMP,BRASS,5 LIGHT CHANDELIER.............................     10.50
LAMP,BRACKET WITH 9 IN. MERCURY REFLECTOR,ELECTRIFIED......     25.00
LAMP,BRASS & TEAKWOOD BASE,GREEN,MOTTLED & WHITE CARVED JADE    325.00
LAMP,BRASS ALI BABA.......................................      8.00
LAMP,BRASS ANGLE,MILK GLASS TOP...........................     32.50
LAMP,BRASS ASTRAL BASE,LACQUERED,17 IN. TALL..............     60.00
LAMP,BRASS BASE GONE WITH THE WIND,FLORAL BALL SHADE........     48.00
LAMP,BRASS BASE PAT.1898,FROSTED & ETCHED TAM-O-SHANTER
   SHADE..................................................     40.00
LAMP,BRASS BASE,WHITE BALL TYPE SHADE WITH DAFFODILS........     55.00
LAMP,BRASS BASE WITH APRICOT MOTHER OF PEARL SATIN GLASS
   SHADE,WIRED............................................    150.00
LAMP,BRASS BASE WITH CAMEO SHADE,WIRED....................    150.00
LAMP,BRASS BASE WITH ROMAN KEY BAND,WHITE GLASS SHADE......     40.00
LAMP,BRASS CARBIDE MINERS.................................      9.50
LAMP,BRASS FONT,EMBOSSED IRON FOOT & HANDLES,GLASS SHADE....     39.50
LAMP,BRASS FONT,IRON BASE,WHITE METAL HANDLES,WHITE SHADE...     25.00
LAMP,BRASS FRAME HANGING,14 IN. DECORATED SHADE,CLEAR
   PATTERN FONT,.........................................     75.00
LAMP,BRASS FRAME HANGING,KITCHEN TYPE,14 IN. WHITE
   HANDPAINTED SHADE......................................     37.50
LAMP,BRASS ,GIRL HEADS ON LACY FOUNT,GREEN CHINA SHADE......     79.50
LAMP,BRASS HALL WITH CLEAR FROSTED & ETCHED GLOBE...........     65.00
LAMP,BRASS HALL WITH CRANBERRY GLOBE......................     90.00
LAMP,BRASS HAND WITH CHIMNEY..............................      4.75
LAMP,BRASS HANGING,YELLOW CASED HALF SHADE,PRISMS,WIRED.....    135.00
LAMP,BRASS HEAT MARKED OPTIMUS #5 MADE IN SWEDEN...........     12.50
LAMP,BRASS,LANTERN STYLE,ELECTRIFIED......................     15.00
LAMP,BRASS PIANO,ADJUSTABLE,FLOOR TYPE WITH BRASS FOUNT.....     69.50
LAMP,BRASS PIANO WITH IRON FRETWORK SHELF,FROSTED CUT GLOBE.    115.00
LAMP,BRASS RAYO...........................................     18.00
LAMP,BRASS RAYO FANCY EMBOSSED BOTTOM,POLISHED.............     25.00
LAMP,BRASS STUDENT,23 IN. TALL,GREEN CASED WITH WHITE SHADE.    130.00
LAMP,BRASS TURKISH,OVAL HALF MOON SHAPE,LACY BRASS SHADE....     75.00
LAMP,BRASS WALL BRACKET, AURENE SIGNED SHADE,WIRED..........    150.00
LAMP,BRASS WITH HANDLE & TUBE BURNER,PAT.1867.............      6.50
LAMP,BRAZILIAN SLAVE,USED BY SLAVES IN BRAZIL
   1690-1900,CASTOR OIL..................................     18.50
LAMP,BRISTOL OVERLAY,ENAMELLED............................     85.00
LAMP,BRONZE GOD THOR ALADIN,4 WICKS.......................     34.00
LAMP,BRONZE HANDEL MARKED BASE............................     17.50
LAMP,BRONZE TABLE,LEADED SHADE,PANES & TULIPS.............    125.00
LAMP,BROODER TIN..........................................      3.00
LAMP,BUGGY DASH LIGHT
   5.00  TO...............................................     10.00
LAMP,BUGGY,PAIR...........................................     10.00
LAMP,BULLS EYE KEROSENE...................................     18.00
LAMP,BURMESE FAIRY,3 IN. SHADE ON CLARKE BASE WITH CLARKE
   CANDLE.................................................    125.00
LAMP,BURMESE FAIRY,CLARKE BASE
   95.00  TO..............................................    125.00
LAMP,BURMESE FAIRY,CLARKE POTTERY BASE....................    120.00
LAMP,BURMESE FAIRY ON SIGNED CLARKE BASE..................    130.00
LAMP,BURMESE MINIATURE FAIRY ON SIGNED CLARKE BASE.........    175.00
LAMP,BUTTERSCOTCH MARBLE TYPE TIFFANY,CHAIN & HANGING
   FIXTURES...............................................     69.00
```

LAMP,CAMEO,4 COLOUR FLORAL SIGNED FRANCISIS,WIRED........... 350.00
LAMP,CAMEO,4 COLOUR SCENIC SIGNED MULLER,WIRED.............. 300.00
LAMP,CAMEO CARVED,HELMET SHELL............................. 15.00
LAMP,CAMEO SIGNED LE GRAS,5 COLOUR,WIRED................... 350.00
LAMP,CANDLE,6 IN.,METAL BOTTOM,RED BEADED FROSTED
   SHADES,PAIR... 16.50
LAMP,CANDLE PAIR BRASS PEDESTAL ON ROUND BRASS BASES,WHITE
   GLASS SHADES.. 69.50
LAMP,CARBIDE MINERS.. 4.75
LAMP,CARRIAGE,BRASS,26 IN. HIGH............................ 38.00
LAMP,CARRIAGE,HEXAGONAL SHAPE WITH 3 OVAL GLASS WINDOWS..... 20.00
LAMP,CARVED CAMEO SHELL.................................... 47.50
LAMP,CARVED CAMEO SHELL,SCENIC............................. 37.50
LAMP,CAST IRON 1875,4-BRANCH CHANDELIER,OIL,BRASS RINGS &
   BURNERS... 98.00
LAMP,CAST IRON HANGING,CLEAR GLASS FONT,WHITE DOME SHADE.... 52.50
LAMP,CAST IRON HANGING DATED ON FOUNT & FRAME 1875,WHITE
   SHADE... 48.50
LAMP,CEILING PRISM LIGHT FIXTURE,1900,2 ROWS PRISMS,AMBER
   GLASS... 22.50
LAMP,CELADON BASE,15 IN.................................... 29.50
LAMP,CHARTREUSE NAILSEA FAIRY ON PRESSED CLARKE BASE........ 50.00
LAMP,CHERUB WITH BURMESE SHADE,WIRED....................... 185.00
LAMP,CHILDS NIGHT PATENT JUNE 23,1863,BASE FIGURE OF CHILD.. 22.00
LAMP,CLARKE CRICKLITE FAIRY,DIAMOND POINT,CLEAR BASE & DOME. 15.00
LAMP,CLEAR DOOLIDGE DRAPE,BASE WITH FOUNT.................. 10.00
LAMP,CLEAR FLINT,THUMBPRINT,BRASS STEM TO MARBLE BASE....... 14.00
LAMP,CLEAR GLASS,FLINT HANDLED,OIL GUARD PAT.1870.......... 10.00
LAMP,CLEAR GLASS MINIATURE,BRASS CONNECTIONS,SWIRL PATTERN.. 8.50
LAMP,CLEAR GOOFUS TYPE,RAISED ROSES........................ 11.00
LAMP,CLEAR LION... 75.00
LAMP,CLEAR PATTERN GLASS OIL,FROSTED FOUNT & SHADE.......... 22.00
LAMP,CLEAR PRESSED GLASS BANDED PRISM,BRASS STEM,MARBLE BASE 15.00
LAMP,CLEAR SPANISH COIN................................... 49.50
LAMP,CLEAR SQUATTY GLOW,WIDE RIBBED CORSET SHAPED CHIMNEY IN
   WHITE... 15.00
LAMP,CLOISONNE,28 IN. HIGH................................. 15.00
LAMP,COACH LIGHT.. 20.00
LAMP,COBALT BLUE ALCOHOL,DOCTORS STYLE..................... 18.00
LAMP,COBALT BLUE GLASS PEDESTAL IN DRAPERY PATTERN......... 39.00
LAMP,COMPLETE BRASS,CLIMAX REFLECTOR LIGHT................. 19.00
LAMP,COMPLETE BRASS LANTERN............................... 9.00
LAMP,COOLIDGE DRAPE PATTERN GLASS HAND.................... 12.00
LAMP,COOLIDGE NO. 2....................................... 17.50
LAMP,COPPER BETTY WITH PICK & HOOK........................ 30.00
LAMP,COPPER BROODER,8 IN. HIGH............................ 15.00
LAMP,COPPER FACTORY 3 WICK SPOUT WITH SNUFFER,DATED BRASS
   CAP 1857.. 25.00
LAMP,COSMOS MINIATURE..................................... 35.00
LAMP,CRANBERRY.. 75.00
LAMP,CRANBERRY BULLS EYE HANGING,14 IN. SHADE,BRASS FONT,30
   4IN. PRISMS... 225.00
LAMP,CRANBERRY HAND WITH BURNER & CLEAR CHIMNEY,BRASS COLLAR 45.00
LAMP,CRANBERRY HANGING,RIBBED............................. 85.00
LAMP,CRANBERRY HOBNAIL 14 IN. SHADE,HANGING,2 SETS
   PRISMS,BRASS FOUNT...................................... 275.00
LAMP,CRANBERRY HOBNAIL HANGING WITH PRISMS................. 265.00
LAMP,CRESOLENE ,MILK GLASS CHIMNEY........................ 8.50
LAMP,CRESOLENE OIL,VAPOURIZER,MILK GLASS GLOBE............. 9.00
LAMP,CRESOLENE VAPO....................................... 6.50
LAMP,CRESOLENE,VAPO,AMBER WITH MILK GLASS CHIMNEY.......... 15.00
LAMP,CUSTARD GLASS SHADE,BRASS FOUNT,38 PRISMS,40 IN....... 195.00
LAMP,CUSTARD SHADE,FLEUR DE LIS RAISED EMBOSSES,CHERUB
   PEWTER.. 78.00
LAMP,CYLINDER,BRONZE FITTINGS,HANDPAINTED SCENE,SHADE SIGNED

```
BACCARAT.................................................  35.00
LAMP,DARK BLUE NUTMEG....................................  17.50
LAMP,DARLING, 14IN. H. CUT & PRESSED GLASS BASE..........  37.50
LAMP,DAUM NANCY SIGNED,4 COLOUR,WIRED.................... 300.00
LAMP,DAUM NANCY SIGNED,8 IN.,PINK & PURPLE,BRONZE BASE... 125.00
LAMP,DAVIS BRASS PATENT DATED 1856.......................  75.00
LAMP,DOLPHIN WITH BLUE FOUNT............................. 375.00
LAMP,DOME FOR CEILING SIGNED HANDLE,BRASS FILIGREE DESIGN... 175.00
LAMP,DOTTED AMERICAN SHIELD HAND.........................  10.00
LAMP,DOUBLE ANGLE,MILK GLASS SHADE,NICKEL FINISHED FONT..  55.00
LAMP,DOUBLE HANDLED RIPLEY 1868 WITH BURNER & CHIMNEY....  11.00
LAMP,DOUBLE OPEN BETTY...................................  25.00
LAMP,DOUBLE OPEN BETTY WITH HANGER.......................  20.00
LAMP,DOUBLE RIBBON FROSTED ,BRASS COLLAR DATED 1867.....  22.50
LAMP,DOUBLE STUDENT,WEIGHT 12 POUNDS,ELECTRIFIED,25 IN.
  HIGH,BRASS.............................................  85.00
LAMP,EFFULGENT STAR,RING HANDLED,4 IN....................  18.50
LAMP,EIGHT LILY LIGHT TABLE QUEZAL,7 SHADES,SIGNED,GREEN
  &WHITE................................................ 600.00
LAMP,ELECTRIC TABLE,METAL BASE,FROSTED GLASS SHADE,SCENIC...  38.00
LAMP,EMBOSSED PINK CASED GLASS MINIATURE,...............  30.00
LAMP,EMBOSSED PINK SATIN GLASS MINIATURE,,SQUARE BASE... 150.00
LAMP,EMBOSSED SAFETY,HORSESHOE HANDLE....................  10.00
LAMP,FAIRY,2 STORY CASTLE WITH TURRETS & WINDOWS........  19.00
LAMP,FAIRY,3 IN. TALL ON SIGNED CLARKES PATTERN GLASS
  BASE,YELLOW SHADE......................................  47.00
LAMP,FAIRY,3 PIECE,BLUE FLOWERED TOP.....................  15.00
LAMP,FAIRY,AMBER SATIN GLASS SWIRL IN RAISED RIBBED & PUFFED
  PATTERN...............................................  45.00
LAMP,FAIRY,CLEAR BASE,3-MOLD-CAMPHOR TOP.................  15.00
LAMP,FAIRY,GREEN SILVERIA SHADE ON PRESSED BASE.........  65.00
LAMP,FAIRY,NAILSEA SHADE IN CITRON COLOR ON MARKED CLARKES
  BASE..................................................  50.00
LAMP,FAIRY OF 2 STORY HOUSE WITH GABLE & CHIMNEY........  37.50
LAMP,FAIRY,OPAQUE BLUE CHIMNEY,MARKED DIAMOND CANDLE CO..  15.00
LAMP,FAIRY,PEG WITH SATIN CRANBERRY SHADE................  42.00
LAMP,FAIRY,PEG STAND WITH VASELINE GLASS PETAL SHADE....  40.00
LAMP,FAIRY,ROSE COLOR IN MOTHER OF PEARL,SATIN SHADE,MARKED
  CLARKES...............................................  70.00
LAMP,FAIRY,SHADE IN CRYSTAL OVERLAPPING LEAVES IN BLUE
  ,CLARKES BASE.........................................  45.00
LAMP,FAIRY SIGNED BACCARAT,BLUE,5 IN. DIAMETER..........  57.50
LAMP,FAIRY,SIGNED CLARKES PATTERN GLASS BASE,CRANBERRY
  NAILSEA SHADE.........................................  45.00
LAMP,FAIRY,SIGNED CLARKES PATTERN GLASS BASE,MOTHER OF PEARL
  SHADE.................................................  50.00
LAMP,FAIRY,STEVENS & WILLIAMS CAMPHOR SATIN SHADE,GREEN
  SATIN TOP.............................................  55.00
LAMP,FAIRY,WHITE CRACKLE GLASS PATTERN ON VASELINE SATIN
  BACKGROUND............................................  42.00
LAMP,FLASHED RED IRIDESCENT HAND CANDLE,OVAL BALL CRYSTAL
  SHADE.................................................  20.00
LAMP,FLINT CLEAR TABLE,ROUGH PONTIL,FLANGE FOOTED,6 IN..  14.00
LAMP,FLINT GLASS WHALE OIL..............................  25.00
LAMP,FLINT FOUNT,LEE PAT.,BRASS STEM,MARBLE BASE........  22.00
LAMP,FLINT SPARKING LIGHT,TUBE BURNER...................   6.00
LAMP,FLINT WHALE OIL,BLOWN FOUNT,APPLIED RINGS,4 STEP BASE..  22.00
LAMP,FLOOR-TYPE STANDING LIGHTING DEVICE,TRIPOD.........  75.00
LAMP,FLORENTINE CAMEO BLUE ON WHITE SIGNED,WIRED........ 150.00
LAMP,FRENCH, 12 IN. TALL,EMBOSSED IN FILIGREED GOLD OVER
  RED,BRASS BASE........................................  75.00
LAMP,FRENCH OPALINE GLASS WITH GILDED METAL HANDLES CIRCA
  1820.................................................. 355.00
LAMP,FRUIT,BOAT SHAPE EMBOSSED BOWL,CHERUB
  HANDLES,ELECTRIFIED...................................  87.50
```

LAMP,GALLE 5 COLOUR,SIGNED,WIRED............................ 650.00
LAMP,GAS FIXTURE,BRONZED FIGURE HUNTER WITH STAFF........... 18.50
LAMP,GEORGE WASHINGTON...................................... 20.00
LAMP,GERMAN CHINA IN DRESDEN STYLE,2 CUPIDS ON FOOTED BASE.. 150.00
LAMP,GLASS,APPLIED HANDLE................................... 9.00
LAMP,GLASS,MUSHROOM TOP,ETCHED FLOWERS...................... 25.00
LAMP,GLASS PEDESTAL,BLUE FOUNT,EMBOSSED HEXAGON PATTERN,13
  IN. TALL... 55.00
LAMP,GLASS PEDESTAL HAND WITH HANDLE,TORPEDO PATTERN........ 8.50
LAMP,GLOBULAR GAS LIGHT FIXTURE BY COLT WITH COLT MARK...... 35.00
LAMP,GONE WITH THE WIND
  70.00 TO... 125.00
LAMP,GONE WITH THE WIND,18 IN. TALL,MILK GLASS FOUNT,PINK
  SHADE.. 50.00
LAMP,GONE WITH THE WIND,21 IN.,CREAM BACKGROUND WITH FLOWERS
  ,YELLOW.. 90.00
LAMP,GONE-WITH-THE-WIND,21 IN. TALL,ELECTRIFIED,RED & WHITE
  SHADE.. 85.00
LAMP,GONE WITH THE WIND,22 IN.,BRASS FOOT & CAN,ROSE TO
  YELLOW SHADE... 95.00
LAMP,GONE WITH THE WIND,AUBURN WITH BLUE FLOWERS............ 75.00
LAMP,GONE WITH THE WIND,ELECTRIFIED,3 WAY,CREAM TO
  PINK,CALLA LILLIES....................................... 65.00
LAMP,GONE WITH THE WIND,GREEN BACKGROUND WITH RED COSMOS.... 65.00
LAMP,GONE WITH THE WIND,GREEN WITH POPPIES IN ORANGE,BRASS
  COLLAR... 85.00
LAMP,GONE WITH THE WIND,PINK SHADE & BASE,BRASS BASE,....... 115.00
LAMP,GONE WITH THE WIND RED SATIN GLASS,25 IN. TALL......... 225.00
LAMP,GONE WITH THE WIND,SATIN GLASS,RED IRIS PATTERN BASE &
  GLOBE.. 200.00
LAMP,GONE WITH THE WIND,SCENES OF LITTLE BO PEEP............ 78.00
LAMP,GRAF ZEPPELIN IRON..................................... 12.00
LAMP,GRAPE BAND KEROSENE.................................... 7.50
LAMP,GREASE,TIN... 12.50
LAMP,GREEN & CLEAR BEADED HEART KEROSENE.................... 10.00
LAMP,GREEN BRISTOL GLASS FOUNT WITH RED ROSED,GOLD DRAPERY.. 27.50
LAMP,GREEN CUT TO CLEAR PEAR SHAPED FOUNT,BRASS STEM,MARBLE
  BASE... 36.00
LAMP,GREEN GLASS OIL BASE,PATTERNED BOWL,FLUTED STEM........ 12.50
LAMP,GREEN MILK GLASS BASE.................................. 22.00
LAMP,GREEN SATIN GLASS DESK,HANDPAINTED NIAGARA FALLS....... 10.00
LAMP,HALF SHADE,BRASS FOOT & CAN,HANDPAINTED SHADE.......... 47.50
LAMP,HALL FOR HANGING,CARAMEL SLAG GLASS PANELS,METAL FRAME. 12.00
LAMP,HAND,CLEAR GLASS,COOLIDGE DRAPE........................ 10.00
LAMP,HAND,CLEAR,MARKED PAT.SEPT.20,1870..................... 12.00
LAMP,HAND WITH MELON RIBBED BOWL ,BURNER PAT.1873........... 6.00
LAMP,HAND WITH TOM THUMB BURNER............................. 15.00
LAMP,HANGING,14 IN. BLUE SHADE,FLOWERED,BRASS FRAME ,30
  PRISMS... 72.50
LAMP,HANGING,14 IN. CHINA SHADE WITH BLUE BIRD,GOLDEN
  WHEAT,LEAVES... 69.50
LAMP,HANGING,14 IN. CHINA SHADE WITH PURPLE AND ORCHID
  PEONIES.. 69.50
LAMP,HANGING,14 IN. ,PINK SATIN GLASS HOBNAIL SHADE,BRASS
  FOUNT,PRISMS... 250.00
LAMP,HANGING,.. 20.00
LAMP,HANGING,BOATS,LIGHT HOUSE,FILIGREE BRASS TRIM & FINIAL. 20.00
LAMP,HANGING BRASS ANGLE,3 BURNER........................... 135.00
LAMP,HANGING,BRASS BASE,PRISMS,VASELINE INVERTED HOBNAIL.... 150.00
LAMP,HANGING,BRASS FILIGREE FRAME,HALF SHADE,WHITE BRISTOL.. 115.00
LAMP,HANGING,BRISTOL SHADE.................................. 30.00
LAMP,HANGING CRANBERRY BULLS EYE SHADE,CRANBERRY FONT....... 400.00
LAMP,HANGING CRANBERRY HALL,8 IN. INVERTED RIB
  SHADE,FONT,CHIMNEY....................................... 57.00
LAMP,HANGING,CRANBERRY INVERTED BULLS EYE WITH WHITE OUTER

```
SHADE.................................................... 200.00
LAMP,HANGING HALL IN AMBER GLASS,HONEYCOMB PATTERN,BRASS
  FITTINGS............................................... 28.00
LAMP,HANGING HALL WITH CRANBERRY OPALESCENT SWIRLED SHADE... 30.00
LAMP,HANGING LEADED TIFFANY TYPE DOME,COSMOS
  FLOWERS,MUSHROOM SHAPE................................. 175.00
LAMP,HANGING MILK GLASS HALL,5 IN. MELON RIBBED SHADE....... 48.00
LAMP,HANGING PAINTED 14 IN. SHADE & FONT,PINK FLOWERS,BRASS
  CONNECTION............................................. 90.00
LAMP,HANGING,PINK SATIN GLASS RIBBED SHADE,BRASS FOUNT...... 250.00
LAMP,HANGING,RED SATIN GLASS BALL SHADE,BRASS
  CHAINS,FITTINGS....................................... 68.00
LAMP,HANGING,STUDENTS,DOUBLE BRASS ACORN FOUNTS,........... 198.50
LAMP,HANGING,WHITE BRISTOL SHADE,COPPER FONT,PRISMS & BEADED
  CHAINS............................................... 85.00
LAMP,HANGING WITH 14 IN. CLEAR SHADE,42 PRISMS,BRASS FONT... 165.00
LAMP,HANGING WITH MILK GLASS FOUNT........................ 49.00
LAMP,HEBREW TEMPLE HANGING,25 IN. BRONZE,7 POINTS.......... 125.00
LAMP,HURRICANE HARNESS MAKERS,TOLE & CRYSTAL.............. 35.00
LAMP,IRON BANQUET,37 IN. TALL,BALL SHADE,WHITE TO CRANBERRY. 85.00
LAMP,IRON BETTY,COPPER TRIM............................... 45.00
LAMP,IRON BETTY,DOUBLE BASE............................... 26.00
LAMP,IRON BRACKET........................................ 7.50
LAMP,IRON DOUBLE BASE PHOEBE.............................. 42.00
LAMP,IRON NIGHT LIGHT WITH PEACOCK....................... 8.50
LAMP,JEWELED BRASS HANGING,CUT OUT FLOWER PATTERN,BALL SHADE 35.00
LAMP,JEWELED FAIRY,GILT BASE,FINGER LOOP HANDLE........... 59.00
LAMP,KEROSENE,9 IN.,PATTERN GLASS BELLFLOWER............. 38.75
LAMP,KEROSENE........................................... 19.50
LAMP,KEROSENE ,CLEAR BOWL,MARKED 1870.................... 18.00
LAMP,KEROSENE,YELLOWISH GREEN,BEADED OVALS & FLUTING....... 32.50
LAMP,KINGS CROWN HANDLED................................. 10.00
LAMP,KITCHEN WALL,TIN REFLECTOR.......................... 6.50
LAMP,KODAK TIN DARKROOM OIL,9 IN......................... 12.00
LAMP,LACY IRON SINGLE BRACKET............................ 4.50
LAMP,LARD OIL,19TH CENTURY,SHEET TIN..................... 47.50
LAMP,LEADED GLASS SHADE,DRAGON DESIGN,ON CLOISONNE
  VASE,MOSAIC.........................................5,000.00
LAMP,LEADED TIFFANY TYPE TABLE,240 PIECES OF LEADED GLASS... 110.00
LAMP,LIMOGES CHINA,SATIN GLASS SHADE..................... 85.00
LAMP,LOW PIANO,CREAM WITH GRAY & GREEN PALMS IN HAND
  PAINT,10 IN. SHADE................................... 72.00
LAMP,MAJOLICA & BRASS STUDENT,WHITE SHADE & CHIMNEY....... 125.00
LAMP,MAJOLICA BASE,COBALT BLUE WITH PINK FLOWERS,TIFFANY
  TYPE SHADE.......................................... 120.00
LAMP,MANTLE GAS-LIGHT,ISINGLASS CHIMNEY,1905............. 2.00
LAMP,MARBLE BASE,BRASS STEM,CUT GLASS FONT............... 15.00
LAMP,MARKED CLARKS CRICKLITE FAIRY,CLEAR BASE............ 35.00
LAMP,MARY GREGORY BLUE,SANDWICH GLASS,BOY & BIRD......... 85.00
LAMP,MATCHED PAIR KEROSENE BEDROOM...................... 29.00
LAMP,METAL ANGLE WITH BRASS,WHITE SHADE................. 22.50
LAMP,METAL BASE,GONE WITH THE WIND...................... 65.00
LAMP,METAL BASE,MILK GLASS FONT,RAISED DESIGN........... 24.50
LAMP,METAL FIGURINE WITH STUDENT SHADE.................. 35.00
LAMP,MILK GLASS CHARTRUESE ALADDIN...................... 30.00
LAMP,MILK GLASS,EMBOSSED NUTMEG,WIRE HANDLE,CHIMNEY...... 14.00
LAMP,MILK GLASS GASLIGHT FLUTED SHADE................... 5.00
LAMP,MILK GLASS MINIATURE
  8.50  TO............................................. 18.00
LAMP,MILK GLASS RECLINING ELEPHANT,FROSTED BALL SHADE.... 65.00
LAMP,MILK GLASS ROUND & RIBBED WITH 2 PAINTED PANELS..... 8.50
LAMP,MILK GLASS WITH 4 ROUND PANELS,EMBOSSED SCROLLS &
  FLOWERS............................................. 8.50
LAMP,MILK GLASS WITH GRAY SHADE......................... 17.50
LAMP,MILKY OPALENE 10 IN.,SWIRLED FONT.................. 25.00
```

```
LAMP,MILLEFIORI...................................................  50.00
LAMP,MILLEFIORI,20 IN. TALL,BLUE,GREEN & RED..................... 225.00
LAMP,MILLEFIORI MINIATURE,BLUE,GREEN & RED.......................  75.00
LAMP,MINE INSPECTORS,MULLENS MFG. CO.,11 IN. TALL...............  15.00
LAMP,MINERS.......................................................   8.00
LAMP,MINERS CARBIDE...............................................   4.50
LAMP,MINIATURE,AMBER CHEMISTS DATED 1893,BRASS HOLDER........  22.50
LAMP,MINIATURE BEAUTY NIGHT,MILK GLASS BEEHIVE SHADE.........  18.50
LAMP,MINIATURE BRASS,BRASS SHADE WITH 3 GREEN GLASS OVAL
  INSERTS.........................................................  27.50
LAMP,MINIATURE BRASS CHAMBER,....................................  21.50
LAMP,MINIATURE BURMESE FAIRY..................................... 135.00
LAMP,MINIATURE CAMEO,10 IN. HIGH,ARTIST SIGNED GALLE,PURPLE
  TO LAVENDER..................................................... 225.00
LAMP,MINIATURE,CLEAR,MARKED BUTTERCUP..........................  10.00
LAMP,MINIATURE CRANBERRY.........................................  30.00
LAMP,MINIATURE CRANBERRY GLASS HAND,DIAMOND RIBBED
  PATTERN,ACID FINISH............................................  20.00
LAMP,MINIATURE CRANBERRY INVERTED THUMBPRINT.................  47.50
LAMP,MINIATURE CRESOLENE WITH MILK GLASS CHIMNEY.............   6.50
LAMP,MINIATURE FISHSCALE,CLEAR..................................  12.50
LAMP,MINIATURE GLOW MARKED,GONE WITH THE WIND SHAPE,CLEAR
  RIBBED..........................................................  30.00
LAMP,MINIATURE,GONE WITH THE WIND,MILK GLASS WITH FLEUR DE
  LIS PATTERN.....................................................  45.95
LAMP,MINIATURE,GREEN,MARKED TWINKLE.............................  15.00
LAMP,MINIATURE GREEN SATIN FAIRY PYRAMID MARKED S.CLARK WITH
  HOBNAIL.........................................................  38.50
LAMP,MINIATURE,MILK GLASS CANDLESTICK GLOW.....................  34.50
LAMP,MINIATURE MILK GLASS IN EMBOSSED FLOWER DESIGN..........  38.50
LAMP,MINIATURE MILK GLASS IN FLOWER PATTERN...................  45.00
LAMP,MINIATURE MILK GLASS,SQUARE BASE WITH RAISED SCROLL
  DESIGN,.........................................................  22.50
LAMP,MINIATURE MILK GLASS WITH LINCOLN DRAPE SHADE,GOLD.....  39.50
LAMP,MINIATURE NELLY BLY TYPE RED FLOWERS,LEAVES.............  39.50
LAMP,MINIATURE NICKLE PLATED EMBOSSED RAYO,ELECTRIFIED......  25.00
LAMP,MINIATURE OIL,BULLS EYE.....................................  10.00
LAMP,MINIATURE,OLD ROSE,DIAMOND QUILTED........................ 385.00
LAMP,MINIATURE OPALESCENT SPOT..................................  20.00
LAMP,MINIATURE RED SATIN GLASS,TULIP SHADE,MEDALLION & PLUME
  BASE............................................................  55.00
LAMP,MINIATURE RED SATIN PAIR,SQUATTY BASE WITH DRAPERY FOLD  90.00
LAMP,MINIATURE,WHITE MILK GLASS.................................   8.00
LAMP,MINIATURE,YELLOW SATIN FAIRY PYRAMID MARKED S.CLARK
  BASE............................................................  32.50
LAMP,MIRROR-TYPE BRACKET,AUSTRIAN..............................  17.50
LAMP,MODEL T FORD KEROSENE......................................   9.50
LAMP,MOTHER OF PEARL SATIN GLASS FAIRY ,YELLOW,DRAPE
  PATTERN,1886....................................................  85.00
LAMP,MT.WASHINGTON CAMEO ON BRONZE BASE,FEMALE PROFILES..... 400.00
LAMP,MULTI-COLOURED JEWEL BRASS HANGING,BEVELED CLEAR
  CENTERS......................................................... 150.00
LAMP,NICKEL ELECTRIFIED,BRISTOL WHITE SHADE...................  27.00
LAMP,NIGHT,CLEAR COSMOS.........................................  18.50
LAMP,NIGHT LIGHT SIGNED G.ARGY,ROUSSEAU,PATE DE VERRE,PURPLE 475.00
LAMP,NIGHT,PRESSED & BLOWN OIL SECTION.........................  20.00
LAMP,OAK,HANDCARVED,5 BRANCHES,MARBLE SHADES,43 IN. HIGH.... 425.00
LAMP,OIL,10 IN. HIGH,IRON BASE,GREEN GLASS STEM PAINTED.....  12.00
LAMP,OIL BASE,IRON BASE,BLUE FLUTED MILK GLASS COLUMN,BRASS
  COLLARS.........................................................  28.50
LAMP,OIL,CLEAR BOWL & BEADED BASE..............................  15.00
LAMP,OIL DESK ,SILVER,CRYSTAL CHIMNEY,12 IN. TALL............  45.00
LAMP,OIL,IRON & BRASS BASE,FROSTED PANELLED BOWL,PAT.1875...  10.50
LAMP,OIL,CLEAR GLASS.............................................   6.50
LAMP,OIL WALL BRACKET WITH REFLECTOR PEG.......................   5.00
```

```
LAMP,OPAQUE BEIGE MANTEL,DRAPE PATTERN....................    15.00
LAMP,ORANGE,PINK & YELLOW SWIRLED END OF DAY MINIATURE......    32.50
LAMP,ORIENTAL OIL,INNER GLASS TUBE,BRASS BASE WITH SILVER
  PLATE....................................................    37.50
LAMP,ORIENTAL VASE NAVY BLUE WITH IMARI HANDPAINTED
  FIGURES,11 IN. TALL......................................    40.00
LAMP,ORNATE SILVER SEALING WAX WITH SEAL HOLDER............     9.00
LAMP,OVAL CHIMNEY GLASS....................................    30.00
LAMP,PAINTED TIN KEROSENE LAMP.............................     4.00
LAMP,PAIR ALADDIN BASES,STRIPPED...........................    30.00
LAMP,PAIR,ALADDIN LINCOLN DRAPE............................    14.95
LAMP,PAIR BELLFLOWER WHALE OIL,MARBLE BASES................    70.00
LAMP,PAIR BLOWN BLACK GLASS,10 IN. TALL....................    85.00
LAMP,PAIR BRASS WEBB LIGHTS,...............................   225.00
LAMP,PAIR BULLS-EYE & FLEUR-DE-LIS ON MARBLE BASE..........   100.00
LAMP,PAIR CARRIAGE,BRASS EAGLE ORNAMENT....................    45.00
LAMP,PAIR CARRIAGE,ELECTRIFIED WITH HANDCUT CRYSTAL........    90.00
LAMP,PAIR CLARKE SIGNED FAIRY,PYRAMID,DIAMOND POINT AMBER
  TOP......................................................    45.00
LAMP,PAIR FLORENTINE,HAND CARVED FRUIT.....................   650.00
LAMP,PAIR HURRICANE CANDLE,SILVER-PLATED,CHERUBS...........    18.50
LAMP,PAIR HURRICANE CANDLE,TURNED WOOD BASES,5 IN. PRISMS,..    45.00
LAMP,PAIR FRENCH BRONZE PEG WITH IRIDESCENT BOWLS WITH
  FLOWER ENAMELING.........................................   125.00
LAMP,PAIR LACY SANDWICH WHALE OIL,HEARTS,PEACOCK EYES......    85.00
LAMP,PAIR MARBLE AND BRASS,SHADES & PRISMS.................    24.00
LAMP,PAIR MATCHED SHIPS ,20 IN. HIGH.......................    60.00
LAMP,PAIR PEG,BLUE FRENCH GLASS,WHITE ENAMEL PAINTED
  DECORATION...............................................    60.00
LAMP,PAIR,PEG,PLATED SILVER CANDLESTICK,SQUARE BASE........   110.00
LAMP,PAIR PEG,WHITE ART GLASS BALL SHAPE,APPLIED PURPLE
  RASPBERRIES..............................................    61.50
LAMP,PAIRPOINT 21 IN. HIGH,MARKED,3 DOLPHINS FORM BRONZE
  BASE.....................................................   120.00
LAMP,PAIRPOINT,21 IN. HIGH,MUSHROOM SHAPED SHADE...........   300.00
LAMP,PAIR TIN JACK-O-LANTERNS ON 36 IN. STAFF,1890.........    25.00
LAMP,PAIR WAFFLE WHALE OIL.................................    70.00
LAMP,PAIR WHALE OIL,QUATREFOIL,9 IN. ETCHED FONT...........   100.00
LAMP,PAIR WHALE OIL SANDWICH,BLOWN FOUNTS,4 STEP DOWNS.....    70.00
LAMP,PAIR WELLER,ROOKWOOD COLOURING,11 IN. HIGH............    60.00
LAMP,PAIR WITH WHITE IRIDESCENT HALF SHADES,BRACKET,YELLOW
  TOP......................................................   125.00
LAMP,PALMETTE KEROSENE.....................................    12.00
LAMP,PANELLED CRANBERRY HALL,BRASS FRAME...................    45.00
LAMP,PATTERN GLASS MOUNTAIN LAUREL,BULLSEYE,CABLE..........    18.00
LAMP,PATTERN QUARTERED BLOCK HANDLE........................     6.50
LAMP,PEG,3 IN. BALL, PEWTER WHALE OIL BURNER...............    15.00
LAMP,PEG,11 IN. TALL,AZURE BLUE SATIN MOTHER OF PEARL
  DIAMOND POINT............................................    48.00
LAMP,PEG FLOAT,LEMON SHAPED................................     6.00
LAMP,PEG,SWIRLED STICK & FOUNT.............................    25.00
LAMP,PEWTER DOUBLE BULLSEYE READING,.......................   225.00
LAMP,PEWTER WHALE OIL HANDLED,2 PRONG......................    25.00
LAMP,PHOENIX,BLUE BIRDS & RED BLOSSOMS,CLOTH SHADE.........    60.00
LAMP,PHOTOGRAPHERS RUBY LIGHT RED PAINT....................    10.00
LAMP,PIE-SHAPED TIN WHALE OIL,STRAP HANDLE.................    12.50
LAMP,PINEAPPLE PATTERN.....................................    15.00
LAMP,PINK DIAMOND QUILTED MOTHER OF PEARL MINIATURE,SATIN
  GLASS SHADE..............................................   185.00
LAMP,PINK DIAMOND QUILTED MOTHER OF PEARL..................   300.00
LAMP,PINK DIAMOND QUILTED MOTHER OF PEARL SATIN FAIRY,SHELL
  FEET.....................................................    65.00
LAMP,PINK FOUNT KEROSENE,CLEAR OVERLAY & BASE..............    48.00
LAMP,PINK MILK GLASS ALADDIN,DRAPE PATTERN.................    15.00
LAMP,PINK MOTHER OF PEARL FAIRY,CLARKS BASE................    65.00
```

```
LAMP,PINK OPALESCENT SWIRL HALL,RUFFLED RIM,BRASS FRAME.....   65.00
LAMP,PINK SATIN CASED MINIATURE,BALL SHADE,SQUARE BASE......  125.00
LAMP,PINK SATIN CASED GLASS PEG,PAIR SET IN BRASS
  CANDLESTICKS............................................... 59.50
LAMP,PINK SATIN GLASS HANGING,5 IN. LONG,PINK TO ROSE,BRASS
  FITTINGS.................................................. 40.00
LAMP,PINK,SCENES,GREEN & WHITE,G.W.T.W.,27 IN. H.......... 110.00
LAMP,POLITICAL PARADE TORCH & HOLDER..................... 12.50
LAMP,POTTERY BROWN OIL.................................. 17.00
LAMP,PRESSED GLASS 101,8 IN. PEDESTAL.................... 17.50
LAMP,PRESSED GLASS 101 & CHIMNEY........................ 14.00
LAMP,PRESSED GLASS BASE,BULLS EYE WITH FLEUR DE LIS...... 32.00
LAMP,PRESSED GLASS DIAMOND POINT BASE WITH HANDLE,BLUE.... 22.00
LAMP,PRINCESS FEATHER PATTERNED WITH CHIMNEY............. 14.00
LAMP,PRINCESS FEATHER ROMAN KEY......................... 15.00
LAMP,PULLDOWN,119 COLOURED GEMS......................... 50.00
LAMP,PYRAMID SHAPE WITH TUBE BURNER....................  4.00
LAMP,QUILTED RED SATIN GLASS STUDENT SHADE.............. 10.50
LAMP,RAILROAD SWITCH 1907.............................. 25.00
LAMP,RAYO OIL ,NICKEL OVER BRASS,WHITE BRISTOL SHADE.... 22.00
LAMP,RAYO TABLE,NICKEL ON BRASS WITH MUSHROOM SHADE,DRAPE
  PATTERN................................................. 32.50
LAMP,RED SATIN GLASS BASE.............................. 25.00
LAMP,RED SATIN GLASS BEADED DRAPE GONE WITH THE WIND,BRASS
  FITTINGS............................................... 145.00
LAMP,RED SATIN GLASS GONE WITH THE WIND,EMBOSSED
  ROSETTES,SCROLLS....................................... 95.00
LAMP,RED SATIN GLASS HALL,BRASS FRAME & CHAINS.......... 85.00
LAMP,RED SATIN GONE WITH THE WIND,23 IN.,ARTICHOKE...... 189.00
LAMP,RED SATIN GONE WITH THE WIND,BRASS CONNECTIONS..... 185.00
LAMP,RED SATIN GONE-WITH-THE-WIND,BRASS OPEN-WORK BASE.. 175.00
LAMP,RED SATIN,MAPLE LEAF,UMBRELLA SHADE................ 200.00
LAMP,REGENCY HALL FROM HOME IN CAMDEN MAINE,36 IN. HIGH.. 200.00
LAMP,ROCHESTER......................................... 27.50
LAMP,ROCHESTER,WHITE CHINA SHADE....................... 10.00
LAMP,ROMAN KEY KEROSENE,TRANSPARENT GREEN OCTAGON...... 22.50
LAMP,ROSE RIBBED SWIRLED SATIN,SIGNED CHARKS FAIRY..... 45.00
LAMP,ROUND TIN,HANDLED................................  5.00
LAMP,RUBY GLOBE FOR RAILROAD LANTERN,NYC...............  4.00
LAMP,RUSH LIGHT & CANDLE HOLDER,15 IN.,WOOD BASE....... 80.00
LAMP,RUSH LIGHT SET IN HAND HEWN WOOD BASE,CIRCA 1700.. 88.00
LAMP,SANDWICH CLEAR FLINT WHALE OIL.................... 25.00
LAMP,SANDWICH GLASS,10 IN. TALL,CLEAR................. 27.50
LAMP,SANDWICH GLASS BELL SHAPED FINGER TYPE WHALE OIL,BRASS
  COLLAR................................................. 15.00
LAMP,SANDWICH GLASS WHALE OIL,6 SIDED PRESSED GLASS BASE.... 25.00
LAMP,SANDWICH GLASS WHALE OIL,CLEAR,9 IN.............. 28.00
LAMP,SANDWICH HAND,CABLE IN RING...................... 25.00
LAMP SANDWICH,LION HEAD ALL FOUR CORNERS BASE & FOUNT,BASE 6
  IN. HT. 8............................................. 75.00
LAMP,SANDWICH-TYPE WHALE OIL,FROSTED BANDS ON FONT.... 20.00
LAMP,SANDWICH WHALE OIL,PANELED WAFFLE................ 40.00
LAMP,SANDWICH WHALE OIL ,WAFFLE....................... 40.00
LAMP,SAPPHIRE BLUE DIAMOND QUILTED FINGER,APPLIED HANDLE.... 35.00
LAMP,SAPPHIRE BLUE OIL HAND,.......................... 35.00
LAMP,SATIN GLASS HANGING WITH FAIRY SCENE............. 220.00
LAMP,SATSUMA,URN TYPE,2 TEMPLE DOG GOLD HANDLES,EMBOSSED
  GOLD.................................................. 165.00
LAMP,SCHOONER WITH SHADE.............................. 30.00
LAMP,SHADE & FONT HANGING............................. 75.00
LAMP,SIGNED KAUFFMANN,HANDLED URN ON PORCELAIN BASE... 125.00
LAMP,SINGLE ANGLE, EMBOSSED FLOWERED METAL........... 40.00
LAMP,SINGLE CANDLEMOLD IN WOODEN HANGING FRAME....... 35.00
LAMP,SPREAD EAGLE MINIATURE MILK GLASS BALL SHADE.... 110.00
LAMP,SQUIRREL TABLE OIL.............................. 75.00
```

```
LAMP,STEAM LOCOMOTIVE ENGINEERS KEROSENE TORCH,12 IN,BRASS &
   IRON..............................................................   22.00
LAMP,STEM,FROSTED FONT,BRASSED FIGURE STEM...................   23.00
LAMP,STICKING TOM MINERS......................................    6.00
LAMP,STUDENT..................................................   95.00
LAMP,STUDENT,BRASS,WHITE SHADE................................   45.00
LAMP,STUDENT,CONVERTED TO ELECTRIC,YELLOW SWIRL SHADE.........   85.00
LAMP,STUDENT,NICKEL OVER BRASS................................   50.00
LAMP,STUDENT,SINGLE SHADE,ORNATE BRASS,ELECTRIFIED...........   85.00
LAMP,TABLE,18 IN. TALL,TIFFANY TYPE SHADE,METAL BASE.........   65.00
LAMP,TABLE,ELECTRIC,SLAG GLASS,CARAMEL PANELS IN METAL FRAME   40.00
LAMP,TABLE,STAINED GLASS SHADE,BRASS PEDESTAL BASE...........   85.00
LAMP,THREE GRACES SALT STONE 11 IN.,NUDES....................   19.50
LAMP,TIFFANY TYPE 20 IN. HIGH,TABLE WITH PANELLED 20 IN.
   SHADE......................................................   25.00
LAMP,TIFFANY TYPE,23 IN. TALL,6 MARBELIZED BLUE PANELS,GOLD
   CUTOUT.....................................................  100.00
LAMP,TIFFANY-TYPE SHADE IN CARAMEL SLAG,TREE TRUNK BASE.....   89.50
LAMP,TIN BETTY IN HOLDER,TIN PEG BASE........................   75.00
LAMP,TIN KEROSENE............................................    3.50
LAMP,TIN MAGIC LANTERN.......................................   25.00
LAMP,TIN MINERS OIL,3IN......................................    5.00
LAMP,TIN WALL................................................   10.00
LAMP,TIN WALL SCONCE KEROSENE HOLDER WITH REFLECTOR.........   28.00
LAMP,TOLE WALL WITH DECORATED RESERVOIR AND SHADE,BRASS TRIM
   WICKMENT...................................................   42.00
LAMP,TRILBY NIGHT,AQUA BULBOUS FOUNT,........................   10.50
LAMP,VIKING FIGURE IN BRONZE,................................  105.00
LAMP,WARMER WHITE METAL BAROQUE WORK,ALCOHOL LAMP,GRASS
   ROUND PANEL................................................   55.00
LAMP,WHALE OIL,7 IN.,WATER FALL BASE.........................   15.00
LAMP,WHALE OIL,AMBER FOUNT,PLATED SILVER STEM AND FOOT......   35.00
LAMP,WHALE OIL BRASS,HANDLED,4 IN............................   12.00
LAMP,WHALE OIL,CLEAR GLASS,INSCRIBED ON BASE,1868...........   20.00
LAMP,WHALE OIL,GREEN FONT,BRASS COLUMN,SQUARE MARBLE BASE...   95.00
LAMP,WHALE OIL,HEART & THUMBPRINT............................   30.00
LAMP,WHALE OIL,ROUND WITH OCTAGON POINTS,BRASS ROOSTER......   45.00
LAMP,WHALE OIL,SHEFFIELD WITH SILVER.........................   60.00
LAMP,WHALE OIL,SWEETHEART PATTERN............................   45.00
LAMP,WHITE BRISTOL...........................................   48.50
LAMP,WHITE HANGING,SHADE 14 IN...............................   12.50
LAMP,WHITE MILK GLASS MINIATURE,BLOCK PATTERN...............   18.00
LAMP,WHITE SATIN TABLE,PINK WITH ORCHID BLUE BELLS,BRASS
   BASE.......................................................   65.00
LAMP,WICKER 2 BULB TABLE,SATIN SHADE.........................   12.50
LAMP,WITH GLASS SHADE SIGNED JEFFERSON 1899,PINK,WHITE &
   GREEN LEAVES...............................................  150.00
LAMP,WOOD & GLASS WITH STUDENT SHADE.........................   19.00
LAMP,WOOL WINDER REFINISHED & MADE INTO FLOOR LAMP,4 ARM....   32.50
LAMP,WORLDS FAIR PYLON & SPHERE FROSTED ELECTRIC...........    3.50
LAMP,WROUGHT IRON RUSH LIGHT.................................   50.00
LANTERN,4 WICK CIRCULAR POLE TORCH FOR FISHING..............   40.00
LANTERN,9 IN. TALL WOOD FRAMED CANDLE........................   75.00
LANTERN,BARN,SILVER COLOR FRAME,BAIL HANDLE..................    5.00
LANTERN,BOAT,GREEN & RED GLOBES..............................   10.00
LANTERN,BOSTON & ALBANY RAILROAD.............................    7.00
LANTERN,BOSTON & MAINE RAILROAD..............................    7.00
LANTERN,BRAKEMANS RAILROAD ,MAINE CENTRAL...................    8.50
LANTERN,BULLS EYE CHIMNEY,15 IN. HIGH,12 IN. DIAMETER,TOLE
   HOODED.....................................................   20.00
LANTERN,CANDLE,DOMED SCREEN..................................   50.00
LANTERN,CARBON MINERS........................................   12.50
LANTERN,CARRIAGE,BEVELED LENS................................   16.75
LANTERN,CARRIAGE,PAIR,CANDLE,BEVELLED GLASS,BRASS & TIN.....   65.00
LANTERN,CHILDS SKATING,PERKO WONDER JUNIOR,PAINTED TIN......   12.50
```

```
LANTERN,DIETZ FIRE DEPARTMENT,CHROME PLATED................... 25.00
LANTERN,DIETZ INSPECTORS HOODED WITH BAIL & HANDLE........... 15.00
LANTERN,DIETZ KEROSENE FIREMANS,COPPER BOTTOM & BRASS BAIL.. 12.00
LANTERN,DIETZ TUBULAR DRIVING,RED REFLECTOR ON BACK,DATED
   JAN.,1897................................................. 32.50
LANTERN,DIETZ WITH RED GLOBE................................. 5.00
LANTERN,ELECTRIFIED WABASH RAIL ROAD......................... 7.50
LANTERN,FARM................................................. 3.50
LANTERN,FARM,OLD DIETZ,BULLSEYE GLOBE........................ 5.00
LANTERN,GERMAN............................................... 22.50
LANTERN,HAND,BULLS EYE GLASS................................. 20.00
LANTERN,IRON WITH COWS HORN PANES............................ 90.00
LANTERN,KEROSENE BURNER,SLIDING SHUTTER...................... 12.50
LANTERN MARKED CITY OF NEW YORK,DIETZ........................ 4.00
LANTERN,MARKED RAILROAD,S.P.CO. ON TIN....................... 15.00
LANTERN,NEW YORK CENTRAL CLEAR RAILROAD...................... 8.00
LANTERN,PAIR CARRIAGE,BEVELED GLASS LENSES................... 50.00
LANTERN,PAIR RAILROAD MARKED MCRR,TIN WITH BRASS ON TOP..... 19.00
LANTERN,PENNSYLVANIA RAILROAD................................ 4.50
LANTERN,PENNSYLVANIA RAILROAD CLEAR.......................... 8.00
LANTERN,PIERCED TIN-TYPE PAUL REVERE......................... 35.00
LANTERN,RAILROAD
   10.00  TO................................................. 15.00
LANTERN,RAILROAD BRAKEMAN,TIN CAP,BAIL HANDLE................ 5.50
LANTERN,RAILROAD,CLEAR GLASS CHIMNEY,BANGOR & ARDASTOAK..... 6.50
LANTERN,RAILROAD CONDUCTORS,RED GLOBE........................ 10.00
LANTERN,RAILROAD MARKED GRAND TRUNK NY....................... 7.00
LANTERN,RAILROAD PAIR........................................ 12.00
LANTERN,RAILROAD,RED GLASS,1908-1922,C.B.& Q MARK............ 12.50
LANTERN,RAILROAD,RED GLOBE................................... 5.00
LANTERN,RAILROAD,RUBY GLOBE.................................. 12.50
LANTERN,ROUND CANDLE MOLD,10 STICKS,TIN...................... 125.00
LANTERN,SCOUT DIETZ,SIGNED GLOBE............................. 10.00
LANTERN,SHIPS,BRASS & METAL,19 IN. HIGH,PORT & STARBOARD.... 48.50
LANTERN,SKATERS
   5.00  TO................................................. 10.00
LANTERN,SKATERS BRASS DATED 1876............................. 15.00
LANTERN,SKATERS,OCTAGONAL SLOPING GLASS BETWEEN PRICKED TIN
   BASE..................................................... 48.00
LANTERN ,SQUARE BRASS POLISHED & ELECTRIFIED................. 65.00
LANTERN,STONEBRIDGE FOLDING,ISINGLASS WINDOWS................ 8.00
LANTERN,TIN SKATERS.......................................... 9.00
LANTERN,TOLE BOAT SIGNAL,KEYSTONE............................ 16.00
LANTERN,TRAFFIC GUARD,RED GLOBE.............................. 15.00
LANTERN,WESTERN PACIFIC RAILROAD,RED GLOBE................... 5.00
LANTERN,WOODEN CIRCA 1900,................................... 38.00
LANTERNS,PR.LARGE ROUND RED GLOVE,SHIP....................... 75.00
LEATHER FIRE BUCKET,BLACK ON RED,MARKED MERRYWEATHER,LONDON. 49.50
LEATHER SHOT FLASK,EMBOSSED SCENE OF MOUNTAIN LION & HUNTER. 15.00
LEATHER SIDE SADDLE EXHIBITOR................................ 17.50
LEATHER SNUFF BOX............................................ 4.50
LEATHER TOBY PITCHER,SEATED FIGURE.......................... 240.00
```

LEEDS POTTERY was made at Leeds, Yorkshire, England, from 1774 to 1878. Most Leeds ware was not marked. Early Leeds pieces had distinctive twisted handles with a greenish glaze on part of the creamy ware. Later ware often had blue borders on the creamy pottery.

```
LEEDS CHESSMEN,SET,CASTLEFORD,CIRCA 1790,BLACK & WHITE......1,600.00
LEEDS CREAMER & SUGAR,RED FLOWERS & GREEN LEAVES............ 20.00
LEEDS CUP & SAUCERS,2,FLORAL DECORATION IN RUST
   RED,HANDLELESS ........................................... 50.00
LEEDS LAVABO WITH GREEN EDGED & BROWN DOLPHIN,CIRCA
   1780,POTTERY.............................................1,400.00
LEEDS PLATE,CHINESE DECORATION IN BLUE WITH FEATHER
   EDGE,SOFT PASTE.......................................... 18.00
```

LEEDS PLATE,MARKED,7 IN.,SIGNED,FLORAL CENTER,LATTICE EDGE.. 22.50
LEEDS PLATE OVAL BASKET WEAVE CREAM WARE PIERCED SCALLOPED
EDGE.. 20.00
LEEDS PLATTER,BLUE FEATHER EDGE.............................. 8.00
LEEDS TEAPOT,COBALT BLUE,GOLD DECORATION,MEDALLIONS.......... 75.00
LEEDS TEAPOT,CREAMWARE,1790,OVOID WITH LEAF MOLDED SPOUT.... 75.00
LEEDS TUREEN,BLUE FEATHER EDGE,............................. 85.00
LEEDS TYPE PEPPER POT WITH BLUE COMB DECORATION & BLUE STAR
CIRCA 1800... 18.50
LEEDS VEGETABLE,MINIATURE,COVERED,BROWN TRIM................ 10.00

LE GRAS is a name that appeared on French cameo glass of the late nineteenth and early twentieth centuries.
LE GRAS LAMP BASE,CAMEO GLASS,LAVENDER FLOWERS,BROWN
LEAVES,SIGNED.. 95.00
LE GRAS SIGNED 8 IN. VASE,PURPLE GRAPES,GOLD LEAVES......... 110.00
LE GRAS VASE,ENAMEL DECORATED,AUTUMN BROWNS IN TREES,10
IN.,SIGNED.. 23.00
LE GRAS VASE,ENAMELED DECORATION,FIELDS,STREAMS,10
IN.,SIGNED.. 27.00
LE GRAS VASE,ENAMEL DECORATED,SIGNED........................ 27.00
LE GRAS VASE,ENAMELED WINTER SCENE.......................... 24.00
LE GRAS VASE,FROSTY CHARTREUSE,3 BLUE 5-PETAL
FLOWERS,SIGNED,PAIR.. 175.00
LE GRAS VASE,GREEN & WHITE,ACID CUTBACK,CLUTHRA,6 IN.
HIGH,SIGNED... 225.00
LE GRAS VASE,SHEPHERD & SHEEP ON MOUNTAIN,SIGNED............ 125.00
LE GRAS VASE,WINTER SCENE,10 IN.,CONICAL,SIGNED............. 62.50
     LENOX, SEE ALSO BELLEEK................................

LENOX CHINA was made in Trenton, New Jersey, after 1906. The firm also makes a porcelain similar to Belleek.
LENOX BETTY WARE 3 PIECE COBALT BLUE CHINA,SUGAR,CREAMER,TEA
POT... 45.00
LENOX BOWL,9 IN.. 5.00
LENOX BOWL WITH BRASS FILIGREE BAND ON RIM,MARKED FRANCE.... 75.00
LENOX CANDLE HOLDER,PAIR,GREEN BASE & BELLEEK HOLDERS....... 24.00
LENOX FISH PLATE,9 IN.,MARKED TIFFANY & CO.,GOLD EDGE....... 18.00
LENOX INSERT IN STERLING HOLDER DEMI CUPS WITH SAUCERS,8.... 75.00
LENOX INSERTS IN STERLING HOLDER SAUCER,8................... 100.00
LENOX PALLETTE SALT,CREAM WITH GOLD EDGE.................... 5.00
LENOX PLACE SET,BREAKFAST,5 PIECE,MYSTIC PATTERN............ 12.50
LENOX PLATE,6 IN.,12... 30.00
LENOX SALT,2 FOOTED,WITH PALLETTE............................ 6.00
LENOX SALT,SET OF 6,HANDPAINTED PINK ROSES,SIGNED........... 32.00
LENOX SALT,WITH WREATH.. 4.00
LENOX SERVICE PLATE,11 IN.,12................................. 70.00
LENOX SWAN,PINK,MARKED.. 9.50
LENOX TEAPOT WITH GOLD AND GARLANDS OF FLOWERS.............. 35.00
LENOX VASE,BLUE,PINK,FLOWERS................................. 13.00
LETTERS,CARTON OF HANDWRITTEN DOCUMTS.ETC.FROM ATTORNEYS
ESTATE OF 1880.. 15.00
LE VERRE FRANCAIS SIGNED EWER,ORANGE & BROWN MUSHROOMS ON
YELLOW... 135.00
LIGHT BULB DATED 1889... 5.50
LIGHT BULB,TAN COLOURED,POINTED TIP.......................... 1.25
LIGHT,RAILROAD SWITCH,COLOURED LENS.......................... 15.00
     LIGHTING DEVICES, SEE CANDLEHOLDER, CANDLESTICK, LAMP,
TOOL..
     LIMOGES, SEE ALSO HAVILAND..............................

LIMOGES CHINA is any china made in Limoges, France. The most famous Limoges was made at the Haviland factory (see HAVILAND). About 100 factories worked in Limoges, France.
LIMOGES ASPARAGUS PLATE,MARKED,10 IN.,GOLD TRIM & DECOR ON

```
WHITE.................................................  12.00
LIMOGES ATOMIZER WITH GOLD,SIGNED,WINE & GOLD..............  10.00
LIMOGES BASKET CREAM COLOURED WITH GOLD HANDLE.............  16.50
LIMOGES BERRY DISH,SET OF 6 MARKED,HANDPAINTED DEPOSE
   STRAWBERRY.............................................  36.00
LIMOGES BERRY SET,BOWL & 6 SAUCES,CREAMER & 2
   SUGARS,HANDPAINTED.....................................  125.00
LIMOGES BIRD GAME SET,PLATTER & 10 PLATES,SIGNED GILLES.....  225.00
LIMOGES BIRD PLATE,9 IN.,2 HANDPAINTED DUCKS................  15.00
LIMOGES BIRD PLATE,FRENCH,WILD TURKEY.......................  12.00
LIMOGES BIRD SET PLATTER,9 PLATES,SIGNED MAX................  150.00
LIMOGES BOUILLON CUP & SAUCER..............................  7.00
LIMOGES BOUILLON CUP & SAUCER,CORONET,DOUBLE GOLD BAND,PINK
   ROSES.................................................  8.00
LIMOGES BOUILLON CUP & SAUCER,FRENCH,WHITE & GOLD...........  4.25
LIMOGES BOUILLON CUP & SAUCER,OLD ABBEY,PINK ROSES..........  4.00
LIMOGES BOUILLON CUP & SAUCER,OPEN PINK POPPY,SCALLOPED RIM.  4.25
LIMOGES BOWL,6-SIDED,SILVER & WHITE........................  17.00
LIMOGES BOWL,9 IN.,PINK ROSES,GOLD BORDER..................  18.00
LIMOGES BOWL,9 IN. PINK ROSE SWAGS,GOLD....................  7.50
LIMOGES BOWL,9 IN.,SCALLOPED,GOLD EDGED,MARKED J. POUYAT....  8.50
LIMOGES BOWL,CORONET,8 IN.,POPPIES DECOR,GOLD..............  16.00
LIMOGES BOWL,FOOTED,HANDPAINTED GRAPES,ARTIST SIGNED & DATED  24.50
LIMOGES BOWL,HANDPAINTED SPRAYS OF FLOWERS IN ORCHID &
   YELLOW................................................  9.50
LIMOGES BOWL,STRETCHED GOLD EDGE,SPRAY PINK & WHITE ROSES
   SIGNED PAUL...........................................  16.00
LIMOGES BOX,COVERED,PAIR,CHATEAU DE LANGEAIS & CHAREAU DE
   CHAUMONT..............................................  25.00
LIMOGES BOX,ENAMEL,RED,MAN & WOMAN SITTING ON BENCH UNDER
   TREE..................................................  225.00
LIMOGES BOX,HANDPAINTED,YELLOW WITH BROWN,OVAL.............  8.50
LIMOGES BREAD TRAY,SIGNED,HANDPAINTED,TANS & BROWNS.........  12.00
LIMOGES BUTTER DISH,3 PIECE,EMBOSSED 24K GOLD..............  15.00
LIMOGES CAKE PLATE,10 IN. DIAMETER,2 OPEN HANDLES,FLORAL
   SPRAYS................................................  4.00
LIMOGES CAKE PLATE,10 IN.,OPEN HANDLES,PINK WITH WHITE WITH
   FLORAL................................................  14.00
LIMOGES CAKE PLATE,FLORALS.................................  3.50
LIMOGES CAKE PLATE,PICKARD SIGNED H. TULLEY,HANDPAINTED
   POINSETTIAS...........................................  12.50
LIMOGES CAKE PLATTER,13 IN. DIAMETER,PAINTED ORCHIDS ON GOLD  35.00
LIMOGES CAKE STAND,FOOTED,PANSIES & HOUSE..................  20.00
LIMOGES CANDLESTICK,HANDPAINTED FLORAL & GOLD,SQUARE BASE...  7.50
LIMOGES CANDLESTICK,PAIR 6 IN.,FRANCE,BLUE,FLOWERS ON STEM &
   BASE..................................................  12.00
LIMOGES CELERY DISH, OPEN HANDLES AT EACH END,WHITE WITH
   MEDALLION.............................................  16.00
LIMOGES CHALICE,ENAMEL,FIGURES & SCENERY...................  235.00
LIMOGES CHIP PLATE,DAISY,GOLD ROCOCO EDGE..................  48.00
LIMOGES CHOCOLATE CUP & SAUCER,ELITE,PINK CARNATIONS.......  8.00
LIMOGES CHOCOLATE CUP & SAUCER,FRENCH......................  10.50
LIMOGES CHOCOLATE POT,BULBOUS BASE,PINK ROSES..............  42.00
LIMOGES CHOCOLATE POT,HANDPAINTED,BLUE LUSTER,ARTIST SIGNED.  17.50
LIMOGES CHOCOLATE POT,LACY FERN-LIKE DECORATION,OVERLAY IN
   GOLD..................................................  18.50
LIMOGES CHOCOLATE POT,PINK FORGET-ME-NOTS & GREEN & WHITE
   LILIES................................................  35.00
LIMOGES CHOCOLATE POT WITH YELLOW ROSES & 6 CUPS &
   SAUCERS,FRANCE,BROWN..................................  85.00
LIMOGES CIDER PITCHER,HANDPAINTED & ARTIST SIGNED,DATED
   1907,RED..............................................  12.50
LIMOGES COMPOTE,ENAMEL,GREEN & RED,LADY SITTING ON WHITE
   CLOUD.................................................  325.00
LIMOGES CRACKER JAR,SIGNED,HANDPAINTED APPLE BLOSSOM........  22.50
```

LIMOGES CREAMER & SUGAR,HANDPAINTED,BLUE LUSTER,ARTIST SIGNED...	10.00
LIMOGES CREAMER,SUGAR,3 DEMITASSE.........................	13.50
LIMOGES CRUET,HANDPAINTED,SIGNED & DATED 1920..............	20.00
LIMOGES CUP & SAUCER & TEA PLATE,MARKED,LAVENDER FLOWERS ON WHITE..	9.00
LIMOGES CUP & SAUCER,FRENCH,GOLD,CORONET MARK,ROSES..........	14.00
LIMOGES CUP & SAUCER,MARKED,FLORAL DESIGN....................	5.50
LIMOGES CUP & SAUCER,SET OF 4,ETELE,SPRAYS PINK ROSES,GOLD..	28.00
LIMOGES CUP,SET OF 6,PINK ROSES............................	20.00
LIMOGES DEMI-TASSE CUP & SAUCER,SET OF 12,WHITE.............	35.00
LIMOGES DEMI-TASSE CUP & SAUCER,SIGNED,FRENCH,MOSAIC TYPE...	4.00
LIMOGES DEMITASSE CUP AND SAUCER,WHITE ,GOLD RIM............	6.00
LIMOGES DEMITASSE CUP & SAUCER,WHITE SWIRLED & GOLD.........	6.00
LIMOGES DEMI-TASSE CUP & SAUCER,WHITE WITH GOLD TRIM........	5.00
LIMOGES DEMITASSE CUPS,FOOTED,GOLD RIM.....................	4.50
LIMOGES DEMI TASSE,GOLD....................................	3.00
LIMOGES DEMI-TASSE SET,23 PIECES...........................	65.00
LIMOGES DEMI-TASSE SET,CLASSIC TRIM,5 CUPS & SAUCERS,POT & TRAY..	55.00
LIMOGES DESK SET MARKED GERMANY,HANDPAINTED,5 PIECE.........	40.00
LIMOGES DEVILED EGG PLATE,RECTANGULAR,SCALLOPED,PINK & BLUE WITH GOLD..	32.50
LIMOGES DINNER PLATE,FRANCE................................	3.50
LIMOGES DINNER PLATE,HOTEL ASTOR,GOLD BORDER & EMBLEM.......	12.50
LIMOGES DINNER SERVICE FOR 6,CH.FIELD HAVILAND GOLD BAND,72 PIECES..	225.00
LIMOGES DINNER PLATE,SET OF 12,FLORAL SPRAYS,GOLDWORK BORDER	30.00
LIMOGES DISH,DEEP,OPEN PINK POPPY,SCALLOPED RIM.............	2.75
LIMOGES DISH,FRENCH,PORTRAIT COVERED,HANDPAINTED............	40.00
LIMOGES DISH,OVAL,PASTEL,GOLD..............................	3.50
LIMOGES DRESSER SET,HANDPAINTED VIOLETS,BLUE & WHITE,GOLD TRIM..	30.00
LIMOGES DRESSER TRAY,OVAL,HANDPAINTED BLACKBERRIES,BLOSSOMS,GOLD...............................	16.50
LIMOGES DRESSER TRAY,YELLOW FLOWERS,12 IN...................	15.00
LIMOGES EWER,ENAMEL,RED BACKGROUND,WHITE FIGURES,SILVER GILT	275.00
LIMOGES FISH PLATE,PAIR,FRENCH.............................	22.50
LIMOGES FISH SET,SIGNED,GOLD TRIM,PLATTER & 12 PLATES.......	175.00
LIMOGES FRUIT PLATE,CORONET,ROCOCO EDGE,12 IN..............	30.00
LIMOGES FRUIT PLATE SIGNED BORDOT,ROCCO EDGE,CORONET........	28.00
LIMOGES GAME BIRD PLATE ARTIST SIGNED,ROCOCO SCALLOPED & EMBOSSED..	20.00
LIMOGES GAME PLATE,10 IN.,MALLARD DUCK SIGNED MAX...........	20.00
LIMOGES GRAVY BOAT & DISH,SIGNED,SPRAY PINK ROSES & BLUE FLOWERS...	10.00
LIMOGES GRAVY BOAT,DEPOSE,COVER,ATTACHED PLATE,HANDPAINTED..	9.00
LIMOGES HAIR RECEIVER MARKED & DATED 1915,FLORAL............	6.50
LIMOGES HAIR RECEIVER MARKED J.P.,OVER L,HANDPAINTED........	8.50
LIMOGES HAIR RECEIVER,VIOLETS..............................	8.00
LIMOGES HANGING PLATE,FRANCE,SIGNED RENE,SAILBOATS AND CANOE	20.00
LIMOGES HATPIN HOLDER,HANDPAINTED DAISIES....................	9.75
LIMOGES HATPIN HOLDER,PANSIES ON GOLD,SATIN FINISH..........	14.00
LIMOGES HATPIN HOLDER,SIGNED & DATED.......................	16.50
LIMOGES HATPIN HOLDER SIGNED & DATED 1915,BLUE WITH ROSES...	9.00
LIMOGES ICE CREAM SET,16 IN. TRAY & 10 PLATES,GOLD,PINK ROSES,BLUE..	70.00
LIMOGES JAM JAR WITH SAUCER,COVERED,ROSES & GOLD............	16.50
LIMOGES JARDINIERE,HANDPAINTED,FOOTED,GREEN TO CREAM,PINK IRIS..	30.00
LIMOGES JELLY JAR & PLATE,COVERED,GOOSEBERRIES..............	18.50
LIMOGES OYSTER PLATE,FRENCH,SET OF 12......................	150.00
LIMOGES PERFUME TRAY,FREE FORM,FLORAL......................	16.00
LIMOGES PERFUME TRAY,FRENCH,GOLD & GREEN ,VIOLETS ON WHITE BACKGROUND..	14.50

```
LIMOGES PICTURE FRAME,HANDPAINTED BLUE FORGET ME NOT,GOLD...     16.50
LIMOGES PIN TRAY,SIGNED H-P...................................    4.00
LIMOGES PITCHER,ARTIST SIGNED,APPLES & LEAVES ON BEIGE......     26.50
LIMOGES PITCHER,DECORATED,GOLD HANDLE........................    38.00
LIMOGES PITCHER,HANDPAINTED,SIGNED & DATED 1897..............     9.00
LIMOGES PLAQUE,HANDPAINTED,COBALT & GOLD BORDER.............     32.00
LIMOGES PLAQUE,HANDPAINTED GRAPES & FLOWERS,FRAMED..........     45.00
LIMOGES PLAQUE,HANGING,HANDPAINTED,ARTIST SIGNED,MONK EATING    28.00
LIMOGES PLAQUE SIGNED BARIN,13 IN.,HANGING,FISH & CORAL REEF    35.00
LIMOGES PLAQUE,WALL,SIGNED FRENCH,HANDPAINTED,GOLD EMBOSSED
  BORDER.....................................................    48.00
LIMOGES PLATE,6 IN. ,ACORNS..................................     3.50
LIMOGES PLATE,6 IN.,BORDER OF FLOWERS,SIGNED J.P.............     1.50
LIMOGES PLATE,7 IN.,OPEN PINK POPPY,SCALLOPED RIM...........     4.25
LIMOGES PLATE,7 IN.,PINK ROSES,BLUE FORGET-ME-NOTS,GOLD.....     4.50
LIMOGES PLATE,8 IN.,1878,HANDPAINTED CHERUB ON BLUE GROUND..    12.00
LIMOGES PLATE,8 IN.,EMBOSSED SCALLOPED EDGE,PINK & WHITE
  ROSES.....................................................     7.50
LIMOGES PLATE,8 IN.,HANDPAINTED FISH.........................     6.50
LIMOGES PLATE,8 IN.,PINK ROSES,BLUE FORGET-ME-NOTS,GOLD LINE     4.50
LIMOGES PLATE,8 IN.,SHAPED LIKE ACANTHUS LEAF,SIGNED
  L.E.RIPPEY.................................................    45.00
LIMOGES PLATE,8 IN.,SHAPED LIKE OPEN WATER LILY,CHERUBS &
  ROSES,MARKED...............................................    42.50
LIMOGES PLATE,9 IN.,FULL FIGURE OF WOMAN....................    15.00
LIMOGES PLATE,9 IN.,OPEN WATER LILY SHAPE,MARKED,BIRDS IN
  CENTER....................................................    75.00
LIMOGES PLATE,10 IN.,CAVALIER AND LADY......................    29.50
LIMOGES PLATE,13 IN.,HANDPAINTED IN BIG ROSES...............    30.00
LIMOGES PLATE,BEADED EDGE,PINK & GREEN DECOR................    18.00
LIMOGES PLATE,CORONET,8 IN.,SCALLOPED,GOLD BORDER & TRIM....     9.00
LIMOGES PLATE,CORONET,9 IN.,IRIS,GREEN LEAVES ,GOLD.........    14.00
LIMOGES PLATE,CORONET,10 IN.,SIGNED COUDARY,,BUST OF GAY
  CAVALIER..................................................    22.00
LIMOGES PLATE,CORONET,ARTIST SIGNED,HANDPAINTED FLOWER......    12.00
LIMOGES PLATE,CORONET,HANDPAINTED,FLORAL,11 IN.,PINK & WHITE
  ROSES.....................................................    18.50
LIMOGES PLATE,FISH PAINTING,HANGS...........................    17.50
LIMOGES PLATE,FRANCE DEPOSE.................................     1.50
LIMOGES PLATE,FRENCH,HANDPAINTED CLASSIC DESIGN,GOLD........    18.00
LIMOGES PLATE,HANDPAINTED BIRD IN FLIGHT....................    12.00
LIMOGES PLATE,HANDPAINTED,MARSHALL FIELD....................     7.50
LIMOGES PLATE,HANDPAINTED ROSES,GREEN RIM...................     5.50
LIMOGES PLATE,HANDPAINTED,SIGNED,10 IN......................    65.00
LIMOGES PLATE,HOLLY,FOR CHRISTMAS...........................    15.00
LIMOGES PLATE MARKED GDA FRANCE,WHITE & PINK FLOWERS........     3.50
LIMOGES PLATE,OPEN HANDLE,FLORAL ON WHITE,SIGNED............     7.50
LIMOGES PLATE,SCENIC,ORNATE RIM.............................    16.00
LIMOGES PLATE,SET OF 5 8 IN.,HAVILAND.......................    35.00
LIMOGES PLATE,SET OF 6 6 IN.,.,............................    15.00
LIMOGES PLATE,SET OF 6 6 IN.,ELITE,PINK FLOWERS,GOLD EDGE...    14.00
LIMOGES PLATE,SET OF 6,HANDPAINTED,CHINOISERIE BORDER.......    50.00
LIMOGES PLATE,SET OF 6,HANDPAINTED,RAISED SCROLLS...........    30.00
LIMOGES PLATE,SET OF 10 CORONET,8 IN.,HANDPAINTED ENAMEL
  PINK TRIM.................................................   110.00
LIMOGES PLATE,SIGNED,SCENIC,ORNATE RIM......................    16.00
LIMOGES PLATE,SIGNED,ROSES..................................     7.00
LIMOGES PLATE WITH PINK ROSES BORDER,OCTAGONAL,SET OF 8.....    35.00
LIMOGES PLATTER,13 X 17 IN.,ENCRUSTED WITH GOLD.............    24.00
LIMOGES PLATTER,14 X 9 IN.,SPRAYS OF PINK APPLE BLOSSOMS....     9.00
LIMOGES PLATTER,16 IN.,WHITE BACKGROUND,GOLD BORDER WITH
  GREEN & RED...............................................    11.00
LIMOGES PLATTER,HAVILAND FRANCE,OVAL WITH PINK FLOWERS......    12.00
LIMOGES PLATTER,OVAL,SCALLOPED RIM,PASTEL FLOWERS...........    18.00
LIMOGES PLATTER,SIGNED,9 X 14 IN.,SPRAY PINK ROSES & BLUE
```

```
FLOWERS........................................................  16.00
LIMOGES PORTRAIT OF A LADY ON EASEL,MINIATURE.................  15.00
LIMOGES PORTRAIT PLATE,MARKED ART NOUVEAU,PROFILE OF WOMAN..  13.50
LIMOGES PORTRAIT PLATE SIGNED COUDERT,CORONET,FRENCH.........  45.00
LIMOGES PORTRAIT PLATE,WOMAN CARRYING BASKET OF FRUIT ON
   HEAD......................................................  35.00
LIMOGES POWDER BOX,COVERED,MELETA LODGE,ROYAL ARCH CHAPTER
   NO.284...................................................  18.00
LIMOGES PUNCH BOWL & 6 GOLD HANDLED CUPS,ARTIST
   SIGNED,MARKED............................................ 150.00
LIMOGES PUNCH BOWL,FRENCH,GRAPE,SIGNED & DATED APRIL 15,
   1896.................................................... 150.00
LIMOGES PUNCH BOWL,HANDPAINTED BLUE & PURPLE GRAPES,SIGNED,4
   FEET....................................................  85.00
LIMOGES RELISH DISH,OVAL,12 IN. LONG,YELLOW ROSE BUDS.......  12.50
LIMOGES RING TREE,GREEN & PASTEL FLOWERS....................   9.00
LIMOGES RING TREE,HANDPAINTED PINK WILD ROSES,SIGNED
   E.K.VAUGHT..............................................  12.00
LIMOGES ROSE BOWL,FOOTED,PINK WILD ROSE DECOR,BLUE BODY.....  12.00
LIMOGES SALT & PEPPER,HANDPAINTED ROSES & VIOLETS,SIGNED....   5.00
LIMOGES SALT,INDIVIDUAL SWAN,FRANCE,24K GOLD................   3.00
LIMOGES SALT,SWAN...........................................   2.00
LIMOGES SALT,WHITE WITH GOLD RIM............................   2.00
LIMOGES SAUCE DISH,FLORAL DECOR,6...........................  18.00
LIMOGES SAUCER,SIGNED,PINK ROSES & BLUE FLOWERS SPRAY.......   2.00
LIMOGES SCREEN WITH WATCH IN CENTER PANEL,ENAMEL,3 PANEL.... 325.00
LIMOGES SERVICE PLATE,SET OF 8,WM.GUERIN & CO. FRANCE.......  90.00
LIMOGES SET OF 46 PIECES,...................................  50.00
LIMOGES SET OF 52 PIECES,FRANCE,WHITE,GOLD EDGE,ROMAN KEY... 195.00
LIMOGES SET OF 94 PIECES,PINK ROSES & GREEN LEAVES,12 OF
   EVERYTHING.............................................. 450.00
LIMOGES SOUP PLATE,SET OF 6,FRENCH,FLOWER DESIGN............  84.00
LIMOGES SOUP TUREEN & 12 SOUP DISHES,SIGNED XMAS............  55.00
LIMOGES TANKARD,4 IN.,HANDPAINTED HOP DECOR.................  15.00
LIMOGES TANKARD,HANDPAINTED.................................  80.00
LIMOGES TEAPLATE,GOLD WITH TURQUOISE ENAMELING,HANDPAINTED
   ROSES...................................................  48.00
LIMOGES TEAPOT & 4 CUPS & SAUCERS,FRANCE....................  30.00
LIMOGES TEAPOT & COVERED SUGAR,CREAMER,FLORAL ON
   WHITE,SIGNED............................................  45.00
LIMOGES TEAPOT,OVAL SHAPED,WHITE WITH GREEN,GOLD HANDLE &
   FINIAL..................................................  20.00
LIMOGES TEA SET DATED 1879,HAVILAND & CO.,26 PIECES,FLORAL
   PINK....................................................  90.00
LIMOGES TRAY,MARTHA & GEORGE WASHINGTON.....................  35.00
LIMOGES TRAY,OVAL,YELLOW & WHITE LUSTER,GOLD RIM............  18.00
LIMOGES VASE,ENAMEL,BEIGE BACKGROUND,FIGURE OF MAN.......... 145.00
LIMOGES VASE,ENAMEL,LADY IN GREEN & WHITE,RED VASE & TOP.... 145.00
LIMOGES VASE,FRANCE,9 IN. HIGH,PINE CONES & GREENS..........  17.50
LIMOGES VASE,FRANCE,GOLD HANDLES,HANDPAINTED IRIS...........  40.00
LIMOGES VASE,FRANCE,HANDPAINTED,MOUNTED ON MAHOGANY BASE,30
   IN. TALL................................................ 250.00
LIMOGES VASE,GREEN ENAMEL WITH MAN PLAYING MANDOLIN,GREEN
   COSTUME,RED............................................. 165.00
LIMOGES VASE,OVAL SHAPED,YELLOW & ORCHID MUMS,GREEN
   LEAVES,BALL FEET........................................  38.00
LIMOGES VASE,WAISTED BODY WITH 3 SCROLL HANDLES,WHITE.......  12.50
LIMOGES VEGETABLE DISH,COVERED,10 IN.,PINK & BLUE FLOWERS...   8.00
LIMOGES VEGETABLE DISH,SHALLOW..............................   4.52
LIMOGES VEGETABLE,OPEN,SIGNED,SPRAY PINK ROSES & BLUE
   FLOWERS.................................................   6.00
LIMOGES WALL PLATE,ARTIST SIGNED,WHARF SCENE ,HOLLAND GIRL..  37.50
LIMOGES WALL PLAQUE,HANDPAINTED,FRENCH,CLASSICAL PORTRAIT...  35.00
LIMOGES WALL PLAQUE,SIGNED,FRENCH,HANDPAINTED,GOLD EMBOSSED
   BORDER..................................................  48.00
```

```
LIMOGES WASTE BOWL,C.H.HAVILAND,FLORAL........................    7.50
LIMOGES WATER PITCHER,FRENCH,SIGNED,HANDPAINTED PEACHES,GOLD     39.50
```

LINDBERGH memorabilia commemorating the events in the life of Charles A. Lindbergh are a special field of collecting.

```
LINDBERGH SILK RIBBON,2 X 7 IN. PICTURE LINDBERGH,PLANE.....     10.00
LINEN,BANQUET CLOTH,HANDMADE ITALIAN LINEN LACE,WHITE........    95.00
LINEN,BEDSPREAD,POPCORN STITCH CROCHETED,90 X 108
   IN.,SCALLOPED EDGE.........................................    67.50
LINEN,BLACK SILK NET KING SIZE BED SPREAD,HAND EMBROIDERED
   FLOWERS...................................................    59.00
LINEN,BLANKET,HOMESPUN,72 X 95 IN............................    15.00
LINEN,BLUE & WHITE TYLER COVERLET DATED 1839................    25.00
LINEN,CHINTZ QUILT,94 X 108 IN..............................    35.00
```

LINEN OR WOOL COVERLETS were made during the eighteenth century. Most of the coverlets date from 1800 to 1850. Four types were made: the double woven, jacquard, summer and winter, and overshot.

```
LINEN,COVERLET DATED 1839,RED,BLUE & WHITE..................    45.00
LINEN,COVERLET DATED 1857,75 X 84 IN.,FRINGED,BLUE &
   WHITE,JACQUARD...........................................    75.00
LINEN,COVERLET DATED 1894,80 X 90 IN.,FRINGED,BLUE &
   WHITE,JACQUARD...........................................    60.00
LINEN,COVERLET,FRINGED,GREEN,BLUE,EAGLES,CIRCA 1860.........   100.00
LINEN,COVERLET,RED,GREEN,BLUE,WHITE & BLACK.................    45.00
LINEN,CRAZY QUILT,DATED 1878,.................................    30.00
LINEN,DAMASK LINEN TABLECLOTH & 6 NAPKINS,72 IN. SQUARE,....    16.50
LINEN,EMBROIDERED WEDDING HANDKERCHIEF......................     4.50
LINEN,FRINGED TOWEL,RED & WHITE,CONSTITUTIONAL,EMBOSSED.....     7.50
LINEN,GRANNY AFGHAN.........................................    39.50
LINEN,HAND CROCHETED BEDSPREAD,10 PAIR MATCHING DRAPES......    69.00
LINEN,HAND CROCHETED WHITE DOUBLE BEDSPREAD,POPCORN STITCH..    18.75
LINEN,HANDMADE QUILT OF SILK & VELVET.......................    75.00
LINEN,HANDMADE SILK & VELVET PATCHWORK......................    25.00
LINEN,HOMESPUN TABLECLOTH 65 X 57 IN.,RED WITH WHITE FLEUR
   DE LIS...................................................    10.00
LINEN,HOOKED RUG...........................................    20.00
LINEN,INDIAN RUG...........................................    65.00
LINEN,INDIAN PRAYER RUG,RED WITH BLACK WHITE DESIGN,WHITE
   FRINGE...................................................    10.00
LINEN,LUNCHEON NAPKIN,12,FRINGED,DAMASK, 15 IN. SQUARE......    10.00
LINEN,NAPKIN,10,WHITE MADERA,SCALLOPED EDGE.................     6.00
LINEN,NECKTIE QUILT.........................................    42.50
LINEN,PAISLEY CREPE SPANISH SHAWL,BLUE & GOLD,36 IN. SQUARE    22.50
LINEN,PAISLEY SHAWL,72 IN. SQUARE,BLACK CENTER..............    15.00
LINEN,PAISLEY THROW,RED CENTER..............................   125.00
LINEN,PIECED QUILT,WOOL & SILK..............................    15.00
LINEN,QUILT,DOUBLE SIZE,MULTI-COLOURED SILK,EMBROIDERED.....    75.00
LINEN,QUILT,DOUBLE WEDDING RING PATTERN.....................    50.00
LINEN,QUILT,RED & WHITE.....................................    35.00
LINEN,QUILT,RED & WHITE PATCH...............................    25.00
LINEN,QUILT,WEDDING RING PATTERN............................    50.00
LINEN,ROUND EMBROIDERED BATTENBURG TABLECLOTH...............     6.00
LINEN,ROUND LINEN TABLE CLOTH,EMBROIDERED FLOWERS,EYELET
   WORK....................................................    16.00
LINEN,SHAWL,22 X 69 IN.,EGYPTIAN,CARMEN RED NET,SILVER MESH.    15.00
LINEN,TABLECLOTH,54 IN. BY 54 IN.,BLUE & GOLD PATTERNED.....    35.00
LINEN,TABLECLOTH,FRINGED,SHAWLS IN THE 20S,2,1 PINK,1
   LAVENDER................................................    50.00
LINEN,TABLECLOTH,HOMESPUN,56 X 58 IN.,RED WITH WHITE CHECK..    10.00
LINEN,TABLECLOTH,LACE,ECRU.................................    60.00
LINEN,TABLECLOTH,LINEN,8 NAPKINS,LILY OF VALLEY PATTERN.....    57.50
LINEN,TABLECLOTH,LINEN,HAND MADE............................    32.00
LINEN,TABLECLOTH,RED,62 X 62 IN.............................    35.00
LINEN,TABLECLOTH,WHITE DAMASK,21 FEET X 88 IN...............    20.00
```

LINEN,TABLE SET 2 LONG RUNNERS & 4 MATCHING SQUARES WITH
LACE CENTERS.. 10.00
LINEN,TEA CLOTH 51 IN. SQUARE,HAND DONE,LACE WORK CENTER &
BORDER.. 14.00
LINEN,TOWEL,3,VICTORIAN,RED BORDERED,FRINGED LINEN.......... 7.50
LINEN,TURKEY RED TABLE CLOTH,52 X 64 IN.,FLORAL & LEAF...... 7.50
LINEN,WHITE & RED FRINGED TABLE CLOTH,2 YARDS............... 16.50
LINEN,WHITE & RED FRINGED TABLECLOTH,POPPY.................. 27.50

*LITHOPHANES are porcelain pictures made by casting clay in layers of various
thicknesses. When a piece is held to the light, a picture of light and shadow is
seen through it. Most lithophanes date from the 1825 to 1875 period. A few are
still being made.*
LITHOPHANE CANDLE SHIELD,METAL HOLDER,SCENIC VIEW OF TREES &
MOUNTAINS... 48.00

*LIVERPOOL, ENGLAND, has been the site of several pottery and porcelain fac-
tories from 1716 to 1785. Some earthenware was made with transfer decora-
tions. Sadler and Green made print-decorated wares from 1756. Many of the
pieces were made for the American market and featured patriotic emblems such
as eagles, flags, and other special-interest motifs.*
LIVERPOOL JUG,SOLDIERS ADIEU.............................. 110.00
LIVERPOOL TRANSFER HANDLED CUPS & SAUCERS,MOSES IN BULRUSHES 40.00
LOETZ BOWL,AUSTRIA,SILVERY GREEN SATIN WITH TRACERY DESIGN.. 55.00
LOETZ BOWL,GOLD & BLUE IRIDESCENT,IN BRASS BASKET
HOLDER,EGYPTIAN FACES.. 125.00
LOETZ EPERGNE IN MULBERRY TO GREEN,BASE BY HOMAN SILVER CO.. 160.00
LOETZ LAMP,IRIDESCENT WHALE OIL,STERLING HALLMARKED COLLAR.. 35.00
LOETZ LAMP,TABLE,GOLD SHADE WITH RAINBOW IRIDESCENCE........ 175.00
LOETZ ROSE BOWL SIGNED,PURPLE WITH SILVER.................. 135.00
LOETZ VASE,4 IN.,IRIDESCENT GREEN,BLUE HIGHLIGHTS........... 45.00
LOETZ VASE,8 IN.,GREEN IRIDESCENT,TREE TRUNK................ 27.00
LOETZ VASE,8 IN.,TIFFANY SHADES BLUE,SILVER & GOLD
IRIDESCENCE.. 35.00
LOETZ VASE,9 IN... 130.00
LOETZ VASE,12 IN.,AMBERINA COLOURING,IRIDESCENT............. 35.00
LOETZ VASE.. 85.00
LOETZ VASE,AMBER... 11.00
LOETZ VASE,AUSTRIA,SIGNED,4 IN.,BLUE & BUTTERSCOTCH SWIRLS.. 120.00
LOETZ VASE,BLUE & GOLD,5 IN.,PAIR.......................... 50.00
LOETZ VASE,BLUE,GREEN & RAINBOW IRIDESCENCE................ 65.00
LOETZ VASE,BLUE GREEN PEACOCK FEATHER DESIGN............... 90.00
LOETZ VASE,BLUE,IRIDESCENT,BULB SHAPE NARROWS TO SHORT NECK. 20.00
LOETZ VASE,COBALT WITH GOLD IRIDESCENCE.................... 32.50
LOETZ VASE GOLD WITH SILVERY BLUE TRACERIES................ 100.00
LOETZ VASE,GREEN... 38.50
LOETZ VASE,PURPLE-GREEN IRIDESCENT,LAVA EFFECT............. 24.00
LOETZ VASE,PURPLE WITH SILVERY GREEN IRIDESCENCE DESIGN..... 47.50
LOETZ VASE,SIGNED,GOLD,RED,BLUE & GREEN.................... 115.00
LOETZ VASE,UNSIGNED,8 IN. ,GREEN RIBBED,IRIDESCENCE......... 35.00
LOETZ VASE,WHITE,8 IN. TALL,APPLIED GREEN GLASS............. 37.50

*LOTUS WARE was made by the Knowles, Taylor and Knowles Company of East
Liverpool, Ohio, from 1890 to 1900.*
LOTUS WARE BOWL,GOLD PICKET,RUFFLED EDGE,GOLD NET WORK &
PINK... 135.00
LOTUS WARE COFFEE POT,SIGNED K.T.K.,RAISED GOLD BLOSSOMS.... 95.00
LOTUS WARE CREAMER,WHITE FISH-NET............................ 150.00
LOTUS WARE PITCHER,SIGNED,5 IN.,FISH NET,LAVENDER & YELLOW
DAISIES,GOLD.. 180.00
LOTUS WARE SPITTOON,SIGNED.................................. 95.00
LOTUS WARE SUGAR BOWL WITH LID............................. 65.00
LOTUS WARE SYRUP PITCHER,BLUE BOTTOM,YELLOW TOP............. 95.00
LOTUS WARE SYRUP PITCHER MARKED,FLOWER DECORATION & WHITE
SWAN... 47.50

LOTUS WARE TEAPOT WITH LID.. 75.00
 LOWESTOFT, SEE CHINESE EXPORT...............................

LUNEVILLE is a French city where pottery has been made since 1731. The factory changed hands several times, but wares marked with the name Lunéville were made during the eighteenth and nineteenth centuries.
LUNEVILLE FRANCE PLATE,8 IN.,BLUE & WHITE WITH FLEUR DE LIS
BORDER.. 5.00

LUSTERWARE was meant to resemble copper, silver, or gold. It has been used since the sixteenth century. Most of the luster found today was made during the nineteenth century.
LUSTER CHILDS TEA SET,GERMANY,9 PIECES....................... 50.00
LUSTER,CHILDS YELLOW TEA SET,GERMANY......................... 45.00
LUSTER,COPPER BONE DISH,TEA LEAF,ALFRED MEAKIN,SCALLOPED
EDGE.. 12.50
LUSTER,COPPER BOWL & PITCHER SET,MINIATURE,BLUE FLORAL BAND. 30.00
LUSTER,COPPER BOWL,FOOTED,BLUE BAND & RAISED FLORAL.......... 38.00
LUSTER,COPPER CHALICE,BLUE BAND.............................. 55.00
LUSTER,COPPER CHALICE,BLUE BAND WITH RAISED COLOURED FLOWERS 40.00
LUSTER,COPPER CREAMER.. 25.00
LUSTER,COPPER CREAMER,2 IN................................... 8.00
LUSTER,COPPER CREAMER,3 IN................................... 11.00
LUSTER,COPPER CREAMER,5 IN.
8.00 TO... 18.00
LUSTER,COPPER CREAMER,BLUE BAND WITH COPPER DECOR........... 24.00
LUSTER COPPER CREAMER,EAGLE ON HANDLE,RAISED DECOR ON TAN... 53.50
LUSTER,COPPER CREAMER WITH BLUE BAND
15.00 TO.. 45.00
LUSTER,COPPER CUP & SAUCER,DECORATED BLUE BAND.............. 35.00
LUSTER,COPPER JUG,BLUE BAND AROUND BASE,BEADED BANDS ON TOP. 35.00
LUSTER,COPPER JUG,BLUE BAND AT TOP,5 IN. TALL............... 37.00
LUSTER,COPPER JUG,FLARE TOP,EMBOSSED MORNING GLORIES........ 19.50
LUSTER,COPPER JUG,SAFFRON BAND & BLUE DECORATION............ 60.00
LUSTER,COPPER,MASTER SALT,SAND FINISH BAND.................. 20.00
LUSTER,COPPER MILK PITCHER,6 IN............................. 25.00
LUSTER,COPPER MILK PITCHER,BULBOUS & FLOWER DECORATION...... 30.00
LUSTER,COPPER MUG
8.50 TO... 20.00
LUSTER,COPPER MUG,3 IN. TALL,BLUE BAND,CIRCA 1820........... 25.00
LUSTER,COPPER MUG,BEIGE BAND,PINK LUSTER INSIDE RIM......... 21.00
LUSTER,COPPER MUG,BLUE BAND,2 IN. HIGH...................... 20.00
LUSTER,COPPER MUG,BLUE BAND & RAISED FLORAL................. 40.00
LUSTER,COPPER,MUG,BLUE AND TAN BANDS........................ 14.00
LUSTER,COPPER MUG,BLUE BAND,MULTI-COLOURED PASTORAL SCENES.. 20.00
LUSTER,COPPER MUG,CHILDS,WITH COLOURED STRIPES.............. 18.50
LUSTER,COPPER MUG,CLEAR,BLUE DECOR OUTSIDE,BEIGE INSIDE..... 26.00
LUSTER,COPPER MUG,DECORATED BLUE BAND....................... 22.00
LUSTER,COPPER MUG,GREEN BAND,RAISED COLOURED FIGURES........ 30.00
LUSTER,COPPER MUG,HANDLED................................... 10.00
LUSTER,COPPER MUG,ORANGE BAND IN CENTER WITH PINK LUSTER
BAND INSIDE... 22.50
LUSTER,COPPER MUG,PINK BAND ON CREAM........................ 20.00
LUSTER,COPPER MUG WITH COVER,SANDED MAJOLICA,PINK,ROSE &
WHITE... 78.00
LUSTER,COPPER MUG WITH SAND BAND............................ 22.00
LUSTER,COPPER PITCHER,4 IN. HIGH
25.00 TO... 30.00
LUSTER,COPPER PITCHER,5 IN.,CABBAGE ROSE ON EACH SIDE....... 38.00
LUSTER,COPPER,PITCHER,6 IN. HIGH,BLUE BAND FLORAL DECORATION 45.00
LUSTER,COPPER PITCHER,6 IN. HIGH,DIAMOND MOLDED BULBOUS BASE 55.00
LUSTER,COPPER PITCHER,6 IN. HIGH,RAISED FLORAL DESIGN OF
PINK & BLUE... 38.00
LUSTER,COPPER PITCHER,7 IN. TALL,PANELS OUTLINED WITH ENAMEL
COLOURS... 60.00

```
LUSTER,COPPER,PITCHER,8 IN. HIGH,BLUE DECORATION,ENGLISH
  MARK..........................................................  50.00
LUSTER,COPPER PITCHER,BLUE BAND,5 IN............................  48.00
LUSTER,COPPER PITCHER,BLUE BAND AT MIDDLE.......................  12.00
LUSTER,COPPER PITCHER,BLUE BAND AT TOP WITH LUSTER DESIGN....  65.00
LUSTER,COPPER PITCHER,BLUE BAND DESIGN..........................  47.00
LUSTER,COPPER PITCHER,BLUE,SANDED BAND..........................  12.00
LUSTER,COPPER PITCHER CIRCA 1820-30.............................  30.00
LUSTER,COPPER PITCHER,CREAM,DOLPHIN HANDLE,PINK BACKGROUND..  90.00
LUSTER,COPPER PITCHER,DIAMOND QUILTED BAND,FLORAL DECOR.....  45.00
LUSTER,COPPER PITCHER,GREEN BAND AROUND CENTER..............  18.00
LUSTER,COPPER PITCHER,LAVENDER BAND,CIRCA 1820..............  23.50
LUSTER,COPPER PITCHER,LONGTON,ENGLAND,BLUE BAND.............   9.00
LUSTER,COPPER,PITCHER,OFF WHITE BAND WITH RED DESIGN........  42.00
LUSTER,COPPER PITCHER,PAIR,GRAPE BORDER,HANDPAINTED.........  35.00
LUSTER,COPPER PITCHER,RAISED FIGURES OF CHILD & FLOWERS IN
  BLUE.........................................................  25.00
LUSTER,COPPER PITCHER,SANDED BAND...............................  60.00
LUSTER,COPPER PITCHER,TURQUOISE & YELLOW BANDS..............  21.00
LUSTER,COPPER,STAFFORDSHIRE PITCHER,HANDPAINTED STAGS & DOGS  23.50
LUSTER,COPPER SUGAR BOWL,OPEN,CREAM GROUND.................  26.50
LUSTER,COPPER TEA LEAF HANDLED BREAD PLATE..................  12.00
LUSTER,COPPER TEA LEAF HANDLELESS CUP & SAUCER.............  16.50
LUSTER,COPPER TEALEAF HANDLELESS TEACUP & SAUCER,MEAKIN.....  11.25
LUSTER,COPPER TEA LEAF PLATTER 7 X 10 IN....................   6.00
LUSTER,COPPER TEA LEAF PLATTER...............................  16.50
LUSTER,COPPER TEA LEAF SUGAR BOWL,MEAKIN....................  18.50
LUSTER,COPPER TEAPOT,BLUE DECOR.............................  55.00
LUSTER,COPPER TEAPOT,EAGLE HANDLE...........................  45.00
LUSTER,COPPER TEAPOT,RAISED NEO-CLASSIC FIGURES............  28.00
LUSTER,COPPER,TOOTHPICK,SANDED BAND WITH COLOURED DOTS......  25.00
LUSTER,COPPER WITH BLUE BAND CHILDS MUG.....................  18.00
LUSTER,ENGLISH PINK CUP & SAUCER...........................  15.00
LUSTER,ENGLISH PINK PLATE 7 IN.............................  10.00
LUSTER,ENGLISH PUDDING MOLD,1830...........................  14.00
LUSTER,ENGLISH SILVER TEA POT CIRCA 1815-25................  45.00
LUSTER,GOLD 4 IN. TALL PITCHER,BLUE BAND WITH FIGURE........  35.00
LUSTER,GOLD,CUP & SAUCER,FLOWERS,REMEMBER ME...............  15.00
LUSTER,GOLD CUP & SAUCER,REMEMBER ME.......................  15.00
LUSTER,GOLD TEA SET,24K,3 PIECE,BAVARIA....................  50.00
LUSTER,MEAKIN GRAVY BOAT....................................  14.50
LUSTER,ORANGE CUP SIGNED GERMANY,REMEMBER ME...............   7.50
LUSTER,PAIR ITALIAN 9 IN. PLATES,RED & BLUE FRESCO WORK.....  25.00
LUSTER,PINK & WHITE CREAMER,GERMANY MARKED,HOME OF G.
  WASHINGTON...................................................   3.95
LUSTER,PINK BOOTS,PAIR SCALLOPED,4 IN. TALL.................  17.00
LUSTER,PINK COFFEE SET,CHILDS,3 PIECES,GERMANY.............  15.00
LUSTER,PINK CUP & SAUCER
  10.00  TO...................................................  25.00
LUSTER,PINK CUP & SAUCER,ENAMEL SPRIG,NO HANDLE............  26.00
LUSTER,PINK CUP & SAUCER,EMBOSSED..........................   8.50
LUSTER,PINK CUP & SAUCER,EMBOSSED PEARS....................  15.00
LUSTER,PINK CUP & SAUCER,FALL RIVER,MASS...................   3.50
LUSTER,PINK CUP & SAUCER,FEATHERY WITH COPPER LUSTER........   7.50
LUSTER,PINK,CUP & SAUCER,FOR-GET-ME NOT....................  18.00
LUSTER,PINK CUP & SAUCER,HANDLELESS........................  23.00
LUSTER,PINK CUP & SAUCER,HANDLELESS,ROSE PATTERN...........  20.00
LUSTER,PINK CUP & SAUCER MARKED STAFFORDSHIRE,PINK
  FLOWERS,COPPER..............................................  15.00
LUSTER,PINK CUP & SAUCER,PRESENT,RAISED FLOWERS............   9.50
LUSTER,PINK CUP & SAUCER,WISHBONE HANDLE,RED,YELLOW,BLUE &
  GREEN.......................................................  10.00
LUSTER,PINK CUP & SAUCER WITH BLACK TRANSFER
  DECORATION,GARDEN SCENES....................................  22.00
LUSTER,PINK CUP,THINK OF ME.................................   5.50
```

```
LUSTER,PINK PITCHER,NAUTILUS PATTERN.........................    37.50
LUSTER,PINK PITCHER,PINK BAND................................    25.00
LUSTER,PINK PLATE,7 IN.......................................    10.00
LUSTER,PINK PLAQUE,RETRIBUTION STEAMER.......................    35.00
LUSTER,PINK PLATE,HOUSE PATTERN..............................    35.00
LUSTER,PINK SHAVING MUG,EMBOSSED WHITE FLOWERS...............    15.00
LUSTER,PINK SLIPPER,5 IN.,ROSES..............................     7.00
LUSTER,PINK TEA SET,BERRY DESIGN,23 PIECES...................   225.00
LUSTER,PINK TEA SET,CHILDS,FLORAL MEDALLION..................    10.00
LUSTER,PINK TEA SET,CHILDS,PINK FLORAL MEDALLION.............    10.00
LUSTER,PINK VASE,PAIR,PICTURE ON FRONT,GOLD HANDLES..........    10.00
LUSTER,SILVER 2 HANDLED CUP,COPPER LUSTER INSIDE.............    30.00
LUSTER,SILVER 10 SIDED PITCHER...............................    48.50
LUSTER,SILVER CREAMER,GADROONED PATTERN,BOAT-SHAPED.........    22.50
LUSTER,SILVER CREAMER,QUEEN ANNE STYLE,ENGLISH CIRCA 1810...    35.00
LUSTER,SILVER MUG,CHILDS.....................................    30.00
LUSTER,SILVER PITCHER,BULBOUS SHAPE,RIBBED PATTERN,SILVER ON
SPOUT........................................................    55.00
LUSTER SILVER PITCHER WITH BLUE STRIPE.......................    15.00
LUSTER,SILVER RESIST COVERED SUGAR,LION MASK HANDLES,CREAMER    85.00
LUSTER,SILVER RESIST MILK PITCHER,PINEAPPLE PATTERN..........    65.00
LUSTER,SILVER TEAPOT.........................................    55.00
LUSTER,SILVER TEAPOT,CREAMER & SUGAR WITH LIDS..............   125.00
LUSTER,SILVER TOBY PITCHER,4 IN..............................    55.00
LUSTER,SUNDERLAND CUP & SAUCER,RED TRANSFER DEER............    12.75
LUSTER,SUNDERLAND GOBLET,PEDESTAL BASE,BLACK TRANSFER OF
FLYING CLOUD.................................................    20.00
LUSTER,SUNDERLAND ON BLUE CIRCA 1840 QUEEN VICTORIA,ALBERT
PITCHER......................................................    40.00
LUSTER,TEA SET,CHILDS,JAPAN,BLUE.............................    12.00
LUSTER,YELLOW BOWL,MARKED MADE IN BELGIUM,BROWN TRANSFER &
FARM SCENE...................................................    15.00
LUSTER,YELLOW SCUTTLE MUG,PINK FLOWERS.......................     8.00
LUSTRE ART SIGNED TORTOISE SHELL GAS SHADE...................    35.00
```

LUSTERS are mantel decorations or pedestal vases with many hanging glass prisms. The name really refers to the prisms, and it is proper to refer to a single glass prism as a luster (either spelling. luster or lustre, is correct).

```
LUSTRE,MANTEL,9 IN. LONG,PRISMS,PIGEON BLOOD &
GOLD,HANDPAINTED.............................................    35.00
LUSTRES,10 CRYSTAL PRISMS,WATERFORD TYPE.....................   251.00
LUSTRES,BLUE ROBINS EGGS,PAIR,12 IN. TALL,ENAMELED
FLOWERS,LONG PRISMS..........................................   150.00
LUSTRES,PAIR,9 IN. HIGH,COBALT BLUE..........................    79.50
LUSTRES,PAIR PINK,TULIP TOP,ENAMELED,8 CRYSTAL PRISMS.......   150.00
LUSTRES,RUBY GLASS,DOUBLE ROW PRISMS,ENAMELED & GOLD
DECORATED,PAIR...............................................   110.00
LUSTRES,WHITE PAIR,BLUE ENAMELLED FLOWERS,CUT SPEAR POINT
PRISMS.......................................................   125.00
```

LUTZ GLASS was made in the 1870's by Nicholas Lutz at the Boston and Sandwich Company. He made a delicate and intricate threaded glass of several colors. Other similar wares are referred to as Lutz.

```
LUTZ OPALESCENT SWIRL FINGER BOWL & PLATE....................    17.50
LUTZ SWIRLED GLASS CANE......................................   100.00
LUTZ THREADED SHADE IN COPPERY-ROSE COLOUR...................    27.50
```

MAASTRICHT, HOLLAND, had a large pottery called the Sphinx, which was established in 1836 by Petrus Regout. The firm made transfer printed ironstone dinner sets marked with the words "Maastricht," or "Petrus Regout." Twentieth-century wares were also made by the firm.

```
MAASTRICHT 8 IN. PINK PLATE,SAMARCAND PATTERN...............     2.00
MAESTRICHT HOLLAND PLATE,9 IN.,RED,BLUE,GREEN & LAVENDER....     4.00
MAESTRECHT MARKED LINCOLN BLUE AND WHITE PORTRAIT PLATE.....    17.00
MAASTRICT MARKED PLATE,ORIENTAL DESIGN......................     6.75
```

```
MAASTRICHT ORIENTAL PLATE,TIMOR PATTERN IN ORANGE & BLUE....   12.00
     MACHINE, SEE ALSO TYPEWRITER..............................
MACHINE,CHEWING GUM DISPENSER,MECHANICAL,PULVER..............   45.00
MACHINE,COIN FOR NUTS & CANDY................................   29.95
MACHINE,COIN FOR SHIPPING & INSURANCE........................   29.95
MACHINE,GUM,BALL,E-Z,CAST IRON,PATENT 1908...................   20.00
MACHINE,GUM,PAT. DEC. 4, 1894, RAILWAY AUTOMATIC SALES CO...   45.00
MACHINE,FORTUNE TELLING,WOOD & METAL BALL GUM................   65.00
MACHINE,IN MAHOGANY,SHOCKING,ELECTRICAL......................   25.00
MACHINE,PENNY SLOT,2 JACKPOTS PLUS GUM.......................   65.00
MACHINE,PENNY,VIEWING,TRIGGER OPERATION......................  135.00
MACHINE,PENNY-SLOT,2 JACKPOTS PLUS GUM.......................   65.00
MACHINE,PIN BALL,7 BALLS FOR 1 CENT,WORKING ORDER............   48.00
MACHINE,PULVER,GUM,TRAFFIC POLICEMAN MODEL...................   37.50
MACHINE,SEWING,SINGER,HAND OPERATED..........................   12.50
MACHINE,SLOT,CRICKET,JUDGE DEWEY,FLOOR MODEL.................  350.00
MACHINE,SLOT,PENNY,5 SPINNING REELS WITH MINIATURE PLAYING
  CARDS......................................................  350.00
MACHINE,STAMP................................................   15.00
MACHINE,VENDING,POSTAGE STAMP,2 & 3 CENT.....................   15.00
MACHINE,VENDING,PUSH CART PEANUT ROASTING....................  500.00
     MAGIC LANTERN, SEE MAJIC LANTERN........................
MAGIC LANTERN WITH ORIG.KEROSENE BURNER,40 GLASS SLIDES,6IN.
  BY 1IN.....................................................   40.00
     LANTERN,BRASS TRIMMED,KEROSENE LAMP.....................   35.00
     LANTERN,GERMAN,KEROSENE.................................   22.50
     LANTERN,HANDPAINTED SET OF 11 SLIDES,WOOD...............   15.00
     LANTERN,KEROSENE TYPE,SLIDE PROJECTOR...................   35.00
     LANTERN,OIL LAMP,6 SLIDES...............................   12.50
     LANTERN,WITH 6 SLIDES,KEROSENE LAMP.....................   35.00
     LANTERN.WITH SLIDES,OIL LAMP............................   28.00
MAH JONG SET,4 DRAWER MAHOGANY CABINET WITH BRASS CORNERS...   21.00
MAH JONG SET,BOX,IVORY TILES & STICKS........................   45.00
MAH JONG SET IN 5 DRAWER BOX W/OLD RACKS.....................   20.00
MAH JONG SET,IVORY BLOCKS IN WOODEN CASE.....................   45.00
MAH JONG SET,IVORY CHARACTERS................................   20.00
MAH JONG TILES,IVORY.........................................   12.00
```

MAJOLICA is any pottery glazed with a tin enamel. Most of the majolica found
today is decorated with leaves, shells, branches, and other natural shapes and
in natural colors. It was a popular nineteenth-century product.

```
MAJOLICA ASPARAGUS HOLDER & TRAY.............................   65.00
MAJOLICA ASPARAGUS SERVING DISH,RIM OF BROWN & GOLD
  LEAVES,GRAPES..............................................   29.00
MAJOLICA BASKET,13 IN. LONG,AQUA CABBAGE LEAVES WITH MAROON
  DAISIES....................................................   22.00
MAJOLICA BASKET WITH HANDLE,PINK LINED,BROWN & GREEN.........   35.00
MAJOLICA BOWL WITH HANDLES,10 IN.............................    9.50
MAJOLICA BREAD PLATE,OVAL,YELLOW WHEAT ON GREEN & BROWN......   15.00
MAJOLICA BUTTER DISH.........................................   40.00
MAJOLICA BUTTER PAT,GREEN LEAF...............................    4.50
MAJOLICA BUTTER PAT,GREEN VINE...............................    2.75
MAJOLICA BUTTER PAT,PAIR,3 GREEN LEAVES WITH COLOUR..........    9.00
MAJOLICA BUTTER PAT,PANSY....................................    3.75
MAJOLICA BUTTER PAT,PHOENIXVILLE.............................    5.00
MAJOLICA CAKE PLATE ON STANDARD,HOLLY & IVY LEAVES & BERRIES   35.00
MAJOLICA CANDLE HOLDER,TOBY..................................   11.50
MAJOLICA COMPOTE,FOOTED,GREEN,PINK LINING....................   22.00
MAJOLICA COMPOTE,LEAF,SCALLOPED EDGE,GREEN LEAF WITH ORCHID
  & GREEN....................................................   35.00
MAJOLICA CREAMER,CORN,PINK LINED.............................   10.00
MAJOLICA CREAMER,YELLOW & GREEN BASKETWEAVE,BROWN
  HANDLE,ORCHID LINING.......................................   10.00
MAJOLICA CREAM PITCHER,FERNS & LEAVES ON BROWN,GREEN &
  YELLOW.....................................................    6.50
```

```
MAJOLICA CUP & SAUCER...................................  25.00
MAJOLICA CUSPIDOR,RIBBED DESIGN,BROWN TO GREEN...........   9.50
MAJOLICA DISH,7 IN.,GREEN,GEOMETRIC DESIGN BACKGROUND....  15.50
MAJOLICA DISH,LEAF,8 IN.,ROSE BORDER.....................   7.50
MAJOLICA DISH,LEAF,BROWN,PINK & GREEN....................  15.00
MAJOLICA DISH,SHELL SHAPE,TURQUOISE,CONCH SHELL ON 3 BROWN
  FEET..................................................  18.50
MAJOLICA ETRUSCAN 8 IN. LEAF DISH.......................   8.75
MAJOLICA ETRUSCAN 9 IN. LEAF DISH,PINK,GREEN & YELLOW....  10.00
MAJOLICA ETRUSCAN BUTTER PAT,LEAF SHAPED,GREEN,YELLOW & PINK   4.50
MAJOLICA ETRUSCAN CUP & SAUCER..........................   6.50
MAJOLICA ETRUSCAN CUP & SAUCER,SHELL & SEAWEED..........  60.00
MAJOLICA ETRUSCAN GERANIUM PATTERN OPEN HANDLE CAKE
  PLATE,SIGNED..........................................  35.00
MAJOLICA ETRUSCAN LEAF DISH,PINK EDGE...................  25.00
MAJOLICA ETRUSCAN MARKED TEAPOT.........................  65.00
MAJOLICA ETRUSCAN MILK PITCHER,PINK RAISED FLORAL MARKED....  45.00
MAJOLICA ETRUSCAN PLATE,2 HANDLED,LAVENDER & GREEN & BROWN..  29.50
MAJOLICA ETRUSCAN SERVING LEAF PLATE....................   6.50
MAJOLICA ETRUSCAN TEAPOT,SUGAR & CREAMER,MARKED,CAULIFLOWER.  90.00
MAJOLICA EWER,GIEN FRENCH,SIGNED,LEGENDARY
  FIGURES,BLACK,BLUE & GOLD.............................  33.00
MAJOLICA INKWELL & PEN HOLDER,4 X 4 SQUARE CUT CORNERS,..  15.00
MAJOLICA JAR,OPEN,EAR OF CORN...........................   8.00
MAJOLICA JARDENIERE.....................................   9.00
MAJOLICA JARDINIERE,PINK,GREEN & BROWN..................  12.00
MAJOLICA MAIZE PITCHER..................................  20.00
MAJOLICA MUG,COBALT BACKGROUND,DEPRESSED CROSSES,RAISED IVY
  LEAVES................................................  28.00
MAJOLICA MUG WITH ETRUSCAN MARK,YELLOW BASKETWEAVE,GREEN OAK
  LEAVES................................................  12.00
MAJOLICA MUSH BOWL & CREAMER,BIRD & FAN.................  27.50
MAJOLICA OYSTER PLATE,10 IN.............................  16.00
MAJOLICA OYSTER PLATE,10 IN.,LAVENDER,BLUE,GREEN & SEAWEED..  18.50
MAJOLICA OYSTER PLATE,MOTTLED BROWN SHELLS,WHITE
  CENTER,YELLOW SEAWEED.................................  12.00
MAJOLICA PITCHER,6 IN...................................   6.00
MAJOKICA PITCHER,7 IN.,BROWN WITH PURPLE FLOWERS........  10.00
MAJOLICA PITCHER 8 IN. CREAM BACKGROUND,YELLOW WATER LILIES,  30.00
MAJOLICA PITCHER,BLACKBERRY SPRAY & PINK FLORAL.........   8.00
MAJOLICA PITCHER,BLUE GREEN BASKETWEAVE.................  15.00
MAJOLICA PITCHER,BROWN TEDDY BEAR TOBY..................  18.00
MAJOLICA PITCHER,CORN
  7.00   TO............................................  16.00
MAJOLICA PITCHER,CORN,6 IN.,YELLOW CORN,GREEN HUSK......  12.00
MAJOLICA PITCHER,DOG,BROWN DOG IN SITTING POSITION......  35.00
MAJOLICA PITCHER,EAR OF CORN,CREAM COLOUR CORN,GREEN HUSKS &
  HANDLE................................................  10.00
MAJOLICA PITCHER,ELK STANDING BENEATH PINK BLOOMING TREE,DOE  17.50
MAJOLICA PITCHER,FISH,10 IN.............................  27.50
MAJOLICA PITCHER,FISH,11 IN. HIGH.......................  65.00
MAJOLICA PITCHER IN BLUE & GREEN DESIGN,GLAZED..........  15.00
MAJOLICA PITCHER,MONKEY,FRENCH,11 IN.,SIGNED F.PERROT,BROWN
  MONKEY................................................  65.00
MAJOLICA PITCHER,PINK LILIES ON WHITE,BASKET WEAVE......  15.00
MAJOLICA PITCHER SIGNED PHOENIXVILLE ETRUSCAN,4 IN.
  TALL,RAISED FLOWERS...................................  15.00
MAJOLICA PITCHER,YELLOW TOP AND BASE....................  15.00
MAJOLICA PLANTER,4 IN. HIGH,ACORNS & FLORALS ,4 PEDESTAL
  FEET..................................................  14.00
MAJOLICA PLATE,8 IN.,BROWN,GREEN LEAF CENTER............   9.00
MAJOLICA PLATE,8 IN.,GREEN,FLOWERS......................  12.00
MAJOLICA PLATE,10 IN.,BIRD IN CENTER,CHERRIES,BLUE
  BACKGROUND............................................  15.00
MAJOLICA PLATE,11 IN.,BLUE CENTER,GREEN LEAVES,PINK
```

```
ROSES,BROWN TRIM.........................................  14.00
MAJOLICA PLATE,11 IN. ,SHAGGY DOG WITH DOG HOUSE IN CENTER,.  24.00
MAJOLICA PLATE,BROWN,9 IN.,YELLOW PEARS & GREEN LEAVES......  30.00
MAJOLICA PLATE,ENGLISH,2 HANDLES,DIAMOND IMPRESSED MARK 1882  16.50
MAJOLICA PLATE,FERN DESIGN,7 IN...........................   7.00
MAJOLICA PLATE,FLORAL.....................................   6.50
MAJOLICA PLATE,IVORY SPRIG................................   4.50
MAJOLICA PLATE,JOAN OF ARC HEAD,GREENISH BLUE,ARTIST SIGNED. 39.50
MAJOLICA PLATE,PAIR FRENCH 8 IN.,L AVIATION & LA COURSEA
 PIED....................................................  25.00
MAJOLICA PLATE,PAIR FRENCH,MARINE BLUE WITH ROBINS & FRUIT.. 26.50
MAJOLICA PLATE,PANELLED GREEN BORDER,GRAPES &
 LEAVES,SARREGUEMINES....................................   5.00
MAJOLICA PLATE,SEATED SHAGGY DOG WITH DOGHOUSE............  15.00
MAJOLICA PLATE,WALL,MAN IN MOON,HANDPAINTED OCEAN & SAILING
 SHIPS..................................................  29.50
MAJOLICA PLATE,YELLOW BACKGROUND WITH WHITE WATER LILIES.... 13.50
MAJOLICA PLATTER,GREEN MAPLE LEAF,YELLOW & RED ON BROWN..... 10.00
MAJOLICA PLATTER,OVAL,FLORAL GREEN & ROSE DESIGN ON IVORY... 45.00
MAJOLICA RELISH TRAY,2 HANDLED,GREEN & YELLOW LEAVES IN
 LAVENDER...............................................  10.00
MAJOLICA RING TREE,DOLLS,GREEN,3 PRONG.....................   4.50
MAJOLICA SALT & PEPPER....................................   9.50
MAJOLICA SHOE,SANDED,GREEN WITH BLUE FLOWERS & PINK
 STREAMERS..............................................  10.00
MAJOLICA SUGAR & CREAMER,CAULIFLOWER......................  10.00
MAJOLICA TANKARD,GRAPE DESIGN WITH LINING.................  70.00
MAJOLICA TILE,SET OF 13,OLIVE GREEN,SIGNED................  13.00
MAJOLICA TOBACCO JAR,6 IN. HIGH,TURQUOISE BACKGROUND......  16.00
MAJOLICA TOBACCO JAR,BULL DOG.............................  27.50
MAJOLICA TOBACCO JAR,CLOWNS HEAD WITH HAT FOR LID.........  12.00
MAJOLICA TOBACCO JAR,CROCODILE SMOKING PIPE..............  15.00
MAJOLICA TOBACCO JAR,DOGS HEAD,SMOKING PIPE ON LID.........  10.00
MAJOLICA TOBACCO JAR,GLAZED BROWN.........................  15.00
MAJOLICA TOBACCO JAR,HIGH-HATTED FAT MAN SMOKING PIPE,HAT IS
 LID...................................................  15.00
MAJOLICA TOBACCO JAR,INDAIN HEAD.........................  16.00
MAJOLICA TOBACCO JAR,INDIAN MANS HEAD WITH FEATHERED HAT.... 16.50
MAJOLICA TOBACCO JAR,MANS HEAD WITH TRICORN RED HAT FOR LID. 19.50
MAJOLICA TOBACCO JAR,PUG DOG,TAN WITH ORCHID LINING......... 30.00
MAJOLICA TOBACCO JAR,RAMS HEAD TOP BETWEEN HORNS........... 22.50
MAJOLICA TOBACCO JAR,ROUND,DECORATED,PIPE ON LID...........   9.00
MAJOLICA TRAY,BROWN BASKET WEAVE,GREEN LEAVES & GRAPES...... 25.00
MAJOLICA UMBRELLA HOLDER..................................  13.00
MAJOLICA VASE,9 IN.,RED,HANDLE,FLORAL,MARKED IX 828......... 19.00
MAJOLICA VASE,13 IN. HIGH,2 HANDLES,AMBER BROWN,BLUE WITH
 WHITE FLORAL...........................................  37.50
MAJOLICA VASE,FISH.......................................  15.00
MAJOLICA VASE,PAIR,TURQUOISE BLUE WITH WHITE FLOWERS........110.00
MAJOLICA WATER PITCHER,LEAF DESIGN........................  17.00
MAJOLICA WATER PITCHER,MARKED.............................  55.00
MAP OF PANAMA CANAL 1914.................................   6.50
MANTLE URNS,3,MADE IN ENGLAND,15 IN.,EBONY COLOURING,ORMOLU. 50.00
```

*MARBLES of glass were made during the nineteenth century. Venetian swirl,
clear glass, and sulfides (marbles with frosted white animal figures imbedded
in the glass) were popular. Handmade clay marbles were made in many places,
but most of them came from the pottery factories of Ohio and Pennsylvania.
Occasionally, real stone marbles of onyx, carnelian, or jasper can be found.*

```
MARBLE,6 CANDY STRIPE....................................   2.00
MARBLE,CANDY STRIPE......................................   8.00
MARBLE,SULPHIDE,ELEPHANT INSIDE..........................  15.00
MARBLE,SULPHIDE,LAMB INSIDE..............................  12.00
MARBLE,SULPHIDE,LION INSIDE..............................  10.00
```

MARY GREGORY GLASS is identified by a characteristic white figure painted on dark glass. It was made from 1870 to 1910. The name refers to any glass decorated with a white silhouette figure and not just the Sandwich glass originally painted by Miss Mary Gregory.

MARY GREGORY ALE GLASS,PEDESTAL STEM AMBER,SET OF 4,FULL WHITE FIGURE...	85.00
MARY GREGORY ALE,PEDESTAL STEM,BOY WITH FISH..................	25.00
MARY GREGORY ALE,PEDESTAL STEM,BLUE WITH WHITE GIRL..........	25.00
MARY GREGORY BARBER BOTTLE,AMETHYST 55.00 TO...	75.00
MARY GREGORY BARBER BOTTLE,AMETHYST,GIRL.....................	45.00
MARY GREGORY BARBER BOTTLE,GREEN.............................	50.00
MARY GREGORY BARBER BOTTLE,GREEN,BOY.........................	27.50
MARY GREGORY BARBER BOTTLE,GREEN,GIRL........................	48.00
MARY GREGORY BARBER BOTTLE,PAIR AMETHYST.....................	245.00
MARY GREGORY BARBER BOTTLE,PAIR AMETHYST SIGNED,GIRL IN WHITE..	225.00
MARY GREGORY BEER GLASS,BOY WITH FOLIAGE.....................	29.00
MARY GREGORY BEER GLASS,WHITE ENAMELED GIRL AND FOLIAGE.....	29.00
MARY GREGORY BOTTLE,CRANBERRY,8 IN.,WHITE BOY & BIRDS........	42.50
MARY GREGORY BOTTLE,LAVENDER,7 IN. TALL,WHITE ENAMEL GIRL...	27.00
MARY GREGORY BOTTLE,WINE,CLEAR,GIRL,BROWN HAIR...............	37.50
MARY GREGORY BOWL,5 IN.,CLEAR,GIRL SITTING IN FIELD..........	22.00
MARY GREGORY BOWL,CRANBERRY,4 IN. BY 5 IN.,ENAMELLED COVER GIRL...	44.00
MARY GREGORY BOX,4 IN.,AMETHYST,LITTLE GIRL,BRASS FEET......	68.00
MARY GREGORY BOX,BLACK GLASS COVERED,4 FOOTED METAL STAND...	85.00
MARY GREGORY BOX,BLUE HINGED,BOY WITH BRANCH & FOLIAGE,FLOWER BAND......................................	70.00
MARY GREGORY BOX,COBLAT BLUE,COVERED,WHITE ENAMELLED FIGURE OF GIRL..	75.00
MARY GREGORY BOX,COBALT BLUE,HINGED LID COVERED,GIRL CHILD ON LID..	150.00
MARY GREGORY BOX,CRANBERRY,ROUND COVERED,GIRL CHILD IN WHITE,DOME LID...	65.00
MARY GREGORY BOX,HINGED,GREEN GLASS,ENAMELED................	45.00
MARY GREGORY BOX,ROUND,COVERED,WHITE ENAMEL DECORATION......	27.00
MARY GREGORY BUD VASE,6 IN.,RUFFLED TOP,GREEN,WHITE DETAIL..	22.00
MARY GREGORY BUD VASE,CLEAR,6 IN.,WHITE DETAIL..............	21.00
MARY GREGORY CASTOR,PICKLE,GIRL CARRYING BASKET OF EGGS,SILVER HOLDER.....................................	125.00
MARY GREGORY CRACKER JAR,COVERED............................	49.50
MARY GREGORY CREAM PITCHER,BOY & FOLIAGE,CLEAR GLASS FOOTED.	22.50
MARY GREGORY CREAM PITCHER,SAPPHIRE BLUE,BOY & FOLIAGE......	62.50
MARY GREGORY CREAM PITCHER,TURQUOISE,4 IN. TALL,GIRL & FLOWERS..	13.00
MARY GREGORY CREAMER,GREEN,WHITE BOY WITH TINTED FACE.......	42.50
MARY GREGORY CRUET,EMERALD GREEN,WHITE ENAMELLED GIRL.......	80.00
MARY GREGORY CRUET,GIRL....................................	39.50
MARY GREGORY CRUET,PAIR CRANBERRY,WHITE ENAMELLED FIGURES,BOY & GIRL.......................................	110.00
MARY GREGORY CRUET,SAPPHIRE BLUE,WHITE ENAMEL FLORAL & GOLD.	67.50
MARY GREGORY CRUET,VINEGAR,COBALT BLUE,GIRL.................	17.50
MARY GREGORY CRUET,VINEGAR,CRANBERRY,1 BOY & 1 GIRL.........	36.50
MARY GREGORY CRUET,VINEGAR,EMERALD GREEN,1 BOY & 1 GIRL.....	36.50
MARY GREGORY DECANTER,GIRL.................................	62.50
MARY GREGORY DECANTER,GREEN,11 IN. TALL,WHITE ENAMEL GIRL...	48.00
MARY GREGORY DECANTER,GREEN,WHITE FIGURE & FOLIAGE..........	45.00
MARY GREGORY DECANTER,PAIR CLEAR CRYSTAL,ENAMELING,APPLIED HANDLES...	60.00
MARY GREGORY DECANTER,PAIR GREEN,GIRL ON ONE,BOY ON OTHER...	60.00
MARY GREGORY DECANTER,PINK PAINTED AT TOP & BOTTOM,GIRL & FLOWERS...	47.50
MARY GREGORY DECANTER,WINE,CLEAR,APPLIED HANDLE,DEER DECOR..	55.00
MARY GREGORY DECANTER,WINE,CLEAR,BOY,MATCHING STOPPER.......	37.50

```
MARY GREGORY DECANTER,WINE,CLEAR,GIRL.....................     38.00
MARY GREGORY DECANTER,WINE,CRANBERRY,11 IN. TALL,WHITE GIRL
  FISHING................................................     62.50
MARY GREGORY DECANTER,WINE,VASELINE,GREEN,BULBOUS,WHITE
  DETAIL.................................................     45.00
MARY GREGORY DRESSER PIECE,MIRROR WITH PAIR OF COBALT BLUE
  VASES..................................................     85.00
MARY GREGORY EWER VASE,CRANBERRY,GIRL & FOLLIAGE ENAMELLED
  IN WHITE...............................................     57.50
MARY GREGORY FAIRY LAMP,BLUE,WHITE FIGURE.................     75.00
MARY GREGORY GOBLET,CLEAR,WHITE ENAMELED DECOR,2
  HOUSES,CASTLE & TREES..................................     30.00
MARY GREGORY GOBLET,PAIR HONEY AMBER,SAPPHIRE BLUE,PEDESTAL
  BASES..................................................     95.00
MARY GREGORY JUICE GLASS,RED,LITTLE GIRL IN WHITE ENAMEL....   32.50
MARY GREGORY LAMP,BLUE GLASS,WHITE ENAMELLED BOY IN GARDEN..   75.00
MARY GREGORY LAMP,TABLE,BLACK AMETHYST,WHITE DETAIL.........   85.00
MARY GREGORY LEMONADE,BOY & GIRL,PAIR,VIOLET COLOUR........    72.50
MARY GREGORY LEMONADE GLASS,DWARF,PINK FACE & HANDS.........   23.50
MARY GREGORY LEMONADE SET IN APPLE GREEN,WHITE ENAMEL.......  150.00
MARY GREGORY LEMONADE TUMBLER,CHARTREUSE PANELLED,GIRL &
  FLOWER.................................................     25.00
MARY GREGORY MILK PITCHER,BOY WITH TINTED FACE...............  45.00
MARY GREGORY MILK PITCHER,CLEAR,7 IN.......................    35.01-
MARY GREGORY MILK PITCHER,CLEAR,BLOWN,APPLIED HANDLE,BOY....   42.50
MARY GREGORY MILK PITCHER,CLEAR,CHILD WITH TINTED FACE.....    55.00
MARY GREGORY MILK PITCHER,LIME GREEN,6 IN. TALL.............   75.00
MARY GREGORY MUG,CRANBERRY CLEAR GLASS HANDLE,BOY FIGURE....   40.00
MARY GREGORY MUG,CRANBERRY,HANDLED,BOY IN WHITE & FLOWER....   40.00
MARY GREGORY MUG IN AMBER GLASS,WHITE ENAMEL GIRL...........   23.00
MARY GREGORY MUG,MARIGOLD,GIRL & FOLIAGE...................    18.00
MARY GREGORY PATCH BOX,AMETHYST,WHITE FIGURE OF GIRL,BRASS
  HINGE..................................................     69.00
MARY GREGORY PITCHER,6 IN.,RIBBED INSIDE,GREEN..............   69.50
MARY GREGORY PITCHER,12 IN. TALL,CLEAR,FULL WHITE FIGURE OF
  BOY & KITE.............................................     55.00
MARY GREGORY PITCHER,AMBER,FULL WHITE FIGURE...............    60.00
MARY GREGORY PITCHER,BLUE,WHITE ANGEL WITH FLOWERS.........    25.00
MARY GREGORY PITCHER,CLEAR,12 IN. HIGH,TINTED FACE.........    55.00
MARY GREGORY PITCHER,ELECTRIC BLUE PANELLED GLASS,WHITE
  ENAMEL GIRL............................................     47.00
MARY GREGORY PLATE,PAIR BLACK AMETHYST,WHITE BOY ON ONE,GIRL
  ON OTHER...............................................     75.00
MARY GREGORY POWDER BOX,BLUE GLASS,ENAMELED BOY & GIRL WITH
  HOOP...................................................     85.00
MARY GREGORY STEIN WITH GLASS COVER,INVERTED THUMBPRINT.....   65.00
MARY GREGORY SUGAR BOWL,GREEN,WHITE FIGURE OF GIRL,TINTED
  FACE...................................................     42.50
MARY GREGORY SUGAR BOWL,VASELINE,COVERED,WHITE ENAMELED
  FLOWERS ON BOWL........................................     55.00
MARY GREGORY TANKARD PITCHER,9 IN.,CLEAR WITH WHITE GIRL....   75.00
MARY GREGORY TANKARD PITCHER,SAPPHIRE BLUE,GIRL IN
  WHITE,BIRDS............................................     62.50
MARY GREGORY TEA WARMER,FOOTED SILVER PLATE HOLDER,LAVENDER.   45.00
MARY GREGORY TEA WARMER,WHITE ENAMELLED CHILDREN SCENES.....   48.00
MARY GREGORY TUMBLER,AMBER BASE & PAINTED FACES.............   25.00
MARY GREGORY TUMBLER,BLUE,BOY WITH TWIG IN HAND............    30.00
MARY GREGORY TUMBLER,BLUE,GIRL IN WHITE....................    20.00
MARY GREGORY TUMBLER,BLUE,DEER............................     20.00
MARY GREGORY TUMBLER,CLEAR,BOY WITH TINTED FACE............    15.00
MARY GREGORY TUMBLER,CLEAR,GIRL,TINTED FACE,ETCHED 1896.....   15.00
MARY GREGORY TUMBLER,CRANBERRY,GIRL & FOLIAGE.............     34.50
MARY GREGORY TUMBLER,CRANBERRY,WHITE ENAMEL...............     30.00
MARY GREGORY TUMBLER,CRANBERRY,WHITE ENAMELED GIRL & FOLIAGE
  AT TOP.................................................     25.00
```

```
MARY GREGORY TUMBLER,FOOTED...............................   45.00
MARY GREGORY TUMBLER,GIRL FIGURE,CRANBERRY HANDLE...........   40.00
MARY GREGORY TUMBLER,GREEN,PANELLED,TINTED FEATURES.........   18.50
MARY GREGORY TUMBLER,GREEN WITH WHITE BIRD ON FENCE.........   20.00
MARY GREGORY TUMBLER,OLIVE GREEN,FIGURE OF BOY..............   30.00
MARY GREGORY TUMBLER,PANELED,WHITE ENAMEL BOY..............   14.00
MARY GREGORY TUMBLE-UP,ROBINS EGG BLUE BRISTOL,BOY ON
 BOTTLE,GIRL...............................................   65.00
MARY GREGORY VASE,5 IN. TALL,BLACK PEDESTAL,BOY............   22.50
MARY GREGORY VASE,6 IN.,BLUE,BULBOUS BOTTOM,BOY,BUTTERFLY...   33.00
MARY GREGORY VASE,6 IN. TALL,SAPPHIRE BLUE,GIRL & BUTTERFLY.   45.00
MARY GREGORY VASE,7 IN.,BLUE SAPPHIRE,WHITE CHILD..........   42.50
MARY GREGORY VASE,9 IN. TALL,BLUE BOY DATED 1895,ATLANTIC
 CITY......................................................   35.00
MARY GREGORY VASE,10 IN.,MARY SITTING ON FENCE,PASTORAL
 BACKGROUND................................................   53.00
MARY GREGORY VASE,11 IN.,AMBER,FOOTED,2 APPLIED
 HANDLES,WHITE GIRL........................................  110.00
MARY GREGORY VASE,BLACK PURPLE,7 IN.,WHITE ENAMEL BOY &
 FOLIAGE...................................................   40.00
MARY GREGORY VASE,BLUE BLOWN,RUFFLED TOP,WHITE ENAMELED
 STORK.....................................................   25.00
MARY GREGORY VASE,BLUE,WHITE GIRL,GOLD RIM.................   65.00
MARY GREGORY VASE,BOTTLE,SAPPHIRE BLUE,WHITE FIGURES &
 FOLIAGE...................................................   45.00
MARY GREGORY VASE,COBALT,GIRL.............................   43.00
MARY GREGORY VASE,CRANBERRY,8 IN. TALL....................   65.00
MARY GREGORY VASE,CRANBERRY GLASS,8 IN. TALL,WHITE ENAMEL
 BOY.......................................................   40.00
MARY GREGORY VASE,CRANBERRY GLASS,8 IN. TALL,WHITE ENAMEL
 GIRL......................................................   40.00
MARY GREGORY VASE,CRANBERRY PANELLED,BOY TIPPING HAT.......   35.00
MARY GREGORY VASE,CRANBERRY,WHITE GIRL IN GARDEN...........   45.00
MARY GREGORY VASE,EMERALD GREEN,7 IN.,BOY,PINK FACE & HANDS.  40.00
MARY GREGORY VASE,GREEN PANEL,6 IN. TALL,BOY & FOLIAGE IN
 WHITE ENAMEL..............................................   18.00
MARY GREGORY VASE,GREEN PANEL GLASS,6 IN. TALL,WHITE ENAMEL
 GIRL......................................................   18.00
MARY GREGORY VASE IN BLACK AMETHYST,......................   75.00
MARY GREGORY VASE IN SAPPHIRE BLUE PANELLED GLASS,WHITE BOY.  40.00
MARY GREGORY VASE IN SAPPHIRE BLUE PANELLED GLASS,WHITE
 ENAMELED GIRL.............................................   40.00
MARY GREGORY VASE,LIME GREEN,WHITE ENAMELLED BOY...........   25.00
MARY GREGORY VASE,PAIR 8 IN.,EMERALD GREEN WITH CLEAR
 APPLIED GLASS.............................................   75.00
MARY GREGORY VASE,PAIR BLACK,10 IN. HIGH...................   80.00
MARY GREGORY VASES,PAIR,BLACK MILK GLASS,10 IN. TALL.......  150.00
MARY GREGORY VASE,PAIR BLUE BRISTOL,BOY ON ONE,GIRL ON OTHER 125.00
MARY GREGORY VASE,PAIR BLUE,FIGURES,TINTED FEATURES........  165.00
MARY GREGORY VASE,PAIR CRANBERRY,9 IN.
 125.00  TO...............................................  295.00
MARY GREGORY VASE,PAIR GREEN,MELON RIBBED,ENAMELED BOY &
 GIRL......................................................  185.00
MARY GREGORY VASE,PAIR SAPPHIRE BLUE,WHITE BOY & GIRL......   65.00
MARY GREGORY VASE RUFFLED TOP,GREEN,GIRL..................   40.00
MARY GREGORY VASE,SAPPHIRE BLUE GLASS,5 IN. TALL,WHITE GIRL
 & FOLIAGE.................................................   30.00
MARY GREGORY VASE,TOPAZ PANEL GLASS,5 IN. TALL,BOY IN WHITE
 & FOLIAGE.................................................   35.00
MARY GREGORY VASE WITH BOY,7 IN. TALL,AMETHYST LUSTER......   55.00
MARY GREGORY WATER PITCHER,CLEAR,GIRL WITH FLOWERS.........   65.00
MARY GREGORY WATER PITCHER,CLEAR GLASS,RUFFLED,INVERTED RIB.  58.00
MARY GREGORY WATER PITCHER,10 IN. TALL,GIRL,REEDED HANDLE...  75.00
MARY GREGORY WATER SET,GIRL & BOY.........................   85.00
MARY GREGORY WINE,PAIR CLEAR,BOY & GIRL,TINTED FACES.......   25.00
```

```
MARY GREGORY WINE,SAPPHIRE BLUE,STEMMED,WHITE ENAMELLED GIRL        35.00
    MASONIC, SEE ALSO PRESSED GLASS, SHRINE.................
MASONIC CHALICE,CLEAR ,ETCHED STEP EMBLEMS...................        40.00
MASONIC CLEAR DISH,GOLD EDGED,EMBOSSED LOS ANGELES MAY 1906.        18.50
MASONIC PLATE..............................................         5.50
MASONIC RAZOR BLADE ENGRAVED WITH MASONIC SYMBOLS...........         6.50
MASONIC SYRIA LOVING CUP,CRANBERRY COLOURED,1908,SHEAF OF
    WHEAT..................................................         35.00
MATCH HOLDER FROM OLD TRAIN COACH...........................         5.00
MATCH HOLDER,IRON,DOUBLE....................................         7.50
MATCH HOLDER,IRON & TIN ON WOOD BASE,PUSH UP................         8.50
MATCH HOLDER,SILVER PLATE,PAIR OF RIDING BOOTS ON ROUND BASE        12.00
MATCH HOLDER,TIN,2 ROUNDED HOLDERS..........................         3.95
MATCH HOLDER,TIN,SOUVENIR OF UNIVERSAL STOVES & RANGES......         3.95
```

MEAKIN is a name used by several Victorian English potter firms. Alfred Meakin produced from 1875 to the present time. Charles Meakin worked from 1883 to 1889; Henry Meakin worked from 1873 to 1882; and J. & G. Meakin produced from 1851 to the present time.

```
MEAKIN BONE DISH,SET OF 6,GOLD TRIM.........................         8.50
MEAKIN GRAVY,WHITE,SCALLOPED................................         3.50
MEAKIN PLATE,9 IN...........................................        15.00
MEAKIN PLATE,10 IN.,MEDALLIONS OF PINK & BLUE FLOWERS.......         4.75
MEAKIN PLATTER,12 X 9 IN.,MARKED............................         3.00
MEAKIN SOUP,HUDSON,10 IN.,FLOWERS,GOLD BAND.................         9.00
MEAKIN TOOTHBRUSH HOLDER,BASKETWEAVE BAND...................         4.50
```

MECHANICAL BANKS were first made about 1870. Any bank with moving parts is considered mechanical, although those most collected are the metal banks made before World War I. Reproductions are being made.

```
MECHANICAL BANK, SEE BANK, MECHANICAL...................
MECHANICAL BIRD IN BRASS ORNATE CAGE, 3 MINUTES OF SONG.....       130.00
```

MEERSCHAUM PIPES and other carved pieces of meerschaum date from the nineteenth century to the present time.

```
MEERSCHAUM CIGAR HOLDER,AMBER STEM..........................         8.50
MEERSCHAUM CIGAR HOLDER,HORSE ON TOP,AMBER BIT..............        15.00
MEERSCHAUM CIGAR HOLDER WITH CARVED DOG.....................        18.00
MEERSCHAUM CIGARETTE HOLDER,CARVED STALLION.................        14.00
MEERSCHAUM 5 IN. PIPE,BRASS TRIM WITH WOMENS FIGURES........        15.00
MEERSCHAUM PIPE.............................................        20.00
MEERSCHAUM PIPE,CARVED......................................        95.00
MEERSCHAUM PIPE,CARVED DEER HEAD,CASE.......................        11.00
MEERSCHAUM PIPE,CARVED HORSE & DOG..........................        35.00
MEERSCHAUM PIPE,CARVED RUNNING DEER,14 IN. CHERRY STEM,HORN
    MOUTHPIECE.............................................        18.00
MEERSCHAUM PIPE,CARVED TIGER AROUND BOWL,CASE...............        12.00
MEERSCHAUM PIPE ,ENGLISH STYLE.............................        20.00
MEERSCHAUM PIPE,HAND CARVED,RUNNING HORSE WITH CASE,5 IN....        27.00
MEERSCHAUM PIPE,TURBANED ARAB,HORN MOUTHPIECE...............        15.00
MEERSCHAUM PIPE,WHITE STALLION CARVED.......................        14.00
```

MEISSEN is a town in Germany where porcelain has been made since 1710. Any china made in that town can be called Meissen, although the famous Meissen factory made the finest porcelains of the area.

```
MEISSEN, SEE ALSO DRESDEN ONION.......................
MEISSEN BOWL WITH PATTERN IN BLUE ON WHITE,8 IN.............        50.00
MEISSEN CANARY,PAIR YELLOW WITH CROSS-SWORD MARK,3
    IN.,FLORAL BASE.......................................       125.00
MEISSEN CHOCOLATE POT WITH CROSS-SWORD MARK,ROSES...........        35.00
MEISSEN COMPORT ON BOLTED BASE,HAND DECORATED,CROSSED SWORDS
    MARK...................................................       175.00
MEISSEN COMPOTE ON TALL FOOT WITH CROSS-SWORD MARK..........        95.00
MEISSEN CUP & SAUCER.......................................        60.00
MEISSEN DEMI-TASSE,CROSSED SWORDS,LARGE PINK ROSE...........        15.00
```

MEISSEN DEMI-TASSE,CROSSED SWORDS,MARKED,SMALL FLOWER SPRIGS	15.00
MEISSEN DISH,FOOTED,5 IN.,CROSS-SWORD MARK UNDERGLAZE BLUE..	50.00
MEISSEN DRESSER TRAY,SIGNED,FUCHSIA,GOLD & WHITE WITH FLORAL DECORATION...	160.00
MEISSEN FIGURINE,PAIR MARKED,COPIES OF GAINSBOROUGH PAINTINGS..	300.00
MEISSEN FRUIT BOWL,PAIR,MARCOLLINI............................	150.00
MEISSEN FRUIT BOWL,19TH CENTURY...............................	40.00
MEISSEN FRUIT PLATE..	40.00
MEISSEN KNIFE & FORK,SET OF 6 PISTOL HANDLED.................	180.00
MEISSEN PLATE,11 IN. ROUND,WITH CROSS-SWORD MARK IN BLUE,GOLD FLORAL...	55.00
MEISSEN PLATE,BLUE CROSS SWORDS MARK UNDERGLAZE,.............	27.50
MEISSEN PLATE,WHITE,9 IN.,RAISED SEA URCHINS.................	40.00
MEISSEN PLATE,WHITE,10 IN.,RAISED GRAPES & LEAVES...........	45.00
MEISSEN PLATTER WITH CROSS-SWORD MARK.......................	75.00
MEISSEN SUGAR & CREAMER......................................	95.00
MEISSEN TEA POT,CROSSED SWORD................................	47.50
MEISSEN TEAPOT,18TH CENTURY..................................	125.00
MEISSEN TEA SET,CROSSED SWORDS,PINK & WHITE & BLUE..........	165.00
MEISSEN TEA SET,CROSSED SWORDS UNDER GLAZE,COBALT & GOLD EDGING,ROSES..	60.00
MEISSEN VEGETABLE DISH,COVERED,WITH CROSS-SWORD MARK........	75.00
MEMORIAL PLATE,METHODIST,CENTENNIAL CONVENTION 1907.........	24.50

MERCURY OR SILVERED GLASS was first made in the 1850's. It lost favor for a while but became popular again about 1910. It looks like a piece of silver.

MERCURY GLASS 6 LONG SPEAR POINT ORNAMENTS,2 TRUMPETS.......	16.00
MERCURY GLASS 6 CHRISTMAS TREE ORNAMENTS.....................	15.00
MERCURY GLASS 9 IN. CANDLESTICKS,PAIR........................	12.50
MERCURY GLASS 9 IN. VASE,GOLD INSIDE,GRAPE,LEAVES,BOWERS,TREES.............................	12.00
MERCURY GLASS 10 IN. VASE,GOLD LINED,PAIR...................	32.00
MERCURY GLASS 14 XMAS TREE ORNAMENTS.........................	50.00
MERCURY GLASS CANDLESTICK,PAIR...............................	18.00
MERCURY GLASS CHRISTMAS TREE BALLS,10,SILVER,GOLD,GREEN,BLUE	39.50
MERCURY GLASS COMPOTE,ETCHED,GOLD LINED......................	25.00
MERCURY GLASS FOOTED SALT DIPS...............................	3.50
MERCURY GLASS GOBLET,GRAPE LEAVES & WORDS MY WIFE............	22.00
MERCURY GLASS MASTER SALT....................................	6.75
MERCURY GLASS MATCHING TIEBACKS..............................	12.00
MERCURY GLASS MUG,GOLD LINER,APPLIED CLEAR HANDLE............	14.00
MERCURY GLASS MULTI-COLOURED PUNCH LADLE.....................	25.00
MERCURY GLASS PAIR MASTER SALTS,PEDESTAL.....................	24.50
MERCURY GLASS PAIR SALT DIPS,PEDESTAL FOOT,WAX SEALS........	14.00
MERCURY GLASS PAIR TIEBACKS..................................	5.00
MERCURY GLASS PRESENTATION CHALICE,GOLD LINED,THE WEDDING CELEBRATION..	35.00
MERCURY GLASS REFLECTOR......................................	4.75
MERCURY GLASS ROSE BOWL......................................	8.00
MERCURY GLASS ROSE BOWL,PEDESTAL SALT DIP,DUCK...............	15.00
MERCURY GLASS SALT DIP.......................................	6.50
MERCURY GLASS SET,PEDESTAL CREAMER,SUGAR,SPOONER,BUTTER DISH,WASTE BOWL..	185.00
MERCURY GLASS SET OF 4 ROSE TIEBACKS........................	20.00
MERCURY GLASS TIEBACKS,GRAPE.................................	10.00
MERCURY GLASS TIE BACKS,RAISED DESIGN,PEWTER SCREWS.........	9.00
MERCURY GLASS VASE,10 IN.,PINK FLOWER ENAMELING.............	4.50
MERCURY GLASS VASE,BLUE......................................	19.50
MERCURY GLASS VASE,HANDPAINTED ROSE..........................	12.00
MERCURY GLASS VASE IN BLUE,BULBOUS...........................	19.50
MERCURY GLASS WINE..	4.50
METTLACH, SEE ALSO STEIN....................................	

METTLACH, GERMANY, is a city where the Villeroy and Boch factories worked.

Steins from the firm are known as Mettlach steins. They date from about 1842.

METTLACH BEAKER, ONE HALF LITRE	27.00
METTLACH BEAKER, 1200 STATE LEIPZIG, QUARTER LITER	17.50
METTLACH BOWL, VEGETABLE, 8 IN., 2-HANDLED, ALPINE DECOR, VILLEROY & BOCH	8.50
METTLACH BOX, RAISED MEDALLION MARK, CIGARETTES, MATCH HOLDER & STRIKER	89.00
METTLACH DISH, OLIVE, GREEN MERCURY MARKED, # 1309, OLIVE LEAVES	13.00
METTLACH FRUIT PLATE, PEACHES & BERRIES	7.50
METTLACH FRUIT PLATE, PEAR, NUTS & CHERRIES	7.50
METTLACH FRUIT PLATE, PEAR, PLUMS & BERRIES	7.50
METTLACH GOBLETS, PAIR, PEDESTAL, 1 QUARTER LITRE	75.00
METTLACH JAM JAR, COVERED, VILLEROY & BOCH	12.50
METTLACH MUG, 1909, HANDLED	12.50
METTLACH MUG, B.P.O.E. 1897 SOUVENIR MINNEAPOLIS BREWING CO...	12.50
METTLACH MUG, BEER, SIGNED, MINIATURE, NUMBERED, SHRINE JULY 1911	17.00
METTLACH MUG, HANDLED, CASTLE MARK #2245, 3/10 LITRE	25.00
METTLACH MUG, VILLEROY & BOCH, DRINK HIRES ROOT BEER	38.00
METTLACH PITCHER, CASTLEMARKED, 2 1/2 LITRES	110.00
METTLACH PITCHER, HINGED, CASTLE MARK, PEWTER LID & THUMB REST.	140.00
METTLACH PITCHER STEIN WITH 6 BEER CUPS, 14 IN. TALL	290.00
METTLACH PITCHER, VILLEROY & BOCH 3 QUART SIZE	110.00
METTLACH PLAQUE, 12 IN.	85.00
METTLACH PLAQUE, 16 IN. DIAMETER, GLAZED, #1110, WOMAN ON HORSE.	95.00
METTLACH PLAQUE, 17 IN. DIAMETER, GLAZED DUTCH SCENE	120.00
METTLACH PLAQUES, PAIR, SIGNED PORTRAIT, #1405 & #1376	325.00
METTLACH PLATE, CASTLE MARK, 12 IN. ONION PATTERN CHOP	55.00
METTLACH PLATE, CASTLE MARK, 8 IN. ONION PATTERN CHOP	35.00
METTLACH PLATTER, ETCHED, #3321, 15 IN. DIAMETER	40.00
METTLACH SET OF 6 MUGS, #675	90.00
METTLACH TUMBLER, 1 QUARTER LITRE, MERCURY MARK, GERMAN TROUBADOUR SCENE	25.00
METTLACH TUMBLER, 1 QUARTER LITRE	22.50
METTLACH TUMBLER, MERCURY MARK	12.00
METTLACH TUMBLER SIGNED & NUMBERED, YOUNG MAN & COUNTRY SCENE	17.00
METTLACH TUREEN, 5 QUART & GLAZED PLATTER	225.00
METTLACH TUREEN WITH COVER, 5 QUART, FLORAL GLAZED DECOR	75.00
METTLACH VASE, 14 IN., CHERUBS, CASTLEMARKED NO. 1537	120.00
METTLACH VASE, PAIR, 9 IN., CHERUBS	80.00
METTLACH VASE, PAIR, WITH CHERUBS, 9 IN. HIGH	90.00

MILK GLASS was named for its milky white color. It was first made in England during the 1700's. The height of its popularity in the United States was from 1870 to 1880. It is now correct to refer to some colored glass as blue milk glass, black milk glass, etc.

MILK GLASS, SEE BOTH LISTINGS, FIRST BY COLOUR OR PATTERN, SECOND BY ITEM.	
MILK GLASS ACTRESS BOTTLE, DRESSER	27.50
MILK GLASS ACTRESS BOX, PIN, COVERED	18.00
MILK GLASS ACTRESS DRESSER SET	18.00
MILK GLASS ADMIRAL DEWEY PLATE, RED TRANSFER CENTER	13.50
MILK GLASS AMBER ATTERBURY DISH, OWL COVERED	50.00
MILK GLASS ANCHOR & YACHT PLATE	11.00
MILK GLASS ANGEL & HARP PLATE, 7 IN	7.00
MILK GLASS ANGEL & HARP PLATE, 8 IN	6.50
MILK GLASS APPLE BLOSSOM COMPOTE, FOOTED, LATTICE EDGE	60.00
MILK GLASS AQUA QUILTED & FLOWER SUGAR SHAKER, EMBOSSED	27.00
MILK GLASS ATLAS COMPOTE 37.00 TO	50.00
MILK GLASS ATLAS COMPOTE, SCALLOPED	40.00
MILK GLASS ATTERBURY ATLAS COMPOTE, OPEN EDGE	59.50
MILK GLASS ATTERBURY BOWL, 9 IN., OPEN, LATTICE	12.00
MILK GLASS ATTERBURY DISH, ENTWINED FISH COVERED, DATED AUG. 1886	75.00

```
MILK GLASS ATTERBURY PLATE,7 IN.,H BORDER....................   6.50
MILK GLASS ATTERBURY SAUCE,KNOTCHED LACY EDGE................   7.00
MILK GLASS ATTERBURY SQUARE BLOCK DISH,SWAN COVERED..........  75.00
MILK GLASS ATTERBURY TRUMPET VINE BOWL,LATTICE...............  32.50
MILK GLASS BASKET TOOTHPICK..................................   6.50
MILK GLASS BASKETWEAVE DISH,7 IN.,MARKED,PATENT 1874.........   6.75
MILK GLASS BASKETWEAVE DISH,HEN ON NEST......................  15.00
MILK GLASS BASKETWEAVE DISH,HEN ON NEST WITH EGGS............  18.50
MILK GLASS BASKETWEAVE EGG CUP DATED PAT.JAN.30,1874.........  10.00
MILK GLASS BASKETWEAVE SALT,MASTER,HANDLED,FOOTED,DATED 1874   9.00
MILK GLASS BASKETWEAVE TUMBLER...............................   4.00
MILK GLASS BATTLESHIP MAINE DISH,COVERED.....................  21.00
MILK GLASS BEADED LOOP INDIAN HEAD PLATE.....................   8.75
MILK GLASS BEADED RIB BOWL,9 IN.,OPEN EDGE...................  27.50
MILK GLASS BEADED SALT SHAKER................................   6.00
MILK GLASS BEADED SWAG SALT & PEPPER.........................   8.75
MILK GLASS BIRDS MUG.........................................  11.50
MILK GLASS BIRDS VASE,11 IN.,PHOENIX.........................  35.00
MILK GLASS BLACK AMETHYST BOWL...............................   3.50
MILK GLASS BLACK AMETHYST BOWL,LEGGED........................   2.50
MILK GLASS BLACK AMETHYST BOX,HANDKERCHIEF,COVERED,FLORAL...   6.50
MILK GLASS BLACK AMETHYST CANDLESTICK........................   6.00
MILK GLASS BLACK AMETHYST DISH,SWAN..........................   6.00
MILK GLASS BLACK BASKET,SATIN................................  25.00
MILK GLASS BLACK BOWL,OCTAGONAL ,3 FEET......................   6.00
MILK GLASS BLACK CERES MUG...................................  18.50
MILK GLASS BLACK CRACKLE VASE,WALL...........................   4.00
MILK GLASS BLACK CREAM & SUGAR,SCALLOPED.....................  15.00
MILK GLASS BLACK DECANTER WITH STERLING SILVER DEPOSIT WORK.  20.00
MILK GLASS BLACK DISH,CHEESE,THE JOLLY DROVER................  15.00
MILK GLASS BLACK DRESSER TRAY,ROUND..........................   3.50
MILK GLASS BLACK LION ON SLAB,SLEEPING.......................  50.00
MILK GLASS BLACK PLATE,7 IN.,GOTHIC BORDER...................   9.00
MILK GLASS BLACK PLATE,8 IN..................................   2.50
MILK GLASS BLACK PLATE,COOKIE,LATTICE EDGE,7 IN..............   6.50
MILK GLASS BLACK PLATE,GOTHIC BORDER.........................   7.50
MILK GLASS BLACK PLATE,S BORDER,SQUARE.......................   8.50
MILK GLASS BLACK SALT,MASTER,SIGNED C IN TRIANGLE............  37.50
MILK GLASS BLACK TOOTHPICK,HAT...............................   9.50
MILK GLASS BLACK VASE,12 IN..................................   7.50
MILK GLASS BLACK VASE SILVER TRIM 2 SELF HANDLES.............   8.00
MILK GLASS BLACK VASE,WORLDS FAIR 1933.......................   4.00
MILK GLASS BLACKBERRY DISH,9 IN..............................  12.50
MILK GLASS BLACKBERRY EGG CUP................................  13.50
MILK GLASS BLACKBERRY SALT,FOOTED,MASTER.....................  10.00
MILK GLASS BLACKBERRY SPOONER................................  10.50
MILK GLASS BLAZE CANDLESTICK,LOW HANDLED,GOLD TRIM,PAIR......  15.00
MILK GLASS BLUE & PINK SALT & PEPPER SHAKER,PAIR.............  25.00
MILK GLASS BLUE BASKETWEAVE CREAMER,3 IN. HIGH...............  22.00
MILK GLASS BLUE BOTTLE,LIDDED,1888...........................  18.00
MILK GLASS BLUE CANDLESTICK FOOTED,ROPE HANDLE...............  16.00
MILK GLASS BLUE CANDLESTICK,MINIATURE,RING HANDLE............   4.50
MILK GLASS BLUE CANOE,6 IN.,DECORATED........................   6.00
MILK GLASS BLUE CHALLINORS FLOWER SPRIG SYRUP WITH TIN TOP..  32.00
MILK GLASS BLUE CHERRIES & GRAPES SUGAR
  BOWL,COVERED,PEDESTAL......................................  17.50
MILK GLASS BLUE CHICKEN WITH WHITE HEAD......................  30.00
MILK GLASS BLUE CHRYSANTHEMUM SPRIG WATER TUMBLER............  60.00
MILK GLASS BLUE CREAMER......................................  15.00
MILK GLASS BLUE DISH,DOG COVERED MARKED VALLERYSTAHL.........  15.00
MILK GLASS BLUE DISH,DUCK ON OVAL BASE,COVERED,VALLERYSTAHL.  22.50
MILK GLASS BLUE DISH,HEN ON NEST.............................   6.50
MILK GLASS BLUE DISH,HEN WITH WHITE HEAD ON BASKETWEAVE BASE  23.00
MILK GLASS BLUE DISH,KITTEN COVERED..........................  22.00
MILK GLASS BLUE DISH,PAIR ROOSTERS COVERED,BASKET BASES.....  29.00
```

```
MILK GLASS BLUE DISH,TURTLE WITH SNAIL ON BACK,COVERED......     16.50
MILK GLASS BLUE DRESSER TRAY,& ROUND DRESSER BOX............     22.00
MILK GLASS BLUE EMBOSSED ACANTHUS LEAF TOOTHPICK,MARKED.....     16.50
MILK GLASS BLUE FORGET ME NOT TOOTHPICK HOLDER.............      20.00
MILK GLASS BLUE FRENCH PINEAPPLE DISH,COVERED,FOOTED........     10.00
MILK GLASS BLUE GRAPE & CHERRY SUGAR & CREAMER,OPAQUE.......     15.00
MILK GLASS BLUE HEN.........................................      7.50
MILK GLASS BLUE HEN MARKED VALLERYSTAHL.....................     35.00
MILK GLASS BLUE HEN,WHITE HEAD,BASKET WEAVE BASE............     22.00
MILK GLASS BLUE LAMP,MINIATURE..............................     10.00
MILK GLASS BLUE LOBULATED SALT & PEPPER SHAKER,PEWTER TOPS..     20.00
MILK GLASS BLUE PANEL FORGET-ME-NOT CONDIMENT SET & TRAY,3
  PIECE.....................................................     50.00
MILK GLASS BLUE PEACOCK FEATHER BOWL,FRUIT..................     10.00
MILK GLASS BLUE PLATE,10 IN.,LATTICE EDGE...................     59.00
MILK GLASS BLUE POND LILY NAPPY,2 HANDLED..................      12.50
MILK GLASS BLUE RAISED GRAPES JAR,POWDER,FOOTED.............     12.50
MILK GLASS BLUE SALT & PEPPER...............................      6.50
MILK GLASS BLUE SALT,LEANING................................     14.50
MILK GLASS BLUE SANDWICH DISH,SHALLOW.......................     15.00
MILK GLASS BLUE SANDWICH EGGCUP,DOUBLE......................     12.00
MILK GLASS BLUE SANDWICH SCROLL & EYE PLATE,8 IN............     15.00
MILK GLASS BLUE SCROLL & NET SALT SHAKER....................     10.00
MILK GLASS BLUE SCROLLED SPRAY CREAMER & COVER..............     23.00
MILK GLASS BLUE SWIRL VASE,CRIMPED & FLUTED MOUTH...........     56.00
MILK GLASS BLUE TEXAS SUGAR & CREAMER.......................     12.50
MILK GLASS BLUE TOOTHPICK HOLDER,ENGLISH REGISTRY MARK 1877.     10.00
MILK GLASS BLUE TOOTHPICK...................................      8.50
MILK GLASS BLUE TRAY,DRESSER................................     12.00
MILK GLASS BLUE TRAY,DRESSER,OVAL,GREY ,GOLD ENAMEL.........     17.00
MILK GLASS BLUE TWIN HORN SUGAR,COVERED.....................     35.00
MILK GLASS BLUE WAFFLE JAR,7 IN. TALL.......................     18.00
MILK GLASS BLUE WITH WHITE RAISED FLOWERS & LEAVES VASE,10
  IN. HIGH..................................................     26.50
MILK GLASS BUTTERFLY MATCH HOLDER,HANGING...................      9.50
MILK GLASS CABBAGE ROSE PLATE,5 IN..........................      5.00
MILK GLASS CANDLEWICK CUP & SAUCER..........................     10.00
MILK GLASS CARDINAL BIRD SHAVING MUG........................     15.00
MILK GLASS CHARTREUSE GREEN DIAMOND QUILTED SUGAR
  SHAKER,OPAQUE.............................................     35.00
MILK GLASS CHARTREUSE SHELL SALT SHAKER.....................      6.00
MILK GLASS CLEAR PITCHER,7 IN.,MARY GREGORY TYPE DECOR,GIRL.     32.50
MILK GLASS COLUMBIAN COIN LAMP..............................    100.00
MILK GLASS COREOPSIS BUTTER,COVERED.........................     30.00
MILK GLASS CORN WITH HUSK SHAKER............................     10.50
MILK GLASS CROSSED FERN COMPOTE,LOW,OPEN,SCALLOPED TOP......     13.50
MILK GLASS CUPID & PSYCHE PLATE.............................      9.75
MILK GLASS CURTAIN SYRUP,GOLD HANDLE........................     27.50
MILK GLASS DEWEY CRUISER DISH,COVERED.......................     19.25
MILK GLASS DEWEY TILE BASE..................................     20.00
MILK GLASS DIAMOND & SHELL PLATE............................      8.00
MILK GLASS DIAMOND GRILL PLATE,BREAD,11 IN..................     15.00
MILK GLASS DOMINECKER HEN...................................     75.00
MILK GLASS DOUBLE C ROSES PLATE.............................      5.00
MILK GLASS EMBOSSED BOX,SQUARE,FOOTED.......................      7.00
MILK GLASS EMBOSSED FLORALS BOTTLE,PAIR 9 IN. BULBOUS
  DRESSER...................................................     30.00
MILK GLASS NIAGARA FALLS PLATE..............................     10.25
MILK GLASS NUTMEG LAMP......................................     14.00
MILK GLASS NUTMEG LAMP,RAISED FLOWERS.......................     18.00
MILK GLASS OWL LOVERS PLATE.................................      9.00
MILK GLASS OWL MUSTARD JAR..................................     18.00
MILK GLASS OWL PLATE........................................      7.50
MILK GLASS PANEL WHEAT SUGAR,OPEN...........................     12.50
MILK GLASS PANELLED DAISY MUFFINEER.........................     12.50
```

MILK GLASS PANELED FLOWER CRUET & TRAY	25.00
MILK GLASS PANELLED GRAPE MATCH HOLDER, HANGING	9.00
MILK GLASS PANSY TRAY	12.00
MILK GLASS PEACOCK & LILY OF THE VALLEY MUG, CHILDS	5.50
MILK GLASS PICKET FENCE DISH, LAMB, OCTAGON	22.00
MILK GLASS PINK & WHITE SALT & PEPPER SHAKER, PAIR	19.00
MILK GLASS PINK BOX, COVERED, DECORATED SCENIC	35.00
MILK GLASS PINK DISH, CANDY, 3 LEGGED, IRIDESCENCE, SCALLOPED BEADED EDGE	5.00
MILK GLASS PINK FEATHER SUGAR, COVERED, OPAQUE	15.00
MILK GLASS PINK HOBNAIL COMPOTE	12.50
MILK GLASS PINK HONEYCOMB SYRUP, BULBOUS	55.00
MILK GLASS PINK LOUIS XV BOWL, BANANA	35.00
MILK GLASS PINK MELON RIBBED & EMBOSSED FLOWERS SUGAR SHAKER	36.00
MILK GLASS PINK PINEAPPLE SALT SHAKER	7.00
MILK GLASS PYRAMID CANDLE HOLDER, PAIR	26.00
MILK GLASS QUILTED ROYAL OAK CREAMER & SUGAR, NORTHWOOD	60.00
MILK GLASS RAISED PINEAPPLE SPOONER	20.00
MILK GLASS RIBBED BOX, POWDER, PAINTED GILT HEAD KNOB	9.50
MILK GLASS RIBBED CREAMER, SUGAR & OPEN BUTTER, LACY TOP	40.00
MILK GLASS RIBBED LAMP, MINIATURE	15.00
MILK GLASS ROMEO SPOONER	7.00
MILK GLASS ROSE LEAF SPOONER	10.00
MILK GLASS ROSE VASE	7.50
MILK GLASS ROSES & POPPIES TRAY, PIN	5.00
MILK GLASS ROYAL OAK SUGAR SHAKER	14.00
MILK GLASS ROYAL OAK SUGAR, SQUARE, PINK BAND, NORTHWOOD	25.00
MILK GLASS SAWTOOTH BUTTER DISH	35.00
MILK GLASS SAWTOOTH SPOONER WITH SAWTOOTH EDGE	12.50
MILK GLASS SCOOP TRAY	7.50
MILK GLASS SCROLL & EYE BOWL, 8 IN., SHALLOW	9.50
MILK GLASS SCROLL & EYE PLATE, 8 IN	8.00
MILK GLASS SCROLL TANKARD	75.00
MILK GLASS SCROLL TRAY, DRESSER	18.00
MILK GLASS SERENADE PLATE	35.00
MILK GLASS SINGLE FORGET-ME-NOT PLATE, 7 IN	5.50
MILK GLASS SPADE & HEART PLATE, PAIR	12.00
MILK GLASS SQUARE PEG PLATE, 8 IN	8.00
MILK GLASS STAR PLATE	5.00
MILK GLASS STARS & STRIPES HAT	9.00
MILK GLASS STRAWBERRY DISH, SAUCE, OPALESCENT	5.50
MILK GLASS STRAWBERRY SAUCE, FLAT, FLINT	5.75
MILK GLASS SUNKEN RABBIT PLATE	12.00
MILK GLASS SWAN CREAMER	25.00
MILK GLASS THE STATES SALT SHAKER, PAIR	10.00
MILK GLASS THREE KITTEN PLATE	10.00
MILK GLASS THREE KITTEN PLATE, 7 IN., OPEN EDGE	7.50
MILK GLASS TOM & JERRY SET MARKED	45.00
MILK GLASS TRUMPET VINE PLATE, 10 IN., LATTICE-EDGE	32.50
MILK GLASS TRUMPET VINE PLATE, OPEN LATTICE EDGE	25.00
MILK GLASS TRUMPET VINE PLATE, PINWHEEL EDGE, 10 IN	54.00
MILK GLASS TULIP VASE, GREEN GLASS ORNAMENTS	35.00
MILK GLASS TURQUOISE PANELLED SHELL SALT, PAIR	18.50
MILK GLASS WAFFLE COMPOTE	12.00
MILK GLASS WAFFLE TUMBLER, RAYED BASE	10.00
MILK GLASS WHEAT SHEAF CREAMER	18.50
MILK GLASS WICKET PLATE	6.50
MILK GLASS WICKET PLATE, 8 IN. DIAMETER	11.00
MILK GLASS WICKET PLATE, 8 IN., RECESSED CENTER WITH PINK FLOWERS	10.00
MILK GLASS WILDFLOWER SALT SHAKER	7.00
MILK GLASS, SEE ALSO LISTINGS BY COLOUR	
MILK GLASS, BANK, COVERED, SCHOOLHOUSE	12.50
MILK GLASS, BANK, LOG CABIN, GOLD & YELLOW PAINT	26.00
MILK GLASS, BANK, UNCLE SAM HAT	17.00

```
MILK GLASS,  BASE FOR LACY EDGE CAT OR HAND & DOVE..........    27.50
MILK GLASS,  BASKET,COVERED,OPALESCENT.....................    12.00
MILK GLASS,  BASKET,SCALLOPED WITH WIRE HANDLE.............     8.00
MILK GLASS,  BASKET WITH PAINTED FLOWERS...................    10.00
MILK GLASS,  BELL,SMOKE....................................     4.00
MILK GLASS,  BELL,SMOKE,7 IN...............................     6.00
MILK GLASS,  BELL,SMOKE,RUFFLES............................     8.00
MILK GLASS,  BOTTLE,1939 WORLDS FAIR.......................     6.00
MILK GLASS,  BOTTLE,A CENTURY OF PROGRESS..................     5.50
MILK GLASS,  BOTTLE,BARBER.................................     6.00
MILK GLASS,  BOTTLE,BARBER,3,OCTAGON SHAPE.................    50.00
MILK GLASS,  BOTTLE,BARBER,NEW YORK WORLDS FAIR 1939.......     5.00
MILK GLASS,  BOTTLE,BARBERS,SHAKER TOP.....................    15.00
MILK GLASS,  BOTTLE,COLOGNE................................    12.50
MILK GLASS,  BOTTLE,COLOGNE,GREEN WITH GOLD TRIM...........    18.00
MILK GLASS,  BOTTLE,DRESSER................................     9.00
MILK GLASS,  BOTTLE,DRESSER WITH HANDPAINTED ROSES.........    10.50
MILK GLASS,  BOTTLE,FIGURAL,CHINESE BOY SEATED.............    20.00
MILK GLASS,  BOTTLE,PAIR,BUREAU
   20.00  TO...............................................    22.50
MILK GLASS,  BOTTLE,PAIR DRESSER...........................    18.00
MILK GLASS,  BOTTLE,PAIR TOILET............................    10.00
MILK GLASS,  BOTTLE,PAIR TOILET 10 IN. HIGH,GLAZED FINISH...   23.00
MILK GLASS,  BOTTLE,PAIR VICTORIAN COLOGNE WITH
   STOPPERS,FLORAL DECOR...................................    24.00
MILK GLASS,  BOTTLE,SATIN FINISH WITH HANDPAINTED CARNATIONS   10.50
MILK GLASS,  BOTTLE,WORLDS FAIR 1939
   7.50  TO................................................     9.00
MILK GLASS,  BOWL,8 IN.,DAISY..............................    60.00
MILK GLASS,  BOWL,LATTICE EDGE,HANDPAINTED CENTER..........    25.00
MILK GLASS,  BOWL ON LOW FOOT,OPEN WORK AT TOP,7 IN.
   DIAMETER................................................    14.50
MILK GLASS,  BOWL,OVAL.....................................    13.00
MILK GLASS,  BOWL,ROSES....................................    22.50
MILK GLASS,  BOX,5 IN. SQUARE,COVERED,RAISED DECOR OF ROSES
   & LEAVES.................................................     6.00
MILK GLASS,  BOX,COVERED...................................     6.50
MILK GLASS,  BOX,COVERED,LION CORNERS......................     5.00
MILK GLASS,  BOX,PIN,THREE KITTENS IN RELIEF ON COVER......    15.00
MILK GLASS,  BOX,POWDER....................................     5.00
MILK GLASS,  BOX,ROUND,COVERED,COW ON COVER................    20.00
MILK GLASS,  BOX,SALT......................................     6.00
MILK GLASS,  BOX SIGNED VALLERYSTAHL.......................    35.00
MILK GLASS,  BUREAU SET,HANDPAINTED SATIN..................    28.00
MILK GLASS,  BUREAU SET,SATIN,HANDPAINTED PINK ROSES & GREEN
   LEAVES...................................................    35.00
MILK GLASS,  BUTTER DISH,HANDPAINTED,EMBOSSED PINK TRIM &
   EDGE.....................................................    17.50
MILK GLASS,  CAKE STAND,9 IN.,PEDESTAL,PINK APPLE BLOSSOM
   DECOR....................................................    12.50
MILK GLASS,  CAKE STAND,LATTICE EDGE,PEDESTAL BASE.........    30.00
MILK GLASS,  CANDLESTICK,7 IN.,CRUCIFIX....................    10.50
MILK GLASS,  CANDY CONTAINER,SUITCASE......................     9.00
MILK GLASS,  CANOE.........................................     3.00
MILK GLASS,  CHICKEN,COVERED,6 EGG CUPS & TRAY SIGNED
   VALLERYSTAHL.............................................    85.00
MILK GLASS,  CHICK ON SLEIGH...............................    14.00
MILK GLASS,  COLOGNE,BULBOUS,RAISED FERN-LIKE SCROLL,LION
   HEADS....................................................    12.50
MILK GLASS,  COMPOTE,COVERED,PLAIN TOP,PIERCED HANDLE,RIBBED
   BASE.....................................................    15.00
MILK GLASS,  COMPOTE,CRINKLED LACY EDGE....................    20.00
MILK GLASS,  CONDIMENT SET IN SILVER PLATE HOLDER,FLORAL
   DECOR....................................................    30.00
MILK GLASS,  CONDIMENT SET,PINK & GREEN DECORATION.........    15.00
```

MILK GLASS,	CREAMER & SUGAR,MINIATURE......................	5.00
MILK GLASS,	CREAMER & SUGAR,NIAGARA FALLS..................	5.00
MILK GLASS,	CUP,EYE,BRISISH MARKED.........................	2.00
MILK GLASS,	CUSPIDOR......................................	10.00
MILK GLASS,	CUSPIDOR,TOP BEADED & EMBOSSED WITH FLEUR DE	
LIS..		25.00
MILK GLASS,	DECANTER......................................	8.50
MILK GLASS,	DECANTER,POINTED DESIGNED.....................	8.00
MILK GLASS,	DISH,2 HANDLED................................	4.50
MILK GLASS,	DISH,BONE,EMBOSSED FISH.......................	12.50
MILK GLASS,	DISH,CAT COVERED,SIGNED W.G...................	7.00
MILK GLASS,	DISH,CHICKS EMERGING COVERED..................	22.50
MILK GLASS,	DISH,COVERED,CRUISER TYPE WARSHIP.............	22.50
MILK GLASS,	DISH,COVERED,LION RECLINING ON COVER..........	18.50
MILK GLASS,	DISH,COVERED,MOSES IN THE BULRUSHES...........	70.00
MILK GLASS,	DISH,COVERED KITTEN RECLINING.................	15.00
MILK GLASS,	DISH,CRAWFISH COVERED.........................	30.00
MILK GLASS,	DISH,CRAWLING TURTLE WITH SNAIL ON BACK COVERED	27.50
MILK GLASS,	DISH,DOG COVERED,5 IN.,RIBBED BASE............	16.00
MILK GLASS,	DISH,DOG ON OVAL BASE.........................	35.00
MILK GLASS,	DISH,DUCK COVERED WITH ENAMELLED COLOURS......	65.00
MILK GLASS,	DISH,EGG,CHICK ON TOP.........................	8.50
MILK GLASS,	DISH,FRENCH,RABBIT............................	4.50
MILK GLASS,	DISH,HEN,BLUE HEAD............................	20.00
MILK GLASS,	DISH,HEN COVERED,THE AMERICAN HEN	
22.00 TO...		25.00
MILK GLASS,	DISH,HEN ON LACY BASE.........................	11.00
MILK GLASS,	DISH,HEN ON NEST	
10.50 TO...		45.00
MILK GLASS,	DISH,HEN ON NEST COVERED......................	12.00
MILK GLASS,	DISH,HEN ON NEST COVERED,PAIR.................	15.00
MILK GLASS,	DISH,HEN ON NEST,OPALINE......................	20.00
MILK GLASS,	DISH,HEN WITH BLUE HEAD COVERED,5 IN..........	20.00
MILK GLASS,	DISH,HONEY,EMBOSSED STANDING FERN ALL AROUND	
SIDES..		21.00
MILK GLASS,	DISH,HORSE ON SPLIT RIBBED BASE...............	45.00
MILK GLASS,	DISH,LION COVERED.............................	40.00
MILK GLASS,	DISH,OBLONG DOG,6 X 4 IN......................	30.00
MILK GLASS,	DISH,POPE LEON XIII,ROUND,COVERED.............	42.50
MILK GLASS,	DISH,QUAIL COVERED...........................	30.00
MILK GLASS,	DISH,QUAIL COVERED,SCROLL BASE................	27.50
MILK GLASS,	DISH,RABBIT...................................	9.00
MILK GLASS,	DISH,RABBIT COVERED,6 IN......................	25.00
MILK GLASS,	DISH,ROBIN ON 3 FOOTED BASE...................	60.00
MILK GLASS,	DISH,SANTA CLAUS ON SLEIGH COVERED............	26.00
MILK GLASS,	DISH,SLEIGH WITH CHICKEN IN EGG LID...........	22.50
MILK GLASS,	DISH,SNARE DRUM CANNON COVERED................	22.50
MILK GLASS,	DISH,SPLIT RIB BASE,TURKEY....................	40.00
MILK GLASS,	DISH,STEAMBOAT COVERED,MARKED WHEELING........	18.50
MILK GLASS,	DISH,STRAIGHT BACK ROOSTER,SPLIT RIB BASE.....	32.00
MILK GLASS,	DISH,SWAN COVERED,SIGNED VALLERYSTAHL.........	22.50
MILK GLASS,	DISH,TURKEY,SPLIT RIB BASE....................	35.00
MILK GLASS,	DISH,UNCLE SAM ON BATTLESHIP COVERED..........	22.00
MILK GLASS,	DISH,WALKING FISH COVERED	
18.00 TO...		28.00
MILK GLASS DUCK ON WAVES PLATE.............................		49.00
MILK GLASS,	EGG	
5.00 TO..		7.50
MILK GLASS,	EGG,CHICK WITH WORD EASTER....................	4.50
MILK GLASS,	EGG,EASTER,BLOWN,WITH LOVING EASTER THOUGHTS...	8.50
MILK GLASS,	EGG,EASTER,EASTER GREETINGS IN RELIEF IN GOLD..	10.00
MILK GLASS,	EGG,NEST,9...................................	15.00
MILK GLASS,	EPERGNE,BLUE RUFFLED FLUTED BOWL ON PEDESTAL	
BASE...		37.00
MILK GLASS,	EWER,PAIR,METAL TOPS & BOTTOMS,HANDPAINTED	

```
SAILING VESSELS..............................................  35.00
MILK GLASS FISH DISH,RELISH,OPEN.............................  11.00
MILK GLASS FLAG PLATE........................................  15.00
MILK GLASS FLEUR DE LIS FLAG & EAGLE PLATE,7 IN..............  15.00
MILK GLASS FLORAL & FEATHER CHAMBERSTICK,PETTICOAT STYLE
  BASE......................................................  12.50
MILK GLASS FLOWER SPRAY SALT & PEPPER SHAKER.................  12.00
MILK GLASS FLOWERED BOX,POWDER...............................   3.50
MILK GLASS FLYING FISH SALT,MASTER...........................  18.50
MILK GLASS FORGET-ME-NOT CRUET,MELON SHAPED..................  25.00
MILK GLASS FRUIT PANELS GOBLET...............................  22.50
MILK GLASS GARFIELD MEMORIAL PLATE...........................  18.50
MILK GLASS GARGOYLE HEAD BOTTLE,PAIR.........................  38.00
MILK GLASS GARGOYLE HEAD PLATTER,11 IN.......................  23.00
MILK GLASS GENERAL FITZUGH LEE PLATE.........................  17.50
MILK GLASS GENERAL LEE & FLAG PLATE..........................  15.00
MILK GLASS, GOBLET...........................................   6.00
MILK GLASS GODDESS OF LIBERTY LAMP...........................  18.00
MILK GLASS GOTHIC PLATE,7 IN.................................   5.00
MILK GLASS GRAPE & LEAF SYRUP,6 IN. HIGH,TIN TOP.............  16.75
MILK GLASS GRAPE LEAF & CLUSTERS GARLAND BANDS SALT..........   7.50
MILK GLASS GRAPE SALT & PEPPER ON TRAY,CHILDS SIZE...........  15.00
MILK GLASS GRAPE WITH OVERLAPPING FOLIAGE CREAMER DATED FEB.
  1870......................................................  21.00
MILK GLASS GRAPES & LEAVES SALT & PAPPER,PAIR EMBOSSED,RED &
  GOLD......................................................  15.00
MILK GLASS GREEN BEADED TASSEL SALT & PEPPER,PAIR............  16.50
MILK GLASS GREEN BOWL,FRUIT,PEDESTAL BASE,FLUTE SCALLOP EDGE   27.50
MILK GLASS GREEN DIAMOND QUILTED SUGAR SHAKER,OPAQUE.........  35.00
MILK GLASS GREEN DISH,CANDY,OVAL VASE ON 4 PAW FEET..........  12.00
MILK GLASS GREEN SHELL & JEWEL PITCHER.......................  12.50
MILK GLASS GREEN SHELL TOOTHPICK HOLDER......................  15.00
MILK GLASS GREEN SUGAR,COVERED...............................  11.50
MILK GLASS GREEN SUGAR SHAKER................................  12.50
MILK GLASS HAND & DOVE DISH,DATED............................  65.00
MILK GLASS, HAT..............................................   9.00
MILK GLASS, HAT,FLAT TOP STRAW...............................   7.00
MILK GLASS, HAT,GREEN BAND...................................  10.00
MILK GLASS, HAT,STRAW SAILOR
  14.00  TO.................................................  15.00
MILK GLASS, HATCHET
  4.50  TO..................................................   8.00
MILK GLASS, HATCHET,SOUVENIR.................................   8.00
MILK GLASS HEART & ANCHOR PLATE..............................  13.50
MILK GLASS HORSES SPOONER....................................   7.50
MILK GLASS, HUMIDOR,RAISED GOLD DECORATION...................  16.50
MILK GLASS IMPRESSED STARS & STRIPES TOOTHPICK HOLDER,UNCLE
  SAMS HAT..................................................   8.00
MILK GLASS INDIAN HEAD MATCH HOLDER,HANGS BY CHAIN...........   7.50
MILK GLASS JADE GREEN SPRAYS OF FLOWERS & BERRIES
  VASE,RUFFLED TOP..........................................  15.00
MILK GLASS JADE GREEN VASE,9 IN.,RAISED SPRAYS OF FLOWERS &
  BERRIES...................................................  17.00
MILK GLASS, JAR,RAISED FLOWERS...............................   8.00
MILK GLASS JENNY LIND COMPOTE,OPEN,7 IN. HIGH...............  67.50
MILK GLASS JEWEL CELERY VASE.................................  22.00
MILK GLASS JOHNNY BULL SALT SHAKER...........................  25.00
MILK GLASS KEYHOLE PLATE,7 IN................................   7.00
MILK GLASS LACY DAISY DISH,BERRY.............................   4.00
MILK GLASS, LAMP,10 IN. TALL,ETCHED SHADE,SHADE RING........  32.00
MILK GLASS, LAMP,BLUE STEPPED BASE WITH WHITE FONT..........  65.00
MILK GLASS, LAMP,KEROSENE,YELLOW PAINTED FLOWERS,GREEN
  LEAVES....................................................  12.50
MILK GLASS, LAMP,PAIR FOOTED MINIATURE.......................  32.50
MILK GLASS, LAMP SHADE.......................................   7.50
```

MILK GLASS LEAF PITCHER,SYRUP		23.50
MILK GLASS LIBERTY BELL MUG		18.75
MILK GLASS MAIZE CONDIMENT SET		50.00
MILK GLASS, MATCH HOLDER		6.50
MILK GLASS, MATCH HOLDER,PIPE		6.75
MILK GLASS, MATCH HOLDER,SKELETONS HEAD		12.00
MILK GLASS MAUVE FEATHER SUGAR,COVERED		25.00
MILK GLASS MEDALLION SPRIG SUGAR SHAKER		15.00
MILK GLASS MELON WITH LEAF & NET SPOONER		15.00
MILK GLASS MEMPHIS PUNCH CUP,SET OF 6,BASE OF BOWL MARKED		49.00
MILK GLASS MONKEY & HAT TOOTHPICK HOLDER		14.00
MILK GLASS MORTAR & PESTLE JAR		7.50
MILK GLASS, MUSTARD ,HORSEHEAD HANDLES		12.00
MILK GLASS, MUSTARD JAR,BANK		17.00
MILK GLASS, MUSTARD MARKED AMORY HOUGHTON,19TH CENTURY		20.00
MILK GLASS, PEPPER SHAKER PAINTED RED & GREEN		4.50
MILK GLASS, PIPE,SOUVENIR IRISH HILLS MICHIGAN		8.50
MILK GLASS, PITCHER,OWL		18.00
MILK GLASS, PITCHER,SYRUP		8.00
MILK GLASS, PLANTER,OVAL,RAISED SWAN DECOR		7.50
MILK GLASS, PLATE,5 IN.,BEADED EDGE		6.50
MILK GLASS, PLATE,5 IN. SQUARE		12.00
MILK GLASS, PLATE,7 IN.,CLUB & SHELL BORDER,U S BATTLESHIP MAINE		6.00
MILK GLASS, PLATE,7 IN.,LACE EDGE		6.50
MILK GLASS, PLATE,7 IN.,LACE EDGE,GOLD		4.50
MILK GLASS, PLATE,7 IN.,THREE BEARS READING BOOK		13.50
MILK GLASS, PLATE,8 IN.,101 BORDER		15.00
MILK GLASS, PLATE,8 IN.,H BORDER		9.00
MILK GLASS, PLATE,9 IN.,GOLD OPEN BORDER		10.00
MILK GLASS, PLATE,10 IN.,ARCH BORDER		16.50
MILK GLASS, PLATE,ANCIENT CASTLE		9.50
MILK GLASS, PLATE,BREAD,GIVE US THIS DAY		14.00
MILK GLASS, PLATE,BREAD,GIVE US THIS DAY OUR DAILY BREAD		30.00
MILK GLASS, PLATE,CALIFORNIA MID-WINTER FAIR		15.00
MILK GLASS, PLATE,CLUB BORDER,7 IN		5.00
MILK GLASS, PLATE,CONTRARY MULE		8.00
MILK GLASS, PLATE,EASTER,2 OWLS,BEADED RIM		15.00
MILK GLASS, PLATE,FISH ON SKIFF		11.00
MILK GLASS, PLATE,FORGET-ME-NOT RIM		6.00
MILK GLASS, PLATE,LACY EDGE 3.50 TO		7.00
MILK GLASS, PLATE,LATTICE EDGE,10 IN.,APPLE BLOSSOMS		47.50
MILK GLASS, PLATE,OPAL EDGES,8 IN.,SQUARE,PUNCHED OPEN WORK SCROLLS		7.00
MILK GLASS, PLATE,OPEN EDGE,HANDPAINTED RURAL SCENE		8.00
MILK GLASS, PLATE,OWL LOVERS		12.00
MILK GLASS, PLATE,PAINTED		6.50
MILK GLASS, PLATE,SCALLOPED ROSE BORDER		10.00
MILK GLASS, PLATE,THREE OWLS,DATED JULY 2,1901,7IN		9.50
MILK GLASS, PLATE,WICKET EDGE,8 IN.,MARKED WITH A		7.00
MILK GLASS, PLATE,SHELL & CLUB BORDER		5.00
MILK GLASS, PLATTER,13 IN.,DOG SWIMMING		55.00
MILK GLASS, PLATTER,FISH,PATENT DATED JUNE 4, 1872		29.50
MILK GLASS, POWDER JAR,COVERED,GOLD TRIM		3.00
MILK GLASS, ROLLING PIN,WOOD HANDLES,NAME IMBEDDED IN GLASS		17.50
MILK GLASS, ROSEBOWL		12.50
MILK GLASS, ROSEBOWL,BLOWN,FLOWERS,STIPPLED GOLD		15.00
MILK GLASS, SALT & PEPPER 7.00 TO		12.50
MILK GLASS, SALT & PEPPER,EGG SHAPED,PAINTED FLOWERS		18.00
MILK GLASS, SALT & PEPPER,G.E.REFRIGERATOR		5.00
MILK GLASS, SALT & PEPPER,G.E.REFRIGERATORS		8.75
MILK GLASS, SALT & PEPPER,GRECIAN LADY,MARKED PATENT 103910		12.00
MILK GLASS, SALT & PEPPER,PAIR,CORN WITH HUSK		15.00

```
MILK GLASS,   SALT & PEPPER SHAKER,PAIR EGG SHAPED
   HANDPAINTED.................................................   18.00
MILK GLASS,   SALT & PEPPER SHAKERS,PAIR,ROSE EMBOSSED........    8.50
MILK GLASS,   SALT & PEPPER SHAKER WITH PEWTER TOP...........     6.00
MILK GLASS,   SALT & PEPPER,SHAPE OF G.E.MONITOR
   REFRIGERATORS............................................     32.50
MILK GLASS,   SALT & PEPPER WITH TOPS,REFRIGERATOR...........    10.00
MILK GLASS,   SALT,CHICKEN HEAD,PEWTER TOP,EGG SHAPE.........    25.00
MILK GLASS,   SALT,HEXAGONAL,PAIR,MINERAL COLOURED FLOWERS...    14.50
MILK GLASS,   SALT,OPEN,SLEIGH..............................     15.00
MILK GLASS,   SALT SHAKER,LIONS HEADS.......................     10.00
MILK GLASS,   SHADE,PAIR PETTICOAT,8 IN.,CRIMPED EDGE........    10.00
MILK GLASS,   SHAVING MUG,BARBER SHOP.......................      3.75
MILK GLASS,   SPOONHOLDER,YELLOW BAND,FLOWERS...............     12.00
MILK GLASS,   SUGAR,COVERED,CREAMER,& BUTTER,COVERED,SCROLLED
   FEET......................................................    18.00
MILK GLASS,   SUGAR,COVERED,SWAN HANDLES & FINIAL............    22.50
MILK GLASS,   SUGAR SHAKER..................................      7.50
MILK GLASS,   SUGAR SHAKER,BATTLE SHIP MAINE................      7.50
MILK GLASS,   SWAN,CLOSED NECK..............................     17.00
MILK GLASS,   SYRUP,HANDPAINTED PINK FLOWERS & FOLIAGE.......    14.00
MILK GLASS,   SYRUP,HANDPAINTED PINK FLOWERS,6 IN...........     16.50
MILK GLASS,   SYRUP PITCHER.................................     10.00
MILK GLASS,   TOOTHPICK,2 HANDLED BASKET....................      5.00
MILK GLASS,   TOOTHPICK HAT WITH PARROT IN BRIM.............     24.50
MILK GLASS,   TOOTHPICK,PARROT ON HAT.......................     25.00
MILK GLASS,   TOOTHPICK,SQUARE,FOOTED.......................     11.00
MILK GLASS,   TRAY & CONTAINER..............................      6.00
MILK GLASS,   TRAY,DRESSER
   7.50  TO................................................       8.00
MILK GLASS,   TRAY,EMBOSSED PEN-PENCIL,8 IN.................      2.75
MILK GLASS,   TRAY,HAIR PIN,LEAF SHAPE,HANDPAINTED..........      5.00
MILK GLASS,   TRAY,LADIES BUST,11 IN........................     23.00
MILK GLASS,   TRAY,OVAL & COVERED BOX,RAISED ROSES..........     12.50
MILK GLASS,   TUMBLER,ST.LOUIS WORLD FAIR...................     12.00
MILK GLASS,   TURTLE........................................     60.00
MILK GLASS,   VASE WITH RUFFLED TOP.........................     10.00
```

MILLEFIORI means many flower. It is a type of glasswork popular in paperweights. Many small flower-like pieces of glass are grouped together to form a
design.

```
MILLEFIORI BOX WITH HINGED LID.............................     85.00
MILLEFIORI CREAMER,BULBOUS,ALTERNATING STRIPS OF BLUE &
   FLOWERED CANES...........................................    100.00
MILLEFIORI CRUET...........................................    125.00
MILLEFIORI CUP & SAUCER....................................     75.00
MILLEFIORI CUP & SAUCER,MULTI-COLOURED.....................     65.00
MILLEFIORI DISH,RUFFLED EDGE...............................     12.50
MILLEFIORI PAPERWEIGHT MARKED CHINA........................     12.00
MILLEFIORI RING TREE,CANDY CANES,RUFFLED BASE,3 IN. CENTER
   POST......................................................    18.00
MILLEFIORI TOOTHPICK,BROWN BACKGROUND......................     36.00
MILLEFIORI TUMBLER
   45.00  TO................................................     70.00
MILLEFIORI URN,3 IN. TALL..................................     85.00
MILLEFIORI VASE,CABINET....................................     32.00
MILLEFIORI VASE,CABINET PIECE,BLUE,YELLOW & GREEN..........     20.00
MILLEFIORI VASE,BLACK & CHINESE RED,11 IN. TALL............     65.00
MILLEFIORI VASE WITH STRIPED HANDLES.......................     95.00
MINIATURE BASKET,GREEN GLASS WITH APPLIED HANDLE...........      3.50
MINIATURE BEER MUG WITH HANDLE,GLASS,2 IN..................       .75
MINIATURE BELL,BRASS,2 IN. HIGH............................      4.50
MINIATURE BELL,BRASS SCHOOLMASTER HAND.....................      2.75
MINIATURE BEVERAGE SET ON WOODEN TRAY,PITCHER & 6 GLASSES,1
   IN. SCALE.................................................     1.75
```

```
MINIATURE BIRD,GOSS CREST.....................................     1.50
MINIATURE BOTTLE,12 PANEL AQUA................................     3.00
MINIATURE BOTTLE,BARREL SHAPED AQUA GLASS.....................    14.00
MINIATURE BOTTLE BASE,4 LAYER,3 COLOUR,WEBB CAMEO,WHITE TO
  PINK........................................................   325.00
MINIATURE BOTTLE,BLUE RIBBED..................................      .75
MINIATURE BOWL,OVAL...........................................    27.00
MINIATURE BOX,SLED,CHILDREN DECOR.............................     7.50
MINIATURE BRIDES BASKET,BLOWN,ROSE & WHITE,ROUGH PONTIL.......    27.00
MINIATURE BUTTER,COVERED,LIBERTY BELL.........................    15.00
MINIATURE BUTTER,COVERED,SUNBURST.............................     8.00
MINIATURE BUTTER MOLD.........................................     5.50
MINIATURE BUTTER MOLD,ROUND...................................     7.50
MINIATURE BUTTER MOLD,WOOD....................................     5.00
MINIATURE BUTTER MOLD,WOODEN,FLOWER...........................     4.50
MINIATURE BUTTER,SUGAR,CREAMER & SPOONER,PANELLED,COVERED....    15.00
MINIATURE CANDLE HOLDER,GLASS,CLEAR,RING......................     2.50
MINIATURE CANDLE HOLDER,PAIR BRASS............................     2.50
MINIATURE CANDLEHOLDER,ROUND BASE,2 IN. DIAMETER..............     2.00
MINIATURE CANDLESTICK,CAST BRASS..............................     3.00
MINIATURE CANDLESTICK,PAIR BRASS..............................     2.50
MINIATURE CANNON,BRASS........................................    18.00
MINIATURE CHAFING DISH,FOOTED,SILVER..........................    15.00
MINIATURE CHAIR,RUSH SEAT,LADDERBACK..........................     4.00
MINIATURE CHAIR,WOOD,CORNER,HAND CARVING......................    19.00
MINIATURE CHEST CIRCA 1820,5-DRAWER MAHOGANY..................   185.00
MINIATURE CHICKEN ON BASKET,MILK GLASS,WESTMORELAND...........     8.00
MINIATURE CLOCK WITH FUSEE MOVEMENT,EMPIRE SHELF,SMITH &
  GOODRICH....................................................   165.00
MINIATURE COAL HOD,VICTORIAN GOLD METAL,BASKETWEAVE HANDLE..      5.00
MINIATURE COOK STOVE MARKED ROYAL,IRON........................     7.50
MINIATURE CRADLE,IRON.........................................     1.75
MINIATURE CREAM PITCHER,RED BLOCK,3 IN. TALL,ROSETTE BASE...    13.50
MINIATURE CREAMER,CHINA,PASTEL ROSES & GOLD DECORATION.......     2.50
MINIATURE CREAMER,CRANBERRY...................................    17.50
MINIATURE CREAMER,DRUM........................................     9.00
MINIATURE CREAMER,GLASS,NURSERY RHYMES........................     7.50
MINIATURE CREAMER,SANDWICH LACY...............................    23.00
MINIATURE CREAMER,SHEEP & RAM.................................    12.00
MINIATURE CREAMER,SUGAR & BUTTER DISH IN MILK GLASS..........    15.00
MINIATURE CREAMER,SUNBURST....................................     7.00
MINIATURE CRUET,MILK GLASS....................................     6.00
MINIATURE CRUET,PRESSED GLASS.................................     9.00
MINIATURE CRUET SET,MILK GLASS,TRAY CUT PINEAPPLE PATTERN...    15.00
MINIATURE CUP,HANDLELESS,BLUE SPATTER GLASS...................    15.00
MINIATURE CUP WITH BLUE FLOWERS,CHINA.........................     1.25
MINIATURE CUP WITH FLOWERS,TIN................................     1.75
MINIATURE DESK,18TH CENTURY SLANT FRONT MAHOGANY SIGNED &
  DATED 1771..................................................   350.00
MINIATURE DESK ON FRAME,ROLL-TOP,DRAWER INSIDE & OUT,CUBBIES    88.00
MINIATURE DESK,ROLL TOP.......................................    25.00
MINIATURE DISH,CAMPHOR GLASS,HEN ON NEST COVERED..............     6.00
MINIATURE DOG,CAST IRON BOSTON TERRIER........................     5.00
MINIATURE DOG,CAST IRON COCKER SPANIEL........................     7.00
MINIATURE DOG,CAST IRON SITTING SCOTTY,HOLLOW.................     3.00
MINIATURE DOLL,2 CELLULOID BABY...............................     3.00
MINIATURE DOLL,LACE-MAKER AT BENCH,3 IN.......................     1.50
MINIATURE DOUGH BOX...........................................     3.50
MINIATURE FIGURE,LEAD,RECLINING DEER..........................     3.00
MINIATURE FIGURINE,PAIR BISQUE IN COLONIAL DRESS..............    55.00
MINIATURE FLOWER POT IN WIRE WALL RACK,POTTERY,SET OF 6......     2.00
MINIATURE FLOWER POT,WHITE....................................      .75
MINIATURE HORSE SHOE,GOOD LUCK................................     2.00
MINIATURE ICE BUCKET,CUT GLASS,CANE PATTERN...................    15.00
MINIATURE ICE TONGS...........................................     3.75
```

```
MINIATURE INCENSE BURNER,CAST IRON CHINESE BUDDHA...........      4.00
MINIATURE IRON,CHILDS.....................................      6.00
MINIATURE IRON FLAT IRON..................................      6.00
MINIATURE IRON,OVAL,ROPE DESIGN HANDLE....................      3.50
MINIATURE IVORY CARVING OF NUDE,EYE & SERPENT.............     75.00
MINIATURE JUG,LIVERPOOL,MASONIC...........................     30.00
MINIATURE JUG WITH LID,PAIR,3 IN.,SALT GLAZE..............      2.50
MINIATURE JUG WITH RING HANDLE,CLOISONNE..................      7.50
MINIATURE LAMP,7 IN.,THOUSAND EYE HOBNAIL PANEL BASE......      2.50
MINIATURE LAMP,8 IN. CRANBERRY BEADED SWIRL...............     40.00
MINIATURE LAMP & BATTERY BOX,BRASS........................      1.95
MINIATURE LAMP,ARTICHOKE,ROSE & GREEN.....................    100.00
MINIATURE LAMP BASE,AMBER,ACORN BURNER,CLEAR CHIMNEY,WILD
  FLOWERS.................................................      8.50
MINIATURE LAMP BASE,CLEAR,APPLIED HANDLE..................     12.00
MINIATURE LAMP BASE ,MILK GLASS,PINK BAND.................     20.00
MINIATURE LAMP BASE,PEDESTAL,AMBER GLASS..................     18.50
MINIATURE LAMP,BEADED HEART...............................     10.00
MINIATURE LAMP,BLUE NUTMEG,................................     18.75
MINIATURE LAMP,BRASS RAYO TYPE WITH SPIDER MARKED LITTLE
  PRINCE..................................................     18.00
MINIATURE LAMP,CHERRY RED CAMPHOR-SATIN,HEXAGON SHAPE,.....     55.00
MINIATURE LAMP,CLEAR COSMOS,COMPLETE WITH SHADE,NO CHIMNEY..     30.00
MINIATURE LAMP,CLEAR COSMOS GLASS.........................     15.00
MINIATURE LAMP,CLEAR GLASS,EAGLE GLASS MFG. CO............     35.00
MINIATURE LAMP,CLEAR GLASS THOUSAND EYE HOBNAIL & PANEL BASE     2.50
MINIATURE LAMP,CLEAR GREEN ACORN..........................     17.50
MINIATURE LAMP,COBALT BASE,WHITE MILK GLASS SHADE.........     28.50
MINIATURE LAMP COMPLETE...................................     25.00
MINIATURE LAMP,FROSTED WHITE ,DAISY & BUTTON..............     29.50
MINIATURE LAMP,GONE WITH THE WIND,MILK GLASS..............     30.00
MINIATURE LAMP,GREEN GLASS,DECOR LEAVES IN RELIEF,HORNET
  BURNER..................................................     45.00
MINIATURE LAMP,HANDLED BLUE GLASS.........................     15.00
MINIATURE LAMP,HANDPAINTED STRIPED CAT,WHITE PORCELAIN BASE.   18.00
MINIATURE LAMP,IRON BRACKET, IRON BASE,MILK GLASS SHADE.....   22.50
MINIATURE LAMP,JADE GLASS,CUT GLASS CHIMNEY...............     47.50
MINIATURE LAMP,LITTLE JEWEL,FOOTED,HANDLED................     12.50
MINIATURE LAMP,METAL BRACKET..............................     10.00
MINIATURE LAMP,MILK GLASS.................................     10.00
MINIATURE LAMP,MILK GLASS BRACKET.........................     15.00
MINIATURE LAMP,MILK GLASS,FLORAL PATTERN..................      7.50
MINIATURE LAMP,MILK GLASS,PANELED ZINC BASE...............     14.00
MINIATURE LAMP,MILK GLASS,WHITE CYLINDRICAL BASE,HANDPAINTED   24.50
MINIATURE LAMP,MOON & STARS...............................     10.00
MINIATURE LAMP,NUTMEG.....................................      5.00
MINIATURE LAMP,NUTMEG,WHITE MILK GLASS,WORD NUTMEG EMBOSSED
  ON BASE.................................................     11.00
MINIATURE LAMP,RED SATIN GLASS BASE WITH BURNER...........     18.00
MINIATURE LAMP,RUBY,RIBBED,PATENT AUGUST 27,1895..........     25.00
MINIATURE LAMP SET IN RING HANDLED BRASS BASE,CLEAR,CHIMNEY.   10.00
MINIATURE LAMP,TIN........................................      4.50
MINIATURE LAMP WITH CHIMNEY,BRASS,KEROSENE................      2.75
MINIATURE LAMP WITH CLEAR GLASS CHIMNEY,ROYAL IVY.........     27.50
MINIATURE LAMP WITH COSMOS GLASS SHADE....................     60.00
MINIATURE LAMP WITH SHADE,MILK GLASS......................     25.00
MINIATURE LANTERN,TOLE....................................      8.00
MINIATURE MIRROR,WOOD,HAND................................      3.00
MINIATURE MORTAR & PESTLE,BRASS...........................      4.50
MINIATURE MUG,FEEDING DEER & DOG..........................     16.00
MINIATURE PAINTING,OIL ON FRENCH IVORY....................     45.00
MINIATURE PAINTING ON IVORY,1910,GREEN VELVET FRAME.......     18.00
MINIATURE PAINTING ON IVORY SIGNED,PORTRAIT OF LADY IN BRASS
  FRAME...................................................     35.00
MINIATURE PITCHER,2 IN.,PINK,TIN,NURSERY RHYME & LAMBS.....     2.50
```

```
MINIATURE PITCHER,CHINA,2 IN.....................................    3.00
MINIATURE PITCHER,COPPER LUSTER,PINK SUNDERLAND BAND.........   30.00
MINIATURE PITCHER,GAUDY WELSH TULIP PATTERN,3 IN. HIGH.......   25.00
MINIATURE PITCHER,TIN,1 IN......................................    2.50
MINIATURE POTATO MASHER,BUTTER MOLD,ROLLING PIN,WOODEN.......   10.00
MINIATURE POTTY,CHINA,EYE INSIDE..............................    1.50
MINIATURE PUNCH BOWL & 4 CUPS,FLEUR DE LIS DRAPE.............   18.00
MINIATURE PUNCH BOWL & 6 CUPS,PRESSED GLASS..................   15.00
MINIATURE PUNCH SET...........................................   40.00
MINIATURE RANGE,BLACK IRON....................................    2.25
MINIATURE RANGE,GAS,IRON,ROYAL,NICKEL COLOUR FINISH.........   10.00
MINIATURE RANGE,KITCHEN.......................................   30.00
MINIATURE ROSEBOWL,WEBB ACID BURMESE,PINK TO YELLOW......... 325.00
MINIATURE SADIRON.............................................    5.50
MINIATURE SAUCE WITH 6 SPOONS,STERLING SILVER...............   15.00
MINIATURE SCREEN,JADE TABLE,OPEN CARVED FLOWERS,MUTTONFAT
JADE..........................................................   67.50
MINIATURE SET OF DISHES MADE IN JAPAN,FLOWERED CHINA........    6.00
MINIATURE SET,WEE GRAPE BUTTER,SUGAR,CREAMER & SPOONER.......   30.00
MINIATURE SEWING MACHINE......................................    9.00
MINIATURE SHAKER OVAL BOX,3 X 2 X 2 IN........................   15.00
MINIATURE SLIPPER,PAIR GERMAN PORCELAIN HIGH HEEL............   12.00
MINIATURE SOUP TUREEN WITH ATTACHED TRAY,COVERED,FRENCH
PORCELAIN.....................................................   18.00
MINIATURE SPOONER,NURSERY RHYMES.............................   10.00
MINIATURE STAGE COACH,COPPERED,A CENTURY OF PROGRESS,CHICAGO
1934..........................................................    4.00
MINIATURE STOVE,IRON,GAS......................................    3.00
MINIATURE STOVE,METAL GAS WITH DISHES........................    1.95
MINIATURE STOVE WITH OVEN,ELECTRIC,DOLLS......................   15.00
MINIATURE SUGAR & CREAMER,CHILDS,OPALESCENT HOBNAIL.........    4.50
MINIATURE SUGAR,COVERED,4 IN. HIGH...........................    1.50
MINIATURE SUGAR,COVERED,TULIP WITH HONEYCOMB.................    5.50
MINIATURE SUGAR,DRUM COVERED..................................   12.00
MINIATURE TABLE,PEDESTAL......................................    3.00
MINIATURE TABLE SET,4 PIECES,TULIP & HONEYCOMB...............   18.50
MINIATURE TABLE,WOOD TRIPOD,CHIPPENDALE STYLE................   29.50
MINIATURE TEA SET,FLORAL & GOLD DECORATED,SUGAR & CREAMER &
POT...........................................................   20.00
MINIATURE TEAKETTLE,BRASS.....................................    2.75
MINIATURE TEAKETTLE,CAST IRON.................................   11.25
MINIATURE TEAPOT,3 LEGS,GREEN.................................   25.00
MINIATURE TEAPOT,CLOISONNE....................................    4.50
MINIATURE TIEBACK,PAIR,MILVILLE PAPERWEIGHT GLASS...........   20.00
MINIATURE TOY,CAST IRON KNIGHT ON HORSE,BLACK,ARM MOVES.....    4.00
MINIATURE VASE,FAN-SHAPED.....................................    1.00
MINIATURE VASE,PAIR DECORATED,4 IN............................    4.00
MINIATURE VASE,ROSE MEDALLION,3 IN. HIGH,ROSES,BUTTERFLIES
ON GOLD.......................................................   27.50
MINIATURE VASE SIGNED KUTANI WITH PAINTING,3 IN..............   18.00
MINIATURE WASH BOWL & PITCHER,FOOTED,FLORAL..................   17.00
MINIATURE WATER CARAFE,CHILDS,3 IN.,FLUTE PATTERN...........    4.75
MINIATURE WATER PITCHER,CLEAR GLASS,GRAPE & VINE............    4.00
MINIATURE WATERING CAN,CHINA..................................    3.00
```

MINTON CHINA has been made in England from 1793 to the present time.

```
MINTON & BOYLE TUREEN,SAUCE,CIRCA 1840,BLACK POLKA DOT &
GOLD..........................................................   18.50
MINTON CAKE TRAY,FLORAL DECORATION...........................    8.00
MINTON CUP & SAUCER...........................................   14.50
MINTON DEMI-TASSE,COBALT WITH COIN GOLD BANDINGS.............    5.50
MINTON GAME PLATE,PAIR,BLUE BORDER,GOLD TRIM,TAN BACKGROUND.   10.00
MINTON GARDEN SEAT,BARREL SHAPE...............................   85.00
MINTON HANDPAINTED DISH,EGG SHAPED...........................    2.50
MINTON JUG,IMPRESSED,PEWTER LID,PORCELAIN THUMB REST.........   50.00
```

```
MINTON LUNCHEON PLATES,BAILEY,BANKS & BIDDLE,6...............   40.00
MINTON PLATE,10 IN.,HANDPAINTED............................   20.00
MINTON PITCHER & BOWL SET CIRCA 1885,WHITE BASKETWEAVE ON
  BASE,GOLD.................................................   47.00
MINTON PLATE,PAIR SIGNED 7 IN.,TURKEYS & FOLIAGE...........   18.00
MINTON PLATTER,FLORAL IN PUCE MONOCHROME...................   18.50
MINTON PLATE,SET OF 6,10 IN.,ENAMELED,PINK & GREY
  BORDER,GOLD EDGE..........................................   35.00
MINTON PLATTER,BLUE ON WHITE,PASSION FLOWER PATTERN........   25.00
MINTON PLATE,11 IN.,FLOWERS,STERLING EDGE..................   12.50
MINTON PLATE,10 IN.,BLUE & GREY WITH COAT OF ARMS..........    5.00
MINTON SOAP BOX,GREEN GROUND..............................    7.50
MINTON SAUCE WITH PLATE,COVERED,MARKED....................   32.00
MINTON SQUARE GREEN PLATE ON SILVER PLATED STAND..........    8.50
MINTON SUGAR BOWL.........................................    7.50
MINTON TILE,ENGLAND,RABBIT................................   10.00
MINTON TILE,ENGLAND,BARBER................................   10.00
MINTON TILE,ENGLAND,HUNTER................................   10.00
MINTON TILE,ENGLAND,PICKPOCKET............................   10.00
MINTON TILE,ENGLAND,MUSICIAN & SPANISH DANCER.............   10.00
MINTON TILE,SHAKESPEARIAN SCENE,TAN.......................    5.00
MINTON WASH BOWL & PITCHER,1866,..........................   75.00
```

MOCHA WARE is an English-made product that was sold in America during the early 1800's. It is a heavy pottery with pale coffee and cream coloring. Designs of blue, brown, green, orange, or black or white were added to the pottery.

```
MOCHA CHAMBER POT,CATS EYE TYPE DESIGN....................   45.00
MOCHA MUG,OYSTER PATTERN,BLUE,BROWN,WHITE & BLACK.........   25.00
MOCHA MUG,STRAP HANDLE,BUFF WITH WHITE STRIPES...........   18.00
MOCHA PEPPERPOT,EARTHWORM................................   55.00
MOCHA PITCHER,6 IN. HIGH,BULBOUS,EARTHWORM
  PATTERN,GREEN,BLACK......................................   37.00
MOCHA PITCHER,BAND OF SEAWEED AROUND CENTER...............   45.00
MOCHA WARE 4 IN. MUG,SEAWEED GREEN CENTER,2 BLACK BANDS,1
  BLUE BAND.................................................   17.50
MOCHA WARE 4 IN. MUG,SEAWEED PATTERN.....................   22.50
MOCHA-WARE HANDLED MUG,BLUE & BROWN BANDS.................   30.00
MOCHA WARE MUG,SEAWEED GREEN CENTER,2 BLACK BANDS,1 GREEN
  BAND.....................................................   19.00
MOCHA WATER PITCHER,EARTHWORM PATTERN.....................   42.00
  MOLD, SEE IRON, KITCHEN, PEWTER, TOOL...................
MORTAR & PESTLE,3 IN. DIAMETER...........................   10.00
MORTAR & PESTLE HEAVY BRASS..............................   21.50
```

MOSER GLASS was made by Kolomon Moser in the early 1900's. The art nouveau type glassware had detailed exotic enamel designs.

```
MOSER BOWL,AMETHYST,SILVERED RIM,FLOWER MOTIF.............   45.00
MOSER BOWL,ENAMELLED INSECTS,9 IN.........................   75.00
MOSER CUP & SAUCER,ENAMELED SEAWEED PATTERN...............   82.50
MOSER JAR,COVERED,GOLD,BROWN,YELLOW,GREEN FLOWERS &
  LEAVES,BEADING...........................................   65.00
MOSER LIQUEUR,KARLSBAD SIGNED & NUMBERED,GOLD ON GREEN....   80.00
MOSER PATCH BOX,DECORATED,CLEAR,ROUND,HINGED..............   17.50
MOSER,PERFUME,CRANBERRY...................................   25.00
MOSER PUNCH CUP,CRANBERRY WITH APPLIED HANDLE,ENAMELED....  110.00
MOSER TUMBLER,DECORATED,SIGNED IN GOLD,4 SIDED IN 4 SCALLOPS 185.00
MOSER TYPE DECORATED CRANBERRY PERFUME BOTTLE,GOLD ENAMEL
  SCROLLING.................................................   40.00
MOSER TYPE WINE,CRANBERRY,ENAMELED.......................   28.00
MOSER VASE,AMBER WITH ATTACHED FISH ON SIDE,GOLD TRIM.....   78.00
MOSER VASE,AMETHYST,TO CLEAR,6 IN.,INTAGLIO CUT
  VIOLETS,MARKED...........................................  100.00
MOSER VASE,AMETHYST TO CLEAR,INTAGLIO....................  100.00
MOSER VASE,KARLSBAD SIGNED,PINK,GREEN LEAVES & BUDS......   75.00
MOSER VASE,PAIR,8 IN.,FLUTED TOPS,RIBBED AMBER
```

GLASS, ENAMELED.. 125.00

MOSS ROSE CHINA was made by many firms from 1808 to 1900. It refers to any china decorated with the moss rose flower.

MOSS ROSE COVERED SUGAR, BLUE TINT ON HANDLES & COVER FINIAL.   18.00
MOSS ROSE COVERED SUGAR......................................   7.00
MOSS ROSE CUP & SAUCER
    5.00   TO..   5.50
MOSS ROSE CUP & SAUCER, BURGESS & CAMPBELL...................   12.00
MOSS ROSE DOUBLE HANDLED SUGAR..............................   9.00
MOSS ROSE MUG...   3.50
MOSS ROSE PITCHER...   26.50
MOSS ROSE SUGAR BOWL, BURGESS & CAMPBELL.....................   5.00
MOSS ROSE TEAPOT, BURGESS & CAMPBELL.........................   12.00

MOTHER-OF-PEARL or pearl satin glass was first made in the 1850's in England and in Massachusetts. It was a special type of mold-blown satin glass with air bubbles in the glass, giving it a pearlized color.

MOTHER OF PEARL, SEE PEARL..................................
MOTHER OF PEARL BLUE HERRINGBONE TUMBLER.....................   55.00
MOTHER OF PEARL BLUE DIAMOND QUILTED VASE CASED 8 IN. TALL..   45.00
MOTHER OF PEARL BLUE SATIN TUMBLER...........................   65.00
MOTHER OF PEARL BOWL, PURPLE, ZIPPER PATTERN................. 1,250.00
MOTHER OF PEARL CANDLESTICK, RAINDROP PATTERN, PINK TO
    WHITE, ENAMEL...   600.00
MOTHER OF PEARL DIAMOND PATTERN RUFFLED TOP VASE, WHITE
    LINING, APRICOT...   26.50
MOTHER OF PEARL DIAMOND QUILTED 10 IN. VASE..................   135.00
MOTHER OF PEARL DIAMOND QUILTED 10 IN. VASE, BLUE............   125.00
MOTHER OF PEARL DIAMOND QUILTED APRICOT STICK VASE, MELON
    BASE..   58.00
MOTHER OF PEARL DIAMOND QUILTED BLUE TUMBLER.................   50.00
MOTHER OF PEARL DIAMOND QUILTED BUTTERSCOTCH
    VASE, BULBOUS, SCALLOPED TOP.............................   32.50
MOTHER OF PEARL DIAMOND QUILTED LAMP BASE....................   45.00
MOTHER OF PEARL DIAMOND QUILTED PINK JUG BY STEVENS &
    WILLIAMS..   60.00
MOTHER OF PEARL DIAMOND QUILTED SATIN GLASS VASE, ROSE SHADE.   75.00
MOTHER OF PEARL DIAMOND QUILTED VASE, APRICOT SHADING TO
    WHITE...   135.00
MOTHER OF PEARL DIAMOND RICK RACK SATIN MOIRE HANDLED
    VASE, PINK..   350.00
MOTHER OF PEARL FINISH 4 PIECE CONDIMENT SET.................   23.00
MOTHER OF PEARL HERRINGBONE APRICOT TO WHITE BASKET.........   185.00
MOTHER OF PEARL MASTER SALT DIP.............................   15.00
MOTHER OF PEARL OUTSIDE, GOLD INSIDE, CALCITE TRUMPET VASE,...   95.00
MOTHER OF PEARL PAIR 9 IN. VASES, ROSE TO PINK AND
    WHITE, WHITE LINER......................................   245.00
MOTHER OF PEARL PAIR GREEN MOIRE SATIN SHADES, WHITE LINED...   65.00
MOTHER OF PEARL PINK LAMP SHADE.............................   70.00
MOTHER OF PEARL PINK TO WHITE TUMBLER, DIAMOND QUILTED.......   35.00
MOTHER OF PEARL PINK QUILTED FAIRY LAMP, CLEAR MARKED CLARKE
    BASE..   95.00
MOTHER OF PEARL SATIN DIAMOND QUILT CYLINDER SHAPED ROSE
    BOWL..   85.00
MOTHER OF PEARL SATIN GLASS GAS SHADE, DIAMOND QUILTED, BLUE..   45.00
MOTHER OF PEARL SATIN GLASS PEDESTAL FOOTED ROSE VASE, MOIRE.   165.00
MOTHER OF PEARL SATIN GLASS SNOW WHITE VASE, 11 IN. TALL.....   182.50
MOTHER OF PEARL SATIN GLASS TUMBLER, HERRINGBONE, PINK.........   65.00
MOTHER OF PEARL SATIN GLASS VASE IN CAMPHOR FEET, DIAMOND
    QUILTED...   85.00
MOTHER OF PEARL SATIN GLASS TEARDROP VASE, SHADES OF BLUE, 6
    IN. HIGH..   75.00
MOTHER OF PEARL SATIN GLASS VASE, AMBERINA COLOURED, STEVENS &
    WILLIAMS..   350.00

```
MOTHER OF PEARL SATIN GLASS VASE,HERRINGBONE PATTERN........   125.00
MOTHER OF PEARL SATIN ROSE BOWL.............................    65.00
MOTHER OF PEARL STEVENS & WILLIAMS LAY-DOWN PERFUME BOTTLE..    87.50
MOTHER OF PEARL SATIN TUMBLER,ROSE OVER WHITE...............    60.00
MOTHER OF PEARL VASE,TREE OF LIFE...........................   135.00
MOTHER OF PEARL VICTORIAN FLAT BASE BRASS TOP PERFUME.......    18.50
MOTHER OF PEARL WEBB SATIN GLASS ROUND BOWL,RED TO WHITE....   185.00
MOTHER OF PEARL WHITE VASE,2 PATTERNS.......................    86.00
```

*MOUNT WASHINGTON GLASS was made at the Mount Washington Glass Co.
located in New Bedford, Massachusetts. Many types of art glass were made there
from 1850 to the 1890's.*

```
MT.WASHINGTON MELON-RIBBED SATIN EWER,CAMPHOR HANDLE.......    77.50
MT.WASHINGTON PAIR RIBBED SALT & PEPPER ,DECORATED..........   35.00
MT.WASHINGTON ROSE AMBER SALT SHAKER,THUMBPRINT.............   25.00
MT.WASHINGTON SALT DIP,BLUE ACID FINISH,HANDPAINTED PANSIES.   26.00
MUELLER FRERES LAMP,LUNEVILLE...............................   300.00
MUELLER FRERES VASE,6 IN.,MOTTLED,SIGNED,OPAQUE TO BRONZE...    45.00
MUELLER FRERES VASE,LUNEVILLE,SCENIC,21 IN. TALL,5 ACID
  CUTTINGS.................................................   425.00
MUELLER FRERES VASE,SIGNED,BULBOUS TO STICK,MOTTLED ORANGE &
  BROWN...................................................    45.00
MULBERRY CUP & SAUCER,HANDLELESS,NING PO...................    12.00
MULBERRY CUP & SAUCER,WASHINGTON VASE......................    12.50
MULBERRY CUP,HANDLELESS & SAUCER,PELEW,BLACKISH............    17.50
MULBERRY DISH,BONE,SCENIC..................................     7.00
MULBERRY DISH,VEGETABLE,COVERED............................    27.50
MULBERRY PLATE,8 IN.,COREAN................................     9.00
MULBERRY PLATE,9 IN.,HONG..................................     8.50
MULBERRY PLATE,7 IN.,WASHINGTON VASE.......................     8.00
MULBERRY PLATE,COREAN PATTERN..............................     7.50
MULBERRY PLATE,9 IN.,NING PO...............................    10.00
MULBERRY PLATE,MILLENIUM...................................    18.50
MULBERRY PLATE,9 IN.,VINCENNES.............................    18.50
MULBERRY PLATTER,BREAD.....................................    10.00
MULBERRY PLATTER,KYBER,10 X 13 IN.,OCTAGONAL...............    19.50
MULBERRY VINCENNES ,59 PIECES..............................   650.00
MUSIC,ACCORDIAN,GERMAN,100 YEARS OLD.......................    22.40
MUSIC,BANJO,5 STRING,......................................    22.00
MUSIC,BOX,6 TUNE,MAHOGANY BOX..............................   125.00
MUSIC,BOX,6 TUNE,ROSEWOOD INLAID TOP.......................   125.00
MUSIC,BOX,GERMAN,CYLINDER-TYPE,8 TUNES.....................   125.00
MUSIC,BOX,MARQUE DE FABRIQUE,8 SONGS.......................   115.00
MUSIC,BOX,OLYMPIA DISC,OAK CASE............................   385.00
MUSIC,BOX,ON TABLE,POLYGHON,19 IN.,UPRIGHT.................. 1,000.00
MUSIC BOX,POLISHED WOOD CASE,2 TUNES.......................    45.00
MUSIC BOX,REGINA,CHERRY WOOD,PLAYS.........................   225.00
MUSIC BOX REGINA,DARK WOOD,MINT COND.PLAYS 15 1/2 IN.METAL
  DISC RECORDS.............................................   500.00
MUSIC,BOX,REGINA FLOOR MODEL,AUTOMATIC CHANGER............. 1,000.00
MUSIC BOX,STELLA...........................................   500.00
MUSIC,BOX,SWISS,8 TUNES,17 IN. LONG,WOOD CASE..............   175.00
MUSIC BOX,SWISS CYLINDER,INLAID CABINET,DRUM,BELLS & ORGAN..   650.00
MUSIC BOX,TURN CRANK,4 TUNES,PORCELAIN BUTTON HANDLE,MAPLE
  BOX.....................................................    25.00
MUSIC,BOX,WALNUT...........................................    22.50
MUSIC,CALLIOPE,STEAM,10 NOTE GABRIEL HORN.................. 1,000.00
MUSIC,CONCERTINA...........................................    12.00
MUSIC,CONCERTINA,BRASS & MOTHER OF PEARL KEYS..............    27.50
MUSIC,CREMONA NICKELODEON.................................. 1,500.00
MUSIC,DISCS,EDISON DIAMOND,12..............................     5.00
MUSIC,DISC FOR BOX,MIRA,9 IN...............................     1.00
MUSIC,DISC FOR BOX,MIRA,15 IN..............................     2.50
MUSIC,DISC FOR MUSIC BOX,MIRA,18 IN........................     3.00
MUSIC,DRUMMERS INSTRUMENTS,25 IN. DRUM,....................    22.00
```

```
MUSIC,GEM ROLLER ORGAN WITH ROLLS..........................    225.00
MUSIC,GEM ROLLER ORGAN,.....................................     65.00
MUSIC,GRAMAPHONE,COLUMBIA,14 IN. BLACK HORN,FLARED BRASS,21
 RECORDS....................................................     95.00
MUSIC,GRAMAPHONE,COLUMBIA,CYLINDERS,METAL HORN..............    130.00
MUSIC,GRAPHOPHONE,COLUMBIA,TABLE MODEL,OAK,BLACK HORN,BRASS
 TRIM.......................................................     59.00
MUSIC,HARP,18TH CENTURY FRENCH 7-PEDAL......................    500.00
MUSIC,HURDY GURDY-PLAYS 10 TUNES PLUS 2 OTHER ROLLERS.......    400.00
MUSIC,HURDY-GURDY,SPANISH,1 ROLL............................    350.00
MUSIC,MANDOLIN..............................................     20.00
MUSIC,MANDOLIN,TATER BUG....................................      6.00
MUSIC,MELODEON,ROSEWOOD CASE,PLAYS,FOOT PUMP,SCREW ON LEGS..     75.00
MUSIC,MOUTH ORGAN,ROLMONICA,MUSIC ROLLS,4...................     10.00
MUSIC,NICKEL FIFE WITH MOUTH PIECE..........................      5.00
MUSIC,NICKELODEON,BERRY WOOD,RESTORED.......................    800.00
MUSIC,NICKELODEON,LINK......................................    495.00
MUSIC,NICKELODEON,MILLS RACEHORSE,PIANO WITH 3 ROLLS........    950.00
MUSIC,ORCHESTRA,WURLITZER THEATRE.........................1,195.00
MUSIC,ORCHESTRION,WURLITZER,STYLE C.......................1,995.00
MUSIC,ORGAN,33 NOTE DEAGAN UNA-FON........................1,500.00
MUSIC,ORGAN,37 NOTE DEAGAN................................1,500.00
MUSIC,ORGAN,48 NOTE,IN CASE,PLAYS PAPER ROLLS.............1,750.00
MUSIC,ORGAN,BELLOWS,WALNUT..................................    500.00
MUSIC,ORGAN,CARVED FRONT & GLOCKENSPIEL BELLS.............2,500.00
MUSIC,ORGAN,CIVIL WAR PIPE,GEORGE JARDINE,6 RANKS PIPES.....3,500.00
MUSIC,ORGAN,GOTHIC WITH MIRROR,1886,STORY & CLARK,PUMP......    500.00
MUSIC,ORGAN,WALNUT..........................................    100.00
MUSIC,ORGAN,WALNUT,PARLOR,TAYLOR & FARLEY,WORCESTER MASS....    275.00
MUSIC,ORGAN,WURLITZER BAND,CARVED FRONT...................3,500.00
MUSIC,ORGAN,WURLITZER BAND,CARVED FRONT & GLOCKENSPIEL BELLS2,500.00
MUSIC,PACKARD BELL RECORD RECORDER WITH MIKE & 5 12 IN.
 BLANK RECORDS..............................................     75.00
MUSIC,PHONOGRAPH,200 DISCS,FOR EDISON,IN CASE...............     40.00
MUSIC,PHONOGRAPH,EDISON,1907,WITH 37 ROLLS..................     40.00
MUSIC,PHONOGRAPH,EDISON,1913 MODEL WITH 6 RECORDS...........     75.00
MUSIC,PHONOGRAPH,EDISON CYLINDER,50 CYLINDERS...............     95.00
MUSIC,PHONOGRAPH,EDISON GEM CYLINDER WITH 6 CYLINDERS.......    120.00
MUSIC,PHONOGRAPH,EDISON GEM,WITH HORN & 40 RECORDS.........    115.00
MUSIC,PHONOGRAPH,EDISON,HOME,RUBBER STAMP WITH EDISONS
 PICTURE....................................................      2.10
MUSIC,PHONOGRAPH,EDISON,RED MORNING GLORY HORN,20 CYLINDER
 SLEEVE.....................................................     75.00
MUSIC,PHONOGRAPH,EDISON STANDARD,12 CYLINDER RECORDS........     45.00
MUSIC,PHONOGRAPH,EDISON STANDARD,CYLINDER RECORD TYPE,HORN..     55.00
MUSIC,PHONOGRAPH HORN.......................................      7.00
MUSIC,PHONOGRAPH,OLD NIPPER,PAPIER MACHE....................    110.00
MUSIC,PHONOGRAPH RECORDS 1908...............................       .50
MUSIC,PHONOGRAPH,VICTOR CRANK SUITCASE......................      8.50
MUSIC,PHONOGRAPH WITH BRASS HORN............................      6.50
MUSIC,PIANO,1864 SQUARE GRAND STEINWAY,CARVED ROSEWOOD CASE.    490.00
MUSIC,PIANO,AMPICO MODEL B GRAND............................    995.00
MUSIC,PIANO,DUO-ART GRAND,STROUD............................    895.00
MUSIC,PIANO,KNABE AMPICO GRAND,1928,LOUIS XV CASE,WALNUT....1,700.00
MUSIC,PIANO,MARSHALL & WENDALL AMPICO.....................1,495.00
MUSIC,PIANO ROLL
 .50  TO....................................................      1.25
MUSIC,PIANO ROLLS,200.......................................     50.00
MUSIC,PIANO,STEINWAY 65 85 NOT PEDAL UPRIGHT,UNRESTORED.....    300.00
MUSIC, PIANO, STEINWAY B DUO-ART REPRODUCER................1,750.00
MUSIC,PIANO,UPRIGHT,LEADED GLASS FRONT......................    300.00
MUSIC,PIANO,UPRIGHT REPRODUCING WITH 10 WELTE ROLLS.........    350.00
MUSIC,PIANO,WELTE GRAND.....................................    895.00
MUSIC,PIANO,WELTE UPRIGHT REPRODUCING WITH 10 ROLLS.........    350.00
MUSIC,PLAY A SAX,5 ROLLS LIKE A PLAYER PIANO................     32.50
```

```
MUSIC,PLAYER PIANO.............................................   400.00
MUSIC,PLAYER PIANO,WEBER AEOLIAN 65 NOTE ROLL,80
  ROLLS,MAHOGANY FINISH........................................   400.00
MUSIC,POLYPHON,9 IN. DISC MUSIC BOX,20 DISCS..................   300.00
MUSIC,POLYPHON COIN OPERATED VERTICAL DISC PHONOGRAPH WITH 7
  DISCS........................................................   650.00
MUSIC,RECORDS,75 1900 78RPM 10 IN.............................    15.00
MUSIC,RECORDS,EDISON 2 & 4 MINUTE,12..........................    11.00
MUSIC,RECORDS OF THE 20 S ,12.................................     5.00
MUSIC,ROLMONICA PLAYER HARMONICA WITH 14 PLAYER ROLLS.........    10.00
MUSIC,ROLMONICA WITH 18 ROLLS,MADE IN GERMANY.................    25.00
MUSIC,SAX,LITTLE ORPHAN ANNIE STOVE,5 ROLLS,LIKE PLAYER
  PIANO........................................................    32.50
MUSIC,SHEET,1900 TO 1945
  .50 TO.......................................................     1.50
MUSIC,SYMPHONIUM,IMPERIAL,6 IN. DISC RECORDS..................   135.00
MUSIC,TALKING MACHINE,STANDARD STYLE X WITH BLUE MORNING
  GLORY HORN...................................................    85.00
MUSIC,TALKING MACHINE,VICTROLA,HORN...........................    75.00
MUSIC,TALKING MACHINE WITH BRASS BELL HORN,VICTOR 11..........   100.00
MUSIC,TAMBOURINE,10 IN.,PAINTING ON HEAD,KICKAPOO
  MED.CO.INSIDE................................................    12.00
MUSIC,VICTROLA OF THE 20S,PORTABLE,PLAYS......................    20.00
MUSIC,VICTROLA WITH RECORDS...................................    50.00
MUSIC,VIOLANO VIRTUOSO WITH 5 ROLLS,QUARTER SLOT..............   900.00
MUSIC, VIOLIN.................................................     5.00
MUSIC,VIOLIN,16 IN. LONG......................................    38.00
MUSIC,ZITHER.................................................    15.00
MUSIC,ZITHER,PAT.DATE 1894...................................    20.00
```

MUSTACHE CUPS were popular from 1850 to 1900. A ledge of china or silver held the hair out of the liquid in the cup.

```
MUSTACHE CUP & SAUCER,6 SIDED,EMBOSSED FLOWERS,GOLD OUTLINED     30.00
MUSTACHE CUP & SAUCER,AQUA & GOLD DECOR......................    14.00
MUSTACHE CUP & SAUCER,BLUE FLOWERS...........................    13.50
MUSTACHE CUP & SAUCER,BLUE OUTSIDE,COLOURED FLOWERS..........    25.00
MUSTACHE CUP & SAUCER,BROWN,YELLOW FLOWERS...................    25.00
MUSTACHE CUP & SAUCER,BURGUNDY UPPER WITH GOLD,BLUE FLOWERS
  & YELLOW.....................................................    16.50
MUSTACHE CUP & SAUCER,CHINA,FLORAL WITH GOLD.................    13.50
MUSTACHE CUP & SAUCER,CHINA,MOLDED TO RESEMBLE FLOWER,PINK
  LUSTER.......................................................    20.00
MUSTACHE CUP & SAUCER,ENGLAND,WHITE WITH GILT TRIM,PINK
  ROSES,BLUE...................................................    14.00
MUSTACHE CUP & SAUCER,FLORAL DECORATED WITH GOLD TRIM........    12.50
MUSTACHE CUP & SAUCER,FLORAL DESIGN..........................    12.00
MUSTACHE CUP & SAUCER,FLUTED,EMBOSSED,GOLD,GERMAN............    16.00
MUSTACHE CUP AND SAUCER,GERMAN,BROWN WITH RAISED
  LETTERS,PRESENT..............................................    15.00
MUSTACHE CUP & SAUCER,GOLD LUSTER,PRESENT....................    15.00
MUSTACHE CUP & SAUCER,GOLD TRIMMED
  22.00 TO.....................................................    29.50
MUSTACHE CUP & SAUCER,GREEN LUSTER...........................    22.50
MUSTACHE CUP & SAUCER,GREEN SHINY FINISH,REMEMBER ME,LOVE
  THE GIVER....................................................    14.50
MUSTACHE CUP & SAUCER,HANDPAINTED YELLOW FLOWER..............    25.00
MUSTACHE CUP & SAUCER,HOLLY LEAVES & BERRIES.................    15.00
MUSTACHE CUP & SAUCER,IMAIR SIGNED,ORANGE,BLUE,& GREEN......    28.50
MUSTACHE CUP & SAUCER IN CERISE-RUST,CHINESE DECOR,FLORAL...    18.50
MUSTACHE CUP & SAUCER IN GREEN WITH GOLD FLOWERS.............    17.50
MUSTACHE CUP & SAUCER,IVORY CHINA............................    55.00
MUSTACHE CUP & SAUCER,LAVENDER FLORAL PATTERN................     6.75
MUSTACHE CUP & SAUCER MARKED GERMANY,BLUE ,PINK & GOLD DECOR    15.00
MUSTACHE CUP & SAUCER,PANELED WITH GOLD ENAMEL FLOWERS......     8.50
MUSTACHE CUP & SAUCER,PINK WITH YELLOW ROSES,MARKED BAVARIA.    23.50
```

```
MUSTACHE CUP & SAUCER,PORCELAIN,GREEN.........................  12.50
MUSTACHE CUP & SAUCER,PRESENT,GOLD LUSTER,FLORAL DECORATION.   15.00
MUSTACHE CUP & SAUCER,RED & BLUE,FOOTED.....................   15.00
MUSTACHE CUP & SAUCER,RED ROSES & GOLD......................   10.50
MUSTACHE CUP & SAUCER,SCENE ANNAPOLIS RIVER AT BRIDGETOWN...   10.00
MUSTACHE CUP & SAUCER,SILVER PLATE..........................   22.50
MUSTACHE CUP & SAUCER,SPRAY OF PINK,ORANGE FLOWERS,GREEN
  LEAVES....................................................   15.00
MUSTACHE CUP & SAUCER,SUNDERLAND LUSTER,BLACK TRANSFER OF
  SCHOONER..................................................   25.00
MUSTACHE CUP & SAUCER,THINK OF ME IN GOLD LETTERS,WILD ROSES  13.50
MUSTACHE CUP & SAUCER,WEIMAR GERMANY........................   10.00
MUSTACHE CUP & SAUCER,WELMAR,GERMANY,WHITE CHINA,FLORAL.....   20.00
MUSTACHE CUP & SAUCER,WHITE & DAISIES.......................   16.00
MUSTACHE CUP & SAUCER,WHITE & GREEN,MARKED LS & S GERMANY...   20.00
MUSTACHE CUP & SAUCER,WHITE CHINA,RC BAVARIAN CROWN & FLORAL  20.00
MUSTACHE CUP & SAUCER,WHITE,FLORAL EMBOSSED.................   16.50
MUSTACHE CUP & SAUCER,WHITE,FLOWER CLUSTER..................   14.75
MUSTACHE CUP & SAUCER,WHITE WITH GOLD & PINK LUSTER
  BANDS,ROSES...............................................   11.50
MUSTACHE CUP & SAUCER,WHITE WITH GOLD GILT,RAISED FLOWERS &
  LEAVES....................................................   15.00
MUSTACHE CUP & SAUCER,WHITE WITH ORCHID & WHITE
  FLOWERS,GREEN LEAVES......................................   14.00
MUSTACHE CUP & SAUCER,WHITE WITH PRESENT....................   17.50
MUSTACHE CUP,A PRESENT,GOLD FLOWERS.........................   12.00
MUSTACHE CUP,BEEHIVE MARK,FLORAL WITH GUARD & HANDLE........    9.50
MUSTACHE CUP,FLOWER DECOR,HANDLE............................   14.00
MUSTACHE CUP,FOOTED,BLUE & WHITE,AUSTRIAN COURT TYPE
  MEDALLION.................................................   18.00
MUSTACHE CUP,GERMANY,GOLD LETTERED POEM WRITTEN IN GERMAN...    6.00
MUSTACHE CUP,GERMAN,HAS BAND OF FLOWERS,TRANSFER PATTERN OF
  HOUSE.....................................................   12.50
MUSTACHE CUP,HAVILAND,RED ROSES ON CREAM WITH GOLD RIM......    9.50
MUSTACHE CUP,LEFT HAND,LARGE GAY 90S DESIGN,NO SAUCER.......   75.00
MUSTACHE CUP MARKED P.M.& B.,ENGLAND........................    8.00
MUSTACHE CUP,PICTURE OF OWL.................................    6.00
MUSTACHE CUP,PINK LUSTER WITH WHITE & GOLD LILY OF VALLEY &
  LEAVES....................................................   18.00
MUSTACHE CUP,QUART SIZE.....................................   35.00
MUSTACHE CUP,REMEMBER ME,GERMAN,WHITE & BLUE & GOLD.........   10.00
MUSTACHE CUP,RAISED DESIGN,PRESENT..........................   12.50
MUSTACHE CUP,SILVER.........................................    9.00
MUSTACHE CUP,THINK OF ME,GOLD,HANDLELESS....................    7.50
MUSTACHE CUP,TRANSLUCENT WHITE SQUATTY SEA SHELL SHAPE
  FOOTED,...................................................   18.00
MUSTACHE CUP,WHITE & PINK LUSTRE WITH GOLD..................   13.50
MUSTACHE CUP,WALTER JACOBY..................................   25.00
MUSTACHE CUP,WHITE ,FLORAL DESIGN...........................    7.50
```

NAILSEA GLASS was made in the Bristol District in England from 1788 to 1873.
Many pieces were made with loopings of colored glass as decorations.

```
NAILSEA ART GLASS WALKING CANE..............................   50.00
NAILSEA FLASK,BLOWN BLUE WITH WHITE LOOPINGS................   65.00
NAILSEA GLASS FLASK BOTTLE,7 IN.,COBALT & WHITE............   75.00
NAILSEA PINK 6 IN. TALL PITCHER,THREADED DESIGN.............  100.00
NAILSEA ROLLING PIN,RUBY LOOPINGS ON GREEN..................   58.00
NAILSEA VERRE MOIRE WHITE LOOPINGS,CRANBERRY TUMBLER........   50.00
```

NAKARA is a trade name for a white glassware made around 1900 that was
decorated in pastel colors. It was made by the C. F. Monroe Company of Meriden,
Connecticut.

```
NAKARA OPEN TRINKET BOX,PINK,TO CREAM,5IN. L. BY 5IN. W.....   41.00
NAKARA SIGNED C.F.MONROE CO.,6 SIDED HINGED BOX.............   50.00
NAKARA SIGNED FLORAL COOKIE JAR.............................   65.00
```

NAKARA SIGNED 6 SIDED BOWL,BURMESE COLOR,FLORAL ,BRASS
COLLAR.. 35.00
NAKARA SIGNED PLANTER WITH BRASS RIM,ENAMELED PANSIES ON
GREEN,PINK.. 45.00
NAKARA SIGNED POWDER BOX,SQUARED-SHAPE,RAISED BLUE DAISIES
IN PINK... 67.50
NAKARA SIGNED TOOTHPICK HOLDER WITH SILVER RIM,FLOWERS IN
GREEN... 42.00

*NANKING CHINA is a blue and white porcelain made in China for export during
the eighteenth century.*
NANKING COVERED CREAMPOT ,TWISTED HANDLE,GOLD............... 75.00
NANKING OBLONG OCTAGONAL TUREEN & STAND,BLUE
DECORATION,CIRCA 1790..................................... 485.00
NANKING PLATE 8 IN... 28.00
NANKING PLATTER,BLUE OCTAGONAL............................. 42.00
NANKING POSSET & SAUCER,COVER & WISHBONE HANDLE............ 55.00
NANKING TRAY,BLUE & WHITE RETICULATED..................... 25.00

NAPKIN RINGS were popular from 1869 to about 1900.
NAPKIN RING,2 LEAVES & BRANCH ON SIDE OF RING WITH CHICK.... 17.50
NAPKIN RING,A B C... 6.50
NAPKIN RING,BLUE & WHITE DUTCH SCENES..................... 7.50
NAPKIN RING,CRANBERRY OVERLAY,WHITE CUT TO CRANBERRY,GERMAN
VILLAGE... 35.00
NAPKIN RING,DOG,SILVER FIGURAL............................ 23.00
NAPKIN RING,FIGURAL,HEN AT SIDE SAYS FROM A FRIEND TO
GEORGIA... 16.00
NAPKIN RING,FLORAL DESIGN,FOOTED.......................... 5.00
NAPKIN RING,FOX TRYING TO REACH GRAPES.................... 15.00
NAPKIN RING,GLASS,4 SIDES WITH CUT FLOWERS & LEAVES....... 7.50
NAPKIN RING,LITTLE GIRL WITH BONNET,SILVER PLATE.......... 20.00
NAPKIN RING,MARKED MERIDEN,EAGLE EACH SIDE................ 19.50
NAPKIN RING,QUILTED WITH BIRD............................. 14.00
NAPKIN RING,RING SET ON LEAF WITH BIRD ON STEM........... 16.50
NAPKIN RING,SILVER FIGURAL,DEER WITH ANTLERS............. 24.00
NAPKIN RING,SILVER FIGURAL,FOX ON TREE TRUNK............. 12.00
NAPKIN RING,SILVER FIGURAL,GREENAWAY BOY WITH BAT & BALL.... 30.00
NAPKIN RING,SILVER FIGURAL,KATE GREENAWAY GIRL........... 28.00
NAPKIN RING,SILVER FIGURAL,NESTING CHICKEN & FLOWER....... 17.00
NAPKIN RING,SILVER FIGURAL,OWL & FIDDLE ON MUSIC SHEEL,BALL
FEET.. 29.00
NAPKIN RING,SILVER,HAND APPLIED ON RING HOLDING FLOWERS..... 12.50
NAPKIN RING,SILVER LACY,2 LIONS ON PLATE................. 16.75
NAPKIN RING,SILVER ,TENNIS RACQUET & BALL................ 18.00
NAPKIN RING,SILVER WITH LYRE............................. 17.50
NAPKIN RING,SILVER....................................... 4.00
NAPKIN RING WITH DOG,WOODEN.............................. 1.75
NAPKIN RING WITH TENNIS RACQUET,SILVER................... 15.00
NAPKIN RINGS,ENAMEL ON BRASS,EACH........................ 2.00
NAPOLEON PLATES,12,BLACK & WHITE TRANSFER PRINTS OF BATTLE
SCENES.. 75.00

*NASH GLASS was made in Corona, New York, by Arthur Nash and his sons after
1919. He had worked at the Webb factory in England and for the Tiffany Glass
Works in the United States.*
NASH SIGNED BLUE IRIDESCENT PEDESTAL VASE.................. 195.00
NASH SIGNED FOOTED 6 IN. LEMONADE,GREEN & BLUE STRIATIONS ON
SMOKY.. 110.00

*NETSUKE are small ivory, wood, metal, or porcelain pieces used as the button on
the end of a cord holding a Japanese money pouch. The earliest date from the
sixteenth century.*
NETSUKE IVORY FROG ON MANS HEAD SIGNED KOSHIN CIRCA
1820-1840... 75.00

```
NETSUKE IVORY MAN.........................................   16.00
NETSUKE IVORY NAKED MAN LIFTING RICE BALE CIRCA 1800-1840...   50.00
NETSUKE IVORY SITTING HO HO CIRCA 1800......................   50.00
NETSUKE IVORY ,THE FIVE POETS,19TH CENTURY..................   45.00
NETSUKE SIGNED IVORY........................................   12.50
NETSUKE WOOD CARVED MAN BEING ATTACKED BY DOG...............   29.00
NEWALL CUP & SAUCER,FAMILY SCENES,WISHBONE HANDLE...........   20.00
NEWSPAPER,CIVIL WAR.........................................    1.25
NEWSPAPER,UNITED STATES,1867 TO 1900.......................    3.00
```

NIPPON MARKED PORCELAIN was made in Japan after 1891.

```
NIPPON BANANA BOAT,HANDPAINTED GOLD & PINK ROSES............   10.50
NIPPON BOWL & PLATE,WATERCRESS.............................    7.00
NIPPON BOWL,6 IN.,FOOTED,DAFFODIL DECOR....................    3.75
NIPPON BOWL,BERRY,HANDPAINTED FLORALS IN & OUT.............   12.50
NIPPON BOWL,BROWN & BEIGE,2 HANDLED,SQUARE,BASKETWEAVE DECOR   8.00
NIPPON BOWL,FOOTED,OVAL BERRY,GOLD SCALLOPED RIM,GREEN &
  PINK.....................................................   35.00
NIPPON BOWL,HANDPAINTED,BRAZIL NUTS IN RELIEF,2 HANDLES.....    9.00
NIPPON BOWL,HANDPAINTED,HANDLES HAVE RAISED ENAMEL WORK.....    6.50
NIPPON BOWL,NUT,5 IN.,HANDPAINTED..........................    3.00
NIPPON BOX,POWDER,COBALT EDGING,HANDPAINTED PINK
  FLOWERS,GOLD.............................................    8.50
NIPPON BOWL,RAISED ACORN IN RELIEF,RUST,YELLOW & BROWN......   10.00
NIPPON BUTTER PAT,SET OF 5,HANDPAINTED.....................    3.00
NIPPON CAKE SET,HANDPAINTED APPLE BLOSSOMS,GOLD TRIM........   17.50
NIPPON CAKE SET,HANDPAINTED PINK ROSETTES ON CREAM.........   22.00
NIPPON CELERY SET,MARKED,PINK ROSES ON WHITE,GOLD TRIM......   18.00
NIPPON CHEESE DIP SERVER,HANDPAINTED.......................    5.00
NIPPON CHOCOLATE POT,HANDPAINTED
  5.00  TO................................................    8.00
NIPPON CHOCOLATE POT,2 CUPS,HANDPAINTED ROSES..............   12.00
NIPPON CHCOOLATE POT,7 IN.,GOLD EDGE,HANDPAINTED ROSES......    8.75
NIPPON CHOCOLATE POT,FLORAL BANDS WITH GOLD................   10.00
NIPPON CHOCOLATE POT,GOLD BEADING,HANDPAINTED PINK GARLANDS.   16.50
NIPPON CHOCOLATE POT,HANDPAINTED MANDERIN FIGURES,COBALT &
  GOLD....................................................   15.00
NIPPON CHOCOLATE POT WITH 3 CUPS,HANDPAINTED...............    9.00
NIPPON CHOCOLATE POT WITH 4 CUPS,MARKED,HANDPAINTED,MELON
  RIBBED..................................................   17.00
NIPPON CHOCOLATE POT WITH 5 CUPS & SAUCERS,HANDPAINTED......   29.50
NIPPON CHOCOLATE SET,FALL SCENE,TREE WITH ORANGE LEAVES.....   55.00
NIPPON CHOCOLATE SET,HANDPAINTED,5 PIECES,COBALT-GOLD.......   27.50
NIPPON CHOCOLATE SET,HANDPAINTED BLUE VIOLETS ON PINK.......   32.00
NIPPON CHOCOLATE SET,HANDPAINTED WHITE WITH BLUE BANDS EDGED
  IN GOLD.................................................   17.00
NIPPON CHOCOLATE SET,PINK & BLUE ROSES,GOLD TRIM...........   25.00
NIPPON CHOCOLATE SET,POT,4 CUPS & SAUCERS..................   18.50
NIPPON CHOCOLATE SET,POT & 6 CUPS & SAUCERS,HANDPAINTED.....   30.00
NIPPON COMPOTE,2 HANDLED,HANDPAINTED FLOWERS WITH GOLD......    6.00
NIPPON CRACKER JAR,HANDPAINTED AQUA BANDS & GREEN
  LEAVES,GOLD,FOOTED......................................   22.50
NIPPON CRACKER JAR WITH LOTS OF HEAVY GOLD,2 HANDLED........    7.50
NIPPON CREAMER & SUGAR,GOLD...............................   25.00
NIPPON CREAMER,COVERED,ROSES,GOLD TRIM....................    3.00
NIPPON CREAMER,GOLD,YELLOW ,ROSE..........................    1.50
NIPPON CREAMER,ROSES,GOLD TRIM............................    3.50
NIPPON CUCUMBER SET,FOOTED BOWL ON PLATE,HANDPAINTED PINK
  ROSES...................................................    7.00
NIPPON CUP & SAUCER & CAKE PLATE,HANDPAINTED,GREEN & GOLD...    5.00
NIPPON CUP & SAUCER,AUTUMN SCENE ON LAKE,ORCHID,PURPLE,GREEN
  & YELLOW................................................    5.00
NIPPON CUP & SAUCER,CHOCOLATE,SET OF 6,HANDPAINTED.........   20.00
NIPPON CUP & SAUCER,DEMI-TASSE,EGGSHELL,BLUE WITH WHITE
  EGRETS..................................................    5.00
```

```
NIPPON CUP & SAUCER,DEMI-TASSE,HANDPAINTED,3 IN. TALL.......          5.25
NIPPON CUP & SAUCER,DEMI-TASSE,HANDPAINTED FLORALS,GOLD TRIM          3.50
NIPPON CUP & SAUCER,HANDPAINTED AZALEA......................          4.00
NIPPON CUP & SAUCER,HANDPAINTED GREEN WITH RED & YELLOW
  ROSES,FOOTED..............................................          3.75
NIPPON CUP & SAUCER,MARKED,HANDPAINTED PINK ROSES,GOLD
  HANDLE...................................................          4.00
NIPPON DISH,2 HANDLES,WHITE CENTER,BLUE & PINK FLOWERS......         12.00
NIPPON DISH,5 IN.,BLUE & GOLD BORDER,ROSES INSIDE WITH
  HANDLE...................................................          2.50
NIPPON DISH,7 IN.,2 OPEN HANDLES,HANDPAINTED BLACK &
  GREEN,GOLD EDGE..........................................          8.50
NIPPON DISH,8 IN.,CHINA,FLOWER DECORATION...................          2.00
NIPPON DISH,BERRY,MARKED,HANDPAINTED........................          2.00
NIPPON DISH,BON BON,HANDPAINTED GREEN WITH ROSES,OPEN WORK
  ROSES....................................................         60.00
NIPPON DISH,CANDY,HANDPAINTED FLOWERS,TRIAGNLE CORNERS
  TURNED IN................................................          3.00
NIPPON DISH,CHEESE,COVERED,BLUEBIRD.........................         .8.00
NIPPON DISH,CHEESE,SLANT TOP................................         12.50
NIPPON DISH,HANDPAINTED CHINA,4 IN.,BROWN,TAN,SAILBOAT......          3.75
NIPPON DISH,JELLY WITH ATTACHED TRAY,HANDPAINTED
  FLOWERS,BIRDS & GOLD.....................................         12.50
NIPPON DISH,NUT,HANDPAINTED.................................          2.50
NIPPON DISH,PAIR NUT,HANDPAINTED PINK ROSES & GREEN LEAVES..          1.50
NIPPON DISH,PANCAKE,HANDPAINTED.............................         10.00
NIPPON DRESSER SET,5 PIÉCES,GOLD WITH PINK ROSES............         25.00
NIPPON DRESSER SET,HANDPAINTED..............................         35.00
NIPPON HAIR RECEIVER & POWDER BOX,HANDPAINTED FLORAL WITH
  GOLD.....................................................          6.75
NIPPON HAIR RECEIVER,HANDPAINTED PINK FLORAL,GREEN & GOLD...          4.00
NIPPON HAIR RECEIVER,HANDPAINTED WINDMILL & TREES,FLORAL
  SPRAY....................................................          8.50
NIPPON HAIR RECEIVER ON 3 LEGS,TAN BAND WITH FLORAL & GOLD..          4.00
NIPPON HATPIN HOLDER,FOOTED,GOLD DOTS.......................          7.50
NIPPON HATPIN HOLDER,HANDPAINTED GOLD ENAMELING & ROSES.....          6.00
NIPPON HATPIN HOLDER,HANDPAINTED,GOLD YELLOW FLORAL.........          7.00
NIPPON HATPIN HOLDER,HANDPAINTED RUST & GOLD WOMEN IN GARDEN          4.00
NIPPON HATPIN HOLDER,HANDPAINTED WHITE WITH GOLD SCROLL TRIM          6.75
NIPPON HATPIN HOLDER,HANDPAINTED WILD ROSES,GILT TRIM,OPEN
  TOP......................................................          6.75
NIPPON HATPIN HOLDER,WHITE WITH RAISED GOLD LEAVES &
  BERRIES,................................................          8.00
NIPPON HATPIN HOLDER WITH BLUE & FLORAL DECOR,WHITE.........          5.00
NIPPON JAR,DRESSER,PAIR,FOOTED,HANDPAINTED..................          7.50
NIPPON JAR,JAM,CROWN DERBY CHINOISERIE IN BLUE & ORANGE.....         12.00
NIPPON JAR,POWDER,HANDPAINTED PINK FLORAL,GREEN & GOLD......          4.00
NIPPON MAYONNAISE POT WITH LADLE & TRAY,COVERED,GOLD........         11.50
NIPPON MAYONNAISE SET,3 PIECE,HANDPAINTED,3 FOOTED
  BOWL,GREEN & GOLD........................................          8.00
NIPPON MAYONNAISE SET,3 PIECE,HANDPAINTED,FOOTED BOWL,BLUE..          7.50
NIPPON MAYONNAISE SET,3 PIECE,MARKED,PRIMROSE ON WHITE......          5.50
NIPPON MAYONNAISE SET,DELFT BLUE,PEARLIZED LINING...........          7.00
NIPPON MUG,SET OF 4,ROYAL,ROSES & GOLD......................         24.00
NIPPON MUSTARD,MARKED,ATTACHED DISH & SPOON.................          6.00
NIPPON MUSTARD POT,WINDMILL SCENE...........................          4.50
NIPPON MUSTARD POT WITH ATTACHED DISH,HANDPAINTED PINK ROSES
  & GOLD...................................................          4.50
NIPPON MUSTARD SET WITH TRAY,HANDPAINTED....................         10.00
NIPPON NAPKIN HOLDER,MARKED,HANDPAINTED SCENE,GOLD ENAMEL...         15.00
NIPPON NUT SET,7 PCS........................................          5.00
NIPPON NUT SET,7 IN. BOWL WITH 3 FEET & 8 DISHES............         22.50
NIPPON NUT SET,7 IN. DISH WITH 2 OPEN HANDLES & 6
  DISHES,HANDPAINTED.......................................          6.95
NIPPON NUT SET,HANDPAINTED,GREEN TRADEMARK,7 PIECE,CHESTNUT
```

DESIGN	13.75
NIPPON NUT SET,HANDPAINTED PINK ROSE BANDS,6 SERVERS	10.00
NIPPON NUT SET,WHITE PORCELAIN WITH RAISED GOLD DECOR	6.00
NIPPON PANCAKE SERVER,COVERED,GOLD FLOWERS & LEAVES	12.00
NIPPON PITCHER,ART NOUVEAU,HANDPAINTED,10 IN. TALL	35.00
NIPPON PITCHER,COVERED,QUART SIZE,GOLD WITH FLORAL BAND	10.00
NIPPON PITCHER,HANDPAINTED PINK FLOWERS,GREEN LEAVES,GOLD TRIM	8.00
NIPPON PITCHER,MILK,HANDPAINTED HOUSE SCENE	25.00
NIPPON PITCHER,MILK,MARKED,HANDPAINTED BLUE MAPLE LEAF & PINK FLORAL	22.50
NIPPON PITCHER,SAUCE,SAUCER	12.00
NIPPON PITCHER,SYRUP,COVERED,HANDPAINTED RED POPPIES,GOLD TRIM	4.50
NIPPON PITCHER,SYRUP,HANDPAINTED FLOWERS	6.00
NIPPON PITCHER,TANKARD TYPE,ROYAL,ROSES & GOLD	20.00
NIPPON PITCHER WITH DEER,11 IN	35.00
NIPPON PLATE,6 IN. DEEP,BABY,CHILDREN & DOG	5.00
NIPPON PLATE,7 IN.,HANDPAINTED MAROON SWAGS,PINK ROSES,GREEN & GOLD	5.00
NIPPON PLATE,10 IN.,HANDPAINTED PASTEL FLORAL EDGES	4.25
NIPPON PLATE,CAKE,10 IN.,HANDPAINTED	4.00
NIPPON PLATE,CAKE,BLUEBIRD,OPEN HANDLED WITH 6 SMALL PLATES.	8.50
NIPPON PLATE,CAKE,HANDLED,MARKED,HANDPAINTED GREEN BORDER WITH GARLANDS	7.00
NIPPON PLATE,CHILDS,ROBINSON CRUSOE,5 IN. DIAMETER	12.50
NIPPON PLATE,HANDPAINTED,6 IN.,SIGNED BY W.ROSE	5.00
NIPPON PLATE,HANDPAINTED GOLD EDGING & SCROLLS & ROSES,7 IN.	8.50
NIPPON PLATE,HANDPAINTED,SIGNED WITH MAPLE LEAF	22.00
NIPPON PLATE,HANGING,HANDPAINTED,10 IN	8.50
NIPPON PLATE,SET OF 6 DESSERT,HANDPAINTED	25.00
NIPPON RELISH,7 IN.,FOOTED,LIME,GOLD	4.00
NIPPON RELISH,FOOTED,LIME TRIM WITH GOLD SCALLOPED EDGE	4.50
NIPPON SALT & PEPPER,HANDPAINTED	3.00
NIPPON SALT & PEPPER SHAKER IN CHINA HOLDER,HANDPAINTED	5.00
NIPPON SALT & PEPPER SHAKERS,MARKED	2.75
NIPPON SALT & PEPPER SHAKER,SQUARE,DECORATED,PAIR	4.00
NIPPON SALT,OPEN HANDLE	3.00
NIPPON SALT,OPEN,SET OF 4 DOUBLE HANDLED	6.00
NIPPON SAUCE BOAT WITH 6 IN. UNDERPLATE,HANDPAINTED,5 IN	6.50
NIPPON SAUCER,PAIR,HANDPAINTED	3.00
NIPPON SHAVING MUG,MORIAGI,GREEN RAISED DECOR OF IRIS,HANDPAINTED	13.50
NIPPON SUGAR & CREAMER,HANDPAINTED AZALEAS	7.00
NIPPON SUGAR & CREAMER,HANDPAINTED PINK FLORAL	12.50
NIPPON SUGAR & CREAMER,HANDPAINTED PINK FLORAL ON TAN BAND	12.50
NIPPON SUGAR & CREAMER,ROYAL MORIYE,FOOTED,CREAM BACKGROUND.	28.00
NIPPON SUGAR BOWL,GOLD	6.00
NIPPON SUGAR,POWDERED,WHITE WITH PINK FLOWERS,GOLD TRIM	5.00
NIPPON SUGAR SHAKER,HANDPAINTED	4.50
NIPPON SUGAR SHAKER,HANDPAINTED ROSES,GILT TRIM,SIDE HANDLED	7.50
NIPPON SYRUP,HANDPAINTED RED POPPIES,GOLD HANDLE	4.50
NIPPON SYRUP WITH PLATE,MARKED	5.00
NIPPON TEAPOT,4 CUP SIZE,MARKED,HANDPAINTED WHITE EGRETS WITH PINK	8.00
NIPPON TEAPOT,HANDPAINTED,GOLD BEADING,MEDALLIONS ON SIDES	16.00
NIPPON TEAPOT,SUGAR & CREAMER,SIGNED,HANDPAINTED WHITE & PINK SWAN	25.00
NIPPON TEA SET,BLUE,IRIDESCENT GOLD LINING	25.00
NIPPON TEA SET,GOLD	25.00
NIPPON TEA SET,HANDPAINTED LAKE SCENE,GOLD	37.50
NIPPON TEA SET,HANDPAINTED ROSES WITH GOLD,25 PIECES	65.00
NIPPON TOBACCO JAR,GREEN WITH HUNT SCENE	15.00
NIPPON TOBACCO JAR,HANDPAINTED SCENIC WITH GOLF BAG ON GREEN	11.50
NIPPON TOOTHPICK,CHINA,HANDPAINTED,8 HANDLED	3.00

```
NIPPON TOOTHPICK,HANDPAINTED,2 IN.............................   3.00
NIPPON TOOTHPICK,HANDPAINTED GOLD & PINK FLOWERS.............    3.50
NIPPON TRAY,CELERY & 6 SALTS,HANDPAINTED PINK ROSES.........    12.00
NIPPON TRAY,DRESSER,10 IN.,HANDPAINTED......................     3.00
NIPPON TRAY,DRESSER,SIGNED,HANDPAINTED LEAVES & FLOWERS......    6.50
NIPPON TRAY,PIN,HANDPAINTED,6 IN.............................    4.00
NIPPON TRAY,PIN,HANDPAINTED SCENE SAIL BOAT IN SUNSET........    2.50
NIPPON TRAY,RELISH,MARKED,HANDPAINTED PERSIMMON FLOWERED
   BORDER & GOLD..............................................    7.50
NIPPON VASE,2 HANDLED........................................   27.50
NIPPON VASE,7 IN. HANDLE EACH SIDE,ORANGE,BLUE..............    15.00
NIPPON VASE,7 IN.,HANDPAINTED FLOWERS,HANDLED................    5.00
NIPPON VASE,7 IN.,HANDPAINTED,HANDLED.......................    10.50
NIPPON VASE,8 IN.,SQUARE,HANDPAINTED HOLLAND SCENES.........     8.00
NIPPON VASE,11 IN.,2 HANDLED,LAVENDER,GREEN,ORANGE & GOLD...    25.00
NIPPON VASE,BUD,3 IN.,HANDPAINTED...........................     3.00
NIPPON VASE,BUD,5 IN.,HANDLED,HANDPAINTED SWAN ON LAKE......     5.50
NIPPON VASE,EWER SHAPED,2 HANDLED,YELLOW WITH PURPLE FLOWERS    10.00
NIPPON VASE,HANDPAINTED,5 IN................................     3.00
NIPPON VASE,HANDPAINTED ORCHID SPRAY DECOR,10 IN............    10.00
NIPPON VASE,HANDPAINTED PASTEL ROSES WITH GOLD LEAVES.......    10.00
NIPPON VASE,HANDPAINTED SAILBOAT,GREEN & FUCHSIA............     2.25
NIPPON VASE,MARKED,6 HANDPAINTED PANELS,GOLD................    16.00
NIPPON VASE MARKED DOW SIE CO URE NIPPON,PINK & ORCHID
   LUSTRE..................................................      12.00
NIPPON VASE,MARKED,HANDPAINTED MORNING GLORIES & GOLD,9 IN..    15.00
NIPPON VASE,PAIR 9 IN.,HANDPAINTED GREEN REEDS & WATER......    28.00
NIPPON VASE,SQUARE,4 HANDLED,SCENERY DECOR..................     6.00
NIPPON VASE,URN,HANDPAINTED FLORAL BOUQUET,FLUTED,GOLD RIM..     6.00
NIPPON VASE WITH FLORAL & GOLD DECORATION...................    12.50
NIPPON VASE WITH SCENIC DECORATION..........................    12.50
```

NODDERS or nodding figures or pagods are porcelain figures with heads and hands that are attached to wires. Any slight movement causes the parts to move up and down. Examples were made in many countries during the eighteenth and nineteenth centuries.

```
NODDER,BANK,POTTERY FIGURE,FOR OUR MISSION..................    75.00
NODDER,BLUE MAN.............................................    21.75
NODDER,CHELSEA,CHILD........................................    36.00
NODDER,CHELSEA,3 IN.........................................    69.50
NODDER,CHINESE COOLIE BOY,SEATED,3 IN. TALL.................    15.00
NODDER,INKWELL,ROUND PIECE OF GLASS LEAVES & FLOWERS........    18.00
NODDER,LADY IN ENGLISH CHINA,BLUE & WHITE...................    22.00
NODDER,LEAD,MINSTRELS.......................................    45.00
NODDER,MANDARIN,CHINA WITH GLASSES..........................    32.00
NODDER,ORIENTAL GENTLEMAN,IMPRESSED ORIENTAL MARKINGS IN
   BASE....................................................     35.00
```

NORITAKE-MARKED PORCELAIN was made in Japan after 1904 by Nippon Toki Kaisha.

```
NORITAKE 12 PLACE SETTING,72 PIECES,AZALEA..................   250.00
NORITAKE BOTTLE,PERFUME,HANDPAINTED BIRD,WHITE FLOWERS,GOLD.     3.50
NORITAKE BOWL,BERRY,OPEN HANDLES,AZALEA PATTERN.............     6.50
NORITAKE BOWL,HANDPAINTED POPPIES..........................     10.00
NORITAKE BOWL,NUT DECOR,ORANGE LINING......................     30.00
NORITAKE BOWL,NUT,PAIR,PINK WILD ROSE CENTER...............      8.00
NORITAKE BOWL,ROUND ON PEDESTAL,HANDPAINTED RED & YELLOW
   ROSES...................................................      6.00
NORITAKE BOWL,SIGNED,6 IN.,FLOWERED........................      4.50
NORITAKE BOWL,WREATH WITH M,GOLD BORDER,STEM,TOP IN INSIDE
   COBALT..................................................      5.00
NORITAKE BUTTER TUB,AZALEA.................................      6.50
NORITAKE CANDY WITH PINK ROSES,5 IN........................      2.50
NORITAKE CELERY & 6 SALT DIPS..............................     10.50
NORITAKE CHOCOLATE POT,PINK FLOWERS........................      8.00
```

```
NORITAKE COMPOTE,JELLY,OPEN,AZALEA,RED MARK,MELON
  RIBBED,FOOTED..................................................   9.00
NORITAKE CONDIMENT SET,AZALEA.....................................   7.50
NORITAKE CREAM & SUGAR,COBALT BLUE & ROSES....................... 10.00
NORITAKE CREAMER & SUGAR,AZALEA.................................. 14.50
NORITAKE CREAMER & SUGAR IN CELTIC PATTERN......................   8.00
NORITAKE CUP & 5 SAUCERS,AZALEA,................................   5.00
NORITAKE CUP & SAUCER,AZALEA....................................   6.50
NORITAKE CUP & SAUCER,LUZON.....................................   3.50
NORITAKE CUP & SAUCER,REGINA...................................   3.00
NORITAKE CUP & SAUCER,SET OF 5,WHITE WITH GOLD LINE.......... 20.00
NORITAKE CUP,CYRIL PATTERN......................................   1.50
NORITAKE DESSERT SET,HANDPAINTED FLORAL IN WHITE,GOLD RIM,5
  PIECES...................................................... 10.50
NORITAKE DISH,BUTTER,COVERED,AZALEA............................ 15.00
NORITAKE DISH,CELERY,AZALEA....................................   4.00
NORITAKE DISH,SAUCE,AZALEA,5 IN................................   4.00
NORITAKE DISH,VEGETABLE,COVERED,AZALEA........................ 10.50
NORITAKE EGG CUP,RED MARK,AZALEA...............................   4.00
NORITAKE JAR,CANDY,LOTUS BUD LID,HANDPAINTED................. 10.00
NORITAKE MAYONNAISE SET,3 PIECES,AZALEA
  5.50  TO................................................... 12.00
NORITAKE MUSTARD,LADLE,GOLD DESIGN............................   5.00
NORITAKE PLATE,AZALEA,7 IN....................................   5.50
NORITAKE PLATE,AZALEA,10 IN...................................   6.50
NORITAKE PLATE,CAKE,FLORAL PATTERN,10 IN.,& 4 6 IN. PLATES.. 15.00
NORITAKE PLATE,CAKE,HANDLED...................................   1.00
NORITAKE PLATE,PIE,CHELSEA....................................   2.50
NORITAKE PLATE,PIE,LUZON......................................   2.50
NORITAKE SALT & PEPPER & COVERED MUSTARD &
  SPOON,AZALEA,GREEN MARK..................................... 12.00
NORITAKE SOUP PLATE,AZALEA.................................... 24.00
NORITAKE SPOONER,............................................   5.00
NORITAKE SUGAR & CREAMER,AZALEA
  6.50  TO................................................... 15.00
NORITAKE SUGAR BOWL,AZALEA....................................   4.50
NORITAKE SUGAR,COVERED,SUPERBA................................   4.00
NORITAKE TEA PLATE,6,GREEN BORDER WITH LEAVES & FLORAL
  DESIGN.....................................................   5.00
NORITAKE TEAPOT,3 CUP SIZE,GOLDENA............................   6.00
NORITAKE TEAPOT,CREAMER & SUGAR,GOLD & ENAMELED JEWELED DOTS 25.00
NORITAKE TEA SERVICE,22 PIECES,MOSS ROSE...................... 42.00
NORITAKE TEA SET,CHILDS,21 PIECES............................. 25.00
NORITAKE TEA SET,TRI-FOOTED,MELON RIBBED...................... 19.00
NORITAKE TOOTHPICK,HANDPAINTED BLUE FLOWERS...................   7.50
NORITAKE TUREEN,LAUREATE......................................   6.00
NORITAKE TUREEN,SOUP,MELSUKUA PATTERN,GOLD HANDLES & FINIAL. 15.00
NORITAKE VASE,AZALEA,FAN SHAPED,RED MARK......................   9.00
NORITAKE VASE,HANDPAINTED,8 IN................................   8.00
```

NORTHWOOD GLASS COMPANY worked in Martins Ferry, Ohio, from 1888.
They marked some pieces with the letter N in a circle. Many pieces of carnival
glass were made by this company.

```
    NORTHWOOD, SEE ALSO CARNIVAL....................................
NORTHWOOD BLUE OPALESCENT GLASS GOLD TRIM 4 PIECE TABLE
  SET,SIGNED................................................... 85.00
NORTHWOOD BLUE OPALESCENT 7 PIECE BERRY SET,GOLD TRIM,MARKED 58.00
NORTHWOOD BLUE & OPALESCENT DRAPE CREAMER.................... 18.50
NORTHWOOD BOWL,6 IN.,SHELLS & WILD ROSE,GREEN,FOOTED........ 18.00
NORTHWOOD CAKE STAND,BLUE,DAISY WITH CROSSBAR & THUMBPRINTS. 30.00
NORTHWOOD CARNIVAL PEACOCK AT FOUNTAIN WATER
  PITCHER,MARIGOLD............................................ 65.00
NORTHWOOD CLEAR TO OPALESCENT BUTTER DISH,SPOONER & CREAMER. 52.00
NORTHWOOD CLEAR TO OPALESCENT DIAMOND QUILTED VASE.......... 20.00
NORTHWOOD CLEAR POPPY TUMBLER............................... 10.00
```

```
NORTHWOOD CORN BOTTLE,GREEN...................................    30.00
NORTHWOOD DIAMOND POINT VASE,MARKED,12 POINTED FLAME TOP....      12.00
NORTHWOOD DRAPE,CLEAR TO OPAL WITH GOLD SPOONER..............      18.00
NORTHWOOD FLUTED GREEN BOWL WITH ORANGE,LEAF & BALL PATTERN.      15.00
NORTHWOOD GRAPE & CABLE BROWN TRIM CREAM PITCHER............      38.00
NORTHWOOD GRAPE & CABLE BROWN TRIM SUGAR BOWL...............      35.00
NORTHWOOD GRAPE GREEN SPOONER...............................      35.00
NORTHWOOD GRAPE & CABLE OPEN SUGAR,NUTMEG BROWN.............      38.50
NORTHWOOD GRAPE COMPOTE,MARIGOLD WITH ROSY IRIDESCENCE......      15.00
NORTHWOOD GRAPES ORANGE TUMBLER.............................       6.50
NORTHWOOD GRAPE PURPLE PUNCH CUP............................      12.50
NORTHWOOD GREEN 2 HANDLED BASKET............................      35.00
NORTHWOOD GREEN & GOLD GRAPES & GOTHIC ARCH CREAMER.........       7.00
NORTHWOOD GREEN CHERRY WATER PITCHER........................      95.00
NORTHWOOD GREEN GOTHIC GRAPE WITH GOLD DECORATION SUGAR &
    CREAMER.................................................      20.00
NORTHWOOD GREEN PEACH WITH GOLD SUGAR BASE..................      12.50
NORTHWOOD GREEN SUNFLOWER PLATE,8 IN. DIAMETER..............       8.50
NORTHWOOD IMPERIAL 10 IN. BOWL..............................      25.00
NORTHWOOD MAPLE LEAF OPALESCENT TO BLUE OPEN JELLY COMPOTE..      12.50
NORTHWOOD MARIGOLD PEACOCK AT FOUNTAIN PUNCH VASE...........      14.00
NORTHWOOD MARKED EMERALD GREEN GLASS PEACH BERRY BOWL & 4
    SAUCES..................................................      42.50
NORTHWOOD MARKED BOWL,FLOWER PATTERN........................       7.00
NORTHWOOD MARKED GREEN FOOTED CANDY COMPOTE,FLOWER PATTERN..      10.75
NORTHWOOD MARKED GRAPE PATTERN TUMBLER,PURPLE...............      15.00
NORTHWOOD MARKED ROSE BOWL,DAISY & PLUME,CRIMPED TOP,BRONZE
    IRIDESCENT..............................................      32.50
NORTHWOOD MARKED SET,CREAMER,COVERED SUGAR,COVERED BUTTER &
    SPOONER.................................................      58.00
NORTHWOOD MARKED SILVER GREEN VASE,SWIRLED RIBBED,& POINT
    TOP.....................................................      15.00
NORTHWOOD MARKED TREE TRUNK VASE,RAISED BARK BURRS,MARIGOLD
    TOP.....................................................      18.00
NORTHWOOD MARKED WHITE VASE,RAINBOW IRIDESCENT,RIBBED &
    FLUTED..................................................      40.00
NORTHWOOD OVOID ROSE BOWL,CHARTREUSE LOOPINGS ON FROSTED....      65.00
NORTHWOOD PAIR VASES,MARKED,4 FOOTED METAL BASES,GREEN
    BRONZE..................................................      35.00
NORTHWOOD PANEL CHERRY 9 IN. BERRY BOWL.....................       8.50
NORTHWOOD PANELLED CHERRY PITCHER & 4 TUMBLERS..............      60.00
NORTHWOOD PANELED CHERRY 7 PIECE BERRY SET,.................      28.50
NORTHWOOD PEACH,GREEN COVERED BUTTER,PANELLED & SCALLOPED
    GOLD SIGNED.............................................      37.50
NORTHWOOD PEACH TUMBLER,GOLD FRUIT,CABLE BANDS..............      15.00
NORTHWOOD PURPLE 3 FOOTED BLACKBERRY 8 IN. COMPOTE,DAISY &
    PLUME OUTER.............................................      25.00
NORTHWOOD PURPLE GRAPE & CABLE HATPIN HOLDER................      10.00
NORTHWOOD ROYAL PURPLE-BLUE VASE,DIAMOND POINT,SCALLOPED 12
    POINT TOP...............................................      12.00
NORTHWOOD RUBY & GOLD GOBLET................................       6.50
NORTHWOOD SIGNED 4 IN. HIGH COMPOTE ON 3 IN. FOOTED BASE....      48.00
NORTHWOOD SIGNED BUTTER DISH,GREEN WITH GOLD PANELLED CHERRY      25.00
NORTHWOOD SIGNED CREAMER....................................      55.00
NORTHWOOD SIGNED CREAMER,GREEN WITH GOLD PANELLED CHERRY....      20.00
NORTHWOOD SIGNED GREEN & GOLD BERRY DISH....................       6.00
NORTHWOOD SIGNED SUGAR,GREEN WITH GOLD PANELLED CHERRY......      20.00
NORTHWOOD SIGNED SPOONER....................................      55.00
NORTHWOOD SIGNED TOOTHPICK HOLDER...........................      45.00
NORTHWOOD SIGNED WATER PITCHER,GREEN WITH GOLD PANELLED
    CHERRY..................................................      22.00
NORTHWOOD SINGING BIRD MUG IN PURPLE GLASS,FOOTED...........      18.50
NORTHWOOD STIPPLED SUNFLOWER 7 IN. BOWL & 6 SAUCES..........      23.50
NORTHWOOD STRAWBERRY SAUCE,CLEAR WITH RED BERRY,GOLD BAND...       5.00
NORTHWOOD STRAWBERRY CREAMER,CLEAR,COLOURED FRUIT WITH GOLD.      15.00
```

NORTHWOOD TUMBLER,BLUE DIAMOND QUILTED,OPALESCENT EDGE......	.15.00
NORTHWOOD WATER PITCHER,CRYSTAL,RED FRUIT,GOLD TRIM,CHERRY LATTICE...	25.00
NORTHWOOD WATER SET,PITCHER & 6 GLASSES,GRAPE & GOTHIC ARCHES..	165.00
NORTHWOOD WHITE BASKET......................................	37.50
NORTHWOOD WHITE OPALESCENT BERRY SET GOLD TRIM,MARKED.......	48.00
NORTHWOOD WHITE OPALESCENT GOLD TRIM 4 PIECE SET SIGNED.....	58.00
NORTHWOOD WHITE OPALESCENT PANELLED HOLLY COVERED SUGAR.....	22.50
NORTHWOOD WHITE OPALESCENT PUMP & TROUGH...................	55.00
NORTHWOOD WILD ROSE PATTERN TRI-FOOTED BOWL IN GREEN IRIDESENCE..	15.00
NOTTINGHAM POTTERY CAT,CIRCA 1810,11 IN. HIGH...............	190.00
NUART BLUE IRIDESCENT BOWL.................................	24.50
NUART SIGNED WHITE IRIDESCENT SHADE........................	7.50
OBERT PAIR SIGNED FRENCH MARK 8 IN. PLATES..................	7.00
OCCUPATIONAL SHAVING MUGS, SEE SHAVING MUGS.............	
OLD IVORY BERRY SET NO. 28,10 IN. BOWL & 6 SAUCES..........	55.00
OLD IVORY BERRY SET,7 PIECES..............................	40.00
OLD IVORY BOWL..	16.00
OLD IVORY BOWL,MARKED,PINK ROSES..........................	12.00
OLD IVORY CAKE DISH,OPEN HANDLE...........................	22.00
OLD IVORY CAKE PLATE,OPEN HANDLE..........................	18.00
OLD IVORY CAKE PLATE,OPEN HANDLES.........................	14.00
OLD IVORY CELERY,FLAT,ROSES...............................	15.00
OLD IVORY COFFEE POT,VIII.................................	38.50
OLD IVORY CREAMER...	15.00
OLD IVORY CUP & SAUCER,NO. 202,POPPY PATTERN..............	12.50
OLD IVORY DISH,CANDY,HANDLED,SILESIA......................	15.00
OLD IVORY PLATE,8 IN. SCROLLED RIM........................	8.00
OLD IVORY PLATE,PAIR ORIENTAL BIRD........................	7.50
OLD IVORY PLATE,ROSE PATTERN..............................	10.00
OLD IVORY SALT & PEPPER SHAKER,PAIR.......................	17.50
OLD IVORY SUGAR BOWL......................................	27.50
OLD IVORY SUGAR,COVERED...................................	12.50
OLD IVORY SUGAR BOWL,COVERED & CREAMER MARKED CROWN & SILESIA...	37.50
ONION BOWL,10 IN.,IMPERIAL,BLUE...........................	14.00
ONION 12 PIECES,BLUE,MEISSEN..............................	350.00
ONION BOWL,BLUE MEISSEN MARKED & IMPRESSED,8 IN. SQUARE.....	25.00
ONION BOWL,SET OF 4 NESTED................................	15.00
ONION BREAD BOARD,GERMAN SAYINGS,FOR HANGING..............	12.50
ONION BUTTER DISH,MEISSEN CROSSED SWORD MARK,COVERED.......	37.50
ONION CANDLE HOLDER,MEISSEN...............................	12.00
ONION CHEESE BOARD,HOLE FOR HANGING,GERMAN SAYING.........	12.00
ONION CONDIMENT SET,3 PIECE,..............................	9.00
ONION CREAM PITCHER,SIGNED COULDON ENGLAND................	17.50
ONION EGG CUP,BLUE,SET OF 4...............................	17.50
ONION EGG CUP,DOUBLE,BLUE.................................	7.00
ONION GRAVY DISH WITH ATTACHED TRAY,MEISSEN MARKED,LOOP HANDLES..	30.00
ONION INVALID FEEDER,BLUE.................................	12.50
ONION KITCHEN UTENSIL HOLDER,BLUE,PLACE FOR 10 PIECES WITH 5 UTENSILS...	87.50
ONION MUSTARD JAR,BLUE,SPOON..............................	12.75
ONION NAPKIN RING,BLUE PATTERN............................	22.50
ONION PLATE,BLUE,7 IN.,MARK MADE IN ENGLAND & ONION........	7.50
ONION PLATE,BLUE,9 IN.....................................	12.50
ONION PLATE,BLUE,9 IN.,GERMAN.............................	6.00
ONION PLATE,CAKE ON STANDARD,10 IN.,MEISSEN...............	32.50
ONION PLATE,STAFFORDSHIRE,9 IN.,REGISTERED & NUMBERED.......	6.50
ONION PLATTER,BLUE,MARKED CROWN ALLERTONS.................	15.00
ONION PLATTER,BLUE MEISSEN GERMANY,TREE & WELL,17 X 11 IN...	45.00
ONION PLATTER,MEISSEN BLUE,23 X 17 IN.,CROSSED SWORDS MARK..	85.00

```
ONION  PLATTER,MEISSEN  BLUE,CROSS  SWORDS  UNDERGLAZE..........    85.00
ONION  RAMEKIN,2  PIECE,BLUE,DRESDEN  MADE  IN  GERMANY...........     9.50
ONION  ROLLING  PIN,BLUE..........................................    28.00
ONION  SET  OF  12  PIECES,BLUE  MEISSEN,LACY....................   350.00
ONION  SHELF,WALL,BLUE,12  HOLES  FOR  SPOONS....................    12.00
ONION  SPOON,9  IN...............................................     9.00
ONION  SPOON,STRAINER  WITH  WOODEN  HANDLE.......................    14.00
ONION  STRAINER,CONE  SHAPED.....................................    12.00
ONION  TEAPOT,SUGAR  &  CREAMER,ROSE  FINIALS,BAVARIA............    30.00
ONION  TEA  SET,CHILDS,15  PIECE.................................    36.00
ONION  TUREEN,BLUE,2  QUART  SIZE................................    35.00
ONIONSKIN  BOWL,IRIDESCENT  BLUE,10  IN.  DIAMETER...............    30.00
ONIONSKIN  PLATE,GREEN  IRIDESCENT,14  IN.......................    38.00
```

OPALESCENT GLASS is transluscent glass that has the bluish-white tones of the opal gemstone. It is often found in pressed glasswares made in Victorian times. (Some dealers use the terms opaline and opalescent for any of the bluish-white translucent wares.)

```
OPALESCENT  BLUE  GLASS  TOOTHPICK  HOLDER........................     8.00
OPALESCENT  BULBOUS  GREEN  COIN  SPOT  PERFUME,DE  VILBISS.......     6.50
OPALESCENT  INVERTED  HOBNAIL,SWIRL  SYRUP  PITCHER,BRASS
  TOP,DATED  1881................................................    35.00
OPALESCENT  SPOT  WATER  PITCHER,RUFFLED  TOP,CLEAR  APPLIED
  HANDLE........................................................    22.00
OPALESCENT  STRIPED  BLUE  BARBER  BOTTLE........................    25.00
OPALESCENT  SWIRL  GLASS  LAMP  GLOBE............................    12.50
OPALESCENT  WHITE  GLASS  14  IN.  TALL  VASE,GOLD  FILIGREE.......   165.00
```

OPALINE GLASS or opal glass was made in white, apple green, and other colors. The glass had a matte surface and a lack of transparency. It was often gilded or painted. It was a popular mid-nineteenth-century European glassware.

```
OPALINE  BLUE  OPAQUE  COLOGNE  BOTTLE,GOLD  ACCENTS.............    25.00
OPALINE  CARD  DISH,MADE  IN  FRANCE,GIRL  PLAYING  MANDOLIN  &
  SUITOR........................................................    70.00
OPALINE  GREEN  FOOTED  COMPOTE.................................     8.50
OPALINE  GREEN  PERFUME  WITH  WHITE  SAUCER  BASE  FOR  RINGS,GOLD
  TRIMMED.......................................................    27.50
OPALINE  GREEN  VASE,TULIP  SHAPE,KNOP  CENTER,GOLD,10  IN.  HIGH.    38.00
OPALINE  MAUVE  TUMBLER  WITH  WHITE  &  GOLD  ENAMELED  FLOWERS....    18.50
OPALINE  PAIR  FROSTED  WHITE  WITH  DECORATION  COLOGNE  BOTTLES..    45.00
OPALINE  PINK  PAIR  VASES,MEDALLIONS  OF  CHILDREN  IN  GRASS.....    85.00
OPALINE  PINK  RIBBED  TUMBLER.................................    15.00
OPALINE  PINK  VASE,ENAMEL  MEDALLIONS,YELLOW,BLUE&WHITE  BANDED
  IN  GOLD......................................................    37.50
OPALINE  PINK  8  IN.  TALL  VASE,2  APPLIED  WHITE  FLOWERS,AMBER
  EDGE..........................................................    50.00
OPALINE  PLATE,8  IN.,SPEAR  PATTERN............................     4.50
OPALINE  ROSE  BOWL,ROSE  LINED,YELLOW  AMBER...................    35.00
OPALINE  ROSE  VASE  9  IN.  ,  APPLIED  FLOWERS.................    60.00
OPALINE  WHITE  PAIR  6  IN.  PERFUME  BOTTLES  &  STOPPERS,RAISED
  FLOWERS.......................................................    40.00
OPERA  GLASSES  IN  CASE........................................    13.00
OPERA  GLASSES,IVORY  FRENCH  TRIM  SIGNED  BREVET...............     5.00
OPERA  GLASSES,LEMAIRE  PARIS,TRIMMED  WITH  PEARL..............     8.00
OPERA  GLASSES,MOTHER  OF  PEARL  MARKED  PANELED,RAIMOND  PARIS..    15.00
OPERA  GLASSES  WITH  LEATHER  CASE.............................    15.00
ORIENTAL  RUG  SADDLE  BAG......................................   135.00
OVERSHOT  7  IN.  TALL  AZURE  PITCHER,REEDED  AMBER  HANDLE.......    95.00
```

OWENS POTTERY was made in Zanesville, Ohio, from 1891 to 1928. Art pottery, Henri Deux ware, Feroza wares, and others were also made there.

```
OWENS  MARKED  HANDLED  JUG,BROWN  GLAZE  WITH  CORN  DECOR........    19.50
OWENS  UTOPIAN  ART  POTTERY  VASE,ORANGE  FLOWER  &  GREEN  LEAF  ON
  BROWN.........................................................    14.00
OWENS  UTOPIAN  VASE,YELLOW  POINSETTIA.........................    18.50
```

```
PAINTING,18TH CENTURY ENGLISH OF DEER HUNT,GOLD LEAF
  FRAME,CIRCA 1730......................................    820.00
PAINTING,AMERICAN SHIP,OIL ON CANVAS,SIGNED J H PUGH 1850...  450.00
PAINTING,CHINESE VELVET TEXTURE RICE PAPER PAINTING WITH
  BLACK FRAME........................................... 32.00
PAINTING,DECORATION DAY BY B F REINHART,CIVIL WAR
  WIDOW,FRAMES..........................................    425.00
PAINTING,FRAMED CAT BOAT RACING OFF ANNAPOLIS CIRCA 1850....1,100.00
PAINTING,FRAMED OIL ON FABRIC CIRCA 1830,GEORGE WASHINGTON..3,500.00
PAINTING,FRAMED VIEW OF BOCA TIGRIS AT MOUTH OF CANTON RIVER
  CIRCA 1840............................................    650.00
PAINTING,GROOM WITH 2 HORSES,CHARLES TOWN 1763-1840,OIL ON
  CANVAS...............................................2,750.00
PAINTING,LION,20 X 25 IN.,OIL PORTRAIT CIRCA 1885 SIGNED
  J.WALKER..............................................     65.00
PAINTING,OIL,HEAD & SHOULDERS OF BABY,AMERICAN.............    225.00
PAINTING,OIL,LOOKING DOWN BLACK RIVER FROM BEEBES ISLAND
  1874..................................................    250.00
PAINTING,OIL,MOUNTAINS,TREES & BROOK,GOLD FRAME............      6.00
PAINTING,OIL ON CANVAS,AMERICAN INDIAN ENCAMPMENT SCENE.....   600.00
PAINTING,OIL ON CANVAS,COW & CALF GRAZING..................     18.50
PAINTING,OIL ON CANVAS,FRAMES,BOY IN RED COAT,SIGNED PONTARY   450.00
PAINTING,OIL PANSIES,36 X 8 IN.,FRAMED....................     15.00
PAINTING,OIL,SIGNED RAUGHTMAKER,APPLE,16 X 24 IN.,CIRCA 1885   30.00
PAINTING,OIL,WINDING MOUNTAIN STREAM DATED 1933.............     5.00
PAINTING ON VELVET,MEMORIAL,GOLD LEAF FRAME................    250.00
PAINTING,ON WOOD,FRUITS,VEGETABLES........................     23.00
PAINTINGS,PAIR ANCESTOR,4 IN. GOLD FRAME,MAN & WOMAN,.......   225.00
PAINTING,PAIR DUTCH REVERSE OIL ON GLASS CIRCA 1635.........   250.00
PAINTING,PORCELAIN MADONNA,OVAL IN VELVET FRAME............     34.50
PAINTING,PORTRAIT IN OIL ON CANVAS BY P PAILLOU 1810,GEORGE
  CHALMERS..............................................    630.00
PAINTING,PORTRAIT OF BOY,NORTHCOTE CIRCA 1790,FRAMED........1,300.00
PAINTING,PORTRAIT OF GENTLEMAN WITH BLUE COAT,GILT FRAME
  CIRCA 1775............................................    635.00
PAINTING,REVERSE ON GLASS,STEAM SHIPS & SAILBOATS ON OCEAN
  SIGNED HAIRE..........................................     52.00
PAINTING,RUSSIAN WOLF HUNT,BY F S LISCHENWITZ 1857..........   400.00
PAINTING,PORTRAIT SEA CAPTAIN.............................    550.00
PAINTING,,SAND,CARRISBROOKE CASTLE SIGNED 1884 AT NEWPORT...   100.00
PAINTING,STILL LIFE CIRCA 1840,FRUIT,NORTH SHORE OF
  MASSACHUSETTS.........................................    550.00
PAINTING,THEOREM,OILS ON VELVET,PANSY DESIGN IN GOLD FRAME..    14.75
PAINTING,WILLIAM POPE STILL LIFE WATERCOLOR SIGNED 1826.....   210.00
```

PAIRPOINT CORPORATION was a silver and glass firm founded in New Bedford, Massachusetts, in 1880.

```
PAIRPOINT 5 FLOWER DATED PAPERWEIGHT.......................    18.00
PAIRPOINT AMBER BOWL WITH DIAMOND POINT BAND...............    20.00
PAIRPOINT AMBER WINE......................................      6.50
PAIRPOINT AMETHYST BUD VASE...............................     18.50
PAIRPOINT,AMETHYST CANDLE HOLDER,POLISHED PONTIL...........    45.00
PAIRPOINT AMETHYST FINGER BOWL,FLINT GLASS BELLTONE........    24.00
PAIRPOINT BRIDES BOWL BASKET HOLDER WITH NUT & LEAF........    21.50
PAIRPOINT BRONZE LIZARD PAPERWEIGHT,TEARDROP PATTERN........   145.00
PAIRPOINT BUD VASE,PAPERWEIGHT BASE.......................      6.50
PAIRPOINT CANDY COMPOTE IN GREEN WITH PEDESTAL ,ETCHED
  FLORAL DESIGN.........................................     48.00
PAIRPOINT COPPER-WHEEL BUTTERFLY CUT RUFFLED EDGE FINGER
  BOWL .................................................      8.00
PAIRPOINT CRANBERRY 6 IN. VASE...........................     18.00
PAIRPOINT CRYSTAL CORNUCOPIA VASE,PEDESTAL BASE............    22.50
PAIRPOINT CUP & SAUCER ENGRAVED LIGHTHOUSE................     15.00
PAIRPOINT DATED BUTTERFLY PAPERWEIGHT.....................    20.00
PAIRPOINT GLASS BASKET,ETCHED FLOWERS,BUDS,LEAVES &
```

```
TENDRILS,.............................................  18.00
PAIRPOINT MARKED PICKLE CASTOR FRAME...................   3.50
PAIRPOINT MARKED COVERED VEGETABLE SILVER PLATE HANDLED DISH  12.50
PAIRPOINT PAIR CRANBERRY CANDLESTICKS,CLEAR TWISTED STEMS &
BASES.................................................  95.00
PAIRPOINT PAPERWEIGHT,DIAMOND CUT FACETED MUSHROOM STOPPER..  72.00
PAIRPOINT RED HAT TOOTHPICK HOLDER WITH LABEL 1861...........  22.00
PAIRPOINT RED VASE....................................   9.00
PAIRPOINT RUBY CREAMER& COVERED SUGAR,COPPER WHEEL ENGRAVED.  38.00
PAIRPOINT RUBY SWAN CANDY DISH WITH CLEAR CRYSTAL NECK HEAD.  48.00
PAIRPOINT RUBY MASTER SALT,CLOVERLEAF DESIGN SIGNED.........  17.50
PAIRPOINT STICK VASE WITH PAPER WEIGHT BASE,BLUE...........  18.00
PAIRPOINT VASE,FLARED RIM..............................  65.00
PAIRPOINT VASE,SIGNED SPOONER..........................  65.00
     PAISLEY SHAWL, SEE LINEN.........................
PANTIN FRANCE SIGNED 5 IN. VASE,IRIDESCENT,GOLD,LILAC,BLUE..  145.00
PAPER DOLL & CLOTHES,DARLING MARGERY,RAPHAEL TUCK,1894......   6.00
PAPER DOLL,NEGRO,SATIN DRESS & SASH,IN PICTURE FRAME........   6.00
PAPER DOLLS, PAGE OF FROM OLD MAGAZINE.....................   1.50
     PAPERWEIGHT, SEE ALSO BACCARAT....................
PAPERWEIGHT,6 FACETED WITH MILLEFIORI MUSHROOM.............  13.00
PAPERWEIGHT ADVERTISING,RECTANGULAR,RED,BLACK,GOLD,FIELD
WOOD WORKING..........................................   4.75
PAPERWEIGHT,AMBER WITH GREEN POLKA DOTS....................   8.50
PAPERWEIGHT,AMERICAN LOCOMOTIVE CO.,SILVER PLATED,ENGINE &
COAL CAR..............................................  18.00
PAPERWEIGHT,A MERRY CHRISTMAS..........................  15.00
PAPERWEIGHT APPLE SIGNED ZIMMERMAN.....................  10.50
PAPERWEIGHT,AUTO RADIATOR MASCOT,MOUNTED ON OAK
BASE,FRANKLIN LION....................................  12.50
PAPERWEIGHT,AUTO RADIATOR MASCOT,MOUNTED ON OAK BASE,ISOTTA
COBRA.................................................  25.00
PAPERWEIGHT,AUTO RADIATOR MASCOT,MOUNTED ON OAK BASE,MINERVA
KNIGHT................................................  20.00
PAPERWEIGHT,AUTO RADIATOR MASCOT,MOUNTED ON OAK BASE,ROLLS
ROYCE LADY............................................  20.00
PAPERWEIGHT,AUTO RADIATOR MASCOT,MOUNTED ON OAK BASE,STUTZ..  15.00
PAPERWEIGHT,BACCARAT BLUE POINSETTIA,RED JASPER GROUND......  375.00
PAPERWEIGHT,BACCARAT CLOSE MILLEFIORI ON LATTICINIO.........  238.00
PAPERWEIGHT,BACCARAT CONCENTRIC MILLEFIORI,2 ALTERNATION
CIRCLES...............................................  88.00
PAPERWEIGHT,BACCARAT CONCENTRIC MILLEFIORI ARROWS,FACETED...  145.00
PAPERWEIGHT,BACCARAT,DAHLIA............................  150.00
PAPERWEIGHT,BACCARAT FACETED CHRISTMAS BROKEN CANDY CANE
MACEDOINE.............................................  24.00
PAPERWEIGHT,BACCARAT,J.F.K.............................  200.00
PAPERWEIGHT,BACCARAT,KENNEDY...........................  225.00
PAPERWEIGHT,BACCARAT,LEE ,COBALT & CLEAR WAFFLE BASE........  120.00
PAPERWEIGHT,BACCARAT PANSY,STAR CUT BASE...................  168.00
PAPERWEIGHT,BACCARAT POPE JOHN.........................  95.00
PAPERWEIGHT,BACCARAT,POPE JOHN,YELLOW BASE.................  100.00
PAPERWEIGHT,BACCARAT PANSY,STAR CUT BASE...................  200.00
PAPERWEIGHT,BACCARAT,ZODIAC WITH COBALT BASE,STATE SIGN.....  47.50
PAPERWEIGHT,BABY CHICK,GREEN CENTER....................   9.50
PAPER WEIGHT,BALL SHAPED BLOWN GLASS WITH COLORED GLASS
STONES................................................  15.00
PAPERWEIGHT BELL SIGNED ST.CLAIR.......................  10.50
PAPERWEIGHT,BLOWN GLASS,GOLD STONES OVER COLOURED STONES....  25.00
PAPERWEIGHT,BLOWN YELLOW & RED APPLE...................  12.00
PAPERWEIGHT BLUE ERICSON VASE,CLEAR 3 FOLD TOP.............  12.50
PAPERWEIGHT,BLUE GLASS,MULTI-COLOURED BASE.................  25.00
PAPERWEIGHT,BRASS ALLIGATOR............................   6.00
PAPERWEIGHT,BRISTOL WITH STAND,BLOWN MULTI-COLOURED FLOWERS.  125.00
PAPERWEIGHT,BUBBLE,NEBRASKA CENTENNIAL.....................  10.00
PAPERWEIGHT,BUBBLY RED & WHITE.........................   5.00
```

```
PAPERWEIGHT,BULBOUS GLASS,WHITE GLASS BLANKET WITH PURPLE
  LETTERS...............................................    45.00
PAPERWEIGHT,BUST OF M.S.OWENS DATED,LIBBEY GLASS............    35.00
PAPERWEIGHT BUTTON,CAPRICORN...............................     9.50
PAPERWEIGHT BUTTON,DOG.....................................     9.50
PAPERWEIGHT BUTTON,HORSEHEAD WITH BRIDLE...................     9.50
PAPERWEIGHT BUTTON,ZODIAC OF THE GOAT......................     9.50
PAPERWEIGHT,CAMEO SULPHIDE,CHRISTOPHER COLUMBUS............    55.00
PAPERWEIGHT,CAMEO SULPHIDE,FRANKLIN D ROOSEVELT............    55.00
PAPERWEIGHT,CAMPHOR GLASS HAND HOLDING CLEAR ,TORTOISE
  INSIDE..................................................    18.00
PAPERWEIGHT CENTENNIAL INTERNATIONAL,PHILADELPHIA,1776-1886.   15.00
PAPERWEIGHT,CHRISTOPHER COLUMBUS...........................    55.00
PAPERWEIGHT,CIGAR STORE,3 IRON CIGARS......................     7.50
PAPERWEIGHT,CIVIL WAR CENTENNIAL 1861-1865.................    18.00
PAPERWEIGHT,CLAMBROTH HORSESHOE DESK,FLUTED BASE,GOOD
  LUCK,JUSTICE............................................    17.50
PAPERWEIGHT,CLEAR FROSTED BOTTOM,28TH NAT,G.A.R.ENCAMPMENT
  1894....................................................    20.00
PAPERWEIGHT,CLEAR GLASS BATTLESHIP MAINE...................     3.75
PAPERWEIGHT CLEAR GLASS,MACKEREL CAVE,BAILEYS ISLAND,MAINE..     2.95
PAPERWEIGHT,CLEAR GLASS,TEMPLE OF MUSIC,PAN AMERICAN
  EXPOSITION 1901.........................................     2.95
PAPERWEIGHT,CLEAR GLASS,STATE LIBRARY,CONCORD,N.H..........     2.95
PAPERWEIGHT,CLEAR GLASS,PLYMOUTH ROCK 1876,PROVIDENCE
  INKSTAND CO.............................................    15.00
PAPERWEIGHT,CLEAR WITH COLOURFUL BUTTERFLY OVER MUSHROOMS IN
  FLOWERS.................................................    24.00
PAPERWEIGHT,CLICHY CONCENTRIC MILLEFIORI CLEAR GROUND......   112.00
PAPERWEIGHT,CLICHY GARLAND.................................   226.00
PAPERWEIGHT,CLICHY SCRAMBLED INCLUDES PINK ROSE............    84.00
PAPERWEIGHT,CLICHY ,18 TYPICAL CLICHY CANES AROUND A PINK
  ROSE....................................................   250.00
PAPERWEIGHT,COLUMBUS SULPHIDE MADE BY D ALBERT.............    55.00
PAPERWEIGHT,CRANE ON TURTLE,9 IN. TALL.....................    15.00
PAPERWEIGHT,DEGENHART.....................................    25.00
PAPERWEIGHT,DEGENHART ROSE,RED & WHITE PETALS.............    60.00
PAPERWEIGHT,DEMPSTER IRON FROG,GREEN......................     3.75
PAPERWEIGHT,DOME TOP GLASS ,FROM A FRIEND..................    10.00
PAPERWEIGHT,DOMED TOP,MULTI-COLOURED BASE WITH FROM A FRIEND   12.00
PAPERWEIGHT,ELEPHANT MADE OF QUARTZ,RAISED TRUNK...........     9.00
PAPERWEIGHT,ELKS..........................................    15.00
PAPERWEIGHT,FACETED ONYX..................................     3.50
PAPERWEIGHT,FACETED IN MINIATURE MILLIFIORE...............     9.00
PAPERWEIGHT,F.D.ROOSEVELT.................................    55.00
PAPERWEIGHT FLAT ADVERTISING BATES STEEL POLES............     3.50
PAPERWEIGHT,FLORAL........................................    18.00
PAPERWEIGHT,FLORAL,SIGNED ST.CLAIR........................     7.50
PAPERWEIGHT,FRENCH BACCARAT FLOWER,CLEAR CRYSTAL DOME,DOUBLE
  PETALED.................................................   300.00
PAPERWEIGHT,FROM A FRIEND.................................    12.00
PAPERWEIGHT,FROSTED LION,SIGNED GILLANDER AND SONS.........    35.00
PAPERWEIGHT,GLASS,B.P.O.E.................................     6.00
PAPERWEIGHT GLASS BUD VASE................................     3.50
PAPERWEIGHT GLASS DATED 1893..............................    28.00
PAPERWEIGHT,GLASS DOME MARKED WASHINGTON D.C..............     3.50
PAPERWEIGHT,GLASS,FLAT WITH PICTURE.......................     3.00
PAPERWEIGHT GLASS PITCHER SIGNED ST.CLAIR.................     7.50
PAPERWEIGHT,GREEN PHEASANT,HOLLOW.........................     2.00
PAPERWEIGHT,HAND DONE,BEVELED GLASS.......................     2.50
PAPERWEIGHT,HANSEN PURPLE ROSE,4 GREEN LEAVES,BLUE GROUND...    60.00
PAPERWEIGHT,HANSEN SUB-MINI GREEN ROSE....................    25.00
PAPERWEIGHT,HANSEN YELLOW ROSE WITH ORANGE STAMEN,4 GREEN
  LEAVES..................................................    55.00
PAPERWEIGHT,HOME SWEET HOME,HOUSE & TREE..................    25.00
```

```
PAPERWEIGHT,INDIANA SESQUICENTENNIAL SIGNED ZIMMERMAN.......    10.50
PAPERWEIGHT,IRIDESCENT SATIN ELEPHANT......................    15.00
PAPERWEIGHT,IRON ALLIGATOR.................................     4.50
PAPERWEIGHT,IRON FROG......................................     2.50
PAPERWEIGHT,IRON FROG SIGNED DEMPSTER......................     3.75
PAPERWEIGHT,JERSEY,DEVILS FIRE.............................    32.00
PAPERWEIGHT,JERSEY,MULTI-COLOURED WITH BILL IN ORANGE.......   17.00
PAPERWEIGHT,J F KENNEDY SIGNED.............................    20.00
PAPERWEIGHT,J F K,SIGNED AND DATED 1963....................    25.00
PAPERWEIGHT,JOHN F. & JACQUELINE KENNEDY,DOUBLE SULPHIDE....   59.00
PAPERWEIGHT,KAZIUN PEDESTAL,TILTED YELLOW FLOWER,1 IN.......  165.00
PAPERWEIGHT,KAZIUN YELLOW ROSE ENFOLDED IN 3 UPSTANDING
   GREEN LEAVES............................................   275.00
PAPERWEIGHT,KENNEDY,SIGNED J.G. 1963.......................    25.00
PAPERWEIGHT,KENNEDY SULPHIDE...............................   300.00
PAPERWEIGHT,KENNEDY SULPHIDE,GREEN BASE....................   250.00
PAPERWEIGHT,KENNEDY SULPHIDE,RED BASE......................   250.00
PAPERWEIGHT,LBJ,SIGNED AND DATED 1963......................    25.00
PAPERWEIGHT,LOG CABIN AND HOME SWEET HOME LEGEND,FIGURE AT
   DOOR...................................................    30.00
PAPERWEIGHT,METAL LIBERTY BELL.............................     3.50
PAPERWEIGHT,MILLEFIORI.....................................    37.50
PAPERWEIGHT,MILLEFIORI DATED 1875..........................    55.00
PAPERWEIGHT,MINIATURE MURANO...............................    13.00
PAPERWEIGHT,MURANO,6 FACETED,MILLEFIORI MUSHROOM...........    13.00
PAPERWEIGHT,MURANO,ITALY,FULL BLOWN RED ROSE,ON STANDARD....   18.00
PAPERWEIGHT,MURANO,ITALY,PEACH COLOURED APRICOT ON GREEN
   WITH GOLD...............................................     9.00
PAPERWEIGHT,MURANO,ITALY,RED CHERRIES,GREEN STEM,BLUE FIELD.    9.00
PAPERWEIGHT,MURANO,MINIATURE,6 FACETED,MILLEFIORI MUSHROOM..   13.00
PAPERWEIGHT,MURANO MULTIFACETED,SPRAY OF FLOWERS & LEAVES...   32.00
PAPERWEIGHT,MURANO YELLOW ROSE,FOOTED......................    25.00
PAPERWEIGHT,N E GLASS CO.,BLUE FLOWER ON LATTICE GROUND.....  150.00
PAPERWEIGHT NAILSEA-TYPE DOOR STOP,GREEN GLASS WITH BUBBLES.   45.00
PAPERWEIGHT,OBLONG GLASS,ENW CO............................     5.00
PAPERWEIGHT,OBLONG PICTURE OF SOUTHERN COOPERAGE CO,ST.LOUIS   10.00
PAPERWEIGHT,OBLONG ST LOUIS FAIR...........................    16.00
PAPERWEIGHT,OBLONG ST.LOUIS FAIR BUILDING..................    16.00
PAPERWEIGHT,OBLONG SOUTHERN COOPERAGE CO,ST.LOUIS..........    10.00
PAPERWEIGHT,OVAL GLASS,MILK WHITE BACKING,FLETCHER MFG. CO..    3.95
PAPERWEIGHT,PAIRPOINT,CLEAR SWIRL GLASS OVER BLUE & WHITE
   CHIPS..................................................    44.00
PAPERWEIGHT PAIRPOINT,CUT & ETCHED ANCHOR..................    40.00
PAPERWEIGHT PEACH SIGNED ZIMMERMAN.........................    10.50
PAPERWEIGHT,PEN TYPE ROCK SHAPE............................     3.00
PAPERWEIGHT,PINK LUSTER HOUSE,OPAQUE GLASS.................    33.00
PAPERWEIGHT,POPE JOHN......................................   100.00
PAPERWEIGHT,POPE JOHN DOUBLE OVERLAY,GOLD ON WHITE ON
   CLEAR,RED BASE..........................................   135.00
PAPERWEIGHT ,RALPH BARBER NAME,V J BARNARD.................    50.00
PAPERWEIGHT,RED STAINED OVAL...............................    10.00
PAPERWEIGHT,ROOKWOOD SIGNED 1922,TAN TURTLE................    50.00
PAPERWEIGHT,ROSE QUARTZ,GREEN JADE BUTTERFLY & AMETHYST
   QUARTZ BEETLE...........................................    32.00
PAPERWEIGHT,ROUND GLASS 2 IN. HIGH,CLOUD
   DESIGN,RED,BLUE,YELLOW..................................    22.50
PAPERWEIGHT,ROUND,KNOB HANDLE..............................     7.50
PAPERWEIGHT,RUBY FLASHED,FLORAL & LEAF,ENGRAVED T.HENDRICK..   11.00
PAPERWEIGHT,RUSSIAN CUT....................................    35.00
PAPERWEIGHT,ST.LOUIS,5 CLUSTERS AROUND CENTER CLUSTER,BLUE &
   WHITE..................................................   145.00
PAPERWEIGHT,ST.LOUIS SCRAMBLED ON WHITE FILIGREE...........    98.00
PAPERWEIGHT SIGNED BACCARAT SET OF 12 ZODIAC SULPHIDES......  420.00
PAPERWEIGHT SIGNED BACCARAT ZODIAC SULFIDE,COBALT BASE......   45.00
PAPERWEIGHT,SIGNED KENNEDY.................................    25.00
```

```
PAPERWEIGHT SIGNED LUTZ,LATTICINO GOLD,PINK,WHITE............5,000.00
PAPERWEIGHT,SIGNED PAUL YSART,5 FLOWER SPRAY & VEINED LEAVES
  ON GREEN.................................................   425.00
PAPERWEIGHT SIGNED WHITTEMORE ON STANDARD,WHITE,TILTED
  ROSE,GREEN...............................................    85.00
PAPERWEIGHT,SNOW,COLOURED MAMMY.............................     5.00
PAPERWEIGHT,SNOW,THE LONE RANGER ROUNDUP....................     6.00
PAPERWEIGHT SPIDER LILY,SIGNED ZIMMERMAN....................    10.50
PAPERWEIGHT,STAR-SHAPED,MERRY CHRISTMAS.....................    16.00
PAPERWEIGHT,STREAM LINED HUDSON LOCOMOTIVE..................    15.00
PAPERWEIGHT,SULPHIDE BACCARAT,JOHN F.KENNEDY................   200.00
PAPERWEIGHT,TEDDY ROOSEVELT INTAGLIO BUST...................    15.00
PAPERWEIGHT,THE FERRIS WHEEL,WORLDS FAIR 1893...............    12.50
PAPERWEIGHT THE LONE RANGER ROUND UP........................     6.00
PAPERWEIGHT,U.A.M.,........................................    16.00
PAPERWEIGHT,UNION GLASS,BLUE SPATTER OVER WHITE IN FLOWER
  FORM....................................................    18.00
PAPERWEIGHT,W.VA.CENTENNIAL.................................    10.50
PAPERWEIGHT,WHITE DAISY ON GREEN GROUND.....................    17.50
PAPER WEIGHT,WHITE PEBBLES AND PINK FLOWER..................    15.00
PAPERWEIGHT,WHITE ROSE ON PEDESTAL BASE.....................   135.00
PAPERWEIGHT,WHITTEMORE YELLOW ROSE & 4 GREEN LEAVES,PEDESTAL    90.00
PAPERWEIGHT WITH DECAL ADMIRAL DEWEY........................     7.50
```

PAPIER-MACHE is a decorative form made from paper mixed with glue, chalk, and other ingredients, then molded and baked. It becomes very hard and can be decorated. Boxes, trays, and furniture were made of papier-mâché. Some of the early-nineteenth-century pieces were decorated with mother-of-pearl.

```
PAPIER-MACHE BLACK SNUFF BOX,MOTHER OF PEARL INLAID TOP.....     4.00
PAPIER-MACHE BOX,9 IN. HIGH,CLOTHES.........................    60.00
PAPIER MACHE BOX,RUSSIAN,SIGNED,3 IN. DIAMETER..............    75.00
PAPIER-MACHE BULL DOG,GLASS EYES,SPRING TAIL................     5.00
PAPIER MACHE BUNNY CIRCA 1910...............................     8.00
PAPIER MACHE CARNIVAL HEAD HOLLOW GROTESQUE MASK 1890.......    55.00
PAPIER MACHE FRENCH SNUFF BOX,HUNTER ON HORSEBACK...........     5.00
PAPIER-MACHE GIRL,10 IN. TALL,CLOTHES.......................    50.00
PAPIER MACHE MATCH BOX,BORDER IN INLAID MOTHER OF PEARL.....    20.00
PAPIER MACHE ORIENTAL ENAMELLED DESIGNED CIGAR BOX..........     5.00
PAPIER MACHE PORTRAIT COVERED SNUFF BOX.....................    35.00
PAPIER MACHE RECTANGULAR SNUFF BOX,MOTHER OF PEARL INLAID
  EDGE....................................................     7.50
PAPIER MACHE ROUND BOX,DIVIDED DISH,YELLOW & ORANGE.........    12.00
PAPIER MACHE RUSSIAN WINTER SCENE IN FRUITWOOD FRAME WITH
  BRASS HANGER............................................    17.50
PAPIER MACHE SANTA CLAUS....................................     3.50
PAPIER MACHE SHELL SHAPED TRAY,PAINTED......................     3.50
PAPIER MACHE SNUFF BOX,PICTURE GIRLS HEAD ON COVER..........     2.75
PAPIER MACHE SNUFF BOX,POLYCHROME,ZACHARY TAYLOR............    50.00
PAPIER MACHE TEA CADDY BOX,PEWTER LINED,ORIENTAL FIGURES....    50.00
PAPIER MACHE TOBACCO CANNISTER,PRE-REVOLUTIONARY RUSSIAN....    55.00
PAPIER MACHE WITH INLAY SNUFF BOX...........................    10.00
```

PARIAN is a fine-grained, hard paste porcelain named for the marble it resembles. It was first made in England in 1846 and gained in favor in the United States about 1860. Figures, tea sets, vases, and other items were made of parian at many English and United States factories.

```
PARIAN BLUE & WHITE 8 IN. VASE..............................    20.00
PARIAN BLUE & WHITE PITCHER,WHEAT PATTERN...................    29.50
PARIAN BLUE & WHITE WATER PITCHER...........................   135.00
PARIAN BUST OF ROBERT BURNS,5 IN. TALL......................    15.00
PARIAN BUST OF VENUS........................................    15.00
PARIAN BUST OF WAGNER,7 IN. TALL............................    12.00
PARIAN BUST OF WAGNER SIGNED................................    50.00
PARIAN BUST ON MARBLE BASE..................................    85.00
PARIAN CABINET VASE,HANDLE,FIGURE OF WOMAN & SHEEP IN REFIEF     6.00
```

PARIAN CAULDON BOX,QUEEN ELIZABETHS DOLL HOUSE...............	7.50
PARIAN COVERED JAR,RIBBED.....................................	12.00
PARIAN DIANA ON THE LION,7 IN. HIGH..........................	26.00
PARIAN FIGURES ON GLAZED COBALT ROCOCO BASE,10 IN. HIGH.....	125.00
PARIAN FIGURINE,GRECIAN GIRL CARRYING GRAPES,14 IN. TALL....	35.00
PARIAN FIGURINE OF FISHER GIRL 1850..........................	15.00
PARIAN FIGURINE,ROBED FIGURE OF GIRL CARESSING BIRD IN LAP..	43.00
PARIAN FIGURINE VASE,11 IN.,GENTLEMAN WITH TRI-CORNERED HAT.	35.00
PARIAN GIRL,10 IN.,PLUMED HAT,FANCY GOWN & PEACOCK...........	25.00
PARIAN HAND,6 IN. TALL..	15.00
PARIAN HAND HOLDING A BASKET,REGISTRY MARK ON BASE...........	37.50
PARIAN HAND HOLDS RUFFLE TOP VASE,BLUE TRIM..................	19.00
PARIAN HAND HOLDS SHELL VASE WITH GOLD & WHITE BEADS.........	14.00
PARIAN HAND TOOTHPICK...	25.00
PARIAN SETTER STANDING WITH HANDLED BASKET OF FRUIT..........	25.00
PARIAN SHELL-SHAPED VASE BASE IS BUST OF ELIZABETHAN FIGURE,	20.00
PARIAN SIGNED BOY & GIRL,ATTACHED CANDELABRA IN BACK ,......	140.00
PARIAN STATUE OF GIRL RESTING ON STONE,MINTON ON BOTTOM.....	100.00
PARIAN VASE,2 HANDLES,RED RIDING HOOD........................	12.50
PARIAN VASE,5 IN.,SHEAF OF WHEAT.............................	20.00
PARIAN VASE,5 IN. TALL,OPEN SHELLS ON SHELL BASE.............	9.00
PARIAN VASE,BASKET WITH MICE.................................	12.00
PARIAN VASE,HAND,2 FINGERS RINGED............................	16.00
PARIAN VASE,PAIR,BLUE DECORATION,8 IN. TALL..................	36.00
PARIAN VASE,PAIR EAGLE.......................................	125.00
PARIAN VASE,PAIR WHITE CORN..................................	30.00
PARIAN VASE,WHITE WITH RAISED FLOWERS,8 IN. TALL.............	8.00
PARIAN WARE FIGURINE GIRL HOLDING PITCHER....................	36.00
PARIAN WHITE COVERED BOX,SHAPE OF CORNUCOPIA.................	25.00
PARIAN WHITE COVERED BOX,SHAPE OF SHELL......................	25.00
PARIAN WHITE HAND VASE HOLDING SHEAF OF WHEAT................	14.50
PARIAN WHITE PITCHER,6 IN. HIGH,SMEAR GLAZE,MARKED ALBION,..	46.50
PARIAN WHITE VASE,HAND HOLDING SHEAF OF WHEAT................	17.50
PASTE SOFT MARKED MAASTRICHT 9 IN. PLATE,WHITE CENTER,GAUDY FLOWERS..	6.00
PASTE SOFT PITCHER,HUNTING SCENE WITH BLUE & PINK LUSTER....	37.00
PASTE,SOFT,SPRIG PLATE.......................................	4.50
PATE-DE-VERRE COVERED BOX,TREFOIL SHAPE,SIGNED A.WALTER NANCY..	440.00
PATE DE VERRE PLATE SIGNED A.WALTER,NANCY & E.ROYER,PINE CONE..	325.00
PATE DE VERRE SIGNED A.WALTER NANCY ASH TRAY WITH BEETLE....	425.00
PATE-DE-VERRE SIGNED G.ARGY ROUSSEAU 6 IN. HIGH FAIRY LAMP ON BRONZE..	195.00
PATE DE VERRE SIGNED G.ARGY ROUSSEAU ARTICHOKE VASE,BLUE,GREEN..	600.00
PATE DE VERRE SIGNED G.ARGY ROUSSEAU VASE,GREEN,PINK & BLUE.	450.00
PATE-DE-VERRE SIGNED DE CORCHMENT GEOMETRIC BOWL.............	450.00
PATE DE VERRE SIGNED WALTER-NANCY CANDLE HOLDER,GREEN & ORANGE DECOR...	410.00

PATE SUR PATE means "paste on paste." The design was made by painting layers of slip (which see) on the piece until a relief decoration was formed. The method was developed at Sèvres factory in France about 1850. It became even more famous at the English Minton factory about 1870.

PATE SUR PATE VASE, LAVENDER W. WHITE FIGURE 10 IN. HG......	84.00

PEACHBLOW GLASS originated about 1883 at Hobbs, Brockunier and Company of Wheeling, West Virginia. It is a glass that shades from yellow to peach. It was lined in white. New England peachblow is a one-layer glass with a lining shading from red to white. Mount Washington peachblow shades from pink to blue. Reproductions of peachblow have been made, but they are of a poor quality and can be detected.

PEACHBLOW 8 IN. FOOTED VASE,CAMPHOR THORN HANDLES............	145.00
PEACHBLOW ACORN TOOTHPICK....................................	18.50

PEACHBLOW BUD VASE,6 IN. HIGH,WHITE TO ROSE AT TOP.......... 135.00
PEACHBLOW DARNER,NEW ENGLAND................................. 50.00
PEACHBLOW GUNDERSON GOBLET,6 IN. HIGH,TAPERED BOWL OF
  RASPBERRY... 150.00
PEACHBLOW LAMP SHADE WITH ACID ENGRAVED DESIGN,NEW ENGLAND.. 65.00
PEACHBLOW MARTINSVILLE 4 IN. SAUCE.......................... 45.00
PEACHBLOW,MARTINSVILLE BRIDES BASKET,RUFFLED,CRIMPED,ROCOCO. 35.00
PEACHBLOW MT.WASHINGTON ROSE BOWL........................... 995.00
PEACHBLOW MT.WASHINGTON SUGAR BOWL WITH ENAMEL DECORATION...1,500.00
PEACHBLOW MUSTARD POT,WHEELING.............................. 160.00
PEACHBLOW NEW ENGLAND ACID TUMBLER,RASPBERRY................ 250.00
PEACHBLOW NEW ENGLAND CREAMER,PEACHBLOW HANDLE.............. 190.00
PEACHBLOW,NEW ENGLAND DARNER,PINK TO WHITE.................. 67.50
PEACHBLOW PEAR WHIMSEY,POLISHED,STEM........................ 250.00
PEACHBLOW THOS.WEBB ROUND VASE.............................. 295.00
PEACHBLOW VASE,5 IN... 150.00
PEACHBLOW VASE,7 IN. HIGH,LONG NARROW NECK,FLARED TOP....... 98.00
PEACHBLOW VASE,GUNDERSON,6 IN. HIGH,NARROW NECK............. 275.00
PEACHBLOW VASE WITH DECOR OF GOLD LEAVES & BLACKBERRIES &
  BUTTERFLY... 250.00
PEACHBLOW WATER PITCHER,WHEELING,PINK OVERLAY............... 175.00
PEACHBLOW WHEELING 11 IN. BOWL.............................. 350.00
PEACHBLOW WHEELING CELERY................................... 400.00
PEACHBLOW,WHEELING SALT SHAKER,BULBOUS,2 IN. HIGH........... 98.00
PEACHBLOW WHEELING SUGAR,ANNEALING MARK..................... 85.00
PEACHBLOW,WHEELING TUMBLER.................................. 200.00
PEACHBLOW,WHEELING TUMBLER,DRAPE PATTERN,CHERRY RED TO AMBER 175.00
PEACHBLOW WHEELING TUMBLER,GLOSSY........................... 265.00
PEARL BOX,CARVED INLAID JEWEL,CHINESE,HAND MADE,PADLOCK..... 520.00
PEARL BOX,INLAID WALNUT..................................... 60.00
PEARL CALLING CARD CASE,DIAMOND SHAPE PATTERN,FELT LINER.... 15.00
PEARL CARD CASE
  8.50 TO... 25.00
PEARL CARD CASE,VELVET LINED................................ 15.00
PEARL CARVED DINNER 12 KNIVES ,STERLING FERRULES............ 95.00
PEARL FRENCH OPERA GLASSES,ENGRAVED JESSIE MC NEEL 1893..... 50.00
PEARL HANDLE 12 DINNER KNIVES,AETNA......................... 45.00
PEARL HANDLE 12 LUNCHEON KNIVES,AETNA....................... 45.00
PEARL HANDLE NUT PICKERS,10................................. 24.00
PEARL HANDLE SET OF 6 BUTTER SPREADERS...................... 24.00
PEARL HANDLED BOXED SET SALAD KNIVES & FORKS,12 PIECES...... 55.00
PEARL HANDLED CARVING SET,GERMAN............................ 27.50
PEARL HANDLED CHEESE SERVER................................. 9.00
PEARL HANDLED DINNER KNIVES,12,OVAL SHAPED HANDLED WITH
  SILVER BANDS... 58.00
PEARL HANDLED KNIFE & FORK SET OF 6,STERLING ROSE DESIGN
  FERRULES... 68.00
PEARL HANDLED KNIVES,6...................................... 18.50
PEARL HANDLED LUNCHEON KNIVES & FORKS,12 EACH............... 100.00
PEARL HANDLED SERVING SPOON,OPENWORK BOWL................... 5.25
PEARL OPERA GLASSES IN LEATHER CASE......................... 28.00
PEARL PEN HOLDER IN VELVET CASE............................. 2.00
PEARL SALAD KNIVES,8.. 36.00
PEARLWARE GERMAN CANISTER SET WITH FLORAL BAND,15 PIECES.... 45.00
PEKING AMBER GLASS CHINESE SNUFF BOTTLE,YELLOW STOPPER...... 22.00
PEKING CARVED GLASS IMITATION OF CORAL SHOWING LOTUS
  BOTTLE,TEAK STAND.. 185.00
PEKING CARVED IMPERIAL YELLOW GLASS BOTTLE,CARVED TEAK
  STAND,... 115.00

  *PEKING GLASS is a Chinse cameo glass of the eighteenth and nineteenth cen-
  turies.*

PEKING GLASS BOTTLE,GREEN CARVED LEAVES,FLOWERS IN RELIEF... 125.00
PEKING GLASS BOTTLE,INSIDE PAINTED CHINESE LANDSCAPES....... 75.00
PEKING GLASS BOWL,OVERLAY,BURNT-ORANGE,5 IN. DIAMETER....... 135.00

```
PEKING GLASS BOWL,OVERLAY,GREEN VINES,FLOWERS & A
  GRASSHOPPER..................................................   140.00
PEKING GLASS CUP & SAUCER,CHINESE,COBALT BLUE WITH METAL
  TRIM & HANDLE................................................    22.50
PEKING GLASS GINGER JAR,WHITE CAMEO,LOTUS LEAVES,BIRDS &
  BLOSSOMS....................................................    150.00
PEKING GLASS MOTTLED SNUFF BOTTLE,IRON RED DOTS IN CLEAR
  GLASS.......................................................     60.00
PEKING GLASS OVERLAY CHINESE SNUFF BOTTLE....................     65.00
PEKING GLASS PERFUME BOTTLE,BLUE & WHITE.....................     95.00
PEKING GLASS PLATE MARKED CHINESE,10 IN.,SCROLL & SWAN.......      2.00
PEKING GLASS ROSE CARVED ROSE BOWL,RED ROSES & LEAVES TO
  WHITE.......................................................    225.00
PEKING GLASS SNUFF BOTTLE,PAIR,WHITE WITH BROWN ORIENTAL
  MOTIFS......................................................     50.00
PEKING GLASS SNUFF BOTTLE,RED ON CLEAR CIRCA 1750-1800......      75.00
PEKING GREEN GLASS WINE CUP & STAND.........................     26.00
```

*PELOTON GLASS is European glass with small threads of colored glass rolled
onto the surface of clear or colored glass. It is sometimes called "spaghetti" or
"shredded coconut" glass.*

```
PELOTON 4 IN. RIBBED & CASED VASE,WHITE BULBOUS BODY........    195.00
PELOTON BOWL,SQUATTY,GREENISH GOLD IRIDESCENCE,IVORY
  IRIDESCENT RIBBING..........................................     45.00
PELOTON BRIDES BASKET,ORNATE BRASS FOOTED HOLDER,HANDLE
  DECORATED...................................................     45.00
PELATON PITCHER,3 IN. TALL,CLOVER LEAF SHAPE TOP............     28.00
PELOTON SWIRLED PITCHER,APPLIED HANDLE,ENAMELED THREADS.....     95.00
PELOTON VASE,GREEN WITH PURPLE & GOLD HIGHLIGHTS............     40.00
```

*PEWTER is a metal alloy of tin and lead. Some of the pewter made after about
1840 has a slightly different composition and is called Britannia metal.*

```
PEWTER ASHTRAY MARKED CROMWELL PRODUCTS GENUINE
  PEWTER,ANIMAL SHAPE.........................................      3.00
PEWTER & BRASS CANDLEHOLDER,SINGLE..........................      3.00
PEWTER & GLASS FLASK,BOTTOM HALF ENCASED IN PEWTER,TOP IN
  LEATHER.....................................................      4.75
PEWTER BASIN,7 IN...........................................     27.50
PEWTER BEAKER
  8.50  TO...................................................     12.00
PEWTER BOWL,L.B.SMITH,BOSTON 175,8 IN.......................     25.00
PEWTER BOWL,ENGLISH HAMMERED.................................      4.25
PEWTER BOWL MARKED,COLONIAL.................................      5.00
PEWTER BOWL MARKED OLD COLONY PEWTER........................      7.50
PEWTER BOWL MARKED PEWTER L S W.............................      8.75
PEWTER BOWL MARKED PILGRIM SOLID PEWTER.....................      3.95
PEWTER BOWL,MUSKMELON SHAPE.................................     10.00
PEWTER BOWL,REVERE BY BENEDICT,3-FOOTED.....................      4.50
PEWTER BUTTER CHIP..........................................      3.50
PEWTER CANDLE HOLDER,SAUCER TYPE WITH HANDLE................      4.75
PEWTER CANDLESTICK,PAIR.....................................     60.00
PEWTER CANDLESTICK,PAIR 2 SOCKETS,MARKED HOMAN & FLAGG
  PEWTER......................................................     80.00
PEWTER CANDLESTICK,PAIR,2-ARM...............................     13.75
PEWTER CANDLESTICKS,PAIR 7 IN.,ENGLISH GADROONED DESIGN.....     60.00
PEWTER CANDLESTICKS,8 IN. H.................................     12.50
PEWTER CANDLESTICKS,PAIR AMERICAN...........................    125.00
PEWTER CANDLESTICKS,PAIR HANDMADE 8 IN......................     24.00
PEWTER CANDLESTICKS,PAIR,J.WEEKES...........................    250.00
PEWTER CANDY COMPOTE,PAIRPOINT..............................      4.00
PEWTER CANDY DISH...........................................      4.00
PEWTER CANDY DISH WITH 6 IN. HIGH BASE......................      7.00
PEWTER CANDY MOLD,FLORAL WREATH.............................      6.50
PEWTER CASE WITH CLEAR BOTTLE,PEWTER SCREW TOP ,LID DATED
  1866........................................................     15.00
```

```
PEWTER CASKET PLATES,1863,1873,1877.........................    7.50
PEWTER CASTOR FRAME FOR 6 BOTTLES,SIGNED GLEASON............   12.00
PEWTER CASTOR FRAME WITH 5 BOTTLES,GOTHIC PATTERN...........   38.00
PEWTER CHANDELIER,23 IN. HIGH,24 IN. SPREAD................   450.00
PEWTER CHARGER.............................................   195.00
PEWTER CHARGER,15 IN.,RICHARDS OR RICHARDSON TOUCHMARK.....   100.00
PEWTER CHARGER,LONDON MARK,15 IN...........................    45.00
PEWTER CHARGER MARKED INITIALS W.F.,16 IN..................    85.00
PEWTER CHARGER,PAIR TOWNSEND & GRIFFEN,LONDON 1793.........   130.00
PEWTER CHARGER PLATE,15 IN.,SIGNED SAMUEL ELLIS WITH TOUCH
 MARKS....................................................    85.00
PEWTER CHARGER PLATTER,ENGLISH,18 IN. MARKED COMPTON.......   110.00
PEWTER CHARGER PLATTER,ENGLISH,23 IN. MARKED ELLIS.........   125.00
PEWTER CHILDS PLATE,3 IN. WIDE............................    12.50
PEWTER CIGARETTE BOX & MATCH HOLDER,CARVED JADE FLORAL
 TOP,ORIENTAL.............................................    20.00
PEWTER COFFEE POT,ACORN FINIAL............................    14.75
PEWTER COFFEE POT,AMERICAN,SELLEW & CO....................   110.00
PEWTER COFFEE POT,COVERED,SIGNED F.PORTER,CIRCA 1835.......   125.00
PEWTER COFFEE POT,IRON BASE,MARKED E.B.MANNING JUNE 5,1862..   37.50
PEWTER COFFEE POT,J.DIXON,11 IN...........................    35.00
PEWTER COFFEE POT,KAYSERZINN MARKED,8 IN. TALL,SWIRLED BODY.   40.00
PEWTER COFFEE POT,PAIR,MARKED R DUNHAM....................   250.00
PEWTER COFFEE POT,SCROLLED HANDLE,BLACKBERRY FINIAL........    20.00
PEWTER COFFEE POT,SELLEWS.................................    60.00
PEWTER COFFEE POT SIGNED G RICHARDSON.....................   100.00
PEWTER COFFEE POT,SUGAR & CREAMER,DIXSON & SON............   150.00
PEWTER COMPOTE,5IN. W. 2 IN. TALL.........................     3.50
PEWTER COMPOTE ON STANDARD,REED & BARTON,SIGNED AMERICAN....   85.00
PEWTER CONSOLE SET,MARKED K.S.CO..........................    12.50
PEWTER CREAMER & SUGAR....................................     7.00
PEWTER CREAMER & SUGAR,5 IN.,............................   125.00
PEWTER CREAM & SUGAR MARKED GENUINE PEWTER................     7.00
PEWTER CREAMER,2 IN. HIGH.................................     2.00
PEWTER CREAMER CIRCA 1830,AMERICAN........................    58.00
PEWTER CREAMER,KAYSERZINN,4 IN.,RAISED POPPY & IRIS DESIGN..   27.00
PEWTER CREAMER,SUGAR & TRAY WITH DRAGON SHAPE HANDLES,JADE
 TRIMMED..................................................    20.00
PEWTER CREAMER,SUGAR,TRAY.................................    17.50
PEWTER CRUCIFIX...........................................     9.50
PEWTER CUP,CHINESE........................................     8.00
PEWTER CUP,FOLDING IN TIN CASE............................     6.50
PEWTER DECANTER,FLAT PINT,JAMES DIXON & SONS ENGLAND.......   150.00
PEWTER DISH,10 IN.........................................    15.00
PEWTER EWER,COVERED,WALLACE...............................    12.50
PEWTER FLASK,ENGRAVED BAND,18TH CENTURY,6 IN..............    25.00
PEWTER FLASK MARKED MADE IN ENGLAND.......................    15.00
PEWTER FUNNEL ,5 IN. HIGH.................................    16.00
PEWTER FUNNEL WITH STRAINER,8 IN. HIGH....................    22.00
PEWTER GOBLET
 4.50 TO.................................................    35.00
PEWTER GOBLET,6..........................................    40.00
PEWTER GRAVY BOAT.........................................     5.00
PEWTER GRAVY BOAT,KAYSERZINN,BUG ON HANDLE................    17.50
PEWTER HALF PINT  IMPERIAL HOTEL KILKENNY IRELAND.........    25.00
PEWTER ICE CREAM DISH MARKED GENUINE PEWTER,B.W.,SET OF 6...   12.00
PEWTER INKWELL ATTACHED TO TRAY,ROUND.....................     8.50
PEWTER INKWELL,ENAMELLED,FACETIOUS SCOTS WOMAN GOLFER......    25.00
PEWTER INKWELL,GLASS INSERT...............................    21.00
PEWTER INKWELL,HOLES FOR QUILLS...........................    20.00
PEWTER INKWELL,LID & 5 QUILL PEN HOLDERS..................    30.00
PEWTER INKWELL,LID & HOLES FOR QUILL......................    25.00
PEWTER INKWELL MARKED S.C.R. & CO.,AMERICAN...............    35.00
PEWTER KNIFE REST,KAYSERZINN MARKED,DASCHUND DOG..........    15.00
PEWTER LADLE WITH WOODEN HANDLE...........................    28.00
```

```
PEWTER LAMP,HAND,BELLS,FIREPROOF..............................   35.00
PEWTER LAMP,PAIR WHALE OIL SIGNED PORTER.....................  295.00
PEWTER LAMP,SPARKING.........................................   35.00
PEWTER LAMP,WHALE OIL,DOUBLE BULLSEYE,AMERICAN...............  200.00
PEWTER MAYONNAISE SET MARKED PAUL REVERE,4 PIECES............   12.00
PEWTER MEASURE,1 HALF GILL,HALL MARK CROWN OVER VR...........    8.00
PEWTER MEASURE,PINT,CIRCA 1820,IRISH.........................   25.00
PEWTER MEASURE SET,7 PIECES..................................   21.00
PEWTER MILK PITCHER SIGNED REED & BARTON,10 IN. HIGH,CIRCA
  1860.......................................................   67.50
PEWTER MILK PITCHER,WOODWARD TAUNTON.........................    4.00
PEWTER MOLD,FRUIT,ARTICHOKE MARKED LACO......................   12.00
PEWTER MOLD,GIRL.............................................    9.25
PEWTER MOLD,ICE CREAM,BANANA SHAPE...........................    8.00
PEWTER MOLD,LOBSTER..........................................   12.50
PEWTER MOLD,SANTA CLAUS......................................   24.50
PEWTER MOLD,SANTA SLEIGH,3 SECTIONS,HINGED...................    6.00
PEWTER MOLD SHAPE OF LILY FLOWER,THREE HINGED PARTS..........   12.00
PEWTER MOLD,SHOE.............................................   12.50
PEWTER MOLD,SPOON............................................   95.00
PEWTER MOLD,TURKEY...........................................   12.50
PEWTER MUG,ENGLISH & IRISH CIRCA 1825........................   20.00
PEWTER MUG,ENGLISH RUM.......................................   10.00
PEWTER MUG MARKED MADE IN CHINA,GLASS BOTTOM.................    6.00
PEWTER MUG,PAIR 1/2 PINT,ENGLISH.............................   60.00
PEWTER MUG WITH GLASS BOTTOM,HANDLED.........................   12.50
PEWTER PITCHER,AMERICAN,WHITLOCK,TROY,NEW YORK...............   65.00
PEWTER PITCHER,COLONIAL,6 IN.................................    8.00
PEWTER PITCHER,KAYSERZINN,11 IN.,METHISTOPELES...............   35.00
PEWTER PITCHER MARKED GENUINE PEWTER.........................   25.00
PEWTER PITCHER,OPEN,9 IN. HIGH...............................   17.50
PEWTER PLAQUE OF NAPOLEON,4 IN...............................   18.00
PEWTER PLATE,8 IN............................................   45.00
PEWTER PLATE,8 IN.,TOWNSEND-FEN CHURCH-LONDON................   25.00
PEWTER PLATE 9 IN. DIAMETER,SMALL HOLE THROUGH EDGE..........   16.50
PEWTER PLATE,10 IN...........................................   20.00
PEWTER PLATE,12 IN.,PLYMOUTH USA.............................   25.00
PEWTER PLATE,13 IN...........................................   70.00
PEWTER PLATE,AMERICAN,SAMUEL
  KILBOURN,BALTIMORE,MARYLAND,1814-39,7 IN...................   68.50
PEWTER PLATE,BUSH & PERKING LONDON 1775......................   40.00
PEWTER PLATE,GERMAN,9 IN.....................................   33.00
PEWTER PLATE,L.H.VAUGHAM,TAUNTON,7 IN........................   17.50
PEWTER PLATE,ROSE & CROWN MARKED GEORGIAN,9 IN...............   35.00
PEWTER PLATE,SCALLOPED,8 IN..................................    7.50
PEWTER PLATE SIGNED WITH TOUCHMARK JOHN GRIFFITH,8 IN........   45.00
PEWTER PLATE,SMITH & FELTMAN.................................   57.50
PEWTER PLATE,SWEDISH,ENGRAVED SCENE SIGNED SVENSKI...........    6.50
PEWTER PLATE,TOWNSEND & COMPTON..............................   38.00
PEWTER PLATTER MARKED OLD ESSEX PEWTER BY JENNINGS,WELL &
  TREE.......................................................    6.75
PEWTER PORRINGER,CROWN HANDLE................................  165.00
PEWTER PORRINGER,DAVID MELVIL................................  225.00
PEWTER PORRINGER,DOUBLE HANDLED..............................   10.00
PEWTER PORRINGER,FLOWER HANDLE...............................  125.00
PEWTER PORRINGER MARKED BENEDICT PEWTER......................   15.00
PEWTER PORRINGER,SINGLE HANDLE...............................   25.00
PEWTER PORRINGER WITH BOARDMAN HANDLE,CIRCA 1840.............   75.00
PEWTER PORRINGER WITHOUT HANDLE,4 IN.........................   22.00
PEWTER POT,MOREY & SMITH,GRAPE & LEAVES FINIAL..............    55.00
PEWTER RELISH,8 IN. OVAL.....................................    2.50
PEWTER SALT & PEPPER.........................................   12.50
PEWTER SALT & PEPPER,PAIR HANDLED MARKED PEERLESS PEWTER....    6.50
PEWTER SALT & PEPPER,PEDESTAL BASES..........................   32.00
PEWTER SALT DIP,SET OF 3.....................................    8.50
```

```
PEWTER SALT SET IN BOX...........................................  10.00
PEWTER SAUCE BOAT................................................  12.00
PEWTER SET,COFFEE & TEAPOT,SUGAR & CREAMER,MARKED SOLID
   PEWTER........................................................  50.00
PEWTER SHAVING BASIN,18TH CENTURY............................... 425.00
PEWTER SOAP DISH,LIDDED..........................................   6.00
PEWTER SPILL....................................................  25.00
PEWTER SPITTOON SIGNED AMERICAN DANFORTH........................ 128.00
PEWTER SPOON,IHS MARKINGS.......................................  12.50
PEWTER STEIN,ENGLISH SIGNED.....................................  37.00
PEWTER SUGAR BOWL MARKED PEWTER IN SCROLL,APPLIED HANDLES...      8.00
PEWTER SUGAR & CREAMER,MAYFLOWER................................  10.00
PEWTER SYRUP & TRAY,FOOTED,WALLACE..............................  20.00
PEWTER TABLESPOON...............................................   4.00
PEWTER TABLESPOON AND FORK......................................  12.00
PEWTER TABLESPOON,SET OF 4......................................  30.00
PEWTER TABLESPOON,SET OF 6 MARKED STEENKESSE...................  45.00
PEWTER TANKARD..................................................  60.00
PEWTER TANKARD,1 QUART,JAMES YATES..............................  50.00
PEWTER TANKARD,8 IN. HIGH,BARTHOLOMEW WALDER...................  42.50
PEWTER TANKARD,COVERED,MANNING BOWMAN & CO.CIRCA 1850.......  16.75
PEWTER TANKARD,PINT.............................................  25.00
PEWTER TANKARD,QUART,MARKED CROWN...............................  42.50
PEWTER TANKARD WITH THUMB FLIP TOP,ENGLISH HALLMARKS........  45.00
PEWTER TEA CADDY,CHINESE........................................  14.00
PEWTER TEA CADDY,CHINESE,6 SIDES WITH INCISED FLORAL DESIGN.  30.00
PEWTER TEA CADDY,ORIENTAL,2 COMPARTMENT........................  45.00
PEWTER TEA SERVICE,DOLLS,3-PIECE................................   5.00
PEWTER TEA SET,3 PIECES.........................................  45.00
PEWTER TEA SET MARKED HOMAN & CO.,CINCINNATI,4 PIECES........  22.00
PEWTER TEA STRAINER.............................................   5.00
PEWTER TEAPOT,A.PORTER,7 IN.....................................  75.00
PEWTER TEAPOT BY MANNING PATENT 1862,BRITANNIA..............  35.00
PEWTER TEAPOT CIRCA 1824-34,SIGNED REED & BARTON,FOOTED.....  45.00
PEWTER TEAPOT CIRCA 1845,AMERICAN...............................  67.50
PEWTER TEAPOT,CREAM & SUGAR,CONCORD.............................  30.00
PEWTER TEAPOT,DIXON.............................................  30.00
PEWTER TEAPOT,DIXON & SON,WOODEN HANDLE & FINIAL,4 CLAW FEET  75.00
PEWTER TEAPOT,DIXON,FLOWER FINIAL,VINE & GRAPES APPLIED
   AROUND BASE...................................................  45.00
PEWTER TEAPOT,DUNHAM............................................  65.00
PEWTER TEAPOT,FISHER-SHEFFIELD..................................  45.00
PEWTER TEAPOT,FOOTED MARKED JAMES DIXON & SONS...............  50.00
PEWTER TEAPOT,GRAPE FINIAL,R.DUNHAM.............................  45.00
PEWTER TEAPOT,HINGED LID,MARKED WILLIAM ROGERS...............  25.00
PEWTER TEAPOT,JAMES DIXON & SON,OVAL DRUM SHAPE WITH FLUTED
   SIDES.........................................................  48.00
PEWTER TEAPOT,JAMES DIXON & SONS,RECTANGULAR SHAPE,..........  40.00
PEWTER TEAPOT,KAYSERZINN,6 IN. TALL.............................  40.00
PEWTER TEAPOT,KAYSERZINN,PORCELAIN INSERTS IN HANDLE........  27.00
PEWTER TEAPOT MARKED J.......................................... 235.00
PEWTER TEAPOT MARKED JAMES DIXON & SONS,MELON SHAPED........  50.00
PEWTER TEAPOT MEASURE,MONOGRAM..................................  15.00
PEWTER TEAPOT,OAK LEAF FEET,HALLMARKED M.HUNTER & SON........  45.00
PEWTER TEAPOT,PEAR-SHAPED,EDGAR & SONS.......................... 250.00
PEWTER TEAPOT,PINK ENAMEL.......................................  22.00
PEWTER TEAPOT,R.DUNHAM
   27.50  TO.....................................................  55.00
PEWTER TEAPOT,R.DUNHAM,LIGHTHOUSE...............................  60.00
PEWTER TEAPOT SIGNED BOARDMAN,7 IN. HIGH....................... 165.00
PEWTER TEAPOT,SUGAR & CREAMER,SQUAT,DIXON & SONS.............  50.00
PEWTER TEAPOT,TOUCHMARK LEW-EL-TYN,BLACK EBONY
   HANDLE,PEDESTAL...............................................  58.00
PEWTER TEAPOT,WHITE ENAMELING...................................  29.50
PEWTER TEAPOT WITH WOOD HANDLE,DIXON & SMITH.................  40.00
```

```
PEWTER TRAY,BOAT SHAPE,KAYSERZINN,10 IN......................    6.50
PEWTER TRAY,KAYSERZINN MARKED,OPEN HANDLES,18 X 10 IN.......   35.00
PEWTER VASE,J.DIXON,COLOURED BEAD DESIGN,9 IN................   22.00
PEWTER WASH BOWL,HAND WROUGHT...............................   55.00
PEWTER WATER PITCHER,DUNHAM.................................  125.00
PEWTER WHISTLE,DOGS HEAD DESIGN.............................    5.00
PEWTER WINE GOBLET,SET OF 5 PURITAN.........................   15.00
PEYNAUD SIGNED OVAL VASE,CAMEO BOATS,SWAMP GRASS,TREES &
BIRDS.......................................................   95.00
```

THE PHONOGRAPH, invented by Thomas Edison in the 1880's, has been made by many firms.

```
PHOTOGRAPH,LEATHER COVERED ALBUM FOR TINTYPES,BRASS CLASP...    4.50
    PHOTOGRAPHY, SEE ALSO ALBUM.............................
PHOTOGRAPHY,19 OLD GLASS WITH OLD SCENES....................   10.00
PHOTOGRAPHY,CAMERA,AUTOGRAPHIC KODAK JUNIOR WITH LEATHER
CASE........................................................   10.00
PHOTOGRAPHY,CAMERA,EASTMAN BOX..............................    3.50
PHOTOGRAHPY,CAMERA,EASTMAN KODAK FOLDING RAINBOW HAWK EYE
NO.2A,......................................................   10.00
PHOTOGRAPHY,CAMERA,FOLDING POCKET BROWNIE...................    7.40
PHOTOGRAPHY,CAMERA,KODAK,LEATHER CASE,1926..................    5.50
PHOTOGRAPHY,CAMERA,KODAK NO. 122............................   15.00
PHOTOGRAPHY,CAMERA,ROCHESTER OPTICAL CO. 1870,TRIPOD STAND..   50.00
PHOTOGRAPHY,CAMERA,TESSINA,35MM,DAYLIGHT LOADER,CASSETTES...  189.00
PHOTOGRAPHY,DAGUERRE,3 IN. SQUARE,CUPID & WREATH,SIGNED
SMITH.......................................................   15.00
PHOTOGRAPHY,DAGUERREOTYPE LEATHER CASE......................    4.00
PHOTOGRAPHY,FAMILY ALBUM & STAND,PURPLE VELVET WITH BRASS...   12.50
PHOTOGRAPHY,GUTTA PERCHA FRAME,GRAPE DECOR..................    6.00
PHOTOGRAPHY,GUTTA PERCHA OCTAGONAL DAGUERREOTYPE............   10.50
PHOTOGRAPHY,GUTTAPERCHA PAIR HANGING CASES WITH CIVIL WAR
MOTIF.......................................................   25.00
PHOTOGRAPHY,GUTTA PERCHA SCROLLS & HANGING BASKET...........   12.00
PHOTOGRAPHY,KODAK FOLDING CAMERA............................    8.00
PHOTOGRAPHY,MEDALLION EMBOSSED DAGUERREOTYPE CASE...........   14.50
PHOTOGRAPHY,NEGATIVES,GLASS.................................    7.00
PHOTOGRAPHY,WOODEN FILM HOLDER..............................   15.00
    PIANO BABY, SEE BISQUE.................................
PICKARD BASKET,GOLD ETCHED FLOWERS,PIERCED HANDLE...........   12.50
PICKARD BOUILLON CUP & 6 SAUCERS,GOLD DECORATED.............   60.00
PICKARD BOWL & PLATE,CONDIMENT,HANDPAINTED..................    8.50
PICKARD CANDLESTICK,ETCHED..................................   12.50
PICKARD COFFEE POT,SUGAR,3 DEMI-TASSE CUPS & SAUCERS,SIGNED.   45.00
PICKARD COMPOTE,HANDPAINTED.................................    8.50
PICKARD CUP & SAUCER........................................   12.50
PICKARD CUP & SAUCER,DEMI-TASSE,SET OF 8,SIGNED,BLACK & GOLD   60.00
PICKARD CUP & SAUCER GOLD...................................   17.00
PICKARD DISH,COVERED,SIGNED,HANDPAINTED,WHITE COIN
GOLD,ORANGE,GREEN...........................................   29.50
PICKARD JAR,POWDER,MARKED,FRANCE,COVERED,IVORY COLOURED.....   10.00
PICKARD MARKED PIN TRAY.....................................    6.50
PICKARD PLATE,GAME,SIGNED FERRINGTON,HANDPAINTED............  100.00
PICKARD PLATE,SIGNED,BAVARIA,HANDPAINTED....................    7.50
PICKARD SALT & PEPPER SHAKERS,GOLD..........................   10.00
PICKARD SALT SHAKER,GOLD....................................    6.00
PICKARD TEA POT,CREAMER & SUGAR.............................   37.50
PICKARD TRAY,DRESSER,SIGNED,BLUE & GOLD.....................    4.50
PICKARD TRAY,MARKED,HANDPAINTED GOLD LEAF...................   12.50
PICKARD VASE,PAIR GOLD MATCHING,5 IN. HIGH..................   25.00
    PICKLE CASTOR, SEE CASTOR..............................
    PICTURE, SEE ALSO CURRIER AND IVES.....................
PICTURE,BLEEDING HEART EMBROIDERED IN SILK,MATTED FRAME.....    5.00
PICTURE,BUST OF TEDDY ROOSEVELT,FRAMED UNDER GLASS..........   25.00
PICTURE,COLOR ADVERTISING PRINT,TURKISH TROPHIES
```

CIGARETTES,FRAMED,1905..	30.00
PICTURE,COLOR,CONFEDERATE GENERAL ROBERT E. LEE..............	2.00
PICTURE,C.M.RUSSELL COLOURED PRINT BY DICK JONES PICTURE CO.	9.00
PICTURE,EDOUART SILHOUETTE SIGNED & DATED 1826,SEATED	
GENTLEMEN..	110.00
PICTURE,FRAMED,BIRD MADE OF FEATHERS.........................	8.50
PICTURE,FRAMED ETCHING BIRTHPLACE OF ABRAHAM LINCOLN SIGNED.	45.00
PICTURE,FRAMED LITHOGRAPH OF GEORGE WASHINGTON SIGNED KELLOG	28.00
PICTURE,FRAMED PENCIL SKETCH OF 5 CUPIDS BY F.H.FUEGER	
1751-1818,...	135.00
PICTURE,FRAMED PRINT HENRY CLAY,12 X 16 IN...................	15.00
PICTURE,FRENCH PRINT,ARTIST FRANCOIS BOUCHER 1703-1770,LE	
GOUTER...	45.00
PICTURE,GEO.WASHINGTON,LIFE SIZE BUST IN COLOR,FRAMED UNDER	
GLASS..	35.00
PICTURE,GODEY PRINT..	20.00
PICTURE,GODEY PRINT,1864,FRAMED.................................	5.00
PICTURE,GODEY PRINT,COLOURED,GOLD FRAME,BATTLE LAKE ERIE....	18.00
PICTURE,GODEY PRINT,FRAMED,PARIS FASHIONS 1851..............	8.00
PICTURE,HISTORICAL PRINT,FRAMES,FLYING SQUADRON,FLEET OF 7	
BATTLE SHIPS...	19.00
PICTURE,HORSE PRINT,FRAMED BY A COOPER........................	200.00
PICTURE,IRON STEAMER PILGRIM BY MAJOR & KNAPP,PRINT.........	110.00
PICTURE,KELLOGS & THAYER,WASHINGTON RECEPTION 1789..........	18.00
PICTURE,MOORES TALLY-HO TO THE SPORTS,FRAMED.................	50.00
PICTURE,PAIR FRAMED SILHOUETTES SIGNED LOTTE GUZLAFF........	22.50
PICTURE,PEN & INK SKETCH,INDIAN ON HORSE,SIOUX,FRAMED,SIGNED	
J HAUSER..	100.00
PICTURE,PETER HURD PRINTS PERSONALLY AUTOGRAPHED IN MARGIN..	25.00
PICTURE,PRINT,DR.SYNTAX 1821,THOMAS ROWLANDSON,9 IN. BY 6	
IN...	4.00
PICTURE,PRINT,FOREST SCENE WITH GREENAWAY TYPE GIRLS & DEER.	12.50
PICTURE,PRINT KELLOGS HAPPY PARTY.............................	12.50
PICTURE,PRINT,MORNING OF SNOW.................................	75.00
PICTURE,PRINT NAVAL PARADE OF BATTLESHIPS PASSING GRANTS	
TOMB 1899..	22.00
PICTURE,PRINT OF HEEMAN-SAYERS BOXING MATCH LONDON	
1860,FRAMED..	150.00
PICTURE,SANDPAPER DRAWING,CHARCOAL,SCHUYLKILL RIVER SCENE...	35.00
PICTURE,SIGNED PAINTING ON IVORY OF PRINCESS VICTORIA,BRASS	
FRAME..	35.00
PICTURE,SILHOUETTE DATED 1860 SIGNED WYBRAND,BLACK & GOLD	
FRAME..	35.00
PICTURE,SILHOUETTE,FRAME,DOCUMENTED DAVID TOWNSEND CABINET	
MAKER,BOSTON...	25.00
PICTURE,SILHOUETTE MAN IN COCKED HAT,FRAMED,.................	100.00
PICTURE,SUNBONNET BABIES,OAK FRAMES,PAIR,MENDING DAY &	
CLEANING DAY...	17.50
PICTURE,THE FALLS OF NIAGARA,1857,COCKBURN,COLOURED	
LITHOGRAPH...	115.00
PICTURE,WALLACE NUTTING FRAMED SIGNED TITLED PRINT..........	4.95
PICTURE,WALLACE NUTTING SIGNED COLOUR PRINT	
9.00 TO..	9.00
PICTURE,WALLACE NUTTING TINTED IN MAHOGANY FRAME,COLONIAL	
DAYS...	10.00
PICTURE,WALNUT FRAME WITH GOLD LINER,BELSHAZZARS FEAST......	25.00
PICTURE,WOOD BLOCK PRINT,CAT WITH LONG TAIL,SIGNED TOMOO	
INAGAKE..	65.00
PICTURE,WORLD WAR I RECRUTING,FRAMED,PAIR....................	40.00

*PIGEON BLOOD GLASS is any glassware with a deep red color. It is a very am-
biguous term.*

PIGEON BLOOD CANDLESTICKS,PAIR,FLOWER & ARABESQUE DESIGN....	35.00
PIGEON BLOOD SALT & PEPPER......................................	42.00
PIN CUSHION,GREEN SATIN HEART SHAPED,HANDPAINTED WITH	

```
FLOWERS & LEAVES..............................................   4.00
     PINK LUSTER, SEE LUSTER.....................................
     PIPE, SEE ALSO MEERSCHAUM...................................
PIPE,13 IN. EMBOSSED STONEWARE BOWL,BRASS COVER,AUSTRIAN....     12.50
PIPE,BLOWN GLASS WITH CURVING STEM,CLEAR WITH WHITE LOOPINGS     55.00
PIPE,BRIAR 8 IN. ATTACHED BOWL WITH HINGED TIN COVER,CORD &
  TASSELS.....................................................   12.00
PIPE,CARVED BRIAR WOOD,DRAGONS,EBONY STEM...................     16.00
PIPE,CIGARETTE PIPE,2 CARVED DOGS,AMBER STEM.................     20.00
PIPE,CLAY & BRASS............................................    2.00
PIPE,CLAY,PAIR,7 IN. LONG....................................    5.00
PIPE,FRENCH BRIER,4IN.CASED..................................    4.00
PIPE,HAND CARVED PAIR BRIAR ,ELEPHANT HEAD & HORSE HEAD.....    42.50
PIPE HOLDER,IVORY CARVED FIGURE ON...........................   35.00
PIPE,INDIAN CLAY.............................................    4.75
PIPE,IVORY OR BONE AND AMBER PIPE,LEATHER CASE,4 CARVED DOGS    35.00
PIPE,MALAY SURABAJA,RED LACQUERED BAMBOO STEM,IVORY
  MOUTHPIECE..................................................   24.00
PIPE,ORIENTAL OPIUM,WHITE METAL..............................   28.00
PIPE,ORNATE 23 IN. LONG WITH CERAMIC LIDDED BOWL.............   15.00
PIPE,PRE WORLD WAR I,PORCELAIN BOWL,HANDPAINTED,GERMAN
  KAISER PORTRAIT.............................................   45.00
PIPE,RUSSIAN ENAMEL ,MARKED..................................   85.00
PIPE,THIN CURVED BLACK STEM MARKED VERANDA...................    5.00
PIPE,WHITE CLAY..............................................    1.00
```

PIRKENHAMMER PORCELAINS were made in Brezova, Bohemia. The factory was founded in 1803, but most of the wares found today date from the late nineteenth century.

```
PIRKENHAMMER PITCHER,PAINTED BUTTERFLIES & FLOWERS ON WHITE
  WITH GOLD...................................................   28.00
PIRKENHAMMER PORTRAIT PLATE,ST.BERNARD DOG,SIGNED............   65.00
PLASTER BUST OF ROBERT E.LEE ON WALNUT BASE..................    5.00
PLASTER COLOURED BUST,CHIEF HIAWATHA.........................   15.00
PLASTER FIGURE COLOURED BOY,ROLLING EYES OPERATED BY CLOCK
  WORKS.......................................................  100.00
PLASTER OF PARIS MUTT & JEFF BUSTS DATED 1915...............     5.25
     PLATE, SEE UNDER SPECIAL TYPES SUCH AS ABC, CALENDAR,
     CHRISTMAS,..............................................
     PORTRAIT, PORCELAIN, ETC................................
     PLATED AMBERINA, SEE AMBERINA...........................
```

PLIQUE A JOUR is an enameling process. The enamel was laid between thin raised metal lines and heated. The finished piece has transparent enamel held between the thin metal wires.

```
PLIQUE A JOUR 5 IN. VASE,TRANSPARENT ENAMEL..................  140.00
PLIQUE A JOUR ENAMELLED TWO HANDLED BOWL,3 IN. BY 2 IN. H...  150.00
PLIQUE A JOUR ON SILVER ENAMELLED VIKING SHIP,FRENCH
  HALLMARKS.................................................1,000.00
POLITICAL CAMPAIGN,ALTON B.PARKER COLOURED PICTURE PIN......   13.50
POLITICAL CAMPAIGN,BRYAN BUTTON..............................    9.00
POLITICAL CAMPAIGN,BRYAN-STEVENSON BUTTON....................   14.00
POLITICAL CAMPAIGN,BULL MOOSE STICKPIN.......................    9.50
POLITICAL CAMPAIGN,BUTTON WITH JFK & LBJ PORTRAITS FOR 1960.    2.50
POLITICAL CAMPAIGN,CARD FOR GARFIELD BY WELCOME SOAP........     2.50
POLITICAL CAMPAIGN,CASEY FOR GOVENOR PIN.....................    1.00
POLITICAL CAMPAIGN,CELLULOID WILSON PORTRAIT BUTTON OF 1912.    9.00
POLITICAL CAMPAIGN,FDR METAL TRAY,KEEP ROOSEVELT IN THE
  WHITE HOUSE................................................   25.00
POLITICAL CAMPAIGN,GENERAL DOUGLAS MC ARTHUR MAN OF THE YEAR
  PIN........................................................    1.00
POLITICAL CAMPAIGN,GENERAL MC ARTHUR.........................    1.00
POLITICAL CAMPAIGN,GEORGE WASHINGTON BUTTON..................  175.00
POLITICAL CAMPAIGN,GLASS TUMBLER,MC KINLEY FIGURE IN BOTTOM.    6.50
POLITICAL CAMPAIGN,GLASS TUMBLER WITH WM. J.BRYAN OUR NEXT
```

PRESIDENT.. 5.00
POLITICAL CAMPAIGN,HARRISON,GOLD COLOURED HEAD STICKPIN..... 6.50
POLITICAL CAMPAIGN,HARRISON,THE PEOPLES CHOICE 1840,TOKEN... 4.50
POLITICAL CAMPAIGN,MC KINLEY,1 IN. PRESIDENTIAL PICTORIAL
BUTTON... 6.00
POLITICAL CAMPAIGN ,MC KINLEY & ROOSEVELT BUTTON............ 4.00
POLITICAL CAMPAIGN,MC KINLEY CAMPAIGN PLATE,7 IN............ 38.50
POLITICAL CAMPAIGN,MC KINLEY FOR CANDIDATE,POSTER.......... 18.00
POLITICAL CAMPAIGN,MC KINLEY-HOBART 1896 JUGATE PORTRAIT PIN 18.75
POLITICAL CAMPAIGN,MC KINLEY PLATE......................... 12.00
POLITICAL CAMPAIGN,MC KINLEY-ROOSEVELT CAMPAIGN,1 IN.,BROWN. 8.50
POLITICAL CAMPAIGN,MC KINLEY ROOSEVELT TINTED JUGATE,GOLD
BACKGROUND.. 11.00
POLITICAL CAMPAIGN,PAIR TORCHES............................ 15.00
POLITICAL CAMPAIGN ,PARADE CHEST BAND,RED,WHITE,BLUE....... 3.00
POLITICAL CAMPAIGN,PARASOL,PORTRAIT OF MC KINLEY & ROOSEVELT 65.00
POLITICAL CAMPAIGN PIN,HARRISON & MORTON PRESIDENTIAL TOKEN. 22.50
POLITICAL CAMPAIGN PIN,TAFT PICTURE........................ 5.00
POLITICAL CAMPAIGN PIN,TAFT PICTURE IN COLOUR.............. 12.50
POLITICAL CAMPAIGN,PLATE,THEODORE ROOSEVELT BREAD
TRAY,PORTRAIT CENTER.. 25.00
POLITICAL CAMPAIGN,PLATE,WHITE TAFT PORTRAIT............... 25.00
POLITICAL CAMPAIGN,PRESIDENT COLLECTION.................... 400.00
POLITICAL CAMPAIGN,REAGAN PIN.............................. 1.00
POLITICAL CAMPAIGN,ROOSEVELT FAIRBANKS SEPIA JUGATE........ 16.00
POLITICAL CAMPAIGN,ROOSEVELT NEW DEAL POTTERY MUG.......... 3.00
POLITICAL CAMPAIGN,SQUARE MEDAL WITH RED SQUARE & SQUARE
DEAL EMBOSSED... 7.00
POLITICAL CAMPAIGN,TAFT PICTURE PIN........................ 7.50
POLITICAL CAMPAIGN,TAFT,SHIELD HANGING FROM EAGLE.......... 25.00
POLITICAL CAMPAIGN TOKEN,BUST OF MC KINLEY,1900............ 5.00
POLITICAL CAMPAIGN TOKEN,NIXON & LODGE,1 IN................ 2.50
POLITICAL CAMPAIGN,WALLACE FOR PRESIDENT BUTTON............ .35
POLITICAL CAMPAIGN,WALLACE FOR PRESIDENT NECKTIE........... 3.50
POLITICAL CAMPAIGN,WM.MC KINLEY PIN........................ 2.00
POLITICAL CAMPAIGN,WOODROW WILSON FOR PRESIDENT CELLULOID
PIN... 3.50
POLITICAL CAMPAIGN,WOODROW WILSON OVAL METAL
PLAQUE,1856-1924.. 4.00

*POMONA GLASS is clear with a soft amber border decorated with pale blue or
rose-colored flowers and leaves. The colors are very, very pale. The background
of the glass is covered with a network of fine lines. It was made from 1885 to
1888 by the New England Glass Company.*
POMONA 7 IN. LILY VASE..................................... 50.00
POMONA DIAMOND QUILTED TUMBLER,CORNFLOWERS,AMBER & BLUE..... 77.50
POMONA FINGERBOWL,CORNFLOWER,RUFFLED TOP................... 38.00
POMONA FROSTED SUGAR & CREAMER,BLUE OAK LEAVES,AMBER ACORNS. 115.00
POMONA GOBLET,AMBER TOP & BOTTOM,PINK & WHITE FLOWERS....... 30.00
POMONA MID-WEST TUMBLER,FROSTED,AMBER STAINED TOP,ENAMELED
FERN.. 55.00
POMONA MIDWEST TUMBLER,OAK LEAF & ACORNS................... 33.00
POMONA MIDWESTERN INVERTED THUMBPRINT WATER PITCHER........ 45.00
POMONA MIDWESTERN SPOONER,GOLD ACORNS,BLUE LEAVES,INVERTED
THUMBPRINT.. 45.00
POMONA MIDWESTERN TUMBLER,INVERTED THUMBPRINT............. 25.00
POMONA NEW ENGLAND FINGER BOWL............................. 20.00
POMONA NEW ENGLAND PUNCH CUP,BLUE CORNFLOWER............... 72.00
POMONA NEW ENGLAND TUMBLER,BLUE CORNFLOWER,YELLOW & BLUE.... 68.00
POMONA PEPPER,PEWTER TOP,BLUE CONRFLOWERS.................. 50.00
POMONA PUNCH CUP... 35.00
POMONA PUNCH CUP,CIRCA 1885................................ 35.00
POMONA PUNCH CUP,PLAIN SCALLOPED DESIGN.................... 37.50
POMONA ROSE BOWL,AMBER TINTED RUFFLED TOP & BORDER & FEET... 21.00
POMONA TOOTHPICK HOLDER,NEW ENGLAND,TRICORN,AMBER.......... 55.00

```
POMONA TOOTHPICK,INVERTED THUMBPRINT,AMBER RIM,.............    90.00
POMONA TUMBLER WITH BLUE CORNFLOWERS....................    65.00
PORCELAIN 6 PIECES,ADAMS,RAISED COLOURED FRUIT..............     9.00
PORCELAIN 6 PIECES,AUSTRIAN,SCALLOP PATTERN WITH BEADING....    25.00
PORCELAIN 14 PIECE CHILDS SET OF WHITE DISHES,GOLD TRIMMED..    10.00
PORCELAIN 15 PIECES MARKED AUSTRIA,GOLD BANDED..............    30.00
PORCELAIN 20 PIECES,FRENCH,GOLD TRACERY.....................   120.00
PORCELAIN ASH TRAY,SHELL,GERMANY............................     4.00
PORCELAIN ASH TRAY WITH MATCH BOX HOLDER IN CENTER..........     5.00
PORCELAIN BABY BOOTIE,WHITE,PINK ROSES & BOW ON TOE,BLUE &
  GOLD.....................................................     5.00
PORCELAIN BABY FEEDER,BLUE & WHITE.........................     5.00
PORCELAIN BASKET,CARLSBAD,AUSTRIA,IMPERIAL,PINK & WHITE
  FLORAL & GOLD............................................     8.50
PORCELAIN
  BASKET,OBLONG,HANDPAINTED,BLACK,YELLOW,TREE,BAVARIA.......     3.50
PORCELAIN BASKET,ORANGE WITH YELLOW SCROLLS,LUSTRE
  LINING,HANDPAINT.........................................     4.50
PORCELAIN BEAKER SIGNED HSUAN TE,BLUE & WHITE ,UNDERGLAZED
  BLUE FLOWERS.............................................    95.00
PORCELAIN BERRY SET,7 PIECES,ROSES.........................    24.00
PORCELAIN BERRY SET,HANDPAINTED,SCALLOPED & EMBOSSED GOLD...    24.00
PORCELAIN BERRY SET, PORTRAIT BLOND MAIDEN WITH PINK ROSE IN
  HAIR....................................................    48.50
PORCELAIN BOOT,4 IN.,SOUVENIR OF BOSTON....................     5.00
PORCELAIN BOOT,PRUSSIAN,GOLD TRIM & FLOWERS................     8.50
PORCELAIN BOTTLE,BLUE & WHITE UNDERGLAZE,FIGURAL & SCENIC...    65.00
PORCELAIN BOTTLE,BLUE & WHITE UNDERGLAZE,SKY DRAGON,CARVED
  TEAK STAND...............................................    65.00
PORCELAIN BOTTLE,BLUE UNDERGLAZE,5 CLAWED SEA DRAGON........    65.00
PORCELAIN BOTTLE,COLOGNE,FRENCH,STOPPER,PASTEL FLOWERS......    16.00
PORCELAIN BOTTLE ON CARVED TEAK STAND,WHITE WITH BLUE
  UNDERGLAZE...............................................    60.00
PORCELAIN BOTTLE,PERFUME,FRENCH,PAIR,SQUARE WITH FLORAL
  DECORATIONS..............................................   125.00
PORCELAIN BOTTLE,SCENT,MOON FACE SHAPED....................    18.00
PORCELAIN BOTTLE,SNUFF,CHINESE.............................    36.00
PORCELAIN BOTTLE,SNUFF,CHINESE,CARVED TEAK STAND,AQUAMARINE
  GLAZE...................................................   110.00
PORCELAIN BOTTLE,SNUFF,CHINESE,FAMILLE VERDE COLOURING,WOMAN
  & CHILDREN...............................................    38.00
PORCELAIN BOTTLE,SNUFF,SQUARE,YELLOW,BROWN FLORAL
  MOTIFS,AMBER STOPPER.....................................    22.50
PORCELAIN BOTTLE WITH 6 UNDERGLAZE BLUE FLORAL
  MEDALLIONS,TAN...........................................    70.00
PORCELAIN BOUILLON CUP & SAUCER,AUSTRIA,IMPERIAL CROWN,PINK
  FLORAL..................................................     4.50
PORCELAIN BOWL,8-SIDED,HANDPAINTED RED ROSES,SIGNED.........    18.50
PORCELAIN BOWL,AUSTRIA,HANDPAINTED,3 GOLD KNOB FEET,GOLD &
  GRAPE...................................................    11.50
PORCELAIN BOWL,AUSTRIA,HANDPAINTED,SIGNED,3 GOLD FEET.......     6.00
PORCELAIN BOWL,BERRY,HANDPAINTED ROSES & PURPLE FLOWERS,9
  IN.,GERMANY.............................................     4.50
PORCELAIN BOWL,BLUE BACKGROUND WITH CLOUDS & BATS IN
  YELLOW,GREEN & RED......................................    45.00
PORCELAIN BOWL,CARLSBAD,AUSTRIA,8 IN.,KING PORTRAITS........    50.00
PORCELAIN BOWL,CENTERPIECE OVAL,FRENCH,COIN GOLD
  BORDER,ENAMEL...........................................    48.00
PORCELAIN BOWL,FRANCE SIGNED CURRAN,12 IN.,HANDPAINTED......    45.00
PORCELAIN BOWL,GERMANY,10 IN.,GOLD RIM,GRAPES & ROSES.......     6.75
PORCELAIN BOWL,JAPANESE,BLUE & WHITE,HOUSE ,MOUNTAINS.......    15.00
PORCELAIN BOWL,JAPANESE,BLUE & WHITE WITH PEWTER
  RIM,HOUSE,MOUNTAINS......................................    18.00
PORCELAIN BOWL MARKED BAVARIA,HANDPAINTED CHRISTMAS LILIES..     8.50
PORCELAIN BOWL MARKED FRANCE,PEDESTAL BASE,FLORAL...........     9.50
```

```
PORCELAIN BOWL MARKED GERMANY,LUSTER,PINK,ROSE WITH VIOLETS
   IN CENTER.....................................................    4.75
PORCELAIN BOWL,RICE,CHINA,MANDARIN...............................    4.50
PORCELAIN BOWL,RICE,WITH PLATE,ORANGE & PANELLED SCENES.......    6.00
PORCELAIN BOWL SIGNED EZAN-FRANCE,10 IN.,OPAQUE,BIRDS........   32.00
PORCELAIN BOWL,TEA,CHINA,YELLOW WITH FLOWERS.................    4.50
PORCELAIN BOWL,VEGETABLE,COVERED,ROUND,GOLD TRIMMED,AUSTRIAN   10.00
PORCELAIN BOX,AUSTRIA,COVERED,ROYAL BRUXANIA.................    8.00
PORCELAIN BOX,BLUE FLOWERED,PATCH............................    3.00
PORCELAIN BOX,COVERED DRESSER WITH HANDLES,GOLD & FLOWERS...   16.50
PORCELAIN BOX,FLOWER DECORATED,HINGED PLATE GLASS COVER.....   18.00
PORCELAIN BOX,FOOTED,PORTRAIT,TRINKET........................    4.50
PORCELAIN BOX,HINGED,BRASS RIMMED,GREEN,PINK ROSES,RAISED
   DOTS........................................................   15.00
PORCELAIN BOX,HINGED,GREEN...................................   14.50
PORCELAIN BOX,PATCH,PORTRAIT.................................   30.00
PORCELAIN BOX,PIN,MANDOLIN,EMBOSSED & HANDPAINTED ROSES ON
   COVER.......................................................    6.50
PORCELAIN BOX,PORTRAIT,HINGED,PINK...........................   14.50
PORCELAIN BOX,ROUND COVERED,PURPLE VIOLETS,CREAM
   BACKGROUND,GOLD.............................................   18.50
PORCELAIN BOX,SALT WITH WOODEN COVER MARKED VICTORIA,HANGING    4.50
PORCELAIN BOX SIGNED A. KAUFFMANN,HINGED,CLASSICAL SCENE....   16.00
PORCELAIN BOX SIGNED MOOR,DECORATED,COVERED,TWIG LEGS.......   35.00
PORCELAIN BOX,SOAP,COVERED,SYDENHAM..........................   25.00
PORCELAIN BOX,STAMP..........................................   15.00
PORCELAIN BOX,WHITE,HANDPAINTED..............................   10.00
PORCELAIN BRUSH WASHER,BLUE & WHITE,BLUE FOO DOGS ON
   WHITE,WOOD STAND............................................   45.00
PORCELAIN BUDDHA,ORANGE,GREEN,BLUE,LAVENDER ON WHITE
   GROUND,SIGNED...............................................   85.00
PORCELAIN BUTTER CHIP........................................    2.00
PORCELAIN BUTTER DISH........................................   10.00
PORCELAIN BUTTER PAT,6,FLOWERS...............................   12.00
PORCELAIN BUTTER PAT,CHILDREN IN REVOLUTIONARY WAR COSTUMES.    2.00
PORCELAIN BUTTER PAT CIRCA 1836..............................    3.00
PORCELAIN BUTTER PAT,WHITE...................................   12.50
PORCELAIN CACHE POT & STAND,PARIS,OCHRE YELLOW,CIRCA 1815...  125.00
PORCELAIN CAKE SERVER,AUSTRIAN,PIERCED HANDLES,MEDALLIONS OF
   PINK ROSES..................................................   15.00
PORCELAIN CANDLE HOLDER,7 IN. TALL,GREEN WITH DAISIES &
   GOLD,MARKED.................................................    8.00
PORCELAIN CANDLE HOLDER, GERMAN,MINIATURE,PASTEL GREEN
   BACKGROUND..................................................    6.50
PORCELAIN CANDLE HOLDER,SAUCER TYPE,WHITE,RED HANDLE........    7.50
PORCELAIN CANDLE HOLDERS,PAIR,AUSTRIAN,HANDPAINTED,8 IN.....   15.00
PORCELAIN CANDLE SNUFFER & CANDLE,CHAMBER,GOLD DECOR........   10.00
PORCELAIN CANDLESTICK,FRENCH,9 IN.,ROSES.....................    9.50
PORCELAIN CANDLESTICK,FRENCH,CUSTARD COLOUR..................    4.50
PORCELAIN CANDLESTICK,HANDLED................................    9.00
PORCELAIN CANDLESTICK,PAIR,AUSTRIA,HANDPAINTED...............   15.00
PORCELAIN CANDLESTICK,SINGLE,WHITE GROUND,COBALT,ORANGE &
   GOLD........................................................   30.00
PORCELAIN CANDLESTICK,SINGLE,WHITE GROUND,ORANGE & GOLD.....   27.00
PORCELAIN CANISTER,GERMAN,15 PIECES,BLUE WINDMILLS..........   40.00
PORCELAIN CHAMBERSTICK,SAUCER TYPE,HANDLE,COBALT BLUE BORDER    9.50
PORCELAIN CHAMBERSTICK WITH GOLD,WHITE EMBOSSED & SCROLLED..    8.50
PORCELAIN CHOCOLATE CUP & SAUCER,VICTORIA,AUSTRIA,PORTRAIT..   18.50
PORCELAIN CHOCOLATE POT & 4 CUPS & SAUCERS,GERMANY,LUSTER
   BIRD DECOR..................................................   35.00
PORCELAIN CHOCOLATE POT & 4 CUPS,GERMANY,COLOURFUL POPPIES..   24.50
PORCELAIN CHOCOLATE POT,CARLSBAD,MEDALLIONS OF
   MUSICIANS,GOLD HANDLE.......................................   26.50
PORCELAIN CHOCOLATE POT,COVERED,GREEN WITH RED ROSES........   22.50
PORCELAIN CHOCOLATE POT,FLOWERS,GOLD.........................   13.50
```

```
PORCELAIN CHOCOLATE POT,GERMANY,ROSES.........................    14.00
PORCELAIN CHOCOLATE POT,JAPANESE,MEDALLION SCENE.............    12.00
PORCELAIN CHOCOLATE POT,PRUSSIA,10 IN.,LAVENDER CLEMATIS....    20.00
PORCELAIN CHOCOLATE POT,VICTORIA,AUSTRIA,GREEN & CREAM,GOLD
  DESIGN...................................................    30.00
PORCELAIN CHOCOLATE POT,VICTORIA,CARLSBAD,MUSICIAN & 2
  LADIES...................................................    18.00
PORCELAIN CHOCOLATE POT,WHITE,PINK ROSES....................    12.50
PORCELAIN CHOCOLATE SET,4 CUPS & SAUCERS,POT PINK
  ROSES,BAVARIA............................................    45.00
PORCELAIN CHOCOLATE SET,BAVARIA,PITCHER & 6 CUPS,TAN
  RINGED,GOLD..............................................    40.00
PORCELAIN CHOCOLATE SET,GERMAN,PASTEL ROSES.................    35.00
PORCELAIN CHOCOLATE SET,JAPANESE,RUST,GOLD WITH GARDEN SCENE    20.00
PORCELAIN CHOCOLATE SET,PITCHER WITH BULBOUS BASE,ARTIST
  SIGNED 1904..............................................    49.50
PORCELAIN CHOCOLATE SET,POT & 4 CUPS & SAUCERS,GERMANY,RED
  OPEN ROSES...............................................    30.00
PORCELAIN CHOCOLATE SET,POT & 6 CUPS ,GERMAN,PINK
  ROSES,GREEN..............................................    32.00
PORCELAIN CHOCOLATE SET,POT WHITE & PINK,5 CUPS &
  SAUCERS,PRUSSIAN.........................................    49.50
PORCELAIN COFFEE POT,SIGNED.................................     8.00
PORCELAIN CREAM & SUGAR,FOLEY,COMMEMORATION QUEEN VICTORIA..    14.00
PORCELAIN CREAM & SUGAR,HANDPAINTED,SIGNED..................    20.00
PORCELAIN CREAM & SUGAR,JAPAN,HANDPAINTED...................     3.50
PORCELAIN CREAM PITCHER,MARKED AUSTRIA,WHITE,BLUE UNDER
  BEIGE....................................................     5.00
PORCELAIN CREAM PITCHER WITH DOUBLE HANDLE,WHITE,HANDPAINTED     9.00
PORCELAIN CREAMER,4 IN. HIGH,ORNATE HANDLE,ROSES & VIOLETS..     2.00
PORCELAIN CREAMER & COVERED SUGAR,AUSTRIA,SIGNED,ROSE &
  YELLOW FLOWERS...........................................    12.00
PORCELAIN CREAMER & SUGAR BOWL,EGG SHELL CHINA,PINK & BLUE..    10.50
PORCELAIN CREAMER & SUGAR MARKED GERMANY RED
  MARK,HANDPAINTED ROSES...................................    12.50
PORCELAIN CREAMER,AUSTRIAN,MOOING COW.......................    16.00
PORCELAIN CREAMER,AUSTRIA,MOOSE.............................    15.00
PORCELAIN CREAMER,AUSTRIA,MOOSE HEAD........................     6.50
PORCELAIN CREAMER,BROWN COW.................................    19.00
PORCELAIN CREAMER,BULBOUS,CALLA LILIES & PASTEL FLOWERS.....     2.00
PORCELAIN CREAMER,CHILDREN AT BEACH.........................     3.50
PORCELAIN CREAMER,CZECHOSLOVAKIA,SITTING COW,BROWN WITH TAN.     5.00
PORCELAIN CREAMER,GERMAN,GOLD HANDLE & TRIM.................     6.50
PORCELAIN CREAMER,GERMAN,RAISED GREEN KELP,RED LOBSTER
  HANDLE...................................................     6.50
PORCELAIN CREAMER,GERMAN,WHITE & BLUE,SCHENECTADY SOUVENIR..     3.00
PORCELAIN CREAMER,HANDPAINTED ROSES WITH GOLD...............     2.75
PORCELAIN CREAMER,KAHLA,GERMANY,CHRYSANTHEMUMS,PINK & WHITE.    12.50
PORCELAIN CREAMER,KIWANIS IN GOLD...........................     2.00
PORCELAIN CREAMER MARKED AUSTRIA,MOOSE HEAD.................     5.50
PORCELAIN CREAMER MARKED GERMANY,HANDPAINTED ROSES..........     3.75
PORCELAIN CREAMER,PRUSSIA,ART NOUVEAU,RAISED STAR IN
  BASE,FLORAL..............................................    18.00
PORCELAIN CREAMER SHAPE OF BACCHUS HEAD,4 IN................    27.50
PORCELAIN CREAMER SHAPE OF PARROT MARKED CZECH..............     3.75
PORCELAIN CUP & SAUCER & CAKE
  PLATE,CARLSBAD,AUSTRIA,VICTORIA..........................     6.00
PORCELAIN CUP & SAUCER,BLUE,PEACOCK ON GARDEN WALL..........     8.50
PORCELAIN CUP & SAUCER,BONE,QUEEN ELIZABETH CORONATION......     4.50
PORCELAIN CUP & SAUCER,BONE,RAISED SWIRLS,DAISIES...........    15.00
PORCELAIN CUP & SAUCER,CZECHOSLOVAKIA,YELLOW LUSTER &
  TURQUOISE................................................     8.00
PORCELAIN CUP & SAUCER,DEMI-TASSE,BAVARIA,PORTRAIT..........    18.50
PORCELAIN CUP & SAUCER,DEMI-TASSE,GERMANY,SET OF 6,FUCHSIA &
  GOLD.....................................................    15.00
```

PORCELAIN CUP & SAUCER,DEMI-TASSE,EGG SHELL,GOLD FLOWER
  PETALS ON WHITE.. 3.50
PORCELAIN CUP & SAUCER,DEMI-TASSE,HANDPAINTED FLORALS,GOLD
  TRIM... 3.50
PORCELAIN CUP & SAUCER,DEMI-TASSE,HANDPAINTED YELLOW ,BLUE
  LEAVES... 16.00
PORCELAIN CUP & SAUCER,DEMI-TASSE,JAPAN,PAIR.................. 50.00
PORCELAIN CUP & SAUCER,EGG SHELL............................. 4.50
PORCELAIN CUP & SAUCER,ELIZABETH II,BONE..................... 7.50
PORCELAIN CUP & SAUCER,FLOWER & GOLD TRIM WITH WORDS
  FORGETMENOT.. 4.25
PORCELAIN CUP & SAUCER,GERMAN,SOUVENIR,ROSWELL NEW MEXICO... 5.00
PORCELAIN CUP & SAUCER,GERMANY,FORGET-ME-NOT,GOLD TRIMMED... 5.00
PORCELAIN CUP & SAUCER,GERMANY,MERRY CHRISTMAS IN GOLD
  LETTERING.. 14.50
PORCELAIN CUP & SAUCER,HANDLELESS,DENMARK,GREEN WITH NATIVE
  FIGURES.. 2.00
PORCELAIN CUP & SAUCER,HANDLELESS,PINK TRANSFER,THE YOUNG
  COTTAGERS.. 17.50
PORCELAIN CUP & SAUCER,HANDPAINTED FLOWERS WITH GOLD........ 4.50
PORCELAIN CUP & SAUCER,NEWHALL,FAMILY SCENE IN PINK,BLUE &
  GREEN... 25.00
PORCELAIN CUP & SAUCER,PAIR,BAVARIA,YELLOW,GOLD TRIM........ 5.00
PORCELAIN CUP & SAUCER,PINK,PUSS IN BOOTS................... 5.00
PORCELAIN CUP & SAUCER,SET OF 12,BONE CHINA................. 42.00
PORCELAIN CUP & SAUCER,TEA,BAVARIA,PINK & WHITE............. 16.00
PORCELAIN CUP & SAUCER,TEA,ENGLISH,QUEEN ELIZABETH
  CORONATION... 5.50
PORCELAIN CUP,BABY,GERMANY,SOUVENIR NIAGARA FALLS IN GOLD
  LETTERS.. 30.00
PORCELAIN CUP,GERMANY,SIP FOR INVALIDS,WHITE WITH GOLD TRIM. 5.50
PORCELAIN CUP,GOLD & BLUE,RAISED DESIGN..................... 6.00
PORCELAIN CUP,HANDLELESS,JAPANESE,BLUE &
  WHITE,FLORAL,BUTTERFLY................................... 10.00
PORCELAIN CUP,HANDLELESS MARKED STONE CHINA,BLUE............ 20.00
PORCELAIN CUP,JUMBO,GERMANY,I AM NOT GREEDY BUT I LIKE A LOT 9.50
PORCELAIN CUP,STEM,WHITE BACKGROUND WITH PAINTINGS OF
  FLOWERS.. 49.00
PORCELAIN DESSERT SERVICE FOR 6,HANDPAINTED FLOWERS......... 66.50
PORCELAIN DINNER SET,SERVICE FOR 6,CARLSBAD,AUSTRIA......... 130.00
PORCELAIN DISH,AUSTRIA,CROWN VICTORIA,PORTRAIT
  CENTER,MEDITATION,SIGNED................................. 15.00
PORCELAIN DISH,BONE,ENGLAND,KIDNEY SHAPE,JOHNSON BROS....... 2.50
PORCELAIN DISH,BONE,GERMAN,PINK LIP,SHADED BLUE & WHITE
  FLOWERS.. 5.00
PORCELAIN DISH,BONE,SET OF 8,ENGLISH....................... 15.00
PORCELAIN DISH,BONE,WHITE.................................. 3.00
PORCELAIN DISH,CAKE,GERMANY,DIVIDED........................ 14.50
PORCELAIN DISH,CELERY,BAVARIA,PRINCES REGENT,GOLD
  BORDER,FLORAL.. 7.50
PORCELAIN DISH,CELERY,KIMONO LADIES,RED TRIM............... 5.50
PORCELAIN DISH,CHEESE,COVERED,GOLD & GREEN................. 16.50
PORCELAIN DISH,CHEESE,COVERED,FLORAL EMBOSSED.............. 11.00
PORCELAIN DISH,CHEESE,SIGNED BONN GERMANY,WEDGE SHAPE...... 22.50
PORCELAIN DISH,CHINA,PEONY & GAME COCK OVAL............... 7.50
PORCELAIN DISH,CHINESE,4-SIDED,FIGHTING ROOSTERS
  DESIGN,CHINA IN RED...................................... 45.00
PORCELAIN DISH,DRESSER,PRUSSIA,HANDPAINTED ROSES & GOLD..... 4.50
PORCELAIN DISH,GERMANY,CHILDS FEEDING,3 CROWN MARK,JACK
  SPRAT.. 10.00
PORCELAIN DISH,GRAVY,COVERED FISH,BAVARIA,IMPERIAL CROWN
  CHINA.. 12.00
PORCELAIN DISH,LOBSTER,PINK & WHITE PANELS,GOLD TRIM........ 25.00
PORCELAIN DISH,LOBSTER,MARKED GERMANY...................... 18.00
PORCELAIN DISH MARKED KPM,FLOWERS ON GREY.................. 20.00

```
PORCELAIN DISH MARKED LEONARD VIENNA,HANDPAINTED,SCALLOPED..      7.00
PORCELAIN DISH MARKED L.P.FRANCE,3 PART SECTIONAL...........     25.00
PORCELAIN DISH,PAIR,COVERED,PARIS CIRCA 1830,PAINTED
  BIRDS,FLOWERS...........................................     250.00
PORCELAIN DISH,PICKLE,HANDPAINTED GREEN WITH PINK
  ROSES,GOLD,SIGNED........................................     15.00
PORCELAIN DISH,SAUCE,BLUE & ROSE SPRIG......................      4.00
PORCELAIN DISH,SAUCE,MARKED CHINA,PEONY.....................      6.00
PORCELAIN DISH,SCALLOPED LEAF,HANDPAINTED,WHITE GLAZE.......     15.00
PORCELAIN DISH,TRIANGULAR BABYS HIGH CHAIR,MARKED...........     10.00
PORCELAIN DRESSER SET,4 PIECES,HANDPAINTED FLOWER GARLANDS..     27.50
PORCELAIN DISH,VEGETABLE MARKED AUSTRIA,SCALLOPED,ROUNDED
  CORNERS.................................................     15.00
PORCELAIN DESSERT SET,17 PIECES,PARIS,WHITE WITH FLORAL
  DESIGN..................................................    375.00
PORCELAIN DRESSER SET SIGNED W.WILSON,PAINTED ROSES ON GREEN
  & IVORY.................................................     75.00
PORCELAIN DRESSER SET,VICTORIAN,YELLOW ROSES,WHITE TRAY.....     22.50
PORCELAIN EGG.............................................      2.00
PORCELAIN EGG,COVERED,HANDPAINTED VIOLETS ON COVER..........      4.00
PORCELAIN EGG CUP SIGNED BAVARIA,WHITE WITH FLORAL..........      3.25
PORCELAIN EGG SERVING SET..................................     12.50
PORCELAIN EWER,PAIR,AUSTRIA,OLIVE GREEN BASE TO WHITE,GIRL..     20.00
PORCELAIN EWER,PORTRAIT,GERMANY,BLUE & GOLD TRIM WITH
  CHERUBS.................................................      7.00
PORCELAIN FIGURE,CHINESE,PAIR 9 IN.,SIGNED..................     55.00
PORCELAIN FIGURE OF HOTEI & A CHILD,11 IN. TALL.............     65.00
PORCELAIN FIGURE WITH QUIVER,ARROWS........................     15.50
PORCELAIN FIGURINE,6 IN. TALL BALLERINA....................     35.00
PORCELAIN FIGURINE,12 IN. TALL FRENCHMAN OF LOUIS XIV PERIOD    150.00
PORCELAIN FIGURINE,BLANC FOO DOGS,PAIR.....................     15.00
PORCELAIN FIGURINE,CAT,FRENCH,7 IN. STRETCHED
  OUT,ENAMELED,GREEN EYES.................................     15.00
PORCELAIN FIGURINE,CAT SITTING ON QUILTED PILLOW...........     24.00
PORCELAIN FIGURINE,CHINESE,ELEPHANT ON TEAK
  STAND,BLUE,STAMPED CHINA................................     30.00
PORCELAIN FIGURINE,DUTCH GIRL,SWINGS SIDEWAYS..............     28.75
PORCELAIN FIGURINE ,FISH SIGNED ROYAL WORCESTER,5 IN. LONG..     58.00
PORCELAIN FIGURINE,GEISHA,20 IN. TALL,BISQUE FACE &
  HANDS,BLACK ROBE........................................     65.00
PORCELAIN FIGURINE,GERMAN,LADY SEATED ON SETTEE,GENTLEMAN
  STANDS..................................................     65.00
PORCELAIN FIGURINES,GERMANY,PAIR,LADY & GENTLEMAN,8 IN. TALL     75.00
PORCELAIN FIGURINE,JAY BIRD IN BOUGH,12 IN. TALL,UNDERGLAZE
  BLUE MARK...............................................     65.00
PORCELAIN FIGURINE,MULE,IMPERIAL AMPHORA,ARTIST SIGNED &
  DATED 1908..............................................     75.00
PORCELAIN FIGURINE,VICTORIAN,PAIR WIRE HAIRED TERRIERS,GOLD.     15.00
PORCELAIN FISH SET,7 PIECES,ARTIST SIGNED,REDDISH BROWN
  BORDER..................................................     35.00
PORCELAIN FISH SET,9 PIECES,VICTORIA,AUSTRIA...............     85.00
PORCELAIN FOOTWARMER......................................     15.00
PORCELAIN FRAME,8 X 6 IN.,HANDPAINTED PANSIES..............     28.00
PORCELAIN GLASS,JUICE,WHITE,ROBERT BURNS GRACE PRINTED.....     10.00
PORCELAIN GRAVY BOAT & TRAY,LAUGHLIN EMPRESS...............      2.50
PORCELAIN GRAVY BOAT,VIENNA,AUSTRIA,CROWN & 2 SHIELDS......      8.00
PORCELAIN HAIR RECEIVER,AUSTRIA,IVORY COLOUR,POPPY DECOR....      7.50
PORCELAIN HAIR RECIEVER,GERMANY,WHITE,PINK,BEIGE,ROSES......      6.00
PORCELAIN HAIR RECEIVER,SQUARISH..........................      6.00
PORCELAIN HAIR RECEIVER,STRAWBERRIES & VINES...............      9.00
PORCELAIN HAIR RECEIVER,STRAWBERRY BLOSSOM COVER...........     12.00
PORCELAIN HAND TO HOLD RINGS,GOLD FINISH...................      5.00
PORCELAIN HAT SIGNED KAUFFMANN............................     15.00
PORCELAIN HATPIN HOLDER,BUST OF WOMAN......................     10.00
PORCELAIN HATPIN HOLDER,HANDPAINTED.......................      7.50
```

PORCELAIN HATPIN HOLDER MARKED GERMANY,ROSES & GREEN LEAVES. ... 12.50
PORCELAIN HATPIN HOLDER,PURPLE ROSES & GREEN................. 8.00
PORCELAIN HATPIN HOLDER,R.G.GERMANY,GOLD,PINK FLOWERS........ 14.00
PORCELAIN HATPIN HOLDER,STOKE ON TRENT,ENGLAND,HANDPAINTED.. 12.50
PORCELAIN HATPIN HOLDER,SUN BONNET,SAUCER BASE.............. 42.00
PORCELAIN HATPIN HOLDER,WHITE,FLOWERS & GOLD................ 6.50
PORCELAIN HATPIN HOLDER WITH ATTACHED SAUCER BASE,AUSTRIAN.. 10.00
PORCELAIN HATPIN,PEARLS,STONES & GOLD TRIM.................. 4.00
PORCELAIN INKWELL,2-WELL.................................... 19.50
PORCELAIN INKWELL,DOMED COVERED,SIGNED,HANDPAINTED.......... 18.00
PORCELAIN INK WELL,DRESDEN TYPE,BRASS HINGED TOP............ 24.00
PORCELAIN INKWELL WITH ATTACHED TRAY,SQUARE................. 12.00
PORCELAIN INVALID FEEDER,OVAL............................... 5.50
PORCELAIN INVALID FEEDER,PINK,ROSE.......................... 9.50
PORCELAIN INVALID FEEDER,PRISTINE WHITE..................... 5.00
PORCELAIN INVALID FEEDER,WHITE
   3.50 TO... 6.00
PORCELAIN JAR,APOTHECARY,FRENCH,PAIR,COVERED,GOLD TRIM,WHITE 75.00
PORCELAIN JAR,CHINA,PAIR COVERED MANDARIN................... 15.00
PORCELAIN JAR,COOKIE,LAVENDER FLOWERS....................... 6.75
PORCELAIN JAR,COOKIE,ORIENTAL,SIGNED,ENAMELLED FLOWERS &
   BUTTERFLIES.. 17.50
PORCELAIN JAR,CRACKER,CARLSBAD,MADALLIONS OF MUSICIANS...... 25.00
PORCELAIN JAR,CRACKER,ENGLISH,HANDPAINTED ENAMEL,PURPLE
   GRAPES.. 27.00
PORCELAIN JAR,CRACKER MARKED G.B.GERMANY,APPLE & GRAPE
   DESIGN.. 25.00
PORCELAIN JAR,GINGER,COVERED,GREEN BACKGROUND WITH FLOWERS.. 95.00
PORCELAIN JAR,JAM,AUSTRIA,COVERED,2 HANDLES................. 8.50
PORCELAIN JAR,JAM,CARLSBAD,FLOW BLUE GOLD WITH ORCHID
   FLOWERS... 21.00
PORCELAIN JAR,JAM,COVER & SAUCER,WHITE WITH PINK
   FLORAL,MARKED... 19.00
PORCELAIN JAR,JAM,COVERED,HANDPAINTED PURPLE GRAPES,GOLD.... 17.50
PORCELAIN JAR,JAM,FLORAL & GOLD DECORATED,HOLE IN
   BOTTOM,HANDLES & LID.................................... 10.00
PORCELAIN JAR,MUSTARD & LADLE,MUTED BLUE & WHITE............ 4.50
PORCELAIN JAR,MUSTARD & SPOON,PINK FLOWERS,RAISED STAR ON
   BASE.. 4.00
PORCELAIN JARDINIERE,CHINESE,OFF WHITE & BLUE ON 3 FEET..... 50.00
PORCELAIN JARDINIERE MARKED BAVARIA,HANDPAINTED............. 24.50
PORCELAIN JUG,WINE,AUSTRIAN,HANDPAINTED GREEN WITH BLACK
   BIRD.. 9.50
PORCELAIN KNIFE REST MARKED PIEFFER,WHITE,ELONGATED
   GREYHOUND... 8.50
PORCELAIN KNIFE REST,WHITE,ELONGATED BULLDOG................ 8.50
PORCELAIN KNOB FOR CABINET,PAIR BLUE....................... 1.00
PORCELAIN LADLE,SAUCE,CHINA,BLUE & WHITE.................... 2.00
PORCELAIN LADLE,SAUCE,CHINA,YELLOW WITH FLOWERS............. 3.50
PORCELAIN MATCH HOLDER,BEARDED DWARF LYING ON BACK &
   BALANCING KEG... 16.50
PORCELAIN MATCH HOLDER,CONE SHAPED......................... 3.00
PORCELAIN MATCH HOLDER,HANGING,ORIENTAL SCENE.............. 6.50
PORCELAIN MATCH HOLDER,ROYAL BLUE MEDALLION,CAMEO PORTRAIT.. 8.75
PORCELAIN MATCH HOLDER,WALL TYPE,DOUBLE COMPARTMENTS,FLOWERS 8.50
PORCELAIN MATCH HOLDER,YELLOW BARREL WITH PINK ROSES........ 6.50
PORCELAIN MENU STAND,STANDS LIKE EASEL,GREEN BACKGROUND WITH
   SCENE... 12.00
PORCELAIN MORTAR & PESTLE,9 IN............................. 25.00
PORCELAIN MUFFINEER,ORANGE POPPIES......................... 10.50
PORCELAIN MUFFINEER,VICTORIA,AUSTRIA,DOMED SILVER LID....... 20.00
PORCELAIN MUG,3 IN.,WITH MONK DRAWING BEER FROM BARREL...... 6.50
PORCELAIN MUG,BARREL SHAPED,HANDPAINTED SCARLET POPPIES IN
   GREEN... 7.50
PORCELAIN MUG,BEER... 3.50

```
PORCELAIN MUG BIRD WHISTLE HANDLE............................  11.00
PORCELAIN MUG,CHILDS,CHILDREN PLAYING SOLDIER...............   5.00
PORCELAIN MUG,CHILDS,WHITE WITH 4 CHILDREN PLAYING..........   7.50
PORCELAIN MUG,DERBY,MANS FACE...............................  200.00
PORCELAIN MUG,GERMANY,DEER..................................   7.50
PORCELAIN MUG,MERRY CHRISTMAS...............................   5.50
PORCELAIN MUG,PRESENTATION DATED MARCH 11, 1860.............  27.50
PORCELAIN MUG,QUEEN ELIZABETH CORONATION,JUNE 2,1953........  10.00
PORCELAIN MUG,SCUTTLE,GERMAN,ROSES..........................  14.50
PORCELAIN MUG SIGNED F.ALM,SCALLOPED GOLD TOP,BLUE FROM BASE
 UP.........................................................  15.00
PORCELAIN MUG,TOM & JERRY,CARLSBAD,AUSTRIA,PINK FLOWERS &
 GOLD TRIM..................................................   4.25
PORCELAIN MUG,TOM & JERRY,J.S.GERMANY,GOLD BAND &
 INSCRIPTION................................................   6.50
PORCELAIN MUG,WHITE WITH STRAWBERRIES.......................   6.00
PORCELAIN MUSTARD,COVERED,RAISED GOLD ON WHITE..............   3.50
PORCELAIN MUSTARD POT ,RUFFLED EDGES ON LID & PLATTER.......   6.50
PORCELAIN MUSTARD POT SHAPE OF SITTING ORIENTAL MAN,WHITE...   7.50
PORCELAIN NAPKIN RING,BLUE & WHITE DUTCH SCENE..............   5.50
PORCELAIN NUT SET,ROYAL AUSTRIA,HANDPAINTED.................  16.50
PORCELAIN PAINTING,FRAMED,7 X 9 IN..........................  150.00
PORCELAIN PAINTING,OVAL PORTRAIT OF JOSEPHINE...............  25.00
PORCELAIN PAINTING SIGNED KPM,OVAL,FRAMED,YOUNG GIRL........  150.00
PORCELAIN PAINTING SIGNED WAGNER,OVAL,WOMAN HOLDING CANDLE..  175.00
PORCELAIN PERFUME,FIGURAL,OLD FASHIONED GIRL................   5.00
PORCELAIN PIPE BOWL,HUNTER WITH DOG,CARVED STEM.............   8.50
PORCELAIN PITCHER & TRAY,CARLSBAD,3 IN.,HANDPAINTED,PURPLE &
 YELLOW.....................................................  11.00
PORCELAIN PITCHER,BAVARIA,FISH SHAPE,OPEN MOUTH,PINK,GREEN
 LUSTER.....................................................  16.00
PORCELAIN PITCHER,BUTTERMILK,HANDPAINTED,ROYAL BAVARIA
 SIGNED LEONI...............................................  30.00
PORCELAIN PITCHER,COBALT BLUE...............................  12.50
PORCELAIN PITCHER,HANDPAINTED,SIGNED,TREE OF LIFE,KT.& K CO.  50.00
PORCELAIN PITCHER,LEMONADE,BURGUNGY TOP,PURPLE GRAPES,LEAVES  15.00
PORCELAIN PITCHER MARKED 3 CROWN CHINA GERMANY,OFF WHITE TO
 GREEN......................................................   7.50
PORCELAIN PITCHER MARKED GERMANY,OFF-WHITE,PEACHES..........   7.50
PORCELAIN PITCHER MARKED GERMANY,OFF WHITE TO GREEN.........   6.00
PORCELAIN PITCHER MARKED MADE IN CZECHOSLOVAKIA,WHITE,BOATS.   7.50
PORCELAIN PITCHER MARKED T.P.FRANCE,HANDPAINTED PURPLE & RED
 GRAPES.....................................................  25.00
PORCELAIN PITCHER,MILK,BAVARIA,6 IN.,2 PINK & YELLOW ROSES..   8.50
PORCELAIN PITCHER,MILK,ENGLISH,PELICAN,FLOW BLUE COLOURING..   3.75
PORCELAIN PITCHER,MILK,HANDPAINTED PURPLE IRIS..............  20.00
PORCELAIN PITCHER,MILK,HANDPAINTED PURPLE IRIS WITH GOLD
 LEAVES.....................................................  20.00
PORCELAIN PITCHER,ROSES,3 GOLD LEGS.........................   4.00
PORCELAIN PITCHER SIGNED A. KAUFMANN,MEDALLION IN CLASSICAL
 SCENE......................................................  20.00
PORCELAIN PITCHER,SIGNED PAINTER M.L.HUGES 90,FLORAL........  32.00
PORCELAIN PITCHER,STONE CHINA,RAISED SCROLL & LEAF DESIGN...  19.00
PORCELAIN PITCHER,SYRUP,VICTORIA,AUSTRIA....................  15.00
PORCELAIN PITCHER,TANKARD,TRENTON,NEW JERSEY,EMPIRE
 CHINA,RED ROSES............................................  38.00
PORCELAIN PITCHER,TANKARD TYPE,AZTEC........................   5.00
PORCELAIN PITCHER,WATER,TOOTHBRUSH HOLDER & MUG,HOLER
 LAUGHLIN,9 IN..............................................  17.50
PORCELAIN PLAQUE,PAIR HANDPAINTED,GOLD LEAF & EBONY FRAMES..  100.00
PORCELAIN PLATE,6 IN.,CHILDREN ON SEE-SAW...................   4.00
PORCELAIN PLATE,6 IN.,WHITE WITH GREEN PHEASANTS IN TREES...   3.00
PORCELAIN PLATE,7 IN.,POMPEII...............................   3.75
PORCELAIN PLATE,9 IN.,HANDPAINTED ROSES.....................   7.00
PORCELAIN PLATE,10 IN.,WHITE,FLORAL CENTER,COBALT BLUE
```

```
BORDER................................................    3.00
PORCELAIN PLATE,1911,TREBLE COUNCIL NO.13,WHITE & GOLD......   13.00
PORCELAIN PLATE,BAREFOOT BOY IN OVERALLS HOEING CORN........    4.50
PORCELAIN PLATE,BAVARIA,7 IN.,SCALLOPED GOLD EDGE,DAFFODILS.    5.00
PORCELAIN PLATE,BAVARIA,7 IN.,SCALLOPED GOLD
  EDGE,DAISIES,SIGNED.................................    5.00
PORCELAIN PLATE,BAVARIA,7 IN.,SCALLOPED GOLD EDGE,POPPIES...    5.00
PORCELAIN PLATE,BAVARIA,HANDPAINTED DUCK,QUAIL,8 IN.........    9.00
PORCELAIN PLATE,BLOOR,DERBY,RED,BLUE & GOLD DECOR...........   20.00
PORCELAIN PLATE,BLUE,8 IN.,MEDALLION,HINDU TEMPLES..........   17.50
PORCELAIN PLATE,BREAD,BOY & GIRL WITH TOP..................   10.50
PORCELAIN PLATE,BREAD,ROSE CENTER..........................    4.50
PORCELAIN PLATE,BREAD,SCHWARZENHAMMER,BAVARIA,WHITE,GIVE US
  THIS DAY..........................................   10.00
PORCELAIN PLATE,CAKE,CARLSBAD,AUSTRIA,HANDLED,ARTIST SIGNED.   13.50
PORCELAIN PLATE,CAKE,DAHLIA,CLOSED HANDLES.................   12.50
PORCELAIN PLATE,CAKE,GERMAN,CUT OUT HANDLES,FLOWERS & GOLD..    6.50
PORCELAIN PLATE,CAKE,GERMANY,OPEN HANDLE,9 IN.,ROSES........    5.50
PORCELAIN PLATE,CAKE,HANDPAINTED BLACKBERRIES WITH FOLIAGE &
  PINK.............................................    3.00
PORCELAIN PLATE,CAKE,IVORY OPEN HANDLED....................   34.50
PORCELAIN,PLATE,CAKE,PINK ROSES,COBALT BLUE & GOLD EDGE.....   20.00
PORCELAIN PLATE,CAKE,VICTORIAN,SQUARE 10 IN.,HANDPAINTED....    9.50
PORCELAIN PLATE,CARLSBAD,VIENNA,SCROLLED GOLD TRIM,2 MALLARD
  DUCKS............................................   24.50
PORCELAIN PLATE,CARLSBAD,AUSTRIA,PINK & YELLOW CABBAGE ROSES   12.50
PORCELAIN PLATE,CHILDS,ROBINSON CRUSOE.....................   12.50
PORCELAIN PLATE,CHOP,GERMAN,11 IN.,ROSES...................   25.00
PORCELAIN PLATE,DERBY IMPRESSED BLUE CROWN,PEACOCK,BLUE &
  WHITE............................................    5.00
PORCELAIN PLATE,DESSERT,SET OF 9,GOLD TRIMMED,FLORAL
  DECORATED........................................   18.50
PORCELAIN PLATE,ELIZABETH II,BONE.........................    4.00
PORCELAIN PLATE,FRENCH,GIRL IN GARDEN.....................   18.00
PORCELAIN PLATE,FRENCH,HANDPAINTED PINK ROSES,GREEN & WHITE
  SCROLLS..........................................    6.50
PORCELAIN PLATE,FRUIT,AUSTRIA,9 IN.,WHITE CENTER,RED APPLES
  BORDER...........................................    5.00
PORCELAIN PLATE,FRUIT MARKED KPM,PAIR,COLOURED BORDERS......   19.00
PORCELAIN PLATE,FRUIT,ROYAL MUNICH,HANDPAINTED CHERRIES IN
  STRAW BASKET.....................................   12.00
PORCELAIN PLATE,GERMAN,3 CROWN MARK,12 IN.,CASTLE SCENE.....   25.00
PORCELAIN PLATE,GERMAN,SET OF 6 ,INITIALED & IMPRESSED MARKS   24.00
PORCELAIN PLATE,GERMANY,9 IN.,3 CROWN MARK,GOLD BORDER,6
  ROSES............................................    4.50
PORCELAIN PLATE,GERMANY,POPPY,8 IN.,ORANGE-AMBER POPPIES....    4.00
PORCELAIN PLATE,HANDPAINTED GRAPES ON GREEN BACKGROUND,9 IN.    7.50
PORCELAIN PLATE,HANDPAINTED WATER LILY ON WATER,GOLD BORDER.   17.50
PORCELAIN PLATE,HISTORICAL,10 IN.,LANDING OF OUR FATHERS....   39.50
PORCELAIN PLATE,HUNT SCENE IN CENTER,FLORAL & GOLD RIM......   18.00
PORCELAIN PLATE,JAMES A.GARFIELD FOR PRESIDENT.............   15.00
PORCELAIN PLATE,KING GEORGE VI & QUEEN ELIZABETH CORONATION.   20.00
PORCELAIN PLATE,MAESTRICHT,HOLLAND,8 IN.,RED THISTLE WITH
  BLUE.............................................    4.50
PORCELAIN PLATE MARKED 3 CROWN GERMANY,PAIR 8
  IN.,HANDPAINTED FRUIT.............................   17.50
PORCELAIN PLATE MARKED ABBEVILLE,9 IN.,BLUE &
  WHITE,FLORENTINE CHINA............................    4.50
PORCELAIN PLATE MARKED AUSTRIA,TRANSFER CHERUBS CENTER,8 IN.    8.00
PORCELAIN PLATE MARKED BAVARIA,8 IN.,GOLD BORDER,WHITE
  ORCHID CENTER....................................    6.00
PORCELAIN PLATE MARKED BAVARIA,HANDPAINTED PHEASANT.........   25.00
PORCELAIN PLATE MARKED CARLSBAD,AUSTRIA,SOUVENIR OF NEW
  ORLEANS..........................................   15.00
PORCELAIN PLATE MARKED ENGLISH,PAIR 9 IN.,GEORGE & MARTHA
```

WASHINGTON...	60.00
PORCELAIN PLATE MARKED FLORENTINE,HANDPAINTED PINK,BLUEBIRD	
CENTER..	6.00
PORCELAIN,PLATE,NAPOLEON MARKED P B X 1821................	18.00
PORCELAIN PLATE,NAPOLEON MARKED VICTORIA,CARLSBAD,AUSTRIA,10	
IN..	35.00
PORCELAIN PLATE,OYSTER,SET OF 6,HALF MOON SHAPE,PINK LUSTER	
& WHITE...	55.00
PORCELAIN PLATE,OYSTER,DATED 1881,UNION WORKS,11 IN..........	40.00
PORCELAIN PLATE,PAIR 7 IN.,HOUSE THAT JACK BUILT & CHILDREN	
RIDING..	10.00
PORCELAIN PLATE,PUSS IN BOOTS............................	5.00
PORCELAIN PLATE,QUEEN LOUISE,7 IN.,ROSE & GOLD BAND.........	18.50
PORCELAIN PLATE,RANSOM,7 IN..............................	3.50
PORCELAIN PLATE,RANSOM,9 IN..............................	3.50
PORCELAIN PLATE,RED RIDING HOOD,SHELLY....................	5.00
PORCELAIN PLATE,SALAD,GERMANY,SET OF 5,ROSES,BLUE	
FORGET-ME-NOTS..	10.00
PORCELAIN PLATE,SALOPIAN,8 IN.,PIERCED BORDER,ORIENTAL SCENE	85.00
PORCELAIN PLATE,SERVING,SELB,BAVARIA,11 IN.,CREAM WITH GREEN	
& GOLD..	8.00
PORCELAIN PLATE,SET OF 5 7 IN.,SCALLOPED,PINK & RED ROSES...	7.50
PORCELAIN PLATE,SET OF 6 SIGNED BOYLE,BAVARIA,BLUE & APRICOT	
SHADING...	28.00
PORCELAIN PLATE,SET OF 6,VICTORIA,CARLSBAD,AUSTRIA..........	15.00
PORCELAIN PLATE SIGNED A.KOCH,GRAPES......................	18.00
PORCELAIN PLATE SIGNED ANGELICA KAUFFMANN,CROWN MARK........	48.00
PORCELAIN PLATE SIGNED ANGELICA KAUFFMANN,PAIR,AUSTRIA......	95.00
PORCELAIN PLATE SIGNED KAUFFMANN,CLASSICAL FIGURES,9 IN.....	24.00
PORCELAIN PLATE SIGNED KAUFFMANN,VICTORIA AUSTRIA,SCENE GIRL	
& MAN...	23.50
PORCELAIN PLATE SIGNED MAJ,HANDPAINTED STAG DEER & BIRDS....	30.00
PORCELAIN PLATE SIGNED ROSE TYLER 1887,HANDPAINTED PINK &	
LAVENDER..	8.25
PORCELAIN PLATE,SIGNED,SOUVENIR DICKENS MR.PICKWICK.........	18.50
PORCELAIN PLATE,VICTORIA,AUSTRIA,SOUVENIR OF BOSTON,PIERCED	
BACK,7 IN...	12.50
PORCELAIN PLATE,WALL SIGNED KAUFFMAN,AUSTRIAN..............	35.00
PORCELAIN PLATE,WALL,SIGNED SADDLER,PAIR,HANDPAINTED........	38.50
PORCELAIN PLATTER,CARLSBAD AUSTRIA,SCALLOPED EDGE WITH SHELL	
DESIGN..	12.50
PORCELAIN PLATTER,CARLSBAD,TURNED UP PINK RIM,HANDPAINTED...	32.00
PORCELAIN PLATTER,CZECHOSLOVAKIA,COLOURS & GOLD,ORNATE......	20.00
PORCELAIN PLATTER MARKED E.B.WITH ROYAL CROWN,BLUE & WHITE..	8.00
PORCELAIN PORTRAIT IN EASEL FRAME,WOMANS HEAD,ENAMEL........	35.00
PORCELAIN PORTRAIT,KPM OVAL SHAPED,FRAMED.................	250.00
PORCELAIN PORTRAIT PLATE,BAVARIA,LOUISE,6 IN...............	10.00
PORCELAIN PORTRAIT PLATE,CARLSBAD, AUSTRIA,8 IN............	10.00
PORCELAIN PORTRAIT PLATE,GERMANY,SIGNED ASTONI,9 IN.,3 CROWN	
MARK,LADY...	48.00
PORCELAIN PORTRAIT PLATE MARKED	
VICTORIA,CARLSBAD,AUSTRIA,SIGNED........................	22.50
PORCELAIN PUNCH BOWL,2 PARTS,DECORATED IN & OUT WITH GREEN &	
PURPLE..	48.00
PORCELAIN PUNCH BOWL,ENGLISH,CHERUBS DECOR................	100.00
PORCELAIN PUNCH SET WITH SILVER LINING,13 PIECES,HANDPAINTED	110.00
PORCELAIN RAMEKIN,SET OF 6,PINK ROSES,AUSTRIAN............	28.50
PORCELAIN RING TREE,4 BRANCH,GREY TO WHITE................	6.00
PORCELAIN RING TREE,GAY COLOURED BIRDS....................	3.00
PORCELAIN RING TREE,WHITE,SPRAY PINK ROSES................	3.50
PORCELAIN RING TREE,YELLOW FLOWERS,GOLD TRIM..............	15.00
PORCELAIN ROSEBOWL,VIENNA,GOLD SCALLOPED TOP,CURVED FEET....	12.00
PORCELAIN SALT & PEPPER,JAPANESE,FLOWERS DECORATION.........	2.50
PORCELAIN SALT & PEPPER,PRUSSIA,CABBAGE ROSE IN COLOUR......	9.50
PORCELAIN SALT & PEPPER,RED TOMATO.......................	4.00

```
PORCELAIN SALT & PEPPER SET,SCALLOPED BASE,COBALT BANDS,ROSE
  FLOWERS.................................................  3.50
PORCELAIN SALT & PEPPER SHAKER,HANDPAINTED BLUE & WHITE
  FLOWERS,GOLD............................................ 10.00
PORCELAIN SALT & PEPPER SHAKER,PAIR PINK DAHLIA........... 20.00
PORCELAIN SALT & PEPPER,WHITE SQUATTY,PAIR,HANDPAINTED.... 12.00
PORCELAIN SALT DIP,COBALT BLUE,ENAMELLED FLOWERS,STERLING
  RIM....................................................  7.50
PORCELAIN SALT DIP,PAIR SWAN.............................  5.50
PORCELAIN SALT DIP,SET OF 4.............................  3.00
PORCELAIN SALT DIP,SIGNED R.W.GERMANY,ORNATE FLORAL......  7.00
PORCELAIN SALT ON STANDARD,SET OF 6..................... 18.00
PORCELAIN SALT SHAKER MARKED GERMANY,DECORATED...........  3.00
PORCELAIN SALT WITH GOLD SPOON,FOOTED,GOLD...............  7.00
PORCELAIN SAUCER,DEMI-TASSE,AUSTRIA,PINK ROSES & GREEN...  1.50
PORCELAIN SAUCER,DEMI-TASSE,SET OF 6,EDWIN KNOWLES,OPEN ROSE
  FLORAL.................................................  5.00
PORCELAIN SAUCER,JAPANESE,BLUE & WHITE,7 MEN AT TABLE GAMING 12.00
PORCELAIN SHAKER,PAIR OWL FIGURAL.......................  2.00
PORCELAIN SHAVING MUG MARKED GERMAN,WHITE,YELLOW,PINK & ROSE 7.00
PORCELAIN SHAVING MUG MARKED GERMANY,GOLD BAND..........  7.50
PORCELAIN SHAVING MUG,WHITE,PINK & GOLD TOP............. 10.50
PORCELAIN SHAVING MUG,WHITE,YELLOW & BLUE...............  5.00
PORCELAIN SHOE,HIGH HEELED PINK,CHERUB ON PILLOW IN
  FRONT,GOLD.............................................  6.50
PORCELAIN SHOE,HIGH HEELED,WHITE WITH FLORAL DESIGN,GOLD
  TRIM.................................................. 12.00
PORCELAIN SHOE,PALE GREEN...............................  8.00
PORCELAIN SLIPPER,BLUE,WHITE,GOLD,CHERUB ON TOE.........  6.75
PORCELAIN SLIPPER,PURPLE LUSTRE WITH LEMON PANELS.......  9.00
PORCELAIN SLIPPER,WHITE,5 IN.,BUTTERFLY EMBOSSED,GOLD TRIM..  5.00
PORCELAIN SOUP PLATE,BAVARIA,SET OF 4,QUEEN LOUISE......  8.00
PORCELAIN SOUP PLATE,HISTORICAL,BLUE,PINE ORCHARD HOUSE..... 53.50
PORCELAIN SUGAR & CREAMER,AUSTRIA....................... 15.00
PORCELAIN SUGAR & CREAMER MARKED GERMANY,OLD ORCHARD BEACH
  MAINE..................................................  5.50
PORCELAIN SUGAR & CREAMER,RAISED GOLD ON WHITE..........  6.00
PORCELAIN SUGAR & CREAMER SIGNED KAYSER,GOLD & GREEN....  6.50
PORCELAIN SUGAR,COVERED,SYDENHAM........................ 35.00
PORCELAIN SUGAR SHAKER,BAVARIA,PURPLE VIOLETS WITH GREEN
  LEAVES................................................ 12.50
PORCELAIN SUGAR SHAKER,HANDPAINTED POPPIES,SIGNED....... 13.00
PORCELAIN SUGAR SHAKER,SIGNED,HANDPAINTED............... 12.00
PORCELAIN SUGAR SHAKER,VICTORIA,AUSTRIA,COUNTRY SCENES.. 15.00
PORCELAIN SYLLABUB SET,TRAY & 6 COVERED CUPS............ 25.00
PORCELAIN SYLLABUBS,SET OF 6,WHITE,COVERED.............. 15.00
PORCELAIN TEAPOT,BLIND EARL WORCESTER................... 35.00
PORCELAIN TEAPOT,BLUE & WHITE,CASTLEFORD................ 85.00
PORCELAIN TEAPOT,CHILDS,CHILDREN IN BOAT POLING.........  8.50
PORCELAIN TEAPOT,CREAMER & COVERED
  SUGAR,WHITE,CARLSBAD,AUSTRIA........................... 20.00
PORCELAIN TEAPOT,CREAMER & SUGAR MARKED GERMANY,LILAC,SILVER
  BANDS................................................. 10.00
PORCELAIN TEAPOT WITH MATCHING COVER,WHITE
  BACKGROUND,PAINTINGS.................................. 85.00
PORCELAIN TEA SET,CHILDS,7 PIECES,PURPLE GRAPES FORM.... 25.00
PORCELAIN TEA SET,CHILDS,17 PIECES,ROSE TO WHITE,GOLD
  HANDLES & TRIM........................................ 24.50
PORCELAIN TEA SET,CHILDS,BLUE & WHITE.................. 15.50
PORCELAIN TEA SET,COIN GOLD............................ 20.00
PORCELAIN TEA SET,GERMANY,HELIOTROPE................... 12.50
PORCELAIN TEA SET MARKED BAVARIA,ARTIST SIGNED,GOLDEN TAN
  LUSTER................................................ 38.00
PORCELAIN TEA SET,WHITE & GOLD,PINEAPPLE FINIALS,OVOID SHAPE 75.00
PORCELAIN TEA SET,WHITE & GOLD,PINEAPPLE FINIALS....... 75.00
```

PORCELAIN TEA STRAINER,GERMANY,2 PIECE....................	4.50
PORCELAIN TEA STRAINER & WASTEBOWL STAND,HANDPAINTED FLORAL SPRAYS...	12.50
PORCELAIN TEA STRAINER WITH MATCHING BASE,PINK & GOLD.......	6.00
PORCELAIN TEA TILE SIGNED MURPHY,BAVARIA,HANDPAINTED YELLOW ROSES..	7.00
PORCELAIN TOAST RACK WITH FAN DIVIDERS,ENGLISH,WHITE,4 SLOT,HANDLE..	18.50
PORCELAIN TOAST RACK,WHITE,4 SLOT,GOLD TRIM.................	7.00
PORCELAIN TOAST RACK,WHITE,4 SLICE.........................	4.00
PORCELAIN TOBACCO JAR,TOBY TYPE CHINA,JOLLY BLUE COATED MAN.	25.00
PORCELAIN TOOTH BRUSH HOLDER,BULBOUS,GOLD & PANSIES.........	2.50
PORCELAIN TOOTHPICK HOLDER,GAUDY WORCESTER COLOURS..........	12.50
PORCELAIN TOOTHPICK HOLDER,GREEN HAT WITH WHITE PARIAN BULLDOG SITTING...	7.50
PORCELAIN TOOTHPICK HOLDER,HANDPAINTED FLORAL DESIGN........	4.00
PORCELAIN TOOTHPICK HOLDER SHAPED LIKE MILITARY CAP,BLUE,WHITE & GOLD.....................................	6.50
PORCELAIN TOOTHPICK HOLDER,PLAYING CARDS....................	8.00
PORCELAIN TOOTHPICK HOLDER,RED ROSE........................	2.75
PORCELAIN TOOTHPICK HOLDER,WHITE WITH PINK ROSES............	5.50
PORCELAIN TOOTHPICK HOLDER WITH BUTTERFLY HANDLE,WHITE & PINK...	4.50
PORCELAIN TOOTHPICK,TOP HAT WITH UMBRELLA,SOUVENIR SWEETSBURG...	8.00
PORCELAIN TRAY,DRESSER,AUSTRIAN,HANDPAINTED BLUE WITH ROSES.	8.00
PORCELAIN TRAY,DRESSER,FRENCH,HANDPAINTED GREEN HYDRANGEA,SIGNED.......................................	65.00
PORCELAIN TRAY,DRESSER,VIOLET SPRAYS.......................	5.50
PORCELAIN TRAY,HANDPAINTED BLACKBERRIES WITH FOLIAGE........	12.50
PORCELAIN TRAY,JAPAN,DIVIDED,HANDPAINTED FLORAL BOUQUET BOTTOM...	5.00
PORCELAIN TRAY,PICKLE,PRUSSIAN,PINK ROSES..................	12.50
PORCELAIN TRAY,ROUND WITH NATIONS SHIELD...................	5.00
PORCELAIN TRAY SIGNED TANN ROYAL AUSTRIA,HANDPAINTED........	10.00
PORCELAIN TRAY WITH HOLLY,DRESSER,GERMAN...................	15.00
PORCELAIN TUREEN,PARIS CIRCA 1830,PAINTED BIRDS,BUTTERFLIES,FLOWERS................................	600.00
PORCELAIN TUREEN,SAUCE WITH ATTACHED BASE,CARLSBAD,AUSTRIA,HANDLED...........................	15.00
PORCELAIN TUREEN,SOUP,CARLSBAD,MARKED MARX,FLOWERS IN MAUVE & BROWN...	27.00
PORCELAIN URN WITH PORCELAIN FLOWERS & HANDPAINTED FIGURES..	240.00
PORCELAIN URN WITH REMOVABLE TOP,FRENCH,BRONZE FOOTED BASE,15 IN. HIGH..	75.00
PORCELAIN VASE,12 IN.,GREEN TOP BAND,MINIATURE ROSES,BIRDS,FLORAL	6.00
PORCELAIN VASE,BUD MARKED HOLLAND,INDIAN CLUB SHAPE,PINK POPPIES,GILT..	15.00
PORCELAIN VASE,BUD,MARKED HOLLAND,INDIAN CLUB SHAPE,PINK & WHITE,GILT...	16.75
PORCELAIN VASE,BURNT ORANGE &GOLD DECOR,14 IN. HIGH.........	11.50
PORCELAIN VASE,FRENCH,PAW FEET,FLORAL......................	5.00
PORCELAIN VASE,GERMAN,4 IN.,ROYAL BLUE & WHITE,SOUVENIR OF BOSTON..	2.75
PORCELAIN VASE,HANDPAINTED PINK & RED ROSES,GOLD TRIM.......	28.00
PORCELAIN VASE,HANDPAINTED PURPLE LILACS,GOLD TRIM..........	32.00
PORCELAIN VASE MARKED BAVARIA,HANDPAINTED PINK ROSES & GREEN LEAVES..	22.00
PORCELAIN VASE,PAIR DECORATED IN MING DESIGN,SIGNED WITH ARTISMIS LEAF..	135.00
PORCELAIN VASE,PAIR JAPANESE KIMONO GIRL,CONE SHAPE,RED TRIM	5.00
PORCELAIN VASE,PAIR,WHITE WITH PAINTED FLOWERS & BUTTERFLIES,SIGNED......................................	150.00
PORCELAIN VASE-PITCHER,FRANCE,LUSTER GLAZE WITH TIGER LILIES	16.50

```
PORCELAIN VASE SIGNED A. KAUFFMANN,CENTER MEDALLION IN
  CLASSICAL SCENE....................................................  18.00
PORCELAIN VASE SIGNED CARLSBAD,TAPESTRY...................... 165.00
PORCELAIN VASE SIGNED CLAUDE LACHAN,VICTORIA,AUSTRIA,PAINTED
  SCENE.............................................................  38.00
PORCELAIN VASE,URN SHAPED MADE INTO LAMP,BRASS BASE,CHINESE.  45.00
PORCELAIN VASE,URN SHAPED,PAINTED ROSES.....................  60.00
PORCELAIN VASE,VICTORIA,CARLSBAD,12 IN.,BEIGE SATIN EMBOSSED
  BODY..............................................................  32.00
PORCELAIN VASE,VIENNA,AUSTRIA,HANDPAINTED VIOLETS,MERRY XMAS
  TO DANNA..........................................................  25.00
PORCELAIN VASE,WHITE,PENGUINS,TRIMMED IN TURQUOISE..........  16.00
PORCELAIN WASH SET,BLUE TO WHITE WITH PINK FLORAL & STIPPLE
  GOLD..............................................................  40.00
PORCELAIN WASTE BOWL,HEAD ON EACH SIDE,ROYAL VITREOUS.......   4.00
PORCELAIN WATERING CAN,HANDPAINTED ROSES,4 IN. HIGH.........   8.00
PORTRAIT COVERED COOKIE JAR,PORTIA AT COURT,GREEN & GOLD....  23.50
PORTRAIT PLATE,8 IN. GOLD TRACERY & GOLD CHAINS,WOMAN.......  20.00
PORTRAIT PLATE,9 IN.,AUSTRIA,BLACK HAIRED LADY,SIGNED.......  25.00
PORTRAIT PLATE, 9 IN. , OPEN LATICE BORDER..................  20.00
PORTRAIT PLATE,9 IN. ROCCO SCALLOPED ,WOMAN,GOLD,PINK   TO
  GREEN.............................................................  21.00
PORTRAIT PLATE, 9 IN. SIGNED BERNARD.......................  27.00
PORTRAIT PLATE,10 IN. BLUE FRANCES WILLARD CENTENNIAL.......   4.75
PORTRAIT PLATE,10 IN. GOLD OPEN HANDLE,WOMAN................  14.00
PORTRAIT PLATE,10 IN.,HANDPAINTED,DUTCH CHILDREN,BAVARIA....  10.50
PORTRAIT PLATE,10 IN. SCALLOPED EDGE SIGNED E.VETTERI,LADY..  14.00
PORTRAIT PLATE,ARTIST SIGNED,LADY IN RED HAT,HANDPAINTED....   6.00
PORTRAIT PLATE,ARTIST SIGNED V.BERNARD,GOLD SCALLOPED EDGE..  27.00
PORTRAIT PLATE,BRIDGPORT & SONS 10 IN. ,BRIDGE & SCANDAL....  25.00
PORTRAIT PLATE,BRIDGPORT & SONS 10 IN.,GAME WON............  25.00
PORTRAIT PLATE,BRIDGPORT & SONS 10 IN. ,WHY AND WHEREFORE...  25.00
PORTRAIT PLATE,COBALT BLUE & WHITE,CAPTAIN JOHN SMITH,SIGNED
  1906..............................................................   8.50
PORTRAIT PLATE,CONSTANCE ARTIST SIGNED 9 IN.,BLONDE WOMAN...  26.00
PORTRAIT PLATE,DARK HAIRED BEAUTY..........................   6.00
PORTRAIT PLATE DIONNE QUINTS,SOUVENIR NIAGARA FALLS.........  12.50
PORTRAIT PLATE,GEORGE,KING 1939.............................   4.75
PORTRAIT PLATE,GEORGE WASHINGTON WITH GOLD EDGE.............  49.00
PORTRAIT PLATE,GERMAN,6 IN.,HORTENSE........................   6.00
PORTRAIT PLATE,GERMAN,6 IN.,MARIE-LOUISE....................   6.00
PORTRAIT PLATE,GERMAN,6 IN.,MADAM RECAMIER..................   6.00
PORTRAIT PLATE,GERMAN,6 IN.,NAPOLEON ON BORDER..............   6.00
PORTRAIT PLATE,HANDPAINTED,LADY,CERISE,GOLD & BEADED EDGE...  19.00
PORTRAIT PLATE,HEAD & SHOULDERS,GOLD EDGE SCALLOP,..........  17.00
PORTRAIT PLATE,JOSEPHINE,NAPOLEON GOT AWAY..................  40.00
PORTRAIT PLATE,LET US HAVE PEACE US GRANT,LEAF BACKGROUND...  16.00
PORTRAIT PLATE,LIMOGES MARKED,FRANCE........................ 110.00
PORTRAIT PLATE,LIMOGES 9 IN.,COURT LADY,ARTIST SIGNED.......  33.00
PORTRAIT PLATE,MARIE ANTOINETTE.............................  24.50
PORTRAIT PLATE,PAIR,GEORGE & MARTHA WASHINGTON SIGNED TATLER  55.00
PORTRAIT PLATE,PORCELAIN 9 IN. BADEN-POWELL.................   4.75
PORTRAIT PLATE,QUEEN ELIZABETH 1939.........................   4.75
PORTRAIT PLATE,RICHARD GINORI SIGNED,GOLD RIM,ARTIST SIGNED
  LAURA.............................................................  22.00
PORTRAIT PLATE,RICHARD GINORI SIGNED,GOLD RIM,ARTIST SIGNED
  PETRARCA..........................................................  22.00
PORTRAIT PLATE,SANTA,GRINDLEY & CO..........................  21.00
PORTRAIT PLATE SPANISH GIRL.................................  38.00
PORTRAIT PLATE TIN 10 IN....................................  11.00
PORTRAIT PLATE,TIN,10 IN.,BASEBALL SCENE....................   7.50
PORTRAIT PLATE,TIN,10 IN.,LADY IN COLOURFUL GOWN............   6.50
PORTRAIT PLATE,TIN,10 IN.,WOODLAND SCENE....................   6.50
PORTRAIT PLATE,TIN,BRUNETTE,GOLD EARRINGS,VIENNA ART,FOR
  HANDING...........................................................  12.00
```

```
         POST CARD, SEE ALSO ALBUM.............................
POST CARD,10 THANKSGIVING................................     2.00
POST CARD,12 GIRLS,WHITE DRESSES,CIRCA 1920..............     7.50
POST CARD,15 HALLOWEEN 1909-10-12-13.....................     3.00
POST CARD,20 HAWAIIAN,1920 PERIOD........................     4.00
POST CARD,25 FOREIGN.....................................     1.00
POST CARD,30 HUGH LEIGHTONS..............................     1.00
POST CARD,1902 FLORIDA ORANGE WOOD.......................     2.00
POST CARD,ADVERTISING
  .10  TO.................................................      .25
POST CARD ALBUM LOADED WITH OLD POST CARDS...............    10.00
POST CARD,ALBUM WITH 56 ,1905-15.........................     6.00
POST CARD,ATTACHED HAIR ORIENTAL ORNAMENTATION...........     1.00
POST CARD,BRUNDAGE.......................................     1.00
POST CARD,CALIFORNIA CHROME..............................     1.00
POST CARD,CALIFORNIA LINEN...............................     1.00
POST CARD,CHRISTMAS,1880-90,FRINGE SILK,2 PICTURES OF CHILD.  3.00
POST CARD,CHRISTMAS CIRCA 1880,SILK FRINGE...............     3.00
POST CARD,CLAPSADDLE.....................................     1.00
POST CARD,DETROIT PHOSTINT...............................      .05
POST CARD,EARLY 1900 VIRGINIA............................     2.50
POST CARD,EASTER,COLOURED................................      .10
POST CARD,EMBROIDERED FROM SPAIN.........................      .50
POST CARD GREETINGS FEATURING FLOWERS,WINTER SCENES8OR
  ANIMALS,40.............................................     1.00
POST CARD,GROUP OF 7 LINCOLN,WASHINGTON POST.............     4.00
POST CARD,KEWPIE DOLL SERIES,6...........................    22.00
POST CARD,KLEIN..........................................     1.00
POST CARD,LEATHER........................................      .25
POST CARD,NEW YORK STATE,EARLY 1900......................     2.50
POST CARD,OCCUPIED POLAND WITH NAZI CANCELLATIONS........     6.00
POST CARD,PRE-1925 ASSORTED,30...........................     1.25
POST CARD,PRE 1915,CHRISTMAS,10..........................     1.00
POST CARD,PRE-1910,GOOD PUBLISHERS.......................     1.00
POST CARD,SANTA CLAUS....................................      .40
POST CARD,TEDDY ROOSEVELT PORTRAIT.......................     1.50
POST CARD,THANKSGIVING,COLOURFUL.........................      .10
POST CARD,VICTORIAN VALENTINE CIRCA 1880,SILVER PAPER
  LACE,PINK ROSES........................................     7.50
POST CARD,WASHINGTON,D.C.,1900,50........................     3.00
POST CARDS,100 OLD.......................................     3.75
POSTER,CIRCUS,CHRISTY CIRCUS INTERIOR MENAGERIE TENT.....     8.50
POSTER,NEIL O BRIEN MINSTREL SHOW MARCHING MINSTREL BAND...   7.50
```

POT LIDS are the lids used on china containers for soap, cosmetics, and other items. The earliest lids often pictured bears because the containers held bear grease for the hair. The most famous English firm to make the lids was R. and R. Pratt Company of Fenton, England, which began making colored lids in 1846. Hundreds of styles of pot lids were made.

```
         POTLID, SEE PRATT...............................
POTTERY BASKET & 2 HANDLED VASE,ZSOLNAY SIGNED,BLUE-GREY....  30.00
POTTERY BED WARMER MARKED,GLAZED.........................    25.00
POTTERY BELL,HEAD,PEAKED HAIR HANDLE.....................     5.00
POTTERY BOWL,9 IN.,SIGNED NANCY,LAVENDER GLAZE...........     9.00
POTTERY BOWL,BLUE BANDED CROCKERY........................     6.75
POTTERY BOWL,FLARED,YELLOW WARE..........................     6.00
POTTERY BOWL,JAPANESE,COVER..............................    22.00
POTTERY BOWL MARKED GRUEBY,ART NOUVEAU,7 IN.,GREEN,LEAF...   65.00
POTTERY BOWL MARKED SOHO POTTERY LTS.,GOLD GRECIAN DESIGN,7
  IN.....................................................     3.00
POTTERY BOWL,RED WARE,SLANTING SIDES.....................    18.00
POTTERY BRUSH WASHER,OXBLOOD & CELADON,CRACKLE GLAZE.....    65.00
POTTERY BUTTER MOLD,CORNFLOWER PATTERN,CARAMEL CLEAR.....     9.50
POTTERY CANDLE LANTERN MARKED SERMA,HOLLAND..............     4.75
POTTERY CHEESE DISH,COVERED,LOSOL
```

```
WARE,BRISTOL,BURSLEM,ENGLAND..................................   15.00
POTTERY COOKIE JAR,RED WING,COVERED,HAPPY FAT BAKER.........   15.00
POTTERY CROCK,TROY NEW YORK,2 GALLON,BLUE PICTURE OF
  ANTEATER....................................................  125.00
POTTERY CROCK WITH BLUE BIRD DESIGN...........................    8.50
POTTERY CUSPIDOR,BLUE OPEN....................................    8.00
POTTERY CUSPIDOR,BROWN,GREEN..................................    8.50
POTTERY CUSPIDOR,EAST LIVERPOOL MARK,MOTTLED BROWN GLAZE....   12.00
POTTERY DISH,BASKET,EMBOSSED DESIGN OF DRAGONS,GREEN BRONZE.   25.00
POTTERY FIGURINE,CERAMIC,SIGNED E.PIERRE,TAN ANIMAL,GREEN
  BASE,WHITE..................................................   75.00
POTTERY FIGURINE,DETAILED 4 IN. CLAY ROBIN HOOD..............    6.50
POTTERY FIGURINE,EARTHENWARE,CHINESE,BLUE DUCK...............    1.50
POTTERY FIGURINE,EARTHENWARE,CHINESE,BROWN GOOSE............    1.00
POTTERY FIGURINE,EARTHENWARE,CHINESE,BROWN ROOSTER,RED COMB.    3.00
POTTERY FIGURINE,EARTHENWARE,CHINESE,GREEN EAGLE............    3.00
POTTERY FIGURINE,EARTHENWARE,CHINESE,MOTTLED BROWN GOOSE....    1.00
POTTERY FIGURINE,EARTHENWARE,CHINESE,SET OF 3 GREEN DUCKS...    1.50
POTTERY FIGURINE,EARTHENWARE,CHINESE,WHITE PEKINESE GOLD
  FISH,PAIR...................................................    1.00
POTTERY FIGURINE,EARTHENWARE,CHINESE,YELLOW ROOSTER,RED COMB    3.00
POTTERY FIGURINE,EARTHENWARE,GREEN PEKINESE GOLD FISH,PAIR..    1.00
POTTERY FIGURINE,ELEPHANT,SET OF 5...........................    5.00
POTTERY FIGURINE,ELEPHANT WITH MAHOUT,BROWN,SIGNED F.C.W....   15.00
POTTERY FIGURINE,PAIR 6 IN. CHINESE GEESE...................   28.00
POTTERY FIGURINE,TERRA COTTA OF LITTLE GIRL.................   22.00
POTTERY FIGURINE,THE BECKONING CAT,10 IN. TALL..............   20.00
POTTERY FIGURINE,ULYSSES S. GRANT BUST,TERRA COTTA,8
  IN.,1885...................................................   45.00
POTTERY FIGURINE,UNICORN,SEA GREEN MONOCHROME GLAZE,9 IN.
  TALL.......................................................   47.50
POTTERY FOOT WARMER,1912 HENDERSON...........................   15.00
POTTERY FOOT WARMER,BAG SHAPE,DOULTON LAMBETH POTTERY.......   15.00
POTTERY FOOT WARMER,BROWN,3-SIDED............................   11.00
POTTERY FOOT WARMER,CREAM WITH BROWN LEAF DESIGN.............   12.50
POTTERY INKWELL,SQUARE,GREEN IN CENTER.......................   10.00
POTTERY JAR MARKED WEYMANS SNUFF.............................    4.75
POTTERY JAR,REDWARE,ORANGE SPOTTED GREEN.....................   35.00
POTTERY JUG,1 GALLON CROCKERY VINEGAR,1 IN. HOLE FOR FILLING    9.00
POTTERY JUG ADVERTISING THE EAGLE BAR,WILKESON,BROWN & WHITE    3.25
POTTERY JUG,AMERICAN BATTER,BROWN GLAZE.....................   22.50
POTTERY JUG,BATTER,BROWN GLAZE,POURING SPOUT................   15.00
POTTERY JUG,GALLON,HANDPAINTED BETSY ROSS HOUSE WITH 13 STAR
  FLAG......................................................   10.00
POTTERY JUG SIGNED MATT MORGAN ART POTTERY CO,ARTIST SIGNED.  150.00
POTTERY MILK PAN,RED WARE,CIRCA 1850........................   58.00
POTTERY MOLD,RABBIT DESIGN INSIDE...........................   12.00
POTTERY MUG MADE IN GERMANY,3 YACHT CLUBS IN
  MARBLEHEAD,MASS...........................................    2.75
POTTERY MUG MADE IN GERMANY,PLYMOUTH ROCK SCENES............    2.75
POTTERY MUG,MOCHA,BLUE & WHITE STRIPES......................   17.50
POTTERY MUG,PAN-AMERICAN EXPOSITION,WHITE,UTICA 1901........   18.00
POTTERY MUG,TAVERN,REDWARE,BROWN GLAZE......................   12.50
POTTERY MUSTARD JAR IN SILVER HOLDER,BROWN EARTHENWARE,WOOD
  SPOON......................................................    1.00
POTTERY PIE PLATE,PENNSYLVANIA DUTCH REDWARE................   10.00
POTTERY PITCHER,11 IN. TALL,TAN WITH BLUE DECORATION........   35.01-
POTTERY PITCHER,BURROUGHS & MONTEFORD EARTHENWARE WATER,IRIS
  FLORAL.....................................................    7.50
POTTERY PITCHER,CREAM WARE,HANDPAINTED DESIGNS,GREEN,BLUE &
  OCHRE......................................................    6.00
POTTERY PITCHER,EARLY AMERICAN HARVEST,BAMBOO DESIGN........   26.50
POTTERY PITCHER,GREEN,VINTAGE PATTERN.......................    4.75
POTTERY PITCHER,STOKE ON TRENT,BROWN TRANSFER...............   45.00
POTTERY PITCHER,WOODS WARE ENGLAND,BLUE & WHITE,ENGLISH
```

SCENES	6.50
POTTERY PLANTER,MARKED HAMPSHIRE,ROUND,GREEN	5.75
POTTERY PLATE,CAULDON EARTHENWARE BLUE & WHITE 1890	5.00
POTTERY PLATE,JAPANESE,SETO-WARE	48.00
POTTERY PLATE,YE OLDE HISTORICAL,BUNKER HILL MONUMENT	10.00
POTTERY PLATE,YE OLDE HISTORICAL FANEUIL HALL	10.00
POTTERY PLATE,YE OLDE HISTORICAL,LANDING OF HENDRICK HUDSON.	10.00
POTTERY PLATTER,TEA LEAF,14 IN.,RECTANGULAR	15.00
POTTERY PLANTER,TERRA COTTA DRAGON,FERN	25.00
POTTERY POSY RING,BLUE RIM	5.50
POTTERY ROSE JAR MARKED WITH BLUE CROSSED SWORDS WITH H UNDER GLAZE	12.50
POTTERY SALT DIP,BEIGE BASE & GLAZED,INCISED BATTERSEA WORKS ENGLAND	27.50
POTTERY SERVING SPOON	1.50
POTTERY SMOKER,TRIANGULAR,DOG,BOAR,GUN,TREES,BROWN GLAZE	24.50
POTTERY SPONGE CAKE DISH,HANDLED,REDWARE	30.00
POTTERY SPOON PIE SERVER	3.00
POTTERY STEWPOT,REDWARE,GLAZED INSIDE	9.00
POTTERY TEA CUP,JAPANESE,CHINO WARE,CEREMONIAL	50.00
POTTERY TEAPOT,BROWN,YELLOW FLOWERS	3.50
POTTERY TEAPOT,TERRA COTTA,BLUE ENAMEL FLOWERS,BUTTERFLIES	10.00
POTTERY TILE,GLAZED TERRA COTTA,SET OF 5,	15.00
POTTERY TOBACCO JAR,TAN & BROWN BEER BARREL,COVER OF MANS HEAD	23.00
POTTERY TOBY JUG,BROWN GLAZED,6 IN. HIGH	24.00
POTTERY TUREEN,WHIELDON WARE ROUND COVERED,PHEASANT PATTERN.	20.00
POTTERY VASE,AMPHORA ART WITH DRAGON HANDLE	28.00
POTTERY VASE,BROWN A.LINCOLN BUST WITH FLAGS & EAGLES	40.00
POTTERY VASE,BROWN,FORM OF FISH,9 IN. TALL	15.00
POTTERY VASE,JARDINIERE SHAPED,MATT MORGAN	22.50
POWDER FLASK,COPPER	15.00
POWDER FLASK, COPPER W/PATENT TOP	12.50
POWDER HORN, SEE WEAPON	
POWDER HORN	5.50
POWDER HORN,COPPER,8 IN	18.00

PRATT WARE means two different things. It was an early Staffordshire pottery, cream-colored with colored decorations, made by Felix Pratt during the late eighteenth century. There was also Pratt ware made with transfer designs during the mid-nineteenth century (see POT LIDS).

PRATT BOX,COVERED,PEACE	26.75
PRATT COMPOTE,MOUNTAIN SCENE	45.00
PRATT LID,PAIR MOUNTED IN CHERRY FRAMES FOR HANGING	25.00
PRATT PITCHER,GREEK PATTERN,FENTON,WHITE ON BLACK WITH GREEK KEY	50.00
PRATT PLATE,7 IN.,ON GUARD,PINK BORDER	19.50
PRATT PLATE SIGNED T.WEBSTER 1834,GREEN WITH ACORN LEAVES & NUTS	40.00
PRATT POT LID,THE TIMES,GENT WITH OPENED PAPER	35.00
PRATT,POT LID,THIRSTY SOLDIER	18.00
PRATT TEAPOT,FENTON,GREEK PATTERN,BLACK & WHITE	75.00
PRATT TEA SET,PINK TRANSFER	120.00
PRESSED GLASS, SEE BOTH LISTINGS, FIRST UNDER PATTERN NAME,	
SECOND UNDER ITEM, SEE ALSO AMBER, CROESUS, CUSTARD, ETC	
PRESSED GLASS, SEE ALSO LISTING BY PATTERN NAME	
PRESSED GLASS 2 PANEL BLUE MASTER SALT	15.00
PRESSED GLASS 2 PANEL BLUE SPOONER	12.50
PRESSED GLASS 3 GRACES BREAD TRAY	18.50
PRESSED GLASS 101 GOBLET	9.50
PRESSED GLASS 101 GREEN PLATE,5 IN	4.50
PRESSED GLASS 101 PLATE,8 IN	9.00
PRESSED GLASS 808 CELERY	9.50

PRESSED GLASS 808 NAPPY,HANDLED.............................. 7.50
PRESSED GLASS 808 PLATE...................................... 14.00
PRESSED GLASS 808 SAUCE,FLAT................................. 9.00
PRESSED GLASS 808 WINE....................................... 7.50
PRESSED GLASS ACANTHUS WITH SCROLL GREEN & GOLD COVERED
SUGAR,.. 19.50
PRESSED GLASS ACORN SAUCE,FLINT.............................. 4.00
PRESSED GLASS ACTRESS CELERY VASE,HMS PINAFORE............... 37.50
PRESSED GLASS ACTRESS CHEESE DISH........................... 68.00
PRESSED GLASS ACTRESS COMPOTE,FROSTED,HIGH STANDARD......... 65.00
PRESSED GLASS ACTRESS COVERED COMPOTE....................... 47.50
PRESSED GLASS ACTRESS DISH.................................. 16.00
PRESSED GLASS ACTRESS FROSTED SAUCE,4 IN.,FLAT.............. 6.50
PRESSED GLASS ACTRESS FROSTED SAUCE,6 IN. FLAT............. 18.75
PRESSED GLASS ACTRESS GOBLET................................ 18.00
PRESSED GLASS ACTRESS SAUCE,FOOTED.......................... 7.00
PRESSED GLASS ACTRESS TRAY & PINAFORE RELISH................ 25.00
PRESSED GLASS ACTRESS WATER PITCHER......................... 68.00
PRESSED GLASS ALABAMA CREAMER............................... 10.00
PRESSED GLASS ALABAMA CRUET................................. 12.00
PRESSED GLASS ALABAMA RING HANDLED CANDY NAPPIE............. 8.50
PRESSED GLASS ALASKA BLUE CREAMER........................... 20.00
PRESSED GLASS ALASKA BLUE OPAL CREAMER...................... 38.00
PRESSED GLASS ALASKA PLATTER,14 X 10 IN..................... 10.50
PRESSED GLASS ALLIGATOR SCALES GOBLET,FLINT................. 15.00
PRESSED GLASS ALMOND THUMBPRINT GOBLET...................... 5.00
PRESSED GLASS ALMOND THUMBPRINT MASTER SALT,PAIR,FLINT...... 12.50
PRESSED GLASS ALTERNATE CLEAR & RUBY SAUCE,PAIR,5 IN.,PETAL
SHAPED.. 12.00
PRESSED GLASS AMBER & CLEAR SERVING BOWL,FLINT.............. 75.00
PRESSED GLASS AMBER CANDLE HOLDER,CHRISTMAS................. 7.50
PRESSED GLASS AMBER DISH,COVERED,GENERALS HAT............... 12.50
PRESSED GLASS AMBER DOG ON RIBBED BASE...................... 22.50
PRESSED GLASS AMBER FAN VASE,ROUND PEDESTAL BASE,BAND OF
GOLD ON TOP... 3.00
PRESSED GLASS AMBER HEN ON NEST,7 X 5 IN.................... 25.00
PRESSED GLASS AMBER MATCHHOLDER,DOG......................... 14.00
PRESSED GLASS AMBER PICKLE CASTOR IN SILVER HOLDER,COVER &
TONGS... 65.00
PRESSED GLASS AMBER TOOTHPICK,CHICKEN BY BASKET............. 16.25
PRESSED GLASS AMBER TOOTHPICK,HAT........................... 10.00
PRESSED GLASS AMBER TRAY,SCENIC,DOG & RABBIT................ 27.50
PRESSED GLASS AMETHYST TOOTHPCIK HOLDER..................... 10.00
PRESSED GLASS AMULET GOBLET................................. 4.50
PRESSED GLASS ANVIL AMBER TOOTHPICK......................... 37.50
PRESSED GLASS AQUA MARINE BLUE TRAY,ROUND,12 IN.,HOUSE...... 25.00
PRESSED GLASS ARCHED FLEUR DE LIS 8 IN. OPEN COMPOTE........ 6.50
PRESSED GLASS ARCHED OVALS RUBY & CLEAR TOOTHPICK HOLDER.... 6.50
PRESSED GLASS ARCHED OVALS WITH GOLD WINE................... 4.75
PRESSED GLASS ARCHED PANEL MILK PITCHER..................... 16.00
PRESSED GLASS ARGUS BAR TUMBLER,4 IN. TALL,FLINT........... 22.50
PRESSED GLASS ARGUS EGG CUP,FLINT........................... 12.00
PRESSED GLASS ARGUS GOBLET,FLINT
12.50 TO.. 22.00
PRESSED GLASS ARGUS THUMBPRINT COMPOTE,OPEN,BELL TONE,9
IN.,FLINT... 30.00
PRESSED GLASS ARGUS VARIANT COMPOTE,HIGH STANDARD,BELL TONE. 32.50
PRESSED GLASS ARTICHOKE SPOONER............................. 5.00
PRESSED GLASS ASHBURTON BARREL GOBLET,FLINT................. 15.00
PRESSED GLASS ASHBURTON DECANTER & 6 WINES,FLINT............ 65.00
PRESSED GLASS ASHBURTON EGG CUP............................. 9.00
PRESSED GLASS ASHBURTON EGG CUP,FLINT....................... 14.00
PRESSED GLASS ASHBURTON GOBLET.............................. 15.00
PRESSED GLASS ASHBURTON GOBLET,FLARED WIDE BAND,FLINT....... 15.00
PRESSED GLASS ASHBURTON GOBLET,POINTED STEM,FLINT........... 15.00

```
PRESSED GLASS ASHBURTON GOBLET,SEMI-SQUARED,FLINT...........    15.00
PRESSED GLASS ASHBURTON GOBLET,STRAIGHT SIDED,FLINT.........    13.50
PRESSED GLASS ASHBURTON OVALS GOBLET,FLINT..................    25.00
PRESSED GLASS ASHBURTON PIE PLATE,FLINT.....................    35.00
PRESSED GLASS ASHBURTON ROUND PANELS GOBLET,FLINT...........    15.00
PRESSED GLASS ASHBURTON ROYAL GOBLET,PONTIL GROUND TOP,FLINT    14.00
PRESSED GLASS ASHBURTON SAUCE DISH,FLINT....................     5.00
PRESSED GLASS ASHBURTON WINE................................    20.00
PRESSED GLASS ASHBURTON WINE,REED STEM,FLINT................    12.50
PRESSED GLASS ASHMAN CLEAR CAKE STAND.......................    18.00
PRESSED GLASS ASHMAN COVERED SUGAR..........................    19.50
PRESSED GLASS ASHMAN SPOONER................................    12.50
PRESSED GLASS ATLANTA FROSTED LION BUTTER,COVERED,SQUARE....    32.50
PRESSED GLASS ATLANTIC CABLE BREAD PLATE,ROUND..............    14.00
PRESSED GLASS ATLAS GOBLET..................................    10.00
PRESSED GLASS ATTERBURY ATLAS COMPOTE.......................    57.50
PRESSED GLASS AURORA RUBY & CLEAR WINE......................    13.50
PRESSED GLASS AZALEA SUGAR..................................     4.00
PRESSED GLASS BABY COINSPOT BLUE TUMBLER....................    12.00
PRESSED GLASS BAKEWELL WINE,BAKEWELL & PAGE 1824............    10.00
PRESSED GLASS BALDER WATER CARAFE...........................     8.50
PRESSED GLASS BALDER WINE...................................     3.75
PRESSED GLASS BALL & SWIRL CAKESTAND,8 IN...................    12.00
PRESSED GLASS BALL & SWIRL CREAMER
 7.50 TO...................................................    14.00
PRESSED GLASS BALL & SWIRL WATER PITCHER....................    15.00
PRESSED GLASS BALL & SWIRL WATERSET TRAY....................    12.50
PRESSED GLASS BALTIMORE PEAR COMPOTE,COVERED................    25.00
PRESSED GLASS BALTIMORE PEAR COMPOTE........................    27.50
PRESSED GLASS BALTIMORE PEAR CREAMER,5 IN...................    11.50
PRESSED GLASS BALTIMORE PEAR SUGAR & CREAMER................    35.00
PRESSED GLASS BALTIMORE PEAR SUGAR BOWL,COVERED.............    16.50
PRESSED GLASS BANDED BEADED GRAPE MEDALLION GOBLET..........     8.00
PRESSED GLASS BANDED BEADED GRAPE MEDALLION
 COMPOTE,COVERED,1870......................................    40.00
PRESSED GLASS BANDED BEADED GRAPE MEDALLION SPOONER.........     4.00
PRESSED GLASS BANDED CRYSTAL GOBLET,BELLTONE,FLINT..........     7.00
PRESSED GLASS BANDED FLEUR-DE-LIS SPOONER...................     9.50
PRESSED GLASS BANDED GRAPE COMPOTE,COVERED,STEMMED,10 X 7
 IN. HIGH.................................................    22.50
PRESSED GLASS BANDED HOBNAIL RUBY PITCHER...................    19.50
PRESSED GLASS BANDED KNIFE & FORK GREEN CREAMER.............     6.50
PRESSED GLASS BANDED KNIFE & FORK GREEN SHERBET.............     4.50
PRESSED GLASS BANDED KNIFE & FORK,GREEN WINE................     5.50
PRESSED GLASS BANDED PORTLAND CELERY........................     9.00
PRESSED GLASS BANDED PORTLAND GOBLET
 6.50 TO...................................................     7.50
PRESSED GLASS BANDED RAINDROP SAUCE,FOOTED..................     6.00
PRESSED GLASS BANDED STAR SALT DIP..........................     8.00
PRESSED GLASS BARBERRY CLEAR MILK PITCHER...................    30.00
PRESSED GLASS BARBERRY COMPOTE,LOW STANDARD.................     6.50
PRESSED GLASS BARBERRY GOBLET...............................     6.00
PRESSED GLASS BARBERRY PLATE,6 IN...........................    10.00
PRESSED GLASS BARBERRY RELISH DISH,OVAL.....................     9.50
PRESSED GLASS BARBERRY SUGAR,OPEN...........................    12.50
PRESSED GLASS BARBERRY SUGAR,OPEN,ROUND BERRY...............    11.50
PRESSED GLASS BARLEY CREAMER
 6.50 TO...................................................     9.00
PRESSED GLASS BARLEY GOBLET.................................     6.50
PRESSED GLASS BARLEY SAUCE,FOOTED,4 IN......................     3.50
PRESSED GLASS BARLEY SPOONER................................     5.00
PRESSED GLASS BARREL TOOTHPICK HOLDER
 4.50 TO...................................................     5.00
PRESSED GLASS BARLEY WATER PITCHER..........................     9.50
PRESSED GLASS BARRED OVAL DISH,RECTANGULAR..................     4.50
```

```
PRESSED GLASS BARRED OVALS PLATE,SQUARE......................   4.00
PRESSED GLASS BARRED OVALS RUBY & CLEAR WATER PITCHER.......  37.50
PRESSED GLASS BARRED OVALS WATER BOTTLE.....................   8.00
PRESSED GLASS BARREL AMBER TOOTHPICK HOLDER.................  12.50
PRESSED GLASS BARREL ARGUS GOBLET,FLINT.....................  22.50
PRESSED GLASS BARREL HONEYCOMB GOBLET,FLINT.................  10.00
PRESSED GLASS BARREL THUMBPRINT GOBLET,FLINT................  22.00
PRESSED GLASS BASKETWEAVE AMBER PITCHER,TANKARD TYPE........  15.00
PRESSED GLASS BASKETWEAVE AMBER SALT SHAKER.................  12.50
PRESSED GLASS BASKETWEAVE AQUA COLOGNE BOTTLE...............  12.50
PRESSED GLASS BASKETWEAVE BLUE TRAY.........................  20.00
PRESSED GLASS BASKETWEAVE BLUE WATER PITCHER................  20.00
PRESSED GLASS BASKETWEAVE CREAMER...........................   8.00
PRESSED GLASS BASKETWEAVE MILK PITCHER......................  10.00
PRESSED GLASS BASKETWEAVE SPOONER...........................   7.50
PRESSED GLASS BASKETWEAVE WATER PITCHER.....................  12.00
PRESSED GLASS BASKETWEAVE WINE..............................   5.00
PRESSED GLASS BASKETWEAVE YELLOW WATER PITCHER,TRAY & 6
GOBLETS.................................................... 125.00
PRESSED GLASS BEACON THUMBPRINT WINE........................   5.50
PRESSED GLASS BEADED ACORN MEDALLION SAUCE,FLAT.............   3.75
PRESSED GLASS BEADED ARCH PANELS CREAMER....................   7.00
PRESSED GLASS BEADED BAND RIBBED BLUE TOOTHPICK
HOLDER,SAWTOOTH EDGE........................................   7.00
PRESSED GLASS BEADED CHAIN PLATE,6 IN.......................   6.50
PRESSED GLASS BEADED DART BAND COVERED SUGAR................   9.75
PRESSED GLASS BEADED DEWDROP PUNCH CUP,SET OF 6.............  15.00
PRESSED GLASS BEADED DEWDROP SALT SHAKER,3 IN...............   6.75
PRESSED GLASS BEADED ECLIPSE SUGAR,COVERED..................  15.00
PRESSED GLASS BEADED FINECUT COVERED SUGAR..................  10.00
PRESSED GLASS BEADED GRAPE BERRY BOWL & 6 SAUCES............  35.00
PRESSED GLASS BEADED GRAPE CLEAR BOWL,SQUARE................  11.00
PRESSED GLASS BEADED GRAPE CLEAR SAUCE DISH,SQUARE..........   3.50
PRESSED GLASS BEADED GRAPE GREEN BOWL,6 IN. SQUARE..........  14.50
PRESSED GLASS BEADED GRAPE GREEN PLATE,8 IN. SQUARE.........  14.50
PRESSED GLASS BEADED GRAPE GREEN RELISH.....................  12.50
PRESSED GLASS BEADED GRAPE GREEN SALT SHAKER................  10.00
PRESSED GLASS BEADED GRAPE GREEN TOOTHPICK HOLDER...........  17.00
PRESSED GLASS BEADED GRAPE MEDALLION GOBLET
6.00   TO...................................................   7.50
PRESSED GLASS BEADED GRAPE MEDALLION SALT DIP...............   3.75
PRESSED GLASS BEADED GRAPE MEDALLION SUGAR,OPEN.............   7.00
PRESSED GLASS BEADED GRAPE PLATTER..........................  18.50
PRESSED GLASS BEADED GRAPE WATER PITCHER....................  22.50
PRESSED GLASS BEADED HEART AMBER TOOTHPICK HOLDER...........   8.00
PRESSED GLASS BEADEM JEWEL & DEW DROP MUG    M
4.00   TO...................................................   5.00
PRESSED GLASS BEADED LOOP MILK PITCHER
10.00   TO..................................................  11.00
PRESSED GLASS BEADED LOOP OVAL PLATTER......................  10.00
PRESSED GLASS BEADED MIRROR BUTTER,COVERED,ACORN
FINIAL,FLINT...............................................  22.00
PRESSED GLASS BEADED MIRROR GOBLET..........................   7.00
PRESSED GLASS BEADED MIRROR SPOONER.........................   5.00
PRESSED GLASS BEADED OVAL AMBER GOBLET......................  12.00
PRESSED GLASS BEADED OVAL & SCROLL GOBLET...................   6.00
PRESSED GLASS BEADED OVAL WITH SCROLL COVERED BUTTER........   9.50
PRESSED GLASS BEADED OVAL WITH SCROLL GOBLET................   9.00
PRESSED GLASS BEADED PANELS CLEAR TOOTHPICK HOLDER,RUBY TOP.  17.50
PRESSED GLASS BEADED PANELS GOBLET..........................   5.00
PRESSED GLASS BEADED SWIRL BAND WATER PITCHER...............  14.00
PRESSED GLASS BEADED SWIRL BOWL,FOOTED......................  14.00
PRESSED GLASS BEAR MUSTARD JAR..............................  10.00
PRESSED GLASS BEARDED MAN CREAMER...........................  13.50
PRESSED GLASS BEATTY HONEYCOMB BLUE CREAMER.................  18.00
```

```
PRESSED GLASS BEATTY RIB BLUE OPALESCENT TOOTHPICK HOLDER...   15.00
PRESSED GLASS BELCHER LOOP GOBLET
  7.50  TO.................................................    9.00
PRESSED GLASS BELFAST GOBLET...............................    4.50
PRESSED GLASS BELLFLOWER & FINE RIB SPOONER,FLINT..........   12.00
PRESSED GLASS BELLFLOWER BUTTERMILK GOBLET,FLINT...........   16.00
PRESSED GLASS BELLFLOWER COARSE RIB GOBLET,FLINT...........   15.00
PRESSED GLASS BELLFLOWER COMPOTE,OPEN......................   30.00
PRESSED GLASS BELLFLOWER COMPOTE,OPEN,SCALLOPED TOP,FLINT...   17.50
PRESSED GLASS BELLFLOWER DOUBLE VINE FINE RIB SUGAR........   15.00
PRESSED GLASS BELLFLOWER FINE RIB GOBLET,RAYED BASE,FLINT...   16.00
PRESSED GLASS BELLFLOWER FINE RIB NARROW BAND GOBLET,FLINT..   16.00
PRESSED GLASS BELLFLOWER FINE RIB RAYED BASE GOBLET,FLINT...   16.00
PRESSED GLASS BELLFLOWER GOBLET,FLINT
 11.50  TO................................................   18.00
PRESSED GLASS BELLFLOWER SAUCE DISH,FLAT...................    5.50
PRESSED GLASS BELLFLOWER SAUCE DISHES,5....................   28.00
PRESSED GLASS BELLFLOWER SINGLE VINE FINE RIB
 COMPOTE,OPEN,SCALLOPED...................................   18.50
PRESSED GLASS BELLFLOWER SPOONER..........................   12.50
PRESSED GLASS BELLFLOWER TUMBLER,FINE RIB,SINGLE VINE,RIBBED
 TO TOP...................................................   22.50
PRESSED GLASS BELLFLOWER VINE GOBLET,BELLTONE.............   15.00
PRESSED GLASS BELLFLOWER VINE SAUCE DISH,FLINT............    5.00
PRESSED GLASS BELTED ICICLE CANDY TRAY,5 X 7 IN.,OBLONG....    2.00
PRESSED GLASS BELTED WORCESTER GOBLET,FLINT...............   14.00
PRESSED GLASS BENT BUCKLE SUGAR & CREAMER.................    8.50
PRESSED GLASS BENT BUCKLE WINE...........................    6.50
PRESSED GLASS BERRY CLUSTER SUGAR,OPEN...................    7.00
PRESSED GLASS BESSIMER FLUTE CHAMPAGNE...................   12.50
PRESSED GLASS BESSIMER FLUTE GOBLET,FLINT................   10.00
PRESSED GLASS BETHLEHEM STAR BUTTER,COVERED..............   15.00
PRESSED GLASS BETHLEHEM STAR JELLY COMPOTE,COVERED.......    6.00
PRESSED GLASS BEVEL DIAMOND WITH STAR WINE...............    5.00
PRESSED GLASS BEVEL STAR GREEN 7 IN. BOWL................   29.50
PRESSED GLASS BIGLER COMPOTE,7 IN.,SANDWICH LOOP BASE,FLINT.   40.00
PRESSED GLASS BIGLER CORDIAL,FLINT.......................   14.50
PRESSED GLASS BIGLER DECANTER,BARLIP,QUART,FLINT.........   26.50
PRESSED GLASS BIGLER GOBLET,FLINT
 10.00  TO...............................................   17.50
PRESSED GLASS BIRCH LEAF PATTERN AMBER BERRY SET,BOWL & 6
 SAUCES..................................................   45.00
PRESSED GLASS BIRD & BERRY JELLY COMPOTE.................   15.00
PRESSED GLASS BIRD & BERRY WATER PITCHER.................   35.00
PRESSED GLASS BIRD & STRAWBERRY BERRY BOWL,FOOTED,OVAL....   16.00
PRESSED GLASS BIRD & STRAWBERRY BOWL,ROUND,FOOTED........   27.50
PRESSED GLASS BIRD & STRAWBERRY BOWL,FOOTED..............   13.50
PRESSED GLASS BIRD & STRAWBERRY CREAMER..................   16.50
PRESSED GLASS BIRD & STRAWBERRY RED COMPOTE,OVAL,FOOTED...   16.00
PRESSED GLASS BIRD & STRAWBERRY SAUCE,FOOTED,4 IN........    5.00
PRESSED GLASS BIRD NEST & LYRE MUG.......................   15.00
PRESSED GLASS BIRD WITH CHERRY AMBER SALT................   12.00
PRESSED GLASS BIRDS & ROSES ETCHED GOBLET................   15.00
PRESSED GLASS BLACKBERRY GREEN CELERY DISH...............   15.00
PRESSED GLASS BLACKBERRY SPRAY GREEN DISH,HAT SHAPED......    3.75
PRESSED GLASS BLAZE TUMBLER,FOOTED,FLINT.................   16.50
PRESSED GLASS BLEEDING HEART BUTTERMILK GOBLET...........   15.00
PRESSED GLASS BLEEDING HEART GOBLET......................   12.00
PRESSED GLASS BLEEDING HEART GOBLET,FLUTED STEM..........    7.00
PRESSED GLASS BLEEDING HEART PITCHER.....................   35.00
PRESSED GLASS BLEEDING HEART RELISH DISH,OVAL............   12.50
PRESSED GLASS BLEEDING HEART SAUCE.......................    5.50
PRESSED GLASS BLEEDING HEART SPOONER
  6.50  TO...............................................    7.50
PRESSED GLASS BLEEDING HEART SUGAR,OPEN..................   11.50
```

```
PRESSED GLASS BLEEDING HEART SUGAR & CREAMER,COVERED........     57.50
PRESSED GLASS BLOCK & CIRCLE CELERY..........................      9.00
PRESSED GLASS BLOCK & FAN AMBER CAKE STAND,SQUARE............     29.50
PRESSED GLASS BLOCK & FAN BOWL...............................     15.00
PRESSED GLASS BLOCK & FAN BOWL,3-CORNERED,FLINT..............      4.50
PRESSED GLASS BLOCK & FAN CAKESTAND,10 IN....................     15.00
PRESSED GLASS BLOCK & FAN MILK PITCHER.......................     15.00
PRESSED GLASS BLOCK & FAN SAUCE,FOOTED.......................      4.50
PRESSED GLASS BLOCK & FAN WATER BOTTLE.......................      7.50
PRESSED GLASS BLOCK & PLEAT GOBLET
  5.00   TO.................................................      6.50
PRESSED GLASS BLOCK & STAR SPOONER...........................      4.00
PRESSED GLASS BLOCK & THUMBPRINT GOBLET......................     12.50
PRESSED GLASS BLOCK AMBER SUGAR BOWL,COVERED.................     18.50
PRESSED GLASS BLOCK ARCHES CLEAR CELERY......................      8.50
PRESSED GLASS BLOCK CREAMER,CLEAR............................      7.50
PRESSED GLASS BLOCK ON STILTS GOBLET.........................      6.00
PRESSED GLASS BLOCK PATTERN GOBLET...........................      8.50
PRESSED GLASS BLOCK PATTERN SHERBET..........................      6.50
PRESSED GLASS BLOCK RED COVERED SUGAR........................     25.00
PRESSED GLASS BLOCK RED WATER PITCHER........................     55.00
PRESSED GLASS BLOCK TUMBLER..................................      3.50
PRESSED GLASS BLOCK TUMBLER,CLEAR............................      5.00
PRESSED GLASS BLOCKADE SAUCE,FLAT............................      2.50
PRESSED GLASS BLOCKADE WINE..................................      7.50
PRESSED GLASS BLOWN-THREE-MOLD SALT,FLINT....................     18.50
PRESSED GLASS BLOWN PITTSBURGH PILLAR-MOLDED CELERY,FLINT...     32.00
PRESSED GLASS BLUE BOX,ROUND,BRASS HINGED....................     12.50
PRESSED GLASS BLUE CANDLE HOLDER,CHRISTMAS...................      4.00
PRESSED GLASS BLUE CANDLESTICK HOLDER,PAIR...................      8.00
PRESSED GLASS BLUE CAR VASE WITH HOLDER......................     10.00
PRESSED GLASS BLUE CRUET,AMBER APPLIED HANDLE & STOPPER......     48.00
PRESSED GLASS BLUE DISH,SWAN,OPEN............................     12.00
PRESSED GLASS BLUE FINGER BOWL,FLINT.........................     10.50
PRESSED GLASS BLUE IRIDESCENT CANDLESTICK....................      8.00
PRESSED GLASS BLUE IRIDESCENT VASE,SHAPE SIMILAR TO OPEN
  TULIP......................................................     15.00
PRESSED GLASS BLUE JEWEL BOX,STUDDED BRASS BANDS,HINGED LID.     24.50
PRESSED GLASS BLUE MATCH HOLDER,DOG..........................     20.00
PRESSED GLASS BLUE OPALESCENT BOWL,3 FEET,...................     17.50
PRESSED GLASS BLUE PITCHER,KING SOLOMON ON FRONT,PHILA.1911.     16.00
PRESSED GLASS BLUE PLAYING CARD HOLDER.......................     11.00
PRESSED GLASS BLUE SALT,SWAN.................................      6.50
PRESSED GLASS BLUE SAPPHIRE & WHITE ENAMEL BUTTER DISH.......     40.00
PRESSED GLASS BLUE SUGAR SHAKER..............................     12.50
PRESSED GLASS BLUE TOOTHPICK HOLDER,BOOT.....................      4.00
PRESSED GLASS BOUQUET CREAMER................................      8.50
PRESSED GLASS BOUQUET BOWL...................................      7.50
PRESSED GLASS BOUQUET SUGAR,OPEN.............................      8.50
PRESSED GLASS BRADFORD GRAPE GOBLET,FLINT....................     35.00
PRESSED GLASS BRICKWORK CREAMER..............................      6.00
PRESSED GLASS BRICKWORK JELLY COMPOTE........................      7.50
PRESSED GLASS BRILLIANT GOBLET,FLINT.........................     15.00
PRESSED GLASS BRITANNIC WATER PITCHER WITH APPLIED HANDLE...     14.40
PRESSED GLASS BROKEN COLUMN CELERY...........................     13.50
PRESSED GLASS BROKEN COLUMN COMPOTE,OPEN.....................     14.00
PRESSED GLASS BROKEN COLUMN CREAMER..........................     13.50
PRESSED GLASS BROKEN COLUMN GOBLET,LADY SIZE,FLINT...........     32.50
PRESSED GLASS BRYCE CELERY VASE..............................      8.50
PRESSED GLASS BRYCE RELISH...................................      5.50
PRESSED GLASS BRYCE SPOONER..................................      5.00
PRESSED GLASS BUCKLE & HOBNAIL SUGAR & CREAMER...............     12.50
PRESSED GLASS BUCKLE & SHIELD GOBLET.........................      6.00
PRESSED GLASS BUCKLE & STAR COMPOTE,OPEN.....................     15.00
PRESSED GLASS BUCKLE & STAR SPOONER,SCALLOPED TOP...........     11.00
```

```
PRESSED GLASS BUCKLE GOBLET
  7.50  TO.........................................  11.50
PRESSED GLASS BUCKLE GOBLET,FLINT
  8.00  TO.........................................  13.50
PRESSED GLASS BUCKLE GREEN SPOONER...............  10.00
PRESSED GLASS BUCKLE SAUCE,FOOTED................   4.50
PRESSED GLASS BUCKLE SPOONER.....................   8.00
PRESSED GLASS BUCKLE STAR SPOONER................   7.50
PRESSED GLASS BUCKLE SUGAR,COVERED...............  22.50
PRESSED GLASS BUCKLE SUGAR,COVERED,ACORN FINIAL,FLINT.......  28.00
PRESSED GLASS BUCKLE SUGAR,COVERED,FLINT.........  37.50
PRESSED GLASS BUCKLE WITH STAR SAUCE FLAT.........   2.75
PRESSED GLASS BUCKLE WITH STAR CREAMER
  8.00  TO.........................................  11.50
PRESSED GLASS BUCKLE WITH STAR SAUCE,FOOTED......   3.75
PRESSED GLASS BUCKLE WITH STAR SUGAR,OPEN........   5.00
PRESSED GLASS BUDDED IVY GOBLET..................  10.50
PRESSED GLASS BULLS EYE & CUBE GOBLET,SET OF 2,FLINT........  65.00
PRESSED GLASS BULLS EYE & DAISY BERRY SET........  38.00
PRESSED GLASS BULLS EYE & DAISY GREEN EYES GOBLET...........   7.50
PRESSED GLASS BULLS EYE & DAISY WINE DECANTER & 4 WINES.....  30.00
PRESSED GLASS BULLS EYE & DIAMOND POINT GOBLET,FLINT........  25.00
PRESSED GLASS BULLS EYE & DIAMOND POINT SAUCE,FLINT.........  15.00
PRESSED GLASS BULLS EYE & DIAMOND VARIANT OPEN SUGAR &
  CREAMER.........................................  15.00
PRESSED GLASS BULLS EYE & FLEUR DE LIS SUGAR,COVERED,FLINT
 26.50  TO.........................................  35.00
PRESSED GLASS BULLS EYE & TEARDROP GOBLET,SET OF 6..........  23.00
PRESSED GLASS BULLS EYE DECANTER,STOPPERS,PAIR..............  25.00
PRESSED GLASS BULLS EYE EGG CUP,COVERED,FLINT..............  45.00
PRESSED GLASS BULLS EYE GOBLET,FLINT
 20.00  TO.........................................  22.50
PRESSED GLASS BULLS EYE PITCHER..................  35.00
PRESSED GLASS BULLS EYE SUGAR,COVERED,FLINT......  48.50
PRESSED GLASS BULLS EYE WINE,FLINT...............  15.00
PRESSED GLASS BULLS EYE WITH FLEUR DE LIS SUGAR,OPEN,FLINT..  25.00
PRESSED GLASS BUNGALOW CLEAR WATER PITCHER.......  21.00
PRESSED GLASS BUTTERFLY & FAN COVERED SUGAR ON TALL FOOT....  15.00
PRESSED GLASS BUTTERFLY & FAN TUMBLER............   5.00
PRESSED GLASS BUTTERFLY CELERY VASE..............   8.50
PRESSED GLASS BUTTERFLY SALT,FOOTED..............   9.75
PRESSED GLASS BUTTERFLY SPOONER..................   7.50
PRESSED GLASS BUTTON ARCHES COVERED SUGAR........  12.50
PRESSED GLASS BUTTON ARCHES RED & CLEAR WATER
  SET,CHRISTMAS,7 PIECES..........................  75.00
PRESSED GLASS BUTTON ARCHES RUBY & CLEAR MILK TANKARD.......  18.50
PRESSED GLASS BUTTON ARCHES RUBY TOP MUG,WORLDS FAIR
  ST.LOUIS 1904...................................  10.50
PRESSED GLASS BUTTON ARCHES WINE.................   4.00
PRESSED GLASS BUTTON BAND CELERY.................  10.00
PRESSED GLASS BUTTON BAND TRAY,ROUND,FOOTED......  15.00
PRESSED GLASS BUTTON BAND WINE TRAY..............  17.50
PRESSED GLASS BUZZ SAW CRUET.....................  12.00
PRESSED GLASS CABBAGE ROSE RELISH DISH,OVAL......  13.75
PRESSED GLASS CABBAGE ROSE SALT & PEPPER,BLOWN PATTERN IN
  RELIEF..........................................   8.50
PRESSED GLASS CABBAGE ROSE WINE, 4IN. H..........  16.50
PRESSED GLASS CABIN GOBLET.......................   6.50
PRESSED GLASS CABLE COMPOTE,OPEN,FLINT...........  22.50
PRESSED GLASS CABLE CREAMER,FLINT................  13.00
PRESSED GLASS CABLE SAUCE........................   9.50
PRESSED GLASS CABLE SPOONER,ENGRAVED,FLINT.......  22.00
PRESSED GLASS CABLE SPOONER,FLINT................  15.50
PRESSED GLASS CABLE SPOONER,FOOTED,FLINT.........  25.00
PRESSED GLASS CABLE WITH RING SUGAR,COVERED,FLINT...........  38.50
```

```
PRESSED GLASS CACTUS BLUE OPALESCENT BOWL,6 IN.,3 FEET......    18.00
PRESSED GLASS CADMUS,6 IN. FLAT BOWL........................    10.00
PRESSED GLASS CAMBRIDGE VIOLET SALT,FOOTED,SQUARE BASE......    30.00
PRESSED GLASS CAMEO SAUCE,FOOTED............................     3.50
PRESSED GLASS CANADIAN CREAMER..............................    18.00
PRESSED GLASS CANADIAN GOBLET
  8.00    TO................................................    10.00
PRESSED GLASS CANADIAN WATER PITCHER........................    25.00
PRESSED GLASS CANDLESTICK,YELLOW,13 IN.,CRUCIFIX,FLINT......    55.00
PRESSED GLASS CANDLEWICK BERRY BOWL.........................     8.00
PRESSED GLASS CANE & ROSETTE SAUCE,FOOTED...................     4.50
PRESSED GLASS CANE AMBER TODDY PLATE,4 IN...................     8.50
PRESSED GLASS CANE AMBER WATER SET,PITCHER WITH 4 GOBLETS...    75.00
PRESSED GLASS CANE APPLE GREEN PLATE,4 IN...................     5.00
PRESSED GLASS CANE AQUA BOAT................................    15.00
PRESSED GLASS CANE BLUE GOBLET..............................    17.50
PRESSED GLASS CANE CLEAR PICKLE DISH,OVAL DOUBLE HANDLED....     5.50
PRESSED GLASS CANE FAIRY LAMP,11 IN. TALL,PAIR..............    35.00
PRESSED GLASS CANE GOBLET...................................     6.00
PRESSED GLASS CANE WATER PTICHER............................     9.50
PRESSED GLASS CANNON BALL CREAMER...........................     9.00
PRESSED GLASS CAPE COD PLATE................................    12.00
PRESSED GLASS CARDINAL BIRD GOBLET
 12.50    TO................................................    14.50
PRESSED GLASS CARMEN WATER PITCHER..........................    22.50
PRESSED GLASS CAROLINA JELLY COMPOTE........................     7.50
PRESSED GLASS CAROLINA MILK PITCHER.........................    10.00
PRESSED GLASS CASED LEAF UMBRELLA BLUE TUMBLER..............    20.01-
PRESSED GLASS CATHEDRAL AMBER BOWL..........................    12.50
PRESSED GLASS CATHEDRAL BLUE BERRY BOEL,8 IN................    17.50
PRESSED GLASS CATHEDRAL BUTTER..............................    25.00
PRESSED GLASS CATHEDRAL COVERED SUGAR.......................    17.50
PRESSED GLASS CATHEDRAL CREAMER.............................     9.00
PRESSED GLASS CATHEDRAL RUBY & CLEAR 7 IN. BOWL.............    16.50
PRESSED GLASS CHAIN & SHIELD BREAD TRAY.....................    10.50
PRESSED GLASS CHAIN & SHIELD CREAMER........................     9.00
PRESSED GLASS CHAIN & SHIELD SPOONER........................     4.50
PRESSED GLASS CHAIN & THUMBPRINT SUGAR & CREAMER............    10.00
PRESSED GLASS CHAIN COVERED BUTTER..........................    10.50
PRESSED GLASS CHAIN COVERED SUGAR...........................    10.00
PRESSED GLASS CHAIN GOBLET..................................     5.50
PRESSED GLASS CHAIN GREEN BREAD PLATTER.....................    17.50
PRESSED GLASS CHAIN WINE
  6.00    TO................................................     6.75
PRESSED GLASS CHAIN WITH STAR 7 IN. PLATE...................     7.50
PRESSED GLASS CHAIN WITH STAR BREAD PLATE WITH HANDLES......    14.50
PRESSED GLASS CHAIN WITH STAR GOBLET........................     6.50
PRESSED GLASS CHAIN WITH STAR PICKLE DISH...................     4.25
PRESSED GLASS CHAIN WITH STAR WINE..........................     5.50
PRESSED GLASS CHALLINOR COSMOS TOOTHPICK,2 HANDLES..........    10.50
PRESSED GLASS CHANDELIER GOBLET.............................    14.50
PRESSED GLASS CHECKERBOARD GREEN CEREAL BOWL................    35.00
PRESSED GLASS CHELSEA SPRIG SUGAR BOWL,COVERED..............    18.00
PRESSED GLASS CHERRIES & FIGS MILK PITCHER..................    15.00
PRESSED GLASS CHERRY SPOONER................................     7.50
PRESSED GLASS CHERUB CLEAR TOOTHPICK HOLDER.................    15.00
PRESSED GLASS CHICK ON WISHBONE CLEAR SALT..................    10.00
PRESSED GLASS CHILSON GOBLET................................    28.00
PRESSED GLASS CHURCH WINDOWS PITCHER........................    16.50
PRESSED GLASS CIRCLE CLEAR SALT SHAKER,PAIR.................    13.50
PRESSED GLASS CIRCLE CLEAR SPOONER..........................     7.50
PRESSED GLASS CIRCLE COMPOTE,JELLY,CLEAR....................     7.00
PRESSED GLASS CIRCLE STAND,JELLY,OPEN,CLEAR.................     8.00
PRESSED GLASS CIRCLE SYRUP WITH BRASS TOP,CLEAR.............    15.00
PRESSED GLASS CLASSIC BOWL,6 FEET...........................    50.00
```

```
PRESSED GLASS CLASSIC CELERY,FOOTED.........................   30.00
PRESSED GLASS CLASSIC CELERY VASE,COLLAR BASE...............   45.00
PRESSED GLASS CLEMATIS GOBLET..............................   12.50
PRESSED GLASS CLIO CREAMER,CLEAR...........................    6.50
PRESSED GLASS CLOVER BERRY BOWL............................   15.00
PRESSED GLASS COBALT BLUE BOWL,GOLD TRIM,HANDPAINTED........   12.00
PRESSED GLASS COBALT BLUE CANDLEHOLDER,3 FOOTED.............    6.00
PRESSED GLASS COBALT BLUE TOOTHPICK HOLDER,TOP HAT..........    4.50
PRESSED GLASS COBALT BLUE TUMBLER,PAIR.....................   13.00
PRESSED GLASS COIN GLASS 1892 RELISH DISH..................  135.00
PRESSED GLASS COBALT CANDLESTICK,FLEUR DE LIS TRIM..........    9.50
PRESSED GLASS COIN SPOT BLUE OPALESCENT SYRUP..............   37.50
PRESSED GLASS COIN SPOT OPALESCENT SYRUP...................   15.00
PRESSED GLASS COLONIAL CREAMER.............................    6.00
PRESSED GLASS COLONIAL GOBLET,FLINT........................   20.00
PRESSED GLASS COLONIAL LOOP DECANTER,FLINT.................   18.50
PRESSED GLASS COLORADO BLUE CREAMER,TRI-CORNER,5 IN........   15.00
PRESSED GLASS COLORADO BLUE NAPPY,TRIANGULAR SHAPE.........   10.00
PRESSED GLASS COLORADO BLUE SUGAR,COVERED..................   43.00
PRESSED GLASS COLORADO BLUE TOOTHPICK HOLDER...............   10.00
PRESSED GLASS COLORADO CLEAR CREAMER.......................   10.00
PRESSED GLASS COLORADO CLEAR RED DISH,3 FOOTED,7 IN........   10.00
PRESSED GLASS COLORADO DISH,TRI-CORNER,6 IN................    6.50
PRESSED GLASS COLORADO ETCHED STAR CLEAR BOWL,8 IN.........   12.00
PRESSED GLASS COLORADO FRINGED DRAPE SPOONER...............    8.00
PRESSED GLASS COLORADO FRUIT GROUPING ADVERTISING PLATE,9
  IN.......................................................    4.50
PRESSED GLASS COLORADO GOLD & BLUE DISH,FLARED.............   14.00
PRESSED GLASS COLORADO GREEN CREAMER.......................   20.00
PRESSED GLASS COLORADO GREEN SUGAR WITH GOLD FEET,SUSIE....   13.50
PRESSED GLASS COLORADO GREEN TABLE SET,4 PIECES............   85.00
PRESSED GLASS COLORADO GREEN TOOTHPICK ETCHED 1905 JOHN
  BAUMANN..................................................    8.00
PRESSED GLASS COLORADO GREEN TUMBLER.......................   14.00
PRESSED GLASS COLORADO GREEN WITH GOLD TUMBLER.............   14.00
PRESSED GLASS COLORADO SAUCE DISH,FOOTED...................   12.50
PRESSED GLASS COLORADO YELLOW POPPIES ADVERTISING PLATE,7
  IN.......................................................    3.00
PRESSED GLASS COLOSSUS COVERED BUTTER......................   10.50
PRESSED GLASS COLUMBIAN COIN BERRY BOWL,8 IN...............   35.00
PRESSED GLASS COLUMBIAN COIN FROSTED TOOTHPICK.............   18.50
PRESSED GLASS COLUMBIAN COIN WATER PITCHER.................   60.00
PRESSED GLASS COLUMBUS MUG.................................   13.50
PRESSED GLASS COLUMBUS WASHINGTON MUG......................   13.50
PRESSED GLASS COLUMNED THUMBPRINT SUGAR,OPEN...............    2.50
PRESSED GLASS CONVEX CLEAR SYRUP WITH LID..................    9.50
PRESSED GLASS CO-OP ROYAL WINE.............................    3.75
PRESSED GLASS CO-OPS COLUMBIA GOLD EYES SPOONER............    5.00
PRESSED GLASS CORCORAN SAUCE,FOOTED........................    2.75
PRESSED GLASS CORD & TASSEL TUMBLER........................    9.75
PRESSED GLASS CORD & TASSEL WINE...........................    7.00
PRESSED GLASS CORD DRAPERY BOWL............................    9.00
PRESSED GLASS CORD DRAPERY JELLY COMPOTE...................   12.50
PRESSED GLASS CORD DRAPERY RELISH DISH.....................    7.00
PRESSED GLASS CORD DRAPERY SAUCE...........................    3.00
PRESSED GLASS CORDOVA RELISH...............................    7.50
PRESSED GLASS CORDOVA SYRUP PITCHER WITH ORIG. PEWTER TOP...   12.50
PRESSED GLASS CORDOVA TOOTHPICK............................    .3.50
PRESSED GLASS CORK & TASSEL CREAMER........................   12.50
PRESSED GLASS CORN DESIGN AQUA BLUE SHAKER.................   10.00
PRESSED GLASS CORNUCOPIA VASE..............................    4.00
PRESSED GLASS COTTAGE CLEAR GOBLET.........................    5.00
PRESSED GLASS COTTAGE GOBLET...............................    8.50
PRESSED GLASS COTTAGE SPOONER..............................    6.50
PRESSED GLASS CRANBERRY CUT TO CLEAR GOBLET,FLINT..........   24.00
```

```
PRESSED GLASS CRANESBILL SPOONER & CREAMER,HANDLED..........    8.50
PRESSED GLASS CROSSBAR DAISY & BUTTON FOOTED SAUCE,CLEAR....    3.50
PRESSED GLASS CROSSED PRESSED LEAF COVERED SUGAR............   10.50
PRESSED GLASS CROWFOOT BUTTER,COVERED......................   22.50
PRESSED GLASS CROWFOOT CREAMER.............................   16.50
PRESSED GLASS CROWFOOT SPOONER.............................    4.75
PRESSED GLASS CROWN JEWEL MUFFINEER........................   18.50
PRESSED GLASS CROWN JEWEL TUMBLER,SET OF 6.................   50.00
PRESSED GLASS CRYSTAL GOBLET,FLINT.........................   20.00
PRESSED GLASS CUBE & BLOCK SPOONER.........................    3.00
PRESSED GLASS CUBE & FAN CREAMER...........................    6.50
PRESSED GLASS CUBE & FAN SUGAR,OPEN........................    5.00
PRESSED GLASS CUBE & FAN WATER JUG.........................    9.50
PRESSED GLASS CUBE WITH FAN SET OF 8 PUNCH CUPS............   22.00
PRESSED GLASS CUPID & VENUS CELERY VASE....................   20.00
PRESSED GLASS CUPID & VENUS MUG............................   15.00
PRESSED GLASS CUPID & VENUS SAUCE,4 IN.,FOOTED.............    6.00
PRESSED GLASS CUPID & VENUS SAUCE,FOOTED...................    5.50
PRESSED GLASS CUPID & VENUS SAUCE,FOOTED,SET OF 6..........   25.00
PRESSED GLASS CUPID & VENUS WATER PITCHER..................   12.00
PRESSED GLASS CUPIDS CLEAR PLATE,CHILDS,5 IN...............    9.50
PRESSED GLASS CUPIDS HEART PLATTER.........................   35.00
PRESSED GLASS CUPIDS HUNT PLATTER..........................   25.00
PRESSED GLASS CURRIER & IVES BALKY MULE TRAY,9 IN..........   23.00
PRESSED GLASS CURRIER & IVES BERRY BOWL,SCALLOPED EDGE,BLUE.  22.50
PRESSED GLASS CURRIER & IVES FINE CUT IONA HERRINGBONE
  GOBLET...................................................    9.00
PRESSED GLASS CURRIER & IVES GOBLET
  6.00    TO...............................................    7.50
PRESSED GLASS CURRIER & IVES MILK PITCHER..................   12.50
PRESSED GLASS CURRIER & IVES PITCHER,WATER.................   12.00
PRESSED GLASS CURRIER & IVES QUART DECANTER WITH CUT FACET
  STOPPER..................................................   17.50
PRESSED GLASS CURRIER & IVES WINE..........................    8.75
PRESSED GLASS CURTAIN COVERED SUGAR........................   16.00
PRESSED GLASS CURVED BROOCH BAND GOBLET,FLINT..............   19.50
PRESSED GLASS CUT ARGUS CHAMPAGNE,FLINT....................   30.00
PRESSED GLASS CUT LOG CAKE COMPOTE.........................   26.00
PRESSED GLASS CUT LOG CAKESTAND............................   12.00
PRESSED GLASS CUT LOG CELERY...............................   18.00
PRESSED GLASS CUT LOG CREAMER..............................   10.50
PRESSED GLASS CUT LOG MUG
  7.50    TO...............................................   10.00
PRESSED GLASS CUT LOG PICKLE DISH 5 BY 8 IN................    7.50
PRESSED GLASS CUT LOG SUGAR,COVERED........................   20.00
PRESSED GLASS CUT LOG WATER PITCHER........................   25.00
PRESSED GLASS CUT LOG WINE.................................    8.00
PRESSED GLASS DAHLIA & FESTOON WINE........................    3.75
PRESSED GLASS DAHLIA BUTTER,COVERED........................   25.00
PRESSED GLASS DAHLIA CHAMPAGNE.............................   16.00
PRESSED GLASS DAHLIA CREAMER...............................   10.50
PRESSED GLASS DAHLIA GOBLET................................   15.00
PRESSED GLASS DAHLIA MILK PITCHER..........................   19.50
PRESSED GLASS DAHLIA MILK PITCHER,7 IN. HIGH...............   22.00
PRESSED GLASS DAHLIA SAUCE.................................    3.00
PRESSED GLASS DAHLIA SPOONER
  5.00    TO...............................................    7.50
PRESSED GLASS DAHLIA WINE
  15.00   TO...............................................   17.50
PRESSED GLASS DAISIES IN OVALS COMPOTE,FOOTED..............    5.00
PRESSED GLASS DAISY AMBER TRAY,OBLONG,HANDLES..............   25.00
PRESSED GLASS DAISY & BUTTON 8 IN. PLATE...................    3.50
PRESSED GLASS DAISY & MEDALLION CREAMER....................    6.50
PRESSED GLASS DAISY & BUTTON & NARCISSUS GOBLET............    6.50
PRESSED GLASS DAISY & BUTTON AMBER BOWL ON 4 SCROLL
```

```
FEET,OVAL..................................................  34.00
PRESSED GLASS DAISY & BUTTON AMBER BUTTER DISH...............  25.00
PRESSED GLASS DAISY & BUTTON AMBER CASTOR,PICKLE............  60.00
PRESSED GLASS DAISY & BUTTON AMBER HAT......................   8.50
PRESSED GLASS DAISY & BUTTON AMBER OWL,SQUARE,TAPERED.......  24.00
PRESSED GLASS DAISY & BUTTON AMBER SAUCE,4 IN. SQUARE.......   6.00
PRESSED GLASS DAISY & BUTTON AMBER SLIPPER PATENT DATED
  OCT.19,1886..............................................  15.00
PRESSED GLASS DAISY & BUTTON AMBER TOOTHPICK HAT............  10.00
PRESSED GLASS DAISY & BUTTON AMBER TOOTHPICK,TOP HAT........   8.50
PRESSED GLASS DAISY & BUTTON AMBER TUMBLER..................  12.00
PRESSED GLASS DAISY & BUTTON AMBERETTE SAUCE................   8.00
PRESSED GLASS DAISY & BUTTON APPLE GREEN CANOE,HANGING......  27.00
PRESSED GLASS DAISY & BUTTON APPLE GREEN TOOTHPICK ON 3 FEET  12.00
PRESSED GLASS DAISY & BUTTON ASH TRAY,KETTLE SHAPE,PLATE &
  SQUARE DISH..............................................   6.50
PRESSED GLASS DAISY & BUTTON BELMONT COMPOTE,COVERED........  55.00
PRESSED GLASS DAISY & BUTTON BELMONT SUGAR & CREAMER,COVERED  50.00
PRESSED GLASS DAISY & BUTTON BLUE ANVIL SALT................  12.00
PRESSED GLASS DAISY & BUTTON BLUE BOWL,OVAL.................  30.00
PRESSED GLASS DAISY & BUTTON BLUE TOOTHPICK,TOP HAT.........   8.50
PRESSED GLASS DAISY & BUTTON BOWL,3 CORNERED................  12.50
PRESSED GLASS DAISY & BUTTON BOWL,CENTER....................  18.00
PRESSED GLASS DAISY & BUTTON BOWL IN SILVER PLATE HOLDER....  28.00
PRESSED GLASS DAISY & BUTTON CANARY HAT.....................   9.50
PRESSED GLASS DAISY & BUTTON CANARY SLIPPER DATED...........  12.00
PRESSED GLASS DAISY & BUTTON CANARY YELLOW ICE CREAM TRAY,9
  IN.......................................................  45.00
PRESSED GLASS DAISY & BUTTON CANOE..........................  35.00
PRESSED GLASS DAISY & BUTTON CELERY DISH,14 IN. LONG........  18.00
PRESSED GLASS DAISY & BUTTON CLEAR HAT......................   4.50
PRESSED GLASS DAISY & BUTTON CLEAR PANELS SYRUP,PEWTER LID..  15.00
PRESSED GLASS DAISY & BUTTON CLEAR PLATE,FAN SHAPED.........   7.50
PRESSED GLASS DAISY & BUTTON CLEAR SLIPPER WITH PERFUME
  BOTTLE INSERT............................................  17.50
PRESSED GLASS DAISY & BUTTON COLOGNE BOTTLE,SQUARE..........   8.50
PRESSED GLASS DAISY & BUTTON COVERED BUTTER.................  18.50
PRESSED GLASS DAISY & BUTTON CROSS BAR AMBER FOOTED SAUCE...   3.75
PRESSED GLASS DAISY & BUTTON CROSSBAR CLEAR WATER PITCHER...  17.50
PRESSED GLASS DAISY & BUTTON CROSSBAR CREAMER...............   6.00
PRESSED GLASS DAISY & BUTTON CUT PANELED VASE,FOOTED........  10.00
PRESSED GLASS DAISY & BUTTON FRUIT COMPOTE..................  45.00
PRESSED GLASS DAISY & BUTTON GREEN BERRY BOWL,OVAL..........  18.00
PRESSED GLASS DAISY & BUTTON GREEN BOWL,CENTER,CLOVER LEAF
  SHAPED...................................................  14.00
PRESSED GLASS DAISY & BUTTON GREEN PANELLED BERRY BOWL & 6
  SAUCES...................................................  26.00
PRESSED GLASS DAISY & BUTTON GREEN SLIPPER..................   7.00
PRESSED GLASS DAISY & BUTTON GREEN TRIANGULAR CELERY........  25.00
PRESSED GLASS DAISY & BUTTON MILK PITCHER...................  27.50
PRESSED GLASS DAISY & BUTTON PANEL CLEAR CRUET..............  15.00
PRESSED GLASS DAISY & BUTTON PICKLE,JUBILEE,ISIS,OVAL END...   2.50
PRESSED GLASS DAISY & BUTTON PLATE,7 IN. SQUARE,DEEP PRESS..   6.00
PRESSED GLASS DAISY & BUTTON PLATE,ROUND....................  12.00
PRESSED GLASS DAISY & BUTTON SHOE...........................   3.50
PRESSED GLASS DAISY & BUTTON SLIPPER........................  12.00
PRESSED GLASS DAISY & BUTTON SLIPPER,1886 BOSTON THEATER ON
  FOOT.....................................................  15.00
PRESSED GLASS DAISY & BUTTON SMOKY AMBER DISH,CANOE,8 IN....  38.00
PRESSED GLASS DAISY & BUTTON SYRUP WITH PEWTER LID..........  15.00
PRESSED GLASS DAISY & BUTTON TRAY,12 IN.,TRIANGULAR,HANDLED.  14.50
PRESSED GLASS DAISY & BUTTON V-ORNAMENT MUG.................   5.00
PRESSED GLASS DAISY AND BUTTON WATER TRAY,CLOVER LEAF SHAPE.  22.50
PRESSED GLASS DAISY AND BUTTON WITH CROSS BARS CELERY.......  15.00
PRESSED GLASS DAISY & BUTTON WITH CROSS BAR MILK PITCHER....  23.00
```

```
PRESSED GLASS DAISY & BUTTON WITH NARCISSUS WITH GOLD  WINE.      7.50
PRESSED GLASS DAISY & BUTTON WITH PANEL BLUE WATER PITCHER..     42.00
PRESSED GLASS DAISY & BUTTON WITH NARCISSUS TRAY.............     6.50
PRESSED GLASS DAISY & BUTTON WITH PANELS ROSE BOWL TYPE VASE
  ON 3 LEGS.................................................     25.00
PRESSED GLASS DAISY & BUTTON WITH RIMMED OVALS CREAMER......      7.50
PRESSED GLASS DAISY & BUTTON WITH RIMMED OVALS GOBLET.......      9.00
PRESSED GLASS DAISY & BUTTON WITH RIMMED OVALS WINE.........      8.00
PRESSED GLASS DAISY & BUTTON WITH SAWTOOTH ELECTRA BLUE CAKE
  STAND...................................................     27.50
PRESSED GLASS DAISY & BUTTON WITH THUMBPRINT BLUE GOBLET....     12.00
PRESSED GLASS DAISY & BUTTON WITH THUMBPRINT CLEAR GOBLET...     18.00
PRESSED GLASS DAISY & BUTTON WITH V,BLUE ,SMALL BOWL........      7.50
PRESSED GLASS DAISY & BUTTON WITH V ORNAMENTS CLEAR
  PITCHER,WATER..........................................     12.00
PRESSED GLASS DAISY & BUTTON YELLOW TOOTHPICK HAT...........      9.00
PRESSED GLASS DAISY CREAMER................................     10.00
PRESSED GLASS DAISY IN CUBE WINE,STEMMED...................      2.00
PRESSED GLASS DAISY MEDALLION COVERED SUGAR................     11.50
PRESSED GLASS DAISY ROUND BREAD PLATE,GIVE US THIS DAY OUR
  DAILY BREAD.............................................     18.00
PRESSED GLASS DAISY SPOONER................................      8.50
PRESSED GLASS DAISY WITH CLEAR STRIPE WINE.................      3.75
PRESSED GLASS DAKOTA CAKESTAND.............................     13.50
PRESSED GLASS DAKOTA COMPOTE ON HIGH STEM,ETCHING..........     16.00
PRESSED GLASS DAKOTA ETCHED CELERY.........................     10.50
PRESSED GLASS DAKOTA ETCHED GOBLET.........................     15.00
PRESSED GLASS DAKOTA ETCHED GRAPE & LEAF COMPOTE...........     15.00
PRESSED GLASS DAKOTA GOBLET................................      6.50
PRESSED GLASS DAKOTA PLAIN COMPOTE WITH LID,11 IN. HIGH.....     22.00
PRESSED GLASS DAKOTA RUBY TUMBLER,MINNIE MYERS 1890.........     12.50
PRESSED GLASS DAKOTA RUBY WINE.............................     19.50
PRESSED GLASS DAKOTA SAUCE,FOOTED & FLAT...................     13.75
PRESSED GLASS DART SUGAR,CREAMER,& SPOONER.................     45.00
PRESSED GLASS DEER & DOE WITH LILY OF VALLEY GOBLET
  28.50  TO..............................................     32.50
PRESSED GLASS DEER & DOG CELERY VASE.......................     25.00
PRESSED GLASS DEER & DOG GOBLET,U SHAPED BOWL..............     25.00
PRESSED GLASS DEER & PINE BUTTER,COVERED...................     32.50
PRESSED GLASS DEER & PINE PLATTER,OBLONG...................     20.00
PRESSED GLASS DEER & PINE SAUCE............................     12.50
PRESSED GLASS DEER & PINE TREE BREAD PLATTER,8 X 13 IN......     13.50
PRESSED GLASS DEER & PINE TREE BREAD TRAY..................     28.00
PRESSED GLASS DEER & PINE TREE CASTOR,PICKLE,TONGS,SILVER
  FRAME..................................................     85.00
PRESSED GLASS DEER & PINE TREE CELERY VASE.................     37.00
PRESSED GLASS DEER & PINETREE SPOONER......................     12.00
PRESSED GLASS DELAWARE BOWL WITH SAUCES,BOAT SHAPE,GOLD.....     60.00
PRESSED GLASS DELAWARE CLEAR WITH CRANBERRY FLOWERS BOAT
  SHAPE BOWL..............................................     25.00
PRESSED GLASS DELAWARE GREEN BOWL..........................     14.00
PRESSED GLASS DELAWARE GREEN BOWL,OVAL IN SILVER FRAME......     20.00
PRESSED GLASS DELAWARE GREEN FRUIT BOWL,OVAL...............     30.00
PRESSED GLASS DELAWARE GREEN WITH GOLD 8 IN. OCTAGON BOWL...     17.50
PRESSED GLASS DELAWARE GREEN WITH GOLD BOWL,BOAT SHAPE
  22.50  TO..............................................     35.00
PRESSED GLASS DELAWARE GREEN WITH GOLD SPOONER.............     16.50
PRESSED GLASS DELAWARE GREEN WITH GOLD SUGAR,OPEN..........     20.00
PRESSED GLASS DELAWARE GREEN WITH GOLD TUMBLER.............     16.00
PRESSED GLASS DELAWARE ROSE & GOLD CREAMER.................     20.00
PRESSED GLASS DELAWARE ROSE PINK BUTTER DISH,COVERED.......     75.00
PRESSED GLASS DELAWARE ROSE RELISH,BOAT SHAPED.............      6.00
PRESSED GLASS DELAWARE VASE,CLEAR WITH CRANBERRY LEAVES,GOLD
  TRIM...................................................     36.50
PRESSED GLASS DEW WITH RAIN DROP CORDIAL...................      6.00
```

```
PRESSED GLASS DEW RAINDROP GOBLET............................    9.00
PRESSED GLASS DEW & RAINDROP PUNCH CUP
   4.00    TO.................................................    5.00
PRESSED GLASS DEW AND RAINDROP SPOONER.......................    8.00
PRESSED GLASS DEW AND RAINDROP WINE..........................    5.50
PRESSED GLASS DEWDROP & STAR SAUCE,FOOTED,SET OF 5...........    5.00
PRESSED GLASS DEWDROP BAND GOBLET
   3.75    TO.................................................    4.75
PRESSED GLASS DEWDROP & DIAMOND PITCHER......................   17.00
PRESSED GLASS DEWDROP & HONEY COMBINATION GOBLET.............    6.50
PRESSED GLASS DEWDROP CLEAR DISH FOR DEVILED EGGS............   20.00
PRESSED GLASS DEWDROP HONEY DISH.............................    3.75
PRESSED GLASS DEWDROP IN POINTS WATER SET TRAY...............    5.00
PRESSED GLASS DEWBERRY CREAMER...............................    7.50
PRESSED GLASS DEWEY GREEN COVERED SUGAR......................   20.00
PRESSED GLASS DEWEY GREEN CREAMER............................   22.50
PRESSED GLASS DEWEY WATER PITCHER............................   22.50
PRESSED GLASS DIAGONAL BAND & FAN GOBLET.....................    7.00
PRESSED GLASS DIAGONAL BAND 9 IN. PEDESTAL CAKESTAND.........   11.50
PRESSED GLASS DIAGONAL BAND CELERY VASE......................    7.00
PRESSED GLASS DIAGONAL BAND CLEAR WATER PITCHER..............    8.00
PRESSED GLASS DIAGONAL BAND COVERED SUGAR....................   13.50
PRESSED GLASS DIAGONAL BAND GOBLET...........................    3.00
PRESSED GLASS DIAGONAL BAND GOBLET,CLEAR.....................    4.75
PRESSED GLASS DIAGONAL BAND GREEN TRAY,RECTANGULAR...........   17.50
PRESSED GLASS DIAGONAL BAND WATER PITCHER....................    8.50
PRESSED GLASS DIAGONAL BAND WITH FAN CHAMBER CANDLESTICK.....   32.00
PRESSED GLASS DIAGONAL BAND WITH FAN COVERED SUGAR...........   15.00
PRESSED GLASS DIAGONAL BAND WITH FAN GOBLET..................    7.50
PRESSED GLASS DIAGONAL BAND WITH FAN PLATE,6 IN..............    6.00
PRESSED GLASS DIAGONAL BAND WITH FAN SAUCE,FOOTED............    2.50
PRESSED GLASS DIAGONAL SAWTOOTH BAND GOBLET,FLINT............   27.50
PRESSED GLASS DIAMOND & DEWDROP GOBLET.......................    6.50
PRESSED GLASS DIAMOND & DOUBLE FAN COVERED BUTTER...........    7.00
PRESSED GLASS DIAMOND & DOUBLE FAN VARIANT COMPOTE,OPEN.....    6.00
PRESSED GLASS DIAMOND & SUNBURST CREAMER.....................   10.00
PRESSED GLASS DIAMOND & SUNBURST VARIANT LEMONADE GLASS......    3.00
PRESSED GLASS DIAMOND & SUNBURST VARIANT WINE................    2.75
PRESSED GLASS DIAMOND BAND GOBLET............................    6.50
PRESSED GLASS DIAMOND MEDALLION BUTTER,COVERED...............   15.00
PRESSED GLASS DIAMOND MEDALLION CAKE STAND...................    7.50
PRESSED GLASS DIAMOND MEDALLION CELERY.......................   14.00
PRESSED GLASS DIAMOND MEDALLION CREAMER......................   14.50
PRESSED GLASS DIAMOND MEDALLION COMPOTE,OPEN.................   10.00
PRESSED GLASS DIAMOND MEDALLION GOBLET
   6.50    TO.................................................    8.00
PRESSED GLASS DIAMOND MEDALLION PLATE,10 IN..................    7.00
PRESSED GLASS DIAMOND MEDALLION RELISH DISH..................    5.50
PRESSED GLASS DIAMOND MEDALLION SAUCE,FLAT...................    2.75
PRESSED GLASS DIAMOND MEDALLION SPOONER......................    7.50
PRESSED GLASS DIAMOND MEDALLION SUGAR........................    7.50
PRESSED GLASS DIAMOND MEDALLION SUGAR,COVERED................   12.50
PRESSED GLASS DIAMOND POINT COVERED SUGAR,FLINT..............   35.00
PRESSED GLASS DIAMOND POINT BAND MILK PITCHER................   22.00
PRESSED GLASS DIAMOND POINT BAND TUMBLER.....................    3.50
PRESSED GLASS DIAMOND POINT COMPOTE ON HIGH STANDARD,FLINT..   38.50
PRESSED GLASS DIAMOND POINT GOBLET,FLINT.....................   16.50
PRESSED GLASS DIAMOND POINT GOBLET,KNOB STEM.................   20.00
PRESSED GLASS DIAMOND POINT SPILL VASE,FLINT.................   16.50
PRESSED GLASS DIAMOND POINT SUGAR,COVERED,CIRCULAR RAYED
  BASE,FLINT.................................................   49.50
PRESSED GLASS DIAMOND POINT SUGAR,COVERED,FLINT..............   35.00
PRESSED GLASS DIAMOND POINT SYRUP,TIN TOP....................   12.50
PRESSED GLASS DIAMOND POINT WATER PITCHER,FLINT..............   55.00
PRESSED GLASS DIAMOND POINT WITH PANELS SUGAR,COVERED,FLINT.   37.50
```

```
PRESSED GLASS DIAMOND QUILTED AMETHYST FLAT SAUCE...........  10.00
PRESSED GLASS DIAMOND QUILTED WINE.........................   7.50
PRESSED GLASS DIAMOND SAWTOOTH CLEAR POWDER JAR............   2.50
PRESSED GLASS DIAMOND SUNBURST BUTTERMILK GOBLET...........   6.50
PRESSED GLASS DIAMOND SUNBURST CELERY VASE.................   7.50
PRESSED GLASS DIAMOND SUNBURST CLEAR RED MILK PITCHER......  22.00
PRESSED GLASS DIAMOND SUNBURST GOBLET......................   5.00
PRESSED GLASS DIAMOND THUMBPRINT CELERY,FLINT..............  95.00
PRESSED GLASS DIAMOND THUMBPRINT COMPOTE,FLINT.............  40.00
PRESSED GLASD DIAMOND THUMBPRINT COMPOTE,OPEN,LOW,FLINT....  30.00
PRESSED GLASS DIAMOND THUMBPRINT SANDWICH DECANTER,FLINT...  60.00
PRESSED GLASS DICKINSON GOBLET.............................  14.00
PRESSED GLASS DICKENSON SAUCE..............................   7.00
PRESSED GLASS DIVIDED SQUARE S BUTTER,COVERED,FLINT........  17.50
PRESSED GLASS DORIC FEATHER SAUCE,SQUARE...................   4.00
PRESSED GLASS DOUBLE DAISY JELLY COMPOTE...................   8.50
PRESSED GLASS DOUBLE FAN & DIAMOND CLEAR COMPOTE,PAIR......  10.00
PRESSED GLASS DOUBLE FAN BOWL,8 IN.........................   7.00
PRESSED GLASS DOUBLE LOOP & DART STIPPLED CELERY,FLINT.....  10.00
PRESSED GLASS DOUBLE LOOP MAYPOLE SPOONER..................   7.50
PRESSED GLASS DOUBLE LOOP SPOON HOLDER.....................   8.50
PRESSED GLASS DOUBLE RIBBON COVERED BUTTER.................  21.50
PRESSED GLASS DOUBLE SCROLL FROSTED CELERY.................  12.50
PRESSED GLASS DOUBLE SCROLL SUGAR,COVERED,CREAMER & SPOONER. 26.00
PRESSED GLASS DOUBLE SPEAR GOBLET..........................   8.00
PRESSED GLASS DOUBLE TEARDROP BOWL,10 IN...................   2.00
PRESSED GLASS DOUBLE TEARDROP CRUET,ORIGINAL STOPPER.......   8.00
PRESSED GLASS DOUBLE VINE COARSE RIB SUGAR.................  14.00
PRESSED GLASS DOUBLE VINE WATER SET TEAY...................  12.50
PRESSED GLASS DRAPERY CREAMER
    7.50   TO.............................................  18.00
PRESSED GLASS DRAPERY GOBLET
    7.00   TO.............................................   9.75
PRESSED GLASS DRAPERY SPOONER..............................  12.00
PRESSED GLASS EDGERTON COVERED SUGAR.......................   8.00
PRESSED GLASS EDGERTON SAUCE,FLAT..........................   2.00
PRESSED GLASS EGG IN SAND GOBLET...........................   9.00
PRESSED GLASS EGG IN SAND PLATTER..........................   7.50
PRESSED GLASS EGYPTIAN CELERY..............................  13.75
PRESSED GLASS EGYPTIAN CLEAR PICKLE DISH...................  10.50
PRESSED GLASS EGYPTIAN CLEOPATRA BREAD PLATE...............  27.50
PRESSED GLASS EGYPTIAN COMPOTE,OPEN........................  37.50
PRESSED GLASS EGYPTIAN CREAMER.............................  10.00
PRESSED GLASS EGYPTIAN GOBLET..............................  12.50
PRESSED GLASS EGYPTIAN SAUCE,FOOTED,4 IN...................   5.50
PRESSED GLASS EGYPTIAN WITH SPHINX COVERED COMPOTE.........  48.50
PRESSED GLASS EIGHT-O-EIGHT WINE...........................   5.00
PRESSED GLASS ELECTRA BLUE DISH,COVERED,RAYED STAR BASE....  25.00
PRESSED GLASS ELONGATED HONEYCOMB GOBLET,FLINT.............  15.00
PRESSED GLASS EMERALD GREEN CANOE,SOUVENIR
    CLARKSTON,WASHINGTON...................................   8.00
PRESSED GLASS EMERALD GREEN CRUET,ENAMELED.................  15.00
PRESSED GLASS ENGLISH HOBNAIL & THUMBPRINT SPOONER.........   5.00
PRESSED GLASS ENGLISH HOBNAIL AMBER FINGER BOWL,FLAT SAUCE..  18.50
PRESSED GLASS ENGLISH HOBNAIL CONDIMENT SET................  12.50
PRESSED GLASS ENGLISH HOBNAIL PICKLE DISH..................   6.00
PRESSED GLASS ENGLISH HOBNAIL SALT,PEDESTAL................   2.50
PRESSED GLASS ENGLISH HOBNAIL SAUCE DISH...................   4.00
PRESSED GLASS ENGLISH HOBNAIL SUGAR........................   8.50
PRESSED GLASS E.PLURIBUS UNUM MUG..........................  13.50
PRESSED GLASS ENGLISH HOBNAIL COMPOTE,STEMMED
    4.75   TO.............................................   6.00
PRESSED GLASS ESTHER GREEN WITH GOLD COVERED SUGAR.........  35.00
PRESSED GLASS ETCHED ADMIRAL DEWEY PLATE...................   8.50
PRESSED GLASS ETCHED BABY THUMBPRINT BUTTER,COVERED........  22.50
```

```
PRESSED GLASS ETCHED BABY THUMBPRINT DAKOTA CELERY,FLAT.....          15.00
PRESSED GLASS ETCHED BABY THUMBPRINT DAKOTA CELERY,FOOTED...          16.00
PRESSED GLASS ETCHED BABY THUMBPRINT DAKOTA COMPOTE,OPEN,6
  IN.................................................................          18.50
PRESSED GLASS ETCHED BABY THUMBPRINT DAKOTA
  COMPOTE,COVERED,5 IN.....................................          25.00
PRESSED GLASS ETCHED BABY THUMBPRINT DAKOTA COMPOTE,9
  IN.,OPEN................................................          35.00
PRESSED GLASS ETCHED BABY THUMBPRINT DAKOTA CREAMER,MAMMA
  1888...................................................          16.50
PRESSED GLASS ETCHED BABY THUMBPRINT DAKOTA CRUET,VINEGAR...          18.50
PRESSED GLASS ETCHED BABY THUMBPRINT DAKOTA GOBLET,SHORT
  STEM...................................................          12.50
PRESSED GLASS ETCHED BABY THUMBPRINT DAKOTA GOBLET...........          15.00
PRESSED GLASS ETCHED BABY THUMBPRINT DAKOTA MILK PITCHER.....          22.50
PRESSED GLASS ETCHED BABY THUMBPRINT DAKOTA SALT SHAKER,PAIR          15.00
PRESSED GLASS ETCHED BABY THUMBPRINT DAKOTA SUGAR,COVERED...          25.00
PRESSED GLASS ETCHED BABY THUMBPRINT DAKOTA WATER PITCHER...          25.00
PRESSED GLASS ETCHED BABY THUMBPRINT DAKOTA WINE.............          8.50
PRESSED GLASS ETCHED BIRD & ROSES GOBLET....................          10.00
PRESSED GLASS ETCHED BIRDS & ROSES GOBLET...................          13.50
PRESSED GLASS ETCHED BIRDS TUMBLER..........................          5.50
PRESSED GLASS ETCHED  CHEESE DISH,FLINT.....................          50.00
PRESSED GLASS ETCHED CLEAR GOBLET...........................          2.00
PRESSED GLASS ETCHED CLEAR TUMBLE-UP........................          7.00
PRESSED GLASS ETCHED DAKOTA BIRD & FERN PITCHER.............          37.50
PRESSED GLASS ETCHED DAKOTA GOBLET..........................          16.00
PRESSED GLASS ETCHED DAKOTA JELLY COMPOTE...................          22.50
PRESSED GLASS ETCHED DAKOTA TANKARD,BIRDS,INSECTS...........          25.00
PRESSED GLASS ETCHED DEER & DOE TUMBLER.....................          5.50
PRESSED GLASS ETCHED FLOWERS TUMBLER........................          5.50
PRESSED GLASS ETCHED GARDEN FRUITS GOBLET...................          13.50
PRESSED GLASS ETCHED GIRAFFE TUMBLER........................          5.50
PRESSED GLASS ETCHED GRAPES 9 PANELLED GOBLET,SHORT
  STEM,FLINT.............................................          6.75
PRESSED GLASS ETCHED HEART STEM CELERY VASE.................          13.50
PRESSED GLASS ETCHED HONEYCOMB WINE.........................          6.00
PRESSED GLASS ETCHED HORSE TUMBLER..........................          5.50
PRESSED GLASS ETCHED OKLAHOMA CLEAR VINEGAR,CO.FORT SMITH...          3.50
PRESSED GLASS ETCHED LEAVES & BABY THUMBPRINT CREAMER.......          8.00
PRESSED GLASS ETCHED LEOPARD TUMBLER........................          5.50
PRESSED GLASS ETCHED PAIR STEMMED COCKTAIL GLASSES,5 IN.....          3.00
PRESSED GLASS ETCHED PINEAPPLE STEM FOOTED SAUCE............          4.50
PRESSED GLASS ETCHED PLUME GOBLET...........................          13.50
PRESSED GLASS ETCHED RED WINE,GOLD BORDER...................          6.50
PRESSED GLASS ETCHED STAG TUMBLER...........................          5.50
PRESSED GLASS ETCHED STORK TUMBLER..........................          5.50
PRESSED GLASS ETCHED THUMBPRINT DAKOTA SAUCE,FOOTED.........          6.50
PRESSED GLASS ETCHED YELLOW CREAMER & SUGAR.................          5.00
PRESSED GLASS EXCELSIOR ALE.................................          39.50
PRESSED GLASS EXCELSIOR ANGULAR GOBLET,FLINT................          10.00
PRESSED GLASS EXCELSIOR BARREL GOBLET,FLINT.................          16.00
PRESSED GLASS EXCELSIOR CARAFE,FLINT........................          27.50
PRESSED GLASS EXCELSIOR COMPOTE.............................          75.00
PRESSED GLASS EXCELSIOR EGG CUP,FLINT.......................          11.00
PRESSED GLASS EXCELSIOR GOBLET,FLINT........................          7.00
PRESSED GLASS EXCELSIOR SUGAR,OPEN,7 IN.,FLINT..............          25.00
PRESSED GLASS EXCELSIOR SUGAR,OPEN,FLINT....................          15.00
PRESSED GLASS EXCELSIOR VARIANT TUMBLER,FOOTED,FLINT........          11.00
PRESSED GLASS EXCELSIOR WITH MALTESE CROSS SPOONER,FLINT....          18.50
PRESSED GLASS EXPANDED DIAMOND DECANTER.....................          29.50
PRESSED GLASS EYEWINKER BUTTER,COVERED......................          25.00
PRESSED GLASS EYE WINKER CAKESTAND..........................          22.50
PRESSED GLASS EYEWINKER CAKE STAND,8 IN.....................          18.00
PRESSED GLASS EYE WINKER COMPOTE,COVERED....................          35.00
```

```
PRESSED GLASS EYEWINKER COMPOTE,SCALLOPED EDGE..............   45.00
PRESSED GLASS EYEWINKER FRUIT COMPOTE......................   48.00
PRESSED GLASS EYE WINKER GREEN TOOTHPICK HOLDER..............   15.00
PRESSED GLASS EYEWINKER SAUCE DISH.........................   12.50
PRESSED GLASS FAIRY VILLA BLUE BOWL,10 IN...................   15.00
PRESSED GLASS FAN & STAR OPEN SUGAR ON PEDESTAL..............    8.50
PRESSED GLASS FAN BAND WINE.................................    5.50
PRESSED GLASS FAN,DIAGONAL DEW & RAINDROP AMBER CREAMER.....   15.00
PRESSED GLASS FANS WITH DIAMONDS GOBLET.....................    7.50
PRESSED GLASS FEATHER & BLOCK CELERY........................    7.50
PRESSED GLASS FEATHER & BLOCK MILK PITCHER..................    9.50
PRESSED GLASS FEATHER BAND CAKE STANDARD
  10.00   TO...............................................   12.00
PRESSED GLASS FEATHER BOWL..................................    5.00
PRESSED GLASS FEATHER BUTTER,COVERED........................   12.50
PRESSED GLASS FEATHER BUTTER DISH...........................   12.00
PRESSED GLASS FEATHER CAKE STAND,QUEEN SIZE..................   16.50
PRESSED GLASS FEATHER CRUET.................................   18.50
PRESSED GLASS FEATHER DUSTER CAKESTAND......................    6.50
PRESSED GLASS FEATHER GOBLET................................   15.00
PRESSED GLASS FEATHER INDIANA SWIRL WATER PITCHER...........   12.50
PRESSED GLASS FEATHER SAUCE.................................    3.50
PRESSED GLASS FEATHER SUGAR.................................    8.50
PRESSED GLASS FEATHER SUGAR,COVERED.........................   12.50
PRESSED GLASS FEATHER TOOTHPICK.............................    5.00
PRESSED GLASS FEATHER VASE,.................................    8.50
PRESSED GLASS FEATHER WATER PITCHER.........................   12.50
PRESSED GLASS FERN GARLAND RELISH...........................    4.00
PRESSED GLASS FERN GARLAND SAUCE,FOOTED.....................    4.50
PRESSED GLASS FERN RUBY & CLEAR WATER SET...................  115.00
PRESSED GLASS FESTOON BUTTER,COVERED........................   10.00
PRESSED GLASS FESTOON BUTTERMILK............................    8.00
PRESSED GLASS FESTOON CAKESTAND.............................    9.00
PRESSED GLASS FESTOON CAKE STAND,10 IN......................   15.00
PRESSED GLASS FESTOON CREAMER
  7.00   TO................................................   12.00
PRESSED GLASS FESTOON SPOONER...............................    5.00
PRESSED GLASS FESTOON SUGAR,COVERED.........................   15.00
PRESSED GLASS FESTOON WATER SET.............................   57.00
PRESSED GLASS FIG & CHERRY MILK PITCHER.....................   18.00
PRESSED GLASS FINE CUT & BLOCK WINE
  4.50   TO................................................    8.25
PRESSED GLASS FINE CUT & FEATHER BOWL,8 IN..................    5.50
PRESSED GLASS FINE CUT & FEATHER COVERED SUGAR..............   10.00
PRESSED GLASS FINE CUT & FEATHER GOBLET.....................    7.00
PRESSED GLASS FINE CUT & FEATHER PITCHER....................   10.00
PRESSED GLASS FINE CUT & FEATHER PURPLE WATER PITCHER.......   17.00
PRESSED GLASS FINE CUT & FEATHER SPOONER....................    4.50
PRESSED GLASS FINECUT AMBER TOP HAT.........................    8.00
PRESSED GLASS FINECUT & PANEL GOBLET........................    7.00
PRESSED GLASS FINE CUT & PANEL RELISH.......................    4.00
PRESSED GLASS FINE CUT & PANEL SAPPHIRE BLUE PLATE..........   10.00
PRESSED GLASS FINECUT PLATE,7 IN............................    5.00
PRESSED GLASS FINE RIB COMPOTE,7 IN. HIGH,FLINT.............   42.50
PRESSED GLASS FINE RIB COMPOTE ON LOW PEDESTAL,FLINT........   22.00
PRESSED GLASS FINE RIB GREEN OPALESCENT VASE................    6.50
PRESSED GLASS FINE RIB MASTER SALT,FOOTED,FLINT.............   12.50
PRESSED GLASS FINE RIB,PLAIN BAND GOBLET....................    6.50
PRESSED GLASS FISHSCALE CAKESTAND...........................    9.50
PRESSED GLASS FISHSCALE COVERED BUTTER......................   11.50
PRESSED GLASS FISHSCALE GOBLET..............................   12.50
PRESSED GLASS FISHSCALE JELLY COMPOTE.......................    9.00
PRESSED GLASS FISHSCALE MILK PITCHER........................   12.50
PRESSED GLASS FISHSCALE PITCHER.............................   14.00
PRESSED GLASS FLAMINGO HABITAT SPOONER,FOOTED...............   17.50
```

```
PRESSED GLASS FLAMINGO SUGAR,COVERED......................    12.50
PRESSED GLASS FLAT DIAMOND & PANEL DECANTER WITH
   STOPPER,FLINT.........................................    25.00
PRESSED GLASS FLAT DIAMOND SPOONER........................     4.75
PRESSED GLASS FLAT SAWTOOTH SALT DIP,FLINT................     6.50
PRESSED GLASS FLEUR DE LIS ARCHED SUGAR BOWL,COVERED,2
   HANDLES..............................................    12.11-
PRESSED GLASS FLEUR DE LIS CELERY VASE....................     8.50
PRESSED GLASS FLEUR DE LIS DRAPE COVERED SUGAR............    10.50
PRESSED GLASS FLEUR DE LIS DRAPE GOBLET...................    10.00
PRESSED GLASS FLEUR DE LIS DRAPE GREEN RECTANGULAR BOWL....    10.50
PRESSED GLASS FLEUR DE LIS & DRAPE JELLY COMPOTE,OPEN......     7.50
PRESSED GLASS FLEUR DE LIS DRAPE PLATE,8 IN...............     5.50
PRESSED GLASS FLEUR DE LIS DRAPE SUGAR,COVERED............    10.00
PRESSED GLASS FLEUR DE LIS DRAPE WATER TRAY...............    14.00
PRESSED GLASS FLEUR DE LIS TOOTHPICK HOLDER...............    27.50
PRESSED GLASS FLEUR DE LIS WITH DRAPE COMPOTE,COVERED......    25.00
PRESSED GLASS FLEUR DE LIS WITH DRAPE SUGAR,COVERED.......    12.00
PRESSED GLASS FLORAL DIAMOND BOWL.........................     5.00
PRESSED GLASS FLORAL ENGRAVED CLEAR SALT SHAKER,STERLING
   SILVER TOP............................................     6.50
PRESSED GLASS FLORAL ETCHED RUBY TOOTHPICK................     8.50
PRESSED GLASS FLORAL OVALS CELERY.........................     9.00
PRESSED GLASS FLORAL OVALS WINE...........................     5.50
PRESSED GLASS FLORIDA EMERALD GREEN WITH GOLD TUMBLER......    12.00
PRESSED GLASS FLORIDA PALM BUTTER.........................    10.50
PRESSED GLASS FLORIDA PALM CAKESTAND......................    10.00
PRESSED GLASS FLORIDA PALM CELERY.........................     9.00
PRESSED GLASS FLORIDA PALM GOBLET.........................     6.50
PRESSED GLASS FLOWER & RIB GREEN OPAQUE SHAKER............    12.50
PRESSED GLASS FLOWER ASSORTMENT BLUE OPAQUE SHAKER,PAIR....    25.00
PRESSED GLASS FLOWER BAND FROSTED SPOONER,DOUBLE HANDLES....   12.00
PRESSED GLASS FLOWER IN SCROLL GOBLET.....................     6.00
PRESSED GLASS FLOWER MEDALLION ETCHED GOBLET,FLINT..........   10.00
PRESSED GLASS FLOWER POT PEPPER SHAKER....................     5.50
PRESSED GLASS FLOWER POT SPOONER..........................     6.50
PRESSED GLASS FLOWER WITH SCROLL SUGAR,COVERED............    10.50
PRESSED GLASS FLUTE & BULLSEYE ALE........................    39.50
PRESSED GLASS FLUTE BESSIMER GOBLET,FLINT.................     9.50
PRESSED GLASS FLUTE GOBLET,FLINT
   7.50     TO...........................................    14.00
PRESSED GLASS FLUTE GOBLET,SQUARE,FLINT...................     9.50
PRESSED GLASS FLUTE PITTSBURGH CLOUDY GOBLET,FLINT...........   4.50
PRESSED GLASS FLUTE SEXTON GOBLET,FLINT...................     9.50
PRESSED GLASS FLUTE TUMBLER,FLINT.........................     7.50
PRESSED GLASS FLUTE WINE..................................     2.75
PRESSED GLASS FLUTE WINE,REED STEM,FLINT..................     7.50
PRESSED GLASS FLUTED DISH,2 HANDLED.......................     4.00
PRESSED GLASS FLUTED SCROLL CREAMER.......................    24.00
PRESSED GLASS FLUTED SCROLL OPAL COVERED JELLY............    15.00
PRESSED GLASS FLUTED SCROLL OPAL CREAMER..................    15.00
PRESSED GLASS FLUTED SCROLLS & FLOWER BAND OPALESCENT
   CREAMER...............................................    14.50
PRESSED GLASS FLUTED SCROLLS OPALESCENT CREAMER...........    12.50
PRESSED GLASS FLUTED SWIRL BLOWN VASE.....................    25.00
PRESSED GLASS FLUTED WINE,FLUTED HALF WAY UP,BELLTONE,KNOB
   STEM,FLINT............................................     3.00
PRESSED GLASS FORGET-ME-NOT IN SCROLL GOBLET..............     7.50
PRESSED GLASS FORGET-ME-NOT IN SCROLL SUGAR,OPEN..........    12.75
PRESSED GLASS FOUR PETAL CREAMER..........................    55.00
PRESSED GLASS FOUR PETAL SUGAR,COVERED....................    55.00
PRESSED GLASS FOUR PETAL SUGAR,COVERED,FLINT..............    39.00
PRESSED GLASS FOUR PETALS & ENGLISH HOBNAIL CREAMER.........    6.50
PRESSED GLASS FOX & CROW PITCHER..........................    45.00
PRESSED GLASS FROG & SPIDER GOBLET........................    50.00
```

```
PRESSED GLASS FROSTED BLOCK GREEN PLATE,SQUARE..............     5.00
PRESSED GLASS FROSTED BLOCK PLATE...........................    10.00
PRESSED GLASS FROSTED BLOCKED ARCHES PICKLE DISH............     6.50
PRESSED GLASS FROSTED CABBAGE LEAF COVERED CANDY DISH SIGNED
  PORTIEUX..................................................    25.00
PRESSED GLASS FROSTED CELERY,SCALLOPED TOP,WHITE & GOLD
  FLORAL...................................................     15.00
PRESSED GLASS FROSTED CIRCLE BUTTER DISH....................    35.00
PRESSED GLASS FROSTED CIRCLE CLEAR & FROSTED TUMBLER........     9.50
PRESSED GLASS FROSTED CIRCLE PITCHER........................    25.00
PRESSED GLASS FROSTED CIRCLE SPOONER........................     9.00
PRESSED GLASS FROSTED DOG & DEER COMPOTE,ETCHED LID,PLAIN
  BASE.....................................................     55.00
PRESSED GLASS FROSTED DUCK BUTTER DISH......................    24.00
PRESSED GLASS FROSTED GREEN ROSE BOWL WITH EMBOSSED FLOWERS.    17.00
PRESSED GLASS FROSTED LION & CABLE CREAMER..................    24.50
PRESSED GLASS FROSTED LION BREAD TRAY,GIVE US THIS DAY......    32.00
PRESSED GLASS FROSTED LION CABLE COMPOTE,OPEN...............    26.00
PRESSED GLASS FROSTED LION,CABLE CREAMER....................    24.50
PRESSED GLASS FROSTED LION COMPOTE,COVERED
  58.00  TO...............................................     75.00
PRESSED GLASS FROSTED LION COMPOTE,COVERED,8 IN.,LOW FOOT...    45.00
PRESSED GLASS FROSTED LION COMPOTE,FROSTED BASE STANDARD....    55.00
PRESSED GLASS FROSTED LION GOBLET...........................    21.50
PRESSED GLASS FROSTED LION PICKLE DISH......................    14.50
PRESSED GLASS FROSTED LION SPOONER..........................    16.50
PRESSED GLASS FROSTED MAPLE LEAF BERRY SET,BOWL & 6 SAUCES..    32.00
PRESSED GLASS FROSTED MAPLE LEAF BOWL,OVAL,FOOTED...........    10.00
PRESSED GLASS FROSTED MEDALLION JELLY COMPOTE...............     6.50
PRESSED GLASS FROSTED PHEASANT COMPOTE,COVERED..............    48.00
PRESSED GLASS FROSTED POLAR BEAR GOBLET.....................    35.00
PRESSED GLASS FROSTED POLAR BEAR WASTE BOWL.................    32.00
PRESSED GLASS FROSTED RIBBON COLOGNE BOTTLE WITH STOPPER....    37.50
PRESSED GLASS FROSTED RIBBON COMPOTE,LARGE STANDARD,COVERED.    18.50
PRESSED GLASS FROSTED RIBBON GOBLET.........................    11.00
PRESSED GLASS FROSTED RIBBON OPEN COMPOTE,7 IN..............    10.00
PRESSED GLASS FROSTED RIBBON PLATTER,RAYED EFFECT,HEXAGON
  SHAPE....................................................     11.00
PRESSED GLASS FROSTED RIBBON WATER TRAY.....................    15.00
PRESSED GLASS FROSTED ROMAN KEY BOWL & 11 SAUCE DISHES,FLINT    75.00
PRESSED GLASS FROSTED ROMAN KEY CHAMPAGNE,FLINT.............    20.00
PRESSED GLASS FROSTED ROMAN KEY GOBLET,FLINT................    20.00
PRESSED GLASS FROSTED ROMAN KEY HONEY DISH,FLINT............     3.50
PRESSED GLASS FROSTED ROMAN KEY GOBLET
  17.00  TO...............................................     20.00
PRESSED GLASS FROSTED ROMAN KEY SUGAR,COVERED,FLINT.........    28.50
PRESSED GLASS FROSTED ROMAN KEY WINE........................    22.00
PRESSED GLASS FROSTED SHELLS ON CORNERS PLATE,BOY & DOG.....    15.00
PRESSED GLASS FROSTED STORK IOWA CITY CLEAR GOBLET..........    50.00
PRESSED GLASS FROSTED THREE FACE SAUCE,FOOTED...............     7.00
PRESSED GLASS FROSTED THREE FACE WATER PITCHER..............   105.00
PRESSED GLASS FRUIT CORNUCOPIA WATER PITCHER................    22.50
PRESSED GLASS FRUIT PANELS GOBLET...........................     7.00
PRESSED GLASS FUCHSIA SPOONER...............................     8.50
PRESSED GLASS FUCHSIA SUGAR,OPEN............................    12.50
PRESSED GLASS GALLOWAY COVERED SUGAR........................    12.50
PRESSED GLASS GALLOWAY TOOTHPICK............................    10.00
PRESSED GLASS GARFIELD DRAPE BREAD PLATE....................    16.50
PRESSED GLASS GARFIELD DRAPE BUTTER,COVERED.................    18.00
PRESSED GLASS GARFIELD DRAPE CELERY.........................    13.00
PRESSED GLASS GARFIELD DRAPE COMPOTE,OPEN...................    15.00
PRESSED GLASS GARFIELD DRAPE CREAMER........................    10.00
PRESSED GLASS GARFIELD DRAPE GOBLET.........................    11.50
PRESSED GLASS GARFIELD DRAPE MILK PITCHER...................    23.50
PRESSED GLASS GARFIELD DRAPE OPEN SUGAR.....................    12.50
```

```
PRESSED GLASS GARFIELD DRAPE PITCHER,BULBOUS,APPLIED HANDLE.    19.50
PRESSED GLASS GARFIELD DRAPE SUGAR,OPEN.....................    12.50
PRESSED GLASS GARFIELD FROSTED PLATE.......................    17.00
PRESSED GLASS GARFIELD MEMORIAL PLATE......................    18.50
PRESSED GLASS GIANT BULLS EYE WATER TRAY,9 IN..............     2.50
PRESSED GLASS GIANT SAWTOOTH SALT,FOOTED...................     3.50
PRESSED GLASS GIBSON GIRL MILK PITCHER,15 IN...............    40.00
PRESSED GLASS GIBSON GIRL TUMBLER..........................    16.50
PRESSED GLASS GILLINDER CLEAR SLIPPER......................    10.00
PRESSED GLASS GIRL & FAN GOBLET............................    16.00
PRESSED GLASS GOLDEN RULE BREAD PLATE,11 IN................    15.00
PRESSED GLASS GOOD LUCK BUTTER,COVERED.....................    22.50
PRESSED GLASS GOOD LUCK CREAMER............................    10.50
PRESSED GLASS GOOD LUCK GOBLET.............................    12.50
PRESSED GLASS GOOD LUCK PLATTER,DOUBLE HANDLE..............    32.00
PRESSED GLASS GOOD LUCK WATER PITCHER......................    17.50
PRESSED GLASS GOOSEBERRY CAKE STAND........................    12.50
PRESSED GLASS GOOSEBERRY CREAMER...........................    13.50
PRESSED GLASS GOOSEBERRY SPOONER...........................     8.00
PRESSED GLASS GOTHIC ARCH SUGAR,COVERED....................    11.50
PRESSED GLASS GOTHIC BOWL,LOW,FOOTED,FLINT.................    20.00
PRESSED GLASS GOTHIC CREAMER...............................    12.50
PRESSED GLASS GRADUATED DIAMONDS GOBLET....................     5.00
PRESSED GLASS GRAND CELERY
  7.75   TO................................................     8.50
PRESSED GLASS GRAND CREAMER................................     7.00
PRESSED GLASS GRAND GOBLET.................................     6.00
PRESSED GLASS GRAND WINE...................................     6.75
PRESSED GLASS GRANT PEACE APPLE GREEN PLATE................    27.50
PRESSED GLASS GRAPE & FESTOON GOBLET.......................     8.00
PRESSED GLASS GRAPE & FESTOON SUGAR,OPEN...................    11.00
PRESSED GLASS GRAPE & FESTOON WITH SHIELD SAUCE,FLAT.......     2.50
PRESSED GLASS GRAPE & GOTHIC ARCHES TUMBLER,BLUE TRIM......    25.00
PRESSED GLASS GRAPE BAND PLATE,6 IN........................    12.50
PRESSED GLASS GRAPE TRAY,HANDLED...........................    16.50
PRESSED GLASS GRAPE WITH GOTHIC ARCHES GREEN WITH GOLD
  TUMBLER..................................................     8.50
PRESSED GLASS GRAPE WITHOUT VINE TUMBLER...................     8.00
PRESSED GLASS GRAPES & HEARTS MUG..........................     8.00
PRESSED GLASS GRAPES WITH ARCHED GREEN WITH GOLD TUMBLER....     7.50
PRESSED GLASS GRASSHOPPER CLEAR CELERY WITH INSECT..........    14.00
PRESSED GLASS GRASSHOPPER FOOTED CREAMER,5 IN. HIGH........     7.50
PRESSED GLASS GRASSHOPPER FOOTED SPOONER,5 IN. HIGH........     7.50
PRESSED GLASS GREEK KEY CHAMPAGNE,GOLD EDGE,FLINT..........     2.00
PRESSED GLASS GREEK KEY PANELED BOWL MARKED US.............    17.50
PRESSED GLASS GREEN BASKET,OPALESCENT BAND.................    35.00
PRESSED GLASS GREEN BUTTER DISH,ENAMEL.....................    35.00
PRESSED GLASS GREEN CRUET..................................     2.00
PRESSED GLASS GREEN DECANTER ,WINE,ROUND TRAY..............    12.00
PRESSED GLASS GREEN DISH,FOOTED,TRICORNE SHAPE.............     8.50
PRESSED GLASS GREEN DISH & 3 SAUCES,CLOVER LEAF SHAPED.....    30.00
PRESSED GLASS GREEN FEATHER RELISH.........................     8.50
PRESSED GLASS GREEN FINGER BOWL,FLINT......................    11.50
PRESSED GLASS GREEN PERFUME BOTTLE,SILVER OVERLAY..........    22.50
PRESSED GLASS GREEN PERFUME,BULBOUS,SILVER PATTERN.........    16.00
PRESSED GLASS GREEN RELISH DISH,PICKLE SHAPE,8 IN. LONG.....     8.50
PRESSED GLASS GREEN SYRUP,TIN LID..........................     6.00
PRESSED GLASS GREEN TANKARD,ENAMELLED FLOWERS..............    28.00
PRESSED GLASS GREEN TOOTHPICK HOLDER,3-MOLD,BUFFALO SOUVENIR   15.00
PRESSED GLASS GREEN TOOTHPICK HOLDER,BOOT..................    20.00
PRESSED GLASS GREEN TUMBLER,ORANGE FLOWER..................     5.00
PRESSED GLASS GREEN VASE EPERGNE,DECORATED.................    25.00
PRESSED GLASS GREEN VASE,GOLD TRACERY WITH WHITE ENAMEL.....    25.00
PRESSED GLASS GREEN WINE,KNOB STEM,ENAMEL DECORATION.......     7.50
PRESSED GLASS GREEN WITH GOLD DESIGN TOOTHPICK HOLDER......     8.00
```

```
PRESSED GLASS GREEN WITH GOLD TOOTHPICK HOLDER...............    7.50
PRESSED GLASS GRATED DIAMOND & FAN VINEGAR CRUET............   12.50
PRESSED GLASS GRILLE CREAMER.................................    5.00
PRESSED GLASS HAIRPIN GOBLET................................   15.00
PRESSED GLASS HAIRPIN WITH LOOP SUGAR,COVERED,FLINT.........   35.00
PRESSED GLASS HAIRPIN WITH THUMBPRINT COVERED SUGAR,FLINT...   35.00
PRESSED GLASS HAIRPIN WITH THUMBPRINT GOBLET................   17.50
PRESSED GLASS HAIRPIN WITH THUMBPRINT GOBLET,FLINT..........   15.00
PRESSED GLASS HALEYS COMET WINE.............................    8.00
PRESSED GLASS HAMILTON COMPOTE,FLINT........................   25.00
PRESSED GLASS HAMILTON GOBLET,FLINT.........................   22.50
PRESSED GLASS HAMILTON OPEN SUGAR,FLINT.....................   22.00
PRESSED GLASS HAMILTON SPOONER,FLINT........................    9.00
PRESSED GLASS HAMILTON SUGAR................................   12.00
PRESSED GLASS HAND CREAMER..................................   15.00
PRESSED GLASS HAND PATTERN 4 BOTTLE CASTOR SET WITH PEWTER
    TOPS....................................................   40.00
PRESSED GLASS HANOVER BLOCK & STAR AMBER WATER PITCHER......   29.50
PRESSED GLASS HANOVER COVERED CHEESE DISH...................   27.50
PRESSED GLASS HARP SPOONER,FLINT
    13.00  TO..............................................   18.50
PRESSED GLASS HARTLEY BLUE SAUCE,FOOTED.....................    8.00
PRESSED GLASS HAWAIIAN LEI MASTER SALT,FOOTED...............    6.00
PRESSED GLASS HAWAIIAN LEI WINE.............................    6.50
PRESSED GLASS HAWAIIAN LEI WITH BEE COVERED BUTTER..........   10.50
PRESSED GLASS HEART-THUMBPRINT SUGAR........................    6.50
PRESSED GLASS HEART & THUMBPRINT SAUCE DISH..................   4.50
PRESSED GLASS HEART & THUMBPRINT SQUARE BOWL,7 IN...........    9.50
PRESSED GLASS HEART BAND SUGAR,MINIATURE....................    6.50
PRESSED GLASS HEARTS CUP PLATE,FLINT........................   10.00
PRESSED GLASS HEART PITCHER,FLINT...........................   35.00
PRESSED GLASS HEART STEM CREAMER
    15.00  TO..............................................   20.00
PRESSED GLASS HEART THUMBPRINT ROSE BOWL,MINIATURE..........    6.50
PRESSED GLASS HEART WITH THUMBPRINT BERRY BOWL,RUFFLE
    SCALLOPED,GOLD..........................................   10.00
PRESSED GLASS HEART WITH THUMBPRINT CARD TRAY...............    4.75
PRESSED GLASS HEART WITH THUMBPRINT ICE TUB.................   15.00
PRESSED GLASS HEART WITH THUMBPRINT RUBY & CLEAR TUMBLER....   27.50
PRESSED GLASS HEART WITH THUMBPRINT SAUCE,GOLD EDGE.........    5.75
PRESSED GLASS HEART WITH THUMBPRINT SUGAR & CREAMER,GOLD
    EDGE...................................................   18.00
PRESSED GLASS HEART WITH THUMBPRINT TUMBLER.................   12.50
PRESSED GLASS HENRIETTA SAUCE,FLAT..........................    1.75
PRESSED GLASS HERCULES PILLAR ALE...........................   19.50
PRESSED GLASS HERCULES PILLAR VEGETABLE DISH,OVAL,FLINT.....    9.75
PRESSED GLASS HERO RUBY & CLEAR 7 IN. BERRY BOWL............   12.50
PRESSED GLASS HERON & PEACOCK CLEAR MUG.....................   12.00
PRESSED GLASS HERRINGBONE BAND EGG CUP......................    4.50
PRESSED GLASS HERRINGBONE BAND WINE.........................    4.00
PRESSED GLASS HERRINGBONE CREAMER...........................    9.50
PRESSED GLASS HERRINGBONE EMERALD GREEN 7 PIECE BERRY SET...   37.50
PRESSED GLASS HERRINGBONE GOBLET............................    6.50
PRESSED GLASS HERRINGBONE GREEN BERRY BOWL..................   11.00
PRESSED GLASS HERRINGBONE GREEN JELLY COMPOTE...............   13.50
PRESSED GLASS HERRINGBONE GREEN SAUCE.......................    6.00
PRESSED GLASS HERRINGBONE GREEN TUMBLER.....................   12.50
PRESSED GLASS HICKMAN GREEN VASE,10 IN......................   10.00
PRESSED GLASS HIDALGO GOBLET, FROSTED TOP...................    8.50
PRESSED GLASS HIDALGO TUMBLER,FOOTED........................    4.50
PRESSED GLASS HIDALGO WATER CARAFE..........................   14.00
PRESSED GLASS HIGH HOBNAIL SPOONER..........................    5.00
PRESSED GLASS HINOTO DRESSER BOTTLE WITH MATCHED
    STOPPER,FLINT...........................................   23.50
PRESSED GLASS HISTORICAL DEWEY WATER PITCHER................   35.00
```

```
PRESSED GLASS HOBNAIL & THUMBRPINT BANANA BOWL,7 IN.........     3.00
PRESSED GLASS HOBNAIL AMBER TOOTHPICK......................      8.00
PRESSED GLASS HOBNAIL AMBER TOOTHPICK HOLDER...............     17.50
PRESSED GLASS HOBNAIL AMBER TRAY,ROUND,12 IN...............     18.00
PRESSED GLASS HOBNAIL AMBER TUMBLER.......................      15.00
PRESSED GLASS HOBNAIL AMBER WATER TRAY
  15.00  TO...........................................          17.00
PRESSED GLASS HOBNAIL BAND CREAMER........................       7.50
PRESSED GLASS HOBNAIL BAND WATER PITCHER..................      10.00
PRESSED GLASS HOBNAIL BLUE & WHITE SUGAR & CREAMER.........      5.00
PRESSED GLASS HOBNAIL BLUE BUTTER DISH,COVERED,FLUTED EDGE..    37.50
PRESSED GLASS HOBNAIL BLUE CREAMER........................      22.00
PRESSED GLASS HOBNAIL BLUE MUG............................      12.00
PRESSED GLASS HOBNAIL BLUE SALT SHAKER....................       8.50
PRESSED GLASS HOBNAIL BOWL,FOOTED,8 IN.,SHIRRED TOP.........    12.50
PRESSED GLASS HOBNAIL CANDLEHOLDER,PAIR,RUFFLED TOPS........     6.70
PRESSED GLASS HOBNAIL CLEAR MILK PITCHER..................      22.50
PRESSED GLASS HOBNAIL CLEAR SALT SHAKER...................       5.00
PRESSED GLASS HOBNAIL CLEAR TRAY,ROUND,12 IN..............      12.00
PRESSED GLASS HOBNAIL CLEAR WATER PITCHER & 4 GLASSES......     24.50
PRESSED GLASS HOBNAIL FAN TOP OBLONG DISH.................       6.00
PRESSED GLASS HOBNAIL MILK PITCHER........................      15.00
PRESSED GLASS HOBNAIL OPALESCENT BASKET WITH FLUTED FLARED
  OPAL EDGE...........................................          16.50
PRESSED GLASS HOBNAIL OPALESCENT CELERY VASE,CLEAR..........    18.50
PRESSED GLASS HOBNAIL OPALESCENT GAS SHADE,PAIR............      30.00
PRESSED GLASS HOBNAIL OPALESCENT PICKLE DISH...............      4.50
PRESSED GLASS HOBNAIL OPALESCENT TOOTHPICK HOLDER,HAT.......    22.50
PRESSED GLASS HOBNAIL RUFFLES AMBER BASKET,CRIMPED EDGE.....     6.50
PRESSED GLASS HOBNAIL SUGAR SHAKER........................      15.00
PRESSED GLASS HOBNAIL TUMBLER,THUMBPRINT BASE..............      6.00
PRESSED GLASS HOBNAIL WATER PITCHER,THUMBPRINT BASE.........    17.50
PRESSED GLASS HOBNAIL WATER PITCHER,THUMBPRINT
  BASE,SCALLOPED TOP..................................          15.00
PRESSED GLASS HOBNAIL WITH FAN CELERY VASE,THUMBPRINT BASE..    14.00
PRESSED GLASS HOBNAIL WITH THUMBPRINT WATER TRAY...........     12.00
PRESSED GLASS HOBSTARS & DIAMOND POINT PUNCH BOWL SET WITH 6
  CUPS..............................................            33.00
PRESSED GLASS HOLLY BAND CELERY...........................      23.50
PRESSED GLASS HOLLY MUG...................................      10.00
PRESSED GLASS HOLLY SPRAY TUMBLER,HANDPAINTED,FLINT.........     2.50
PRESSED GLASS HOLLY TOOTHPICK.............................      28.00
PRESSED GLASS HONEYCOMB & DIAMONDS GOBLET,FLINT.............    10.00
PRESSED GLASS HONEYCOMB ALE
  10.00  TO...........................................          12.50
PRESSED GLASS HONEYCOMB ALE GLASS,FLINT...................       9.50
PRESSED GLASS HONEYCOMB CELERY,FOOTED.....................      12.50
PRESSED GLASS HONEYCOMB CHAMPAGNE.........................      10.00
PRESSED GLASS HONEYCOMB CLEAR TOOTHPICK HOLDER,FLOWER RIM...    17.50
PRESSED GLASS HONEYCOMB COMPOTE,FLINT.....................      23.00
PRESSED GLASS HONEYCOMB COMPOTE,OPEN FLINT................      30.00
PRESSED GLASS HONEYCOMB CORDIAL...........................       4.50
PRESSED GLASS HONEYCOMB CREAMER...........................      18.00
PRESSED GLASS HONEYCOMB EGG CUP,FLINT.....................       5.00
PRESSED GLASS HONEYCOMB GOBLET
  2.50  TO............................................           6.50
PRESSED GLASS HONEYCOMB GOBLET,ENGRAVED NEW YORK...........      4.00
PRESSED GLASS HONEYCOMB GOBLET,FLINT
  4.50  TO............................................          12.50
PRESSED GLASS HONEYCOMB GOBLET,PAIR FOOTED,FLINT...........     20.00
PRESSED GLASS HONEYCOMB GOBLET,TAPERED,FLINT...............     11.00
PRESSED GLASS HONEYCOMB GREEN WITH OPALESCENT BOWL.........     10.00
PRESSED GLASS HONEYCOMB MASTER SALT.......................       2.50
PRESSED GLASS HONEYCOMB OPEN COMPOTE,FLINT...............       18.00
PRESSED GLASS HONEYCOMB SPOONER...........................       6.00
```

```
PRESSED GLASS HONEYCOMB TUMBLER..............................  5.00
PRESSED GLASS HONEYCOMB WINE
   3.75   TO...................................................  6.00
PRESSED GLASS HONEYCOMB WITH DIAMOND GOBLET,FLINT............ 10.00
PRESSED GLASS HONEYCOMB WITH OVALS GOBLET,FLINT............. 12.00
PRESSED GLASS HONG KONG BUTTER DISH,COVERED................. 18.00
PRESSED GLASS HOOKS & EYES GOBLET
   6.00   TO...................................................  8.50
PRESSED GLASS HOPS BAND WINE................................  3.75
PRESSED GLASS HORIZONTAL RIBBED AMBER HAT...................  4.00
PRESSED GLASS HORIZONTAL RIBBED BLACK HAT................... 12.00
PRESSED GLASS HORN OF PLENTY AMBER TUMBLER..................  8.00
PRESSED GLASS HORN OF PLENTY BAR BOTTLE,FLINT............... 50.00
PRESSED GLASS HORN OF PLENTY BLUE VASE...................... 15.00
PRESSED GLASS HORN OF PLENTY COMPOTE,HIGH STAND,FLINT....... 65.00
PRESSED GLASS HORN OF PLENTY COMPOTE,LOW STANDARD........... 40.00
PRESSED GLASS HORN OF PLENTY EGG CUP,FLARE TOP.............. 13.50
PRESSED GLASS HORN OF PLENTY GOBLET,FLINT
  20.00   TO................................................... 25.00
PRESSED GLASS HORN OF PLENTY HONEY DISH.....................  4.75
PRESSED GLASS HORN OF PLENTY OPEN COMPOTE,FLINT............. 35.00
PRESSED GLASS HORN OF PLENTY OPEN SUGAR,FLINT............... 25.00
PRESSED GLASS HORN OF PLENTY SUGAR,COVERED,FLINT............ 75.00
PRESSED GLASS HORSEHEAD-IN-HORSESHOE WATER TUMBLER.......... 17.50
PRESSED GLASS HORSEHEAD MEDALLION BUTTERMILK GOBLET......... 18.50
PRESSED GLASS HORSEHEADS MEDALLION SPOONER..................  6.00
PRESSED GLASS HORSEMINT WINE................................  6.00
PRESSED GLASS HORSESHOE BREAD PLATE......................... 18.00
PRESSED GLASS HORSESHOE BREAD PLATE,SINGLE HANDLES.......... 12.00
PRESSED GLASS HORSESHOE BREAD TRAY
  18.00   TO................................................... 20.00
PRESSED GLASS HORSESHOE CAKE STAND.......................... 12.00
PRESSED GLASS HORSESHOE COVERED BUTTER...................... 15.00
PRESSED GLASS HORSESHOE COVERED COMPOTE..................... 20.00
PRESSED GLASS HORSESHOE CREAMER
   9.50   TO................................................... 12.50
PRESSED GLASS HORSESHOE GOBLET.............................. 14.00
PRESSED GLASS HORSESHOE GOBLET,KNOB STEM....................  1.50
PRESSED GLASS HORSESHOE PATTERN CREAMER.....................  9.50
PRESSED GLASS HORSESHOE PLATE............................... 18.00
PRESSED GLASS HORSESHOE SALT DIP............................  5.75
PRESSED GLASS HORSESHOE SAUCE...............................  6.50
PRESSED GLASS HOTEL THUMBPRINT GOBLET,SET OF 6,FLINT........ 50.00
PRESSED GLASS HUBER BARREL GOBLET,FLINT.....................  9.00
PRESSED GLASS HUBER COMPOTE,PAIR ON LOW STANDARDS,FLINT..... 50.00
PRESSED GLASS HUBER EGG CUP,FLINT...........................  6.50
PRESSED GLASS HUBER GOBLET
   6.00   TO................................................... 10.00
PRESSED GLASS HUBER GOBLET,FLINT............................  7.50
PRESSED GLASS HUBER OPEN COMPOTE ON HIGH STANDARD,8
IN.,FLINT................................................... 50.00
PRESSED GLASS HUBER STRAIGHT GOBLET,FLINT...................  9.50
PRESSED GLASS HUCKLE CELERY.................................  9.00
PRESSED GLASS HUCKLE COVERED BUTTER......................... 10.50
PRESSED GLASS HUCKLE CREAMER................................  7.50
PRESSED GLASS HUCKLE GREEN TUMBLER.......................... 10.00
PRESSED GLASS HUCKLE JELLY COMPOTE..........................  7.00
PRESSED GLASS HUMMING BIRD AMBER TUMBLER.................... 16.00
PRESSED GLASS HUMMING BIRD AMBER WATER PITCHER.............. 18.50
PRESSED GLASS HUMMING BIRD AMBER WATER TRAY................. 18.50
PRESSED GLASS HUMMING BIRD CELERY,7 IN. TALL................ 12.50
PRESSED GLASS HUMMING BIRD CREAMER.......................... 10.00
PRESSED GLASS HUMMING BIRD GOBLET........................... 18.50
PRESSED GLASS HYBRED SALT & PEPPER DATED 1895...............  4.50
PRESSED GLASS IMPERIAL GRAPES BOWL..........................  9.00
```

```
PRESSED GLASS IMPERIAL JEWEL BLUE BOWL,BULBOUS.............    13.50
PRESSED GLASS IMPERIAL JEWEL BLUE FRUIT BOWL,10 IN. DIAMETER   16.50
PRESSED GLASS IMPERIAL JEWEL BLUE PANEL CAKE STAND,FOOTED...   19.50
PRESSED GLASS IMPERIAL JEWEL GREEN BOWL & CANDLE HOLDERS....   35.00
PRESSED GLASS IMPERIAL JEWELS GREEN TO PURPLE BOWL..........   50.00
PRESSED GLASS INDIANA PANELLED GRAPE GOBLET.................   12.00
PRESSED GLASS INDIANA PATTERN BOWL..........................    4.00
PRESSED GLASS INVERNESS GOBLET..............................    3.75
PRESSED GLASS INVERTED FERN COVERED BUTTER,FLINT............   40.00
PRESSED GLASS INVERTED FERN EGG CUP,PLAIN...................   12.00
PRESSED GLASS INVERTED FERN EGG CUP,RAYED...................   12.00
PRESSED GLASS INVERTED FERN GOBLET..........................   17.50
PRESSED GLASS INVERTED FERN GOBLET,FLINT....................   15.00
PRESSED GLASS INVERTED FERN OPEN SUGAR......................   11.00
PRESSED GLASS INVERTED FERN SAUCE...........................    3.00
PRESSED GLASS INVERTED MELON RIBBED ROSE BOWL,ENAMELED BLUE
  & WHITE...................................................   20.00
PRESSED GLASS INVERTED PRISM GOBLET.........................   12.50
PRESSED GLASS INVERTED STRAWBERRY BOWL
  12.50  TO................................................    18.50
PRESSED GLASS INVERTED THUMBPRINT AMBER DECANTER,HAND BLOWN.   13.50
PRESSED GLASS INVERTED THUMBPRINT AMBER PITCHER.............   30.00
PRESSED GLASS INVERTED THUMBPRINT AMBER SPOONER,COLLARED
  BASE.....................................................     8.50
PRESSED GLASS INVERTED THUMBPRINT AMBER SYRUP JUG...........   25.00
PRESSED GLASS INVERTED THUMBPRINT AMBER TANKARD PITCHER,9
  IN.......................................................    52.50
PRESSED GLASS INVERTED THUMBPRINT AMBER TUMBLER.............   13.50
PRESSED GLASS INVERTED THUMBPRINT AMBER WATER PITCHER.......   27.50
PRESSED GLASS INVERTED THUMBPRINT CASTOR,PICKLE,ORNATE
  FRAME,TONGS..............................................    65.00
PRESSED GLASS INVERTED THUMBPRINT CASTOR,PICKLE,SILVER FRAME   85.00
PRESSED GLASS INVERTED THUMBPRINT CLEAR TO BLUE PITCHER.....   28.50
PRESSED GLASS INVERTED THUMBPRINT SAPPHIRE BLUE FINGER BOWL.   18.00
PRESSED GLASS INVERTED THUMBPRINT SYRUP JUG.................   12.00
PRESSED GLASS IONIA GOBLET..................................    5.00
PRESSED GLASS IOWA CITY BEE-HIVE PLATE,OVAL.................   50.00
PRESSED GLASS IOWA CITY BEE HIVE PLATTER,BE INDUSTRIOUS.....   85.00
PRESSED GLASS IOWA CITY CUBE AMBER HAT......................   16.50
PRESSED GLASS IOWA CITY ELAINE PLATE,ROUND..................   75.00
PRESSED GLASS IOWA CITY GOBLET,STORK TRIM...................   45.00
PRESSED GLASS IOWA CITY STORK PLATTER,STORKS FEEDING........   75.00
PRESSED GLASS IOWA PUNCH CUP................................    7.00
PRESSED GLASS IOWA SALT SHAKER..............................    7.00
PRESSED GLASS IRIS & HERRINGBONE CLEAR CREAM PITCHER........    1.25
PRESSED GLASS IRIS & HERRINGBONE CLEAR GOBLET...............    2.50
PRESSED GLASS IRIS & HERRINGBONE SHERBET....................    1.00
PRESSED GLASS ISIS GOBLET...................................    7.00
PRESSED GLASS ISIS WINE.....................................    4.75
PRESSED GLASS IVY IN SNOW GOBLET............................    6.50
PRESSED GLADD JACOBS COAT GREEN SPOONER.....................   12.50
PRESSED GLASS JACOBS LADDER BOWL,6 IN.......................    7.50
PRESSED GLASS JACOBS LADDER CELERY,PEDESTAL.................   15.00
PRESSED GLASS JACOBS LADDER COMPOTE,OPEN....................   12.50
PRESSED GLASS JACOBS LADDER CREAMER
  9.00  TO.................................................    17.50
PRESSED GLASS JACOBS LADDER PICKLE DISH.....................    6.50
PRESSED GLASS JACOBS LADDER PLATE,9 IN......................    2.00
PRESSED GLASS JACOBS LADDER SYRUP...........................   22.50
PRESSED GLASS JACOBS LADDER WINE............................    8.50
PRESSED GLASS JASPER BUCKLE WITH STAR WINE..................    6.00
PRESSED GLASS JEDDO PLATTER 12 X 15 IN......................   25.00
PRESSED GLASS JEFFERSON 271 SPOONER,OPAL TOP................    5.00
PRESSED GLASS JERSEY SWIRL CELERY...........................   12.50
PRESSED GLASS JERSEY SWIRL MILK PITCHER.....................   27.50
```

```
PRESSED GLASS JEWEL & DEWDROP TUMBLER......................  6.00
PRESSED GLASS JEWEL & DEWDROP WATER PITCHER.................  12.50
PRESSED GLASS JEWEL & FESTOON RELISH DISH...................  8.00
PRESSED GLASS JEWEL BAND PICKLE DISH........................  3.25
PRESSED GLASS JEWEL MOON & STAR CELERY......................  13.50
PRESSED GLASS JEWEL MOON & STAR WINE........................  12.50
PRESSED GLASS JEWEL WITH DEWDROP MUG,HANDLED................  16.50
PRESSED GLASS JEWELED MOON & STAR AMBER & BLUE SUGAR,COVERED  45.00
PRESSED GLASS JOBS TEARS VASE,4 MOLD,4 IN...................  6.00
PRESSED GLASS KAHLIA WATER PITCHER..........................  15.00
PRESSED GLASS KENTUCKY GREEN WINE...........................  16.50
PRESSED GLASS KEYSTONE GRAPE GOBLET.........................  7.50
PRESSED GLASS KINGS 500 BLUE CUP,GOLD TRIM..................  8.50
PRESSED GLASS KINGS CROWN BOWL,9 IN.........................  18.00
PRESSED GLASS KINGS CROWN CELERY............................  15.00
PRESSED GLASS KINGS CROWN GOBLET............................  7.50
PRESSED GLASS KINGS CROWN GOLD BAND AMETHYST THUMBPRINT
   GOBLET...................................................  16.50
PRESSED GLASS KINGS CROWN OLIVE GREEN GOBLET,SOUVENIR.......  18.50
PRESSED GLASS KINGS CROWN SPOONER...........................  5.00
PRESSED GLASS KINGS CROWN TOOTHPICK HOLDER..................  22.50
PRESSED GLASS KINGS CROWN WINE
   6.00    TO...............................................  7.50
PRESSED GLASS KINGS CROWN WINE,RUBY TOP.....................  12.00
PRESSED GLASS KLONDIKE BERRY BOWL,SQUARE....................  165.00
PRESSED GLASS KNIVES & FORKS GOBLET,FLINT...................  7.50
PRESSED GLASS KOKOMO CRUET & STOPPER........................  12.50
PRESSED GLASS LACY BACCARAT PLATE,7 IN.,FLINT...............  16.00
PRESSED GLASS LACY PITTSBURG BOWL,FLINT.....................  55.00
PRESSED GLASS LACY PITTSBURG HEARTS CUP PLATE,FLINT.........  8.50
PRESSED GLASS LACY SANDWICH OCTAGONAL BEEHIVE PLATE,FLINT...  60.00
PRESSED GLASS LACY SUGAR,OPEN...............................  5.00
PRESSED GLASS LADDER CREAMER................................  3.50
PRESSED GLASS LADDER PLATE,5 IN.............................  2.00
PRESSED GLASS LADDER TUMBLER................................  3.00
PRESSED GLASS LADDER WINE...................................  5.00
PRESSED GLASS LADDER WITH DIAMOND PUNCH BOWL,2 PIECES.......  15.00
PRESSED GLASS LADDER WITH DIAMONDS WINE.....................  3.00
PRESSED GLASS LADY CELERY VASE..............................  5.00
PRESSED GLASS LAMINATED PETALS GOBLET,FLINT.................  35.00
PRESSED GLASS LAMINATED PETALS WINE,FLINT...................  18.00
PRESSED GLASS LATE BARREL HONEYCOMB GOBLET..................  4.00
PRESSED GLASS LATE BUCKLE CREAMER...........................  10.50
PRESSED GLASS LATE BUCKLE JASPER CREAMER....................  12.00
PRESSED GLASS LATE BUCKLE JASPER WATER PITCHER..............  22.00
PRESSED GLASS LATE PANEL CANE COVERED SUGAR.................  9.50
PRESSED GLASS LATTICE CAKESTAND.............................  7.50
PRESSED GLASS LATTICE PLATE,6 IN............................  6.00
PRESSED GLASS LATTICE SYRUP.................................  8.50
PRESSED GLASS LEAF & BERRY ETCHED DAKOTA GOBLET.............  12.00
PRESSED GLASS LEAF & DART CELERY VASE.......................  10.00
PRESSED GLASS LEAF & DART DISH,OVAL.........................  4.50
PRESSED GLASS LEAF & DART FLANGED COVERED BUTTER............  22.50
PRESSED GLASS LEAF & DART GOBLET
   6.00    TO...............................................  6.75
PRESSED GLASS LEAF & DART GOBLET & COVERED SUGAR............  15.00
PRESSED GLASS LEAF & DART TUMBLER,FOOTED....................  9.00
PRESSED GLASS LEAF & DART WINE
   6.00    TO...............................................  7.50
PRESSED GLASS LEAF & FLOWER AMBER & CLEAR TUMBLER...........  25.00
PRESSED GLASS LEAF & FLOWER AMBER SALT......................  14.50
PRESSED GLASS LEAF EGG CUP..................................  7.50
PRESSED GLASS LEAF MEDALLION GREEN WITH GOLD CREAMER........  15.00
PRESSED GLASS LEGGED BANDED STAR CREAMER....................  10.50
PRESSED GLASS LENS & STAR CELERY............................  8.00
```

```
PRESSED GLASS LENS & STAR TUMBLER,FROST & CLEAR.............     4.50
PRESSED GLASS LE VERNE MILK PITCHER........................    12.50
PRESSED GLASS LIBERTY BELL BREAD TRAY......................    18.00
PRESSED GLASS LIBERTY BELL CREAMER,APPLIED HANDLE..........    25.00
PRESSED GLASS LIBERTY BELL GOBLET
  10.50  TO...............................................    15.00
PRESSED GLASS LIBERTY BELL GOBLET,FLINT....................    22.00
PRESSED GLASS LIBERTY BELL SPOONER.........................    12.50
PRESSED GLASS LIBERTY BELL SUGAR,COVERED...................    35.00
PRESSED GLASS LIBERTY BELL TRAY,OVAL.......................    28.50
PRESSED GLASS LILY OF THE VALLEY CREAMER
  12.50  TO...............................................    20.00
PRESSED GLASS LILY OF THE VALLEY MILK PITCHER
  37.50  TO...............................................    42.00
PRESSED GLASS LINCOLN DRAPE COMPOTE,OPEN,FLINT.............    35.00
PRESSED GLASS LINCOLN DRAPE GREEN PLATE,8 IN...............    15.00
PRESSED GLASS LINCOLN DRAPE MINIATURE LAMP,................    20.00
PRESSED GLASS LINED SMOCKING TUMBLER,FLINT.................    25.00
PRESSED GLASS LINED STARS GOBLET...........................     4.50
PRESSED GLASS LION CELERY..................................    24.00
PRESSED GLASS LION COMPOTE,COVERED,7 IN.,FROSTED LION HEAD
  FINIAL..................................................    45.00
PRESSED GLASS LION COMPOTE,OVAL,COVERED....................    40.00
PRESSED GLASS LION ETCHED CREAMER..........................     9.50
PRESSED GLASS LION JAM JAR.................................    38.00
PRESSED GLASS LION SPOONER.................................    16.50
PRESSED GLASS LION TOOTHPICK ON PEDESTAL BASE,STERLING BAND
  AT TOP..................................................    15.00
PRESSED GLASS LION WITH CABLE CREAMER......................    13.50
PRESSED GLASS LION WITH CABLE SUGAR,OPEN...................    10.00
PRESSED GLASS LOCKET & CHAIN GREEN PITCHER,7 IN............     5.00
PPRESSED GLASS LOCKET ON CHAIN CREAMER.....................    10.00
PRESSED GLASS LOCKET ON CHAIN PLATE,7 IN...................     8.00
PRESSED GLASS LOG CABIN CREAMER............................    32.50
PRESSED GLASS LOG CABIN CUP PLATE,FLINT....................    22.50
PRESSED GLASS LOOP & DART BUTTER,COVERED...................    13.50
PRESSED GLASS LOOP & DART CREAMER..........................    13.50
PRESSED GLASS LOOP & DART EGG CUP..........................     8.00
PRESSED GLASS LOOP & DART GOBLET...........................     6.50
PRESSED GLASS LOOP & DART SUGAR,COVERED....................    13.50
PRESSED GLASS LOOP AND DART WITH ROUND ORNAMENT CREAMER.....   12.50
PRESSED GLASS LOOP & DART WITH ROUND ORNAMENT GOBLET,FLINT..   45.00
PRESSED GLASS LOOP & DEWDROP GOBLET
  6.50   TO...............................................     8.50
PRESSED GLASS LOOP & DEWDROP JELLY COMPOTE.................     8.00
PRESSED GLASS LOOP & JEWEL BERRY BOWL......................     5.00
PRESSED GLASS LOOP COMPOTE,OPEN,LOW STANDARD,FLINT.........    27.50
PRESSED GLASS LOOP DECANTER,FLINT..........................    18.50
PRESSED GLASS LOOP EGG CUP,FLINT...........................    13.00
PRESSED GLASS LOOP VARIANT COMPOTE,7 IN. HIGH,8 IN. WIDE....   25.00
PRESSED GLASS LOTUS GOBLET.................................     9.00
PRESSED GLASS LOTUS WATER PITCHER,PORTLAND.................    40.00
PRESSED GLASS LOTUS WITH SERPENT BREAD PLATTER,GIVE US THIS
  DAY....................................................    22.00
PRESSED GLASS LOUISIANA COVERED SUGAR......................    12.50
PRESSED GLASS LOUISIANA GOBLET.............................     8.00
PRESSED GLASS MAGNET & GRAPE FROSTED LEAF GOBLET,FLINT......   20.00
PRESSED GLASS MAGNET & GRAPE WITH FROSTED LEAF GOBLET.......   25.00
PRESSED GLASS MAIDEN BLUSH BERRY BOWL 9 IN 4 SAUCES........    34.50
PRESSED GLASS MAIDENS BLUSH SAUCE..........................    15.00
PRESSED GLASS MAINE GREEN 8 IN. CAKESTAND..................    18.50
PRESSED GLASS MAINE GREEN BOWL.............................    12.50
PRESSED GLASS MAINE JELLY COMPOTE..........................     8.00
PRESSED GLASS MAINE RELISH.................................     5.00
PRESSED GLASS MAIZE MUSTARD CASTOR POT WITH HINGED TIN TOP..    7.50
```

```
PRESSED GLASS MAIZE SUGAR SHAKER,LIBBEY,5 IN. TALL..........    65.00
PRESSED GLASS MANHATTAN BERRY BOWL...........................     7.50
PRESSED GLASS MANHATTAN BERRY BOWL,AMBER CANE BOTTOM.........    35.00
PRESSED GLASS MANHATTAN BERRY DISH,SET OF 5..................    15.00
PRESSED GLASS MAPLE LEAF BLUE BOWL...........................    35.00
PRESSED GLASS MAPLE LEAF GOBLET..............................     7.50
PRESSED GLASS MAPLE LEAF SAPPHIRE BLUE BOWL,FOOTED,OVAL......    22.00
PRESSED GLASS MARQUIS & MARCHIONESS CREAMER..................    20.00
PRESSED GLASS MARQUISETTE GOBLET.............................     7.00
PRESSED GLASS MARTHAS TEARS WINE.............................     4.00
PRESSED GLASS MARYLAND GOBLET................................     7.50
PRESSED GLASS MARYLAND JELLY COMPOTE.........................     7.50
PRESSED GLASS MARYLAND MILK PITCHER..........................     9.50
PRESSED GLASS MARYLAND PLATE,7 IN............................     4.75
PRESSED GLASS MARYLAND RELISH................................     4.75
PRESSED GLASS MARYLAND WINE..................................     6.50
PRESSED GLASS MASCOTTE ETCHED TUMBLER........................     7.75
PRESSED GLASS MASCOTTE WINE..................................     5.75
PRESSED GLASS MASONIC CHAMPAGNE GLASS DATED 1910,SET OF
  6,COMMEMORATION............................................    75.00
PRESSED GLASS MASONIC CREAMER................................     7.50
PRESSED GLASS MASONIC PATTERN SPOONER........................     4.50
PRESSED GLASS MASONIC SUGAR,COVERED..........................    10.00
PRESSED GLASS MASSACHUSETTS CLEAR WITH GOLD 7 IN. VASE.......     6.50
PRESSED GLASS MASSACHUSETTS GREEN 10 IN. VASE................    12.50
PRESSED GLASS MASTER ARGUS GOBLET,FLINT......................    45.00
PRESSED GLASS MEDALLION AMBER CAKESTAND......................    29.50
PRESSED GLASS MELON RIB AMBER BOTTLES........................     8.00
PRESSED GLASS MELROSE FRUITSTAND.............................    12.50
PRESSED GLASS MELROSE JELLY COMPOTE..........................     7.50
PRESSED GLASS MEPHISTOPHELES WATER PITCHER...................    85.00
PRESSED GLASS MICHIGAN CELERY VASE...........................     9.00
PRESSED GLASS MICHIGAN CLEAR CHILDS TABLE SETTING,4 PIECES..    26.50
PRESSED GLASS MICHIGAN PATTERN CREAMER, 4 IN. H..............     5.50
PRESSED GLASS MIDWAY SUGAR & CREAMER WITH BAND ENAMELED
  FLOWER....................................................    16.00
PRESSED GLASS MIDWEST LACY BOWL,7 IN. DIAMETER,FLINT.........    50.00
PRESSED GLASS MIKADO FAN GOBLET..............................     4.00
PRESSED GLASS MILADYS WORK BOX GOBLET........................     7.00
PRESSED GLASS MILTON GOBLET..................................     5.50
PRESSED GLASS MINERVA CAKE STAND
  18.50    TO...............................................    24.50
PRESSED GLASS MINERVA SPOONHOLDER............................    12.50
PRESSED GLASS MINNESOTA GOBLET...............................     7.50
PRESSED GLASS MITERED DIAMOND POINT WINE,2...................     3.50
PRESSED GLASS MITERED FRIEZE SAUCE,FOOTED....................     2.75
PRESSED GLASS MONGOLIA SAUCE.................................     3.00
PRESSED GLASS MOON & STAR BOWL,SQUARE........................     9.00
PRESSED GLASS MOON & STAR CAKE STAND.........................    24.50
PRESSED GLASS MOON & STAR CLARET.............................    15.00
PRESSED GLASS MOON & STAR COMPOTE,COVERED,7 IN..............    15.00
PRESSED GLASS MOON & STAR COMPOTE,COVERED,10 IN.............    25.00
PRESSED GLASS MOON & STAR COMPOTE,KNOB STEM..................    30.00
PRESSED GLASS MOON & STAR COMPOTE,OPEN.......................    12.00
PRESSED GLASS MOON & STAR COMPOTE,OPEN,8 IN.................    27.00
PRESSED GLASS MOON & STAR COMPOTE,OPEN,ON STANDARD...........    20.00
PRESSED GLASS MOON AND STAR GOBLET...........................     7.00
PRESSED GLASS MOON & STAR RELISH
  8.50    TO...............................................     9.50
PRESSED GLASS MOON & STAR SALT,INDIVIDUAL OPEN,FLINT.........     4.00
PRESSED GLASS MOON & STAR SAUCE,4 IN.........................     6.00
PRESSED GLASS MOON & STAR SPOONER,FLINT......................    17.50
PRESSED GLASS MOON & STAR SPOONER,FOOTED,FLINT...............    22.50
PRESSED GLASS MOON & STAR TRAY,ROUND.........................    10.00
PRESSED GLASS MOON & STAR TUMBLER,FOOTED.....................    25.00
```

```
PRESSED GLASS MOONPRINT CREAMER,FLINT........................  18.00
PRESSED GLASS MOONPRINT WHISKEY SHOT GLASS,FLINT.............  15.00
PRESSED GLASS MORNING GLORY FOOTED TUMBLER..................  150.00
PRESSED GLASS MOUNTAIN LAUREL GOBLET........................   7.50
PRESSED GLASS NAIL RUBY & CLEAR GOBLET......................  16.50
PRESSED GLASS NAIL SHERBET..................................   8.00
PRESSED GLASS NAILHEAD CAKE STAND,11 IN. DIAMETER...........  10.00
PRESSED GLASS NAILHEAD CAKESTAND............................  10.00
PRESSED GLASS NAILHEAD COMPOTE,OPEN.........................  10.00
PRESSED GLASS NAILHEAD COMPOTE,COVERED......................  25.00
PRESSED GLASS NAILHEAD FRUITSTAND,8 IN.,SCALLOPED...........  10.00
PRESSED GLASS NAILHEAD GOBLET...............................   7.50
PRESSED GLASS NAILHEAD PLATE,9 IN. ROUND....................   8.50
PRESSED GLASS NAILHEAD PLATE,9 IN...........................   8.00
PRESSED GLASS NAILHEAD SPOONER..............................   5.00
PRESSED GLASS NAIL HEAD SUGAR BOWL,4 IN. HIGH...............  10.50
PRESSED GLASS NAILHEAD WATER PITCHER........................  18.00
PRESSED GLASS NAILHEAD WINE.................................   6.00
PRESSED GLASS NARCISSUS SPRAY BUTTER DISH...................  10.00
PRESSED GLASS NEW ENGLAND PINE SPOONER......................  15.00
PRESSED GLASS NEW ENGLAND PINEAPPLE CELERY VASE,STEMMED.....  20.00
PRESSED GLASS NEW ENGLAND PINEAPPLE COMPOTE,FLINT
  32.00  TO..................................................  40.00
PRESSED GLASS NEW ENGLAND PINEAPPLE COMPOTE,OPEN,FLINT......  50.00
PRESSED GLASS NEW ENGLAND PINEAPPLE GOBLET..................  17.00
PRESSED GLASS NEW ENGLAND PINEAPPLE SPOONER,FLINT...........  20.00
PRESSED GLASS NEW ERA CELERY................................   6.50
PRESSED GLASS NEW HAMPSHIRE TOOTHPICK.......................   5.00
PRESSED GLASS NEW JERSEY CLEAR WITH RUBY SUGAR,COVERED......  20.00
PRESSED GLASS NEW JERSEY CREAMER............................   6.75
PRESSED GLASS NEW YORK HONEYCOMB BUTTERMILK.................  12.00
PRESSED GLASS NEW YORK HONEYCOMB GOBLET,FLINT...............   8.00
PRESSED GLASS NEW YORK STATE GREEN MILK BASIN WITH POURING
  LIP.......................................................  75.00
PRESSED GLASS NOVA SCOTIA GOTHIC GOBLET.....................  20.00
PRESSED GLASS OAK LEAF SUGAR,OPEN...........................   6.50
PRESSED GLASS OAK WREATH COVERED BUTTER.....................  13.50
PRESSED GLASS OAKEN BUCKET WATER PITCHER....................  12.00
PRESSED GLASS OHIO INVERTED THUMBPRINT GREEN GOBLET.........  16.50
PRESSED GLASS OLIVE GREEN WINE,FROSTED LETTERS GRANDMA......   3.50
PRESSED GLASS OLYMPIA PLATTER,17 X 12 IN....................  10.50
PRESSED GLASS ONE HUNDRED ONE MOTTO BREAD PLATE.............  12.50
PRESSED GLASS ONE-O-ONE CELERY..............................  13.75
PRESSED GLASS OPALESCENT SPOT WATER PITCHER,RUFFLED TOP.....  22.00
PRESSED GLASS OPEN PLAID GOBLET.............................   4.50
PRESSED GLASS OPEN ROSE COMPOTE.............................  18.00
PRESSED GLASS OPEN ROSE GOBLET
   7.00  TO..................................................   8.50
PRESSED GLASS OPEN ROSE SPOONER.............................   5.50
PRESSED GLASS OPEN ROSE SUGAR...............................   9.50
PRESSED GLASS OPPOSING DROPS CELERY VASE....................   7.50
PRESSED GLASS ORANGE PEEL BAND SPOONER......................   8.00
PRESSED GLASS ORION THUMBPRINT CELERY.......................  13.50
PRESSED GLASS ORION THUMBPRINT GOBLET.......................   7.50
PRESSED GLASS OVAL MEDALLION GOBLET,DEARBORN,FLINT..........  17.50
PRESSED GLASS OVAL MITRE COMPOTE............................  10.00
PRESSED GLASS OVAL MITER GOBLET,FLINT.......................  10.00
PRESSED GLASS OWL & PUSSYCAT CHEESE DISH,COVERED............  89.50
PRESSED GLASS OWL CREAMER,4 IN..............................   6.50
PRESSED GLASS OWL GREEN SALT & PEPPER SHAKERS WITH CAST IRON
  HEADS.....................................................  22.50
PRESSED GLASS OWL IN FAN GOBLET.............................   6.00
PRESSED GLASS OWL SALT & PEPPER SHAKERS,PAIR................   6.00
PRESSED GLASS PAISLEY PURPLE DOTS SAUCE.....................   4.50
PRESSED GLASS PALM LEAF FAN CAKE STAND,FOOTED...............   6.00
```

```
PRESSED GLASS PALM LEAF FAN SALT DIP,INDIVIDUAL.............    3.00
PRESSED GLASS PALM LEAF FAN SALTS..........................    7.00
PRESSED GLASS PALM STUB GOBLET.............................    4.50
PRESSED GLASS PALMETTE CELERY..............................   16.50
PRESSED GLASS PANEL & CHERRY GOBLET........................   15.00
PRESSED GLASS PANEL & STAR CELERY,VASELINE COLOUR..........   29.00
PRESSED GLASS PANEL AMBER GOBLET...........................   10.00
PRESSED GLASS PANEL CANE CREAMER...........................    9.75
PRESSED GLASS PANEL DAISY & BUTTON AMBER SAUCE,SET OF 4.....   25.00
PRESSED GLASS PANEL DAISY CELERY...........................   12.00
PRESSED GLASS PANEL DAISY COVERED BUTTER...................   13.50
PRESSED GLASS PANEL DEWDROP CREAMER........................   10.00
PRESSED GLASS PANEL DEWDROP RELISH.........................    6.50
PRESSED GLASS PANEL DIAMONDS RUBY & CLEAR GOBLET...........   12.00
PRESSED GLASS PANEL DIAMONDS WINE..........................    4.00
PRESSED GLASS PANEL GOBLET,SET OF 6........................   30.00
PRESSED GLASS PANEL HERRINGBONE MILK PITCHER...............   10.00
PRESSED GLASS PANEL SHERBET,SET OF 6.......................   25.00
PRESSED GLASS PANEL THISTLE BOWL,8 IN......................   11.00
PRESSED GLASS PANEL THISTLE CELERY.........................    9.00
PRESSED GLASS PANELED CHERRY GOBLET........................    7.50
PRESSED GLASS PANELLED CREAMER,PEWTER HINGED LID...........   12.00
PRESSED GLASS PANELLED DAISY BUTTER,COVERED................   10.00
PRESSED GLASS PANELED DAISY CASTOR JAR,PICKLE..............    3.50
PRESSED GLASS PANELED DAISY CELERY.........................   15.00
PRESSED GLASS PANELED DAISY PICKLE DISH....................    4.75
PRESSED GLASS PANELED DEWDROP BREAD PLATE,MOTTO............   12.50
PRESSED GLASS PANELED DEWDROP CELERY VASE..................   11.00
PRESSED GLASS PANELED DEWDROP WINE.........................    4.50
PRESSED GLASS PANELLED DIAMOND GOBLET......................    4.50
PRESSED GLASS PANELED DIAMONDS & FLOWERS GOBLET
   5.00   TO.................................................    8.50
PRESSED GLASS PANELLED FERN CREAMER........................   12.00
PRESSED GLASS PANELLED FERN SUGAR..........................   12.00
PRESSED GLASS PANELED FORGET-ME-NOT COMPOTE................   11.00
PRESSED GLASS PANELED FORGET-ME-NOT GOBLET.................   12.50
PRESSED GLASS PANELLED GRAPE & FRUIT WEDDING CAKE COMPOTE...   10.00
PRESSED GLASS PANELLED GRAPE GOBLET
  10.00   TO.................................................   12.00
PRESSED GLASS PANELLED GREEN TUMBLER,ENAMEL DECOR,FLINT.....    7.00
PRESSED GLASS PANELED IVY CREAMER..........................    6.50
PRESSED GLASS PANELED IVY PLATE,FOOTED.....................    5.00
PRESSED GLASS PANELLED IVY WATER PITCHER...................   15.00
PRESSED GLASS PANELED JEWEL GOBLET.........................    7.00
PRESSED GLASS PANELED LONG JEWELS GOBLET...................    4.50
PRESSED GLASS PANELLED SAWTOOTH CELERY.....................   12.00
PRESSED GLASS PANELLED STIPPLED SCROLL GOBLET..............    3.50
PRESSED GLASS PANELLED SUGAR SHAKER,FLINT..................    5.50
PRESSED GLASS PANELLED THISTLE 8 IN. RELISH................    8.50
PRESSED GLASS PANELLED THISTLE BERRY BOWL..................   12.00
PRESSED GLASS PANELED THISTLE BOWL,5 IN.,FLAT..............    8.50
PRESSED GLASS PANELLED THISTLE BOWL,6 IN...................    9.75
PRESSED GLASS PANELLED THISTLE BOWL,OBLONG.................   15.00
PRESSED GLASS PANELED THISTLE BUTTER,COVERED,GOLD TRIM......   18.00
PRESSED GLASS PANELED THISTLE CAKE STAND...................   15.00
PRESSED GLASS PANELED THISTLE CAKESTAND,9 IN. DIAMETER......   14.00
PRESSED GLASS PANELED THISTLE CELERY.......................   16.00
PRESSED GLASS PANELED THISTLE COMPOTE......................   12.00
PRESSED GLASS PANELED THISTLE CREAMER......................   16.00
PRESSED GLASS PANELLED THISTLE CRUET
   7.00   TO.................................................   10.50
PRESSED GLASS PANELED THISTLE PLATE,10 IN..................   12.50
PRESSED GLASS PANELLED THISTLE PLATE,FOOTED................   15.50
PRESSED GLASS PANELED THISTLE SPOONER......................   14.00
PRESSED GLASS PANELED THISTLE SUGAR,OPEN...................   15.00
```

```
PRESSED GLASS PANELED WILD DAISY SPOONER....................    4.00
PRESSED GLASS PANELLED WINE...............................    2.75
PRESSED GLASS PANSY & MOSS ROSE CREAMER....................    8.00
PRESSED GLASS PARIS PLATE,7 IN. SQUARE.....................    7.50
PRESSED GLASS PARROT & FAN WITH BEE GOBLET.................   16.50
PRESSED GLASS PARROT GOBLET...............................   10.00
PRESSED GLASS PAVONIA TUMBLER,RUBY TOP.....................   10.00
PRESSED GLASS PEACOCK & URN CAKE DISH......................   50.00
PRESSED GLASS PEACOCK FEATHER BERRY BOWL...................    6.50
PRESSED GLASS PEACOCK FEATHER LAMP BASE,HANDLED............   10.00
PRESSED GLASS PEACOCK FEATHER PICKLE DISH..................    4.50
PRESSED GLASS PEACOCK FEATHER RELISH.......................    6.50
PRESSED GLASS PEACOCK FEATHER SAUCE.......................    3.75
PRESSED GLASS PEACOCK FEATHER SYRUP CAN,ORIGINAL TIN TOP...   14.00
PRESSED GLASS PEACOCK FEATHER TUMBLER.....................    8.75
PRESSED GLASS PEACOCK FEATHER WATER PITCEHR
   11.00  TO....................................................   15.00
PRESSED GLASS PEAR SPOONER................................    5.00
PRESSED GLASS PENGUIN CREAMER.............................    3.00
PRESSED GLASS PETAL & LOOP COMPOTE & CANDLESTICKS,FLINT.....   90.00
PRESSED GLASS PETAL LOOP COMPOTE,COVERED,1830,FLINT.........   25.00
PRESSED GLASS PICKET CELERY...............................   14.00
PRESSED GLASS PICKET COMPOTE,OPEN,9 IN. DIAMETER...........   22.50
PRESSED GLASS PICKET FENCE SAUCE,SQUARE 5 IN.,FLINT........    3.50
PRESSED GLASS PICKET SAUCE WITH HANDLE,4 IN. FLAT..........    6.50
PRESSED GLASS PIGEON BLOOD BOWL,FLUTES ON TOP FORM FEET ON
BASE........................................................   35.00
PRESSED GLASS PIGEON BLOOD PITCHER........................  110.00
PRESSED GLASS PILLAR ALE..................................   13.50
PRESSED GLASS PILLAR & BULLS EYE GOBLET...................   10.00
PRESSED GLASS PILLAR GOBLET,FLINT.........................   22.50
PRESSED GLASS PILLOW & SUNBURST CREAMER & COVERED SUGAR.....    7.50
PRESSED GLASS PILLOW & SUNBURST CREAMER & OPEN SUGAR........    9.00
PRESSED GLASS PILLOW & SUNBURST SUGAR,OVAL,COVERED.........    5.50
PRESSED GLASS PILLOW & SUNBURST SUGAR,OPEN.................    3.50
PRESSED GLASS PILLOW ENCIRCLED CAKESTAND..................   10.00
PRESSED GLASS PINEAPPLE & FAN CELERY......................    8.50
PRESSED GLASS PINEAPPLE & FAN DECANTER & 2 WINES,SILVER
   OVERLAY & BLUE..............................................   30.00
PRESSED GLASS PINEAPPLE & FAN SUGAR BOWL,ROUND,FLINT.......   12.50
PRESSED GLASS PINEAPPLE & FAN VASE,PAIR...................   12.00
PRESSED GLASS PINEAPPLE BUTTER MOLD,ROUND.................   12.00
PRESSED GLASS PINEAPPLE CLEAR CELERY VASE.................    4.50
PRESSED GLASS PINEAPPLE DECANTER..........................    5.00
PRESSED GLASS PINEAPPLE FAN & HOBNAIL WATER CARAFE.........   12.50
PRESSED GLASS PINEAPPLE FAN CELERY........................   15.00
PRESSED GLASS PINEAPPLE PUNCH CUP.........................    2.00
PRESSED GLASS PINEAPPLE SPOONER...........................    6.50
PRESSED GLASS PINEAPPLE STEM GOBLET,FLINT.................   21.50
PRESSED GLASS PINEAPPLE WITH FAN COMPOTE,OPEN.............   25.00
PRESSED GLASS PINK SUGAR & CREAMER........................   11.00
PRESSED GLASS PINPRICK AMBER VASE,BLOWN,HAT FORM..........   12.50
PRESSED GLASS PINWHEEL BERRY BOWL & 6 SAUCES..............   19.00
PRESSED GLASS PINWHEEL DRESSER SET........................   20.00
PRESSED GLASS PINWHEEL PUNCH BOWL,SETS ON 3 MOLDED BASE.....   25.00
PRESSED GLASS PITTSBURG 8 RIBBED CLEAR INK WELL,FLINT.......   13.00
PRESSED GLASS PITTSBURGH CASTOR,PICKLE,SILVER PLATE HOLDER
   WITH TONGS..................................................   22.50
PRESSED GLASS PITTSBURGH DAISY CREAMER....................    7.50
PRESSED GLASS PITTSBURGH FLUTE GOBLET,FLINT...............   12.50
PRESSED GLASS PITTSBURGH LOOP CELERY COMPOTE,FLINT..........   50.00
PRESSED GLASS PITTSBURGH WATER PITCHER,9 IN. HIGH..........   47.50
PRESSED GLASS PLAIN MASCOTTE CELERY.......................    9.75
PRESSED GLASS PLEAT & PANEL BOWL..........................   14.00
PRESSED GLASS PLEAT & PANEL BREAD TRAY....................   16.00
```

```
PRESSED GLASS PLEAT & PANEL CAKE STAND,11 IN...............  23.00
PRESSED GLASS PLEAT & PANEL CELERY........................  15.00
PRESSED GLASS PLEAT & PANEL CREAMER
   10.00  TO.............................................  14.00
PRESSED GLASS PLEAT & PANEL DARBY CAKE STAND,8 IN. TALL.....  35.00
PRESSED GLASS PLEAT & PANEL GOBLET
    8.50  TO.............................................  10.50
PRESSED GLASS PLEAT & PANEL MASTER SALT...................   6.50
PRESSED GLASS PLEAT & PANEL OPEN COMPOTE..................  22.50
PRESSED GLASS PLEAT & PANEL PLATTER,CLOSED HANDLE.........  12.50
PRESSED GLASS PLEAT & PANEL SAUCE,FOOTED.................   4.00
PRESSED GLASS PLEAT & PANEL SPOONER
    5.50  TO.............................................   8.50
PRESSED GLASS PLEAT & PANEL SQUARE COVERED DISH ON
   STANDARD,6 IN........................................  25.00
PRESSED GLASS PLEAT & PANEL SUGAR,OPEN...................  10.00
PRESSED GLASS PLEAT & PANEL SUGAR,COVERED................  18.00
PRESSED GLASS PLEAT & PANEL VASE,CELERY..................  17.00
PRESSED GLASS PLEAT & TUCK COVERED SUGAR.................   8.50
PRESSED GLASS PLUME & PEACOCK FEATHERS BOWL,OVAL.........  40.00
PRESSED GLASS PLUME BERRY BOWL & 4 SAUCES................  18.50
PRESSED GLASS PLUME GOBLET...............................  14.50
PRESSED GLASS PLUME RELISH...............................   6.50
PRESSED GLASS PLUME SUGAR BOWL,COVERED...................  14.50
PRESSED GLASS POGO STICK CELERY,2 HANDLES................   7.00
PRESSED GLASS POINTED ARCHES MUG,RED FLASHED TOP.........   6.00
PRESSED GLASS POINTED ARCHES WINE,RED FLASHED TOP,SOUVENIR..   4.50
PRESSED GLASS POLAR BEAR GOBLET
   45.00  TO.............................................  70.00
PRESSED GLASS POLAR BEAR WATER PITCHER...................  80.00
PRESSED GLASS POLAR BEAR WATER TRAY,OVAL.................  65.00
PRESSED GLASS POND LILIES & FROSTED BUDS CAKE STAND......   7.50
PRESSED GLASS POPCORN CREAMER............................  15.00
PRESSED GLASS POPCORN LINED EAR PITCHER,BULBOUS,APPLIED
   HANDLE..............................................  30.00
PRESSED GLASS POPCORN WITH EAR GOBLET....................  12.50
PRESSED GLASS PORTLAND SALT & PEPPER SHAKER..............   7.50
PRESSED GLASS PORTLAND WITH DIAMOND POINT BAND TOOTHPICK....   5.00
PRESSED GLASS POWDER & SHOT CELERY.......................   6.50
PRESSED GLASS POWDER & SHOT COMPOTE,8 IN.................  25.00
PRESSED GLASS POWDER & SHOT SPOONER,FLINT
   11.50  TO.............................................  15.00
PRESSED GLASS PRESSED DIAMOND AMBER COMPOTE,OPEN,PEDESTAL...  22.00
PRESSED GLASS PRESSED LEAF COMPOTE,LOW,ROPE EDGE.........  15.00
PRESSED GLASS PRESSED LEAF EGG CUP.......................   6.00
PRESSED GLASS PRESSED LEAF GOBLET........................   5.50
PRESSED GLASS PRESSED LEAF WATER SET,PITCHER & 6 GOBLETS....  65.00
PRESSED GLASS PRIMROSE PICKLE DISH.......................   5.00
PRESSED GLASS PRIMROSE SPOONER...........................   6.50
PRESSED GLASS PRIMROSE WATER SET TRAY....................  17.50
PRESSED GLASS PRINCE ALBERT PITCHER......................  10.00
PRESSED GLASS PRINCESS FEATHER GOBLET
    8.50      TO.........................................  12.00
PRESSED GLASS PRINCESS FEATHER SUGAR.....................  11.00
PRESSED GLASS PRISCILLA CAKESTAND........................  22.00
PRESSED GLASS PRISCILLA COMPOTE,OPEN.....................  27.50
PRESSED GLASS PRISCILLA FRUIT COMPOTE....................  25.00
PRESSED GLASS PRISCILLA JELLY COMPOTE,5 IN...............  16.50
PRESSED GLASS PRISCILLA ROSE BOWL........................  24.50
PRESSED GLASS PRISCILLA SPOONER..........................  12.00
PRESSED GLASS PRISCILLA VARIANT BUTTER DISH,COVERED......  15.00
PRESSED GLASS PRISM & BROKEN COLUMN GOBLET,FLINT.........  35.00
PRESSED GLASS PRISM & BROKEN COLUMN WINE.................   6.50
PRESSED GLASS PRISM AND FLUTE GOBLET.....................   7.00
PRESSED GLASS PRISM ARC CELERY...........................   7.50
```

```
PRESSED GLASS PRISM CHAMPAGNE.................................   15.00
PRESSED GLASS PRISM COMPOTE ON LOW STANDARD,FLINT...........   11.50
PRESSED GLASS PRISM GOBLET,FLINT............................   12.00
PRESSED GLASS PRISM SUGAR BOWL,COVERED,FLINT................   15.00
PRESSED GLASS PRISM WITH NOTCHES WATER CARAFE,ROUGH PONTIL..   20.00
PRESSED GLASS PSYCHE & CUPID BOWL,ROUND.....................   17.50
PRESSED GLASS PSYCHE & CUPID CELERY VASE,STEMMED............   17.50
PRESSED GLASS PURPLE PITCHER & 6 GLASSES,SILVER DECOR.......   67.50
PRESSED GLASS QUAKER LADY TUMBLER...........................    8.50
PRESSED GLASS QUEEN AMBER CAKE STAND........................   25.00
PRESSED GLASS QUEEN ANNE SPOONER............................   10.00
PRESSED GLASS QUEEN PITCHER.................................   14.75
PRESSED GLASS QUEEN VICTORIA TODDY PLATE,FLINT..............   25.00
PRESSED GLASS QUEENS NECKLACE PERFUME.......................    8.75
PRESSED GLASS RAIL FENCE BAND GOBLET........................    6.00
PRESSED GLASS RAINBOW WINE..................................    4.75
PRESSED GLASS RAINDROP & DEW PUNCH CUP......................    4.00
PRESSED GLASS RAINDROP AMBER 7 IN. COMPOTE..................   12.00
PRESSED GLASS RAINDROP BLUE FINGER BOWL,SCALLOPED EDGE......   17.50
PRESSED GLASS RAIN DROP BLUE SAUCE DISH.....................    6.00
PRESSED GLASS RAYED PEACOCK EYE SAUCE DISH..................   12.00
PRESSED GLASS RECESSED OVAL GOBLET..........................    5.50
PRESSED GLASS RED CANDLESTICK,ROUND BASE....................    3.50
PRESSED GLASS RED BLOCK GOBLET..............................   12.50
PRESSED GLASS RED BLOCK MUG,HANDLED.........................    8.00
PRESSED GLASS RED BLOCK MUG WITH HANDLE, ETCHED MOTHER
1901,SARATOGA...............................................   16.50
PRESSED GLASS RED BLOCK PITCHER.............................   45.00
PRESSED GLASS RED BLOCK RUBY & CLEAR COVERED SUGAR..........   25.00
PRESSED GLASS RED BLOCK RUBY TUMBLER,SET OF 4...............   45.00
PRESSED GLASS RED BLOCK SUGAR,OPEN..........................    8.00
PRESSED GLASS RED BLOCK TUMBLER.............................   10.00
PRESSED GLASS RED BLOCK WINE................................    7.50
PRESSED GLASS RED MUG,SOUVENIR,MABEL........................    6.50
PRESSED GLASS RED TOOTHPICK HOLDER SIGNED ROCKWELL,SILVER
TRIM........................................................   14.00
PRESSED GLASS REPEAT S SAPPHIRE BLUE TUMBLER................   14.00
PRESSED GLASS REXFORD NAPPY,TRIANGULAR,HANDLED..............    6.00
PRESSED GLASS RIB & ACORN GOBLET,SET OF 8,OVAL PICTURE OF
CAPITOL.....................................................   40.00
PRESSED GLASS RIB & ACORN SHERBET,SET OF 8,PICTURE OF
INDEPENDENCE HALL...........................................   35.00
PRESSED GLASS RIB & SCROLL RED SALT SHAKER..................    5.00
PRESSED GLASS RIBBED ACORN BUTTER,COVERED...................   10.50
PRESSED GLASS RIBBED BELLFLOWER SPOONER,FLINT...............   15.00
PRESSED GLASS RIBBED CLEAR HAT,STOVEPIPE....................   12.50
PRESSED GLASS RIBBED FORGET-ME-NOT CREAMER
6.00    TO..................................................   12.50
PRESSED GLASS RIBBED GRAPE GOBLET...........................   10.00
PRESSED GLASS RIBBED GRAPE GOBLET,FLINT
16.00   TO..................................................   20.00
PRESSED GLASS RIBBED GRAPE SPOONER..........................   13.00
PRESSED GLASS RIBBED HERRINGBONE CLEAR BASKET...............   16.50
PRESSED GLASS RIBBED IVY COMPOTE,OPEN,8 IN. HIGH,LOW
STANDARD....................................................   24.00
PRESSED GLASS RIBBED IVY GOBLET,BELLTONE,FLINT..............   14.50
PRESSED GLASS RIBBED IVY GOBLET,FLINT.......................   12.50
PRESSED GLASS RIBBED IVY SUGAR BOWL,COVERED,FLINT...........   38.00
PRESSED GLASS RIBBED OPAL BLUE MUG..........................   12.50
PRESSED GLASS RIBBED OPAL BLUE MUG,HANDLED..................   15.00
PRESSED GLASS RIBBED OPAL BLUE TOOTHPICK....................   15.00
PRESSED GLASS RIBBED OPAL CREAMER...........................   15.00
PRESSED GLASS RIBBED OPAL TOOTHPICK, 2 IN...................   18.00
PRESSED GLASS RIBBED OPALESCENT WHITE VASE,11 IN............   35.00
PRESSED GLASS RIBBED OVAL MEDALLION GOBLET,FLINT............   17.50
```

```
PRESSED GLASS RIBBED PALM CELERY,FLINT...................... 18.50
PRESSED GLASS RIBBED PALM CREAMER........................... 40.00
PRESSED GLASS RIBBED PALM EGG CUP,SET OF 6.................. 7.00
PRESSED GLASS RIBBED PALM GOBLET,FLINT
  11.00   TO................................................ 15.00
PRESSED GLASS RIBBED PALM SPOONER,FLINT
  10.00   TO................................................ 12.00
PRESSED GLASS RIBBED PALM SUGAR,OPEN,FLINT
  12.00   TO................................................ 25.00
PRESSED GLASS RIBBED PALM WATER PITCHER,FLINT............... 55.00
PRESSED GLASS RIBBED RUBY & CLEAR COMPOTE ON LOW STANDARD... 27.50
PRESSED GLASS RIBBED WHITE OPALESCENT TOOTHPICK............. 7.50
PRESSED GLASS RIBBON CANDY CREAMER.......................... 9.00
PRESSED GLASS RIBBON CANDY PLATE,7 IN....................... 6.50
PRESSED GLASS RIBBON CANDY SPOONER.......................... 5.00
PRESSED GLASS RIBBON CELERY................................. 17.50
PRESSED GLASS RIBBON COMPOTE,DOLPHIN STEM,FROSTED........... 125.00
PRESSED GLASS RIBBON CREAMER................................ 15.00
PRESSED GLASS RIBBON GOBLET,CLEAR........................... 10.00
PRESSED GLASS RIBBON GOBLET................................. 6.00
PRESSED GLASS RIPPLE BUTTER DISH,COVERED.................... 11.00
PRESSED GLASS RIPPLE BUTTERMILK GOBLET...................... 6.50
PRESSED GLASS RIPPLE RELISH DISH............................ 6.50
PRESSED GLASS RISING SUN WITH GOLD WINE..................... 6.50
PRESSED GLASS ROCK OF AGES BREAD TRAY....................... 24.00
PRESSED GLASS ROMAN KEY CASTOR SET,4 BOTTLE,FLINT........... 45.00
PRESSED GLASS ROMAN KEY CELERY,FLINT........................ 27.50
PRESSED GLASS ROMAN KEY COMPOTE,ENGLISH,FOOTED,CLEAR CUT
  BASE...................................................... 75.00
PRESSED GLASS ROMAN KEY GOBLET,FLINT........................ 16.50
PRESSED GLASS ROMAN ROSETTE CREAMER
  9.00   TO................................................. 11.00
PRESSED GLASS ROMAN ROSETTE CUP PLATE....................... 7.50
PRESSED GLASS ROMAN ROSETTE RELISH DISH..................... 8.75
PRESSED GLASS ROMAN ROSETTE SALT SHAKER WITH TOP,BULBOUS.... 8.50
PRESSED GLASS ROMAN ROSETTE SHAKERS,PAIR.................... 15.00
PRESSED GLASS ROMEO SPOONER................................. 5.00
PRESSED GLASS ROSE IN SNOW CLEAR GOBLET..................... 7.00
PRESSED GLASS ROSE IN SNOW CREAMER,SQUARE,4 IN. HIGH........ 16.75
PRESSED GLASS ROSE IN SNOW WATER PITCHER.................... 37.50
PRESSED GLASS ROSE MEDALLION BOWL,PEOPLE,2 IN. HIGH......... 6.50
PRESSED GLASS ROSE OF SHARON GOBLET......................... 8.00
PRESSED GLASS ROSE SPRIG CELERY VASE........................ 7.50
PRESSED GLASS ROSE SPRIG MILK PITCHER....................... 22.50
PRESSED GLASS ROSE SPRIG WATER PITCHER...................... 12.00
PRESSED GLASS ROSETTE & PALM BANANA COMPOTE................. 28.00
PRESSED GLASS ROSETTE & PALMS SUGAR,COVERED................. 15.00
PRESSED GLASS ROSETTE & ZIPPER PUNCH BOWL & CUPS............ 20.00
PRESSED GLASS ROSETTE CAKE STAND,10 IN...................... 12.00
PRESSED GLASS ROSETTE CREAMER............................... 9.50
PRESSED GLASS ROSETTE JELLY COMPOTE......................... 8.50
PRESSED GLASS ROSETTE MUG,HANDLED........................... 8.50
PRESSED GLASS ROSETTE PLATE,HANDLED......................... 6.50
PRESSED GLASS ROSETTE RUBY TUMBLER.......................... 9.50
PRESSED GLASS ROSETTE WATER SET TRAY........................ 9.50
PRESSED GLASS ROSETTE WITH PINWHEELS CAKE STANDARD,9 IN..... 10.00
PRESSED GLASS ROYAL IVY FROSTED TO CRANBERRY TUMBLER........ 4.00
PRESSED GLASS ROYAL OAK RUBY & CLEAR WATER PITCHER.......... 65.00
PRESSED GLASS RUBY & CLEAR WINE,SOUVENIR.................... 5.00
PRESSED GLASS RUBY COVERED SUGAR............................ 10.50
PRESSED GLASS RUBY PUNCH SET,11 IN. BOWL & 12 CUPS.......... 62.00
PRESSED GLASS RUBY WATER SET,ENAMELLED...................... 135.00
PRESSED GLASS RUSSIAN & FAN SET OF 4 PUNCH CUPS............. 15.00
PRESSED GLASS SADDLE AMBER TOOTHPCIK HOLDER................. 25.00
PRESSED GLASS SANDWICH CANDLESTICK,CRUCIFIX,YELLOW,13
```

```
IN.,FLINT.................................................    47.50
PRESSED GLASS SANDWICH EAGLE CUP PLATE IN CLEAR,FLINT.......    15.00
PRESSED GLASS SAHDWICH HONEY DIP,FLINT......................     2.50
PRESSED GLASS SANDWICH LOOP GOBLET,FLINT....................    16.50
PRESSED GLASS SANDWICH LOOP SPOONER,FLINT...................    20.00
PRESSED GLASS SANDWICH RIPPLE GOBLET........................     6.50
PRESSED GLASS SANDWICH STAR DECANTER,FLINT..................    25.00
PRESSED GLASS SANDWICH STAR SPILL HOLDER,ROUND,FOOTED.......    16.00
PRESSED GLASS SANDWICH STAR SPOONER,FLINT...................    12.00
PRESSED GLASS SAPPHIRE BLUE COMPOTE,COVERED,FOOTED..........    12.50
PRESSED GLASS SAPPHIRE BLUE ICE CREAM TRAY..................    35.00
PRESSED GLASS SAPPHIRE BLUE INKWELL,ELK IN RELIEF ON PEWTER
 TOP........................................................     9.50
PRESSED GLASS SAPPHIRE BLUE VASE,DOLPHIN,8 IN. HIGH.........    42.00
PRESSED GLASS SAWTOOTH & LEAF PANELS TUMBLER,FOOTED,FLINT...    16.50
PRESSED GLASS SAWTOOTH & STAR PLATE,10 IN...................    10.00
PRESSED GLASS SAWTOOTH & TULIP TUMBLER,FOOTED,FLINT.........    12.00
PRESSED GLASS SAWTOOTH CAKE COMPOTE.........................    24.00
PRESSED GLASS SAWTOOTH CELERY VASE,KNOB STEM,FLINT..........    35.00
PRESSED GLASS SAWTOOTH CELERY,FOOTED........................     8.50
PRESSED GLASS SAWTOOTH CELERY...............................    22.00
PRESSED GLASS SAWTOOTH CLEAR CELERY HOLDER..................    13.00
PRESSED GLASS SAWTOOTH COMPOTE,6 IN.........................    12.00
PRESSED GLASS SAWTOOTH COMPOTE ON STANDARD,FLINT............    15.00
PRESSED GLASS SAWTOOTH COMPOTE ON STAND,OPEN................    35.00
PRESSED GLASS SAWTOOTH COMPOTE,OPEN.........................    15.00
PRESSED GLASS SAWTOOTH COMPOTE,OVAL,LIONS HANDLES & KNOBS...    15.00
PRESSED GLASS SAWTOOTH COMPOTE WITH LID.....................    25.00
PRESSED GLASS SAWTOOTH CREAMER
 10.50   TO.................................................    40.00
PRESSED GLASS SAWTOOTH CREAMER,APPLIED HANDLE...............    11.00
PRESSED GLASS SAWTOOTH CREAMER,FLINT........................    15.00
PRESSED GLASS SAWTOOTH CRICKLITE,PAIR.......................    20.00
PRESSED GLASS SAWTOOTH DISH,OVAL,COVERED,LION HANDLES &
 KNOBS......................................................    28.00
PRESSED GLASS SAWTOOTH FOOTED SUGAR & CREAMER,4 IN. HIGH,...     8.50
PRESSED GLASS SAWTOOTH HONEYCOMB NAPPY,SCALLOPED EDGE.......     6.00
PRESSED GLASS SAWTOOTH MILK PITCHER,BULBOUS WITH APPLIED
 HANDLE.....................................................    28.00
PRESSED GLASS SAWTOOTH MILK PITCHER WITH APPLIED
 HANDLE,FLINT...............................................    38.50
PRESSED GLASS SAWTOOTH OVAL COMPOTE LIONS HANDLES & KNOB....    15.00
PRESSED GLASS SAWTOOTH PITCHER,BULBOUS,APPLIED HANDLE.......    32.50
PRESSED GLASS SAWTOOTH SALT,COVERED,FOOTED..................    38.00
PRESSED GLASS SAWTOOTH SPOONER..............................     6.00
PRESSED GLASS SAWTOOTH SPOONER,FLINT
 9.50    TP.................................................    18.00
PRESSED GLASS SAWTOOTH TUMBLER,FOOTED,FLINT.................    16.50
PRESSED GLASS SAWTOOTH WATER PITCHER........................    25.00
PRESSED GLASS SAWTOOTH WATER TUMBLER........................     2.50
PRESSED GLASS SAWTOOTH WINE
 7.00    TO.................................................    10.00
PRESSED GLASS SAWTOOTH WINE,3 IN. HIGH......................     3.25
PRESSED GLASS SAWTOOTH WITH STAR GREEN 10 IN. PLATE.........    15.00
PRESSED GLASS SCALLOPED LINES EGG CUP.......................     6.00
PRESSED GLASS SCALLOPED LINES SUGAR BOWL,COVERED............    12.50
PRESSED GLASS SCOTTISH RITES GOBLET.........................    10.00
PRESSED GLASS SCROLL BLUE OPALESCENT TUMBLER................    10.00
PRESSED GLASS SCROLL BLUE OPAQUE SHAKER,FOOTED..............    12.00
PRESSED GLASS SCROLL GREEN OPAQUE SHAKER,FOOTED.............    12.00
PRESSED GLASS SCROLL WITH FLOWERS SPOONER,2 HANDLED.........     6.00
PRESSED GLASS SEDAN WINE....................................     8.75
PRESSED GLASS SENECA LOOP GOBLET............................     7.50
PRESSED GLASS SEQUOIA PLATE,7 IN............................     5.00
PRESSED GLASS SEQUOIA WINE..................................     6.75
```

```
PRESSED GLASS SERRATED SPEARPOINT WINE......................    3.75
PRESSED GLASS SHASTA DAISY AMETHYST 9 IN. SHALLOW PLATE.....   22.50
PRESSED GLASS SHEAF & DIAMOND CAKE STAND...................   10.50
PRESSED GLASS SHEAF & DIAMONDS PEDESTAL BANANA STAND........   11.50
PRESSED GLASS SHEAF OF WHEAT BREAD TRAY,OVAL................   16.00
PRESSED GLASS SHEAF OF WHEAT PLATTER,MOTTLED................   12.50
PRESSED GLASS SHELL & JEWEL BOWL...........................    6.00
PRESSED GLASS SHELL & JEWEL CREAMER........................    8.50
PRESSED GLASS SHELL & JEWEL FROSTED WATER SET,7 PIECES......   26.00
PRESSED GLASS SHELL & JEWEL MILK PITCHER...................   16.50
PRESSED GLASS SHELL AND JEWEL SAUCE DISH...................    3.75
PRESSED GLASS SHELL & JEWEL SPOONER........................    4.25
PRESSED GLASS SHELL & JEWEL WATER PITCHER
  6.00    TO.................................................   14.50
PRESSED GLASS SHELL & SEAWEED GREEN TOOTHPICK..............   14.00
PRESSED GLASS SHELL & TASSEL BOWL IN SILVER PLATED HOLDER,10
  IN........................................................   22.00
PRESSED GLASS SHELL & TASSEL BOWL,OVAL
 12.00    TO.................................................   18.00
PRESSED GLASS SHELL & TASSEL CAKESTAND,SQUARE..............   18.50
PRESSED GLASS SHELL & TASSEL COMPOTE,OPEN,PEDESTAL.........   15.00
PRESSED GLASS SHELL & TASSEL GOBLET........................   18.50
PRESSED GLASS SHELL & TASSEL OBLONG ROUND CORNERED
  PLATTER,HANDLES...........................................   21.00
PRESSED GLASS SHELL & TASSEL ROUND CREAMER.................   12.75
PRESSED GLASS SHELL & TASSEL ROUND SPOONER.................    7.50
PRESSED GLASS SHELL & TASSEL SAUCE,SET OF 6,SQUARE,HANDLED..   24.50
PRESSED GLASS SHELL & TASSEL SQUARE HANDLED SAUCE DISH......    6.50
PRESSED GLASS SHELL & TASSEL SQUARE JELLY COMPOTE..........   15.00
PRESSED GLASS SHELL & TASSEL TRAY,OBLONG,9 X 12 IN.........   20.00
PRESSED GLASS SHELL & WREATH BLUE BUTTER,COVERED...........   45.00
PRESSED GLASS SHELL MEDALLION SAUCE DISH,8 SIDED...........   20.00
PRESSED GLASS SHERATON BUTTER,COVERED
 12.00    TO.................................................   16.00
PRESSED GLASS SHERATON CREAMER.............................    7.00
PRESSED GLASS SHERATON PATTERN OPEN COMPOTE................   50.00
PRESSED GLASS SHERATON MILK PITCHER........................   12.50
PRESSED GLASS SHIP & STARS CLEAR PLATE.....................    6.00
PRESSED GLASS SHORT LOOPS RING STEM GOBLET.................    7.00
PRESSED GLASS SHOSHONE CAKE STAND..........................   15.00
PRESSED GLASS SHOSHONE CLEAR WITH GOLD TOOTHPICK...........    7.50
PRESSED GLASS SHOSHONE COMPOTE,SHALLOW.....................    6.00
PRESSED GLASS SHOSHONE COMPOTE,8 IN........................    7.50
PRESSED GLASS SHOSHONE GREEN CRUET.........................   35.00
PRESSED GLASS SHOSHONE GREEN DOUGHNUT PLATE................   13.50
PRESSED GLASS SHOVEL GOBLET................................    6.50
PRESSED GLASS SHRINE GOBLET................................   10.00
PRESSED GLASS SHRINE MUG...................................   12.00
PRESSED GLASS SHRINE MUG WITH 3 SCIMITAR HANDLES...........   22.50
PRESSED GLASS SHRINE PITCHER...............................   18.50
PRESSED GLASS SHRINE SHAKER,PAIR...........................   12.50
PRESSED GLASS SHRINE WATER PITCHER.........................   18.50
PRESSED GLASS SHUTTLE PUNCH CUP............................    3.00
PRESSED GLASS SHUTTLE WINE
  3.00    TO.................................................    5.00
PRESSED GLASS SKILTON CELERY,CLEAR.........................    8.00
PRESSED GLASS SLEWED HORSESHOE FOOTED SAUCE................    2.50
PRESSED GLASS SMOCKING BOWL,3 IN. HIGH,FLINT...............   24.00
PRESSED GLASS SMOCKING COMPOTE,FLINT.......................   60.00
PRESSED GLASS SMOCKING GOBLET,KNOB STEM,FLINT
 20.00    TO.................................................   28.50
PRESSED GLASS SMOCKING RUMMER GOBLET,FLINT.................   27.50
PRESSED GLASS SMOCKING RUMMER SUGAR,OPEN,FLINT.............   30.00
PRESSED GLASS SMOCKING WINE,KNOB STEM......................   12.50
PRESSED GLASS SNAIL BOWL...................................    7.50
```

```
PRESSED GLASS SNAIL COVERED BUTTER........................... 22.50
PRESSED GLASS SNAIL RELISH,BOAT-SHAPED....................... 7.00
PRESSED GLASS SNAKE DRAPE GOBLET............................. 6.00
PRESSED GLASS SNAKE ENTWINED AROUND TREE CLEAR TOOTHPICK.... 10.00
PRESSED GLASS SNAKE SKIN DOT GOBLET.......................... 7.00
PRESSED GLASS SNOW ON MOUNTAIN PINWHEEL CAKE STAND.......... 10.50
PRESSED GLASS SPANISH FLOWER BLUE OPALESCENT SUGAR SHAKER... 38.00
PRESSED GLASS SPANISH SWIRL OPAL BLUE SYRUP.................. 55.00
PRESSED GLASS SPIRAL WITH MALTESE CROSS CREAMER............. 7.50
PRESSED GLASS SPIREA BAND AMBER TUMBLER...................... 11.00
PRESSED GLASS SPIREA BAND CREAMER & SUGAR.................... 12.00
PRESSED GLASS SPIREA BLUE WINE............................... 14.00
PRESSED GLASS SPRIG CELERY................................... 15.00
PRESSED GLASS SPRIG SPOONER,DOUBLE HANDLES................... 5.00
PRESSED  GLASS SPRIG WATER PITCHER.......................... 22.50
PRESSED GLASS STAR & DIAMOND GOBLET,RUBY TOP................. 15.00
PRESSED GLASS STAR & FILE BOWL,7 IN......................... 10.50
PRESSED GLASS STAR & OVAL BUTTER,OVAL....................... 15.00
PRESSED GLASS STAR & OVAL COMPOTE,COVERED................... 20.00
PRESSED GLASS STAR & PALM GOBLET............................. 4.50
PRESSED GLASS STAR & PILLAR BREAD PLATE,DO UNTO OTHERS,ETC.. 6.00
PRESSED GLASS STAR & PUNTY WHALE OIL LAMP WITH PEWTER
  COLLAR,FLINT.............................................. 49.50
PRESSED GLASS STARS & STRIPES RELISH DISH................... 6.00
PRESSED GLASS STARS & STRIPES SALT.......................... 2.50
PRESSED GLASS STARS & STRIPES WINE.......................... 5.00
PRESSED GLASS STAR & THISTLE BERRY DISH..................... 11.50
PRESSED GLASS STAR BAND BUTTER DISH......................... 10.00
PRESSED GLASS STAR IN BULLS EYE GOBLET...................... 6.50
PRESSED GLASS STAR KNIFE REST,4 IN.......................... 5.00
PRESSED GLASS STAR MEDALLION & CANE GOBLET.................. 6.00
PRESSED GLASS STAR MEDALLION BOWL........................... 7.00
PRESSED GLASS STAR MEDALLION BUTTER,COVERED................. 6.50
PRESSED GLASS STAR ROSETTE SAUCE,FLAT....................... 4.00
PRESSED GLASS STAR ROSETTED CREAMER......................... 16.00
PRESSED GLASS STAR WHIRL GOBLET............................. 6.50
PRESSED GLASS STAR WINE..................................... 7.50
PRESSED GLASS STAR WITH FEATHER AMBER PLATE,7 IN............ 8.75
PRESSED GLASS STAR WITH FEATHER PLATE,7 IN.................. 5.75
PRESSED GLASS STARBURST WINE................................ 5.50
PRESSED GLASS ST.BERNARD PLATE.............................. 25.00
PRESSED GLASS STEDMAN GOBLET................................ 12.50
PRESSED GLASS STEDMAN GOBLET,FLINT.......................... 13.50
PRESSED GLASS STIPPLED BAND GOBLET.......................... 6.50
PRESSED GLASS STIPPLED BAND SAUCE,FLAT...................... 2.00
PRESSED GLASS STIPPLED BAND SPOONER......................... 5.00
PRESSED GLASS STIPPLED BUDDED IVY BUTTER,COVERED............ 12.50
PRESSED GLASS STIPPLED CHERRY SAUCE......................... 2.75
PRESSED GLASS STIPPLED CHERRY SAUCE,FLAT.................... 2.00
PRESSED GLASS STIPPLED DAISY SPOONER........................ 9.00
PRESSED GLASS STIPPLED DOUBLE LOOP CREAMER.................. 6.50
PRESSED GLASS STIPPLED FORGET ME NOT CREAM PITCHER.......... 12.50
PRESSED GLASS STIPPLED FORGET-ME-NOT GOBLET................. 15.00
PRESSED GLASS STIPPLED FORGET-ME-NOT MUSTARD,COVERED........ 15.00
PRESSED GLASS STIPPLED FORGET-ME-NOT TUMBLER................ 18.75
PRESSED GLASS STIPPLED FORGET-ME-NOT WATER PITCHER.......... 12.00
PRESSED GLASS STIPPLED FORGET-ME-NOT WINE................... 15.00
PRESSED GLASS STIPPLED GRAPE & FESTOON CLEAR LEAF WATER
  PITCHER.................................................. 25.00
PRESSED GLASS STIPPLED GRAPE & FESTOON SUGAR,OPEN........... 7.00
PRESSED GLASS STIPPLED GREEN TABLE SETTING,3 PIECE,ROSE IN
  GOLD..................................................... 22.00
PRESSED GLASS STIPPLED IVY BUD GOBLET....................... 9.00
PRESSED GLASS STIPPLED LEAF GOBLET.......................... 8.00
PRESSED GLASS STIPPLED MEDALLION GOBLET,FLINT............... 10.00
```

```
PRESSED GLASS STIPPLED PANEL & BAND BUTTERMILK GOBLET.......      10.00
PRESSED GLASS STIPPLED PANEL & BAND SPOONER.................       5.00
PRESSED GLASS STIPPLED SAUCE,FLAT...........................       3.75
PRESSED GLASS STIPPLED STAR GOBLET..........................      11.50
PRESSED GLASS STIPPLED STAR SPOONER.........................       8.50
PRESSED GLASS STIPPLED STAR SUGAR BOWL......................      25.00
PRESSED GLASS STORK FROSTED PLATTER,101 BORDER..............      35.00
PRESSED GLASS STRAWBERRY & FAN KNIFE REST...................       8.00
PRESSED GLASS STRAWBERRY BOWL...............................       8.50
PRESSED GLASS STRAWBERRY DIAMOND PATTERN BASKET.............       3.00
PRESSED GLASS STRAWBERRY RELISH,TAPERED.....................       8.00
PRESSED GLASS STRAWBERRY SUGAR,OPEN.........................      22.00
PRESSED GLASS STRAWBERRY WITH GOLD CABLE TUMBLER............       4.50
PRESSED GLASS STRAWBERRY WITH GOLD CABLE WATER PITCHER......      20.00
PRESSED GLASS STRIGIL CELERY................................       6.50
PRESSED GLASS STRIGIL PLATE,5 IN............................       4.50
PRESSED GLASS STRUTTING TURKEY CLEAR COVERED DISH...........      15.00
PRESSED GLASS SUNBURST & FAN GOBLET.........................       6.00
PRESSED GLASS SUNBURST CREAMER,INDIVIDUAL...................       3.50
PRESSED GLASS SUNBURST ELECTRA BLUE TRAY FOR DEVILED EGGS...      20.00
PRESSED GLASS SUNBURST PLATE,8 IN...........................       6.75
PRESSED GLASS SUNBURST WINE.................................       3.25
PRESSED GLASS SUNK DAISY CELERY VASE........................       7.00
PRESSED GLASS SUNK HONEYCOMB CREAMER,RUBY TOP...............      10.00
PRESSED GLASS SUNK HONEYCOMB TUMBLER........................      10.00
PRESSED GLASS SUNK TEARDROP CREAMER.........................       6.75
PRESSED GLASS SUNSET SALT SHAKER............................      12.50
PRESSED GLASS SWAN 4 IN. FOOTED DISH........................       5.50
PRESSED GLASS SWAN WITH TREE CREAMER........................      22.50
PRESSED GLASS SWIRL & DIAMOND CREAMER.......................       6.50
PRESSED GLASS SWIRL AMBER TUMBLER...........................      15.00
PRESSED GLASS SWIRL BLUE & OPALESCENT WATER PITCHER.........      35.00
PRESSED GLASS SWIRL BLUE CASTOR,PICKLE,MARKED,HOLDER,COVER &
  TONGS.....................................................      68.00
PRESSED GLASS SWIRL GREEN SHADED VASE,3 BALLS AT BASE.......      18.00
PRESSED GLASS SWIRL STRIPE OPAL SAPPHIRE BLUE TUMBLER.......      18.00
PRESSED GLASS SWIRLED & BEADED GREEN TOOTHPICK HOLDER.......       8.00
PRESSED GLASS SWIRLED BUBBLES AMBER VASE,9 IN...............      12.00
PRESSED GLASS SWIRLED OPALESCENT CELERY VASE................      28.50
PRESSED GLASS SWIRLED PRISM CAKE STAND,CHRISTMAS............       9.50
PRESSED GLASS TACKLE BLOCK GOBLET,FLINT.....................      35.00
PRESSED GLASS TAILORED FROSTED BAND WINE,...................       2.00
PRESSED GLASS TANDEM BICYCLE GOBLET.........................       6.50
PRESSED GLASS TANDEM DIAMONDS & THUMBPRINT GOBLET...........       4.50
PRESSED GLASS TAPE MEASURE GOBLET...........................       8.00
PRESSED GLASS TASSEL VARIANT CREAMER........................       9.50
PRESSED GLASS TAUNTON SAUCE,FOOTED..........................       3.00
PRESSED GLASS TEARDROP & TASSEL SUGAR,OPEN..................       6.00
PRESSED GLASS TEARDROP GOBLET...............................      10.00
PRESSED GLASS TEARDROP WINE.................................       7.00
PRESSED GLASS TEDDY ROOSEVELT PLATTER,OVAL,FROSTED CENTER...      20.00
PRESSED GLASS TENNESSEE CELERY..............................       7.50
PRESSED GLASS TENNESSEE COMPOTE.............................       6.50
PRESSED GLASS TENNESSEE CREAMER.............................      13.00
PRESSED GLASS TEXAS CREAMER
  5.00      TO..............................................       8.00
PRESSED GLASS TEXAS CREAMER AND SUGAR.......................       8.50
PRESSED GLASS TEXAS GOLD CREAMER............................       4.75
PRESSED GLASS TEXAS TEEPEE TOOTHPICK........................       4.50
PRESSED GLASS TEXAS VASE,CLEAR..............................       5.00
PRESSED GLASS THE STATES CREAMER............................       7.00
PRESSED GLASS THE STATES FRUIT BOWL,SQUARE..................      15.00
PRESSED GLASS THE STATES PATTERN BOWL.......................      10.50
PRESSED GLASS THE STATES PUNCH BOWL & STAND.................      35.00
PRESSED GLASS THE STATES PUNCH CUP..........................       5.00
```

```
PRESSED GLASS THISTLE CAKE STANDARD..........................  12.50
PRESSED GLASS THISTLE CAKESTAND,9 IN.,UPTURNED EDGE.........  18.50
PRESSED GLASS THISTLE COMPOTE ON HIGH STANDARD,6 IN.........  10.00
PRESSED GLASS THISTLE EGG CUP...............................  10.00
PRESSED GLASS THISTLE GOBLET................................  12.50
PRESSED GLASS THISTLE GREEN & GOLD SUGAR,CREAMER & SPOONER..  10.00
PRESSED GLASS THISTLE OPEN COMPOTE,6 IN. DIAMETER...........  10.00
PRESSED GLASS THISTLE PICKLE................................   9.00
PRESSED GLASS THISTLE TUMBLER,FOOTED........................  12.50
PRESSED GLASS THOUSAND EYE AMBER COMPOTE....................  21.50
PRESSED GLASS THOUSAND EYE AMBER MUG,HANDLED................   8.00
PRESSED GLASS THOUSAND EYE AMBER PLATTER....................  16.50
PRESSED GLASS THOUSAND EYE AMBER SAUCE......................   4.75
PRESSED GLASS THOUSAND EYE BLUE CHRISTMAS LIGHT.............  20.00
PRESSED GLASS THOUSAND EYE BLUE PLATE,8 IN. DIAMETER,FOLDED
   CORNERS.................................................  12.00
PRESSED GLASS THOUSAND EYE BLUE TOOTHPICK...................  12.50
PRESSED GLASS THOUSAND EYE CELERY
   9.50   TO..............................................  19.50
PRESSED GLASS THOUSAND EYE CLEAR CAKE PLATE,10 IN. SQUARE...  12.50
PRESSED GLASS THOUSAND EYE CLEAR SALT SHAKER................   5.00
PRESSED GLASS THOUSAND EYE CLEAR SAUCE DISH,FOOTED..........   5.00
PRESSED GLASS THOUSAND EYE HAT,CLEAR........................  19.50
PRESSED GLASS THOUSAND EYE WATER TRAY,ROUND.................  12.50
PRESSED GLASS THOUSAND EYE PLATE,10 IN.,SQUARE CUT CORNERS..  18.00
PRESSED GLASS THOUSAND LEAF ROSE SAUCE,FOOTED...............   2.50
PRESSED GLASS THREADING CELERY..............................  15.00
PRESSED GLASS THREE FACE CAKESTAND..........................  48.00
PRESSED GLASS THREE FACE COMPOTE,OPEN.......................  35.00
PRESSED GLASS THREE FACE FROSTED SALT
   12.50   TO.............................................  26.00
PRESSED GLASS THREE FACE FROSTED TOOTHPICK HOLDER...........  17.50
PRESSED GLASS THREE FACE FROSTED TOOTHPICK HOLDER WITH
   MATCHING SALT...........................................  17.50
PRESSED GLASS THREE FACE GOBLET,FOOTED......................  39.50
PRESSED GLASS THREE FACE SALT...............................  10.00
PRESSED GLASS THREE FACE SALT & PEPPER,PAIR,SILVER TOPS.....  45.00
PRESSED GLASS THREE FACE SAUCE,FOOTED,4 IN..................  15.00
PRESSED GLASS THREE FACE TOOTHPICK HOLDER...................   9.50
PRESSED GLASS THREE GRACES PLATTER FROSTED CENTER DATED.....  20.00
PRESSED GLASS THREE GRACES WATER SET TRAY...................  12.50
PRESSED GLASS THREE IN ONE NAPPIE...........................   8.00
PRESSED GLASS THREE PANEL CELERY............................  12.50
PRESSED GLASS THREE PANEL CELERY VASE.......................   9.75
PRESSED GLASS THREE PANEL CREAMER...........................   8.00
PRESSED GLASS THREE PANEL YELLOW SPOONER....................  10.00
PRESSED GLASS THREE PRESIDENTS PLATTER......................  20.00
PRESSED GLASS THREE STORKS A FEEDING PLATTER................  90.00
PRESSED GLASS THUMBPRINT ALE GLASS,FLINT....................  12.50
PRESSED GLASS THUMBPRINT AMBER PITCHER......................  25.00
PRESSED GLASS THUMBPRINT CELERY,FLINT.......................  75.00
PRESSED GLASS THIMBPRINT COMPOTE,COVERED,1830,FLINT.........  45.00
PRESSED GLASS THUMBPRINT COMPOTE,FLINT......................  25.00
PRESSED GLASS THUMBPRINT COMPOTE,PAIR ,FLINT................  50.00
PRESSED GLASS THUMBPRINT COVERED SUGAR,FLINT................  38.50
PTRSSED GLASS THUMBPRINT GRAPE & CABLE GREEN SAUCE..........   9.00
PRESSED GLASS THUMBPRINT HONEY DISH.........................   2.75
PRESSED GLASS THUMBPRINT OPEN COMPOTE,LOW STAND,FLINT.......  24.50
PRESSED GLASS THUMBPRINT OPEN SUGAR,BELL TONE,FLINT.........  22.00
PRESSED GLASS THUMBPRINT RUBY CELERY........................  26.50
PRESSED GLASS THUMBPRINT RUBY CELERY VASE...................  22.50
PRESSED GLASS THUMBPRINT RUBY CREAMER.......................  10.00
PRESSED GLASS THUMBPRINT RUBY GOBLET,SOUVENIR...............   6.50
PRESSED GLASS THUMBPRINT RUBY JELLY.........................  20.00
PRESSED GLASS THUMBPRINT RUBY RED MUG WITH HANDLE...........   3.50
```

```
PRESSED GLASS THUMBPRINT RUBY SPOONER........................    14.00
PRESSED GLASS THUMBPRINT RUBY TOOTHPICK......................     9.50
PRESSED GLASS THUMBPRINT RUBY TUMBLER........................    10.00
PRESSED GLASS THUMBPRINT RUBY WINE,SOUVENIR..................    10.00
PRESSED GLASS THUMBPRINT TUMBLER,OPALINE EDGE................     4.00
PRESSED GLASS THUMBPRINT VINTAGE ETCHED RUBY TOOTHPICK.......    13.50
PRESSED GLASS THUMBPRINT VINTAGE RUBY GOBLET.................    18.50
PRESSED GLASS THUMBPRINT WINE................................     2.50
PRESSED GLASS THUMBPRINT WINE GOBLETS,SET OF 6...............    13.00
PRESSED GLASS TOKYO BLUE SALT SHAKER,PEWTER TOP..............     8.50
PRESSED GLASS TOKYO OPAL GREEN CREAMER.......................    17.50
PRESSED GLASS TOMATO COVERED BUTTER..........................    16.50
PRESSED GLASS TONG CELERY,FLINT..............................    27.50
PRESSED GLASS TORPEDO BERRY BOWL.............................     6.00
PRESSED GLASS TORPEDO BOWL,9 IN..............................    15.00
PRESSED GLASS TORPEDO CUP & SAUCER...........................    12.00
PRESSED GLASS TORPEDO GOBLET
  10.00  TO................................................    17.50
PRESSED GLASS TORPEDO RUBY & CLEAR SYRUP WITH TOP............    37.50
PRESSED GLASS TORPEDO TUMBLER,RUBY TOP.......................    13.75
PRESSED GLASS TORPEDO WINE...................................    18.50
PRESSED GLASS TREE OF LIFE AMBER SAUCE,LEAF SHAPE............     7.50
PRESSED GLASS TREE OF LIFE BLUE FINGER BOWL..................     9.00
PRESSED GLASS TREE OF LIFE BOWL,PORTLAND.....................    10.00
PRESSED GLASS TREE OF LIFE BREAD TRAY,OVAL,GIVE US THIS DAY.    16.00
PRESSED GLASS TREE OF LIFE COBALT FINGER BOWL,PORTLAND......    45.00
PRESSED GLASS TREE OF LIFE COMPOTE,COVERED,HAND HOLDING BALL    30.00
PRESSED GLASS TREE OF LIFE COMPOTE,HAND HOLDING,8 IN. HIGH..    18.00
PRESSED GLASS TREE OF LIFE CREAMER...........................    12.00
PRESSED GLASS TREE OF LIFE ICE CREAM TRAY....................     6.50
PRESSED GLASS TREE OF LIFE JAR,COVERED,SILVER PLATE BASKET..    85.00
PRESSED GLASS TREE OF LIFE PORTLAND COVERED COMPOTE,FLINT...    38.50
PRESSED GLASS TREE OF LIFE SAUCE DISH,STEM...................     4.50
PRESSED GLASS TREE OF LIFE SAUCE,LEAF SHAPED.................     5.00
PRESSED GLASS TREE OF LIFE SAUCE,ROUND.......................     5.00
PRESSED GLASS TREE OF LIFE SPOONER...........................    12.50
PRESSED GLASS TREE OF LIFE SUGAR.............................    12.00
PRESSED GLASS TREE OF LIFE WATER PITCHER & 6 TUMBLERS.......    35.00
PRESSED GLASS TREE TRUNK WITH HERON RED TOOTHPICK HOLDER....    20.00
PRESSED GLASS TREMONT CREAMER................................     5.50
PRESSED GLASS TRIANGULAR MEDALLION GOBLET,FLINT..............    10.00
PRESSED GLASS TRIANGULAR PRISM GOBLET,FLINT..................    18.00
PRESSED GLASS TRIANGULAR PRISM MASTER SALT,FOOTED,FLINT.....    10.00
PRESSED GLASS TRIPLE BAND TUMBLER,FOOTED.....................     4.50
PRESSED GLASS TRIPLE TRIANGLE CLEAR RED CREAMER.............    15.00
PRESSED GLASS TRIPLE TRIANGLE RUBY & CLEAR COVERED SUGAR....    22.50
PRESSED GLASS TRIPLE TRIANGLE RUBY & CLEAR WATER PITCHER....    35.00
PRESSED GLASS TRIPLE TRIANGLE RUBY WINE......................    15.00
PRESSED GLASS TRIPLE TRIANGLE TUMBLER........................    12.50
PRESSED GLASS TROPICAL VILLA CELERY,ETCHED SCENES...........    25.00
PRESSED GLASS TULIP & SAWTOOTH CELERY VASE..................    20.00
PRESSED GLASS TULIP COMPOTE,FLINT............................    45.00
PRESSED GLASS TULIP COVERED BUTTER...........................    12.50
PRESSED GLASS TULIP GOBLET,FLINT.............................    10.00
PRESSED GLASS TULIP GOBLET,KNOB STEM,FLINT...................    12.00
PRESSED GLASS TULIP GOBLET,PLAIN STEM,FLINT..................    12.00
PRESSED GLASS TULIP PETAL GOBLET.............................     5.00
PRESSED GLASS TULIP SAWTOOTH CELERY VASE.....................    12.50
PRESSED GLASS TULIP VARIANT CELERY...........................     7.50
PRESSED GLASS TULIP WITH SAWTOOTH GOBLET,FLINT..............    19.50
PRESSED GLASS TULIP WITH SAWTOOTH OPEN SALT,FOOTED,POINTED
  TOP,FLINT.................................................    10.00
PRESSED GLASS TWO BAND CREAMER...............................     6.50
PRESSED GLASS TWO PANEL AMBER BOWL...........................    17.50
PRESSED GLASS TWO PANEL CELERY VASE..........................     7.00
```

PRESSED GLASS U S COIN BUTTER DISH,DOLLARS...................	48.00
PRESSED GLASS U S COIN GLASS CAKE STAND,SILVER DOLLARS &	
QUARTERS..	300.00
PRESSED GLASS U S COIN GLASS CLARET,6 HALF DIMES............	195.00
PRESSED GLASS U S COIN GLASS,DOLLARS & QUARTERS WITH 1892	
CAKESTAND...	250.00
PRESSED GLASS U S COIN GLASS FROSTED CAKE	
STAND,DOLLARS,QUARTERS......................................	250.00
PRESSED GLASS U S COIN GLASS SPOONER,1892 QUARTERS	
70.00 TO...	110.00
PRESSED GLASS U.S.COIN GLASS TOOTHPICK,SQUARE WITH FROSTED	
DOLLARS 1892..	35.00
PRESSED GLASS U S COIN GLASS TUMBLER,1892 DIMES.............	110.00
PRESSED GLASS VALENCIA WAFFLE AMBER COMPOTE,SQUARE,COVERED..	35.00
PRESSED GLASS VALENCIA WAFFLE APPLE GREEN CELERY VASE.......	17.50
PRESSED GLASS VALENCIA WAFFLE BLUE SPOONER & OPEN SUGAR.....	28.00
PRESSED GLASS VALENCIA WAFFLE CELERY........................	10.00
PRESSED GLASS VALENCIA WAFFLE COVERED BUTTER................	15.00
PRESSED GLASS VASELINE COLOUR FOOTED TUMBLER................	15.00
PRESSED GLASS VENETIAN BLUE TUMBLER,HANDPAINTED.............	12.50
PRESSED GLASS VENUS & CUPID ENGRAVED PLATTER,OVAL...........	125.00
PRESSED GLASS VERA FROSTED SAUCE,SET OF 3,FLAT..............	12.00
PRESSED GLASS VERNON HONEYCOMB CREAMER WITH APPLIED	
HANDLE,FLINT..	16.00
PRESSED GLASS VICTORIAN LOOP EMERALD GREEN VASE,PAIR FOOTED.	17.50
PRESSED GLASS VIKING CELERY.................................	15.00
PRESSED GLASS VIKING SUGAR,COVERED..........................	22.50
PRESSED GLASS VINE ELECTRA BLUE SUGAR,COVERED...............	15.00
PRESSED GLASS VINTAGE ETCHED CRYSTAL WINE,FLINT.............	12.50
PRESSED GLASS VINTAGE ETCHED RUBY FINGER BOWL...............	15.00
PRESSED GLASS VIRGINIA BANDED PORTLAND BUTTER,COVERED.......	14.00
PRESSED GLASS VIRGINIA BANDED PORTLAND SUGAR,COVERED........	12.00
PRESSED GLASS VIRGINIA CREAMER..............................	4.25
PRESSED GLASS VIRGINIA GALLOWAY SUGAR,OVAL..................	4.50
PRESSED GLASS VIRGINIA GALLOWAY TOOTHPICK HOLDER............	5.00
PRESSED GLASS VIRGINIA TOOTHPICK............................	4.00
PRESSED GLASS WAFFLE & SPEARPOINT COVERED SUGAR.............	8.50
PRESSED GLASS WAFFLE & THUMBPRINT COMPOTE,FLINT.............	22.50
PRESSED GLASS WAFFLE & THUMBPRINT DECANTER,QUART............	38.50
PRESSED GLASS WAFFLE & THUMBPRINT EGG CUP,FLINT.............	10.00
PRESSED GLASS WAFFLE & THUMBPRINT OPEN COMPOTE,FLINT........	22.50
PRESSED GLASS WAFFLE & THUMBPRINT SPOONER,FLINT.............	9.50
PRESSED GLASS WAFFLE & THUMBPRINT SUGAR,COVERED.............	35.00
PRESSED GLASS WAFFLE BAR BOTTLE,QUART,FLINT.................	20.00
PRESSED GLASS WAFFLE BUTTER DISH,COVERED,FLINT..............	24.00
PRESSED GLASS WAFFLE CELERY VASE............................	10.00
PRESSED GLASS WAFFLE CELERY VASE,PAIR,FLINT.................	60.00
PRESSED GLASS WAFFLE CLEAR OPAL FINGER BOWL.................	8.50
PRESSED GLASS WAFFLE COMPOTE................................	9.75
PRESSED GLASS WAFFLE COVERED BUTTER DISH,FLINT..............	22.00
PRESSED GLASS WAFFLE SWEET MEAT BOWL & COVER,FOOTED,FLINT...	40.00
PRESSED GLASS WAFFLE THUMBPRINT BAR BOTTLE,FLINT............	20.00
PRESSED GLASS WAFFLE WHITE OPALESCENT CREAMER...............	4.00
PRESSED GLASS WAHOO GOBLET..................................	4.50
PRESSED GLASS WASHBOARD BOWL,OVAL...........................	2.50
PRESSED GLASS WASHBOARD PLATE,10 IN.........................	5.00
PRESSED GLASS WASHBOARD WATER SET TRAY......................	7.50
PRESSED GLASS WASHINGTON CENTENNIAL BUTTERMILK GOBLET.......	8.50
PRESSED GLASS WASHINGTON MASTER SALT,FLINT..................	18.50
PRESSED GLASS WASHINGTON SALT...............................	9.50
PRESSED GLASS WEDDING RING GOBLET,BELLTONE,FLINT............	15.00
PRESSED GLASS WESTMORLAND WATER CARAFE......................	12.50
PRESSED GLASS WESTWARD HO BUTTER,COVERED....................	65.00
PRESSED GLASS WESTWARD HO CELERY VASE.......................	60.00
PRESSED GLASS WESTWARD HO COMPOTE,COVERED,9 IN..............	125.00

```
PRESSED GLASS WESTWARD HO COMPOTE,COVERED,INDIAN FINIAL.....   40.00
PRESSED GLASS WESTWARD HO COMPOTE,OPEN,9 IN.................   65.00
PRESSED GLASS WESTWARD HO CREAMER
  45.00  TO.................................................   58.00
PRESSED GLASS WESTWARD HO FROSTED SUGAR,OPEN................   25.00
PRESSED GLASS WESTWARD HO GOBLET...........................   25.00
PRESSED GLASS WESTWARD HO SAUCE DISH.......................   18.50
PRESSED GLASS WESTWARD HO SPOONER
  35.00  TO.................................................   50.00
PRESSED GLASS WHEAT & BARLEY AMBER MUG.....................   12.50
PRESSED GLASS WHEAT & BARLEY BLUE SALT.....................   10.50
PRESSED GLASS WHEAT AND BARLEY CLEAR CREAMER AND SUGAR BOWL.  25.00
PRESSED GLASS WHEAT & BARLEY COMPOTE,OPEN..................   14.00
PRESSED GLASS WHEAT & BARLEY CREAMER.......................    8.00
PRESSED GLASS WHEAT & BARLEY GOBLET........................    8.50
PRESSED GLASS WHEAT & BARLEY SPOONER.......................   15.00
PRESSED GLASS WHEAT & BARLEY SUGAR,COVERED.................   14.50
PRESSED GLASS WHEAT & BARLEY TUMBLER.......................   11.00
PRESSED GLASS WHEAT BREAD PLATE,GIVE US THIS DAY...........   12.50
PRESSED GLASS WHEAT CLEAR WATER PITCHER....................   17.50
PRESSED GLASS WHEAT SHEAF GOBLET...........................    8.00
PRESSED GLASS WHEAT SHEAF WATER PITCHER....................   14.50
PRESSED GLASS WHITE CREAMER,2 PANELS OF FLOWERS IN BROWN....   2.75
PRESSED GLASS WILD CHERRY SUGAR,OPEN.......................    6.50
PRESSED GLASS WILD ROSE STIPPLED CLEAR BUTTER,COVERED,CHILDS  15.00
PRESSED GLASS WILD FLOWER AMBER DISH,CUT CORNERS...........   17.00
PRESSED GLASS WILDFLOWER AMBER PLATE,10 IN. SQUARE.........   16.50
PRESSED GLASS WILDFLOWER AMBER TRAY,10 IN..................   22.00
PRESSED GLASS WILDFLOWER APPLE GREEN GOBLET................   14.00
PRESSED GLASS WILDFLOWER BLUE 6 IN. COMPOTE................   25.00
PRESSED GLASS WILDFLOWER BLUE BUTTER,COVERED...............   37.00
PRESSED GLASS WILDFLOWER BLUE CREAMER......................   25.00
PRESSED GLASS WILDFLOWER BLUE FOOTED ROUND SAUCE,SET OF 6...  45.00
PRESSED GLASS WILDFLOWER BLUE GOBLET,FOOTED PAIR...........   19.00
PRESSED GLASS WILDFLOWER BLUE SAUCE,FOOTED.................    7.50
PRESSED GLASS WILDFLOWER BLUE SAUCE DISH,FLAT..............   22.00
PRESSED GLASS WILDFLOWER BLUE SPOONER......................   20.00
PRESSED GLASS WILDFLOWER BLUE SUGAR,COVERED................   30.00
PRESSED GLASS WILDFLOWER BLUE TRAY 11 IN. X 8 IN...........   35.00
PRESSED GLASS WILDFLOWER BLUE TUMBLER......................   19.00
PRESSED GLASS WILDFLOWER BLUE WATER TRAY...................   38.00
PRESSED GLASS WILDFLOWER BUTTER,7 IN.......................   15.00
PRESSED GLASS WILDFLOWER CLEAR CAKE BASKET WITH METAL HANDLE  32.50
PRESSED GLASS WILDFLOWER CLEAR CAKESTAND...................   20.00
PRESSED GLASS WILDFLOWER CLEAR PLATE.......................   10.00
PRESSED GLASS WILDFLOWER CLEAR TUMBLER.....................   12.50
PRESSED GLASS WILDFLOWER CLEAR WATER PITCHER...............   15.00
PRESSED GLASS WILDFLOWER CREAMER
  11.00  TO.................................................   15.00
PRESSED GLASS WILDFLOWER GOBLET............................    8.00
PRESSED GLASS WILDFLOWER GREEN PLATE,10 IN.................   16.50
PRESSED GLASS WILDFLOWER PICKLE............................    6.00
PRESSED GLASS WILDFLOWER PITCHER...........................   12.50
PRESSED GLASS WILDFLOWER SPOONER...........................   12.00
PRESSED GLASS WILDFLOWER SUGAR.............................   16.00
PRESSED GLASS WILDFLOWER SUGAR,OPEN........................   10.00
PRESSED GLASS WILD FLOWER SUGAR,COVERED....................   20.00
PRESSED GLASS WILLOW OAK AMBER GOBLET
  13.00  TO.................................................   21.50
PRESSED GLASS WILLOW OAK BUTTER............................    7.00
PRESSED GLASS WILLOW OAK BUTTER,COVERED....................   22.50
PRESSED GLASS WILLOW OAK COMPOTE,8 IN......................   20.00
PRESSED GLASS WILLOW OAK COMPOTE,OPEN......................    9.50
PRESSED GLASS WINDFLOWER COMPOTE,8 IN.,LOW,OPEN............    3.00
PRESSED GLASS WINDFLOWER GOBLET............................   10.00
```

```
PRESSED GLASS WINDFLOWER NAPPY,HANDLED....................... 14.00
PRESSED GLASS WINDFLOWER SPOONER.............................  7.50
PRESSED GLASS WINDFLOWER  TRAY,GREEN CURVED EDGE............. 18.50
PRESSED GLASS WINDFLOWER WINE................................ 17.50
PRESSED GLASS WINDMILL PLATE................................. 10.00
PRESSED GLASS WINGED SCROLL BUTTER,SUGAR & SPOONER,COVERED.. 175.00
PRESSED GLASS WISCONSIN JELLY COMPOTE........................ 10.00
PRESSED GLASS WISCONSIN MILK PITCHER......................... 17.50
PRESSED GLASS WITCHS HEAD TOOTHPICK HOLDER...................  6.50
PRESSED GLASS YELLOW CANDY COMPOTE...........................  8.50
PRESSED GLASS YOKE BAND GOBLET...............................  6.50
PRESSED GLASS YOKED LOOP GOBLET,FLINT........................ 10.00
PRESSED GLASS YORK COLONIAL GOBLET,FLINT..................... 18.50
PRESSED GLASS ZIPPER CELERY VASE.............................  7.50
PRESSED GLASS ZIPPER CREAMER
  6.00    TO.................................................  7.50
PRESSED GLASS ZIPPER MILK PITCHER............................  9.50
PRESSED GLASS ZIPPER PANELLED SUGAR SHAKER,..................  5.50
PRESSED GLASS ZIPPERED BLOCK CELERY..........................  6.50
PRESSED GLASS ZODIAC PLATE,14 IN............................ 30.00
PRESSED GLASS,  ALE GLASS,SET OF 6,DATED 1886............... 30.00
PRESSED GLASS,  BABY DISH,3 BEARS & VERSES IN CENTER,SIDE
  ANIMALS................................................... 10.00
PRESSED GLASS,  BANANA DISH..................................  8.00
PRESSED GLASS,  BANANA DISH,HALF INCH RIDGES FLANGE......... 22.50
PRESSED GLASS,  BASKET,BLUE & WHITE LINING,WISHBONE HANDLE.. 29.00
PRESSED GLASS,  BASKET,CLEAR,SECTIONS TO HOLD SALT & PEPPER.  2.50
PRESSED GLASS,  BASKET,RIBBED SWIRLED BODY,................. 58.00
PRESSED GLASS,  BERRY BOWL,OVAL,HANDLE ON EACH END..........  8.50
PRESSED GLASS,  BIRD PLATE,SCALLOPED GOLD EDGE,10 IN.
  DIAMETER.................................................. 15.00
PRESSED GLASS,  BOTTLE,PERFUME,CLEAR WITH STERLING OVERLAY.. 15.00
PRESSED GLASS,  BOWL,9 IN...................................  5.00
PRESSED GLASS,  BOWL,COMMEMORATIVE,QUEEN VICTORIA DATED 1887 15.00
PRESSED GLASS,  BOWL,HINGED LID.............................  6.00
PRESSED GLASS,  BOWL,PUNCH,CLEAR,CHILDS,PEDESTAL BASE & 4
  CUPS...................................................... 22.00
PRESSED GLASS,  BOWL,SIGNED IMPERIAL MARK................... 20.00
PRESSED GLASS,  BOX,POWDER,FIGURE LADY,HANDPAINTED VIOLIN...  5.50
PRESSED GLASS,  BREAD PLATE,3 PRESIDENTS.................... 19.00
PRESSED GLASS,  BREAD PLATE,10 IN.,OPEN HANDLED,GIVE US THIS
  DAY....................................................... 10.00
PRESSED GLASS,  BREAD PLATE,CENTENNIAL,GIVE US THIS DAY..... 18.00
PRESSED GLASS,  BREAD PLATE,CONTINENTAL CONGRESS,OLD WHITE
  HOUSE..................................................... 30.00
PRESSED GLASS,  BREAD PLATE,CONTINENTAL CENTENNIAL MARKED... 23.00
PRESSED GLASS,  BREAD PLATE,FAITH,HOPE & CHARITY............ 16.00
PRESSED GLASS,  BREAD PLATE,GIVE US THIS DAY,10 IN.......... 16.00
PRESSED GLASS,  BREAD PLATE,HEROES OF BUNKER HILL........... 13.50
PRESSED GLASS,  BREAD PLATE,IT IS GODS WAY,HIS WILL BE DONE.  7.50
PRESSED GLASS,  BREAD PLATE,JENNY LIND...................... 28.50
PRESSED GLASS,  BREAD PLATE,MC KINLEY GODS WILL BE DONE..... 10.00
PRESSED GLASS,  BREAD PLATE,RAILROAD TRAIN................. 30.00
PRESSED GLASS,  BRIDES BASKET,BLUE & OPALESCENT CROSSBARS... 75.00
PRESSED GLASS,  BUTTER DISH WITH LID,CHILDS.................  5.00
PRESSED GLASS,  BUTTER MOLD................................. 15.00
PRESSED GLASS,  CAKE PLATE,10 IN.,WHITE BACKGROUND WITH PINK
  ROSES.....................................................  5.00
PRESSED GLASS,  CAKE PLATE,12 IN.,WHITE & PINK WITH GOLD
  DECORATION................................................ 20.00
PRESSED GLASS,  CAKE PLATE,HANDPAINTED,GOLD EDGE............ 12.00
PRESSED GLASS,  CAKE PLATE,SQUARE,HANDPAINTED ENAMEL ENGLISH
  SCENE.....................................................  7.00
PRESSED GLASS,  CAKE STAND..................................  6.00
PRESSED GLASS,  CANDLE HOLDER,CLEAR CRYSTAL PRISMS ON EACH
```

END.. 32.50
PRESSED GLASS, CANDLEHOLDER,CLEAR,ROUND BASE................. 3.00
PRESSED GLASS, CANDLESTICK,PAIR 7 IN.,PASTELS............... 9.50
PRESSED GLASS, CANDLESTICKS,PAIR,FLINT..................... 30.00
PRESSED GLASS, CANDLESTICKS WITH PEWTER INSERTS,PAIR,CIRCA
1850,FLINT... 35.00
PRESSED GLASS, CANDY MEASURE,MINIATURE BEER-MUG,SET OF 4... 3.50
PRESSED GLASS, CASTOR SET,4 BOTTLE......................... 37.50
PRESSED GLASS, CEREAL BOWL,SIGNED ,BUNNYKINS............... 5.00
PRESSED GLASS, CEREAL BOWL,TOM PIPERS SON.................. 3.00
PRESSED GLASS, CELERY,7 IN. TALL,SCALLOPED RIM,THUMBPRINT
BOTTOM... 4.50
PRESSED GLASS, CELERY VASE,CLEAR,FLINT..................... 40.00
PRESSED GLASS, CELERY VASE ON PEDESTAL,CLEAR,9 IN.......... 8.50
PRESSED GLASS CHILDS CUP RED RIDING HOOD & THE WOLF....... 12.50
PRESSED GLASS, CHOCOLATE POT,GREEN,LILAC,GOLD & WHITE
FLORAL PATTERN... 8.50
PRESSED GLASS, COFFEE & TEA SET,CHILDS..................... 3.00
PRESSED GLASS, COMPOTE,CLEAR,COVERED,7 IN.................. 12.00
PRESSED GLASS, COMPOTE,COVERED,FLINT...................... 25.00
PRESSED GLASS, COMPOTE,OPEN,8 IN. DIAMETER................. 14.00
PRESSED GLASS, COMPOTE,SIGNED ST.LOUIS,4 IN.,PEDESTAL BASE. 55.00
PRESSED GLASS, CORDIAL SET,9 PIECES,GREEN,BLUE & PINK
ENAMEL... 55.00
PRESSED GLASS, CREAM & SUGAR,CRYSTAL STARS ON EACH SIDE.... 7.00
PRESSED GLASS, CREAM PITCHER,LONG HORNED COW WITH FRONT
LEGS DRAWN UP.. 20.00
PRESSED GLASS, CREAMER MARKED POST CEREALS,CLEAR........... 1.00
PRESSED GLASS, CREAMER,PINEAPPLE STEM..................... 16.00
PRESSED GLASS, CREAMER,WASHINGTON CENTENNIAL.............. 25.00
PRESSED GLASS, CRUET WITH BLOWN STOPPER................... 12.50
PRESSED GLASS, CUP & SAUCER,4 FOOTED CUP,CABINET TYPE...... 12.00
PRESSED GLASS, CURTAIN TIEBACK............................ 7.50
PRESSED GLASS, DECANTER,BLOWN WITH STOPPER................ 8.50
PRESSED GLASS, DECANTER,WINE,HANDLED,MATCHING STOPPER...... 8.50
PRESSED GLASS, DIPPER,CUP SIZE WITH WOOD HANDLE DATED
1896,CLEAR... 8.00
PRESSED GLASS, DISH,CLEAR,COVERED,SHAPED LIKE AN IRON,FLINT 8.50
PRESSED GLASS, DISH,CLEAR,MERRY CHRISTMAS,10 IN........... 35.00
PRESSED GLASS, DISH,COVERED,CHICK IN EGG ON SLEIGH......... 25.00
PRESSED GLASS, DISH,POWDER,CLEAR,ROSE FINIAL IN LID........ 5.00
PRESSED GLASS, DISH SIGNED MARIE LOUISE,PORTRAIT CENTER.... 16.50
PRESSED GLASS, DISH,THE QUEENS JUBILEE DATED 1837-1887..... 14.50
PRESSED GLASS, DOG IN HARNESS PULLING CART,CABLE EDGE
BASE,CLEAR... 15.00
PRESSED GLASS, DRESSER TRAY,ROUND,HANDPAINTED PANSIES...... 12.00
PRESSED GLASS, EPERGNE,METAL BASE,SINGLE FLOWER............ 85.00
PRESSED GLASS, EYE-CUP,CLEAR,PANELED STEM,JOHN BULL USA.... 5.00
PRESSED GLASS, FISH PLATE,9 IN.,SCALLOPED FISH WITH 4 GOLD
MEDALLIONS... 17.50
PRESSED GLASS, FISH PLATTER,SCALLOPED EDGE................ 35.00
PRESSED GLASS, FRUIT PLATE,9 IN.,HANDPAINTED.............. 7.50
PRESSED GLASS, FRUIT PLATE,12 IN.,PIERCED FOR HANGING...... 17.00
PRESSED GLASS, FRUIT PLATE,PAIR,9 IN...................... 12.00
PRESSED GLASS, GAME PLATE,SCALLOPED,QUAIL WALKING IN
UNDERGROWTH.. 15.00
PRESSED GLASS, GOBLET,CLEAR,SET OF 6,DOUBLE ROW OF
ETCHING,FLINT.. 36.00
PRESSED GLASS, GOBLET,KNOB STEM,FLINT..................... 20.00
PRESSED GLASS, GOBLET,PHILADELPHIA CENTENNIAL............. 12.50
PRESSED GLASS, HAIR RECEIVER,CLEAR,SILVER TOP,MARKED HAIR
TIDY... 10.00
PRESSED GLASS, HANGING PLATE,THE LAST SUPPER.............. 6.00
PRESSED GLASS, HAT,4 IN.,FEDORA,SOUVENIR ADAMS,NEW YORK.... 5.50
PRESSED GLASS, HAT,CLEAR.................................. 20.00

PRESSED GLASS,	HAT,TOP,CLEAR..................................	1.00
PRESSED GLASS,	HATPIN HOLDER,CORSET SHAPE,HANDPAINTED	
FLOWERS..		6.50
PRESSED GLASS,	HATPIN HOLDER,SWIRL SHAPE WITH HANDPAINTED	
FLOWERS..		4.50
PRESSED GLASS,	JAR,POWDER,CLEAR,ELEPHANT ON TOP.............	4.75
PRESSED GLASS,	KNIFE REST,4 IN...............................	5.50
PRESSED GLASS,	KNIFE REST,KNOB ENDS.........................	5.00
PRESSED GLASS,	KNIFE REST,PAIR...............................	15.00
PRESSED GLASS,	LADLE,PUNCH,2 POURING SPOUTS,FLINT,CLEAR....	12.00
PRESSED GLASS,	LAMP,CLEAR,SPIRIT BURNER,WICK & GLASS COVER.	5.00
PRESSED GLASS,	MASTER SALT,OVAL,RIBBED BOTTOM...............	5.00
PRESSED GLASS,	MATCH HOLDER,SUITCASE SHAPE..................	5.00
PRESSED GLASS,	MUFFINEER,BRASS TOP..........................	12.50
PRESSED GLASS,	MUG,2 IN.,CATS FIGHTING ON FENCE.............	10.00
PRESSED GLASS,	MUG,4 IN. TALL,MARKED NELLIE,ATLANTIC CITY	
1906...		11.00
PRESSED GLASS,	MUG,CLEAR,CHILDS,PUPPY ON EACH SIDE,3 IN....	15.00
PRESSED GLASS,	MUG,GOLD EAGLE ON SIDE,GOLD TRIM.............	10.00
PRESSED GLASS,	MUSTARD POT,CLEAR,SQUARE,HINGED COVER........	8.50
PRESSED GLASS,	NAPKIN PLATE,WHITE BACKGROUND,GOLD RIM.......	7.00
PRESSED GLASS,	OPAL GREEN TOKYO CREAMER.....................	17.50
PRESSED GLASS,	OPEN SALT....................................	5.00
PRESSED GLASS,	OWL FIGURE,CLEAR,4 IN........................	5.00
PRESSED GLASS,	OYSTER PLATE,SEPARATE GLASS INSERTS FOR	
SAUCE..		5.00
PRESSED GLASS,	PICKLE CASTOR INSERT WITH SILVER PLATE	
HOLDER & TONGS...		35.00
PRESSED GLASS,	PITCHER,5 IN. HIGH,SCALLOPED TOP.............	8.50
PRESSED GLASS,	PITCHER,CLEAR,SHAPE OF WOMAN.................	10.00
PRESSED GLASS,	PITCHER,EMERALD GREEN,ENAMELED DECORATION...	18.00
PRESSED GLASS,	PITCHER,NURSERY RHYME........................	30.00
PRESSED GLASS,	PITCHER,OVERSHOT,BULBOUS,REEDED HANDLE.......	18.00
PRESSED GLASS,	PITCHER,SCALLOPED GOLD RIM AT TOP,FLORAL....	42.00
PRESSED GLASS,	PITCHER,SYRUP,CLEAR,ROUGH PONTIL.............	12.00
PRESSED GLASS,	PITCHER,WATER,CLEAR,SILVER PLATE RIM & SPOUT	15.00
PRESSED GLASS,	PLATE,5 IN.,CHILD WITH DOG...................	12.50
PRESSED GLASS,	PLATE,7 IN. SQUARE...........................	6.50
PRESSED GLASS,	PLATE,BABYS..................................	10.00
PRESSED GLASS,	PLATE,BREAD,CLEAR,GENERAL GRANT..............	17.50
PRESSED GLASS,	PLATE,CLEAR,SHIP RAISED IN CENTER............	6.50
PRESSED GLASS,	PLATE,COLUMBUS MEMORIAL......................	12.00
PRESSED GLASS,	PLATE,COMMEMORATION POPE LEO XII,PAPAL	
INSIGNIA...		20.00
PRESSED GLASS,	PLATE,COMMODORE MAC DONOUGHS VICTORY.........	65.00
PRESSED GLASS,	PLATE,DIAMOND & SHELL BORDER,7 IN............	8.75
PRESSED GLASS,	PLATE,GENERAL ULYSSES S. GRANT...............	15.50
PRESSED GLASS,	PLATE,HANDPAINTED,7 IN.......................	5.00
PRESSED GLASS,	PLATE,HANDPAINTED ROSES,SIGNED MARTIN........	12.00
PRESSED GLASS,	PLATE,LAST SUPPER............................	7.50
PRESSED GLASS,	PLATE,QUEEN VICTORIA 50TH JUBILEE 1887.......	25.00
PRESSED GLASS,	PLATE,SCENIC,NIAGARA FALLS,8 IN..............	11.00
PRESSED GLASS,	PLATE,SIGNED SARAH & CHRISTMAS 1909,A K D	
FRANCE...		16.00
PRESSED GLASS,	PLATE,ST.LOUIS EXPOSITION....................	8.00
PRESSED GLASS,	PLATE,THE WORLDS FAIR ST.LOUIS 1904..........	5.00
PRESSED GLASS,	PLATE,U S GRANT,10 IN.,LET US HAVE PEACE....	18.50
PRESSED GLASS,	PLATE,U.S.GRANT,LET US HAVE PEACE,PORTRAIT	
CENTER...		12.50
PRESSED GLASS,	PLATE,VIEW OF BOSTON.........................	7.00
PRESSED GLASS,	PLATTER,RAILROAD TRAIN.......................	20.00
PRESSED GLASS,	PUNCH BOWL,12 CUPS,LADLE,STAND...............	150.00
PRESSED GLASS,	PUNCH BOWL SET MARKED IG,16 PIECES...........	22.50
PRESSED GLASS,	PUNCH BOWL WITH 4 CUPS,MINIATURE,CHILDS.....	14.50
PRESSED GLASS,	PUNCH CUP,SET OF 6 MINIATURE.................	18.00

PRESSED GLASS,	RELISH,BOAT SHAPED	6.50
PRESSED GLASS,	RING TREE,CLEAR,TRIANGULAR	3.00
PRESSED GLASS,	RING TREE,GREEN ENAMELED BASE,3 IN. CENTER POST	12.00
PRESSED GLASS,	ROSE BOWL	20.00
PRESSED GLASS,	ROSE BOWL,PINK,PORTRAIT CENTER,GOLD ENAMEL	55.00
PRESSED GLASS,	ROSE BOWL,SCALLOPED PUSHED IN TOP	79.50
PRESSED GLASS,	SALAD DISH,2 PART,RED LOBSTER HANDLE,GOLD DECOR.	30.00
PRESSED GLASS,	SALT & PEPPER,STERLING LIDS	3.50
PRESSED GLASS,	SALT SHAKER,BOOT,PEWTER TOP	6.00
PRESSED GLASS,	SALT SHAKER,CLEAR,LIGHTHOUSE WITH TOP	10.00
PRESSED GLASS,	SAUCE,SET OF 5 BELL FLARED	25.00
PRESSED GLASS,	SERVING PLATE,HANDPAINTED,PIERCED GOLD RIM	7.50
PRESSED GLASS,	SLIPPER,COLOURED,2	13.00
PRESSED GLASS,	SLIPPER,HIGH HEEL	9.50
PRESSED GLASS,	SNUFF BOTTLE,PAINTED INSIDE,ATTACHED IVORY SPOON	35.00
PRESSED GLASS,	SPOONER	6.50
PRESSED GLASS,	SPOONER,NURSERY RHYME	15.00
PRESSED GLASS,	STAND,WEDDING CAKE,CLEAR	37.50
PRESSED GLASS,	SUGAR & CREAMER DATED 1954,SIGNED,HANDPAINTED	7.50
PRESSED GLASS,	SUGAR & CREAMER MARKED PRESS-CUT	8.50
PRESSED GLASS,	SUGAR,FOOTED,PINK,SCALLOPED EDGE	2.50
PRESSED GLASS,	SUGAR SHAKER,HOOSIER ON COVERED TIN TOP	6.00
PRESSED GLASS,	SUGAR,SHIELD SHAPED	22.50
PRESSED GLASS,	SWAN ON NEST,7 IN.,CLEAR	25.00
PRESSED GLASS,	SYRUP,6 IN.	7.50
PRESSED GLASS,	SYRUP PITCHER,TIN POURING TOP,ROUGH PONTIL	15.00
PRESSED GLASS,	TEA SET,CHILDS 8 PIECE,MOTHER HUBBARD AT CUPBOARD	18.50
PRESSED GLASS,	TEA STRAINER,FLORAL DECOR,CURVED HANDLE,6 IN.	6.00
PRESSED GLASS,	TOBY JUG,COACHMAN	25.00
PRESSED GLASS,	TOBY PITCHER,FULL SQUAT FIGURE,SATIN FINISH IN FACE.	8.50
PRESSED GLASS,	TOOTHPICK,3 HANDLES.	12.00
PRESSED GLASS,	TOOTHPICK,CLEAR,3-HANDLED,GOLD TRIM	17.50
PRESSED GLASS,	TOOTHPICK,GREEN	13.00
PRESSED GLASS,	TOOTHPICK HOLDER,3 HANDLES	15.00
PRESSED GLASS,	TOOTHPICK HOLDER,AMETHYST FLEUR DE LIS BASE.	15.00
PRESSED GLASS,	TOOTHPICK HOLDER,EMERALD FLEUR DE LIS BASE	22.50
PRESSED GLASS,	TOOTHPICK HOLDER,FANCY VASE SHAPED	5.00
PRESSED GLASS,	TOOTHPICK HOLDER,GREEN WITH GOLD DESIGN	7.00
PRESSED GLASS,	TOOTHPICK HOLDER SIGNED ROCKWELL,SILVER TRIM,BLUE.	14.00
PRESSED GLASS,	TOOTHPICK HOLDER,VASE SHAPED	5.50
PRESSED GLASS,	TOOTHPICK,SQUARE	6.50
PRESSED GLASS,	TOOTHPICK WITH KEWPIE STANDING BESIDE,FLINT,CLEAR.	6.50
PRESSED GLASS,	TRAY,BREAD,CLEAR,GIVE US THIS DAY OUR DAILY BREAD.	8.00
PRESSED GLASS,	TRAY,BREAD,THREE GRACES,FAITH,HOPE & CHARITY	21.00
PRESSED GLASS,	TRAY,REVERSE PAINT	10.00
PRESSED GLASS,	TUMBLER,CLEAR,HEAVILY ENAMELLED WITH FLOWERS	5.00
PRESSED GLASS,	TUMBLER,GARFIELD PORTRAIT BASE	9.00
PRESSED GLASS,	TUMBLER,SET OF 6 APPLE GREEN ENAMELED	25.00
PRESSED GLASS,	TUMBLE-UP,TANKARD SHAPE,AMETHYST CLEAR APPLIED HANDLE	55.00
PRESSED GLASS,	VASE,AMPHORA SHAPE,FREE BLOWN IN DOUBLE GATHER	62.50
PRESSED GLASS,	VASE,HANDPAINTED,CLEAR	9.00
PRESSED GLASS,	VASE,HANDPAINTED PINK ROSES,GOLD HANDLES,8 IN.	15.00

```
PRESSED GLASS,  VASE,LOVING CUP,2 HANDLES,5 IN. HIGH........      5.00
PRESSED GLASS,  WATER PITCHER,OPALESCENT CRIMPED TOP........     18.00
PRINTING PRESS,SMALL,CAST IRON,HAND OPERATED W/ 14 DRAWER
  CASE OF TYPE..................................................     40.00
    PURPLE SLAG, SEE SLAG.......................................

QUARTZ,CARVED WISE OLD OWL,PINK,3 IN. TALL INCLUDING STAND..     48.00
```

QUEEN'S ROSE is a Gaudy Dutch pottery design made in England and exported
to the United States about 1810 to 1820.

```
QUEENS ROSE HANDLELESS CUP................................     40.00
QUEENS ROSE HANDLELESS CUP & SAUCER,......................     75.00
```

QUEZAL GLASS was made from 1901 to 1920 by Martin Bach, Sr. He made
iridescent glass of the same type as Tiffany.

```
QUEZAL CANDLESTICK IN GOLD IRIDESCENT SIGNED..............     12.50
QUEZAL CUP & SAUCER WITH BLUE IRIDESCENCE SIGNED..........    245.00
QUEZAL ELECTRIC SHADES PAIR GOLD RIBBED...................     37.50
QUEZAL GAS SHADE FEATHER..................................     20.00
QUEZAL GAS SHADE, GOLD....................................     18.00
QUEZAL GAS SHADE, GOLD FEATHER PATTERN ON WHITE SIGNED....     22.50
QUEZAL GAS SHADE,GOLD WITH PEARLY WHITE CASTING, SIGNED...     20.00
QUEZAL GAS SHADE SIGNED GOLD..............................     17.00
QUEZAL GAS SHADE, SIGNED GOLD LEAVES ON IRIDIZED WHITE PEARL   28.00
QUEZAL GAS SHADES, GOLD CALCITE OUTSIDE, WHITE CASTING
  INSIDE SIGNED PAIR......................................     29.00
QUEZAL GAS SHADES ORANGE..................................     25.00
QUEZAL GAS SHADES,PAIR 5 IN. GOLD IRIDESCENT,RIBBED.......     35.00
QUEZAL GAS SHADES SET OF 3 SIGNED GOLD RIBBED.............     51.00
QUEZAL GAS SHADES SIGNED 2 YELLOW.........................    120.00
QUEZAL GAS SHADES,SIGNED DECORATED.PR.....................     40.00
QUEZAL SALT,GOLD & BLUE HIGHLIGHTS,3 IN. ACROSS TOP.......     76.50
QUEZAL SALT RIBBED GOLD IRIDESCENCE SIGNED................     80.00
QUEZAL TOOTHPICK HOLDER,GREEN BLUE & PURPLE SIGNED........    210.00
QUEZAL VASE, GOLD IRIDESCENT SIGNED.......................     95.00
QUEZAL VASE, 8 IN.H.,SILVER OVERLAY SIGNED................    235.00
QUEZAL VASES PAIR, 13 IN. HIGH VARIEGATED COLOUR..........    200.00
QUEZAL VASE,PURPLE & GOLD WITH SILVER OVERLAY,6 IN. SIGNED.   255.00
QUEZAL VASE, WHITE & BROWN ON AMBER GLASS SIGNED & NUMBERED.   90.00
    QUILTS, SEE LINEN......................................
```

QUIMPER POTTERY was made in Finistère, France, after 1900. Most of the
pieces found today were made during the twentieth century. A Quimper factory
has worked in France since the eighteenth century.

```
QUIMPER 6 IN. SCALLOPED EDGE PLATE,BLUE TRIM,WOMAN..........      9.00
QUIMPER 7 IN. PLATE,PAIR,BLUE & GRAY GARLAND & FLORAL.......     10.00
QUIMPER 8 IN. PITCHER WITH MAN.............................     25.00
QUIMPER 8 YELLOW TUMBLERS,4 LADIES & 4 MEN.................     40.00
QUIMPER BASKET,7 IN........................................      8.00
QUIMPER CUP & SAUCER,3 BREAD & BUTTERS.....................     10.00
QUIMPER DUCK INKWELL.......................................     10.00
QUIMPER DUTCH SHOE.........................................     22.00
QUIMPER INKWELL............................................     12.50
QUIMPER MARKED 2 HANDLED COVERED SUGAR.....................     16.00
QUIMPER PAIR SIGNED YELLOW & SCALLOPED 7 IN. PLATES,MALE &
  FEMALE...................................................     15.00
QUIMPER PITCHER,6 IN.......................................      8.00
QUIMPER SAUCER,FLOWER DESIGN...............................      2.50
QUIMPER SIGNED 2 HANDLED BOWL..............................      6.50
QUIMPER SIGNED 4 IN. PITCHER...............................     10.50
QUIMPER SIGNED FRANCE 8 IN. PLATE,TAN,BLUE,GREEN & RED......     10.00
QUIMPER SIGNED PARI 5 IN. PLATES,YELLOW GROUND,MAN & WOMAN..     10.00
QUIMPER SIGNED SLIPPER 6 IN. LONG..........................     12.00
QUIMPER SIGNED STATUE, 6IN. H..............................     30.00
QUIMPER SIGNED TEAPOT,BLACK WITH YELLOW DECOR..............      7.50
```

```
QUIMPER SQUARE 5 IN. PLAQUE,COLOURED BIRD & FLORAL..........    6.50
QUIMPER TUMBLER...............................................   10.00

R S GERMANY BASKET,OBLONG,HANDPAINTED,RED MARK...............   17.50
R S GERMANY BOTTLE,DRESSER,HANDPAINTED SUNFLOWERS & GREEN
  LEAVES.....................................................    8.50
R.S.GERMANY BOWL & PLATE,5IN.................................   28.00
R S GERMANY BOWL,4 EASTER LILIES INSIDE,WHITE ON BEIGE
  OUTSIDE....................................................   35.00
R S GERMANY BOWL,4 IN.,FOOTED,CUT OUTS AROUND SCALLOPED TOP.   28.00
R S GERMANY BOWL,9 IN.,FLORAL,RED MARK.......................   35.00
R S GERMANY BOWL,10 IN.,GOLD WHITE BORDER,TEA ROSES,GREEN
  MARK.......................................................   22.50
R S GERMANY BOWL,BERRY,YELLOW WITH WHITE FLOWERS,BLUE MARK..   12.50
R S GERMANY BOWL,CALLA LILIES ON GREEN.......................    6.50
R S GERMANY BOWL,FLOWER,DOUBLE TIERED REMOVABLE TOP..........   17.00
R S GERMANY BOWL,FOOTED,FLORAL DECORATED.....................    8.50
R S GERMANY BOWL,FOOTED,OPEN HANDLES,6 DISHES,BLUE MARK......   28.00
R S GERMANY BOWL,FOOTED,RED MARK.............................   26.00
R S GERMANY BOWL,GREEN WITH OPAL FLUTED EDGE,JEWEL HEART....   11.00
R S GERMANY BOWL,POPPY,9 IN..................................   17.50
R S GERMANY BOX,PIN,OVAL,GREEN WITH PINK ROSE................    6.00
R S GERMANY BOX,TALC,LILIES OF THE VALLEY,SHAKER TYPE........   12.50
R S GERMANY CAKE SET,7 PIECE,SWEET PEAS......................   30.00
R S GERMANY CHOCOLATE CUPS & SAUCERS,4,WHITE & YELLOW
  ROSES,6 PLATES............................................   60.00
R S GERMANY CHOCOLATE CUP & SAUCER,ROSES.....................   10.00
R S GERMANY CHOCOLATE POT,BLUE STAR MARK,HANDPAINTED
  VIOLETS,GOLD TRIM..........................................   25.00
R S GERMANY CHOCOLATE POT,FLORAL WITH GOLD & ROCCO EDGE.....   35.00
R S GERMANY CHOCOLATE POT,MINIATURE,WHITE BACKGROUND,PINK
  ROSES......................................................   12.00
R S GERMANY CHOCOLATE POT,PINK ROSES,BROWN-GREEN.............   37.50
R S GERMANY CHOCOLATE POT,ROSES..............................   18.00
R S GERMANY CHOCOLATE POT,SATIN FINISH,HANDPAINTED PINK
  ROSES......................................................   20.00
R S GERMANY CHOCOLATE SET,POT WITH 6 CUPS,SATIN FINISH......   60.00
R S GERMANY CHOCOLATE SET,7 PIECES,BEIGE GREEN BACKGROUND...   75.00
R S GERMANY COMPOTE,8 IN.,ROSES..............................   12.50
R S GERMANY COMPOTE,FOOTED...................................   10.00
R S GERMANY CREAMER..........................................    5.00
R S GERMANY CREAM & SUGAR,PALE ROSES SHADING TO PALE GREEN..   14.00
R S GERMANY CREAMER & 2 HANDLED COVERED SUGAR,GREEN & GOLD,.   25.00
R S GERMANY CREAMER & SUGAR,FLORAL PATTERN,RED MARK..........   13.00
R S GERMANY CREAMER & SUGAR,HANDPAINTED FLOWERS,BLACK MARK..   22.50
R S GERMANY CREAMER,COVERED,ROSES,YELLOW.....................    6.00
R S GERMANY CREAMER,ROSES....................................    3.50
R S GERMANY CUP & SAUCER,DEMITASSE...........................    7.50
R S GERMANY CUP & SAUCER,RED MARK............................   12.50
R S GERMANY CUP & SAUCER,YELLOW DAFFODILS....................   10.00
R S GERMANY DESSERT SET,TRAY WITH INSERT FOR CUP,LUSTER
  FINISH.....................................................   10.00
R S GERMANY DISH,BERRY,SET OF 6,BLUE WREATH & STAR..........   20.00
R S GERMANY DISH,BERRY,SET OF 6,ROSES ON SATINY
  BACKGROUND,BLUE MARK.......................................   20.00
R S GERMANY DISH,BONE,ROSES,FAN SHAPED,6 IN..................    4.50
R S GERMANY DISH,CANDY,OBLONG,HANDPAINTED ROSES,WISHBONE
  HANDLED....................................................    7.00
R S GERMANY DISH,CANDY,SCENIC,SHEPHERD & SHEEP,BEIGE & GOLD.   30.00
R S GERMANY DISH,LOBSTER,DIVIDED.............................   30.00
R S GERMANY DISH,PICKLE,GREEN WITH POPPIES...................    7.50
R S GERMANY DISH,SQUARE,PANSIES ON GREEN,GOLD................    8.00
R S GERMANY HAIR RECEIVER & POWDER BOX,POPPIES...............   14.00
R S GERMANY HAIR RECEIVER,BLUE FLOWERS,BLACK MARK............   11.00
R S GERMANY HAIR RECEIVER,HANDPAINTED,GREEN STAR............   16.00
```

```
R S GERMANY HAIR RECEIVER,IVORY TEAROSES,GREEN WREATH MARK..      7.50
R.S.GERMANY HAIR RECEIVER,SIGNED,OCTAGON WITH 8 FEET........      7.75
R S GERMANY HAIR RECEIVER,YELLOW & WHITE,LILY ON GREEN......      8.50
R S GERMANY HAT PIN HOLDER...............................      9.50
R S GERMANY HAT PIN HOLDER,4 IN. TALL,FLORALS.............     12.50
R S GERMANY HATPIN HOLDER,CALLA LILY DECOR,GREEN MARK......      8.50
R S GERMANY HATPIN HOLDER,FLORAL DECOR....................     16.50
R S GERMANY HATPIN HOLDER,FORGET ME NOT...................     10.00
R S GERMANY HAT PIN HOLDER,GREEN,BLUE,LILY & LEAVES........     14.50
R S GERMANY HATPIN HOLDER,HANDPAINTED.....................     10.00
R S GERMANY HAT PIN HOLDER,LILY ON CREAM..................     12.50
R S GERMANY HATPIN HOLDER,PINK & WHITE ROSES..............     12.00
R S GERMANY HATPIN HOLDER,ROSES, FOOTED...................     37.00
R S GERMANY HATPIN HOLDER WITH FLORAL SPRAYS,GOLD TRIM......     17.50
R S GERMANY HAT PIN HOLDER,WHITE FLORAL ON GREEN..........     15.00
R S GERMANY HAT PIN HOLDER,WHITE LILIES...................     10.00
R S GERMANY HAT PIN HOLDER,WHITE LILY ON CREAM-BEIGE-GREEN
  GROUND..................................................     15.00
R S GERMANY HAT PIN HOLDER,WHITE WITH PINK ROSES..........     15.00
R S GERMANY ICE CREAM SET,GOLD SCALLOPED EDGES,PINK ROSES...     35.00
R S GERMANY JAR,COOKIE,2 HANDLED,CALLA LILIES ON GREEN,RED
  MARK...................................................     20.50
R S GERMANY JAR,COOKIE,SQUATTY SHAPE WITH YELLOW ROSES......     21.00
R S GERMANY JAR,CRACKER,BEIGE & GREEN.....................     12.50
R S GERMANY JAR,CRACKER,GREEN WITH HYDRANGEA DECOR.........     22.50
R S GERMANY JAR,POWDER,COVERED............................     12.00
R S GERMANY JAR,POWDER,ROUND,GREEN WITH PINK ROSE.........      7.75
R S GERMANY JUG,TOBY,SILVER LUSTER,BLUE MARK..............     65.00
R S GERMANY MUSTARD,BLACK MARK...........................     10.00
R S GERMANY PITCHER,COBALT BLUE DECORATIONS WITH GOLD.......     18.50
R S GERMANY PITCHER,DOGWOOD FLOWERS ON GREEN..............     45.00
R S GERMANY PITCHER,LILY DESIGN..........................     15.00
R S GERMANY PITCHER,TANKARD TYPE,EMBOSSED, BLUE TO
  WHITE,GOLD,FLORAL......................................     28.00
R S GERMANY PLATE,6 IN.,GREEN WITH APPLE BLOSSOMS,ARTIST
  SIGNED.................................................      7.00
R S GERMANY PLATE,6 IN.,ROSES............................      5.00
R S GERMANY PLATE,6 IN.,TULIPS...........................      5.00
R S GERMANY PLATE,8 IN.,3 HANDLED........................      7.50
R S GERMANY PLATE,8 IN.,ROSES............................     10.00
R S GERMANY PLATE,8 IN.,SPRAY OF WHITE TULIPS,GREEN & GOLD.     10.50
R S GERMANY PLATE,AZALEAS & BUDS ON CREAM-BEIGE-YELLOW -PINK
  GROUND.................................................     20.00
R S GERMANY PLATE,CAKE,SLIT HANDLES,WHITE & YELLOW FLOWERS..     13.50
R S GERMANY PLATE,CAKE,WHITE BACKGROUND WITH FLOW BLUE
  COLOURING..............................................     18.00
R S GERMANY PLATE,CHRYSANTHEMUM..........................     10.00
R S GERMANY PLATE,GREEN & WHITE WITH TULIPS...............     25.00
R S GERMANY PLATE,RED MARK...............................     12.00
R S GERMANY PLATE,ROUND,HOLLY PATTERN.....................     22.50
R S GERMANY PLATE,SET OF 4,SCALLOPED,WHITE & TAN,TEA
  ROSES,LUSTER...........................................     20.00
R S GERMANY PLATE,SET OF 8,& 8 SAUCE DISHES,GREEN BACKGROUND    20.00
R S GERMANY PLATE,SET OF 8,HANDPAINTED,ENAMELED SHELLS,BLUE
  MARK...................................................     50.00
R S GERMANY PLATE,TAN & WHITE BACKGROUND..................      1.50
R S GERMANY PLATE,WHITE WITH TAN EDGES,TEAROSES...........     20.00
R S GERMANY RELISH WITH ORANGE POPPIES,OPEN HANDLE,RED MARK.     20.00
R S GERMANY RELISH WITH WHITE ROSES......................     10.00
R S GERMANY ROSEBOWL,BLUE SPANISH LACE,4 IN...............     35.00
R S GERMANY SALT & PEPPER,PAIR,GREEN MARK.................      8.00
R S GERMANY SALT & PEPPER SHAKER,.........................     12.00
R S GERMANY SAUCE,BLUE-GREY WHITE FLOWERS &
  LEAVES,LEMON,BLUE MARK..................................      5.25
R.S.GERMANY SAUCE,TULIPS & GOLD...........................      3.25
```

```
R S GERMANY SHAVING SET,7 PIECES,GOLD EDGED,LEAFY FLOWER
  DECOR.................................................  27.50
R S GERMANY SUGAR & CREAMER,COVERED,MELON SHAPED,GREEN MARK.  18.00
R S GERMANY SUGAR BOWL & CREAMER,COVERED,RIBBED MELON SHAPE.  25.00
R S GERMANY SUGAR BOWL & CREAMER,COVERED,RIBBED MELON
  SHAPE,GREEN TOPS.....................................  25.00
R S GERMANY SUGAR & CREAMER,DOGWOOD.......................  17.50
R S GERMANY SUGAR BOWL & CREAMER,SWEET PEAS,GREEN MARK......  10.00
R S GERMANY SUGAR & CREAMER,TAN WITH WHITE FLOWERS..........  14.00
R S GERMANY SUGAR BOWL,FORGET-ME-NOTS......................   8.00
R S GERMANY SUGAR BOWL,HANDPAINTED PINK & YELLOW ROSES ON
  BLUE.................................................  15.00
R S GERMANY SUGAR BOWL,LILIES............................  12.00
R S GERMANY SUGAR,COVERED................................   2.50
R S GERMANY SUGAR,COVERED,APPLE BLOSSOMS ON BEIGE TO GREEN..  10.00
R S GERMANY SUGAR,COVERED,FLORAL SPRAYS ON WHITE,GOLD TRIM..   8.50
R S GERMANY SUGAR,COVERED,WHITE FLORAL WITH GREEN..........  12.00
R S GERMANY TEA SET,GREEN MARK...........................  50.00
R S GERMANY TOOTHPICK HOLDER,2 HANDLED....................   7.50
R S GERMANY TOOTHPICK HOLDER,2 HANDLES....................   6.00
R S GERMANY TRAY,CELERY,RED ROSE.........................  10.50
R S GERMANY TRAY,OBLONG,SATIN FINISH,GREEN MARK...........  12.00
R S GERMANY TRAY,PIN,LILY SHAPED,........................   7.75
R S GERMANY TRAY,RELISH,12 IN.,OPEN ENDED,GREEN WREATH &
  STAR.................................................  20.00
R S GERMANY VASE,HANDLED,BLUE,GOLD.......................   9.50
R S GERMANY VASES,PAIR,8 IN. HIGH,MOTTLED APRICOT & GOLD....  25.00
R S GERMANY VASE,URN SHAPED,OPEN HANDLED,WHITE WITH SILVER
  OVERLAY..............................................   8.50
R S PRUSSIA BERRY SET,RED ROSES ON TURQUOISE,RED MARK.......  72.50
R S PRUSSIA BOWL,3 FOOTED................................  30.00
R S PRUSSIA BOWL,3-FOOTED,MELON RIBBED,ROSES,..............   7.50
R S PRUSSIA BOWL,5 IN.,ASSORTED FLOWERS,RED MARK...........   9.50
R S PRUSSIA BOWL,9 IN....................................  50.00
R S PRUSSIA BOWL,9 IN.,BLUE BACKGROUND,EMBOSSED WATER
  LILIES,GOLD,.........................................  29.00
R S PRUSSIA BOWL,9 IN.,FLOWER SHAPED,SOFT SATIN BEIGE
  FINISH,WHITE,........................................  75.00
R S PRUSSIA BOWL,9 IN.,ROSE,PINK & WHITE ROSES............  45.00
R S PRUSSIA BOWL,9 IN.,WHITE LILIES,GREEN LEAVES,RED MARK...  44.00
R S PRUSSIA BOWL,9 IN.,WIDE GOLD RIM BAND,WHITE & PINK ROSE
  DECOR................................................  37.50
R S PRUSSIA BOWL,10 IN.,...............................  30.00
R S PRUSSIA BOWL,10 IN.,FLORAL DESIGN,RED MARK.............  32.00
R S PRUSSIA BOWL,10 IN.,GOLD & LIME & ORANGE FLOWERS,RED
  MARK.................................................  55.00
R S PRUSSIA BOWL,10 IN.,IVORY,GREEN,ROSES IN CENTER,RED MARK  47.50
R S PRUSSIA BOWL,10 IN.,LILY OF THE VALLEY,SCALLOPED.......  45.00
R S PRUSSIA BOWL,10 IN.,ORCHIDS,GREEN LANDSCAPE,PORTRAIT OF
  LADY.................................................  85.00
R S PRUSSIA BOWL,10 IN. PINK ROSES,BLUE BACKGROUND,RED MARK.  45.00
R S PRUSSIA BOWL,10 IN.,PINK & WHITE POPPIES,RED MARK.......  52.00
R S PRUSSIA BOWL,10 IN.,RED & GOLD BEADING,FLOWERS.........  50.00
R S PRUSSIA BOWL,10 IN.,RIBBED,PINK ROSES,GREEN & WHITE,RED
  MARK.................................................  52.50
R S PRUSSIA BOWL,10 IN.,SCALLOPED EDGE,PINK & YELLOW,RED
  MARK.................................................  40.00
R S PRUSSIA BOWL,11 IN.,GREENISH BLUE WITH PINK & WHITE,RED
  MARK.................................................  50.00
R S PRUSSIA BOWL 11 IN. POPPIES & DAISIES OVER WATER.......  45.00
R S PRUSSIA BOWL,11 IN.,WHITE BEAD SCALLOPS,FLOWER
  CHAIN,AQUA...........................................  22.50
R S PRUSSIA BOWL,19 IN.,& 5 SAUCES,PINK & YELLOW ROSES,RED
  MARK.................................................  60.00
R S PRUSSIA BOWL,BERRY,11 IN.,SET WITH 5 SAUCE DISHES,WHITE
```

```
    & GOLD.............................................................   75.00
R S PRUSSIA BOWL,BERRY,PINK ROSES.............................   26.50
R S PRUSSIA BOWL,BERRY,SATIN FINISH...........................   52.50
R S PRUSSIA BOWL,CENTER,WHITE WITH LILIES,11 IN.,RED MARK...   27.50
R S PRUSSIA BOWL,EXPANDING FLOWER FORM,FOOTED.................   39.00
R S PRUSSIA BOWL,FLARING EDGE IN TORTOISE & RABBIT STEPS,RED
    MARK..........................................................   58.00
R S PRUSSIA BOWL,FLUTED EDGE WITH PINK FLOWERS................   55.00
R S PRUSSIA BOWL,FOOTED,SCALLOPED,GOLD TRIM,ROSES............   22.00
R S PRUSSIA BOWL,GOLD RIM ON SCALLOPED EDGE,RED MARK.........   37.50
R S PRUSSIA BOWL,GREEN WITH WHITE FLORAL,GOLD TRIM..........   15.00
R S PRUSSIA BOWL,OBLONG,FLORAL,PURPLE BORDER,RED MARK........   45.00
R S PRUSSIA BOWL ON SMALL FEET,LILIES RED MARK...............   28.00
R S PRUSSIA BOWL,OVAL,IVORY,TURQUOISE GROUND,WHITE FLORAL
    WITH GOLD.....................................................   45.00
R S PRUSSIA BOWL,OVAL,PASTEL FLORAL,GREEN MARK...............   30.00
R S PRUSSIA BOWL,PAIR,10 IN.,10 PANELS,5 CHARTREUSE,5
    GREEN,RED MARK................................................  127.50
R S PRUSSIA BOWL,PEACOCKS & MULTI-COLOURED TREES,RED MARK...   48.50
R S PRUSSIA BOWL,PINK FLOWERS,EMBOSSED EDGE,10 IN.,RED MARK.   34.00
R S PRUSSIA BOWL,PINK ROSES...................................   33.00
R S PRUSSIA BOWL,PINK ROSES,10 IN. DIAMETER,RED MARK.......   39.50
R S PRUSSIA BOWL,PINK ROSES WITH BEIGE TONES.................   55.00
R S PRUSSIA BOWL,RAISED GOLD DOTS,MAUVE,PINK ROSES,RED MARK.   49.00
R S PRUSSIA BOWL,RED MARK.....................................   52.00
R S PRUSSIA BOWL,ROSES CENTER,GREEN BORDER,PINK IRIS........   65.00
R S PRUSSIA BOWL,ROSES CENTER,GREEN WITH PINK IRIS AROUND
    EDGE..........................................................   65.00
R S PRUSSIA BOWL,SATIN FINISH,9 IN.,YELLOW WITH PASTEL,RED
    MARK..........................................................   70.00
R S PRUSSIA BOWL,WHITE PEARLIZED,GOLD SCALLOPED EDGE,FLORALS   37.00
R S PRUSSIA BOX,COVERED,GREEN,4 IN............................   14.00
R S PRUSSIA BOX,COVERED,YELLOW ROSES,GREEN LEAVES,RED MARK..   38.00
R S PRUSSIA CAKE SET,7 PIECES,HANDPAINTED ROSE DECOR,GOLD
    TRIM..........................................................   25.00
R S PRUSSIA CELERY,IVORY & ROSE,GOLD EMBOSSED EDGE...........   40.00
R S PRUSSIA CHOCOLATE POT,8 IN.,DAISIES,RED MARK.............   58.50
R S PRUSSIA CHOCOLATE POT,FLORAL DECOR........................   38.00
R S PRUSSIA CHOCOLATE POT,GREEN LUSTER WITH WHITE
    FLOWERS,RED MARK..............................................   16.00
R S PRUSSIA CHOCOLATE POT,SATIN FINISH,SCULPTURED
    PANSIES,RED MARK..............................................   68.00
R S PRUSSIA CHOCOLATE SET,POT & 6 CUPS & SAUCERS,GREEN MARK.   65.00
R S PRUSSIA CHOCOLATE SET,YELLOW FLOWERS,RAISED GOLD BEADING   40.00
R S PRUSSIA COMPOTE,GREEN BANDS,GOLD,PINK ROSE BUDS,RED STAR   45.00
R S PRUSSIA COOKIE,COVERED,RAISED GOLD,MARKED ROYAL VIENNA..   23.50
R S PRUSSIA CREAMER & 2 HANDLED COVERED SUGAR,PEDESTAL,RED
    MARK..........................................................   47.00
R S PRUSSIA CREAMER & COVERED SUGAR,PEDESTALED,PINK
    ROSES,RED MARK................................................   40.00
R S PRUSSIA CREAMER & SUGAR,STAR-FLOWER FINIAL WITH GOLD,RED
    MARK..........................................................   68.00
R S PRUSSIA CREAMER,BREAKFAST,FOOTED,EMBOSSED BOTTOM,RED
    MARK..........................................................   25.00
R S PRUSSIA CREAMER,FLORAL,RED MARK...........................   28.00
R S PRUSSIA CREAMER,GREEN LUSTER & LILY OF VALLEY............   15.00
R S PRUSSIA CREAMER,RED STAR..................................   22.50
R S PRUSSIA CREAMER,SATIN FINISH,FOOTED,FLORAL,RED MARK.....   23.00
R S PRUSSIA CUP & SAUCER......................................   25.00
R S PRUSSIA CUP & SAUCER,CHOCOLATE,CONICAL SHAPE.............   22.50
R S PRUSSIA CUP & SAUCER,CHOCOLATE,SCALLOPED & BEADED
    RIMS,RED MARK.................................................   18.50
R S PRUSSIA CUP & SAUCER,DEMI-TASSE,GREEN & WHITE,RED MARK..   15.00
R S PRUSSIA CUP & SAUCER,DEMITASSE,WHITE & GREEN.............   15.00
R S PRUSSIA CUP & SAUCER,FLARED-SHAPED,WHITE,BEIGE &
```

PINK,RED MARK.. 25.00
R S PRUSSIA CUP & SAUCER,GREEN LEAVES & WHITE FLOWER,RED
MARK.. 29.50
R S PRUSSIA CUP & SAUCER,IVORY LILIES,RED MARK............... 15.00
R S PRUSSIA CUP & SAUCER,RED MARK........................... 22.00
R S PRUSSIA CUP & SAUCER,RED ROSES,RED MARK................. 12.50
R S PRUSSIA CUP & SAUCER,TEA,FLORAL SPRAY,EGG SHELL,RED MARK 24.50
R S PRUSSIA CUP & SAUCER WITH GREEN DECORATION,RED MARK..... 27.50
R S PRUSSIA CUP,CHOCOLATE,PEARLIZED EMBOSSED LILY OF
VALLEY,RED MARK....................................... 15.00
R S PRUSSIA CUP,SET OF 4,RED MARK........................... 37.00
R S PRUSSIA DISH,3-FOOTED,5 IN. DIAMETER,RED MARK........... 26.00
R S PRUSSIA DISH,CELERY,WHITE WITH FLORAL,RED & GREEN MARK.. 28.00
R S PRUSSIA DISH,RELISH,11 IN.,PIERCED HANDLES,GREEN WITH
PINK.. 11.00
R S PRUSSIA DISH,RELISH,OPEN HANDLES,WHITE APPLIED
FLORAL,RED MARK....................................... 18.00
R S PRUSSIA DISH,SAUCE,HANDLE & TRAY,WHITE,PURPLE,GREEN,RED
MARK.. 20.00
R S PRUSSIA DISH,SAUCE,TRAY & HANDLE,WHITE FLOWERS,RED MARK. 20.00
R S PRUSSIA DISH,SWEETMEAT,FOOTED,6 IN.,PINK ROSES ON
GREEN,RED MARK.. 35.00
R S PRUSSIA DISH,WHITE BACKGROUND,PINK POPPIES,GREEN,RED
MARK.. 28.00
R S PRUSSIA HAIR RECEIVER,CREAM BACKGROUND,PINK & BLUE,RED
MARK.. 12.00
R S PRUSSIA HAIR RECEIVER,RED MARK.......................... 12.00
R S PRUSSIA HAIR RECEIVER,RED ROSES & LEAVES,RED MARK....... 32.00
R S PRUSSIA HAIR RECEIVER,RIBBED WITH GOLD CHAINS,RED MARK.. 27.50
R S PRUSSIA HAIR RECEIVER,ROSES............................. 17.00
R S PRUSSIA HAIR RECEIVER,SQUARE,FLORAL DECOR,RED MARK...... 37.50
R S PRUSSIA HAIR RECEIVER,WHITE FLOWERS,RED MARK............ 22.00
R S PRUSSIA HATPIN HOLDER,3 FEET,PINK & WHITE FLOWERS....... 15.00
R S PRUSSIA HAT PIN HOLDER ATTACHED TO COVERED TRINKET
BOX,PINK ROSES.. 42.50
R S PRUSSIA HATPIN HOLDER,PINK ROSES........................ 12.50
R S PRUSSIA JAR,COOKIE,PINK ROSES ON WHITE,SCALLOP TOP WITH
FANS.. 59.00
R S PRUSSIA JAR,COOKIE , SYRUP,FOOTED,WHITE FLORALS,GOLD ON
GREEN... 55.00
R S PRUSSIA JAR,CRACKER,BLUE BASE TO WHITE TO ROSE
TOP,FLORAL.. 35.00
R S PRUSSIA JAR,CRACKER,ROSES,SATIN FINISH.................. 25.00
R S PRUSSIA JAR,POWDER,COVERED,RED MARK..................... 30.00
R S PRUSSIA MUG,SHAVING,SATIN FINISH,GOLD LEAVES............ 32.50
R S PRUSSIA MUG,SHAVING,SOAP SHELF,PINK & RED ROSES,GREEN &
WHITE... 38.50
R S PRUSSIA MUG,SHAVING WITH BEVELED MIRROR,PURPLE & GOLD... 42.00
R S PRUSSIA MUG WITH MIRROR INSET IN SIDE,SHAVING,GREEN WITH
PINK.. 49.50
R S PRUSSIA MUG,SHAVING WITH WELL,RED MARK.................. 28.00
R S PRUSSIA MUSTARD POT,RED MARK............................ 22.00
R S PRUSSIA MUSTARD WITH CHINA LADLE,COVERED,RED MARK....... 20.00
R S PRUSSIA MUSTARD WITH LADLE.............................. 25.00
R S PRUSSIA MUSTARD,UNMARKED................................ 8.50
R S PRUSSIA PITCHER,HANDLED,EMBOSSED LILY OF THE VALLEY,RED
MARK.. 17.00
R S PRUSSIA PITCHER,LEMONADE,SQUAT TYPE,RED MARK............ 65.00
R S PRUSSIA PITCHER,TANKARD TYPE,6 FOOTED,ROSES,10 IN.,RED
MARK.. 38.00
R S PRUSSIA PITCHER,TANKARD TYPE,RED,PINK ROSES,GREEN &
GOLD,RED MARK... 125.00
R S PRUSSIA PLANTER,RUFFLED TOP,BISQUE INSERT,8 IN.,RED MARK 65.00
R S PRUSSIA PLATE,6 IN...................................... 20.00
R S PRUSSIA PLATE,6 IN.,CHURCH SCENE,RED MARK............... 22.50

R S PRUSSIA PLATE,6 IN.,PEARLIZED LUSTER,GREEN WITH WHITE
FLOWERS.. 10.00
R S PRUSSIA PLATE,6 IN.,ROSES,NOTCHED BORDER................ 10.50
R S PRUSSIA PLATE,8 IN.,GOLD BORDER,PINK & WHITE POPPIES,RED
MARK... 23.50
R S PRUSSIA PLATE,8 IN.,PEARLIZED LUSTER,GREEN & WHITE
FLOWERS,RED MARK... 22.00
R S PRUSSIA PLATE,8 IN.,PINK ROSES,SATIN FINISH,RED MARK.... 23.00
R S PRUSSIA PLATE,8 IN.,ROSES,RED MARK..................... 17.50
R S PRUSSIA PLATE,8 IN.,VIOLETS,RED MARK................... 24.50
R S PRUSSIA PLATE,8 IN.,WATER LILIES,RED MARK.............. 17.50
R S PRUSSIA PLATE,8 IN.,WILD ROSE PATTERN,RED MARK........... 17.00
R S PRUSSIA PLATE,10 IN.,EMBOSSED CLAM SHELL & GOLD EDGE,RED
MARK... 49.00
R S PRUSSIA PLATE,11 IN.,OPEN HANDLES,PINK POPPIES,RED MARK. 35.00
R S PRUSSIA PLATE,11 IN.,PINK POPPIES REFLECTED IN WATER.... 35.00
R S PRUSSIA PLATE,11 IN.,SATIN FINISH,GREEN WITH PINK &
WHITE FLOWERS.. 60.00
R S PRUSSIA PLATE,CAKE,2 OPEN HANDLES,LUSTER,.............. 32.50
R S PRUSSIA PLATE,CAKE,6 IN.,WHITE DOGWOOD FLOWERS & GREEN.. 10.00
R S PRUSSIA PLATE,CAKE,10 IN.,PIERCED SIDE HANDLES,RED MARK. 39.50
R S PRUSSIA PLATE,CAKE,10 IN.,RED MARK..................... 26.00
R S PRUSSIA PLATE,CAKE,11 IN.,2 HANDLES,RED MARK........... 12.00
R S PRUSSIA PLATE,CAKE,11 IN.,OPEN HANDLES,FLORAL DESIGN,RED
STAR... 27.00
R S PRUSSIA PLATE,CAKE,11 IN.,PEONY & DAISIES,RED MARK...... 32.50
R S PRUSSIA PLATE,CAKE,11 IN.,PINK ROSES,GREEN
BACKGROUND,RED MARK...................................... 65.00
R S PRUSSIA PLATE,CAKE.................................... 10.00
R S PRUSSIA PLATE,CAKE,DICE THROWERS,10 IN.,RED MARK........ 180.00
R S PRUSSIA PLATE,CAKE,FALL SEASONS,9 IN.,RED MARK......... 175.00
R S PRUSSIA PLATE,CAKE,LILACS,RED MARK..................... 25.00
R S PRUSSIA PLATE,CAKE,OPEN HANDLED,2 SWANS,RED MARK........ 57.00
R S PRUSSIA PLATE,CAKE,SATINIZED WITH PINK,WHITE,PEACH,ROSES
& GOLD... 29.50
R S PRUSSIA PLATE,DICE THROWERS,8 IN.,GOLD WITH ROSES &
PEARL,RED MARK... 185.00
R S PRUSSIA PLATE,FLEUR DE LIS,SCALLOPED & BEADING,RED MARK. 14.00
R S PRUSSIA PLATE,GOLD EMBOSSED FLOWER FORMS............... 19.50
R S PRUSSIA PLATE,GREEN,WHITE,GOLD,8 IN.,RED MARK.......... 14.50
R S PRUSSIA PLATE,HEART SHAPE SCALLOPS & EMBOSSEMENTS,9
IN.,RED MARK... 42.00
R S PRUSSIA PLATE,LEAF-SHAPED,PINK ROSES ON BEIGE &
GREEN,RED MARK... 75.00
R S PRUSSIA PLATE,OPEN HANDLE,11 IN.,PINK & YELLOW ROSES.... 42.50
R S PRUSSIA PLATE,PINK ROSES,WHITE TO GREEN,SCALLOPED
BORDER,7 IN.,.. 30.00
R S PRUSSIA PLATE,RED MARK................................ 6.50
R S PRUSSIA PLATE,SET OF 4,6 IN.,PINK ROSES............... 32.00
R S PRUSSIA PLATE,SPRING SEASONS,9 IN.,PINK ROSES ON
GOLD,RED MARK.. 180.00
R S PRUSSIA PLATE,SWIRLED RELIEFS IRREGULAR EDGE,RED MARK... 55.00
R S PRUSSIA PLATE,WHITE FLOWERS ON CREAM TO BROWN
BACKGROUND,6 IN.,.. 25.00
R S PRUSSIA PLATE,WHITE GROUND,PINK & WHITE POPPIES,7
IN.,RED MARK... 13.25
R S PRUSSIA PLATE,WINDBLOWN TULIPS,6 IN................... 15.00
R S PRUSSIA PLATE,WINTER SEASONS,9 IN.,PINK ROSES ON
GOLD,RED MARK.. 180.00
R S PRUSSIA RELISH,RED STAR............................... 20.00
R S PRUSSIA RELISH,SATIN FINISH,OPEN HANDLED,8
IN.,BLUE,ROSES,RED MARK.................................. 28.00
R S PRUSSIA SAUCE,APPLES,GRAPES,PINK,RED & GOLD............ 5.00
R S PRUSSIA SAUCE,MAUVE BORDER,WHITE & PINK ROSES.......... 10.00
R S PRUSSIA SUGAR & CREAMER,COVERED,GREEN,RED MARK......... 30.00

```
R S PRUSSIA SUGAR & CREAMER,COVERED,WHITE & GREEN,RED MARK..        37.50
R S PRUSSIA SUGAR & CREAMER,FOOTED,GREEN WITH GOLD ROSES....        27.50
R S PRUSSIA SUGAR & CREAMER,LUSTER FINISH,GREEN & ROSE,RED
  MARK.............................................................  50.00
R S PRUSSIA SUGAR & CREAMER,MOTHER OF PEARL,GREEN
  BACKGROUND,RED MARK..............................................  47.50
R S PRUSSIA SUGAR & CREAMER,PEDESTAL FOOTED,RED MARK........        35.00
R S PRUSSIA SUGAR & CREAMER,PEDESTAL,GREEN BACKGROUND &
  WHITE,ROSES.....................................................  55.00
R S PRUSSIA SUGAR & CREAMER,PINK ROSES,IVORY GROUND,RED MARK        55.00
R S PRUSSIA SUGAR & CREAMER,SATIN FINISH....................        45.00
R S PRUSSIA SUGAR,4 FEET,GOLD BEADING,PINK ROSES,RED MARK...        20.00
R S PRUSSIA SUGAR BOWL,COVERED,PINK ROSES & GREEN LEAVES,RED
  MARK............................................................  27.00
R S PRUSSIA SUGAR,COVERED,2 HANDLED,RIBS,RUFFLED WITH FANS..        25.00
R S PRUSSIA SUGAR,COVERED,BLUE BASE,GOLD & RED ROSE DECOR,3
  IN..............................................................  20.00
R S PRUSSIA SUGAR,COVERED,RED STAR.........................         8.00
R S PRUSSIA SUGAR,COVERED,PEARLY LUSTER & 3 SWANS,RED MARK..        37.00
R S PRUSSIA SUGAR,FRUIT & FLOWERS..........................        24.00
R S PRUSSIA SUGAR SHAKER,SATINIZED,PINK ROSES..............        29.50
R S PRUSSIA SUGAR SHAKER,WHITE,GREEN & GOLD................        25.00
R S PRUSSIA SUGAR,SWAN COVERED,SATIN FINISH,RED MARK........        22.00
R S PRUSSIA TEAPOT & COVERED SUGAR,GREEN & WHITE FLORAL,RED
  MARK............................................................  50.00
R S PRUSSIA TEAPOT,COVERED,SCALLOPED FANS AT BASE,CRIMSON
  FLOWERS.........................................................  22.00
R S PRUSSIA TEAPOT,COVERED SUGAR,CREAMER,PINK,YELLOW ROSES..       120.00
R S PRUSSIA TEAPOT,FLOWERS,GOLD,RED STAR...................        42.50
R S PRUSSIA TEAPOT,PINK ROSES,RED MARK.....................        65.00
R S PRUSSIA TOOTHPICK HOLDER,2 HANDLED,GREEN & PINK
  SHADING,ROSES...................................................  17.50
R S PRUSSIA TOOTHPICK HOLDER,2 HANDLED,RED ROSES,GREEN
  LEAVES,RED MARK.................................................  65.00
R S PRUSSIA TOOTHPICK HOLDER,HANDLED,RED MARK..............        30.00
R S PRUSSIA TOOTHPICK HOLDER,ROSES,GOLD,2-HANDLED,RED MARK..        28.50
R S PRUSSIA TRAY,BOUDOIR,WHITE,GLOSSY TURQUOISE PASTELS,RED
  MARK............................................................  32.00
R S PRUSSIA TRAY,CEDARS & SWAN DESIGN,RED MARK.............        58.50
R S PRUSSIA TRAY,CELERY,12 IN.,OPEN HANDLES,FRUIT DESIGN,RED
  STAR............................................................  25.00
R S PRUSSIA TRAY,CELERY,RED STAR...........................        24.50
R S PRUSSIA TRAY,DRESSER,..................................        35.00
R S PRUSSIA TRAY,DRESSER,OPEN HANDLES,PINK FLORALS IN WHITE.        24.50
R S PRUSSIA TRAY,DRESSER,PIERCED HANDLES...................        32.00
R S PRUSSIA TRAY,DRESSER,SLOT HANDLES,WHITE,YELLOW,GREY,RED
  MARK............................................................  27.50
R S PRUSSIA TRAY,DRESSER,WHITE SATIN,WHITE FLOWERS,OPEN
  HANDLES.........................................................  45.00
R S PRUSSIA TRAY,OPEN HANDLED,ROSES, 9 IN.,RED MARK........        18.50
R S PRUSSIA TRAY,PINK ROSES................................        35.00
R S PRUSSIA TRAY,PIN,RECTANGLE,BASKET ROSES CENTER,RED MARK.        22.50
R S PRUSSIA TRAY,PIN,ROSES,RED MARK........................        19.00
R S PRUSSIA TRAY,SERVING,OPEN-HANDLED,SCALLOPED BEADED
  EDGE,RED MARK...................................................  38.00
R S PRUSSIA URN,JEWELED & FLORAL,RED MARK..................        90.00
R S PRUSSIA VASE,COBALT,COTTAGE SCENE,3 IN.,...............        26.00
R S PRUSSIA VASE,GREEN TO YELLOW,ROSES,RED MARK............        42.00
R S PRUSSIA VASE,PINK,YELLOW & GREEN FLOWERS,RED MARK,MADE
  IN GERMANY......................................................  33.00
R S PRUSSIA VASE,YELLOW,CARAMEL,APRICOT,COTTAGE SCENE,RED
  MARK............................................................  30.00
REDWARE 9 IN. PIE PLATE,YELLOW SLIP DECORATION.............        45.00
REDWARE FLOWER POT SIGNED JOHN BELL,ONE-HANDLED............        29.50
REDWARE FLUTED CAKE JELLO MOLD,CENTER TUBE.................        12.00
```

REDWARE JUG WITH HANDLE LIKE BEAN POT.......................   4.00

RIDGWAY POTTERY has been made in the Staffordshire district in England since 1808 by a series of companies with the name Ridgway. The transfer design dinner sets are the most widely known product. They are still being made.

RIDGWAY DESSERT SET CIRCA 1860,IVORY BACKGROUND,MAUVE
  BORDER,YELLOW..   48.00
RIDGWAY DISH,BLUE TRANSFER,BUILDINGS,TREES,PEOPLE & BOAT....   17.50
RIDGWAY MUG,COACHING DAYS & WAYS,SILVER LUSTER TRIM.........   23.00
RIDGWAY PITCHER,5 IN. HIGH,BAMBOO PATTERN,ROPE
  HANDLE,GREEN,1835......................................   15.00
RIDGWAY PITCHER,COACHING DAYS & WAYS.......................   42.00
RIDGWAY PLATE,9 IN.,CHINESE MOTIF..........................   3.50
RIDGWAY PLATE,9 IN.,CITY HALL NEW YORK,BLUE................   90.00
RIDGWAY PLATE,HARPERS FERRY,10 IN.,BLUE SEAWEED BORDER......   20.00
RIDGWAY PLATE,TYROLEAN LAVENDER............................   5.00
RIDGWAY PLATTER,11 X 16 IN.,BLUE & WHITE,EUPHRATES.........   15.00
RIDGWAY PLATTER,ENGLAND,ORIENTAL BLUE,OBLONG...............   8.50
RIDGWAY PLATTER,ORIENTAL BLUE & WHITE WITH GOLD............   23.00
RIDGWAY PORTRAIT PLATE OF KING EDWARD VII..................   15.00
RIDGWAY SOUP PLATE,SET OF 8,ETON PATTERN IN BLUE...........   8.00
RIDGWAY TEA TILE,THE CAPITOL,WASHINGTON IN BLACK ON YELLOW..   8.00
RIDGWAY TEAPOT,SQUARE,WHITE & GREEN,SEPIA & PINE-CONE,1871
  REGISTRY...   18.00
RIDGWAY SUGAR BOWL WITH COVER,SQUARE,1871 REGISTRY,PINE-CONE   15.00

ROCKINGHAM in the United States is a brown glazed pottery with a tortoiseshell-like glaze. It was made from 1840 to 1900 by many American potteries. The mottle brown Rockingham wares were first made in England at the Rockingham factory. Other wares were also made by the English firm.

ROCKINGHAM TYPE BOTTLE,HIGH SHOE..........................   35.00
ROCKINGHAM TYPE BOWL,SHELL SHAPE,FLORAL CENTER,GOLD TRIM....   47.50
ROCKINGHAM TYPE CUP & SAUCER,PEDESTAL CUP,QUAKER ACCENTS....   13.50
ROCKINGHAM TYPE CUP & SAUCER,ROSE & GOLD BORDER,MARKED ROYAL
  ROCK WORKS...   45.00
ROCKINGHAM TYPE CUSPIDOR 9.00
ROCKINGHAM TYPE DRAWER PULLS,4 PAIR........................   16.00
ROCKINGHAM TYPE FIGURE GROUP,WHITE,POODLE WITH 2 PUPS,BLUE
  BASE...   59.00
ROCKINGHAM TYPE FIGURINE,SITTING CAT,OBLONG BASE,DARK
  SLIP,18TH CENTURY...................................... 125.00
ROCKINGHAM TYPE MUG,HANDLED................................   18.50
ROCKINGHAM TYPE MUG,TOBY FIGURE,BENNET BROS................   85.00
ROCKINGHAM TYPE PITCHER,2 IN. TALL,SINGING BIRD IN RELIEF...   6.50
ROCKINGHAM TYPE PITCHER,10 IN.,HUNTING SCENE...............   15.00
ROCKINGHAM TYPE PITCHER,BROWN-YELLOW SPATTER..............   15.00
ROCKINGHAM TYPE PITCHER,EMBOSSED DEER,DOGS IN WOODS,HOUND
  HANDLE...   75.00
ROCKINGHAM TYPE PITCHER,GLAZE,HUNTER & DOG PATTERN.........   22.00
ROCKINGHAM TYPE PITCHER,HOUND HANDLED,MASK SPOUT,DEER,DOGS..   75.00
ROCKINGHAM TYPE PITCHER,IMPRESSED A.CADMUS,CONGRESS POTTERY
  CIRCA 1850... 117.00
ROCKINGHAM TYPE PITCHER,RAISED PEACOCK DESIGN..............   20.00
ROCKINGHAM TYPE PITCHER,REBEKAH AT WELL...................   20.00
ROCKINGHAM TYPE PITCHER,TULIP DESIGN,CIRCA 1850...........   20.00
ROCKINGHAM TYPE PLATE,BLUE & WHITE SCENE OF LADY AT SPINNING
  WHEEL.. 150.00
ROCKINGHAM TYPE PLATE,STEAM,PERFORATED,9 IN...............   18.00
ROCKINGHAM TYPE SERVICE,DESSERT,APPLE GREEN & BUFF
  YELLOW,GOLD,1820-...................................... 875.00
ROCKINGHAM TYPE WARMER,FOOT,BLIND PIG.....................   18.50
ROGERS STATUARY WHITE 11 IN. HIGH,IS THAT YOU TOMMY.........   55.00

ROOKWOOD POTTERY was made in Cincinnati, Ohio, after 1800. All of this art pottery is marked, most with the famous flame mark. The R is reversed and placed back to back with the letter P. Flames surround the letters.

ROOKWOOD ASHTRAY,1922,GREEN ALLIGATOR......................	28.00
ROOKWOOD ASHTRAY,ART NOUVEAU,WHITE KNEELING NUDE WITH FLOWING HAIR...	35.00
ROOKWOOD BASKET WITH 2 HANDLES,1887.......................	85.00
ROOKWOOD BOTTLE,SCENT,MINIATURE,GREEN WITH INCISED LEAVES...	75.00
ROOKWOOD BOOK ENDS IN WHITE,PAIR,1919,CHILD SEATED ON EACH..	31.00
ROOKWOOD BOWL,DATED 1916,YELLOW...........................	5.00
ROOKWOOD BOWL,1917..	4.00
ROOKWOOD BOWL,BLUE WITH YELLOW ,1907 SIGNED...............	13.00
ROOKWOOD BOWL,HOLLY & BERRIES,SIGNED L.N.L. 1899...........	45.00
ROOKWOOD BOWL,MARKED XX...................................	16.50
ROOKWOOD BOWL,PINK TO GREEN AT TOP,1931...................	7.50
ROOKWOOD CANDLESTICK,MATTE GLAZE,PINK-SAGE................	10.00
ROOKWOOD CANDLESTICKS,PAIR 6 IN. HIGH,BLUE,1914...........	22.50
ROOKWOOD CANDLESTICKS,PAIR,15 FLAMES,FEMALE FIGURE IN WHITE.	35.00
ROOKWOOD CANDLESTICKS,PAIR,1919,6 IN.,FLUTE PANEL RIBBED,MATTE GREEN...	12.00
ROOKWOOD DISH,RED,BOAT SHAPED.............................	11.00
ROOKWOOD EWER SIGNED MAD & DATED 1894,BROWN & RUST ,LEAF & FLOWER..	135.00
ROOKWOOD EWER,1897,SIGNED H.L.STRAFER,WIDE STRAP HANDLE.....	95.00
ROOKWOOD FIGURE OF RECLINING HORSE WITH FEMALE NUDE.........	22.00
ROOKWOOD FLOWER FROG,MARKED XXI...........................	4.75
ROOKWOOD FLOWER FROG,GREEN,SHINY..........................	9.50
ROOKWOOD FROG,BLUE,DATED..................................	6.50
ROOKWOOD JARDINIERE,1906,8 IN.,GREEN......................	40.00
ROOKWOOD JUG SIGNED ED BAILEY 1900,BROWN GLAZE,GREEN LEAVES AND GRAPES..	45.00
ROOKWOOD JUG WITH STOPPER & CORK,GREEN,TAN,GRAPES,SIGNED....	40.00
ROOKWOOD MUG,1907,5 IN.,GREEN MATTE,SIGNED C.DUELL..........	17.00
ROOKWOOD PAPERWEIGHT,1926,SIGNED MC DONALD,3 IN. HIGH,ELEPHANT...	45.00
ROOKWOOD PAPERWEIGHT,BLUE ROOK 1930......................	25.00
ROOKWOOD PAPERWEIGHT,GRAY ROOK ADVERTISING FINE TILES 1926..	29.00
ROOKWOOD PAPERWEIGHT ON GLOSS GREEN,3 IN. FROG.............	35.00
ROOKWOOD PAPERWEIGHT,ORANGE MONKEY ON BOOK 1927............	30.00
ROOKWOOD PAPERWEIGHT,WHITE ELEPHANT 1933..................	29.00
ROOKWOOD PITCHER,15 FLAMES,BURGUNDY & GREEN...............	18.00
ROOKWOOD PITCHER SIGNED ALBERT R.VALENTIEN & DATED 1884,9 IN. HIGH,..	150.00
ROOKWOOD PLATE PASTEL FLORAL,SIGNED HEW,8IN.DIA............	65.00
ROOKWOOD RABBIT,ORANGE BROWN COLOR........................	15.00
ROOKWOOD VASE,4 IN. TALL,YELLOW MATTE,1928 ,BIRDS...........	10.00
ROOKWOOD VASE,5-SIDED,ROSE COLOURED,ROOK & BRANCH...........	17.50
ROOKWOOD VASE,5 IN.,SIGNED MR & DATED 1885,BROWN GLAZE WITH YELLOW..	75.00
ROOKWOOD VASE,6 IN.,CLASSIC SHAPE,TURQUOISE.................	16.00
ROOKWOOD VASE,7 IN. HIGH,SILVER OVERLAY...................	120.00
ROOKWOOD VASE,7 IN.,ROSE TO GREEN AT TOP,1921..............	14.00
ROOKWOOD VASE,7 IN.,INVERTED BALUSTER SHAPE,GLAZE BROWN,RED & ORANGE..	55.00
ROOKWOOD VASE,7 FLAMES,BROWN TO TAN,TIGER HEAD ON SIDE,URN SHAPE..	23.00
ROOKWOOD VASE 8IN. T. 1921................................	10.00
ROOKWOOD VASE,14 FLAMES,GREENISH-BLUE,RAISED FIGURE OF MERMAID & FISH...	22.00
ROOKWOOD VASE,1899,BROWN GLAZE WITH BERRY-LEAF PAINTING.....	80.00
ROOKWOOD VASE,1903,ARTIST J.SWING,YELLOW DAISIES ON BROWN...	35.00
ROOKWOOD VASE,1914,GREEN PETAL DESIGN......................	12.75
ROOKWOOD VASE,1925,LAVENDER...............................	12.50
ROOKWOOD VASE,1926,......................................	9.50
ROOKWOOD VASE ARTIST SIGNED,BROWNS WITH YELLOW PANSIES......	35.00
ROOKWOOD VASE,AQUA GREEN,1937.............................	4.50

```
ROOKWOOD VASE,BLOOMS ON BROWN SIGNED.........................    38.00
ROOKWOOD VASE,BLUE,14 FLAMES,RAISED DESIGN OF POPPIES........    45.00
ROOKWOOD VASE,BLUE & GREEN,BELL FLOWERS AROUND TOP...........    20.00
ROOKWOOD VASE,BROWN,ARTIST SIGNED............................    29.50
ROOKWOOD VASE,BROWN TO GREEN.................................    12.50
ROOKWOOD VASE,COVERED,ROSE TO TAN,CRACKLE MATTE FINISH 1917.    17.50
ROOKWOOD VASE,DATED 1891,BROWN GLAZE,YELLOW-GREEN,ROSES.....    30.00
ROOKWOOD VASE,FLAMES MARK,ROSE COLOURED BASE WITH BLUE TONES     8.50
ROOKWOOD VASE,GREEN & PINK...................................    10.00
ROOKWOOD VASE,GRAY WITH GRAPES & LEAVES,1904 SIGNED..........    20.00
ROOKWOOD VASE,GREEN,2 HANDLES,1926...........................    10.00
ROOKWOOD VASE,JAR,1906,CARRIE STEINLE,HANDLED,TAN & GREEN...    45.00
ROOKWOOD VASE,MARKED,DATED XVIII,13 IN.,BROWN & GREEN.......    35.00
ROOKWOOD VASE,MARKED SARAH SAX VELLUM 1914...................    27.50
ROOKWOOD VASE,MARKED XXI,VELLUM PINK & GREEN.................    16.00
ROOKWOOD VASE MARKED XXS,DECORATED...........................    16.50
ROOKWOOD VASE,MATT FINISH,GRAY-GREEN TO PINK,15 FLAMES......    18.00
ROOKWOOD VASE,OVOID SHAPED,DATED 1891,ARTIST A.R.VALENTIEN..    40.00
ROOKWOOD VASE,OXBLOOD,ARTIST SIGNED,9 IN.,BLUE FLOWERS......    45.00
ROOKWOOD VASE,PINK DECORATED VELLUM..........................    17.50
ROOKWOOD VASE,PINK TO MOTTLED GRAY AT TOP,1921,..............    10.00
ROOKWOOD VASE,RED WITH WISTERIA TYPE FLOWERS,1921,SIGNED....    12.00
ROOKWOOD VASE,SARAH SAX 1903,7 IN. HIGH,PINK TO WHITE.......    45.00
ROOKWOOD VASE SIGNED C.A.B.;BROWN,ROSES UNDER GLAZE,4 IN.
  TALL.......................................................    25.00
ROOKWOOD VASE,SIGNED C A B ,BROWN TONES,ROSES UNDER GLAZE...    25.00
ROOKWOOD VASE SIGNED WITH FLAME MARK & NUMERAL XXI,GREEN....    15.00
ROOKWOOD VASE,SPECIMEN,FISH BORDER...........................    85.00
ROOKWOOD VASE,TAN,8 IN. TALL,1920 ROOKS IN RELIEF AROUND TOP    18.00
ROOKWOOD VASE,XLIV.9 IN.,BLACK GLAZE WITH WATERLILY DECOR...    35.00
```

ROSALINE GLASS is a rose-colored jade glass that was made by the Steuben Glass Works in Corning, New York.

```
ROSALINE 8 PLATES...........................................   100.00
ROSALINE BOWL...............................................    75.00
ROSALINE BOWL SIGNED CARDER.................................    80.00
ROSALINE COMPOTE SIGNED STEVENS &
WILLIAMS,S.W.ENGLAND,SCALLOPED EDGE.........................    95.00
```

ROSE BOWLS were popular during the 1880's. Rose petals were kept in the open bowl to add fragrance to a room. The glass bowls were made with crimped tops which kept the petals inside. Many types of Victorian art glass were made into rose bowls.

```
ROSE BOWL,3 FOOTED,CUT FLOWERS & PRESSED FOLIAGE............    38.00
ROSE BOWL,4 IN. DIAMETER,BLUE SATIN,LINED IN WHITE..........    38.50
ROSE BOWL,5 IN. DIAMETER,YELLOW TO WHITE....................    40.00
ROSE BOWL BEADED CABLE,FOOTED...............................    35.00
ROSE BOWL,BLOCK MILK GLASS ON PEDESTAL,FLAT HOBS............    15.00
ROSE BOWL,BLOWN RED.........................................    12.00
ROSE BOWL,BLUE MARY GREGORY.................................    85.00
ROSE BOWL,BLUE SATIN........................................    32.00
ROSE BOWL,BLUE SATIN GLASS RUFFLED TOP......................    35.00
ROSE BOWL,BUTTERFLY & SPRAY,5 IN............................    12.50
ROSE BOWL,CARNIVAL GREEN LEAF & BEADS.......................    23.00
ROSE BOWL,CARNIVAL PURPLE GRAPE DELIGHT.....................    40.00
ROSE BOWL,CARNIVAL,TURQUOISE................................    47.50
ROSE BOWL,CASED GLASS,3 IN.,ROSE TO GREY....................    40.00
ROSE BOWL,CASED,OFF WHITE SATIN FINISH,ENAMELED PINK & BLUE
  FLOWERS....................................................    38.00
ROSE BOWL,CLEAR GLASS PRISCILLA PATTERN.....................    14.25
ROSE BOWL,CRANBERRY,3 IN. HIGH,FOOTED,RUFFLED BASE IN CLEAR
  GLASS......................................................    27.50
ROSE BOWL,CRAQUELLE,5 IN. HIGH,LIGHT GREEN..................    29.00
ROSE BOWL,CRAQUELLE,5 IN. HIGH,LIGHT ORCHID.................    29.00
ROSE BOWL,CREAM WHITE SATIN GLASS,HANDPAINTED FLORALS.......    27.00
```

```
ROSE BOWL,CUT GLASS.........................................   45.00
ROSE BOWL,CUT GLASS 7 IN. TALL,HOBSTAR & STRAWBERRY DIAMOND.  100.00
ROSE BOWL,CUT GLASS,FOOTED..................................   12.50
ROSE BOWL,FENTONS FLOWERS,TWIG FEET,MARIGOLD................   24.50
ROSEBOWL,FINE CUT & ROSES,CUSTARD...........................   35.00
ROSE BOWL,FLUTED SCROLL,OPALESCENT & CLEAR..................   10.00
ROSE BOWL,FOOTED BEAD CABLE.................................   12.50
ROSE BOWL,FOOTED,CARNIVAL MARIGOLD BEADED CABLE.............   15.00
ROSE BOWL,FOOTED,PRESSED CUT PATTERN,HARVARD & FLOWERS......   22.50
ROSE BOWL,FRAMED JEWEL CLEAR................................   12.50
ROSE BOWL,GREEN DAISY & PLUME CARNIVAL......................   49.00
ROSE BOWL,GREEN TRANSPARENT,YELLOW ENAMEL SCROLL WORK.......   15.00
ROSE BOWL,HANDPAINTED PANSIES,PORCELAIN,3 GOLD BALL FEET....   15.00
ROSE BOWL,LIONS LEG,GREEN...................................   12.00
ROSE BOWL,LOETZ,MOTHER OF PEARL,7 IN........................   52.50
ROSE BOWL,MOTHER OF PEARL DIAMOND QUILTED BLUE SATIN........   75.00
ROSE BOWL,NORTHWOOD SIGNED,IRIDESCENT CALCITE,RAISED LEAF
DESIGN......................................................   28.00
ROSE BOWL,PINK,RIC RAC,MOTHER OF PEARL......................  120.00
ROSE BOWL,PINK SATIN GLASS..................................   25.00
ROSE BOWL,PINK TO WHITE,NEW ENGLAND PEACHBLOW,MARKED WORLDS
FAIR 1893...................................................  250.00
ROSE BOWL,POMONA,6 IN. HIGH,CRIMPED TOP,DECORATED...........  175.00
ROSE BOWL,RAINBOW COLOURS,CRIMPED TOP,VASA MURRHINA.........   29.50
ROSE BOWL,RED IRIDESCENT,NOUVEAU ART........................   35.00
ROSE BOWL,ROSE TO PINK,WHITE LINED,SATIN FINISH.............   50.00
ROSE BOWL,SATIN,CRIMPED TOP,WHITE LINING....................   29.75
ROSE BOWL,SATIN GLASS,4 IN.,PINK,BLUE,LEMON.................   38.00
ROSE BOWL,SATIN GLASS,WHITE TO BLUE,CRIMPED TOP.............   48.50
ROSE BOWL,SATIN,PINK,3 IN. TALL,PRIMPED TOP.................   40.00
ROSE BOWL,SATIN,PINK,ENAMELED FLOWERS,MULTICOLOURED.........  100.00
ROSE BOWL,SATIN,YELLOW......................................   35.00
ROSE BOWL,SHADED VASA MURRHINA YELLOW,OVERLAY WITH SILVER
SPANGLES....................................................   37.50
ROSE BOWL SIGNED SMITH ON 3 LEGS WITH MARKED STERLING SILVER
DEPOSIT.....................................................    7.50
ROSE BOWL,SPATTER GLASS,CRANBERRY & WHITE ON CLEAR..........   23.50
ROSE BOWL,SPATTER GLASS,YELLOW ,WHITE & BROWN,WHITE LINED,4
IN. HIGH....................................................   30.00
ROSE BOWL,SWIRLED BLOWN MOLD WITH OPALESCENT EDGE,CRANBERRY
ON EDGE.....................................................   15.00
ROSE BOWL,TIFFANY IRIDESCENT COLOURS,5 IN. DEEP,SATINY GREEN
GLASS.......................................................   35.00
ROSE BOWL,TRANSPARENT,SWIRL RIBBING,BLUE TO GREEN...........   25.00
ROSE BOWL,WHITE CARNIVAL GRAPE..............................   35.00
ROSE BOWL,WHITE CARNIVAL GRAPE,FOOTED.......................   38.00
ROSE BOWL,YELLOW CASED GLASS,EGG-SHAPED.....................   22.00
ROSE BOWLS,PAIR,GREEN,APPLIED PINK GLASS FLOWERS............   50.00
ROSE JAR,PERFORATED COVER,6 IN..............................   45.00
```

ROSE MEDALLION china was made in China during the ninetenth and twentieth centuries. It is a distinctive design picturing people, flowers, birds, and butterflies. They are colored in greens, pinks, and other colors.

```
ROSE MEDALLION BOWL & SAUCER,COVERED.......................   22.00
ROSE MEDALLION BOWL OR PLATTER,OVAL........................   90.00
ROSE MEDALLION BOWL,RICE...................................   38.00
ROSE MEDALLION BOWL,RICE,MARKED CHINA,5 IN. DIAMETER.......   25.00
ROSE MEDALLION BOWL,RICE,ON STAND,COVERED..................   30.00
ROSE MEDALLION BOX,COVERED,FLOWERS,BIRDS & PEOPLE..........  155.00
ROSE MEDALLION BOX,COVERED,FORM OF GARDEN SEAT,3 IN. HIGH...   75.00
ROSE MEDALLION BOX WITH LID,RECTANGULAR....................  150.00
ROSE MEDALLION BUTTER,COVERED,3 PIECE......................   50.00
ROSE MEDALLION CHARGER,13 IN. DIAMETER,....................   65.00
ROSE MEDALLION COFFEE POT,FOOTED...........................  165.00
ROSE MEDALLION CUP & SAUCER
```

```
20.00 TO.................................................  22.50
ROSE MEDALLION CUP & SAUCER,DEMI-TASSE......................   9.00
ROSE MEDALLION CUP & SAUCER,DEMITASSE,HANDLED...............   5.00
ROSE MEDALLION CUP & SAUCER,DEMI-TASSE,HANDLELESS..........  10.00
ROSE MEDALLION CUP & SAUCER,DEMI TASSE,SET OF 4.............  60.00
ROSE MEDALLION CUP & SAUCER MARKED CHINA,TEA,HANDLED.......  10.00
ROSE MEDALLION CUP & SAUCER,PRE 1900......................   7.50
ROSE MEDALLION CUP & SAUCER,RIBBED........................  21.00
ROSE MEDALLION CUSPIDOR...................................  70.00
ROSE MEDALLION DISH,9 IN. LONG,OVAL,OPEN..................  65.00
ROSE MEDALLION DISH,GOLD IN LADIES HAIR,BIRDS & FLOWERS
  DESIGN.................................................. 125.00
ROSE MEDALLION DISH,PAIR..................................  48.00
ROSE MEDALLION DISH,SCALLOPED EDGE........................  22.00
ROSE MEDALLION GARNITURE SET,3 PIECES,2 SPILL VASES & TEMPLE
  JAR.................................................... 145.00
ROSE MEDALLION JARDINIERE,10 X 9 IN....................... 125.00
ROSE MEDALLION LADLE,SPOON................................   5.00
ROSE MEDALLION PLATE,6 IN.,PRE 1900.......................   6.50
ROSE MEDALLION PLATE,7 IN.................................  18.50
ROSE MEDALLION PLATE,7 IN.,FLOWERS,BIRDS..................  13.00
ROSE MEDALLION PLATE,7 IN.,MATCHING DEMITASSE WITH SAUCER...  22.50
ROSE MEDALLION PLATE,8 IN.................................   8.00
ROSE MEDALLION PLATE,8 IN.,PEOPLE,BUTTERFLIES &
  BIRDS,GREYISH..........................................  18.00
ROSE MEDALLION PLATE,PAIR 8 IN.,FLORAL & SCENIC WITH GOLD...  33.00
ROSE MEDALLION PLATE,8 IN.,SCALLOPED EDGE,SET OF 6..........  32.50
ROSE MEDALLION PLATE,9 IN.................................   9.50
ROSE MEDALLION PLATE MARKED MADE IN CHINA.................   8.00
ROSE MEDALLION PLATE,PAIR,9 IN............................  45.00
ROSE MEDALLION PLATE,SCALLOPED EDGE,10 IN. LONG........... 115.00
ROSE MEDALLION PLATE,SET OF 6,6 IN.,PEOPLE & BIRD & FLOWER..  30.00
ROSE MEDALLION PLATES,10 IN...............................  25.00
ROSE MEDALLION PLATTER,OVAL,5 IN..........................  38.00
ROSE MEDALLION PLATTER,OVAL,13 X 11 IN....................  48.00
ROSE MEDALLION PLATTER,TREE AND WELL,19 IN. LONG.......... 210.00
ROSE MEDALLION PLATTER WITH INSERT........................ 225.00
ROSE MEDALLION PUNCHBOWL,16 IN. ACROSS.................... 375.00
ROSE MEDALLION SAUCER,SCALLOPED EDGE......................   5.00
ROSE MEDALLION SPOON......................................   8.75
ROSE MEDALLION SUGAR BOWL,MELON SHAPED,HANDLED............  12.50
ROSE MEDALLION SUGAR,GOLD FRUIT FINIAL,COVERED,2 TWIST SHAPE
  HANDLES................................................  65.00
ROSE MEDALLION TEA SET,FLORAL,3 PIECES....................  95.00
ROSE MEDALLION TEAPOT..................................... 125.00
ROSE MEDALLION TEAPOT & 6 CUPS,WIRE HANDLE................  38.00
ROSE MEDALLION TEAPOT & COVER.............................  32.00
ROSE MEDALLION TEAPOT & COVER,CHINA HANDLE................  40.00
ROSE MEDALLION TEAPOT & CUP...............................  39.00
ROSE MEDALLION TEAPOT,2 CUPS,IN BASKET....................  70.00
ROSE MEDALLION TEAPOT IN BASKET...........................  50.00
ROSE MEDALLION TEAPOT IN WICKER BASKET....................  40.00
ROSE MEDALLION TEAPOT,INVERTED COVER,WICKER BASKET WITH
  CLASPS & LOCK..........................................  75.00
ROSE MEDALLION TEAPOT,ONE CUP,IN BASKET...................  60.00
ROSE MEDALLION TEAPOT,OVOID SHAPE.........................  10.00
ROSE MEDALLION TEAPOT,WHITE SPOUT & HANDLE................  32.50
ROSE MEDALLION TEAPOT WITH CUP & SAUCER IN WICKER BASKET...  85.00
ROSE MEDALLION TEAPOT WITH HANDLELESS CUP.................  38.00
ROSE MEDALLION TRAY WITH HANDLE,RELISH,FLORAL.............  55.00
ROSE MEDALLION VASE,8 IN. H...............................  55.00
ROSE MEDALLION VASE,BALUSTER..............................  55.00
ROSE MEDALLION VASE,CYLINDER,12 X 5 IN....................  45.00
ROSE MEDALLION VASE,CYLINDER SHAPED,10 IN. HIGH...........  75.00
ROSE MEDALLION VASE,GOLD IN LADIES HAIR,BLUE DRAGONS...... 150.00
```

```
ROSE MEDALLION VASE,PAIR 8 IN.,ON WOODEN STANDS.............   96.00
ROSE MEDALLION VASE,PAIR CIRCA 1830........................  225.00
ROSE MEDALLION VEGETABLE,COVERED,DIAMOND SHAPE.............   57.50
ROSE MEDALLION VEGETABLE,OPEN,CIRCA 1830...................  115.00
     ROSE O'NEILL, SEE KEWPIE...............................
```

ROSENTHAL PORCELAIN was established in Sels, Bavaria, in 1880. The German
factory still continues to make fine-quality tableware and figurines.

```
ROSENTHAL BOWL,OVAL........................................   25.00
ROSENTHAL CUP & SAUCER,COFFEE,HANDPAINTED & SIGNED,PINK
  BORDER...................................................    3.50
ROSENTHAL CUP & SAUCER,DEMI-TASSE,MOSS ROSE................    3.50
ROSENTHAL CUP & SAUCER,SET OF 8............................   30.00
ROSENTHAL CUP & SAUCER,SET OF 8 PEDESTALED,BAVARIA,WHITE &
  PINK ROSES...............................................   55.00
ROSENTHAL DACHSHUND........................................   17.50
ROSENTHAL DISH,HANDPAINTED,RED POPPIES,GOLD HANDLES,SIGNED
  MC BRIDE.................................................   20.00
ROSENTHAL DISH,SARDINE,7 IN.,HANDPAINTED & SIGNED..........   15.00
ROSENTHAL FIGURINE,PAIR AFRICAN BLACK-A-MOORS HOLDING TRAY
  ON SHOULDER..............................................   10.00
ROSENTHAL JAR,COOKIE,COVERED,2 HANDLES,WHITE WITH WHEAT
  PATTERN..................................................   12.50
ROSENTHAL JARDINIERE SIGNED & HANDPAINTED,PURPLE
  VIOLETS,GREEN LEAVES.....................................   27.50
ROSENTHAL PITCHER,WATER,PRE WORLD WAR II,CREAM COLOURED.....   12.00
ROSENTHAL PLATE,6 IN.,HANDPAINTED,PAIR,GOLD EDGE...........    6.00
ROSENTHAL PLATE,IVORY,7 IN.,FLORAL DECORATIONS.............    6.00
ROSENTHAL SUGAR & CREAMER,COVERED,AIDA PATTERN.............    9.00
ROSENTHAL SAUCER,PAIR,GREEN & GOLD.........................   10.00
ROSENTHAL TEA SET,CREAM COLOURED,PRE WORLD WAR II..........   36.00
ROSENTHAL TEAPOT WITH SUGAR & CREAMER,ISOLDE PATTERN.......   17.50
ROSENTHAL VASE,PORTRAIT,PSYCHE,SIGNED FRENZEL,COBALT BLUE
  35.00  TO...............................................   38.00
ROSETTES,BRASS,U.S.CAVALRY.................................    7.00
ROSETTES BRIDLE,PAIR.......................................    2.00
ROSETTES,BRIDLE,PAIR,PONY EXPRESS..........................    2.00
ROSETTES,BRIDLE,PONY EXPRESS...............................    2.00
ROSETTES CAVALRY BRASS.....................................    4.00
```

ROSEVILLE POTTERY COMPANY was established in 1891 in Zanesville, Ohio.
Many types of pottery were made including flower vases.

```
ROSEVILLE BASKET
  15.00  TO...............................................   32.50
ROSEVILLE BASKET,8 IN.,BLUE & WHITE FLOWERS................   12.00
ROSEVILLE BASKET,BITTERSWEET DECORATION,BROWN..............   18.50
ROSEVILLE BASKET,BROWNS,YELLOWS,RAISED LILY................   10.00
ROSEVILLE BASKET,GREY WITH WHITE FLOWER....................    8.00
ROSEVILLE BASKET,SUNFLOWERS WITH GREEN LEAVES..............   15.00
ROSEVILLE BASKET,WATER LILIES,7 IN.........................    8.00
ROSEVILLE BASKET WITH HANDLE,ART NOUVEAU TYPE,GREEN & BROWN.   16.50
ROSEVILLE BOTTLE,CASTOR....................................   35.00
ROSEVILLE BOWL,I HANDLED,BLEEDING HEART DECOR..............    8.50
ROSEVILLE BOWL,8 IN........................................    5.50
ROSEVILLE BOWL,11 IN.,PINK WITH GREEN,2 HANDLES,HANGING MOSS   7.50
ROSEVILLE BOWL,18 IN. ON 3 FEET,GREEN WITH BROWN & YELLOW...   6.50
ROSEVILLE BOWL,BLUE........................................    8.50
ROSEVILLE BOWL,BLUE,2 HANDLED,FUCHSIA FLOWER...............   10.50
ROSEVILLE BOWL,HANDLED.....................................   14.00
ROSEVILLE BOWL,SAND COLOUR,WHITE RAISED FLOWERS............    8.50
ROSEVILLE BOWL WITH MATCHING CANDLESTICKS,9 IN.............   15.00
ROSEVILLE CANDLE HOLDERS,PAIR..............................  550.00
ROSEVILLE CANDLEHOLDERS,PAIR,GLAZED,GREEN..................    8.75
ROSEVILLE CANDLESTICK,GREEN,WHITE & BROWN..................    4.50
ROSEVILLE CANDLESTICKS,BLUE WITH DAYLILIES.................    8.00
```

```
ROSEVILLE CANDLESTICKS,PR............................................  6.50
ROSEVILLE CANDLESTICKS,PAIR 2 IN.,WHITE FLOWERS,ROSE-GREEN..  6.00
ROSEVILLE CONSOLE SET PAIR CANDLESTICKS & BOWL,..............  8.50
ROSEVILLE DISH,ORANGE,8 IN.,TRIANGULAR,HANDLED..............  5.50
ROSEVILLE DISH WITH 3 DOGS,CHILDS............................  6.50
ROSEVILLE EWER,HOLLY DECOR...................................  8.00
ROSEVILLE FLOWER CONTAINER MARKED POTTERY NO.455,AQUA &
   FLOWERS....................................................  4.95
ROSEVILLE FLOWER POT,GLAZED,RELIEF FIGURES OF LEAVES........  6.00
ROSEVILLE FLOWER POT WITH MATCHING SAUCER,FLOWERS...........  4.95
ROSEVILLE JARDINIERE,GREEN WITH WHITE GARDENIA..............  15.00
ROSEVILLE PITCHER-VASE,ALICE BLUE WITH CREAMY FLORAL
   TWIGS,LEAVES...............................................  7.50
ROSEVILLE PITCHER,WATER,10 IN.,BLUE & WHITE FLOWERS.........  16.00
ROSEVILLE PITCHER,WATERING...................................  9.00
ROSEVILLE PLANTER,6 IN.,BLUE WITH MAGNOLIAS.................  6.00
ROSEVILLE PLANTER,6 IN.,CONCH SHELL,BLUE WITH WHITE FLOWERS.  7.00
ROSEVILLE PLANTER,17 IN. LONG,AUTUMN COLOURS.................  12.50
ROSEVILLE PLANTER,MARKED POTTERY NO.429,2 HANDLES,GREEN WITH
   LILIES....................................................  6.50
ROSEVILLE PLANTER WITH INSERT & CHAINS......................  19.00
ROSEVILLE PLATE,OVENWARE,SAUCER & 2 BREAD & BUTTERS.........  11.00
ROSEVILLE SAUCER,SET OF 6,GREEN.............................  6.00
ROSEVILLE SHELL,ORANGE TO BROWN WITH MAHNOLIA DECOR.........  10.00
ROSEVILLE SUGAR & CREAMER....................................  15.00
ROSEVILLE SUGAR & CREAMER,BLUE WITH FLOWERS.................  6.50
ROSEVILLE SUGAR,CREAMER & TEAPOT............................  55.00
ROSEVILLE TEAPOT,AUTUMN COLOURS.............................  15.00
ROSEVILLE TEAPOT,BLUE WITH WHITE BERRIES & LEAVES..........  8.00
ROSEVILLE TEAPOT,CREAMER & SUGAR,BLUE WITH CREAM COLOURED
   IRIS......................................................  15.00
ROSEVILLE TEAPOT,TAN WITH RAISED FLORAL DESIGN..............  15.00
ROSEVILLE TRAY,SIGNED,GREENS,TANS,EMBOSSED SPRAY OF
   FOXGLOVES.................................................  8.50
ROSEVILLE VASE,2 HANDLED,GREEN,PINK,YELLOW PEONIES..........  7.00
ROSEVILLE VASE,2 HANDLED,LAVENDER & WHITE FLOWER DECOR......  10.00
ROSEVILLE VASE,2 HANDLES,DARK TO LIGHT GREEN,PURPLE & WHITE
   FLOWERS...................................................  13.00
ROSEVILLE VASE,6 IN.,PINK TO GREEN,HOLLYHOCKS...............  5.50
ROSEVILLE VASE,PAIR 7 IN....................................  8.00
ROSEVILLE VASE,7 IN.,2 HANDLED,GREEN ON CREAM BACKGROUND....  8.00
ROSEVILLE VASE,BLUE,6 IN.,HANDLES,APPLE BLOSSOM.............  4.50
ROSEVILLE VASE,BLUE,PINE CONE...............................  6.00
ROSEVILLE VASE,BLUE WITH FLOWERS & 2 HANDLES................  6.50
ROSEVILLE VASE,BROWN & GREEN FLOWERS........................  8.30
ROSEVILLE VASE,BUD,7 IN.,GREEN WITH WHITE FLOWERS...........  5.00
ROSEVILLE VASE,CORNUCOPIA,6 IN.,BLUE WITH WHITE FLOWER......  7.00
ROSEVILLE VASE,DOUBLE HANDLE ENCIRCLING,YELLOW FLOWERS......  8.00
ROSEVILLE VASE,DOUBLE TRUMPET STYLE,ROSE COLOUR
   TRUMPETS,GREEN...........................................  8.50
ROSEVILLE VASE,FAN SHAPED,BLUE LILY.........................  7.00
ROSEVILLE VASE,GREEN,5 IN.,PINK FLOWER,HANDLES.............  6.50
ROSEVILLE VASE,OBLONG,2 HANDLED,BLUE WITH WHITE & PINK
   FLOWERS...................................................  8.00
ROSEVILLE VASE,PINK,LILY OF VALLEY DECOR....................  5.00
ROSEVILLE VASE,SLANT TOP,1 HANDLE,GREEN & IVORY.............  8.50
ROSEVILLE VASE,TAN & GREEN,2 HANDLED........................  7.50
ROWLAND & MARCELLUS BLUE & WHITE PLATE,SOUVENIR OF HARTFORD.  10.00
ROWLAND & MARCELLUS BLUE PLATE,LONGFELLOWS HOME.............  10.00
ROWLAND & MARCELLUS SOUVENIR OF BRIDGEPORT,CONN. PLATE......  12.50
ROWLAND & MARCELLUS SOUVENIR OF SCRANTON,PA. PLATE.........  12.50
ROYAL ALBERT CROWN CHINA TOAST RACK,ENGLISH,RECTANGULAR
   SHAPE....................................................  17.50
ROYAL AUSTRIA HANDPAINTED COVERED SUGAR & CREAMER,BLUE WITH
   BLACK....................................................  12.50
```

```
ROYAL AUSTRIA SALT & PEPPER SHAKERS,ROSES...................  4.25
ROYAL AUSTRIAN PLATE,RANSOM PATTERN,9 IN...................  3.00
ROYAL AUSTRIAN RANSOM PATTERN 5 IN. PLATE.................  1.50
ROYAL AUSTRIAN RANSOM PATTERN CUP & SAUCER.................  4.00
     ROYAL BAYREUTH, SEE ALSO TAPESTRY, SUNBONNET...........
```

*ROYAL BAYREUTH PORCELAIN was made in Germany during the late nine-
teenth and twentieth centuries. Many types of wares were made.*

```
ROYAL  BAYREUTH ASHTRAY,HANDLED,MOOSE WITH HOUNDS,BLUE MARK..  17.00
ROYAL  BAYREUTH BASKET...................................  7.50
ROYAL  BAYREUTH BOWL,8 IN.,OPENWORK BORDER,PAINTED ROSES.....  18.00
ROYAL  BAYREUTH BOWL,10 IN.,3 HORNS OF PLENTY INSIDE.........  60.00
ROYAL  BAYREUTH BOWL,10 IN.,8 MEDALLIONS,PINK,WHITE ROSES....  45.00
ROYAL  BAYREUTH BOWL,BERRY,SATIN FINISH,BLUE MARK...........  35.00
ROYAL  BAYREUTH BOWL,BERRY,TOMATO,7 IN.....................  30.00
ROYAL  BAYREUTH BOWL,FRUIT,TOMATO,9 IN.,DIAMETER...........  35.00
ROYAL  BAYREUTH BOWL IN 3 FEET,LADIES HERDING LAMBS,BLUE MARK  18.00
ROYAL  BAYREUTH BOWL,PEDESTAL,MINIATURE,RUNNING CHILDREN.....  15.00
ROYAL  BAYREUTH BOWL,ROSE TAPESTRY.........................  44.00
ROYAL  BAYREUTH BOWL,ROSE TAPESTRY,10 IN...................  125.00
ROYAL  BAYREUTH BOWL,WHITE WITH ROSES PATTERN,GOLD BORDER....  14.75
ROYAL  BAYREUTH BOX,COVERED,ROSE TAPESTRY..................  50.00
ROYAL  BAYREUTH BOX,PIN,OVAL,TAPESTRY,COLONIAL COUPLE.......  55.00
ROYAL  BAYREUTH BOX,ROSE TAPESTRY,COVERED,ROUND,2 IN. TALL...  47.50
ROYAL  BAYREUTH BOX,ROSE TOP COVERED ON 3 GOLD FEET,ROSES....  37.50
ROYAL  BAYREUTH BOX,TRINKET,OVAL FRONT,SQUARE SIDES.........  33.00
ROYAL  BAYREUTH BOX,TRINKET,ROSE TAPESTRY,ROSE DESIGN.......  35.00
ROYAL  BAYREUTH CANDLEHOLDER,HANDLED,GOATS,BLUE MARK........  17.00
ROYAL  BAYREUTH CANDLEHOLDER,PAIR 6 IN. ,GOLD & FLOWER TRIM..  28.50
ROYAL  BAYREUTH CANDLEHOLDER,SCENE MAN & WOMAN RIDING WITH
  DOGS..................................................  14.75
ROYAL  BAYREUTH CHICKEN,YELLOW,5 IN.,BLUE MARK.............  9.00
ROYAL  BAYREUTH COMPOTE,COVERED...........................  16.00
ROYAL  BAYREUTH COMPOTE,GOATS,TREES.......................  15.00
ROYAL  BAYREUTH COMPOTE,LITTLE BO-PEEP WITH VERSE..........  36.00
ROYAL  BAYREUTH COMPOTE,PASTORAL SCENE,BLUE MARK...........  13.50
ROYAL  BAYREUTH CREAMER,3 IN.,GOATS,BLUE MARK.............  14.00
ROYAL  BAYREUTH CREAMER,3 IN.,SUNBONNET...................  12.00
ROYAL  BAYREUTH CREAMER,4 IN.,DEVIL & CARDS,BLUE MARK......  23.00
ROYAL  BAYREUTH CREAMER,5 IN.,5 SHEEP IN PASTURE..........  15.00
ROYAL  BAYREUTH CREAMER,APPLE,BLUE MARK
  11.00  TO............................................
ROYAL  BAYREUTH CREAMER,BAREFOOT BOY SITTING ON LOG,2 BURROS.  24.00
ROYAL  BAYREUTH CREAMER,BLACK TEXAS LONG HORN..............  36.00
ROYAL  BAYREUTH CREAMER,CONCH SHELL,MOTHER OF PEARL
  GLAZE,BLUE MARK.......................................  18.00
ROYAL  BAYREUTH CREAMER,CORINTHIAN WARE....................  15.00
ROYAL  BAYREUTH CREAMER,ELK
  4.00  TO............................................  12.00
ROYAL  BAYREUTH CREAMER,FOX HUNT..........................  8.50
ROYAL  BAYREUTH CREAMER,HUNTING SCENE,4 IN. TALL,GREEN WITH
  SCENE.................................................  15.00
ROYAL  BAYREUTH CREAMER,LOBSTER
  15.00  TO...........................................  22.00
ROYAL  BAYREUTH CREAMER,LOBSTER,BLUE MARK..................  16.50
ROYAL  BAYREUTH CREAMER,LOBSTER,RED MARK...................  19.00
ROYAL  BAYREUTH CREAMER,MINIATURE,RUNNING CHILDREN.........  18.00
ROYAL  BAYREUTH CREAMER,PEAR..............................  12.50
ROYAL  BAYREUTH CREAMER,RED BOTTOM WITH FISHERMAN SCENE,BLUE
  MARK..................................................  17.50
ROYAL  BAYREUTH CREAMER,RED DEVIL,HANDLED,GREEN MARK.......  27.50
ROYAL  BAYREUTH CREAMER,ROSE TAPESTRY,BLUE WITH GOLD,BLUE
  MARK..................................................  65.00
ROYAL  BAYREUTH CREAMER,ROSE TAPESTRY,GOLD TRIM,BLUE MARK....  42.00
ROYAL  BAYREUTH CREAMER,ROSE TAPESTRY,PINK ON GREEN,BLUE MARK  80.00
```

```
ROYAL BAYREUTH CREAMER,ROSE TAPESTRY,PINK ROSES.............    55.00
ROYAL BAYREUTH CREAMER,ROSE TAPESTRY,ROSE DESIGN............    38.00
ROYAL BAYREUTH CREAMER,ROSE TAPESTRY,YELLOW,PINK,WHITE,BLUE
 MARK......................................................    70.00
ROYAL BAYREUTH CREAMER,SHELL PATTERN,BLUE LUSTRE
 10.00  TO.................................................    15.00
ROYAL BAYREUTH CREAMER,SIGNED,NASTY RED DEVIL FIGURAL,BLUE
 MARK......................................................    23.00
ROYAL BAYREUTH CREAMER,SNAKE,ROGANE & BROWN COLOUR &
 MARKINGS..................................................    25.00
ROYAL BAYREUTH CREAMER,THE GLEANERS,BAND AT TOP WITH FARM
 BUILDINGS.................................................    25.00
ROYAL BAYREUTH CREAMER,THE HUNT,BLUE MARK..................    19.50
ROYAL BAYREUTH CREAMER,TOMATO
 10.00  TO.................................................    18.00
ROYAL BAYREUTH CREAMER,WATERMELON..........................    15.00
ROYAL BAYREUTH CREAMER,YELLOW WITH STAGECOACH SCENE,BLUE
 MARK......................................................    19.00
ROYAL BAYREUTH CUP,POPPY...................................    10.00
ROYAL BAYREUTH CUP,WEDDING,3 HANDLED,SUNBONNET BABIES SEWING   22.00
ROYAL BAYREUTH DESK BLOTTER,CORINTHIAN PATTERN,TOP FINIAL
 UNSCREWS..................................................    27.50
ROYAL BAYREUTH DISH,4 IN. LEAF,BLUE MARK...................     3.00
ROYAL BAYREUTH DISH,7 IN.,CARD-SHAPED......................    28.00
ROYAL BAYREUTH DISH,7 IN. HANDLED LEAF,BLUE MARK...........     4.00
ROYAL BAYREUTH DISH,COVERED LOBSTER,GREEN MARK.............     7.50
ROYAL BAYREUTH DISH,COVERED TOMATO
 3.00  TO..................................................    15.00
ROYAL BAYREUTH DISH,COVERED TOMATO,BLUE MARK...............     9.00
ROYAL BAYREUTH DISH,COVERED TOMATO ON LETTUCE LEAF,BLUE MARK   13.50
ROYAL BAYREUTH DISH,HEART SHAPED,OPEN LATTICE WORK AS HANDLE   11.00
ROYAL BAYREUTH DISH,LEAF...................................     8.00
ROYAL BAYREUTH DISH,LETTUCE LEAF,BLUE MARK.................     4.50
ROYAL BAYREUTH DISH,OLIVE,8 IN.,GIRL WITH CHICKENS,BLUE MARK   15.00
ROYAL BAYREUTH DISH,SAUCE,TAPESTRY.........................    29.00
ROYAL BAYREUTH DISH,SCOUP SHAPE,HANDLED,FOX HUNTER ON
 HORSE,BLUE MARK...........................................    25.00
ROYAL BAYREUTH DISH,TOMATO ON LEAF.........................    15.00
ROYAL BAYREUTH HAIR RECEIVER,3 GOLD FEET,ROSE TAPESTRY,BLACK
 MARK......................................................    45.00
ROYAL BAYREUTH HAIR RECEIVER,BLUE MARK.....................    12.00
ROYAL BAYREUTH HAIR RECEIVER,HANDPAINTED IVORY,BLUE MARK....    16.00
ROYAL BAYREUTH HAIR RECEIVER,RAMS,BLUE MARK................    16.00
ROYAL BAYREUTH HAIR RECEIVER,ROSE TAPESTRY.................    25.00
ROYAL BAYREUTH HAIR RECEIVER,TAPESTRY......................    12.00
ROYAL BAYREUTH HAIR RECEIVER,TAPESTRY,YELLOW ROSES,GOLD FEET   40.00
ROYAL BAYREUTH HAT PIN HOLDER,FLORAL DECOR & GOLD TRIM,BLUE
 MARK......................................................    16.50
ROYAL BAYREUTH HATPIN HOLDER,POPPY.........................    22.00
ROYAL BAYREUTH HUMIDOR,PORTRAIT OF GIRL WITH CANDLE........    70.00
ROYAL BAYREUTH INVALID FEEDER,2 SPOUTS,BEN HUR,NERO &
 FIDDLE,BLUE MARK..........................................    27.00
ROYAL BAYREUTH JUG,MILK,GREEN..............................     7.50
ROYAL BAYREUTH MUG,3 HANDLED,GOATS.........................    15.00
ROYAL BAYREUTH MUG,3 HANDLED,MINSTREL & DRINKING SCENE,GREEN   22.50
ROYAL BAYREUTH MUG,HANDLED,CHILDREN & TEDDY BEAR ON ICE.....    20.00
ROYAL BAYREUTH MATCH HOLDER,HANGING,RED EAGLE..............    28.50
ROYAL BAYREUTH MUSTARD,COVERED,BLUE MARK...................    12.50
ROYAL BAYREUTH MUSTARD JAR,TOMATO,BLUE MARK................    10.00
ROYAL BAYREUTH MUSTARD POT,TOMATO COVERED..................    12.00
ROYAL BAYREUTH NAPPY,HEART SHAPE,1 HANDLE,GOLD RING
 HANDLE,BLUE MARK..........................................    15.00
ROYAL BAYREUTH PITCHER,ARABIAN MOTIF.......................    10.00
ROYAL BAYREUTH PITCHER,BLACK CROW FIGURAL,BLUE MARK........    18.00
ROYAL BAYREUTH PITCHER,BULBOUS,SCENE WITH GRASS,TREES,BLUE
```

```
MARK.............................................................   22.00
ROYAL BAYREUTH PITCHER,CARD,RED DEVIL HANDLE,GREEN MARK.....   17.50
ROYAL BAYREUTH PITCHER,ELK..................................   27.50
ROYAL BAYREUTH PITCHER,ELK,BROWN,HORN TIP...................   12.50
ROYAL BAYREUTH PITCHER,ELK,HORN TIP.........................   13.75
ROYAL BAYREUTH PITCHER,GREEN BAND AT TOP & BASE,BLUE MARK...   18.00
ROYAL BAYREUTH PITCHER,LOBSTER,
   12.50 TO...............................................   17.50
ROYAL BAYREUTH PITCHER,LOBSTER,GREEN MARK...................   25.00
ROYAL BAYREUTH PITCHER,MILK,BULBOUS SHAPE CAVALIER DRINKING
   SCENE...................................................   35.00
ROYAL BAYREUTH PITCHER,MILK,DEVIL & CARDS,BLUE MARK.........   65.00
ROYAL BAYREUTH PITCHER,MILK,TAPESTRY........................   85.00
ROYAL BAYREUTH PITCHER,MINIATURE,RED DEVIL CARD.............   35.00
ROYAL BAYREUTH PITCHER,ROSE TAPESTRY,BLUE MARK..............   54.00
ROYAL BAYREUTH PITCHER,ROSE TAPESTRY,WHITE,YELLOW,PINK ROSES   78.00
ROYAL BAYREUTH PITCHER,SUNBONNET BABIES IRONING.............   30.00
ROYAL BAYREUTH PITCHER,SUNBONNETS FISHING,5 IN. TALL........   85.00
ROYAL BAYREUTH PITCHER,TOMATO...............................   45.00
ROYAL BAYREUTH PITCHER,TOMATO,BLUE MARK.....................   14.00
ROYAL BAYREUTH PITCHER,WATER,LOBSTER,1794 MARK..............   85.00
ROYAL BAYREUTH PITCHER,WATERMELON...........................   45.00
ROYAL BAYREUTH PLANTER,ROSE TAPESTRY,BLUE MARK..............   60.00
ROYAL BAYREUTH PLATE,3-SIDED,PINK WITH ROSES & GOLD,BLUE
   MARK....................................................   12.00
ROYAL BAYREUTH PLATE,6 IN.,LITTLE JACK HORNER,BLUE MARK.....   32.50
ROYAL BAYREUTH PLATE,7 IN.,LONG HAIRED GOATS IN MEADOW......   12.50
ROYAL BAYREUTH PLATE,9 IN. FLORAL CENTER,SCALLOPED BORDER
   WITH GOLD...............................................   14.00
ROYAL BAYREUTH PLATE,9 IN.,GRAPE DESIGN,GOLD EDGE,GREEN
   BACKGROUND..............................................   13.50
ROYAL BAYREUTH PLATE,11 IN.,ROSES...........................   35.00
ROYAL BAYREUTH PLATE,BUD & LEAF,TWIG HANDLE,BLUE MARK.......   12.00
ROYAL BAYREUTH PLATE,CAKE,3 COWS STANDING UNDER WHITE BIRCH
   TREE....................................................   25.00
ROYAL BAYREUTH PLATE,CAKE,OPEN,HANDLES,SUNBONNET BABIES.....   40.00
ROYAL BAYREUTH PLATE,MILL MUFFET............................   18.50
ROYAL BAYREUTH PLATE,SUNBONNET BABIES CLEANING HOUSE........   18.50
ROYAL BAYREUTH PLATE,SUNBONNET BABIES FISHING...............   21.00
ROYAL BAYREUTH PLATE,TOMATO PLANT,BLUE MARK.................    9.50
ROYAL BAYREUTH POT,SCENT,FLAT,2 TOP HANDLES,SCENIC
   BACKGROUND..............................................   14.00
ROYAL BAYREUTH RELISH,COVERED TOMATO........................    8.00
ROYAL BAYREUTH SALT & PEPPER,ROSE TAPESTRY..................   75.00
ROYAL BAYREUTH SALT & PEPPER SHAKER,LOBSTER.................   22.00
ROYAL BAYREUTH SALT & PEPPER SHAKERS,GRAPE..................   18.00
ROYAL BAYREUTH SALT & PEPPER SHAKERS,FLOWERS................   18.00
ROYAL BAYREUTH SALT & PEPPER SHAKERS,TOMATO.................   18.00
ROYAL BAYREUTH SALT,COVERED LOBSTER,PURPLE SATIN FINISH,BLUE
   MARK....................................................    7.00
ROYAL BAYREUTH SALT SHAKER,TOMATO...........................    3.50
ROYAL BAYREUTH SAUCE,ROSE TAPESTRY..........................   30.00
ROYAL BAYREUTH SHOE,PAIR MENS TAN DATED 1911,BLUE MARK......   37.50
ROYAL BAYREUTH SHOE,ROSE TAPESTRY,LADYS HIGH BUTTON.........   50.00
ROYAL BAYREUTH STRAINER,FLOWER FORM,MOTHER OF PEARL.........   14.00
ROYAL BAYREUTH SUGAR & CREAMER,CONCH SHELL..................   18.00
ROYAL BAYREUTH SUGAR & CREAMER IN SHAPE OF GRAPE
   CLUSTERS,MARKED.........................................   25.00
ROYAL BAYREUTH SUGAR & CREAMER,MOTHER OF PEARL,BLUE MARK....   18.75
ROYAL BAYREUTH SUGAR & CREAMER,SUNBONNET BABIES,BLUE MARK...   60.00
ROYAL BAYREUTH SUGAR & CREAMER,TOMATO.......................   32.50
ROYAL BAYREUTH SUGAR BOWL,GREEN,COVERED.....................   12.50
ROYAL BAYREUTH SUGAR BOWL,LOBSTER SHAPED,BLUE MARK..........   15.00
ROYAL BAYREUTH SUGAR BOWL,PURPLE SATIN FINISH,COVERED
   LOBSTER,BLUE MARK.......................................   22.50
```

ROYAL BAYREUTH SUGAR BOWL,SUNBONNET BABIES IRONING..........	18.50
ROYAL BAYREUTH SUGAR,CLASSIC.................................	20.00
ROYAL BAYREUTH SUGAR,COVERED LOBSTER,LAVENDER,IRIDESCENT & GOLD...	13.00
ROYAL BAYREUTH SUGAR,COVERED,ROSE TAPESTRY,MAN & LADY........	25.00
ROYAL BAYREUTH SUGAR,COVERED TOMATO..........................	12.00
ROYAL BAYREUTH SUGAR,COVERED TOMATO,BLUE MARK................	12.50
ROYAL BAYREUTH SUGAR SHAKER,ROSE TAPESTRY....................	105.00
ROYAL BAYREUTH SUGAR,TOMATO COVERED,2 HANDLES................	13.50
ROYAL BAYREUTH TEAPOT,COVERED SUGAR & CREAMER,TOMATO,BLUE MARK..	49.00
ROYAL BAYREUTH TEAPOT,COVERED TOMATO.........................	25.00
ROYAL BAYREUTH TEAPOT,CREAMER & COVERED SUGAR,TOMATO.........	53.50
ROYAL BAYREUTH TEAPOT,PINK,HORSEMEN..........................	75.00
ROYAL BAYREUTH TEAPOT,ROSE TAPESTRY,MAN & LADY,BLUE MARK.....	45.00
ROYAL BAYREUTH TEAPOT,TOMATO.................................	18.00
ROYAL BAYREUTH TOBACCO HUMIDOR,TAPESTRY,SCENIC WITH GOATS...	100.00
ROYAL BAYREUTH TOBACCO JAR...................................	45.00
ROYAL BAYREUTH TOBACCO JAR,BROWN MOOSE.......................	10.00
ROYAL BAYREUTH TOOTHPICK HOLDER,LITTLE JACK HORNER,HANDLED,BLUE MARK...	19.00
ROYAL BAYREUTH TOOTHPICK HOLDER,ROSE TAPESTRY,2 HANDLED,BLUE MARK..	45.00
ROYAL BAYREUTH TOOTHPICK,RED LOBSTERS APPLIED ON 2 SIDES....	9.50
ROYAL BAYREUTH TOOTHPICK,ROSE TAPESTRY,FOOTED,ROSE DESIGN...	32.00
ROYAL BAYREUTH TOOTHPICK,YELLOW,3 CORNERED,FOOTED,PENGUINS ON SIDES...	25.00
ROYAL BAYREUTH TRAY,CLOWN....................................	10.00
ROYAL BAYREUTH TRAY,COVERED TOMATO WITH LEAF.................	10.00
ROYAL BAYREUTH TRAY,DRESSER,SCENE 3 CHILDREN RUNNING WITH ROPE...	27.50
ROYAL BAYREUTH TRAY,DRESSER,WOMAN & CHICKENS IN FIELD.......	30.00
ROYAL BAYREUTH TRAY,PEN & CLIP,HANDLED,BLUE MARK.............	13.50
ROYAL BAYREUTH TRAY,PERFUME,GOOSE GIRL.......................	25.00
ROYAL BAYREUTH TRAY,ROSE TAPESTRY,SIGNED,7 X 11 IN...........	85.00
ROYAL BAYREUTH VASE,2-HANDLED,ARAB & HORSES..................	25.00
ROYAL BAYREUTH VASE,3 HANDLED,3 IN.,HUNTING SCENE,BLUE MARK.	20.00
ROYAL BAYREUTH VASE,4 IN.,GOOSE GIRL,BLUE MARK...............	15.00
ROYAL BAYREUTH VASE,4 IN.,VICTORIAN CHILD WITH PUPPY.........	9.75
ROYAL BAYREUTH VASE,5 IN.,MOUNTAIN SCENERY,BLUE MARK.........	19.00
ROYAL BAYREUTH VASE,5 IN.,RED & YELLOW ROSES,BLUE MARK.......	10.00
ROYAL BAYREUTH VASE,BUD,4 IN.,HUNTER WITH DOGS,BLUE MARK....	14.00
ROYAL BAYREUTH VASE,BUD,HANDLED,CAVALIER,BLUE MARK...........	14.50
ROYAL BAYREUTH VASE,CATTLE SCENE,FLUTED TOP.................	10.00
ROYAL BAYREUTH VASE,EMBOSSED FLARE HORN TOP,SCENIC OF 3 GOATS...	7.00
ROYAL BAYREUTH VASE,FOOTED,3 IN.,CURLICUE SIDE HANDLES......	15.50
ROYAL BAYREUTH VASE,HORSE SCENERY............................	22.00
ROYAL BAYREUTH VASE,MINIATURE,5 IN. HIGH,POLAR BEARS,BLUE MARK..	20.00
ROYAL BAYREUTH VASE,SCENIC,BLACK MARK........................	16.50
ROYAL BAYREUTH VASE,TAPESTRY,SCENIC,BLUE MARK................	22.50
ROYAL BAYREUTH VASE,URN,ROSE TAPESTRY,SIDE HANDLES,BLUE MARK	50.00
ROYAL BONN CRACKER JAR,CASTLE MARK,GERMANY,PINK BANDS ON CREAM...	10.00
ROYAL BONN DECORATED WITH ORCHIDS HOT PLATE.................	5.00
ROYAL BONN PITCHER,MILK,HANDPAINTED GRAPES & LEAVES,CHINA CASTLE MARK...	15.00
ROYAL BONN RELISH,OVAL,HANDPAINTED GRAPES & LEAVES,CHINA CASTLE MARK...	9.00
ROYAL BONN VASE,11 IN.,MULTICOLOURED FLORAL DECOR...........	15.00
ROYAL BONN VASE,DARK BLUE,CASTLE MARK VILLEROY BOCH.........	10.00
ROYAL BONN VASE,EWER TYPE,IVORY BACKGROUND,GREEN LEAVES,GOLD	38.00
ROYAL BONN VASE,PAIR,DATED 1775,IMPRESSED REGISTRY MARKS,GOLD & GREEN...	75.00

```
ROYAL BONN VASE SIGNED GERMANY,RED AND BLUE FLOWERS,GREEN
  LEAVES,GOLD.........................................   12.00
ROYAL CHELSEA CUP AND SAUCER,BLUE & GOLD...............    4.50
```

ROYAL COPENHAGEN PORCELAIN AND POTTERY has been made in Denmark since 1772. It is still being made. One of their most famous wares is the Christmas plate series (see also CHRISTMAS PLATES).

```
  ROYAL COPENHAGEN, SEE ALSO CHRISTMAS PLATE............
ROYAL COPENHAGEN COMPOTE,BLUE & WHITE,PIERCED EDGE...........   37.50
ROYAL COPENHAGEN GRAVY BOAT,BLUE WAVE LINES HALLMARK........   18.00
ROYAL COPENHAGEN PLAQUE,LINCOLN...............................    2.25
ROYAL COPENHAGEN PORTRAIT PLAQUE,FDR..........................    2.25
ROYAL COPENHAGEN PORTRAIT PLAQUE,JFK..........................    2.25
ROYAL COPENHAGEN PORTRAIT PLAQUE,WASHINGTON...................    2.25
ROYAL COPENHAGEN PORTRAIT PLATE,JEFFERSON T.ROOSEVELT........    2.55
ROYAL COPENHAGEN POTTERY BOWL,GREEN SPOTS ON BROWN & BLACK..   25.00
ROYAL COPENHAGEN TEA PLATE,9,GOLD LEAF BORDERS..............  120.00
ROYAL COPENHAGEN VASE, 6 IN. H., SIGNED, FISH WITH SEA WEED.   70.00
```

ROYAL CROWN DERBY COMPANY, LTD. was established in England in 1876.

```
  ROYAL CRONW DERBY, SEE CROWN DERBY.....................
ROYAL CROWN DERBY BLUE MIKADO CUP & SAUCER..................    8.00
ROYAL CROWN DERBY GAME BIRD PLATE,SCALLOPED GOLD EDGE.......   16.00
ROYAL CROWN DERBY TOOTHPICK IN BLUE,ORANGE & GOLD...........   23.00
ROYAL CROWN DUCAL 10 IN. MULBERRY PLATE,GOING TO CHURCH.....    6.50
ROYAL CROWN DUCAL 10 IN. MULBERRY PLATE,THE FIRST
  THANKSGIVING...............................................    6.50
ROYAL DEVON ENGLAND CROWN MARK TONGUE DISH..................    8.00
ROYAL DIX STATUE,MAN POURING FRUIT INTO TUB.................  125.00
```

ROYAL DOULTON was the name used on pottery made after 1902. The Doulton factory was founded in 1815. Their wares are still being made.

```
  ROYAL DOULTON, SEE ALSO DOULTON......................
ROYAL DOULTON BEAKER,KING EDWARD 7TH,QUEEN ALEXANDRIA
  CORONATION.................................................   16.00
ROYAL DOULTON BOWL,BLUE DECORATION.........................    3.50
ROYAL DOULTON BOWL,BROWN,WATCHMAN,WHAT OF THE NIGHT,STREET
  SCENE......................................................  100.00
ROYAL DOULTON BOWL,MUSH,CHILDS,TO MARKET,TO MARKET ETC......    6.50
ROYAL DOULTON BOWL,OCTAGON SHAPED,YELLOW POPPY & GREEN
  PODS,LEAVES................................................   23.00
ROYAL DOULTON CREAMER & SUGAR,ENGLAND,TENIERS TAVERN SCENE..   28.50
ROYAL DOULTON CREAMER,LONGFELLOW MANSION....................   35.00
ROYAL DOULTON CREAMER,OCTAGONAL,BLUE WITH PINK FLOWERS......    7.50
ROYAL DOULTON CREAMER,TITARIAN..............................   12.50
ROYAL DOULTON CREAMER WITH HORSES...........................    6.50
ROYAL DOULTON CUSPIDOR,KING SIZE,MARKED WITH CROWN & LION
  ,SIGNED NOKE...............................................   25.00
ROYAL DOULTON DICKENSWARE PLATE,BARNABY RUDGE..............   12.50
ROYAL DOULTON DICKENSWARE TEAPOT SIGNED BILL SYKES.........   15.00
ROYAL DOULTON DINNER PLATES,OCTAGONAL,BLUE WITH PINK
  FLOWERS,EA.................................................    6.50
ROYAL DOULTON DISH,SOAP,COVERED,INSERT.....................   12.00
ROYAL DOULTON DISH,VEGETABLE,COVERED,SUNFLOWER.............   25.00
ROYAL DOULTON FIGURE OF SITTING HINDU......................   35.00
ROYAL DOULTON FIGURE OF THE BRIDE,MARKED,8 IN. HIGH.........   37.50
ROYAL DOULTON GINGER JAR,SQUARE ,GOLD & BLUE FLOWERS........   65.00
ROYAL DOULTON LAMP,TABLE,WHITE BASE WITH GOLD
  SPATTER,HANDPAINTED........................................   75.00
ROYAL DOULTON MUG & EGG CUP,CHILDS,MARKED,BUNNYKINS.........    8.00
ROYAL DOULTON MUG,BROWN & TAN WITH DRINKING FIGURES,HOUNDS..   20.00
ROYAL DOULTON MUG,COMMEMORATION QUEEN VICTORIA
  1837-97,PEWTER RIM.........................................   30.00
ROYAL DOULTON MUG,TAN & BROWN,3 CLASSICAL DRINKING FIGURES..   20.00
ROYAL DOULTON MUG,TOBY.....................................    5.00
```

```
ROYAL DOULTON MUG,TOBY,JESTER................................    8.50
ROYAL DOULTON PITCHER & BOWL,LILY PATTERN....................   75.00
ROYAL DOULTON PITCHER,7 IN. TALL,FALSTAFF & DAME............   75.00
ROYAL DOULTON PITCHER,8 IN. TALL............................   20.00
ROYAL DOULTON PITCHER,BUTTERMILK,CREAMER & COVERED SUGAR....   85.00
ROYAL DOULTON PITCHER,COMMEMORATION KING GEORGE & QUEEN MARY
  1911.......................................................   32.00
ROYAL DOULTON PITCHER,DUTCH.................................    8.75
ROYAL DOULTON PITCHER,IRIS PATTERN,BLUE & WHITE.............   30.00
ROYAL DOULTON PITCHER,ISAAC WALTON WARE,BEHOLD THE FISHERMAN   23.00
ROYAL DOULTON PITCHER,MINIATURE,SHAKESPEARE,BEIGE &
  BROWN,STERLING EDGE........................................   16.50
ROYAL DOULTON PLATE,7 IN.,3 GIRLS IN WOODEN SHOES &
  WINDMILLS..................................................   15.00
ROYAL DOULTON PLATE,7 IN.,STORY BOOK,THE BLUE CATERPILLAR...   26.00
ROYAL DOULTON PLATE,10 IN.,CAP N CUTTLE & SAIREY............   25.00
ROYAL DOULTON PLATE,10 IN. FULL FIGURE OF SPANIEL..........   13.00
ROYAL DOULTON PLATE,10 IN.,GIBSON GIRL.....................    7.50
ROYAL DOULTON PLATE,10 IN.,GIBSON GIRL,MR.WADDLES ARRIVES
  LATE.......................................................   22.50
ROYAL DOULTON PLATE,10 IN.,MONK IN WINE CELLAR.............   12.00
ROYAL DOULTON PLATE,10 IN.,PRYDE GOETH BEFORE A FALL.......   18.00
ROYAL DOULTON PLATE,10 IN.,SAIL BOATS,YELLOW,GREEN & BROWN..   17.50
ROYAL DOULTON PLATE,10 IN.,SHAKESPEARE.....................   10.00
ROYAL DOULTON PLATE,10 IN.,THE BOOKWORM....................   18.00
ROYAL DOULTON PLATE,10 IN.,THE DOCTOR......................   16.50
ROYAL DOULTON PLATE,10 IN.,THE GYPSIES.....................   15.00
ROYAL DOULTON PLATE,10 IN.,THE OLD WITCH...................   15.00
ROYAL DOULTON PLATE,10 IN.,WHALE BOATS WITH SAILS..........   25.00
ROYAL DOULTON PLATE,BABY,ARTIST SIGNED,JACK & JILL.........    8.00
ROYAL DOULTON PLATE,BABY,ARTIST SIGNED,OLD WOMAN WHITHER SO
  HIGH.......................................................    9.00
ROYAL DOULTON PLATE,BABY,ARTIST SIGNED,SUSAN RABBIT & SON...   12.00
ROYAL DOULTON PLATE,BLUE ON WHITE,MARTHA & GEORGE
  WASHINGTON,PAIR............................................   12.50
ROYAL DOULTON PLATE,BUNNYKINS,RUNNING RABBITS EDGE..........    6.50
ROYAL DOULTON PLATE,DICKENSWARE,8 IN. SQUARE,MR.MICAWBER....   10.00
ROYAL DOULTON PLATE,DICKENSWARE,10 IN.,LITTLE NELL.........   12.00
ROYAL DOULTON PLATE,ENGLISH COTTAGE SCENE,10 IN............   10.00
ROYAL DOULTON PLATE FOR CHILD,RIDE A COCK HORSE.............    4.50
ROYAL DOULTON PLATE,GIBSON GIRL,SHE GOES INTO COLOURS.......   22.00
ROYAL DOULTON PLATE,PAIR 9 IN. PICTURE,ORLANDO & ROSALIND...   35.00
ROYAL DOULTON PLATE,PAIR,EXPOSITION,HEART SHAPED............   16.00
ROYAL DOULTON PLATE,PAIR,FAGIN.............................   22.00
ROYAL DOULTON PLATE,WALL,PAIR,9 IN.,SHAKESPEAREAN..........   50.00
ROYAL DOULTON PLATTER,OCTAGONAL,BLUE WITH PINK FLOWERS......   10.00
ROYAL DOULTON PUNCH BOWL,PEDESTAL BASE,GREEN MARK,STAGE
  COACH SCENES...............................................  150.00
ROYAL DOULTON SALAD PLATES,OCTAGONAL,BLUE WITH PINK FLOWERS.    4.50
ROYAL DOULTON SOUP BOWLS,OCTAGONAL,BLUE WITH PINK FLOWERS...    5.50
ROYAL DOULTON SUGAR,COVERED.................................   12.50
ROYAL DOULTON SUGAR,COVERED,LEEDS SPRAYS,OCTAGON SHAPED.....    5.00
ROYAL DOULTON SUGAR,OCTAGONAL,BLUE WITH PINK FLOWERS........    7.50
ROYAL DOULTON TEAPOT,HANDPAINTED............................   15.00
ROYAL DOULTON TEAPOT,YELLOW POPPY & GREEN PODS..............    8.00
ROYAL DOULTON TOOTHBRUSH HOLDER,OLIVE GREEN.................   10.00
ROYAL DOULTON TUMBLER,CREAM,GREEN RIM,COACHING SCENE........    8.50
ROYAL DOULTON TUREEN,COVERED,SUNFLOWER PATTERN.............   25.00
ROYAL DOULTON VASE,PAIR 8 IN. HANDLED,THE JACKDAW OF RHEIMS.   35.00
ROYAL DOULTON VASE,RED BACKGROUND WITH LANDSCAPE,FLAMBE
  MARKED.....................................................   53.50
ROYAL DUX BOWL,OVAL SHELL-LIKE.............................   75.00
ROYAL DUX FIGURE,GRECIAN,18 IN. TALL.......................  165.00
ROYAL DUX FIGURINE,BOY & GIRL LOVERS,DOUBLE,BOHEMIA.........  165.00
ROYAL DUX FIGURINE,GIRL CLINGING TO SHOULDER OF ROMAN
```

```
WARRIOR,BOHEMIA...................................................  85.00
ROYAL DUX FIGURINE,MAIDEN IN GRECIAN CLOTHES,RED TRIA MARK..  75.00
ROYAL DUX FIGURINE MAN,17 IN. TALL......................... 150.00
ROYAL DUX FIGURINES,PAIR BOY & GIRL CARRYING BASKETS,MARKED
  BOHEMIA................................................... 155.00
ROYAL DUX PLANTER,FIGURINE BOY-CHILD PLAYING FLUTE,BOHEMIA..  50.00
ROYAL DUX PLANTER,RED TRIA MARK,IVORY BEIGE BACKGROUND WITH
  GOLD.....................................................  32.00
ROYAL DUX VASE,10 IN.,WHITE WITH GOLD,BOHEMIA..............  90.00
ROYAL DUX VASE,11 IN. TALL,GOLD CHERRIES & LEAVES,HANDLED...  40.00
```

ROYAL FLEMISH GLASS was made during the late 1880's in New Bedford, Massachusetts, by the Mount Washington Glass Works. It is a colored satin glass decorated in dark colors with gold designs.

```
ROYAL FLEMISH STEEPLE-TOP COVERED ROSE JAR,GREEN,YELLOW &
  MULBERRY.............................................1,650.00
ROYAL MUNICH SHAVING MUG,ROSES.............................  18.50
    ROYAL RUDOSTADT, SEE RUDOSTADT.........................
ROYAL RUDOLSTADT CHEESE DISH,BEIGE WITH PINK ROSES..........  25.00
ROYAL RUDOLSTADT DRESSER TRAY,HOTEL ASTOR,LAVENDER MUMS.....   5.50
ROYAL RUDOLSTADT OPEN HANDLES CAKE PLATE,MOSS GREEN,MARKED
  PRUSSIA..................................................  10.00
ROYAL RUDOLSTADT OVAL-SHAPED COVERED SUGAR,SATIN FINISH,PINK  10.00
ROYAL RUDOLSTADT PICKLE DISH,OPEN HANDLES,WHITE ROSES,GOLD
  TRIM.....................................................   5.75
ROYAL RUDOLSTADT PICKLE,OPEN HANDLED,8 IN...................   6.85
ROYAL RUDOLSTADT PRUSSIA HANDPAINTED SIGNED 6 IN.
  PLATE,ORANGE POPPIES.....................................  16.50
ROYAL VIENNA 15 PIECE TEA SET,BEEHIVE MARK,IN THIN WOOD CASE 175.00
ROYAL VIENNA CELERY,HANDPAINTED GREEN,YELLOW & RED ROSES....  25.00
ROYAL VIENNA CHOCOLATE POT,PINK & WHITE ROSES..............   8.50
ROYAL VIENNA COMPOTE ON CIRCULAR BASE,BEEHIVE MARK..........  32.50
ROYAL VIENNA COVERED URN,BLUE BEEHIVE MARK,HANDPAINTED SCENE
  2 FEMALES................................................  75.00
ROYAL VIENNA CUP & SAUCER,DEMI-TASSE,BLUE BEEHIVE MARK,PINK
  BORDER...................................................  12.00
ROYAL VIENNA CUP & SAUCER,DEMI-TASSE,SCROLLS WITH GOLD......  10.00
ROYAL VIENNA DISH,OBLONG,HANDPAINTED GREEN,YELLOW & RED
  ROSES....................................................  12.50
ROYAL VIENNA PLATE,10 IN.,WOMAN BY FOUNTAIN,BLUE BEEHIVE
  MARK.....................................................  60.00
ROYAL VIENNA PLATE,HANDPAINTED PINK & WHITE ROSES & FOLIAGE.   8.75
ROYAL VIENNA PLATE,PORTRAIT,8 IN.,........................  32.50
ROYAL VIENNA PLATE,PORTRAIT,9 IN.,CERISE-BURGUNDY,AMICITIA..  39.00
ROYAL VIENNA PLATE,PORTRAIT ROMAN MATRON,BEEHIVE MARK.......  75.00
ROYAL VIENNA PLATE,QUEEN LOUISE,BLUE MARK UNDER GLAZE.......  62.50
ROYAL VIENNA TEA CADDY,HANDPAINTED GRECIAN WOMEN,BEEHIVE
  MARK.....................................................  95.00
ROYAL VIENNA VASE,8 IN. TALL..............................  75.00
ROYAL VIENNA VASE,BLUE BEEHIVE MARK.......................  40.00
ROYAL VIENNA VASE,BLUE BEEHIVE MARK,2 GOLD HANDLES..........  45.00
ROYAL VIENNA VASE,URN TYPE,CLASSICAL FIGURES
  HANDPAINTED,BEEHIVE MARK.................................  90.00
```

ROYAL WORCESTER PORCELAIN AND POTTERY was made in England from 1862 to the present time. The factory was founded in 1751 but a different name was used.

```
    ROYAL WORCESTER, SEE ALSO WORCESTER.....................
ROYAL WORCESTER BISCUIT JAR,PURPLE MARK,PEACH BACKGROUND
  WITH FLORAL..............................................  95.00
ROYAL WORCESTER BOWL,CONCH SHELL SHAPE & PATTERN,PINK.......  24.50
ROYAL WORCESTER BOX,1 X 2 IN.,LIFT TOP,HANDPAINTED FLOWERS..  18.00
ROYAL WORCESTER BOX,PILL,COVERED...........................  20.00
ROYAL WORCESTER CAKE SET,7 PIECES,CIRCA 1830,CREAM
  BACKGROUND...............................................  38.50
```

```
ROYAL WORCESTER CAKE SET,STAND & 6 PLATES,HANDPAINTED
  ,PEDESTAL BASE......................................   125.00
ROYAL WORCESTER CONCH SHELL,RIBBED PATTERN ON BEIGE.........  18.00
ROYAL WORCESTER CREAMER,2-HANDLED,2-SPOUTED,1862-91.........  15.00
ROYAL WORCESTER CREAMER,JASPER,PINK,GREEN MEDALLION,OVAL....  22.00
ROYAL WORCESTER CUP & SAUCER,DEMI-TASSE,FOOTED,CREAM WITH
  RUST FLOWERS.....................................          12.00
ROYAL WORCESTER CUP & SAUCER,DEMI-TASSE,PURPLE MARK ENGLAND
  1893.............................................          17.50
ROYAL WORCESTER DISH,OPEN,SHELL,ENAMELED DECORATED..........  82.50
ROYAL WORCESTER EGG CUP,PURPLE MARK ,GOLD LINER & BANDS.....  15.00
ROYAL WORCESTER EWER,9 IN.,DATED 1862-91,SALAMANDER IN GOLD.  75.00
ROYAL WORCESTER EWER,SALAMANDER WITH RED EYES FORMING HANDLE  85.00
ROYAL WORCESTER FIGURE,PAIR,2 FEMALES HOLDING BIRD.......... 250.00
ROYAL WORCESTER FIGURINE,SEATED LADY,PLAYING MANDOLIN.......  45.00
ROYAL WORCESTER FIGURINE,SOLDIER,CITY IMPERIAL
  VOLUNTEER,GOLD TRIM..............................          45.00
ROYAL WORCESTER HOLDER,FLOWER,BASKETWEAVE PATTERN ON BEIGE..  12.00
ROYAL WORCESTER JAR,PAIR,RETICULATED ROSE LEAF,PEDESTAL.....  75.00
ROYAL WORCESTER MUG,MINIATURE KINGS........................  12.00
ROYAL WORCESTER PITCHER,4 IN. TALL,GOLD HANDLE,YELLOW & BLUE  28.00
ROYAL WORCESTER PITCHER,6 IN. TALL,MARKED,HANDPAINTED.......  38.00
ROYAL WORCESTER PITCHER,GREEN CIRCLE & CROWN MARK...........  55.00
ROYAL WORCESTER PITCHER,HELMET SPOUT,HANDPAINTED............  23.00
ROYAL WORCESTER PITCHER,IVORY WHITE WITH EMBOSSED LEAVES....  22.00
ROYAL WORCESTER PITCHER,MINIATURE,HANDPAINTED...............  12.00
ROYAL WORCESTER PITCHER,PINK ROSES,YELLOW DAISIES,BACHELOR
  BUTTONS..........................................          59.00
ROYAL WORCESTER PITCHER,SPRAYS OF FLOWERS ON BEIGE,GOLD.....  89.50
ROYAL WORCESTER PITCHER,TANKARD SHAPE,ELEPHANT TRUNK
  HANDLE,GREEN MARK................................          35.00
ROYAL WORCESTER PITCHER-VASE,ENGLAND,PURPLE MARK,HANDPAINTED
  & SIGNED.........................................          50.00
ROYAL WORCESTER PLANTER,RAMS HEAD HANDLES,CAPO-DI-MONTE
  DECOR............................................          85.00
ROYAL WORCESTER PLATE,BIRD,PINK & GOLD BORDER...............  22.50
ROYAL WORCESTER PLATE,GAME,PAIR,ENGLAND,2 STORKS OVER COIN
  MOON.............................................          35.00
ROYAL WORCESTER PLATE,HANDPAINTED MOSS ROSE,LOW
  PEDESTAL,BLUE & GOLD.............................          35.00
ROYAL WORCESTER PLATE,LEAF,PURPLE CIRCLE & CROWN MARK.......  35.00
ROYAL WORCESTER PLATE,PAIR 8 IN.,YELLOW DESIGN..............   6.00
ROYAL WORCESTER PLATE,PORCELAIN MARK CIRCA 1839,PAIR........ 195.00
ROYAL WORCESTER PLATE,SET OF 6,PURPLE MARK MADE IN ENGLAND
  1893.............................................          65.00
ROYAL WORCESTER PLATE,SET OF 12,8 IN.,SQUARE,CHANTILLY......  60.00
ROYAL WORCESTER ROSEBOWL,GOLD RIM AT RUFFLED TOP............  20.00
ROYAL WORCESTER SALT SHAKER,PURPLE MARK,GOLD BANDS,2 IN.....  15.00
ROYAL WORCESTER SERVICE,BREAKFAST,12 PIECES,ENGADINE........  35.00
ROYAL WORCESTER TEAPOT,MARKED,CIRCA 1870,6 IN. HIGH,CHINESE
  DECOR............................................          60.00
ROYAL WORCESTER SOUP TUREEN WITH PLATTER,BROWN IVY LEAF
  PATTERN..........................................         125.00
ROYAL WORCESTER TURKEY PLATTER,CHANTILLY PATTERN............  35.00
ROYAL WORCESTER VASE,2 GOLD LEAF HANDLES,CREAM BACKGROUND
  WITH FLOWERS.....................................          60.00
ROYAL WORCESTER VASE,6 IN. TALL,HANDPAINTED................  28.00
ROYAL WORCESTER VASE, 9IN. ,HANDLES, MATT FINISH...........  57.00
ROYAL WORCESTER VASE,9 IN. TALL,INVERTED SNAIL SHAPE,YELLOW
  & BROWN..........................................          95.00
ROYAL WORCESTER VASE,DATE 1901,10 IN. TALL,FLORAL ON MATT...  50.00
ROYAL WORCESTER VASE,DECORATED IN HANDPAINTED ROSES & RED...  16.50
ROYAL WORCESTER VASE,DOUBLE OPENING WITH HANDLE,GREEN MARK,8
  IN. LONG.........................................          45.00
ROYAL WORCESTER VASE,RUFFLED TOP,FLORALS & BUDS ON BEIGE....  28.00
```

ROYAL WORCESTER VASE,URN SHAPE,GOLD BAND TOP,PEDESTAL BASE..	22.00
ROZANNE HANDLED VASE,DOG PORTRAIT OF A ST.BERNARD............	45.00
ROZANNE SIGNED ART POTTERY 10 IN. VASE,BROWN TO RUST & OLIVE GREEN..	22.00
ROZANNE VASE,SIGNED..	15.00
ROZANNE VASE,TIGER EYE,BROWN,10 IN. TALL......................	19.50
ROZANNE WARE ROYAL 6 IN. GREEN VASE,GRAY LEAVES..............	12.50
RUBINA VERDE BASKET,RIBBED,VASELINE TO CRANBERRY EDGE........	38.00
RUBINA VERDE BASKET,OVERSHOT,CRIMPED CRANBERRY EDGE..........	32.00
RUBINA VERDE BOAT,BANANA,FOOTED...............................	32.50
RUBINA VERDE BOTTLE,PERFUME...................................	37.50
RUBINA VERDE BOWL,FINGER,EXPANDED DIAMOND.....................	22.00
RUBINA VERDE BUCKET,ENAMEL DECOR,SILVER RIM & HANDLE.........	45.00
RUBINA VERDE CASTOR,PICKLE,BABY THUMBPRINT,SILVER PLATE FRAME...	79.00
RUBINA VERDE CUP,PUNCH,SET OF 4...............................	12.50
RUBINA VERDE DECANTER,APPLIED ROPE HANDLE & CUT STOPPER......	75.00
RUBINA VERDE JELLY DISH,SILVER PLATE HANDLE & LID............	48.50
RUBINA VERDE LIQUOR BOTTLE....................................	45.00
RUBINA VERDE MUFFINEER,ENGLISH,PANELLED,SILVER PLATED TOP...	30.00
RUBINA VERDE MUFFINEER,SILVER PLATE TOP,CUT GLASS............	27.50
RUBINA VERDE PITCHER,WATER,OPALESCENT SWIRL..................	85.00
RUBINA VERDE ROSEBOWL...	35.00
RUBINA VERDE SALT,MASTER,CANE PATTERN,CUT GLASS,SILVER RIM..	16.00
RUBINA VERDE SPOONER,SCALLOPED RIM,INVERTED THUMBPRINT......	25.00
RUBINA VERDE TUMBLER..	24.00
RUBINA VERDE TUMBLER,BABY INVERTED THUMBPRINT................	20.00
RUBINA VERDE VASE,9 IN. TALL,ENAMEL DECORATION..............	150.00
RUBINA VERDE VASE,10 IN.,APPLIED CLEAR RUFFLE................	60.00
RUBINA VERDE VASE,APPLIED CLEAR GLASS RIGAREE AROUND BODY...	23.00
RUBINA VERDE VASE,BLOWN,RUBY TO CLEAR,APPLIED GREEN LEAF....	27.00
RUBINA VERDE VASE,CONE SHAPED,RUFFLE TOP WITH APPLIED GLASS.	35.00
RUBINA VERDE VASE,EPERGNE,WITH OPALESCENT GLASS..............	40.00
RUBINA VERDE VASE,HANDLED & FOOTED,GREEN TO PINK.............	50.00
RUBINA VERDE VASE,JACK IN PULPIT,CRIMPED TOP.................	27.00
RUBINA VERDE VASE,JACK-IN-THE-PULPIT,DECORATED,CRANBERRY TO VASELINE..	57.50
RUBINA VERDE VASE,NOTCHED COLUMNS.............................	20.00
RUBINA VERDE VASE,PAIR,PANELED GOLD & WHITE ENAMEL DECOR....	34.00
RUBINA VERDE WATER PITCHER,INVERTED THUMBPRINT,YELLOW TO CRANBERRY..	135.00

RUBY GLASS is a dark red color. It was a Victorian and twentieth-century ware. Unfortunately the name means many different types of red glass.

RUBY GLASS BERRY BOWL & 6 DISHES,FLASHED.....................	55.00
RUBY GLASS BOX,JEWEL,HINGED,ENAMELED DECOR,BRASS RIM & FEET.	32.00
RUBY GLASS CHAMPAGNE GLASS,BOHEMIAN...........................	8.00
RUBY GLASS COMPOTE,STEMMED,EGGERMAN PATTERN DEER & CASTLE,BOHEMIAN,1884..	45.00
RUBY GLASS COMPOTE,THUMBPRINT.................................	20.00
RUBY GLASS CONSOLE SET,DISH & SINGLE CANDLESTICK.............	50.00
RUBY GLASS CORDIAL,FOOTED,THUMBPRINT,PAIR.....................	14.00
RUBY GLASS CREAMER,KINGS CROWN................................	12.50
RUBY GLASS CUP AND SAUCER.....................................	1.50
RUBY GLASS CUP & SAUCER,THUMBPRINT............................	16.00
RUBY GLASS DECANTER & 6 WINES,BOHEMIAN,DEER,CASTLE..........	70.00
RUBY GLASS PITCHER & 6 TUMBLERS,EGGERMAN,INTAGLIO CARVED & FROSTED...	75.00
RUBY GLASS PITCHER,TANKARD,SOUVENIR,WITH CLEAR...............	27.00
RUBY GLASS SALT & PEPPER SHAKERS WITH THUMBPRINT BOTTOM.....	20.00
RUBY GLASS SUGAR,SPOONER & CREAMER,COVERED,TRIPLE TRIANGLE..	50.00
RUBY GLASS SUGAR BOWL & CREAMER,BOHEMIAN......................	30.00
RUBY GLASS TUMBLER,EGGERMAN PATTERN DEER & CASTLE,BOHEMIAN..	7.50
RUBY GLASS VASE,PAIR,EGGERMAN PATTERN DEER & CASTLE,1900,BOHEMIAN...	35.00

RUBY GLASS VASE,6 IN.,ETCHED BIRD & CASTLE,DATED
1884,BOHEMIAN... 12.00
RUBY GLASS WINE SET DATED 1886,DECANTER & 6 GLASSES,BOHEMIAN 62.50
RUBY GLASS WINE SET,DEER & CASTLE PATTERN,DATED
1894,BOHEMIAN... 28.50

RUDOLSTADT PORCELAIN was made in Thuringia, Germany, from 1854 to the twentieth century.
RUDOLSTADT 12 IN. VASE...................................... 15.00
RUDOLSTADT COPPER LUSTER VASE............................... 24.00
RUDOLSTADT PITCHER,GOLD BOW HANDLE.......................... 15.00
RUDOLSTADT PLATE,LITTLE CHILDREN AT PLAY.................... 2.50
RUDOLSTADT VASE,SIGNED GERMANY,FLORAL DECOR................. 25.00
RUG,HOOKED,31 X 57 IN.,3 HORSES & SULKIES,AMERICAN
FLAG,FARMER,COWS... 350.00
RUSSIAN, DECORATED GOOSE SIZE EGG.......................... 92.00
RUSSIAN ENAMEL SPOON,HALLMARKED,ENAMELED PIERCED BOWL....... 125.00
RUSSIAN MARKED ENAMEL SILVER SPOON,TWISTED
HANDLE,ST.PETERSBURG....................................... 35.00
RUSSIAN SILVER MARKED DEMI-TASSE SPOON,RIBBED HANDLES,...... 12.00
RUSSIAN SILVER MARKED TEA SPOON,EMBOSSED HANDLE DATED 1859.. 22.50

SADDLE, CIVIL WAR.. 20.00
SADDLE,SIDE,LEATHER.. 50.00
SADDLE STIRRUP FROM SIDE SADDLE,LADIES..................... 2.50
SADDLE STIRRUP TO SIDE SADDLE,METAL,METAL SHOE SOLE INSIDE.. 50.00
SADDLE US CAVALRY,IRON STIRRUPS............................ 15.00
SADDLE,WOOD TREE,RAWHIDE COVERED,SILVER PLAQUE IN PUMMEL.... 175.00

SALOPIAN WARE was made by the Caughley factory of England during the eighteenth century. The early pieces were decorated in blue and white with some colored decorations. Many of the pieces called Salopian are elaborate, colored-transfer design, decorated tablewares made during the late nineteenth century.
SALOPIAN 8 IN. SHALLOW DISH................................ 25.00
SALOPIAN CUP & SAUCER,BLUE EDGE............................ 35.00
SALOPIAN HANDLELESS CUP & SAUCER,PRINCE & PEASANT.......... 95.00
SALT BOX,FLOW BLUE TRIM,PORCELAIN,HINGED WOODEN LID........ 12.00
SALT BOX,WOODEN OPEN HANGING PINE.......................... 16.00
SALT GLAZE APOSTLE TEAPOT,SUGAR BOWL,CREAMER,SIGNED,CHARLES
MEIGH.. 450.00

SALT GLAZE is a hard, shiny glaze that was developed for pottery during the eighteenth century. It is still being made.
SALT GLAZE BEER MUG ,1/2 LITRES,BLUE,MADE IN GERMANY....... 25.00
SALT GLAZE CHARGER,15 IN.,ENGLISH,CIRCA 1750............... 90.00
SALT GLAZE CREAMER,WHITE,BRICK PATTERN,2 ROYAL BLUE BANDS... 9.50
SALT GLAZE PITCHER,7 IN. HIGH,WHEAT TOP BAND.............. 25.00
SALT GLAZE PITCHER,BEIGE,HUNTING SCENE WITH 4 HOUNDS,TAVERN
SCENE.. 43.00
SALT GLAZE PITCHER,COBALT FLORAL DECORATED IN RELIEF....... 21.50
SALT GLAZE PITCHER,GREEN,BAMBOO DESIGN,ROPE HANDLE......... 20.00
SALT GLAZE PITCHER,MILK,MORNING GLORY...................... 21.00
SALT GLAZE PITCHER,SYRUP WITH PEWTER LID,JAMES & WALLEY,GOOD
SAMARITAN.. 35.00
SALT GLAZE PITCHER,WATER,HUNTING SCENE..................... 65.00
SALT GLAZE PITCHER,WATER,NAPOLEON BATTLE,BACKGROUND
VIOLET,CIRCA 1830.. 100.00
SALT GLAZE PITCHER,WATER,RIDGEWAYS,1835,EMBOSSED DEER...... 50.00
SALT GLAZE PITCHER,WHITE,9 IN.,RAISED CORAL PATTERN,1861... 22.00
SALT GLAZE PITCHER WITH HINGED PEWTER LID,SIGNED,BLUE WITH
ACANTHUS... 38.00
SALT GLAZE PITCHER WITH PEWTER LID &
FINIAL,WHITE,KNIGHTS,SHIELDS............................... 33.50
SALT GLAZE SUGAR,MORNING GLORY............................. 25.00

```
SALT GLAZE SYRUP,PEWTER TOP,EMBOSSED LEAVES AND FLOWERS.....     22.00
SALT GLAZE TEAPOT,MINIATURE,BASKETWEAVE,PEWTER TOP,1871.....     26.00
SALT GLAZE TEAPOT,WHITE WITH EMBOSSED LEAVES &
  FLOWERS,SIGNED.................................................     40.00
```

SAMPLERS were made in the United States during the early 1700's. The best examples were made from 1790 to 1840. Long narrow samplers are usually older than the square ones. Early samplers just had stitching or alphabets. The later examples had numerals, borders, and pictorial decorations. Those with mottos are mid-Victorian

```
SAMPLER,8 X 8 IN.,MAROON,BIRDS & FLOWERS......................      7.50
SAMPLER,9 IN. BY 10 IN. ,NOT DATED............................      5.00
SAMPLER,A LITTLE PEACEFUL HOME POEM WITH SETTING..............      6.00
SAMPLER,BIRDS,FLOWERS & VERSES DATED 1841,FRAMED.............     50.00
SAMPLER DATED 1805,MAHOGANY FRAME............................     60.00
SAMPLER,DARAH SHEE,NOV.10,1813,ALPHABET & NUMBERS AND FLOWER
  CLUSTERS...................................................     65.00
SAMPLER DATED 1821..........................................     24.25
SAMPLER DATE 1837,FRAMED....................................     47.25
SAMPLER DATED 1847..........................................     25.00
SAMPLER DATE 1848...........................................     15.00
SAMPLER,DOUBLE..............................................     28.00
SAMPLER,FRAMED,HOMESPUN ECRU,SIGNED.........................     17.50
SAMPLER,FRAMED,TURNER FAMILY CIRCA 1838.....................     50.00
SAMPLER,NEW YORK WITH NAME OF SYMON CRYGIER DATED 1734......    275.00
SAMPLER,SWEET HOME,BIRD AT NEST.............................      9.00
SAMPLER,THE LORDS PRAYER,11 IN. X 14 IN.....................      6.00
SAMPLER,WALNUT FRAME WITH GOLD LINER,GOD BLESS OUR HOME.....      8.50
SAMPLER,WALNUT FRAME WITH GOLD LINER,THE OLD OAKEN BUCKET...      8.50
```

SANDWICH GLASS is any one of the myriad types of glass made by the Boston and Sandwich Glass Works in Sandwich, Massachusetts, between 1825 and 1888. It is often very difficult to be sure whether a piece was really made at the Sandwich factory because so many types were made there and similar pieces were made at other glass factories.

```
SANDWICH GLASS BASKET,BLOWN SWIRL-PANELED RUBY,GOLD SPATTER
  IN GLASS..................................................     20.00
SANDWICH GLASS BASKET,TORTOISE SHELL........................     45.00
SANDWICH GLASS BASKET WITH HANDLE,PINK WITH FLUTED GREEN....     30.00
SANDWICH GLASS BERRY,FESTOON,FLINT..........................      6.00
SANDWICH GLASS BOTTLE,SMELLING,AMETHYST WITH FLORAL
  DECOR,METAL TOP...........................................      8.50
SANDWICH GLASS BOTTLE,SMELLING,BLACK AMETHYST WITH METAL CAP      8.50
SANDWICH GLASS BOTTLE,TOILET,CANARY YELLOW..................     42.00
SANDWICH GLASS BOWL,BERRY,FESTOON,FLINT.....................     14.50
SANDWICH GLASS BOWL,FINGER,COBALT BLUE......................     10.00
SANDWICH GLASS BOWL,FINGER,OVERSHOT.........................     10.00
SANDWICH GLASS BOWL,FINGER,SET,RIBBED,THREADED CRANBERRY ON
  CLEAR....................................................     35.00
SANDWICH GLASS BOWL,FINGER,THREADED,DIAMOND QUILTED.........     33.00
SANDWICH GLASS BOWL,LACY HEART & LYRE BORDER................     95.00
SANDWICH GLASS BUTTER,COVERED,RIPPLE........................     16.00
SANDWICH GLASS BUTTER DISH,LACY DAISY.......................     16.50
SANDWICH GLASS CANDLEHOLDER,PAIR,LACY GREEN.................      5.00
SANDWICH GLASS CANDLESTICK,DOLPHIN,CANARY,DOUBLE BASE,PAIR,9
  IN. TALL.................................................    295.00
SANDWICH GLASS CANDLESTICK,PAIR,8 IN.,CLEAR.................     35.00
SANDWICH GLASS CANDLESTICK,PAIR,DOLPHIN,BLUE TOPS,CLAMBROTH
  BASE.....................................................    475.00
SANDWICH GLASS CELERY,TREE OF LIFE..........................     15.00
SANDWICH GLASS CELERY VASE,IVY,CLEAR........................     85.00
SANDWICH GLASS COLOGNE,BLUE.................................     38.50
SANDWICH GLASS COMPOTE,COVERED,LACY,FRENCH..................     85.00
SANDWICH GLASS COMPOTE,COVERED,PEDESTAL,OVAL MITRE PATTERN..     75.00
SANDWICH GLASS COMPOTE,OPALESCENT,MINIATURE.................     30.00
```

```
SANDWICH GLASS CREAM PITCHER,TANKARD TYPE,FESTOON,FLINT.....      12.50
SANDWICH GLASS CREAMER,COVERED SUGAR & SPOONER,CHAIN........      30.00
SANDWICH GLASS CREAMER & SUGAR,OPEN........................      40.00
SANDWICH GLASS CUP PLATE
  14.00  TO...............................................      15.00
SANDWICH GLASS CUP PLATE,52 SCALLOPS ON EDGE,4 FLEUR DE LIS
  CENTER..................................................      15.00
SANDWICH GLASS CUP PLATE,BENJAMIN FRANKLIN FRIGATE.........      15.00
SANDWICH GLASS CUP PLATE,HEARTS...........................      10.50
SANDWICH GLASS CUP PLATE,LACY,12 HEARTS WITH 4 HEART CENTER.      7.50
SANDWICH GLASS CUP PLATE,RAY PATTERN......................      8.50
SANDWICH GLASS CUP PLATE,SANDWICH STAR....................      5.00
SANDWICH GLASS CUP,PUNCH,PINK OVERSHOT,CLEAR HANDLE........      24.00
SANDWICH GLASS DECANTER,FLAT DIAMOND & PANEL..............      40.00
SANDWICH GLASS DECANTER,PAIR,2 BLOWN STOPPER,1 PRESSED.....     135.00
SANDWICH GLASS DISH,CANDY,LACY,4 IN.,HANDLE...............      6.00
SANDWICH GLASS DISH,CELERY,FESTOON,FLINT..................      14.00
SANDWICH GLASS DISH,COVERED,GOLD DECORATED BOTTOM TO WHITE..     125.00
SANDWICH GLASS DISH,COVERED,PAIR..........................      18.00
SANDWICH GLASS DISH,CRANBERRY OVERSHOT....................      35.00
SANDWICH GLASS DISH,HONEY.................................      3.00
SANDWICH GLASS DISH,HONEY,& 6 DISHES,OCTAGONAL............      37.50
SANDWICH GLASS DISH,HONEY,4 IN.,ROMAN ROSETTE.............      6.00
SANDWICH GLASS DISH,HONEY,INDIVIDUAL......................      12.50
SANDWICH GLASS DISH,HONEY,PEACOCK EYE.....................      6.50
SANDWICH GLASS DISH,OAK LEAF..............................      32.50
SANDWICH GLASS DISH,OVAL,LACY
  75.00  TO...............................................      85.00
SANDWICH GLASS DISH,OVERSHOT,SHELL SHAPED.................      15.00
SANDWICH GLASS DISH,PICKLE,PALMETTE.......................      7.00
SANDWICH GLASS DISH,RAYED PEACOCK EYE,5 IN................      25.00
SANDWICH GLASS DISH,SAUCE,LACY PLUME......................      8.00
SANDWICH GLASS DISH,SAUCE,LACY,RAYED PEACOCK EYE..........      22.50
SANDWICH GLASS DOOR KNOBS,PAIR,COBALT.....................      22.50
SANDWICH GLASS DRAWER PULL,PAIR,LACY OPALESCENT...........      12.50
SANDWICH GLASS EGG CUP,FOOTED,RIBBED PALM,FLINT...........      15.00
SANDWICH GLASS EPERGNE,GREEN & OPALESCENT.................      97.50
SANDWICH GLASS EWER,FIREGLOW,7 IN.,DECORATED..............     125.00
SANDWICH GLASS JAR,CONDIMENT IN SILVER PLATE
  FRAME,COVERED,OVERSHOT..................................      79.00
SANDWICH GLASS JAR,JAM,FESTOON,FLINT......................      17.50
SANDWICH GLASS JAR,POMADE,TRANSLUCENT BLUE................      50.00
SANDWICH GLASS LAMP FONT FOR BRACKET HOLDER,CLAMWATER,BRASS
  COLLAR..................................................      22.00
SANDWICH GLASS LAMP,HAND,BLUE OPAQUE,OPAL APPLIED
  HANDLE,GOLD.............................................      50.00
SANDWICH GLASS MUSTARD MUG,LACY PEACOCK EYE...............      35.00
SANDWICH GLASS NUT CUP,FUCHSIA,FLUTED EDGE WITH WHITE
  THREADING...............................................      25.00
SANDWICH GLASS OBELISK,INTAGLIO CUT.......................      17.50
SANDWICH GLASS PICKLE,RIBBED PALM,FLINT...................      15.00
SANDWICH GLASS PITCHER,4 IN. TALL.........................      25.00
SANDWICH GLASS PITCHER,BLADDER............................      65.00
SANDWICH GLASS PITCHER,BULLS EYE & FLEUR DE LIS,APPLIED
  HANDLE..................................................      48.00
SANDWICH GLASS PITCHER,OVERSHOT...........................      95.00
SANDWICH GLASS PITCHER,OVERSHOT,ROPE HANDLE & AROUND NECK...      60.00
SANDWICH GLASS PITCHER,OVERSHOT SAPPHIRE BLUE.............      62.00
SANDWICH GLASS PITCHER,TANKARD SHAPE,OVERSHOT RUBINA......      50.00
SANDWICH GLASS PITCHER,WATER,OPALESCENT COIN SPOT.........      47.50
SANDWICH GLASS PITCHER,WATER,RUBY & WHITE SPLOTCHED,SILVER
  MICA....................................................      88.50
SANDWICH GLASS PITCHER,WATER,TANKARD TYPE,FESTOON,FLINT.....      19.50
SANDWICH GLASS PLATE,7 IN.,LUTZ THREADED,BLUE,OPAQUE RIBBONS      20.00
SANDWICH GLASS PLATE,11 IN.,FISH SCALE....................      7.00
```

SANDWICH GLASS PLATE,CAKE,9 IN.,HANDLED,DAHLIA.............. 12.50
SANDWICH GLASS PLATE,CAKE,LACY BEEHIVE PATTERN,OCTAGONAL.... 55.00
SANDWICH GLASS PLATE,FAN & WAFFLE,CIRCA 1828................ 25.00
SANDWICH GLASS PLATE,LACY PEACOCK EYE,6 IN.................. 45.00
SANDWICH GLASS PLATE,LACY,RAYED PEACOCK EYE................. 57.50
SANDWICH GLASS PLATE,OVERLAY,WHITE ENAMEL,GOLD TRIM,MIXED
  FLOWERS... 85.00
SANDWICH GLASS PLATE,TODDY,LACY,PEACOCK EYE................. 19.50
SANDWICH GLASS PLATE WITH AMBERINA COLOURING,LUTS-TYPE
  THREADING.. 25.00
SANDWICH GLASS ROSEBOWL,OVERSHOT SAPPHIRE BLUE.............. 135.00
SANDWICH GLASS SALT.. 16.00
SANDWICH GLASS SALT,FOOTED................................. 32.50
SANDWICH GLASS SALT,LACY,AMBER BEARDED MAN................. 37.50
SANDWICH GLASS SALT,LACY,BOAT.............................. 10.00
SANDWICH GLASS SALT,MASTER,3 IN. TALL...................... 12.00
SANDWICH GLASS SALT,MASTER,FOOTED,LILY PAD................. 10.00
SANDWICH GLASS SALT,MASTER,OPEN,RAYED PEACOCK EYE.......... 25.00
SANDWICH GLASS SAUCE,RIBBED PALM,FLINT..................... 8.00
SANDWICH GLASS SPILLHOLDER................................. 10.00
SANDWICH GLASS SPILL,RIBBED PINEAPPLE,FLINT................ 18.00
SANDWICH GLASS SPOONER,FESTOON,FLINT....................... 11.00
SANDWICH GLASS SPOONER,RIBBED PALM,FLINT................... 17.50
SANDWICH GLASS SUGAR & CREAMER,FOOTED,IVY IN SNOW,BLACK
  AMETHYST... 37.50
SANDWICH GLASS SUGAR BOWL,GOTHIC WITH COVER,CLEAR,5 IN. HIGH 40.00
SANDWICH GLASS SUGAR,COVERED,LACY GOTHIC ARCH.............. 50.00
SANDWICH GLASS SUGAR,RIBBED PALM,FLINT..................... 17.50
SANDWICH GLASS TIEBACKS,CURTAIN,BLUE ROSETTE,PEWTER
  ENDS,PAIR.. 6.00
SANDWICH GLASS TIEBACKS,OPALESCENT WITH METAL SHANKS....... 10.00
SANDWICH GLASS TIEBACKS,PAIR OPALESCENT LACY............... 40.00
SANDWICH GLASS TIEBACKS,PAIR PINK,PETAL & LOOP............. 10.00
SANDWICH GLASS TOOTHPICK,AMETHYST,IVY,FOOTED............... 75.00
SANDWICH GLASS TUMBLER,FESTOON,FLINT....................... 10.00
SANDWICH GLASS TUMBLER,INVERTED THUMBPRINT,COBALT TO CLEAR.. 27.50
SANDWICH GLASS TUMBLER,PINK & WHITE SPATTER................ 20.00
SANDWICH GLASS TUMBLER,RIBBED PALM,FLINT................... 17.00
SANDWICH GLASS TUMBLER,SAPPHIRE BLUE,ENAMELLED,GOLD........ 10.00
SANDWICH GLASS TUMBLER,THREADED GLASS,CANARY THREADS ON
  CANARY... 20.00
SANDWICH GLASS TUMBLER,THREADED TOP,CRANBERRY TO CLEAR...... 65.00
SANDWICH GLASS TUMBLER,TREE OF LIFE........................ 15.00
SANDWICH GLASS VASE,BUD,THREADED,CLEAR TO CRANBERRY,4 IN.
  HIGH... 20.00
SANDWICH GLASS VASE,CHRYSANTHEMUM LEAF,10 IN............... 25.00
SANDWICH GLASS VASE,CRANBERRY,9 IN.,PANELLED,ENAMELED
  FLOWERS & GOLD... 30.00
SANDWICH GLASS VASE,FROSTED MAIDEN HAIR FERN............... 23.00
SANDWICH GLASS VASE,GREEN TO PURPLE WITH RIGAREE AROUND..... 15.50
SANDWICH GLASS VASE,OPALESCENT,7 IN.,CASED,HOBNAIL ,AMBER
  FEET... 395.00
SANDWICH GLASS VASE,OVERSHOT,BULBOUS,GREEN................. 20.00
SANDWICH GLASS VASE,PAIR,CIRCLE & ELLIPSE,AMETHYST,7 IN..... 290.00
SANDWICH GLASS VASE,RUBY,BELLTONE,6 IN.,FOOTED,WHITE GRAPE &
  LEAF... 30.00
SANDWICH GLASS VASE,STICK,CLEAR PETAL & HEXAGON,7 IN........ 25.00

SARREGUEMINES POTTERY was first made in Lorraine, France, about 1770.
Most of the pieces found today date from the late nineteenth century.
SARREGUEMINES 8 IN. PLATE,FRENCH INSCRIPTION,FROG ON WATER
  BARREL... 7.00
SARREGUEMINES GREEN 10 IN. CAKE PLATE & 8 7 IN. MATCHING
  PLATES... 40.00
SARREGUEMINES FRENCH PLATE,ARTIST SIGNED,GUARDS SLEEPING

```
QUARTERS..............................................    9.00
SARREGUEMINES FRENCH PLATE,ARTIST SIGNED,THREE GUARDS AT
  PALACE GATE.........................................    9.00
SARRAGUEMINES JUG,BROWN GLAZE,2 TAN TREE BARK HANDLES.......   10.00
SARREGUEMINES NAPOLEONIC MILITARY PLATE,8 IN.
  ,MULTI-COLOURED.....................................   12.50
SARREGUEMINES NAPOLEON PLATE,WHITE BACKGROUND,BLACK
  TRANSFERS,GREEN.....................................    6.00
SARREGUEMINES PLATE,HUNTING SCENES....................    5.50
SARREGUEMINES PORTRAIT PLATE,GARFIELD.................   11.50
SARREGUEMINES SONG PLATE,SHEEP,BOY & GIRL SHEPHERDS,WINDMILL    9.00
```

SATIN GLASS is a late-nineteenth-century art glass. It has a dull finish that is caused by a hydrofluoric acid vapor treatment. Satin glass was made in many colors and was sometimes decorated with applied decorations.

```
SATIN GLASS BASKET BLACK..............................   35.00
SATIN GLASS BASKET,BRIDES,8 IN.,HOLDER,LAVENDER TO MAROON...   75.00
SATIN GLASS BASKET,BRIDES,11 IN.,WHITE TO PINK,RUFFLED BOWL.   80.00
SATIN GLASS BASKET,BRIDES,SILVER PLATE HOLDER,WHITE OUTSIDE.   75.00
SATIN GLASS BASKET,HANDLED,BLUE.......................   40.00
SATIN GLASS BERRY SET WITH ENAMEL FLOWERS,PINK........   37.50
SATIN GLASS BOBECHE,PAIR 3 SIDED WITH RUFFLED TOPS,YELLOW TO
  CLEAR..............................................   48.00
SATIN GLASS BOTTLE,DRESSER,WHITE,HANDPAINTED FLOWERS........   10.00
SATIN GLASS BOTTLE,PAIR BLUE OVERLAY,PERFUME..........   25.00
SATIN GLASS BOTTLE,WATER..............................    6.00
SATIN GLASS BOWL & BASE,CENTER,BLUE,11 IN.............   20.00
SATIN GLASS BOWL,BANANA,RUFFLED TOP,BLUE OBLONG.......   79.50
SATIN GLASS BOWL,BLUE,ON STAND........................   30.00
SATIN GLASS BOWL,BLUE OVER BLUE INLAID ORANGE SPLOTCHES,3
  IN.................................................   22.50
SATIN GLASS BOWL,BRIDES,GREEN,10 IN. DIAMETER,HANDPAINTED
  FLOWERS............................................   42.00
SATIN GLASS BOWL IN PURPLE,GRAPES & STEMS,ART NOUVEAU.......   28.00
SATIN GLASS BOWL,PEARLIZED,RIBBED TRIANGLE PATTERN,PURPLE
  HIGHLIGHTS.........................................   42.00
SATIN GLASS BOWL,PEDESTAL,FROSTED,RUFFLED,9 X 7 IN.........   30.00
SATIN GLASS BOWL,YELLOW,ON EXTRA STAND & TALL CANDLESTICKS..   85.00
SATIN GLASS BOX,JEWEL,BLUE............................   45.00
SATIN GLASS BOX,JEWEL,HINGED,HANDPAINTED WINTER SCENE......   27.00
SATIN GLASS BUTTER DISH...............................    6.95
SATIN GLASS CANDLE,SWIRLED,4 IN.......................    5.00
SATIN GLASS CELERY,PINK,FLEURETTE PATTERN.............   45.00
SATIN GLASS CELERY VASE,DIAMOND QUILTED MOTHER OF PEARL.....   85.00
SATIN GLASS COMPOTE,AZURE BLUE........................   50.00
SATIN GLASS COMPOTE BLACK.............................   30.00
SATIN GLASS CREAM PITCHER,SILVER,COVERED,ENAMELED RAISED
  FLOWERS............................................   65.00
SATIN GLASS CREAMER,TANKARD TYPE,DECORATED APRICOT.........   75.00
SATIN GLASS DECANTER IN SHAPE OF BUNCH OF GRAPES,AMETHYST...   29.00
SATIN GLASS DISH,CHICKENS,HEN & ROOSTER COVERED.......   14.95
SATIN GLASS DISH,POWDER,WHITE FROSTED,COVERED,ELEPHANT
  FINIAL.............................................   12.00
SATIN GLASS EGG,WHITE,EASTER DECOR....................    3.50
SATIN GLASS EPERGNE,PINK TO RUFFLED GREEN.............   80.00
SATIN GLASS EWER,BLUE,11 IN.,HERRINGBONE,WHITE TO BLUE......   75.00
SATIN GLASS EWER,BLUE HERRINGBONE,MOTHER OF PEARL,FROSTED
  HANDLE.............................................   87.50
SATIN GLASS EWER,DECORATED,SHADED PINK,9 IN. TALL.........   45.00
SATIN GLASS EWER,DIAMOND QUILTED,FROSTED,7 IN. TALL........   15.00
SATIN GLASS EWER,PAIR BLUE TO TURQUOISE,9 IN. TALL,FLORAL &
  GOLD...............................................  150.00
SATIN GLASS EWER,PAIR,GREEN,MELON RIBBED BASES........   52.50
SATIN GLASS EWER,PINK HERRINGBONE,RUFFLED TOP CLEAR HANDLE..   63.00
SATIN GLASS EWER,PISTACHIO GREEN,HANDPAINTED FLOWERS IN
```

```
    GREEN & BROWN..........................................  65.00
SATIN GLASS EWER,SHADED PINK,BULBOUS ,MELON SECTIONED.......  45.00
SATIN GLASS EWER,STEVENS & WILLIAMS,9 IN. TALL,RUFFLED
    TURNED DOWN TOP,......................................... 40.00
SATIN GLASS EWER,STEVENS & WILLIAMS,AZURE BLUE,ENAMELED
    PANSIES................................................. 40.00
SATIN GLASS EWER,STEVENS & WILLIAMS,PINK TO
    APRICOT,HANDPAINTED..................................... 37.00
SATIN GLASS EWER,VICTORIAN,9 IN.,PINK TO WHITE FLORAL....... 62.00
SATIN GLASS JAR,COOKIE,PINK FLEURETTE,SILVER PLATE COVER.... 45.00
SATIN GLASS JAR,COOKIE,SILVER PLATED HANDLE & COVER,SIGNED.. 30.00
SATIN GLASS JAR,COVERED,RASPBERRY DIAMOND QUILTED........... 40.00
SATIN GLASS JAR,CRACKER,AMBER,DECORATED WITH FLOWERS,ENAMEL. 60.00
SATIN GLASS JAR,CRACKER,ARCHED PANELS,PINK ROSE,GREEN
    PAINTED FLOWERS......................................... 50.00
SATIN GLASS JAR,CRACKER,BELL SHAPE,GREEN TO WHITE........... 40.00
SATIN GLASS JAR,CRACKER,EMBOSSED,QUILTED,ROSE SHADES,SILVER
    BAND................................................... 75.00
SATIN GLASS JAR,CRACKER,RED DRAPE PATTERN................... 90.00
SATIN GLASS JAR,CRACKER,WHITE TO YELLOW,FLORAL DECOR,SILVER. 35.00
SATIN GLASS JAR,CRACKER,WHITE TO YELLOW,PANSIES WITH SILVER. 55.00
SATIN GLASS JAR,MARMALADE WITH SILVER TOP & BAIL,PINK SHELL
    & SEAWEED.............................................. 65.00
SATIN GLASS JAR,PICKLE,PINK DIAMOND QUILTED,IN FRAME........ 97.50
SATIN GLASS JAR,TOBACCO,BLUE,SILVER OVERLAY................. 15.00
SATIN GLASS LAMP BASE,MINIATURE,RAINBOW MOTHER OF PEARL..... 250.00
SATIN GLASS LAMP BASE,RED,4 IN............................. 22.00
SATIN GLASS LAMP BASE,RED ,MINIATURE....................... 25.00
SATIN GLASS LAMP,RED ARTICHOKE,GONE WITH THE WIND.......... 179.00
SATIN GLASS LAMP,RED,MINIATURE,TULIP SHADE................. 75.00
SATIN GLASS PITCHER,PAIR,9 IN.,TURQUOISE................... 75.00
SATIN GLASS PITCHER,WATER,ROSE,WHITE SPATTER,FROSTED REED
    HANDLE................................................. 67.50
SATIN GLASS PLATE,MILK WHITE,ROSES P BUDS WITH HANDPAINTED
    LEAVES................................................. 21.00
SATIN GLASS PLATE,WHITE,HANDPAINTED CARNATIONS IN RED &
    YELLOW................................................. 12.50
SATIN GLASS ROSEBOWL,BLUE.................................. 30.00
SATIN GLASS ROSEBOWL,BLUE,ENAMELLED FLOWERS & LEAVES....... 60.00
SATIN GLASS ROSE BOWL,BLUE TO LIGHT BLUE,CRIMPED EDGE...... 75.00
SATIN GLASS ROSE BOWL,BLUE TO WHITE,CRIMPED................ 35.00
SATIN GLASS ROSE BOWL,CRIMPED TOP,YELLOW TO WHITE.......... 32.00
SATIN GLASS ROSEBOWL,DECORATED,BLUE TO GOLD,ENAMELLED FLORAL 37.50
SATIN GLASS ROSEBOWL,DECORATED,SHADED RICH YELLOW OVERLAY,3
    IN. TALL............................................... 60.00
SATIN GLASS ROSEBOWL,MOTHER OF PEARL,LINED,QUILTED,3 IN..... 29.50
SATIN GLASS ROSEBOWL,MOTHER OF PEARL,QUILTED,LINED.......... 29.50
SATIN GLASS ROSEBOWL,MOTHER OF PEARL,SHADED BLUE HERRINGBONE 95.00
SATIN GLASS ROSE BOWL,OPAQUE WHITE DECORATED IN
    ENAMEL,SIGNED.......................................... 22.00
SATIN GLASS ROSEBOWL,WHITE,ENAMELLED FLOWERS WITH WORDS
    HINDEAD HEATHER........................................ 16.50
SATIN GLASS ROSEBOWL,WHITE,LINED IN PINK,ENAMELED FLOWERS... 60.00
SATIN GLASS ROSEBOWL WITH APPLIED AMBER STEM & LEAVES,5
    IN.,WHITE.............................................. 55.00
SATIN GLASS ROSEBOWL,YELLOW............................... 60.00
SATIN GLASS ROSEBOWL,YELLOW TIPPED WHITE.................. 25.00
SATIN GLASS SALT & PEPPER,PAIR,OPEN,DECORATED.............. 24.00
SATIN GLASS SALT & PEPPER,PAIR,RIBBED,3 IN. TALL.......... 50.00
SATIN GLASS SALT DIP,PAIR................................. 5.95
SATIN GLASS SALT,PEWTER TOP,BLUE,BULBOUS,QUILTED.......... 15.00
SATIN GLASS SALT,YELLOW,RUFFLED........................... 16.00
SATIN GLASS SHADE,GAS,GREEN WITH OPALESCENT STRIPES....... 10.00
SATIN GLASS SHADE,LIGHT,PAIR WHITE........................ 19.00
SATIN GLASS SHADE,RED BALL................................ 36.50
```

```
SATIN GLASS SUGAR & CREAMER,GREEN PUFF WITH BEADED PANEL....    55.00
SATIN GLASS SUGAR SHAKER,MT.WASHINGTON,WHITE,MELON RIB......    35.00
SATIN GLASS SYRUP WITH WAFFLE PATTERN IN OPAL DATED.........    28.50
SATIN GLASS TOOTHPICK HOLDER
5.75 TO.....................................................    18.50
SATIN GLASS TOOTHPICK,PAIR..................................     4.95
SATIN GLASS TUMBLER,BLUE,DAISY & FERN PATTERN...............    18.00
SATIN GLASS TUMBLER,BLUE HERRINGBONE MOTHER OF PEARL........    47.50
SATIN GLASS TUMBLER,BLUE,TEARDROP,WHITE LINING..............    35.00
SATIN GLASS TUMBLER,MULBERRY................................    32.00
SATIN GLASS TUMBLER,NUDE,BOTTOMS UP.........................    18.50
SATIN GLASS TUMBLER,PINK AT BASE TO APRICOT AT TOP,ENAMEL
DECOR.......................................................    35.00
SATIN GLASS TUMBLER,PINK,FLORETTE...........................    17.50
SATIN GLASS TUMBLER,RASPBERRY ROSE,INVERTED DRAPE PATTERN...    65.00
SATIN GLASS TUMBLER,WATER,BLUE DIAMOND QUILTED MOTHER OF
PEARL.......................................................    65.00
SATIN GLASS TUMBLER,WATER,DIAMOND QUILTED MOTHER OF
PEARL,LEMON.................................................    65.00
SATIN GLASS TUMBLER,WATER,HERRINGBONE MOTHER OF PEARL,ROSE
TO WHITE....................................................    95.00
SATIN GLASS VASE,5 IN. HIGH,CRANBERRY TO LIGHT ,GOLD,RAISED
HUCKLEBERRY.................................................    42.50
SATIN GLASS VASE, 5IN. TALL.................................    95.00
SATIN GLASS VASE,6 IN.,ROSE TO LAVENDER PINK,RIBBED.........    18.50
SATIN GLASS VASE,8 IN.,BLUE WITH CUT QUILT PATTERN..........    80.00
SATIN GLASS VASE,7 IN.,HANDPAINTED,OPAQUE BACKGROUND........    18.00
SATIN GLASS VASE,APPLE GREEN RIBBED CUT
VELVET,6IN.TALL,3IN.DIAMETER................................    85.00
SATIN GLASS VASE,BLUE CUT VELVET,8 IN. TALL.................   125.00
SATIN GLASS VASE,BLUE DECORATED,FOOTED,9 IN.,RUFFLED TOP....    45.00
SATIN GLASS VASE,BLUE HERRINGBONE MOTHER OF PEARL...........    67.50
SATIN GLASS VASE,BLUE HERRINGBONE PATTERN,APPLIED CAMPHOR
HANDLES.....................................................    65.00
SATIN GLASS VASE,BLUE JACK IN PULPIT........................    12.00
SATIN GLASS VASE,BLUE,WHITE FLOWERS WITH GOLD LEAVES,PAIR...    75.00
SATIN GLASS VASE,BUD,BURGUNDY,PEPPERMINT,MOTHER OF
PEARL,SILVER................................................    97.50
SATIN GLASS VASE,BUD,RUFFLED TOP,7 IN. HIGH,PINK TO WHITE AT
TOP.........................................................    75.00
SATIN GLASS VASE,BUD,WHITE,MT.WASHINGTON,FOOTED.............    14.00
SATIN GLASS VASE,CORAL BRANCH CORALENE,CHERRY RED TO PINK
WHITE.......................................................   275.00
SATIN GLASS VASE,CRANBERRY IRIDESCENT,11 IN. TALL...........    20.00
SATIN GLASS VASE,DIAMOND QUILTED,PINK,7 IN. TALL............    55.00
SATIN GLASS VASE,ENAMELED TURQUOISE,RUFFLED CLEAR GLASS EDGE    65.00
SATIN GLASS VASE,EWER,GREEN CASED,TWISTED FROSTED
HANDLE,GOLD & WHITE.........................................    40.00
SATIN GLASS VASE,EWER TYPE,VICTORIAN PINK,RUFFLED
TOP,CAMPHOR HANDLE..........................................    40.00
SATIN GLASS VASE,GREEN,5 IN.,BULB SHAPE,RUFFLED TOP.........    12.50
SATIN GLASS VASE,GREEN,12 IN. TALL,NOUVEAU ART..............    15.00
SATIN GLASS VASE,GREEN,WHITE LINING,RUFFLED TOP.............    22.00
SATIN GLASS VASE,GREEN WITH SILVER DESPOIT TRIM.............    32.00
SATIN GLASS VASE,JACK IN THE PULPIT,GREEN,WHITE,ROUGH PONTIL    42.00
SATIN GLASS VASE,LEMON YELLOW WITH ENAMEL DECOR,FLOWERS &
FOLIAGE.....................................................    30.00
SATIN GLASS VASE,PAIR 8 IN.,BUTTERSCOTCH TO WHITE...........    85.00
SATIN GLASS VASE,PAIR,BEIGE DECORATED,9 IN. TALL............    95.00
SATIN GLASS VASE,PAIR,BLACK,10 IN. HIGH.....................    14.00
SATIN GLASS VASE,PAIR,DECORATED,PEACH TO PALER OVERLAY SATIN    85.00
SATIN GLASS VASE,PAIR DIAMOND QUILTED.......................   175.00
SATIN GLASS VASE,PAIR,QUILTED,9 IN.,1 BLUE,1 PINK...........   250.00
SATIN GLASS VASE,PAIR,TEAR DROP,MOTHER OF PEARL,MELON RIBBED
BASE........................................................   175.00
```

SATIN GLASS VASE,PEACH HERRINGBONE MOTHER OF PEARL..........	65.00
SATIN GLASS VASE,PEACH-PINK,WHITE LINING,RIBBED.............	12.50
SATIN GLASS VASE,STEVENS & WILLIAMS,6 IN. TALL,HANDPAINTED,PINK...................................	30.00
SATIN GLASS VASE,STEVENS & WILLIAMS,HANDPAINTED PURPLE PANSIES..	42.00
SATIN GLASS VASE,STEVENS & WILLIAMS,PEACHBLOW COLOUR,PINK,WHITE LINED.....................................	37.00
SATIN GLASS VASE,WHITE..	10.50
SATIN GLASS VASE,WHITE ART NOUVEAU,IRIDESCENT,8 IN. TALL....	38.00
SATIN GLASS VASE,WHITE JACK IN THE PULPIT,BLUE SCALLOPED PETALS..	30.00
SATIN GLASS VASE,WHITE WITH GREEN LOOPINGS,WHITE OPAL LINING	38.00
SATIN GLASS VASE WITH ENAMEL FLOWERS,ATTRIBUTED TO GALLE....	55.00

SATSUMA is a Japanese pottery with a distinctive creamy beige crackled glaze. Most of the pieces were decorated with blue, red, green, orange, or gold. Almost all the Satsuma found today was made after 1860. Japanese faces are often a part of the decorative scheme.

SATSUMA BOWL,EAGLE SCENES,14 IN. DIAMETER....................	125.00
SATSUMA CREAMER & COVERED SUGAR,RED MARK.....................	20.00
SATSUMA CREAMER,MARKED,ROYAL,3 IN.,SCALLOPED TOP,GOLD.......	5.00
SATSUMA CUP & SAUCER,6.......................................	65.00
SATSUMA CUP & SAUCER,EARLY MARK..............................	18.00
SATSUMA CUP & SAUCER,IMPERIAL................................	24.50
SATSUMA FIGURINE,LADY,12 IN. TALL............................	265.00
SATSUMA INCENSE BURNER,3 LEGS,ENAMELING,HANDLED..............	32.50
SATSUMA JAR,CRICKET,LID,3 IN. HIGH...........................	165.00
SATSUMA JARDINIERE,11 IN. TALL...............................	70.00
SATSUMA JUG,WINE,PINE BRANCHES DECOR,CIRCA 1840..............	12.50
SATSUMA PLATE,8 IN...	6.00
SATSUMA POT,BRUSH,CIRCULAR PANEL FRONT & REAR,BIRD & FLORAL,SIGNED...	35.00
SATUSMA POT-POURRI,3 IN. HIGH,DARK BLUE WITH GOLD,TREES & BIRDS..	21.50
SATSUMA SALT AND PEPPER SHAKERS..............................	15.00
SATSUMA TEAPOT,EARLY MARK....................................	45.00
SATSUMA TEA POT,GOLD...	10.00
SATSUMA TEAPOT,IMPERIAL,BEIGE WITH GEISHA GIRLS..............	55.00
SATSUMA TEAPOT,PAGODA & BRANCHES	35.00
SATSUMA TEA SET,7 PIECES,PAGODAS,TREES & BIRDS...............	40.00
SATSUMA TEA SET,MARKED.......................................	145.00
SATSUMA TEA SET, POT,SUGAR,CREAMER,COVERS ON ALL.............	65.00
SATSUMA TUREEN...	50.00
SATSUMA URN,SIGNED,18 IN.,COBALT COLOURING...................	75.00
SATSUMA VASE 2 IN. HIGH......................................	9.50
SATSUMA VASE,2 PANELS,BLUE BACKGROUND,10 IN. HIGH,PAIR......	65.00
SATSUMA VASE,4 IN.,FIGURES & FLOWERS.........................	15.00
SATSUMA VASE,12 IN.,WARRIORS & GOLD..........................	35.00
SATSUMA VASE,FROGS AT WAR WITH BIRDS,NARROW-NECK,10 IN. HIGH	48.00
SATSUMA VASE,IMPERIAL,7 IN.,OF MANY FACES....................	55.00
SATSUMA VASES,PAIR 7 IN. TALL,LADIES IN GARDEN,GOLD DECORATION...	60.00
SATSUMA VASE,PAIR FOOTED,CIRCA 1850,FIGURES IN COURT COSTUMES..	195.00
SATSUMA VASE,WOOD BASE,8 IN. TALL,BIRD & FLOWERS PANELS,GOLD TRIM...	35.00
SCALE,BALANCE,STEELYARD......................................	7.50
SCALE, MARBLE BASE, BRASS FIXTURES, 8 WEIGHTS................	42.00
SCALE,POSTAGE DATED 1906.....................................	7.50
SCALE WITH SMALL TRAY..	12.50

SCHNEIDER GLASS is an art nouveau glass made in France.

SCHNEIDER BOWL,7 IN.,TURQUOISE & BROWN & GOLD................	42.50
SCHNEIDER CANDLESTICK,SIGNED,MUSHROOM,ROYAL BLUE TO LEMON...	58.00

SCHNEIDER COMPOTE,7 IN.,BLUE FOOT & STEM,YELLOW CINTRA KNOB,SIGNED..	125.00
SCHNEIDER COMPOTE ON AMETHYST FOOT & STEM,SIGNED,WHITE & SALMON...	90.00
SCHNEIDER COMPOTE,SIGNED,LOW PEDESTAL......................	125.00
SCHNEIDER SHADE,LIGHT,SIGNED,ORANGE & MOTTLED BLUE,SILVER AT FRAME...	16.50
SCHNEIDER URN,SIGNED,18 IN.,BELL SHAPED,MOTTLED GREEN TO CLEAR...	135.00
SCHNEIDER VASE,9 IN..	46.50
SCHNEIDER VASE,18 IN.,SIGNED..................................	110.00
SCHNEIDER VASE IN METAL STAND,SIGNED........................	125.00
SCHNEIDER VASE,SIGNED,7 IN.,MOTTLED BLUE TO AMETHYST WITH ORANGE...	95.00
SCHNEIDER VASE,SIGNED,APRICOT COLOUR,18 IN. TALL.............	165.00
SCHNEIDER VASE,SIGNED,CASED,ROSE TO BITTERSWEET.............	75.00
SCHNEIDER VASE,SIGNED,FRANCE,FOOTED,15 IN. HIGH.............	95.00
SCHNEIDER VASE SIGNED,FOOTED,ROSE TO BLUE,5 IN. HIGH........	97.00
SCHNEIDER VASE SIGNED IN SCRIPT,7 IN.,MOTTLED BLUE TO AMETHYST,ORANGE..	95.00
SCHNEIDER VASE,SIGNED IN WROUGHT IRON STAND,14 IN. HIGH.....	125.00
SCHNIEDER VASE,SIGNED,ROSE TO BLUE MOTTLED AMETHYST,FOOTED..	98.00
SCHOENHUT TOYS, SEE TOYS..................................	
SCHUMANN CUP & SAUCER,DEMI-TASSE,SET OF 6....................	60.00
SCHUMANN PLATE,CAKE,SET OF 6,LATTICE WORK...................	42.00
SCHUMANN PLATTER,CAKE,ROUND..................................	20.00
SCRAPBOOK,1900 THROUGH 1920,COLOURED ADVERTISING CARDS......	6.00

SCRIMSHAW was bone or ivory or whales' teeth carved by sailors and others for entertainment during the sailing ship days. Some scrimshaw was carved as early as 1800.

SCRIMSHAW BUSK OF WHALEBONE,12 IN.,ROUNDED ENDS,PANELS OF FLOWERS & URN..................................	175.00
SCRIMSHAW CARVED CLOTHES PIN,4 IN.,CIRCA 1850..............	12.50
SCRIMSHAW CARVED ROLLING PIN,CIRCA 1840-50,13 IN.,..........	47.50
SCRIMSHAW CARVED SPERM WHALE TOOTH CIRCA 1830,FIGURE OF MAIDEN..	84.50
SCRIMSHAW LETTER OPENER,CARVED HANDLE HOLDS PEN POINTS......	22.50
SCRIMSHAW ON WHALE TOOTH CARVING OF WOMAN IN HEADDRESS & GOWN,MAN...	68.00
SCRIMSHAW,PIE CRIMPER,5 IN.,OCTAGON & RING,CARVED BONE HANDLE...	34.50
SCRIMSHAW TUSK..	27.50
SCRIMSHAW WHALEBONE PIE CRIMPER OR JAGGING WHEEL,7 IN.,......	44.50
SCRIMSHAW,WHALES TOOTH,4 IN.,.................................	10.00
SCRIMSHAW,WHALES TOOTH,ENGRAVED SAILING MAN O WAR FIRING CANNON..	75.00
SCRIMSHAW WHALES TEETH,ENGRAVED WITH SAILING VESSELS........	35.00
SCRIMSHAW,WHALES TUSK FASHIONED INTO RING FOR SAILORS NECKERCHIEF..	55.00
SCUTTLE MUG, SEE SHAVING MUG...............................	

SEVRES PORCELAIN has been made in Sèvres, France, since 1769. Many copies of the famous ware have been made. The name originally referred to the works of the royal factory. The name now includes any of the wares made in the town of Sèvres, France.

SEVRES BOWL,CHINA,PORTRAIT,COLONIAL COUPLE,WHITE WITH PINK RIM...	9.50
SEVRES BOX,JEWEL,HINGED,FRENCH,WHITE BISQUIT-WARE,CUPIDS PLAYING FLUTE..	45.00
SEVRES BOX,JEWEL,HINGED,FRENCH,WHITE BISQUIT-WARE WITH CLASSIC SCENE.......................................	55.00
SEVRES CHOCOLATE POT,HANDPAINTED,MARKED,CIRCA 1780..........	65.00
SEVRES CUP & SAUCER,DEMI-TASSE,BLUE & COIN GOLD,PORTRAIT,ARTIST MORPAU..............................	33.50

```
SEVRES INKWELL,CHINA,FLORAL PATTERN,BIRD ON LID..............    22.50
SEVRES JAR,CRACKER,METAL TOP & HANDLE,CREAM & GREEN.........      17.00
SEVRES LAMP BASE,PORTRAIT SIGNED ALBERT,12 IN. HIGH.........      75.00
SEVRES PITCHER,WATER,OWL.........................................   14.00
SEVRES PLATE,1840,SIGNED,CHATEAU ST.CLOUD....................     28.50
SEVRES PLATE,FLEUR DE LIS,10 IN.,MARKED,WHITE WITH PINK &
  GREEN.........................................................   45.00
SEVRES PLATE,MARKED, PURPLE & WHITE GRAPES....................    18.00
SEVRES PLATE,PAIR,LOUIS PHILIPPE 1846,SIGNED DEBRIE.........     140.00
SEVRES PLATE,PORTRAIT,SIGNED,DATED 1846,MEMBERS OF FRENCH
  COURT.........................................................   70.00
SEVRES PLATE,RED MARK,ANGELUS CENTER,8 IN.,GOLD DECORATED...       8.00
SEVRES PLATE,SIGNED,1846,9 IN.,BLUE BORDER WITH GOLD
  DESIGN,SCENE..................................................   65.00
SEVRES PLATE SIGNED MADAME DE DAUPHANE PORTRAIT,YELLOW
  BORDER,FLORAL.................................................  135.00
SEVRES PLATE SIGNED MADAME DE GENEES PORTRAIT,YELLOW
  BORDER,FLORAL.................................................  135.00
SEVRES PLATE SIGNED NELLIE LOUISE PORTRAIT,PINK BORDER &
  FLORAL........................................................  135.00
SEVRES PLATE,YELLOW,PANEL CENTER..............................   165.00
SEVRES SAUCER,COBALT & ROSES..................................    45.00
SEVRES SOUP,PAIR,CIRCA 1850...................................    95.00
```

SGRAFFITO is slip-decorated pottery that has been further decorated by scratch decorations in the slip (which see).

```
SGRAFFITO 8 IN. PLATE,SPINNER.................................  700.00
SHAVING MIRROR,...............................................    7.50
SHAVING MIRROK UN STAND WITH BRUSH & MILK GLASS CUP.........     12.50
```

SHAVING MUGS were popular from 1860 to 1900. Many types were made including occupational mugs featuring pictures of the man's job. There were scuttle mugs, silver-plated mugs, glass-lined mugs, and others.

```
SHAVING MUG, SEE ALSO SHAVING MUG, SCUTTLE TYPE  SILVER
  PLATE SHAVING...............................................
    MUG, STERLING SILVER MUG..................................
SHAVING MUG,3-CROWN GERMANY,GOLD RIM,GREEN WITH GOLD
  LACE,DOUBLE ROSES...........................................    12.50
SHAVING MUG,BAND OF RED & YELLOW ACCENTED WITH GOLD.........       7.00
SHAVING MUG,BLUISH-GREEN LUSTER...............................    17.50
SHAVING MUG,BUTCHERS OCCUPATIONAL.............................    37.50
SHAVING MUG,CARNIVAL MARIGOLD ORANGE TREE.....................     8.00
SHAVING MUG,CARPENTERS TOOLS OCCUPATIONAL.....................    37.50
SHAVING MUG,CHINA,LEFT HAND...................................    20.00
SHAVING MUG,CHINA,PINK ON WHITE...............................     6.50
SHAVING MUG,ELVES & SQUIRREL ROUTED BY BEE,GREEN.............      7.50
SHAVING MUG,FATHER IN GOLD,IMPERIAL VITRIFIED CHINA.........      25.00
SHAVING MUG,FLORAL BORDER,1870................................    12.50
SHAVING MUG,FLORAL DECORATED,NAME IN GOLD.....................    10.00
SHAVING MUG,FLOWER DECORATIONS................................     6.00
SHAVING MUG,FLOWERED WITH NAME & BRUSH........................    12.50
SHAVING MUG,FRATERNAL,ELK WITH CLOCK..........................    25.00
SHAVING MUG,GERMAN,PINK BORDER,GOLD TRIM......................    22.50
SHAVING MUG,GILT & FLORAL DECOR WITH NAME T M HODSON JR.....      12.50
SHAVING MUG,GOLD BAND,PINK,GREEN & BLUE FLORAL...............      9.50
SHAVING MUG,GOLD BANDS,M.A.EAMES IN GOLD LETTERS.............      22.00
SHAVING MUG,GOLD MARKED 7-F,SAPPHIRE BLUE
  ,DAISIES,BUDS,GREEN LEAVES...................................    13.50
SHAVING MUG,HANDPAINTED.......................................     6.50
SHAVING MUG,HANDPAINTED FLORAL................................     8.50
SHAVING MUG,HANDPAINTED,IVORY,PINK VASE,YELLOW & PINK ROSES.      8.50
SHAVING MUG,HANDPAINTED,MAROON & WHITE WITH FLOWERS,NAME
  JOHN SAUTER..................................................     9.75
SHAVING MUG,HANDPAINTED SCENE & WISHING WELL.................     19.50
SHAVING MUG,HANDPAINTED SCENE,HUNTER WITH FAMILY IN FRONT OF
```

```
HOUSE..................................................  21.50
SHAVING MUG,LEFT-HANDED,HANDPAINTED PANSIES ARTIST SIGNED...  15.00
SHAVING MUG,LEFT HANDED,MEDALLION WITH 2 DUCKS,3 CROWNS
  CHINA MARK............................................  25.00
SHAVING MUG,LEFT-HANDED,VIOLETS WITH BLUE,GREEN &
  RUSSET-ORANGE.........................................  16.50
SHAVING MUG,LONGHORN OR STEER HEAD,NAME GUS.ARNOLD...........  35.00
SHAVING MUG,MADE IN GERMANY,HANDPAINTED FLOWERS,SOAP TRAY...  9.75
SHAVING MUG,MANS NAME,TAN BACKGROUND,GOLD,ROSES.............  14.00
SHAVING MUG MARKED LIMOGES FRANCE,MASONIC SQUARE COMPASS....  32.00
SHAVING MUG,MASONIC,COLOUR WITH GOLD & NAME.................  22.50
SHAVING MUG,MASONIC,SQUARE P COMPASS WITH MANS NAME.........  22.50
SHAVING MUG,MERRY CHRISTMAS MARKED 3 CROWN CHINA,GERMANY....  12.50
SHAVING MUG,MONKEYS WITH BARBER EQUIPMENT...................  40.00
SHAVING MUG,MOSS ROSE.......................................  6.00
SHAVING MUG,OCCUPATIONAL,AUTO & DRIVER......................  70.00
SHAVING MUG,OCCUPATIONAL,BAKERS AT WORK.....................  40.00
SHAVING MUG,OCCUPATIONAL,BARBER,STRAIGHT RAZOR AT CENTER,...  65.00
SHAVING MUG,OCCUPATIONAL,BICYCLE SALESMAN PICTURED..........  35.00
SHAVING MUG,OCCUPATIONAL,BUTCHER............................  50.00
SHAVING MUG,OCCUPATIONAL,ENGINEER...........................  40.00
SHAVING MUG,OCCUPATIONAL,FLOWERS WITH BAND ACROSS & NAME IN
  GOLD.................................................  40.00
SHAVING MUG,OCCUPATIONAL,GRIST MILL.........................  55.00
SHAVING MUG,OCCUPATIONAL,HARDWARE STORE.....................  75.00
SHAVING MUG,OCCUPATIONAL,HARNESS MAKER,GOLD NAME............  70.00
SHAVING MUG,OCCUPATIONAL,HORSES.............................  60.00
SHAVING MUG,OCCUPATIONAL,HUNTER MAN WITH GUN & DOG..........  50.00
SHAVING MUG,OCCUPATIONAL,MACHINE LATHE......................  58.00
SHAVING MUG,OCCUPATIONAL,MACHINIST AT LATHE.................  40.00
SHAVING MUG,OCCUPATIONAL,PRIEST,NAME ROCCO ZUONU,BARBER
  SUPPLY STAMP.........................................  125.00
SHAVING MUG,OCCUPATIONAL,RAILROAD CONDUCTOR.................  75.00
SHAVING MUG,OCCUPATIONAL STATIONARY ENGINE..................  45.00
SHAVING MUG,OWNERS NAME IN GOLD,MARKED T & V LIMOGES........  12.00
SHAVING MUG,PAIRPOINT WITH SOAP REST........................  12.00
SHAVING MUG,PASTEL FLOWERS,TURQUOISE & PINK BANDS...........  7.50
SHAVING MUG,PINK BAND TOP,ROSE GARLAND......................  8.00
SHAVING MUG,PINK LUSTER,FLORAL DECOR IN RELIEF,GERMANY......  18.50
SHAVING MUG,PINK ROSES......................................  3.00
SHAVING MUG,POLICEMAN.......................................  15.00
SHAVING MUG,PORCELAIN,MOSS ROSE DECOR.......................  12.00
SHAVING MUG,RAILROAD ENGINE.................................  75.00
SHAVING MUG RAISED LILY OF THE VALLEY PRESENT...............  7.00
SHAVING MUG,RED ROSES,LILY OF THE VALLEY,GREEN FOLIAGE,GOLD.  7.50
SHAVING MUG,ROSES & FLORAL..................................  6.50
SHAVING MUG,ROYAL BLUE ,NAME JOSEPH VOGEL...................  14.00
SHAVING MUG,RUFFLED & FLUTED TOP,WILD ROSES,PETUNIAS,PANSIES  12.00
SHAVING MUG,SHADED IVORY & GREEN,RED ROSE,LILY OF VALLEY....  7.50
SHAVING MUG,SHAKER..........................................  115.00
SHAVING MUG,SHOVEL TYPE,WHITE CHINA,FLORAL DECOR............  16.00
SHAVING MUG SHOWING HEAD & NECK OF HORSE....................  16.00
SHAVING MUG,SILVER 2 PART,PAIRPOINT,BEADING AROUND TOP &
  BASE................................................  22.50
SHAVING MUG,SILVER,PAIRPOINT,SCROLL DESIGN ON EACH SIDE.....  22.50
SHAVING MUG,SILVER PLATE,ENGRAVED LEAF SPRAYS...............  12.00
SHAVING MUG,SOAP DECK,PORCELAIN,...........................  5.00
SHAVING MUG,SOAP SECTION,RED AND YELLOW ROSES..............  7.00
SHAVING MUG,SPRAY PINK DAISIES,BLUE PETAL FLOWERS,BEADING...  12.00
SHAVING MUG,SOAP TRAY,ROSES,PORCELAIN......................  18.00
SHAVING MUG,TIN.............................................  8.50
SHAVING MUG,TIN,WITH INSERT.................................  15.00
SHAVING MUG,UNDERTAKERS,HANDPAINTED,PURPLE
  SWAG,DRAPING,FLOWERS.................................  75.00
SHAVING MUG,WHITE...........................................  4.00
```

```
SHAVING MUG,WHITE CHINA,DRAIN TYPE,RED FLORAL DECOR.........      18.00
SHAVING MUG,WHITE,LEFT-HAND,DATED 1887.....................      11.00
SHAVING MUG,WHITE WITH FLORAL DECOR IN RAISED ENAMEL........      12.00
SHAVING MUG,WHITE WITH GOLD BANDS,NAME  W S DE VOE..........      10.00
SHAVING MUG,WHITE WITH PURPLE & WHITE,GOLD.................       7.00
SHAVING MUG WITH SOAP,FLORAL SPRIGS........................       8.00
SHAVING MUG WITH SOAP REST,FLORAL WITH LEAF WITH PINK.......      8.00
SHAVING MUG WITH SOAP REST,TAN BAND WITH BOW KNOT PINK BAND
  BLUE FLORAL..............................................       5.00
SHAVING MUG WITH SOAP TRAY,FLOWERS ON ORCHID,WORD PRESENT IN
  GOLD....................................................        9.95
SHAVING MUG WITH U S FLAG.................................        9.00
SHAVING MUG,SCUTTLE TYPE,2 CUP MUG,RED ROSES...............      20.00
SHAVING MUG,SCUTTLE TYPE,BLUE & WHITE CHINA,FUCHSIA FLOWERS.     16.00
SHAVING MUG,SCUTTLE TYPE,CHINA,HANDPAINTED HORSES HEAD......     13.50
SHAVING MUG,SCUTTLE TYPE,EMBOSSED SHELL,BULBOUS
  BASE,FLOWERS,PINK.......................................       15.00
SHAVING MUG,SCUTTLE TYPE,FISH,BLUE,IVORY TRIM ON TOP........     16.00
SHAVING MUG,SCUTTLE TYPE,FISH WITH HEAD ABOVE WATER,SEA WEED     45.00
SHAVING MUG,SCUTTLE TYPE,FLORAL
  7.00    TO.............................................        14.00
SHAVING MUG,SCUTTLE TYPE,FLORAL,RIBBED CHINA...............      15.00
SHAVING MUG,SCUTTLE TYPE,FLOWERS AND GOLD TRIM.............      17.50
SHAVING MUG,SCUTTLE TYPE,LEDGE FOR BRUSH,DEER ON FRONT......     16.50
SHAVING MUG,SCUTTLE TYPE,LUSTER,YELLOW TO CREAM AT TOP......     11.50
SHAVING MUG,SCUTTLE TYPE,ORANGE FLOWERS,ORCHID BERRIES,GREEN
  LEAVES..................................................       15.75
SHAVING MUG,SCUTTLE TYPE,PINK,IVORY TRIM ON TOP............      16.00
SHAVING MUG,SCUTTLE TYPE,PINK LUSTER CHINA,GOLD BAND
  DECORATED TOP...........................................       15.00
SHAVING MUG,SCUTTLE TYPE,PINK ROSES,PINK EMBOSSED SCALLOPED
  EDGE....................................................       15.00
SHAVING MUG,SCUTTLE TYPE,PLAIN............................        6.50
SHAVING MUG,SCUTTLE TYPE,PORCELAIN,SPRAY PINK GARDEN FLOWERS     12.00
SHAVING MUG,SCUTTLE TYPE,PURPLE DOUBLE ROSES & YELLOW
  VIOLETS.................................................       18.00
SHAVING MUG,SCUTTLE TYPE,RIBBED IRONSTONE WITH HANDPAINTED
  CAT & DOG...............................................       23.50
SHAVING MUG,SCUTTLE TYPE,ROSE BORDER......................       15.00
SHAVING MUG,SCUTTLE TYPE,SILVER...........................       22.50
SHAVING MUG,SCUTTLE TYPE,SOAP REST,BLUE FLORAL............       10.00
SHAVING MUG,SCUTTLE TYPE,TIN..............................       15.00
SHAVING MUG,SCUTTLE TYPE,VARI-COLOURED,LUSTER
  PINK,BLUE,GREEN,GOLD....................................       14.00
SHAVING MUG,SCUTTLE TYPE,WHITE,FLORALS....................       14.00
SHAVING MUG,SCUTTLE TYPE,WHITE,GOLD.......................        7.50
SHAVING MUG,SCUTTLE TYPE,WHITE & FLORALS..................       12.50
SHAVING MUG,SCUTTLE TYPE,WHITE & PURPLE & YELLOW FLOWERS....     13.50
SHAVING MUG,SCUTTLE TYPE,WHITE,GREEN RIMS,PEACHES & PLUMS...     15.00
SHAVING MUG,SCUTTLE TYPE,WHITE PORCELAIN,NARROW & WIDE GOLD
  BANDS...................................................       15.00
SHAVING MUG,SCUTTLE TYPE,WHITE WITH FLORAL DECOR...........       9.00
SHAVING MUG,SCUTTLE TYPE,WHITE WITH GOLD HANDLE & RIM,GOLD
  MEDALLIONS..............................................        8.00
SHAVING MUG,SCUTTLE TYPE,WHITE WITH GOLD TRIM.............        7.50
SHAVING MUG,SCUTTLE TYPE,WHITE WITH PINK FLORAL & GREEN.....     11.50
SHAVING MUG,SCUTTLE TYPE,YELLOW WITH GREEN BAND............       8.75
SHIP,ISLANDER,HONOLULU RACE 1959,SLOOP RIGGED,BUILT UP FROM
  KEEL...................................................       150.00
SHIP,JUAN SEBASTIAN ELCANO,4 MASTED SPANISH SCHOONER,......     150.00
SHIP,MECHANICAL IN CASE,..................................      750.00
SHIP,MINIATURE,IN DRY DOCK,MAHOGANY & GLASS CASE...........      85.00
SHIP MODEL 6 FEET LONG,SINGLE MAST,8 FEET TALL............      250.00
SHIP MODEL,BONE OF 32-GUN HMS FRIGATE PALLAS CIRCA
  1804,GLASS CASE...................................... 6,200.00
```

SHIP,MODEL OF THE NEWSBOY,A BIRGANTINE OF 1854,BOSTON.......	250.00
SHIP MODEL,MAYFLOWER..	100.00
SHIP MODEL,WOODEN OF MAYFLOWER,LARGE,......................	50.00
SHIP,SCALE MODEL OF 1851 SCHOONER YACHT AMERICA,MOUNTED.....	265.00
SHIP,SHIPS BINNACLE BY JOHN LILLEY & SON LTD.,BRASS WITH OAK BASE..	375.00
SHIP,SHIPS WHEEL ,5 FEET DIAMETER,WALNUT...................	175.00
SHIP,THERMOPOLAE,19TH CENTURY SQUARE RIGGER,MAHOGANY & GLASS CASE..	35.00

SHIRLEY TEMPLE dishes, blue glassware, and any other souvenir-type objects with her name and picture are now collected.

SHIRLEY TEMPLE 5 IN. BLUE PITCHER...........................	5.00
SHIRLEY TEMPLE 15 IN. COMPOSITION DOLL,DRESSED..............	18.50
SHIRLEY TEMPLE BLUE CREAMER.................................	3.50
SHIRLEY TEMPLE BLUE GLASS BREAKFAST SET.....................	4.75
SHIRLEY TEMPLE BLUE MILK PITCHER............................	5.00
SHIRLEY TEMPLE BOWL,MUG & PITCHER SET.......................	8.50
SHIRLEY TEMPLE CEREAL BOWL..................................	5.00
SHIRLEY TEMPLE DOLL 12 IN. VINYL IDEAL DRESSED..............	10.00
SHIRLEY TEMPLE DOLL,18 IN. TALL,MARKED IDEAL CO.............	35.00
SHIRLEY TEMPLE DOLL BY IDEAL,...............................	6.00
SHIRLEY TEMPLE DOLL,COMPOSITION.............................	27.00
SHIRLEY TEMPLE DOLL,DRESSED,FLIRTY EYES,25 IN. TALL.........	35.00
SHIRLEY TEMPLE DOLL,DRESSED,ROOTED HAIR,17 IN. TALL.........	12.00
SHIRLEY TEMPLE DOLL,MARKED,COMPOSITION,24 IN. TALL..........	58.50
SHIRLEY TEMPLE DOLL PIN.....................................	15.00
SHIRLEY TEMPLE DOLL,SIGNED COMPOSITION HEAD,18 IN.,IDEAL CORP,DRESSED...	35.00
SHIRLEY TEMPLE DOLL SIGNED,DRESSED,9 IN. TALL...............	25.00
SHIRLEY TEMPLE DOLL,SIGNED,DRESSED,BLOND WIG,18 IN. TALL....	32.00
SHIRLEY TEMPLE MUG,COBALT...................................	5.00
SHIRLEY TEMPLE PRESSED GLASS BLUE CHILDS MILK PITCHER.......	7.00
SHIRLEY TEMPLE PRESSED GLASS PITCHER........................	4.50
SHIRLEY TEMPLE STORY BOOK...................................	5.00
SHOE,AMBER BOOT,CLEAR.......................................	3.60
SHOE,BISQUE,MOUSE AT TOP,BROWN,GREEN & PINK.................	11.70
SHOE,BLACK CHINA,WHITE & BLACK DOG ON TOE,CAT ON TOP EDGE...	4.75
SHOE,BLACK PAPIER MACHE LOW SLIPPER.........................	5.50
SHOE,BLUE MILK GLASS DAISY & BUTTON,BLUE BOW................	14.75
SHOE,BOOT WITH SPUR,CHINA,BLUE,WESTERN STYLE................	3.85
SHOE,CAMPHOR BOOTIES..	12.00
SHOE,CHINA,GERMANY,OFF WHITE WITH RAISED FLOWER,RED CENTER & LEAVES..	5.75
SHOE,CHINA HIGH HEEL ,RAISED SCROLL WITH GOLD TRIM,SOUVENIR ILLINOIS...	7.00
SHOE,CHINA PALE YELLOW AND PINK, ABOUT 3 IN.................	5.00
SHOE,CHINA SLIPPER,BLUE AT FRONT,WHITE IN CENTER............	4.25
SHOE,CHINA SLIPPER,GERMANY,GOLD TRIM........................	6.75
SHOE,CHINA SLIPPER,GREEN WITH STIPPLED GREEN TOE,VIOLETS & LEAVES..	12.50
SHOE,CHINA,WHITE,BOUQUET OF VARI-COLORED FLOWERS ON TOE.....	6.50
SHOE,CLEAR & FROSTED GLASS,BABY SHOE,LACED..................	9.50
SHOE,CLEAR & FROSTED GLASS,BOOT,LACED.......................	7.50
SHOE,CLEAR & FROSTED GLASS,DAISY & BUTTON SLIPPER,HIGH FRONT	7.75
SHOE,CLEAR GLASS BOOT,2 IN. HIGH............................	4.75
SHOE,CLEAR GLASS BOOT,3 IN. HIGH............................	3.50
SHOE,CLEAR GLASS DAISY & BUTTON SLIPPER.....................	6.25
SHOE,CLEAR GLASS HIGH HEEL,BOW ON FRONT.....................	4.50
SHOE,DUTCH SLIPPER SHAPED LIKE WOODEN SHOE,HANDPAINTED,MARKED QUIMPER...........................	3.25
SHOE,EGG SHELL PORCELAIN LADIES SLIPPER.....................	5.75
SHOE,GILDED METAL,RAISED BUCKLE ON FRONT,BEADING AROUND OPENING...	5.75
SHOE,GILT OVER WHITE,BEADING AROUND FLORAL DESIGN,CHINA.....	12.00

```
SHOE,GREEN BOOT,STAR UNDER TOE...............................  10.00
SHOE,GREEN CHINA MOCCASIN TYPE,RAISED SCROLL,BIRD ON FRONT
  IN GOLD....................................................   5.50
SHOE,GREEN GLASS SLIPPER SOUVENIR OF SKIDMORE &
  SONS,COLORADO..............................................   7.75
SHOE,HIGH HEEL SLIPPER,TINTED GREEN EDGE,PAINTED FLOWER ON
  FRONT.....................................................    2.25
SHOE MARKED GERMANY,SLIPPER,LOW CUT,APPLIED FLOWER & LEAVES.   3.75
SHOE,METAL BABY BOOT,PEWTER COLOUR,BOW ON FRONT.............   5.50
SHOE,METAL HIGH HEEL SLIPPER,PIN CUSHION...................    2.75
SHOE,METAL OXFORD,SILVER COLOUR,OPEN EYELETS...............    5.50
SHOE,METAL SLIPPER,GOLD COLOUR,BOW IN FRONT................    5.00
      SHOE, MILK GLASS, SEE ALSO PRESSED GLASS..............
SHOE,MILK GLASS BOOT.......................................    3.25
SHOE,MILK GLASS DAISY & BUTTON SLIPPER WITH BOW ON FRONT....  12.50
SHOE,PAIR DUTCH SLIPPERS MARKED ROTTERDAM,BLUE DESIGN ON TOE   3.25
SHOE,PAIR HIGH HEEL SLIPPERS MADE IN JAPAN,GOLD COLOUR......   2.75
SHOE,PARIAN TYPE BABY BOOT,KNIT EFFECT.....................    8.50
SHOE,PINK LUSTER OVER WHITE CHINA,BLUE WHITE LUSTER & GILT..  12.75
SHOE,POTTERY TYPE MANS OXFORD,BLACK WITH GOLD COLOUR LACES &
  BEADING...................................................   2.25
SHOE,WHITE CHINA,GOLD,RAISED BEADED DESIGN,SOUVENIR
  BURLINGTON IOWA...........................................   6.75
SHOE,WHITE CHINA,RAISED DESIGN,GILT,BLUE...................    6.50
SHOE,WHITE CHINA WITH GILT,PUMP TYPE,BUCKLE IN FRONT.......    6.75
SHOE,YELLOW CHILD BUTTON SHOE..............................    2.75
```

SHRINE GLASSWARE was made from 1893 to 1917. It is occasionally called Syrian Temple Shrine glassware. Most pieces are dated.

```
SHRINE GLASS SARATOGA 1903 INDIAN HEAD MUG,DECORATED.......  25.00
SHRINE MUG,3 SCIMITAR HANDLES,SYRIA PITTSBURG..............  22.50
SHRINE PATTERN TUMBLER....................................   10.00
SILESIA BOWL,GERMANY,PEARLIZED,LILY OF VALLEY IN
  GREEN,WHITE,GOLD TRIM.....................................  23.50
SILESIA CHOCOLATE POT & 12 CUPS & SAUCERS,HANDPAINTED ROSES
  & GOLD....................................................  57.00
SILESIA PLATE,5,SCALLOPED,FLOWERS,EMBOSSED BORDERS,FISH IN
  CENTER....................................................  18.00
SILESIA PLATE,6 IN.,HANDPAINTED POINSETTIA.................   18.00
SILESIA PLATE,SET OF 12,CIRCA 1870-80,WHITE,GOLD DESIGNED
  BORDER....................................................  50.00
SILESIA POWDER JAR,FORGET ME NOTS.........................    8.00
      SILVER, ALSO SEE COIN SILVER, STERLING SILVER.........
```

SILVER DEPOSIT GLASS was made during the late nineteenth and early twentieth centuries. Solid sterling silver was applied to the glass by a chemical method so that a cutout design of silver metal appeared against a clear or colored glass.

```
SILVER DEPOSIT 5 IN. BUD VASE.............................    6.00
SILVER DEPOSIT 6 IN. PLATE................................    4.00
SILVER DEPOSIT AND GREEN GLASS DECANTER,MONOGRAMMED,9 IN.
  TALL......................................................  65.00
SILVER DEPOSIT ARTIST SIGNED BOWL,........................   12.50
SILVER DEPOSIT BOTTLE,STERLING OVERLAY ON BLOWN
  GLASS,SCENT,ORCHID........................................  25.00
SILVER DEPOSIT BOWKNOT PATTERN OPEN SUGAR & CREAMER.........   9.00
SILVER DEPOSIT CANDY......................................    2.00
SILVER DEPOSIT CHEESE & CRACKER DISH,HEISEY MARKED.........  14.00
SILVER DEPOSIT CLEAR GLASS WATER PITCHER,APPLIED HANDLE....   18.00
SILVER DEPOSIT CREAMER....................................    4.50
SILVER DEPOSIT CREAMER & SUGAR............................   12.00
SILVER DEPOSIT CUP........................................    4.50
SILVER DEPOSIT DECANTER & 4 TUMBLERS,STERLING OVERLAY......   95.00
SILVER DEPOSIT DISH,NUT,FOOTED,UNDERPLATE,SIGNED ROCKWELL...  15.00
SILVER DEPOSIT GLASS GREEN 8 IN. PLATE....................    4.00
```

```
SILVER DEPOSIT MUFFINEER...................................   5.00
SILVER DEPOSIT PAIR CANDLESTICKS,SQUARE,8 IN. TALL..........  12.00
SILVER DEPOSIT PATTERN WATER PITCHER & 6 TUMBLERS,GREEN.....  35.00
SILVER DEPOSIT PERFUME BOTTLE...............................  12.50
SILVER DEPOSIT PERFUME BOTTLE,PAIR..........................  25.00
SILVER DEPOSIT PERFUME MARKED STERLING......................  13.00
SILVER DEPOSIT SUGAR,STERLING OVERLAY ON CLEAR GLASS........   4.00
SILVER DEPOSIT SUGAR,SYRUP PITCHER,PLATE & CREAMER,PEDESTAL
  BASE......................................................  10.50
SILVER DEPOSIT TUMBLER......................................   4.00
SILVER DEPOSIT VASE,GREEN,FLORAL SPRAYS & CAMEO.............  14.00
SILVER DEPOSIT VASE,GREEN GLASS,FLORAL & CAMEO..............  14.00
SILVER DEPOSIT WATER PITCHER................................  27.00
SILVER DEPOSIT WHISKEY SHOT GLASS...........................   7.00
SILVER,ENGLISH,ASPARAGUS TONGS,REEDED,LONDON 1791...........  89.00
SILVER,ENGLISH,BEAKER,ENGRAVED ARMS,GILT LINED,LONDON 1812.. 295.00
SILVER,ENGLISH,BEAKER,ENGRAVED,LONDON 1790.................. 295.00
SILVER,ENGLISH CHAMBER CANDLESTICK & SNUFFER,SHEFFIELD 1823. 265.00
SILVER,ENGLISH CHILDS HOOPED MUG,GILT LINED,LONDON 1805..... 185.00
SILVER,ENGLISH,CHILDS HOOPED MUG,LONDON 1821................ 135.00
SILVER,ENGLISH CHILDS WHISTLE WITH CORAL TEETHER,LONDON
  CIRCA 1780............................................... 450.00
SILVER,ENGLISH,CORAL BELLS & RATTLE,CIRCA 1735............. 175.00
SILVER,ENGLISH FISH SLICE,ENGRAVED,LONDON 1813.............  51.00
SILVER,ENGLISH FISH SLICE,LONDON 1872,WILLIAM CHAWNER......  54.00
SILVER,ENGLISH FOOTED SALVER,CRESTED,LONDON 1768,JOHN CARTER 465.00
SILVER,ENGLISH,FOOTED SALVER,LONDON 1773,JOHN CARTER....... 325.00
SILVER,ENGLISH,FOOTED SALVER,REEDED BORDER,CRESTED,LONDON
  1806.................................................... 575.00
SILVER,ENGLISH,FOOTED SALVER,SHELL & GADROON,CRESTED,LONDON
  1817.................................................... 800.00
SILVER,ENGLISH,FOOTED SALVER,SQUARE,FLUTED,CRESTED,LONDON
  1802.................................................... 265.00
SILVER,ENGLISH,GEORGE III CASTER,LONDON 1777,5 IN. TALL.... 195.00
SILVER,ENGLISH,GEORGE IV ENTREE OR GAME DISH,LONDON 1822,12
  IN. LONG.............................................1,386.00
SILVER,ENGLISH,GEORGE III CREAM JUG,LONDON 1765,4 IN. TALL.. 140.00
SILVER,ENGLISH,GEORGE III SOUP LADLE,FIDDLE PATTERN........  56.00
SILVER,ENGLISH GRAVY SPOON,CRESTED,LONDON 1790.............  55.00
SILVER,ENGLISH,HELMET EWER,ENGRAVED,BEADED,LONDON 1787..... 235.00
SILVER,ENGLISH HELMET EWER,ENGRAVED,LONDON 1794,HENRY COWPER 215.00
SILVER,ENGLISH,MARROW SCOOP,LONDON 1786,HESTER BATEMAN..... 180.00
SILVER,ENGLISH MUSTARD POT,BLUE GLASS LINING,LONDON 1782... 335.00
SILVER,ENGLISH,MUSTARD POT,BLUE GLASS LINING,LONDON 1810... 275.00
SILVER,ENGLISH,ONSLOW GRAVY SPOON,CRESTED,LONDON 1761......  95.00
SILVER,ENGLISH OPEN PAIR SALTS,BLUE GLASS LINING,LONDON 1780 335.00
SILVER,ENGLISH OPEN SALT,REEDED,GILT LINED,LONDON 1795,SET
  OF 6..................................................1,050.00
SILVER,ENGLISH PAIR SALT SPOONS,LONDON 1892 ,JACOB WINTLE...  17.00
SILVER,ENGLISH,RATTLE WITH CORAL,BIRMINGHAM 1809........... 150.00
SILVER,ENGLISH SALT SPOON,PAIR,CRESTED,LONDON 1823.........  17.00
SILVER,ENGLISH SAUCE BOAT,LONDON 1783..................... 700.00
SILVER,ENGLISH,SAUCE BOAT,LONDON 1753,WALTER BRIND........ 325.00
SILVER,ENGLISH SAUCE BOAT,PUNCHED BORDER,LONDON 1772...... 245.00
SILVER,ENGLISH SAUCE LADLE,CRESTED,LONDON 1824............  30.00
SILVER,ENGLISH,SAUCE TUREEN,GADROON BORDER,CRESTED,2
  CUPS,LONDON 1805....................................... 650.00
SILVER,ENGLISH,SNUFFER & TRAY,SHELL & GADROON,LONDON 1815... 340.00
SILVER,ENGLISH SOUP LADLE,LONDON 1805.....................  72.00
SILVER,ENGLISH,SUGAR BASKET,CRESTED,DUBLIN 1796........... 785.00
SILVER,ENGLISH SUGAR TONGS,ENGRAVED,LONDON 1813...........  18.00
SILVER,ENGLISH SUGAR TONGS,ENGRAVING,LONDON 1800,GEORGE
  BASKERVILLE............................................  16.00
SILVER,ENGLISH TABLESPOON,CRESTED,LONDON 1771.............  55.00
SILVER,ENGLISH TEA POT,6 CUPS,LONDON 1788................. 445.00
```

```
SILVER,ENGLISH,TEAPOT,ENGRAVED,8 CUPS,LONDON 1804............   475.00
SILVER,ENGLISH TEAPOT,ENGRAVED & CRESTED,8 CUP,LONDON 1792..   465.00
SILVER,ENGLISH,TEA URN,BEADED,CRESTED,7 PINTS,LONDON 1779...1,650.00
SILVER,ENGLISH,WAX BOX,LONDON 1810..........................   225.00
SILVER INLAY SPANISH SPURS PAIR.............................    32.50
SILVER,IRISH,8 IN. FORK.....................................    25.00
SILVER,IRISH 10 CUP TEA POT,DUBLIN CIRCA 1803...............   475.00
SILVER,IRISH BOWL ON 3 FEET,JOHN EBBS.......................   395.00
SILVER,IRISH DESSERT SPOON..................................    25.00
SILVER,IRISH FOOTED SALVER CIRCA 1730,WILLIAM TOWNSEND......   350.00
SILVER,IRISH,FORK,CUT WITH STAR MOTIF.......................    25.00
SILVER,IRISH MARROW SPOON CIRCA 1750,CRESTED,JOHN LAUGHLIN..   110.00
SILVER,IRISH PAIR GEORGE II CANDELABRA,DUBLIN CIRCA 1734....4,200.00
SILVER,IRISH SET OF 4 RATTAIL SPOONS,DUBLIN CIRCA 1766......   175.00
SILVER,IRISH SUGAR & CREAMER,BALL FEET 1809.................   275.00
SILVER,IRISH SUGAR BOWL,DUBLIN CIRCA 1807...................   135.00
SILVER,IRISH TABLESPOONS,PAIR...............................    65.00
SILVER,IRISH TEA POT & 6 CUPS,DUBLIN 1805 BY JAMES SCOTT....   295.00
SILVER,IRISH TEASPOON.......................................    20.00
SILVER,IRISH,TEASPOON,CUT WITH STAR MOTIF...................    20.00
SILVER PLATE BABY CUP,MARKED CARRIE MAY,GOLD LINED..........    10.00
SILVER PLATE BASKET,9 IN. DIAMETER,JAMES TUFTS..............    25.00
SILVER PLATE BASKET,CAKE,HANDLED............................    10.00
SILVER PLATE BASKET,FOOTED..................................     6.50
SILVER PLATE BASKET,FOOTED,ETCHING OF LEAVES,F B ROGERS
  SILVER CO.................................................    14.50
SILVER PLATE BASKET,JAMES TUFTS.............................    25.00
SILVER PLATE BASKET ON STANDARD,FRUIT,SOUTHINGTON QUADRUPLE.    18.00
SILVER PLATE BASKET,SCALLOPED EFFECT,ORNATE,VICTORIAN.......    35.00
SILVER PLATE BASKET,SQUARE,FOOTED,ROPE HANDLE...............     6.50
SILVER PLATE BASKET WITH SWINGING BAIL,FRUIT,PAIRPOINT......    20.00
SILVER PLATE BELL,EAR OF CORN HANDLE MARKED STERLING........     3.50
SILVER PLATE BOWL,OPEN,4 STAG HEAD LEGS,EMBOSSED TOP WITH 2
  HANDLES..................................................     8.50
SILVER PLATE BOWL,ROUND FLUTED..............................     3.50
SILVER PLATE BOX,COVERED,ROUND,TUFTS,3 IN. HIGH.............    13.00
SILVER PLATE BOX,CUPID SITTING LID,EMBOSSED
  LILIES-OF-THE-VALLEY.....................................    22.50
SILVER PLATE BRIDES BASKET,TRAY,VICTORIAN,SWINGING
  HANDLE,PEDESTAL..........................................    22.50
SILVER PLATE BRIDES BOWL HOLDER ON STEM PEDESTAL,WEBSTER &
  SON......................................................    30.00
SILVER PLATE BRIDES CAKE DISH,FOOTED,MARKED ROCKFORD 1875...    12.00
SILVER PLATE BUTTER DISH....................................    35.00
SILVER PLATE BUTTER DISH & KNIFE WITH GLASS INSET...........    25.00
SILVER PLATE BUTTER DISH,COVERED,KNIFE & LINER,ROGERS.......    17.50
SILVER PLATE BUTTER DISH,DOMED,RAISED ACORNS & LEAVES AT TOP    42.50
SILVER PLATE BUTTER DISH,HORSE FINIAL,LINER.................    18.00
SILVER PLATE,BUTTER DISH,NATURE ENGRAVINGS & FINIAL.........    30.00
SILVER PLATE BUTTER PAT,6,BUTTERFLY IN CENTER...............    15.00
SILVER PLATE BUTTERFLY NAPKIN HOLDER........................    12.00
SILVER PLATE CANDLE SNUFFER & TRAY..........................    25.00
SILVER PLATE CANDLEHOLDER WITH HANDLE & THUMBHOLD,SAUCER
  TYPE,PAIR................................................     7.00
SILVER PLATE CANDLESTICK,PAIR,FRENCH,ETCHED,OVAL BASES......   125.00
SILVER PLATE CANDLESTICK,PAIR,PAIRPOINT.....................    65.00
SILVER PLATE CANDLESTICK,PAIR SIGNED EDW.SAN GIOVANNI.......    42.00
SILVER PLATE CARD TRAY......................................     3.50
SILVER PLATE CASKET PLATE,OVAL 1884.........................     1.75
SILVER PLATE CASKET PLATE,RECTANGULAR 1868..................     1.75
SILVER PLATE CASTOR,5 BOTTLE SET............................    45.00
SILVER PLATE CASTOR,PICKLE,4 FEET,DAISY & BUTTON
  INSERT,VICTORIAN.........................................    35.00
SILVER PLATE CASTOR,PICKLE WITH TONGS,DOG FINIAL ON COVER...    22.50
SILVER PLATE CASTOR SET, 4 BOTTLE...........................    30.00
```

```
SILVER PLATE CASTOR SET,4 BOTTLE,LAZY SUSAN..................   35.00
SILVER PLATE CASTOR SET,6 BOTTLE,FROSTED RIBBON..............   67.50
SILVER PLATE CASTOR WITH 5 AMBER BOHEMIAN GLASS BOTTLES.....,   55.00
SILVER PLATE CHEESE SCOOP,ENGRAVED HANDLE...................    6.00
SILVER PLATE CHILDS NAPKIN RING,COX BROWNIES................    4.00
SILVER PLATE COFFEE POT,1 QUART,PEDESTAL,WILCOX SILVER CO...   22.00
SILVER PLATE COFFEE POT,PORCELAIN LINED,MERIDEN SILVER CO.
  1872.......................................................   65.00
SILVER PLATE COFFEE SERVER..................................   95.00
SILVER PLATE COMPOTE,GRAPE,9 IN. WIDE.......................   19.50
SILVER PLATE COMPOTE,PEDESTAL & EDGE SCALLOPED,RIBBON
  ETCHING....................................................   37.50
SILVER PLATE COOKIE JAR,COVER,FLORAL DECOR..................   35.00
SILVER PLATE COVERED SUGAR & CREAMER,REED & BARTON..........    8.50
SILVER PLATE COVERED SUGAR,CREAMER & SPOONER,REPOUSSE.......   35.00
SILVER PLATE COVERED SYRUP JUG MARKED PAIRPOINT.............   10.00
SILVER PLATE COVERED VEGETABLE DISH OVAL....................    6.00
SILVER PLATE CRACKER JAR,CLEAR GLASS WITH PATTERN OF FLOWERS   35.00
SILVER PLATE CREAMER & OPEN SUGAR,FORBES....................   15.00
SILVER PLATE CREAMER,WALDORF................................    6.00
SILVER PLATE CUP & SAUCER,DEMI-TASSE........................   10.00
SILVER PLATE CUP,COLLAPSIBLE CYCLISTS,GOLD PLATED INTERIOR..    7.00
SILVER PLATE,DEER ON 6 X 2 IN. OBLONG BASE,8 IN. TALL.......   22.50
SILVER PLATE DISH,3-FOOTED,SCALLOPED........................    3.00
SILVER PLATE DISH,CHAFING,ON COPPER,5 PIECES................   17.50
SILVER PLATE DISH,CONDIMENT,HINGED COVER,FOOTED ,CAMPHOR
  INSERT,ENGLISH.............................................    6.50
SILVER PLATE DISH,FOOTED,ROUND,ORNATE HANDLES...............   10.00
RILVER PLATE DISH,FRUIT,OVAL ,REED & BARTON,EMBOSSED
  STRAWBERRIES...............................................   20.00
SILVER PLATE DISH,NUT,2 HANDLED,GILT INSIDE,2 IN. HIGH,TUFTS   10.00
SILVER PLATE DISH,REPOUSSE RIM..............................    7.00
SILVER PLATE FRAME ENGLISH CONDIMENT SET,6 IN. HIGH.........   36.00
SILVER PLATE FRUIT BOWL,RAISED FLORAL DECOR & RIM MARKED
  EVELNY.....................................................   12.50
SILVER PLATE GOBLET.........................................   15.00
SILVER PLATE,GOBLET,FESTOONS................................    5.00
SILVER PLATE GOBLET MARKED MERIDAN B CO.....................    9.50
SILVER PLATE GRAVY & TRAY...................................    7.00
SILVER PLATE,HAIR RECEIVER,4 IN. DIAMETER...................   12.00
SILVER PLATE,HAND MIRROR,ORNATE DESIGN......................    8.50
SILVER PLATE HOLDER FOOTED WITH LITHOPHANE TEA WARMER.......   27.00
SILVER PLATE HOLDER,PIE PLATE,WM.ROGERS.....................    6.00
SILVER PLATE HOLDER WITH BLUE GLASS TEA WARMER,FOOTED HOLDER   22.00
SILVER PLATE HOLDER WITH EMERALD ART GLASS BOWL.............   22.50
SILVER PLATE HORN OF PLENTY.................................    4.50
SILVER PLATE JAR,ROSE,COVERED,VICTORIAN,MARKED MIDDLETOWN
  PLATED.....................................................   14.00
SILVER PLATE JEWEL BOX ON 4 FEET,RAISED SCROLL DESIGN.......    7.50
SILVER PLATE KNIFE & FORK,SET OF 6 PEARL HANDLED...........   48.00
SILVER PLATE KNIFE,BUTTER,PAIR WITH PEARL HANDLES IN VELVET
  BOX........................................................   12.50
SILVER PLATE KNIFE,POCKET,2 BLADE...........................    2.50
SILVER PLATE KNIFE REST,LIONS AT ENDS.......................    4.75
SILVER PLATE KNIFE REST,PAIR ,GRAPE,LEAF DESIGN,VICTORIAN....   25.00
SILVER PLATE KNIFE REST,SHELL & ARCH ENDS...................    2.95
SILVER PLATE KNIFE REST SUPPORTED BY 2 BIRDS................    6.00
SILVER PLATE KNIFE REST,TWIRLED CENTERBAR...................    5.00
SILVER PLATE KNIFE,SAWTOOTH EDGED...........................    9.00
SILVER PLATE LADLE,PUNCH,ROGERS BROS........................   14.50
SILVER PLATE MIRROR,HAND,PIERCED HANDLE
  HOLDER,FLORAL,VICTORIAN....................................   10.00
SILVER PLATE MUG,CHILDS,MARKED GUSSIE,AUG.21,1897,TRIPLE
  PLATED.....................................................    9.00
SILVER PLATE MUG,CHILDS,MARKED JOHNIE,AUG.12,1900,TRIPLE
```

```
PLATE.......................................................    9.00
SILVER PLATE MUG,ENGRAVED BIRD IN BUDDED BRANCH,REED &
BARTON......................................................    8.50
SILVER PLATE,MUG WITH FLORAL SPRAYS.........................    8.50
SILVER PLATE MUSTARD POT,COBALT GLASS LINER.................    7.50
SILVER PLATE NAPKIN HOLDER,BOY ON FENCE,ROGERS TRIPLE PLATE.   18.00
SILVER PLATE NAPKIN HOLDER,BUTTERFLY & FAN..................   16.00
SILVER PLATE NAPKIN HOLDER,HORSE DRAWN CHARIOT..............   18.00
SILVER PLATE NAPKIN HOLDER,TRIANGLE SHAPE WITH MYTHICAL
NAKED BOY...................................................   15.00
SILVER PLATE NAPKIN RING,BIRD ON EACH SIDE..................   16.75
SILVER PLATE NAPKIN RING,CHERUB & ANGEL.....................   27.50
SILVER PLATE NAPKIN RING,CHICK ON FOOTED OVAL BASE..........   27.50
SILVER PLATE NAPKIN RING,CHUNKY CHILD WITH FISHTAIL,BLOWING
HORN........................................................   32.50
SILVER PLATE NAPKIN RING,COLUMBIAN EXPOSITION 1892..........    6.00
SILVER PLATE NAPKIN RING,DONKEY.............................    4.00
SILVER PLATE NAPKIN RING,EAGLE ON ROUND BASE,UPTURNED WINGS.   27.50
SILVER PLATE NAPKIN RING,FOX................................   16.00
SILVER PLATE NAPKIN RING,HORSE WITH REINS PULLING RING,.....   35.00
SILVER PLATE,NAPKIN RING OF STATE CAPITOL,ST.PAUL,MINN......    8.50
SILVER PLATE NAPKIN RING ON PEDESTAL........................    9.00
SILVER PLATE NAPKIN RING ON BACK OF SPHINX..................    6.75
SILVER PLATE NAPKIN RING,OVAL BASE,CAT PERCHED ON RING,DOG..   27.50
SILVER PLATE,NAPKIN RING,ROGERS TRIPLE PLATE,BEST WISHES ON
RING........................................................   13.50
SILVER PLATE NAPKIN RING,SQUIRREL WITH GLASS EYES BLOWING
HORN........................................................   25.00
SILVER PLATE NAPKIN RING,TWO WISHBONES ENGRAVED BEST WISHES.    6.00
SILVER PLATE NUT DISH,SQUIRREL FIGURE RESTING IN
HANDLE,FOOTED...............................................   18.00
SILVER PLATE OPEN SUGAR.....................................    3.50
SILVER PLATE OPEN SUGAR & CREAMER,BEADED TOP,TORONTO SILVER
PLATE CO....................................................    7.50
SILVER PLATE PASTRY SERVER,SHELL DESIGN IN BLADE,FLORAL
HANDLE......................................................    5.00
SILVER PLATE,PEARL-HANDLE KNIVES............................    2.00
SILVER PLATE PEARL HANDLED BUTTER...........................    7.00
SILVER PLATE PEARL HANDLED SUGAR SPOON,EPNS.................    5.00
SILVER PLATE PEN TRAY,CURVED RIM REPOUSSE SCROLL............   10.00
SILVER PLATE,PICKLE CASTOR AND TONGS,AMBER DAISY & BUTTON
INSERT......................................................   48.00
SILVER PLATE,PICKLE CASTOR SET WITH 2 FORKS.................   24.50
SILVER PLATE PICKLE CASTOR WITH TONGS.......................   27.50
SILVER PLATE PICKLE FORK MARKED 1835 R.WALLACE PAT. 1902....    3.50
SILVER PLATE PITCHER........................................    6.00
SILVER PLATE PLATE,BREAD & BUTTER,SET OF 4,ROGERS...........    5.00
SILVER PLATE PLATTER COVER,ENGLISH 1857 REGISTRY MARK.......   47.00
SILVER PLATE PLATTER,GADROON RIM,PAIRPOINT CO...............   12.00
SILVER PLATE POCKET MATCH SAFE,FLOWERS & SCROLLS............    3.50
SILVER PLATE PUNCH LADLE,EPNS...............................   18.00
SILVER PLATE RELISH BASKET,APRON,FITTED RUBY & CLEAR GLASS
DISH........................................................   21.50
SILVER PLATE SALT,PAIR FOOTED,3 ORIENTAL FIGURES...........    8.00
SILVER PLATE SALT SCOOP.....................................    1.75
SILVER PLATE SERVER,CHEESE..................................   18.00
SILVER PLATE SHAVING MUG,DERBY SILVER.......................   12.00
SILVER PLATE SHAVING MUG,HINGED MIRRORED LID................   15.00
SILVER PLATE SHAVING MUG,MILK GLASS INSERT..................    5.00
SILVER PLATE SHAVING MUG WITH BRUSH REST,FOOTED.............    5.00
SILVER PLATE SHAVING MUG WITH PEWTER HANDLE,APOLLO SILVER CO
1870........................................................   25.00
SILVER PLATE SHAVING SET DATED 1910,STANDING MIRROR & BRUSH.   17.50
SILVER PLATE,SHEFFIELD ALE MUG MARKED TUDOR & LEADER CIRCA
1760........................................................  200.00
```

```
SILVER PLATE,SHEFFIELD BEAKER CIRCA 1790,BARREL STAVE DESIGN      60.00
SILVER PLATE,SHEFFIELD BUTTER CIRCA 1820,PAIR...............     325.00
SILVER PLATE,SHEFFIELD CAKE BASKET CIRCA 1815...............     125.00
SILVER PLATE,SHEFFIELD CAKE BASKET,CRESTED,CIRCA 1825.......     115.00
SILVER PLATE,SHEFFIELD CANDELABRA CIRCA 1810,PAIR..........      550.00
SILVER PLATE,SHEFFIELD,CANDLESTICK,PAIR,CIRCA 1800-1820.....      50.00
SILVER PLATE SHEFFIELD CANDLESTICK,PAIR OVAL BASES,CIRCA
  1790......................................................     235.00
SILVER PLATE,SHEFFIELD CANDLESTICKS,PAIR,ADAM STYLED,CIRCA
  1786......................................................     140.00
SILVER PLATE,SHEFFIELD CHAMBER CANDLESTICK & SNUFFER CIRCA
  1800......................................................      85.00
SILVER PLATE,SHEFFIELD CHILDS HOOPED MUG CIRCA 1790.........      65.00
SILVER PLATE,SHEFFIELD COFFEE URN & 16 CUPS,BEADED,CIRCA
  1790......................................................     265.00
SILVER PLATE,SHEFFIELD DISH CROSS CIRCA 1800...............      345.00
SILVER PLATE,SHEFFIELD EGG CUP CRUET SET WITH SLIDING TOAST
  RACKS.....................................................     210.00
SILVER PLATE,SHEFFIELD ENTREE DISH,GADROON
  BORDERS,PAIR,CIRCA 1815...................................     425.00
SILVER PLATE,SHEFFIELD FOOTED SALVER,BEADED
  ,CRESTED,OVAL,CIRCA 1780..................................     150.00
SILVER PLATE,SHEFFIELD GEORGE III MUFFINEER,LONDON 1786.....     125.00
SILVER PLATE,SHEFFIELD GOBLET,ENGRAVED,GILT LINED,CIRCA 1790     85.00
SILVER PLATE,SHEFFIELD HOT WATER JUG,BEADED,9 CUPS,CIRCA
  1770......................................................     200.00
SILVER PLATE,SHEFFIELD INK STAND CIRCA 1815.................     200.00
SILVER PLATE,SHEFFIELD JUG,ENGRAVED,8 CUP,CIRCA 1790........     215.00
SILVER PLATE,SHEFFIELD KETTLE & STAND,3 QUARTS,CIRCA 1800...     325.00
SILVER PLATE,SHEFFIELD MEAT DISH,OVAL,SHELL & GADROON,CIRCA
  1810......................................................     165.00
SILVER PLATE,SHEFFIELD OPEN SALT,GILT LINED,CIRCA 1800,PAIR.      75.00
SILVER PLATE SHEFFIELD PLATTER,ROAST,TREE,OBLONG,LONG
  LEGS,PAIRPOINT............................................      65.00
SILVER PLATE,SHEFFIELD SET OF 4 CANDLESTICKS,9 IN.
  HIGH,CIRCA 1825..........................................      500.00
SILVER PLATE,SHEFFIELD SET OF 4 CANDLESTICKS CIRCA 1780,13
  IN. TALL...............................................1,100.00
SILVER PLATE,SHEFFIELD SNUFFER & TRAY CIRCA 1825...........       90.00
SILVER PLATE,SHEFFIELD SUGAR BASKET,BLUE GLASS LINING CIRCA
  1770......................................................     125.00
SILVER PLATE,SHEFFIELD TANKARD,2 PINTS,WOODEN BASE,CIRCA
  1790......................................................     275.00
SILVER PLATE,SHEFFIELD TEA CADDY,BEADED,LONDON 1810.........     115.00
SILVER PLATE,SHEFFIELD TEA CADDY LION RING
  HANDLES,ROUND,CIRCA 1850..................................      25.00
SILVER PLATE,SHEFFIELD TEA POT,CRESTED,6 CUP,CIRCA 1800.....     125.00
SILVER PLATE,SHEFFIELD TELESCOPIC CANDLESTICK CIRCA
  1790,PAIR.................................................     150.00
SILVER PLATE,SHEFFIELD TELESCOPIC CANDLESTICKS,PAIR,CIRCA
  1810......................................................     150.00
SILVER PLATE SHEFFIELD TRAY,BREAD,13 IN.,OPEN LACY BORDER
  WITH HEART................................................      15.00
SILVER PLATE,SHEFFIELD WAX JACK & SNUFFER CIRCA 1790........     100.00
SILVER PLATE,SHEFFIELD WAX JACK CIRCA 1800..................     135.00
SILVER PLATE,SHEFFIELD WINE COOLER CIRCA 1820..............      400.00
SILVER PLATE,SHEFFIELD WINE COOLER,CRESTED,CIRCA 1825,PAIR..     950.00
SILVER PLATE,SHEFFIELD WIRE BOWL,OVAL,CIRCA 1800...........       85.00
SILVER PLATE SHOEHORN,EMBOSSED HANDLE......................        2.50
SILVER PLATE SOUVENIR SPOON,DIONNE QUINTUPLETS.............       10.00
SILVER PLATE SPOON,BERRY,ROGERS 1847 GRAPE PATTERN.........        4.00
SILVER PLATE SPOON,BERRY,SHELL & BEADED,WM.ROGERS.........         5.00
SILVER PLATE SPOON,DEMI-TASSE,SET OF 6,ROGERS BROS 1847
  MARKED....................................................       8.00
SILVER PLATE SPOON,DEMI-TASSE,SET OF 8.....................       12.00
```

```
SILVER PLATE SPOON,GRAPE,ROGERS 1847........................    2.00
SILVER PLATE SPOON HOLDER WITH CUT GLASS BOWL INSERT........   35.00
SILVER PLATE SPOON,ICE CREAM,SET OF 8,ORNATE,W.ROGERS.......   28.00
SILVER PLATE SPOON,SOUVENIR WILLIAMSBURG...................     2.50
SILVER PLATE SPOON WITH HINGED COVER FOR MAKING TEA IN CUP..    3.00
SILVER PLATE SPOON WITH TINES,STUFFING,HALLMARKED J.DIXON &
  SONS.....................................................   12.00
SILVER PLATE STAND WITH BRISTOL COMPOTE,HANDPAINTED,REED &
  BARTON...................................................   40.00
SILVER PLATE STRAINER,TEA,ENGLISH..........................    6.50
SILVER PLATE,SUGAR BOWL & SPOON HOLDER,HOOKS FOR 12
  SPOONS,BIRD FINIAL.......................................   14.50
SILVER PLATE SUGAR BOWL SPOON HOLDER,DOME PEDESTAL..........   25.00
SILVER PLATE,SUGAR BOWL WITH LEAF,FORMED SPOON HOLDERS......   48.00
SILVER PLATE SUGAR ,CREAMER & TRAY.........................   10.00
SILVER PLATE SUGAR SPOONER WITH BIRD ON TOP................   25.00
SILVER PLATE SUGAR TONGS MARKED WM.ROGERS DERBY SILVER CO...    3.50
SILVER PLATE SYRUP JUG,ENGRAVED DESIGN OF FLOWERS...........   17.00
SILVER PLATE SYRUP PITCHER
  4.50  TO...............................................     15.00
SILVER PLATE SYRUP PITCHER ON TRAY HELD WITH SILVER PEG.....   30.00
SILVER PLATE SYRUP WITH TRAY,PAIRPOINT.....................    9.00
SILVER PLATE TEA CADDY,....................................   18.00
SILVER PLATE TEA CADDY,CHINESE DESIGNS.....................   16.00
SILVER PLATE TEA SERVICE,4 PIECE BY ESSEX SILVER CO.........  100.00
SILVER PLATE TEA SERVICE,4 PIECES,VAN BERGH SILVER PLATE CO.   35.00
SILVER PLATE TEA SERVICE ON TRAY...........................   15.00
SILVER PLATE TEA SERVICE,VICTORIAN,EACH PIECE ON 4 FEET.....   75.00
SILVER PLATE TEA SET,3 PIECES..............................   35.00
SILVER PLATE TEA SET,5 PIECES,LINED IN GILT,ENGRAVED OPEN
  ROSE....................................................   75.00
SILVER PLATE TEA SET,FOOTED,FLORAL
  MOUNTS,POOLE,TAUNTON,MASS................................   45.00
SILVER PLATE TEA SET MARKED WILCOX & CO.,VICTORIAN.........   45.00
SILVER PLATE TEA STRAINER,WOOD HANDLE......................    2.25
SILVER PLATE TEAPOT & OPEN SUGAR BY WILCOX & CO.,QUADRUPLE..   45.00
SILVER PLATE TEAPOT,CANADIAN,ROGERS........................   18.50
SILVER PLATE TEAPOT,COLUMBIA,SQUATTY,SCROLL EMBOSSED HANDLE.   15.50
SILVER PLATE TEAPOT,QUEEN ANNE SHAPED......................   25.00
SILVER PLATE TEAPOT,REED HANDLE............................    5.00
SILVER PLATE,TEAPOT SIGNED JAMES ALLAN SHEFFIELD...........   35.00
SILVER PLATE TEAPOT,ON COPPER..............................   10.00
SILVER PLATE TEASPOON,SET OF 8,GRAPE PATTERN,ROGERS BROS....   10.00
SILVER PLATE TEASPOON WITH HINGED COVER MARKED WILLIAMS.....    4.50
SILVER PLATE TOAST RACK,RIBBED,FOOTED......................    8.50
SILVER PLATE TOAST RACK WITH EGG CUP.......................    8.00
SILVER PLATE TONGS,SUGAR...................................    4.50
SILVER PLATE TOOTHPICK,CHICK & WISHBONE....................   10.00
SILVER PLATE TOOTHPICK ,EGG ON WISHBONE CHICK AT SIDE.......    9.50
SILVER PLATE TOOTHPICK HOLDER,FOOTED TREE STUMP &
  BEETLE,SIGNED KNAPP......................................   10.00
SILVER PLATE TOOTHPICK HOLDER,MAN DRESSED AS BAKER..........   12.50
SILVER PLATE TOOTHPICK HOLDER,ROGERS TRIPLE PLATE..........   13.50
SILVER PLATE TOOTHPICK HOLDER,SCALLOPED TOP BASKET,BULLDOG..   12.00
SILVER PLATE TRAY,BREAD,12 IN.,QUADRUPLE...................   12.00
SILVER PLATE TRAY,CARD,ROUND,6 IN.,ELK IN CENTER...........    6.00
SILVER PLATE TRAY,MONOGRAM G.G.G...........................    6.50
SILVER PLATE TRAY ON COPPER,ENGRAVING......................    5.50
SILVER PLATE TRAY WITH 2 HANDLES,RECTANGULAR SHAPE,15 X 19
  IN......................................................   12.00
SILVER PLATE TRAY WITH HANDLES,12 X 15 IN.,HALLMARKED......    7.50
SILVER PLATE WARMER,SPOON,ENGLISH..........................   18.00
SILVER PLATE WATER COOLER,IRONSTONE LINED,MARKED REED &
  BARTON 1860.............................................   85.00
SILVER PLATE WATER PITCHER,BULBOUS SHAPE...................   22.50
```

SILVER WIRE CORNUCOPIA.. 30.00

SINCLAIRE CUT GLASS was made by the H. P. Sinclaire & Company, New York, from 1905 to 1929.

SINCLAIR BOWL,CELESTE BLUE,SIGNED S IN WREATH............... 45.00
SINCLAIR BOWL,HANDLED,VINTAGE PATTERN....................... 155.00

SLAG GLASS is streaked with several colors. There were many types made from about 1880. Caramel or chocolate glass was made by the Indiana Tumbler and Goblet Company of Greentown, Indiana, from 1900 to 1903. Pink slag was an American Victorian product of unknown origin. Purple and blue slag were made in American and English factories. Red slag is a very late Victorian product. Other colors are known, but are of less importance to the collector.

SLAG BLUE BASKET,OVAL...................................... 11.00
SLAG,BLUE COMPOTE... 23.50
SLAG BUTTERSCOTCH FLOWER POT,AKRO AGATE MARK............... 4.50
SLAG BUTTERSCOTCH MATCH HOLDER............................ 22.50
SLAG,BUTTERSCOTCH SPILL HOLDER,4 IN. TALL................. 25.00
SLAG,BUTTERSCOTCH VASE,10 IN. ,FLARED BEADED TOP,RIBBED..... 37.50
SLAG,CARAMEL ACANTHUS LEAF BUTTER DISH,SPOONER & COVERED
  SUGAR.. 85.00
SLAG,CARAMEL AMBER HOLLY VINE CREAMER..................... 27.50
SLAG,CARAMEL AMBER HOLLY VINE TOOTHPICK HOLDER............ 16.50
SLAG,CARAMEL AMBER HOLLY VINE TUMBLER..................... 15.00
SLAG,CARAMEL BUTTER DISH,COVER IS CAT ON HAMPER........... 150.00
SLAG,CARAMEL CACTUS BOWL,ROUND,7 IN....................... 32.50
SLAG,CARAMEL CACTUS BUTTER,COVERED
  25.00 TO.. 65.00
SLAG,CARAMEL CACTUS COMPOTE.............................. 55.00
SLAG,CARAMEL CACTUS COOKIE JAR........................... 30.00
SLAG,CARAMEL CACTUS CREAMER.............................. 10.00
SLAG,CARAMEL CACTUS CRUET................................ 68.00
SLAG,CARAMEL CACTUS JAR,CRACKER,COVERED.................. 65.00
SLAG,CARAMEL CACTUS MUG,HANDLED.......................... 18.50
SLAG,CARAMEL CACTUS SAUCE................................ 13.50
SLAG,CARAMEL CACTUS SHAKER............................... 15.00
SLAG,CARAMEL CACTUS SUGAR,COVERED........................ 38.00
SLAG,CARAMEL CACTUS SUGAR,COVERED,GREENTOWN.............. 45.00
SLAG,CARAMEL CACTUS TABLE SET,4 PIECES................... 182.50
SLAG,CARAMEL CACTUS TUMBLER.............................. 10.00
SLAG,CARAMEL CACTUS TUMBLER,4 IN......................... 19.00
SLAG,CARAMEL CORD DRAPERY JUG,SYRUP...................... 65.00
SLAG,CARAMEL CREAM PITCHER,RECTANGULAR SHAPE ON STANDARD.... 22.50
SLAG,CARAMEL CREAMER,OPEN EDGE,GREENTOWN.................. 25.00
SLAG,CARAMEL CRUET WITH STOPPER.......................... 35.00
SLAG,CARAMEL DEWEY DISH,COVERED.......................... 45.00
SLAG,CARAMEL DEWEY SAUCE................................. 10.00
SLAG,CARAMEL DEWEY SUGAR BOWL,OPEN....................... 15.00
SLAG,CARAMEL DEWEY SUGAR,COVERED......................... 37.50
SLAG,CARAMEL DISH,BERRY,FOOTED,4 IN...................... 13.50
SLAG,CARAMEL DOLPHIN SUGAR............................... 22.50
SLAG,CARAMEL EGG,BLUE & MULBERRY......................... 16.50
SLAG,CARAMEL LEAF BRACKET CELERY DISH.................... 27.50
SLAG CARAMEL LEAF BRACKET TUMBLER........................ 22.50
SLAG,CARAMEL MUG... 15.00
SLAG,CARAMEL NAPPY,HANDLED,TRI-CORNERED.................. 22.00
SLAG,CARAMEL PALM COMPOTE,OPEN........................... 32.50
SLAG,CARAMEL SAUCE,FOOTED................................ 10.00
SLAG CARAMEL SERENADE PLATE.............................. 55.00
SLAG,CARAMEL SHELL & LEAF BOWL ON 3 FEET,8 IN............ 22.00
SLAG,CARAMEL SHELL & LEAF DISH,SAUCE,FOOTED.............. 16.00
SLAG,CARAMEL SHELL NAPPY,TRI-CORNERED.................... 21.00
SLAG,CARAMEL SHOE,PAIR CHILDS HIGH....................... 18.00
SLAG CARMEL SPOONER...................................... 20.00
SLAG,CARAMEL SPOONER WITH 3 SWANS........................ 27.50

```
SLAG,CARAMEL SQUIRREL WATER PITCHER.........................  150.00
SLAG,CARAMEL UNEEDA BISCUIT TUMBLER.........................   15.00
SLAG,CARAMEL VASE,GREENTOWN,SCALLOPED FLANGE................   18.50
SLAG,CARAMEL VASE,SCALLOPED FLANGE..........................   21.50
SLAG,CARAMEL WILD ROSE & BOWKNOT TUMBLER....................   24.00
SLAG,CARAMEL WITCHS HEAD TOOTHPICK HOLDER...................    8.00
SLAG,CHARTREUSE LACY CREAMER & SUGAR,OPEN...................   37.50
SLAG GREEN 8 IN. BOWL.......................................   27.50
SLAG,GREEN & WHITE TOOTHPICK................................   12.50
SLAG,GREEN COMPOTE..........................................   23.50
SLAG,GREEN PAIR 10 IN. VASES,NOTCHED EDGE...................   16.50
SLAG ORANGE OVAL OPEN CANDY DISH............................    5.00
SLAG,PINK 6 FOOTED PUNCH CUPS,3 TUMBLERS IN FAN & INVERTED
  FAN.....................................................2,000.00
SLAG,PINK BUTTER DISH,4 BALL FEET...........................  195.00
SLAG,PINK,CUP...............................................  400.00
SLAG PINK FEATHER & FAN TUMBLER.............................  400.00
SLAG PINK FOOTED SAUCE DISH,INVERTED FAN AND FEATHER DESIGN.  165.00
SLAG,PINK PAIR SALT & PEPPER SHAKERS,INVERTED FAN & FEATHER.  300.00
SLAG,PINK PUNCH CUP.........................................  270.00
SLAG,PURPLE 10 PANEL TUMBLER................................   22.50
SLAG,PURPLE ACANTHUS LEAF SPOONER...........................   20.00
SLAG,PURPLE ACANTHUS LEAVES VASE,GOBLET TYPE,TULIP SHAPE....   38.00
SLAG,PURPLE & WHITE RAISED CABLE & FLUTE SALT,MASTER........   15.00
SLAG,PURPLE BASKET DATED FEB. 13,1877,MINIATURE,4 IN. LONG..   25.00
SLAG,PURPLE BOOT,COWBOY.....................................   25.00
SLAG,PURPLE BOTTLE,3 IN. HIGH,BELL FLOWER...................   12.50
SLAG,PURPLE BOWL,DART & BAR.................................   50.00
SLAG,PURPLE BOWL ON FOOT,SHELL FORM.........................   28.00
SLAG,PURPLE BOWL,RUFFLED,INDENTED DESIGN....................   28.00
SLAG,PURPLE BUTTER COVER,FLOWER & PANEL.....................   20.00
SLAG,PURPLE BUTTER DISH,FLUTED,COVERED......................   55.00
SLAG,PURPLE CAKE STAND
  38.00  TO.................................................   50.00
SLAG,PURPLE CELERY,FLUTED...................................   42.00
SLAG,PURPLE COMPOTE,CAKE....................................   50.00
SLAG,PURPLE COMPOTE,CAKE,FLUTED.............................   75.00
SLAG,PURPLE COMPOTE,DART & BAR..............................   65.00
SLAG,PURPLE COMPOTE,FRUIT,DART & BAR........................   75.00
SLAG,PURPLE COMPOTE,JELLY,4 IN. HIGH........................   37.50
SLAG,PURPLE COMPOTE,JENNY LIND..............................   75.00
SLAG PURPLE COMPOTE ON SHORT STANDARD,RUFFLED BORDER........   20.00
SLAG PURPLE CREAMER,6 SIDES.................................   32.00
SLAG,PURPLE DART & BAR BOWL.................................   45.00
SLAG,PURPLE DART & BAR CAKE STAND...........................   65.00
SLAG,PURPLE DART & BAR COMPOTE,FRUIT........................   70.00
SLAG,PURPLE DART & BAR PITCHER,WATER........................   60.00
SLAG,PURPLE DISH,COVERED,DUCK IN MOTTLED COLOURS............   65.00
SLAG,PURPLE DISH,COVERED,SWAN IN MOTTLED COLOURS............   65.00
SLAG,PURPLE DISH,SOAP.......................................   17.00
SLAG,PURPLE FLUTED BUTTER DISH,COVERED......................   50.00
SLAG,PURPLE FLUTED CELERY,8 IN..............................   49.50
SLAG,PURPLE FLUTED DISH,VEGETABLE,OBLONG....................   45.00
SLAG,PURPLE GOBLET,TWIG FOOT................................   27.00
SLAG,PURPLE JENNY LIND COMPOTE..............................   75.00
SLAG,PURPLE MATCH HOLDER....................................    9.00
SLAG,PURPLE MATCHHOLDER,PAIR................................   12.00
SLAG,PURPLE MATCHHOLDER,POST CORNERS........................   18.00
SLAG,PURPLE PITCHER,4 IN....................................   17.50
SLAG,PURPLE PITCHER,RAIN DROP...............................   70.00
SLAG,PURPLE PLATE,CLOSED LATTICE EDGE
  42.50  TO.................................................   55.00
SLAG,PURPLE PLATTER,NOTCHED EDGE............................   45.00
SLAG,PURPLE RAINDROP PITCHER,WATER..........................   70.00
SLAG,PURPLE ROSE BOWL.......................................   29.50
```

```
SLAG,PURPLE SCROLL WITH ACANTHUS COMPOTE...................   25.00
SLAG,PURPLE SHELL VARIANT BUTTER,COVERED
   53.00  TO.................................................   57.00
SLAG,PURPLE SPOON HOLDER.....................................   22.50
SLAG,PURPLE SUGAR,COVERED,& CREAMER.........................   75.00
SLAG,PURPLE SUGAR WITH LID...................................   22.50
SLAG,PURPLE TABLE SET,6 PIECES..............................  295.00
SLAG,PURPLE TAM-O-SHANTER PLATTER...........................   90.00
SLAG,PURPLE TAPER HOLDER.....................................   12.00
SLAG,PURPLE THIMBLE TOOTHPICK...............................   20.00
SLAG,PURPLE TOOTHPICK HOLDER................................   20.00
SLAG,PURPLE,TOOTHPICK,RAISED FLORAL,SQUARE,HANDLES..........   15.00
SLAG,PURPLE TRAY,FLUTED,OBLONG,9 IN.........................   45.00
SLAG,PURPLE TUMBLER
   12.00  TO.................................................   18.00
SLAG,PURPLE TUMBLER,ANCHOR MARK IN BASE.....................   25.00
SLAG,PURPLE TUMBLER,ENGLISH MARK............................   16.50
SLAG,PURPLE TUMBLER,MARKED BOTTOM HALF PINT LION & CROWN....   25.00
SLAG,PURPLE TUMBLER,WATER,10 SIDED..........................   20.00
SLAG,PURPLE VASE,3 HANDLED,TREE SHAPED,BASE IN SHAPE OF LEAF   24.00
SLAG,PURPLE VASE,11 IN.,BEADED SCALLOPED TOP,5 CORNERED.....   14.00
SLAG,PURPLE VASE,JEWEL......................................   65.00
SLAG,PURPLE VASE WITH FLUTED TOP,12 IN......................   25.00
SLAG,PURPLE WATER GLASS,MARBELIZED COLOUR,RIBBED
   BASE,ENGLISH MARK.........................................   20.00
SLAG,PURPLE WATER PITCHER,DART & BAR........................   60.00
SLAG RED 3-PIECE SET,BOWL WITH CANDLEHOLDERS................  225.00
SLAG,RED COVERED FOOTED URN SHAPED GLASS CANDY COMPOTE......   25.00
SLAG RED MELON RIBBED BOWL..................................   85.00
```

SLIP is a thin mixture of clay and water, about the consistency of sour cream, that is applied to the pottery for decoration. If the pottery is made with red clay, the slip is mixed with yellow clay.

```
SLIPWARE BIRD WHISTLE.......................................   95.00
```

SMITH BROTHERS GLASS was made after 1878. The owners had worked for the Mount Washington Glass Company in New Bedford, Massachusetts, for seven years before going into their own shop. Some of the designs were similar.

```
SMITH BROS.,MT.WASHINGTON COVERED POWDER JAR,SIGNED RAMPANT
   LION......................................................  125.00
SMITH BROS. PASTEL BLUE VASE,SIGNED,8 IN....................  187.50
SMITH BROTHERS RIBBED MUSTARD,FLORAL & LEAF DECORATION......   25.00
SMITH BROS.SIGNED CRACKER JAR,SILVER LID,PANSY DECOR........  200.00
SMITH BROS.SIGNED DECORATED MELON RIBBED BOWL,SILVER PLATED
   COVER.....................................................  125.00
SMITH BROS.SIGNED MELON SECTIONAL BOWL,PINK & BLUE..........  115.00
SMITH BROS.SUGAR & CREAMER,MELON RIBBED,SILVER TOPS.........  150.00
SNOW EAGLES,PR. WITH BRACKETS,ORIGINAL......................   17.50
SNUFF BOTTLE,BLUE ON WHITE DESIGN,SIGNED,ROSE QUARTZ STOPPER   60.00
SNUFF BOTTLE,CHINESE PEKING.................................   15.00
SNUFF BOTTLE,SQUARE AMBER...................................    1.00
SNUFF BOTTLE,WHITE CYLINDER,INCISED DESIGN OF BIRDS
   FLYING,MEN RIDING.........................................   60.00
SNUFF BOTTLE,WHITE,PICTURE OF MAN,LONG POEM ON BACK,GREEN
   STOPPER...................................................   45.00
SNUFF BOTTLE,YELLOW WITH ROSE ,WHITE,FLOWERS & BIRDS,CORAL
   COLLAR....................................................   55.00
SNUFF BOX,FRENCH ENAMEL,CARDINAL HAT SHAPE,HINGED...........  125.00
SNUFF BOX,MOTHER OF PEARL DECOR,2IN.........................    6.00
SNUFF BOX,SILVER ON COPPER WITH CHAIN & SPOON,..............   40.00
```

SOAPSTONE is a mineral that was used for footwarmers or griddles because of its heat-retaining properties. Chinese soapstone carvings of the nineteenth and twentieth centuries are found in many antique shops.

```
SOAPSTONE 3 MONKEYS TOOTHPICK...............................    4.00
```

```
SOAPSTONE 8 IN. HIGH FLOWERS & LEAVES CARVINGS.............     15.00
SOAPSTONE BOX,GRAVESTONE TYPE CARVING,SKULL &
  CROSSBONES,EAGLE........................................     25.00
SOAPSTONE BURMESE FIGURE OF WARRIOR.......................     65.00
SOAPSTONE CABINET PIECE,CARVING OF SLEEPING MONK..........     47.50
SOAPSTONE CANDLESTICK,EATING DEER & BIRD CARVINGS.........     15.00
SOAPSTONE CARVED 3 MONKEYS................................      8.50
SOAPSTONE CARVED KUAN YIN  IN SEATED POSITION WITH VASE IN
  HANDS..................................................     45.00
SOAPSTONE CARVED MONKEY...................................     10.00
SOAPSTONE CARVED PAIR SEALS,2 IN. TALL,JAPANESE..........     20.00
SOAPSTONE CARVED PAIR VASES,FLOWERS,LEAVES IN RELIEF......     27.50
SOAPSTONE CARVED VASE,2 IN. TALL.........................      5.00
SOAPSTONE CIGARETTE HOLDER WITH 3 ASH TRAYS,WHITE.........     12.00
SOAPSTONE FOOT WARMER.....................................      6.00
SOAPSTONE GOD ON BASE.....................................     23.00
SOAPSTONE GREEN & BEIGE VASE..............................     12.00
SOAPSTONE GRIFFIN HORSE CIRCA 1840........................     65.00
SOAPSTONE LYING GOAT CIRCA 1850...........................     45.00
SOAPSTONE ORNAMENT,2 VASES WITH SPRAY FLOWERS ON 3 FEET...      9.00
SOAPSTONE ORNAMENT,BIRD AT FOUNTAIN.......................     12.00
SOAPSTONE PAIR CARVED BOOK
  ENDS,SQUARE,FLOWERS,LEAVES,BUTTERFLIES..................     19.50
SOAPSTONE TAN & ROSE DOUBLE VASE,CARVING OF BIRDS & FLOWERS.   34.50
SOAPSTONE TOOTHPICK HOLDER,3 BIRDS........................      6.00
SOAPSTONE TRAY............................................      6.50
SOAPSTONE VASE,MADE IN CHINA MARK,DOUBLE,FLORAL ETCHING...     52.00
SOAPSTONE VASE WITH CARVED FLOWERS........................     15.00
SOAPSTONE VASE WITH FLOWERS MARKED CHINA..................      8.00
SOAPSTONE VASE WITH MONKEYS...............................     16.00
SOFT PASTE GERMAN CREAMER SHAPE LITTLE DUTCH GIRL.........      6.50
SOFT PASTE HANDLELESS CUP & SAUCER,GREEN LEAVES,LAVENDER
  SPRAY..................................................     15.00
SOFT PASTE ODD FELLOWS MUG CIRCA 1800,POLYCHROME DECORATION.   30.00
SOUVENIR BUTTON,BALLOON ROUTE TROLLEY TRIP................      2.00
SOUVENIR BUTTON,VETERANS OF 1861-1865.....................      4.00
SOUVENIR DEMI-TASSE CUP & SAUCER,AUGUSTA MAINE............      3.00
SOUVENIR PIN,ALASKA-YUKON-PAC.EXPO.SEATTLE 1909...........      4.00
SOUVENIR PIN,PAN-PAC.INTER.EXPO.1915......................      1.00
SOUVENIR PIN,TRANS-MISS.INTER.EXPO.OMAHA,NEB.1898.........      5.00
SOUVENIR PITCHER,4 IN. TALL,SIGNED MADE IN GERMANY,GOLD ON
  WHITE..................................................      2.50
SOUVENIR PLATE,6 IN.,SIGNING DECLARATION INDEPENDENCE.....      3.50
SOUVENIR PLATE,8 IN.,BLUE & WHITE,PITTSBURGH,PA.,OLD BLOCK
  HOUSE..................................................      4.75
SOUVENIR PLATE,9 IN.,MUNCY VALLEY PA.,WHITE & GREEN FLOWERED
  EDGE...................................................      8.50
SOUVENIR PLATE, 9 IN. , NIAGARA FALLS.....................      4.00
SOUVENIR PLATE,10 IN.,BLUE COLORADO SPRINGS VERNON KILNS...     2.50
SOUVENIR PLATE,BLUE,BOSTON VIEWS,MARKED ENGLAND...........      6.00
SOUVENIR PLATE,BOSTON STATE HOUSE.........................      5.00
SOUVENIR PLATE,NEW YORK WORLDS FAIR 1939,THE AMERICAN POTTER   9.50
SOUVENIR PLATE,NIAGARA FALLS,PINK EMBOSSED EDGE...........      8.00
SOUVENIR PLATE,PIERCED RIM,LIBERTY-BELL...................      6.50
SOUVENIR PLATE,PIERCED RIM,TULLAMORE......................      6.50
SOUVENIR SPOON,1893 WORLDS FAIR...........................      2.50
SOUVENIR SPOON,1933 CHICAGO FAIR..........................      1.50
SOUVENIR SPOON,ACTRESS MARION DAVIES......................      2.00
SOUVENIR SPOON,ATLANTIC CITY..............................      3.50
SOUVENIR SPOON,BATTLESHIP MAINE...........................      2.00
SOUVENIR SPOON,BEACH HAVEN,NEW JERSEY.....................      3.50
SOUVENIR SPOON,BERMUDA....................................     44.00
SOUVENIR SPOON,BROOKLYN BRIDGE,NEW YORK,PATENT 1896.......      3.95
SOUVENIR SPOON,CANADA,GOLD DIPPED & ENAMEL................      6.50
SOUVENIR SPOON,CAPITOL,COLUMBUS,OHIO......................      5.50
```

```
SOUVENIR SPOON,CHARLIE MCCARTHY................................   4.50
SOUVENIR SPOON,COLUMBIAN EXPOSITION........................   4.50
SOUVENIR SPOON,COLUMBIAN WORLDS FAIR,ART PALACE IN BOWL.....   5.00
SOUVENIR SPOON,COLUMBIAN WORLDS FAIR,FISHERIES BUILDING IN
  BOWL....................................................   5.00
SOUVENIR SPOON,COLUMBIAN WORLDS FAIR,TRANSPORTATION BUILDING
  IN BOWL.................................................   5.00
SOUVENIR SPOON,CORONATION GEORGE VI,ELIZABETH 1937.........   2.95
SOUVENIR SPOON,CURACAO,ENAMEL HANDLE & BOWL................   8.00
SOUVENIR SPOON,DEMITASSE,STERLING SILVER,CAPITOL
  BUILDING,WASHINGTON.....................................   2.00
SOUVENIR SPOON,DEMITASSE,STERLING SILVER,ST.LOUIS
  CATHEDRAL,NEW ORLEANS...................................   2.00
SOUVENIR SPOON,DIONNE QUINTUPLET,MARIE....................   5.00
SOUVENIR SPOON,DOUGLAS FAIRBANKS PORTRAIT & SIGNATURE.......   4.00
SOUVENIR SPOON,FALLS AT BALA MUSKOKA......................   6.00
SOUVENIR SPOON,FLAGSHIP OLYMPIA,BATTLE OF MANILA,MAY 1898...   2.00
SOUVENIR PLATE,FRIAR TUCK,MANCHESTER,NEW HAVEN.............   9.00
SOUVENIR SPOON,GRANTS TOMB,NEW YORK.......................   2.00
SOUVENIR SPOON,GREATER NEW YORK...........................   3.50
SOUVENIR SPOON,ILLINOIS..................................   1.50
SOUVENIR SPOON,IOWA,COMMUNITY PLATE.......................   1.75
SOUVENIR SPOON,KENTUCKY..................................   1.50
SOUVENIR SPOON,LOG CABIN.................................   1.50
SOUVENIR SPOON,LOGAN STATUE,OGDEN,UTAH....................   2.75
SOUVENIR SPOON,LOUISIANA PURCHASE EXPOSITION..............   6.75
SOUVENIR SPOON,MARIE.....................................   1.50
SOUVENIR SPOON,MARKED BOSTON WITH PAUL REVERE ON RIDE,REED &
  BARTON..................................................   6.00
SOUVENIR SPOON,MARKED IOWA ON HANDLE......................   4.50
SOUVENIR SPOON,MARKED WORLDS FAIR CITY,BUST OF COLUMBUS.....   5.50
SOUVENIR SPOON,MARYLAND..................................   1.50
SOUVENIR SPOON,MASONIC...................................   8.00
SOUVENIR SPOON,MASS......................................   1.50
SOUVENIR SPOON,MERRY CHRISTMAS AND HAPPY NEW YEAR..........   3.50
SOUVENIR SPOON,MISSOURI COAT OF ARMS......................   5.00
SOUVENIR SPOON,MONTREAL,ENAMEL HANDLE.....................   4.00
SOUVENIR SPOON,MONTREAL,QUEBEC...........................   7.50
SOUVENIR SPOON,MORMON TEMPLE,SALT LAKE CITY,UTAH..........   9.00
SOUVENIR SPOON,MORRO CASTLE,HAVANA.......................   4.95
SOUVENIR SPOON,MT.HOOD,PORTLAND,INDIAN WITH BUFFALO 1911....   6.00
SOUVENIR SPOON,MT.WASHINGTON.............................   5.00
SOUVENIR SPOON,NEW JERSEY................................   1.50
SOUVENIR SPOON,NEW YORK..................................   1.50
SOUVENIR SPOON,NEW YORK 1939 WORLDS FAIR..................   1.50
SOUVENIR SPOON,NEW YORK 1939 WORLDS FAIR,AMPHITHEATER......   1.50
SOUVENIR SPOON,NEW YORK WORLDS FAIR,1939,AVIATION BUILDING..   1.50
SOUVENIR SPOON,NEW YORK 1939 WORLDS FAIR,CONSUMERS BUILDING.   1.50
SOUVENIR SPOON,NEW YORK 1939 WORLDS FAIR,RAILROAD
  TRANSPORTATION BLDG.....................................   1.50
SOUVENIR SPOON,NEW YORK 1939 WORLDS FAIR,TEXTILE BUILDING...   1.50
SOUVENIR SPOON,NEW YORK COAT OF ARMS,NIAGARA FALLS.........   4.50
SOUVENIR SPOON,OFFICIAL CENTURY OF PROGRESS 1933..........   1.50
SOUVENIR SPOON,OREGON,LEWIS & CLARK......................   5.00
SOUVENIR SPOON,PAN AMERICAN EXPOSITION 1901...............   4.50
SOUVENIR SPOON,PENNSYLVANIA..............................   1.50
SOUVENIR SPOON,PLATTSBURG,NEW YORK.......................   4.50
SOUVENIR SPOON,QUEBEC,ENAMEL HANDLE......................   5.00
SOUVENIR SPOON,ROGERS BROS.SILVER PLATE,ILLINOIS..........   2.50
SOUVENIR SPOON,SAN FRANCISCO EXPOSITION...................   3.50
SOUVENIR SPOON,ST.LOUIS WORLDS FAIR......................   3.50
SOUVENIR SPOON,SAN GABRIEL MISSION LOS
  ANGELES,ORANGES,OSTRICH,GRAPE...........................   6.00
SOUVENIR SPOON,SANTA FE,NEW MEXICO.......................   7.00
SOUVENIR SPOON,STERLING SILVER,ARKANSAS..................   4.50
```

```
SOUVENIR SPOON,STERLING SILVER,BATTLESHIP MAINE.............    3.00
SOUVENIR SPOON,STERLING SILVER,BIG RAPIDS..................    5.00
SOUVENIR SPOON,STERLING SILVER,BISBEE ARIZONA.................    5.00
SOUVENIR SPOON,STERLING SILVER,CALIFORNIA..................    4.50
SOUVENIR SPOON,STERLING SILVER,CALUMET MICHIGAN..............    5.00
SOUVENIR SPOON,STERLING SILVER,CATALINA ISLAND..............    3.00
SOUVENIR SPOON,STERLING SILVER,CHICAGO WORLDS FAIR 1892-3...    2.95
SOUVENIR SPOON,STERLING SILVER,COLORADO...................    5.00
SOUVENIR SPOON,STERLING SILVER,COLUMBIAN EXPOSITION.........    9.50
SOUVENIR SPOON,STERLING SILVER,DEMITASSE,SAN
DIEGO,CALIFORNIA........................................    3.50
SOUVENIR SPOON,STERLING SILVER,DENVER.....................    3.00
SOUVENIR SPOON,STERLING SILVER,FATHER MARQUETTE,MARQUETTE
MICHIGAN...............................................    2.95
SOUVENIR SPOON,STERLING SILVER,GENESEE FALLS,NEW YORK........    4.00
SOUVENIR SPOON,STERLING SILVER,HARRISBURG.................    3.00
SOUVENIR SPOON,STERLING SILVER,HOTEL-DEL CORONADO CALIFORNIA    4.00
SOUVENIR SPOON,STERLING SILVER,HUDSON-FULTON................    4.00
SOUVENIR SPOON,STERLING SILVER INDIAN HEAD................    8.00
SOUVENIR SPOON,STERLING SILVER,JACKSONVILLE,FLORIDA,ORANGES
& PALMS................................................    3.00
SOUVENIR SPOON,STERLING SILVER,LANDING OF THE PILGRIMS......    3.00
SOUVENIR SPOON,STERLING SILVER,LINCOLN,GETTYSBURG...........    3.50
SOUVENIR SPOON,STERLING SILVER,LOS ANGELES................    4.50
SOUVENIR SPOON,STERLING SILVER,MANITOWOC,WISCONSIN HARBOUR..    3.50
SOUVENIR SPOON,STERLING SILVER,MASONIC
TEMPLE,CHICAGO,MASONIC SYMBOLS...........................    4.95
SOUVENIR SPOON,STERLING SILVER,MEXICO.....................    5.00
SOUVENIR SPOON,STERLING SILVER,MEXICO BULLFIGHT DATED
7-23-14................................................    5.00
SOUVENIR SPOON,STERLING SILVER,MINOT,NORTH DAKOTA...........    3.95
SOUVENIR SPOON,STERLING SILVER,MT.GREYLOCK,NO.ADAMS,MASS....    3.50
SOUVENIR SPOON,STERLING SILVER,MT.HAMILTON,CALIFORNIA.......    8.00
SOUVENIR SPOON,STERLING SILVER,MUSCOGEE,INDIANA TERRITORY
1891...................................................    8.00
SOUVENIR SPOON,STERLING SILVER,NEBRASKA EXPOSITION 1893.....    3.00
SOUVENIR SPOON,STERLING SILVER,NEW BRANFELS TEXAS..........    3.50
SOUVENIR SPOON,STERLING SILVER,NEW HAVEN TIP TOP HOUSE......    5.00
SOUVENIR SPOON,STERLING SILVER,NEW YORK...................    3.50
SOUVENIR SPOON,STERLING SILVER,NORTH DAKOTA................    3.95
SOUVENIR SPOON,STERLING SILVER,OGDEN.....................    4.50
SOUVENIR SPOON,STERLING SILVER,ORANGE,NEW ORLEANS...........    2.50
SOUVENIR SPOON,STERLING SILVER,PAN AMERICAN,INDIAN BUFFALO..    7.00
SOUVENIR SPOON,STERLING SILVER,PAUL REVERE................    7.00
SOUVENIR SPOON,STERLING SILVER,ROCHESTER,NEW YORK,CUT OUT
HANDLE.................................................    3.00
SOUVENIR SPOON,STERLING SILVER,SAN FRANCISCO CALIFORNIA 1915   50.00
SOUVENIR SPOON,STERLING SILVER,SHIELD CROSSED AXES &
INITIALS W.C...........................................    4.50
SOUVENIR SPOON,STERLING SILVER,ST.LOUIS
3.25  TO...............................................    7.00
SOUVENIR SPOON,STERLING SILVER,TEDDY ROOSEVELT ON HORSE.....   10.50
SOUVENIR SPOON,STERLING SILVER,TIFFANY....................    9.00
SOUVENIR SPOON,STERLING SILVER,U S MILITARY
POST,PLATTSBURGH,NEW YORK...............................    3.95
SOUVENIR SPOON,STERLING SILVER,WASHINGTON.................    5.00
SOUVENIR SPOON,STERLING SILVER,WELLESLEY..................    3.00
SOUVENIR SPOON,STERLING SILVER,WHITTIERS LIBRARY,SIGNATURE..    3.95
SOUVENIR SPOON,STERLING SILVER WITH GOLD WASH ,ST.PETERS
CHURCH,1907............................................    4.95
SOUVENIR SPOON,TEXAS YELLOW ROSE IN BOWL,HOUSTON WITH STAR..    9.00
SOUVENIR SPOON,TORONTO ,ENAMEL HANDLE....................    5.00
SOUVENIR SPOON,TOWELS LOG CABIN.........................    2.00
SOUVENIR SPOON,TRINIDAD,ENAMEL HANDLE....................    4.50
SOUVENIR SPOON,WINNIPEG.................................    2.50
```

```
SOUVENIR SPOON WITH BUST OF COLUMBUS ON HANDLE..............      3.50
SOUVENIR SPOON,YELLOWSTONE FALLS,BEAVERS.....................      6.00
```

SPANGLE GLASS is multicolored glass made from odds and ends of colored glass rods. It includes metallic flakes of mica covered with gold, silver, nickel, or copper. Spangle glass is usually cased glass with a thin layer of clear glass over the multicolored layer.

```
SPANGLE GLASS BASKET,BLUE WITH GOLD FLECKS,THORN
  HANDLE,RUFFLED TOP........................................     65.00
SPANGLE GLASS BASKET,TRIPLE CASED YELLOW WITH MICA FLAKES...     39.00
SPANGLE GLASS LILY SHAPED BUD VASE,RAINBOW STRIPED.........      29.50
SPANGLE GLASS ROSE BOWL,4 IN. HIGH ,PINK CASED WITH WHITE
  SILVER MICA..............................................      28.00
SPANGLE GLASS VASE,MOTTLED DEEP & LIGHT YELLOW,CASED WITH
  WHITE...................................................       42.00
SPANGLED GLASS VASE, WHITE CASED 4IN. H...................       33.00
SPANISH LACE BLUE GOBLET..................................       15.00
SPANISH LACE OPAL SYRUP...................................       40.00
SPANISH LACE TUMBLER......................................       12.00
SPANISH LACE WHITE OPALESCENT CELERY VASE.................       32.00
```

SPATTER GLASS is a multicolored glass made from many small pieces of different colored glass.

```
SPATTER GLASS 9 IN. SCALLOPED BOWL........................       35.00
SPATTER GLASS BASKET,APPLIED HANDLE,LEAF..................       32.50
SPATTER GLASS BASKET,CASED RUFFLED TOP....................       30.00
SPATTER GLASS BASKET,CRANBERRY OPAQUE,THORN LOOP HANDLE...       55.00
SPATTER GLASS BASKET,THORN HANDLE.........................       57.50
SPATTER GLASS BASKET WITH THORN HANDLES...................       35.00
SPATTER GLASS BLOWN TUMBLER,BROWN & CREAM.................       15.00
SPATTER GLASS CASED DECANTER,7 IN. TALL,CUSTARD COLOUR
  BACKGROUND..............................................       25.00
SPATTER GLASS CASED EWER,7 IN. TALL,APPLIED HANDLE & CRYSTAL
  LEAF....................................................       18.00
SPATTER GLASS CASED EWER,WHITE SPATTERINGS AGAINST PURPLE...     18.00
SPATTER GLASS CASED RUFFLED BOWL..........................       23.00
SPATTER GLASS CASED SUGAR & CREAMER,RED,BLUE & GREEN ON
  PINK,FOOTED.............................................       28.00
SPATTER GLASS CRANBERRY & WHITE MUFFINEER,BULBOUS ,DOME TOP.     30.00
SPATTER GLASS CREAMER,RAINBOW.............................       60.00
SPATTER GLASS CUP,RAINBOW WITH THISTLE....................       30.00
SPATTER GLASS DECANTER,YELLOW,GREEN & RED SPATTERINGS.......     25.00
SPATTER GLASS EWER,10 IN. TALL,CLOVER LEAF SHAPE TOP........     27.00
SPATTER GLASS FINGER BOWL,PINK,ORANGE & OPALESCENT SWIRL RIB    20.00
SPATTER GLASS JACK IN THE PULPIT VASE,PINK FLECKS,6 IN......     17.50
SPATTER GLASS MINIATURE RAINBOW RED & BLUE CUP & SAUCER.....     50.00
SPATTER GLASS OVERLAY BASKET WITH THORN HANDLE,MOTTLED
  RED,GREEN,PINK..........................................       40.00
SPATTER GLASS PINCH CRUET,RUBY AND BLUE IN SECTIONS.........     35.00
SPATTER GLASS PINK LEAF UMBRELLA TOOTHPICK................       30.00
SPATTER GLASS PITCHER.....................................       50.00
SPATTER GLASS PITCHER,CRANBERRY & WHITE,MELON RIBS........       37.50
SPATTER GLASS PITCHER,END OF DAY,CRANBERRY & WHITE........       45.00
SPATTER GLASS PLATE,THISTLE...............................       80.00
SPATTER GLASS RED & YELLOW 8 IN. VASE.....................       25.00
SPATTER GLASS ROSE BOWL,YELLOW,WHITE & BROWN,CRIMPED TOP....     27.00
SPATTER GLASS SILVERIA PITCHER,GOLD SILVERIA FOIL BETWEEN
  SPATTERINGS.............................................       45.00
SPATTER GLASS SUGAR SHAKER,OVERLAY,ROYAL IVY,4 IN. TALL.....     42.50
SPATTER GLASS SUGAR SHAKER WITH BRASS TOP,PINK & WHITE......     16.00
SPATTER GLASS VASE IN TORTOISE SHELL COLOURING,ENAMELED.....     25.00
SPATTER GLASS VASE,WHITE WITH SAPPHIRE BLUE FLECKS ON CLEAR.    22.00
SPATTER GLASS WHITE RIBBED TOOTHPICK......................       18.50
SPATTER GLASS YELLOW CASED WATER PITCHER,7 IN. TALL,GOLD
  DECOR...................................................       75.00
```

SPATTERWARE is a creamware or soft paste dinner ware decorated with spatter designs. The earliest pieces were made during the late eighteenth century, but most of the wares found today were made from 1800 to 1850. The spatterware dishes were made in the Staffordshire district of England for sale in the American market.

```
SPATTERWARE  6 IN. BROWN PLATE...............................    10.00
SPATTERWARE  CREAMER,TAN & BLUE
  16.00 TO...................................................    24.00
SPATTERWARE  DEMI-TASSE ,YELLOW WITH TULIP...................    20.00
SPATTERWARE  DUTCH 5 IN. BOWL...............................     25.00
SPATTERWARE  HANDLESS CUP & SAUCER,BLUE,FORT OR CASTLE
  PATTERN....................................................    50.00
SPATTERWARE  PEAFOWL CUP & SAUCER,GREEN WITH PURPLE GREEN....   125.00
SPATTER WARE PLATE,10 IN. BLUE WITH PEACOCK AT FOUNTAIN.....    32.00
SPATTERWARE  RAINBOW SUGAR BOWL..............................   100.00
SPATTERWARE  SPONGE BOWL.....................................    15.00
SPATTERWARE  SPONGE PITCHER..................................    22.50
SPATTERWARE  STICK VASES,PAIR,PINK OUTSIDE,WHITE INSIDE......    30.00
SPATTERWARE  VASE...........................................     18.50
SPICE BOX,7 ROUND BOXES INSIDE..............................     12.50
SPICE RACK, 6 SMALL & ONE LONG DRAWER, STENCILED............     18.00
SPITTOON,GLAZED GRANITE,MARKED A.T.& S.F.,RAILROAD..........      5.00
```

SPODE POTTERY, porcelain, and bone china were made by the Stoke-on-Trent factory of England founded by Josiah Spode about 1770. The firm became Copeland and Garrett from 1833 to 1847. Then W. T. Copeland or W. T. Copeland and Sons until the present time. The word "Spode" appears on many pieces made by the Copeland factory. Most antique dealers included all of the wares under the more familiar name of Spode.

```
  SPODE, SEE ALSO COPELAND SPODE............................
SPODE 8 IN. PLATE,BLUE BORDER,RAISED WHITE PATTERN,ROSES
  CIRCA 1800.................................................   195.00
SPODE BLUE PLATE,DEATH OF BEAR..............................     14.00
SPODE BOWL,BLUE & FLORAL SPRAYS WITH GOLD,CIRCA 1820........     85.00
SPODE COPELAND 2 PART SPONGE DISH...........................      8.50
SPODE,COPELAND 1937 CORONATION SPOONER......................      5.00
SPODE,COPELAND,ENGLAND,PITCHER,HUNTING SCENE................     36.00
SPODE COPELAND ENGLAND WATER PITCHER,BLUE WITH WHITE FIGURES    37.50
SPODE CUP & SAUCER,RED & BLUE FLOWERS.......................      8.50
SPODE CUP AND SAUCER,CIRCA 1810,FLORAL......................     35.00
SPODE EGG CUP...............................................      6.00
SPODE FELSPAR PORCELAIN PLATE,HANDPAINTED & ENAMELED........     12.00
SPODE MARKED BLUE & WHITE DIVIDED SOAP DISH..................    22.00
SPODE MINIATURE CUP & SAUCER,ROSE & WHITE,SIGNED............     10.00
SPODE PLATE,CIRCA 1800,GREEN AND GOLD DECORATION............     20.00
SPODE TEA SET PAINTED WITH SCENES IN SEPIA & GOLD,CIRCA 1790   425.00
SPODE WATER PITCHER,IMARI DESIGN............................     65.00
```

SPONGEWARE is very similar to spatterware in appearance. The designs were applied to the ware by daubing the color. Many dealers do not differentiate between the two wares and use the names interchangeably.

```
SPONGEWARE BEAN POT.........................................     12.50
SPONGEWARE BOWL,4 X 6 IN....................................     10.50
SPONGEWARE BOWL,BLUE,BALE HANDLE............................     10.00
SPONGEWARE BOWL,GREEN & WHITE,9 IN..........................     12.50
SPONGEWARE BOWL WITH HANDLE.................................     11.00
SPONGEWARE CUSPIDOR,BLUE & WHITE............................     12.50
SPONGEWARE INKWELL..........................................     35.00
SPONGEWARE MUG,BLUE,STRAP HANDLE............................     15.00
SPONGEWARE PITCHER,6 IN.....................................     22.50
SPONGEWARE PITCHER,BLUE,TANKARD TYPE........................     18.50
SPONGEWARE PITCHER,BLUE ON TAN..............................     20.00
SPONGEWARE PITCHER,GREY ON BUFF.............................     18.00
SPONGEWARE PITCHER,MOTTLED YELLOW & GREEN,6 IN. TALL........      8.00
SPONGEWARE PITCHER,WATER,BLUE...............................     25.00
```

```
SPONGEWARE PITCHER,WATER,BLUE & WHITE.....................   18.50
SPONGEWARE VASE,BLUE & WHITE,CYLINDRICAL,2 FEET HIGH........   50.00
SPURS,IRON,SPANISH.........................................    1.25
SPURS,SILVER INLAY SPANISH.................................    3.50
SPURS,SPANISH ROWELS OVER 5IN..............................   22.50
SPURS,SPANISH ROWELS OVER 5IN. WITH LOTS OF SILVER INLAY....   32.50
```

STAFFORDSHIRE is a district in England where pottery and porcelain have been
made since the 1600's. Thousands of types of pottery and porcelain have been
made in the hundreds of factories that worked in the area. Some of the most
famous factories have been listed separately (see Royal Doulton, Royal Worcester, Spode, Wedgwood, and others).

```
STAFFORDSHIRE BARREL,SPIRIT,DEER WITH FOLIAGE,GOLD LEAF
 BANDS.....................................................   95.00
STAFFORDSHIRE BASKET,FRUIT,BLUE,RETURN OF FISHERMAN........   85.00
STAFFORDSHIRE BOTTLE,COLOGNE,FLOWERS & PETALS..............   17.50
STAFFORDSHIRE BOWL & PITCHER,PINK,CHINESE JUVENILE SPORTS...   67.50
STAFFORDSHIRE BOX,COVERED,OVAL,FLOWERS WITH GOLD CENTERS IN
 RELIEF....................................................   12.00
STAFFORDSHIRE BOX,DOVE,CIRCA 1820.........................  215.00
STAFFORDSHIRE BOX,MATCH,COVERED,BOY & NEWFOUNDLAND DOG.....   29.00
STAFFORDSHIRE BOX,MATCH,COVERED,FOOTED,OVAL,3 IN...........   22.00
STAFFORDSHIRE BOX,MATCH,COVERED,FORM OF TRAIN ENGINE.......   18.00
STAFFORDSHIRE BOX,PATCH,RELIEF,GREEN LEAVES AROUND BASE....   25.00
STAFFORDSHIRE BOX,RED RIDING HOOD & WOLF..................   15.00
STAFFORDSHIRE BOX,STORK FORMS COVER WITH BABY..............   18.00
STAFFORDSHIRE BOX,TRINKET,CHILD SITTING ON COUCH..........   19.50
STAFFORDSHIRE BOX,TRINKET,COVERED,MINIATURE,LITTLE GIRL WITH
 DOLL......................................................   15.00
STAFFORDSHIRE BOX,TRINKET,DOG RECLINING ON BLUE
 CUSHION,MIRROR FRAME......................................   22.00
STAFFORDSHIRE BOX,TRINKET,GOLD DOVES ON NEST OF GREEN MOSS..   14.00
STAFFORDSHIRE BOX,TRINKET,HAND HOLDING JEWEL CASKET........   28.50
STAFFORDSHIRE BOX,TRINKET,WHITE,DRUM,STICKS & HORN ON COVER.   20.00
STAFFORDSHIRE BUBBLE PIPE,MINIATURE,HEN...................   12.00
STAFFORDSHIRE CALLING CARD HOLDER.........................   17.00
STAFFORDSHIRE CHINA PIECE,THE CHESS GAME,LADY & GENT AT
 TABLE.....................................................   49.50
STAFFORDSHIRE CREAM PITCHER,BLUE & WHITE,CHERUBS & GOAT ON
 SIDE......................................................   18.00
STAFFORDSHIRE CREAMER,BROWN FLORAL DESIGN.................    9.00
STAFFORDSHIRE,CREAMER,THE CRYSTAL GARDENS 1851,BLACK
 TRANSFER,.................................................   15.00
STAFFORDSHIRE CREAMER,TOBY,BROWN HAIR,COBALT JACKET,TAN VEST  35.00
STAFFORDSHIRE CUP & SAUCER,CHOCOLATE,BROWN,TUNIS...........    6.00
STAFFORDSHIRE CUP & SAUCER,GREEN,GIRAFFE PATTERN..........   12.50
STAFFORDSHIRE CUP & SAUCER,HANDLELESS,BLUE,BIRD ON NEST.....   50.00
STAFFORDSHIRE CUP & SAUCER,HANDLELESS,BLUE & FLORAL........   10.00
STAFFORDSHIRE CUP & SAUCER,HANDLELESS,RED,ORIENTAL........   15.00
STAFFORDSHIRE CUP & SAUCER,HANDLELESS,SWIMMING SWANS.......   15.00
STAFFORDSHIRE CUP PLATE,BROWN TRANSFER....................   15.00
STAFFORDSHIRE CUP PLATE,HALL,BLUE,FAKEERS ROCK............   23.00
STAFFORDSHIRE DESK SET,WHITE,3 PIECE......................   10.00
STAFFORDSHIRE DINNER SET,17 PIECE,CHILDS,MAY PATTERN......   60.00
STAFFORDSHIRE DINNER SET,DOLLS,BLUE & WHITE,CIRCA 1895.....   42.50
STAFFORDSHIRE DISH,BLUE TRANSFER DECORATED,SHELL SHAPED
 OVAL,NONPAREIL............................................    8.50
STAFFORDSHIRE DISH,CHEESE.................................   32.00
STAFFORDSHIRE DISH,CHEESE,COVERED,SLANT-TOP,ACORN FINIAL....   18.00
STAFFORDSHIRE DISH,CHICKEN COVERED,2 IN.,CARAMEL NEST......   40.00
STAFFORDSHIRE DISH,HEN ON NEST,WHITE ON CARAMEL BROWN BASKET  85.00
STAFFORDSHIRE DISH,HONEY,4 IN.,RIDGWAY,BLUE,WILKES-BARRE....   10.00
STAFFORDSHIRE DISH,SOAP,COVERED,ENGLISH SCENE.............   19.00
STAFFORDSHIRE DISH,VEGETABLE,ADAMS,PINK,LAKE GEORGE USA.....   55.00
STAFFORDSHIRE DISH,VEGETABLE,BROWN,EASTERN PLANTS..........   15.00
```

```
STAFFORDSHIRE DISH,VEGETABLE,COVERED,HISTORICAL,BLUE........    100.00
STAFFORDSHIRE FIGURINE,3 IN.,GIRL WITH ROOSTER...............     6.25
STAFFORDSHIRE FIGURINE,4 IN. BOY & GIRL......................    14.50
STAFFORDSHIRE FIGURINE,4 IN.,LADY IN EARLY DRESS,HANDS IN
   MUFF.......................................................    10.00
STAFFORDSHIRE FIGURINE,15 IN. TALL,SCOTCHMAN AND HIS LASSIE.     22.50
STAFFORDSHIRE FIGURINE,BLACK & WHITE POODLE,5 IN.............    15.00
STAFFORDSHIRE FIGURINE,BLOOMER GIRL..........................    27.00
STAFFORDSHIRE FIGURINE,BOY ON FENCE,GIRL STANDING BACK......     18.50
STAFFORDSHIRE FIGURINE,BOY SKATING,7 IN. TALL................    24.00
STAFFORDSHIRE FIGURINE,COTTAGE 1840,PORCELAIN................    55.00
STAFFORDSHIRE FIGURINE,COTTAGE,ANNE HATHAWAY COTTAGE.........    20.00
STAFFORDSHIRE FIGURINE,COTTAGE,MOSS APPLIED AROUND ROOF,DOOR    42.50
STAFFORDSHIRE FIGURINE,COTTAGE,THE OLD CUROSITY SHOP.........    20.00
STAFFORDSHIRE FIGURINE,COUPLE IN BOWER.......................    12.50
STAFFORDSHIRE FIGURINE,DOG,5 IN.,RED WITH GOLD COLLAR.......     15.00
STAFFORDSHIRE FIGURINE,DOG,COPPER LUSTER ON WHITE,PAIR......     55.00
STAFFORDSHIRE FIGURINE,DOG,PAIR,BROWN & WHITE................    55.00
STAFFORDSHIRE FIGURINE,DOG WITH BLACK DECOR,WHITE,GOLD
   COLLAR.....................................................    12.00
STAFFORDSHIRE FIGURINE,ELEPHANT & INDIAN TEMPLE,BLUE........      8.00
STAFFORDSHIRE FIGURINE,FLAT BACK,8 IN.,WOMAN IN SCOTCH PLAID    30.00
STAFFORDSHIRE FIGURINE,FRENCH POODLE,7 IN.,GOLD COLLAR......     35.00
STAFFORDSHIRE FIGURINE,GLADSTONE,10 IN.
   TALL,WHITE,GOLD,BLACK & GREY...............................    25.00
STAFFORDSHIRE FIGURINE GROUP,FLAT BACK,BOY & GIRL STANDING..     25.00
STAFFORDSHIRE FIGURINE,LADY SITTING IN HIGH-BACK CHAIR
   READING....................................................    18.00
STAFFORDSHIRE FIGURINE,LADY WITH HAT,3 IN....................     6.50
STAFFORDSHIRE FIGURINE,LION,10 IN. HIGH......................    25.00
STAFFORDSHIRE FIGURINE,MAN WITH PLUMED HAT,GIRL SITTING ON
   FENCE......................................................    18.00
STAFFORDSHIRE FIGURINE,MINIATURE POODLE......................    14.50
STAFFORDSHIRE FIGURINE,PAIR ANGELS,WHITE.....................    13.00
STAFFORDSHIRE FIGURINE,PAIR CHOW DOGS,TAILS CURLED OVER
   BACKS......................................................    55.00
STAFFORDSHIRE FIGURINE,PAIR DOGS,BLOWN GLASS EYES,RAISED
   COLLARS....................................................    65.00
STAFFORDSHIRE FIGURINE,PAIR DOGS,WHITE.......................    45.00
STAFFORDSHIRE FIGURINE,PAIR DOGS,WHITE,GOLD CHAIN............    25.00
STAFFORDSHIRE FIGURINE,PAIR DOGS,WHITE WITH GOLD FLECKS.....     25.00
STAFFORDSHIRE FIGURINE,PAIR ENGLISH DOGS,3 IN...............     15.00
STAFFORDSHIRE FIGURINE,PAIR,FISHERMAN & WIFE.................    50.00
STAFFORDSHIRE FIGURINE,PAIR KING CHARLES SPANIEL TYPE
   DOGS,GOLD DECOR............................................    35.00
STAFFORDSHIRE FIGURINE,PAIR LIONS,11 IN.
   LONG,RECLINING,REDDISH BROWN...............................    65.00
STAFFORDSHIRE FIGURINE,PAIR,MAN & WOMAN ON HORSES...........     25.00
STAFFORDSHIRE FIGURINE,PAIR POODLES,8 IN.
   TALL,WHITE,GOLD,BLACK NOSES................................    30.00
STAFFORDSHIRE FIGURINE,PAIR SEATED SPANIELS,WHITE COATS WITH
   ORANGE.....................................................    60.00
STAFFORDSHIRE FIGURINE,PAIR SITTING DOGS,BROWN & WHITE ON
   GOLD.......................................................    80.00
STAFFORDSHIRE FIGURINE,PAIR SPANIELS,9 IN.,TRIM COPPER
   LUSTER.....................................................    70.00
STAFFORDSHIRE FIGURINE,PAIR WHITE SITTING DOGS,BLACK NOSES..     52.00
STAFFORDSHIRE FIGURINE,PAIR WHITE WITH ORANGE MARKINGS
   DOGS,CHAINS................................................    37.50
STAFFORDSHIRE FIGURINE,PARROT ON PERCH,4 IN. TALL...........     23.00
STAFFORDSHIRE FIGURINE,PASTE,WIDOW IN MAUVE,SEATED,CIRCA
   1800.......................................................    80.00
STAFFORDSHIRE FIGURINE,POODLE,ORCHID SPATTER,COPPER GOLD
   COLLAR.....................................................    12.00
STAFFORDSHIRE FIGURINE,QUEEN VICTORIA,14 IN.,INSCRIBED 1837.    75.00
```

```
STAFFORDSHIRE FIGURINE,RECLINING POODLE ON OVAL BASE........      12.00
STAFFORDSHIRE FIGURINE,REINDEER............................       6.50
STAFFORDSHIRE FIGURINE,SITTING CLIPPED WHITE POODLE........       7.50
STAFFORDSHIRE FIGURINE,STANDING MASTIFF....................      22.50
STAFFORDSHIRE FIGURINE,VICTORIAN,CHRIST ON CROSS WITH 2
  ANGELS..................................................      25.00
STAFFORDSHIRE FIGURINE,VICTORIAN,GUARDIAN ANGEL & 2 SLEEPING
  CHILDREN................................................      25.00
STAFFORDSHIRE FIGURINE,VICTORIAN,ROBERT BURNS & HIS MARY....     28.00
STAFFORDSHIRE FIGURINE,WHITE POODLE DOG ON OVAL BASE........      9.00
STAFFORDSHIRE FIGURINE,YELLOW LION ON BASE.................      40.00
STAFFORDSHIRE FLASK,1820,RELIEF-MOLDED MAN WITH ALE & PIPE..     45.00
STAFFORDSHIRE GRAVY BOAT & TRAY,THE ROMAN FURNIVAL.........       4.50
STAFFORDSHIRE HEN,6 IN.....................................      57.50
STAFFORDSHIRE HEN,9 IN.,WHITE BISQUE WITH COLOURED
  HEAD,CREAM BASE.........................................      90.00
STAFFORDSHIRE HEN ON NEST
  37.50 TO................................................      75.00
STAFFORDSHIRE HEN ON NEST,COLOURED........................       35.00
STAFFORDSHIRE HEN ON NEST,RED,7 IN........................       50.00
STAFFORDSHIRE HEN ON NEST,WHITE...........................      110.00
STAFFORDSHIRE HEN-ON-NEST,WICKER PATTERN NEST..............      45.00
STAFFORDSHIRE INKWELL,PHRENOLOGIST HEAD,SIGNED............      150.00
STAFFORDSHIRE JAR,HONEY,2 WHITE LOVE BIRDS & CAT,BEEHIVE
  SHAPE..................................................       22.00
STAFFORDSHIRE JUG,HANDPAINTED FARMERS ARMS,DATED 1791.......    125.00
STAFFORDSHIRE JUG,TOBY,6 IN. HIGH,BLACK HAT & COAT,PINK
  VEST,YELLOW.............................................      85.00
STAFFORDSHIRE JUG,TOBY,PINK,YELLOW,4 IN....................      45.00
STAFFORDSHIRE JUG,TOBY,SEATED MAN WITH TRICORN HAT WITH JUG
  OF ALE..................................................      65.00
STAFFORDSHIRE LADLE,BLUE,ENGLISH SCENE.....................     12.00
STAFFORDSHIRE LADLE,GREEN,ENGLISH SCENE....................     12.00
STAFFORDSHIRE LAMP,13 IN. TALL,BOY & GIRL & DOG............      85.00
STAFFORDSHIRE LAMP,MINIATURE,CHILD STANDING................      27.50
STAFFORDSHIRE MUG,2 HANDLED,LAVENDER ON WHITE,BLACK
  LETTERING..............................................       65.00
STAFFORDSHIRE MUG,BLUE & WHITE,TRANSFER DESIGN VASE........       6.50
STAFFORDSHIRE MUG,DR.FRANKLINS,2 FRANKLIN QUOTES...........      20.00
STAFFORDSHIRE MUG,MILKMAID WITH PAIL,COWS BESIDE BARN,......      9.50
STAFFORDSHIRE MUG,TOBY,SNIFTER.............................      35.00
STAFFORDSHIRE MUSTARD & LADLE,WHITE,LEAF SHAPE COVER.......       7.00
STAFFORDSHIRE NAPPY,SEPIA,AMERICAN MARINE..................       8.00
STAFFORDSHIRE PITCHER,BROWN BAMBOO HANDLE,FLORALS ON
  WHITE,MARKED...........................................       25.00
STAFFORDSHIRE PITCHER,CASTLE SCENERY......................       18.00
STAFFORDSHIRE PITCHER,CHASING THE OSTRICH PINK TRANSFER
  HUNTING SCENE..........................................       38.00
STAFFORDSHIRE PITCHER,HOUSE,GREY GREEN WITH DECORATION......     45.00
STAFFORDSHIRE PITCHER,PAIR,BLUE & WHITE CHINESE LANDSCAPE...     36.00
STAFFORDSHIRE PITCHER WITH PEWTER RIM AND COVER, 1858.......     75.00
STAFFORDSHIRE,PLATE,6 IN.,ADAMS,SEPIA,CONNECTICUT..........      19.00
STAFFORDSHIRE PLATE,6 IN.,ROSE,HORSE & FLOWERS.............       6.00
STAFFORDSHIRE PLATE,7 IN.,JACKSON,BLUE,DEAF & DUMB
  ASYLUM,PHILADELPHIA....................................       25.00
STAFFORDSHIRE,PLATE,7 IN.,MAC DONNOUGHS VICTORY BY E.
  WOOD,BLUE..............................................       80.00
STAFFORDSHIRE,PLATE,7 IN.,RIDGWAY,BLACK,VALLEY OF THE
  SHENANDOAH.............................................       19.00
STAFFORDSHIRE,PLATE,7 IN.,SCOTTS WAVERLEY-DAVENPORT,PINK....      8.00
STAFFORDSHIRE PLATE,8 IN.,CASHIBURY,ENOCH WOOD.............      12.00
STAFFORDSHIRE,PLATE,8 IN.,FULHAM CHURCH,HISTORICAL BLUE.....     48.00
STAFFORDSHIRE PLATE,8 IN.,MOSELLE.........................       7.50
STAFFORDSHIRE PLATE,8 IN.,PARISIAN CHATEAU................       8.00
STAFFORDSHIRE PLATE,9 IN.,CLEWS,PINK,BAKERS FALLS,HUDSON
```

RIVER.. 30.00
STAFFORDSHIRE PLATE,9 IN.,JACKSON,BLACK,CITY HALL,NEW YORK.. 28.00
STAFFORDSHIRE PLATE,9 IN.,PINK,CORINTHIA PATTERN,E.CHALLINOR 4.00
STAFFORDSHIRE,PLATE,9 IN.,TEXAN CAMPAIGN,MULBERRY,HISTORICAL
BLUE.. 30.00
STAFFORDSHIRE PLATE,9 IN.,WOOD,SEPIA ON YELLOW,CASTLE OF
NEPI,ITALY.. 21.00
STAFFORDSHIRE,PLATE,10 IN.,AMERICAN CRYSTAL
PALACE,HISTORICAL BLUE.................................. 10.00
STAFFORDSHIRE PLATE,10 IN.,BLUE,SHELTERED PEASANTS.......... 15.00
STAFFORDSHIRE PLATE,10 IN.,CALEDONIA,BLACK................. 21.00
STAFFORDSHIRE,PLATE,10 IN.,EAGLE PASS CENTENNIAL 1849-1949,
HISTORICAL.. 3.00
STAFFORDSHIRE PLATE,10 IN.,ELIZABETH II,BUCKINGHAM IN
BACKGROUND,BLUE... 13.75
STAFFORDSHIRE PLATE,10 IN.,ROYAL SKETCHES.................. 6.75
STAFFORDSHIRE,PLATE,10 IN.,TABLE ROCK NIAGARA,HISTORICAL
BLUE... 80.00
STAFFORDSHIRE,PLATE,10 IN.,U.S.CAPITOL,HISTORICAL........... 3.00
STAFFORDSHIRE PLATE,10 IN.,WOOD,SEPIA ON YELLOW,OBERWESSEL
ON THE RHINE... 23.00
STAFFORDSHIRE,PLATE,AMERICAN HISTORICAL,W.PENNS TREATY BY
THOS. GREEN.. 28.00
STAFFORDSHIRE PLATE,ANTIQUARIAN SEPIA,10 IN................ 16.00
STAFFORDSHIRE,PLATE,BLACK & WHITE,CLEWS,FISHKILL,HUDSON
RIVER.. 22.50
STAFFORDSHIRE PLATE,BLUE,7 IN.,CASTLE HUNTLY,PERTHSHIRE..... 18.50
STAFFORDSHIRE PLATE,BLUE,8 IN.,ITALIAN SCENERY,VESUVIUS..... 19.00
STAFFORDSHIRE PLATE,BLUE,10 IN.,LANDING OF HENRY HUDSON..... 12.00
STAFFORDSHIRE PLATE,BLUE ABBEY RUINS,8 IN................. 6.00
STAFFORDSHIRE PLATE,BLUE,10 IN.,THEODORE ROOSEVELT......... 12.00
STAFFORDSHIRE PLATE,BLUE & WHITE,BATTLE OF BUNKER HILL...... 12.50
STAFFORDSHIRE PLATE,BLUE & WHITE,COMMEMORATIVE............. 6.50
STAFFORDSHIRE PLATE,BLUE & WHITE,MARKED,DONT GIVE UP THE
SHIP... 15.00
STAFFORDSHIRE PLATE,BLUE & WHITE,WASHINGTON PRAYS AT VALLEY
FORGE.. 12.50
STAFFORDSHIRE PLATE,BLUE,ADAMS,MILL SCENE.................. 32.00
STAFFORDSHIRE PLATE,BLUE CANOVA,9 IN...................... 10.00
STAFFORDSHIRE PLATE,BLUE,ENGLISH HISTORICAL,DEEP,WRITTLE
LODGE.. 3.00
STAFFORDSHIRE PLATE,BLUE,FRUIT CENTER..................... 12.00
STAFFORDSHIRE PLATE,BLUE,PHILLIPS,POLISH VIEW,9 IN......... 10.00
STAFFORDSHIRE PLATE,BLUE,RURAL SCENERY.................... 12.50
STAFFORDSHIRE PLATE,BLUE,WASHINGTON CROSSING THE DELAWARE... 9.00
STAFFORDSHIRE PLATE,BROWN,10 IN.,FISHKILL ON HUDSON........ 12.00
STAFFORDSHIRE,PLATE,BROWN & WHITE,OSBORNE-RIDGEWAY......... 15.00
STAFFORDSHIRE PLATE,BROWN LEAF AND BERRY BORDER,CIRCA 1850.. 8.00
STAFFORDSHIRE PLATE,CHOP,14 IN.,SCALLOPED EDGE,RED ROSES.... 18.00
STAFFORDSHIRE,PLATE,ENOCH & RALPH WOOD.................... 10.00
STAFFORDSHIRE PLATE,ENOCH WOOD,BLUE,9 IN.,ENGLISH SCENERY... 15.00
STAFFORDSHIRE PLATE,FAIRY VILLAS,7 IN.,ADAMS.............. 8.00
STAFFORDSHIRE PLATE,GAME,SET OF 3,HANDPAINTED,DATED 1877... 50.00
STAFFORDSHIRE PLATE,HISTORICAL,10 IN.,MARKED CHARLES MEIGH.. 15.00
STAFFORDSHIRE PLATE,HISTORICAL,BLUE,THE NARROWS FROM FORT
HAMILTON... 27.50
STAFFORDSHIRE PLATE,HISTORICAL,GREEN,8 IN................. 22.00
STAFFORDSHIRE PLATE,HISTORICAL,PURPLE,AT RICHMOND.......... 37.00
STAFFORDSHIRE PLATE,LIVERPOOL,BLACK,BUILDINGS IN WOODS
ENGLISH CITIES... 10.00
STAFFORDSHIRE PLATE,MARKED,BLUE & WHITE,BOSTON MASSACRE..... 15.00
STAFFORDSHIRE PLATE,MARKED,BLUE & WHITE,WHIRLPOOL RAPIDS.... 15.00
STAFFORDSHIRE PLATE,PAIR,BLUE,IMPRESSED ADAMS MARK,SPANISH
CONVENT.. 11.00
STAFFORDSHIRE PLATE,PAIR,RURAL SCENE...................... 13.00

```
STAFFORDSHIRE PLATE,PINK,7 IN.,ADAMS,FAIRY VILLAS...........     8.00
STAFFORDSHIRE PLATE,PINK,7 IN.,CANOVA.......................     7.00
STAFFORDSHIRE PLATE,PINK,8 IN.,ADAMS.......................     10.00
STAFFORDSHIRE PLATE,PINK,8 IN.,HALL,PARISIAN CHATEAU........     8.00
STAFFORDSHIRE PLATE,PINK,SET OF 4,CHINESE PASTIME...........    33.00
STAFFORDSHIRE PLATE,PINK,THE ARCHERS........................     8.50
STAFFORDSHIRE PLATE,PINK TRANSFER,GRECIAN FONT BY ADAMS &
  SON.......................................................    15.00
STAFFORDSHIRE PLATE,SEPIA & WHITE,HISTORICAL,COMMODORE PAUL
  JONES.....................................................    18.00
STAFFORDSHIRE PLATE,SERVICE,BIRD,CHELSEA,SIGNED,SET OF
  8,MYOTT...................................................    56.00
STAFFORDSHIRE PLATE,THE RESIDENCE OF THE LATE RICHARD
  JORDAN,HEATH..............................................    45.00
STAFFORDSHIRE PLATE,TRANSFER,7 IN.,SWISS SCENERY,BLUE.......     6.50
STAFFORDSHIRE,PLATTER,13 IN.,RIDGWAY,BLACK,COLUMBIA BRIDGE..    85.00
STAFFORDSHIRE PLATTER,BLACK & WHITE,CORINTHIA PATTERN.......    10.00
STAFFORDSHIRE PLATTER,BLUE & WHITE,GYPSY PATTERN............    15.00
STAFFORDSHIRE PLATTER,BLUE,ADAMS,MORPETH CASTLE,15 IN. LONG.    45.00
STAFFORDSHIRE PLATTER,BLUE,STUBBS,FRUIT & FLOWERS...........    27.00
STAFFORDSHIRE PLATTER,BLUE,8-SIDED,VENUS....................    25.00
STAFFORDSHIRE PLATTER,BROWN,15 X 13 IN.,VIEW OF NEWBURGH ON
  HUDSON....................................................    30.00
STAFFORDSHIRE PLATTER,CANOVA,BLUE,13 X 15 IN................    35.00
STAFFORDSHIRE PLATTER,GREEN & WHITE,21 IN.,ARABIAN SKETCHES.    35.00
STAFFORDSHIRE PLATTER,ITALIAN BUILDINGS,BLUE,14 IN..........    24.00
STAFFORDSHIRE,PLATTER,MAYER MARKED,BLUE CANOVA,ORIENTAL
  SCENE.....................................................    23.00
STAFFORDSHIRE PLATTER,OCTAGONAL,BLUE SCENIC,JOHN RIDGWAY
  MARKED 1844...............................................    17.50
STAFFORDSHIRE PLATTER,PINK,16 IN.,MAYERS CANOVA.............     9.00
STAFFORDSHIRE PLATTER,PINK,CORINTHIA PATTERN,12 X 9
  IN.,CHALLINOR.............................................     8.00
STAFFORDSHIRE PLATTER RIDGEWAY BLUE.........................    16.50
STAFFORDSHIRE PLATTER,ROSE,T MAYER..........................    45.00
STAFFORDSHIRE PORTRAIT BUST OF CZAR ALEXANDER,11 IN. TALL...   115.00
STAFFORDSHIRE QUILL HOLDER,3 IN. HIGH,TIPSY MAN IN BRIGHT
  CLOTHES...................................................    18.50
STAFFORDSHIRE SALT,PAIR MASTER,FLORAL.......................     7.50
STAFFORDSHIRE SAUCE,5 IN.,BIRDS,TREES,FLOWERS,FLORILLA SCENE     4.50
STAFFORDSHIRE SHAVING MUG,BLUE BORDER,PAINTED FLOWERS,GOLD,.    17.50
STAFFORDSHIRE SOUP PLATE,8 IN.,PINK,CHINESE FIGURES.........    10.00
STAFFORDSHIRE SOUP PLATE,10 IN.,ADAMS,PINK,HEADWATERS OF THE
  JUNIATA...................................................    45.00
STAFFORDSHIRE SOUP PLATE,10 IN.,WOOD,BLUE,PINE ORCHARD HOUSE    80.00
STAFFORDSHIRE SOUP PLATE,SET OF 5,10
  IN.,RIDGWAY,GREEN,ORIENTAL................................    60.00
STAFFORDSHIRE STATUETTE,4 IN.,FISH GIRL ON BASE,PASTEL DRESS    35.00
STAFFORDSHIRE SUGAR & CREAMER,BROWN.........................    15.00
STAFFORDSHIRE SUGAR & CREAMER,MINIATURE,CROWN NO. 15646.....     5.00
STAFFORDSHIRE SUGAR BOWL,LEEDS,QUEENS ROSE..................    50.00
STAFFORDSHIRE SUGAR,COVERED,BLUE,ADAMS WARRANTED,BIRD CAGE
  PATTERN...................................................    38.50
STAFFORDSHIRE TEA POT,DENTON PART,BLUE MORNING GLORY BORDER.    60.00
STAFFORDSHIRE TEAPOT,PAIR,8 IN.,X MARK,BROWN ON WHITE.......    50.00
STAFFORDSHIRE TEAPOT,PINK LUSTER DECORATED,QUART SIZE.......    20.00
STAFFORDSHIRE TEA SET,CHILDS,BLUE & WHITE,PUNCH & JUDY......    48.50
STAFFORDSHIRE TOAST RACK,2 PIECE,WHITE TRIMMED IN GOLD......    12.50
STAFFORDSHIRE TUREEN,GRAVY,BLUE,AMERICAN VILLAS HISTORIC....    65.00
STAFFORDSHIRE TUREEN,FOOTED,FLARED TOP,URN SHAPED BODY......    65.00
STAFFORDSHIRE TUREEN,GRAVY,LAVENDER,LADLE & COVER...........    48.00
STAFFORDSHIRE TUREEN,SOUP,OVAL TRAY,LADLE,BEATRICE PATTERN..    55.00
STAFFORDSHIRE TUREEN WITH 2 HANDLED PLATTER,BLUE,BRUNSWICK
  PATTERN...................................................    15.00
STAFFORDSHIRE VASE,BLUE,7 IN................................    10.00
```

STAFFORDSHIRE VASE,FIGURAL,SCOTTISH SHEPHERD & SHEPHERDESS.. 37.50
STAFFORDSHIRE VEGETABLE,COVERED.CITY OF CANTERBURY.......... 45.00

STAR HOLLY is a milk glass type of glass made about 1902 by the Imperial Glass Company of Bellaire, Ohio. The pieces were made to look like Wedgwood Jasper ware. White holly leaves appear against colored borders of blue, green, or rust. I G is marked on the bottom of every piece.

STAR HOLLY BOWL,5 IN. ACROSS TOP,BLUE STAINING,SIGNED....... 75.00
STEIN,1/2 LITRE,GRAY WITH RAISED FIGURES,PEWTER TOP,GERMANY
ON BOTTOM... 30.00
STEIN,1 HALF LITRE,PEWTER,10 IN. TALL,MARKED GUT HEIL....... 28.00
STEIN,1/2 LITRE,PRESSED GLASS,PURPLE SUN COLOURED,INLAY LID. 28.00
STEIN,1/2 LITRE,P.U.G.SIGNED SCHLITT 1909/727.............. 50.00
STEIN,1 LITER,BLUE & GRAY,MAN HOLDING JUG.................. 30.00
STEIN,1 LITRE,INCISED GERMANY,HUNTER & WOMAN,CREAM,GREEN.... 30.00
STEIN,1 1/2 LITRES,INCISED GERMANY,ORANGE LUSTER,HUNTERS.... 50.00
STEIN,2 LITRES,CREAM ON GREEN BACKGROUND,LADY & MAN DANCING. 60.00
STEIN,2 LITRES,DOE DECORATION,MARKED GERMANY,#11228......... 30.00
STEIN,4 LITRES,CREAM COLOURED MEN AT TABLE,INCISED GERMANY.. 80.00
STEIN 7 IN. H. WHITE METAL SOUVENIR OF MINNEAPOLIS......... 3.00
STEIN,8 IN.,EMBOSSED FIGURE & SCENE,PEWTER LID & THUMBPIECE. 8.00
STEIN,9 IN. HIGH,MEN & WOMAN CAROUSING..................... 30.00
STEIN,10 IN. TALL ,PEWTER TOP,GERMANY,3 MEN DRINKING BEER
OFF KEG.. 47.00
STEIN,16 IN. TALL MARKED GERMANY.......................... 27.50
STEIN,#1488,1 LITRE,INCISED GERMANY,ORANGE LUSTER,BLUE
BACKGROUND... 50.00
STEIN,AMBER & 9 PIN AMBER HANDLE & PEWTER TOP,BOY HOLDING
HAT... 28.00
STEIN,AMBER,NINE PIN HANDLE & PEWTER TOP.................. 28.00
STEIN,AMBER PITCHER,HINGED PEWTER LID & THUMBPIECE,........ 60.00
STEIN,AMBER POKAL GERMAN BEER GLASS,APPLIED AQUA NIPPLED
ORNAMENTS... 39.50
STEIN,BEER,1 HALF LITRE,COBALT BLUE & GREN................ 6.00
STEIN,BEER,1 HALF LITRE,PEWTER LID,GASTHAUS SCENE.......... 8.00
STEIN,BEER,1 HALF LITRE,PEWTER LID,HUNTING DESIGN.......... 8.00
STEIN,BEER,1 LITRE.. 12.00
STEIN,BEER,1 LITER,MAN AT TABLE SERVED BY MAIDEN,GERMAN
MOTTOES... 20.00
STEIN,BEER,4 MEN AT TABLE SERVED BY BAR MAID,MARKED........ 25.00
STEIN,BEER,13 IN. HIGH.................................... 20.00
STEIN,BEER,GLASS.. 8.00
STEIN,BEER,GRAY-BLUE,1 HALF LITRE......................... 10.00
STEIN,BEER MADE IN GERMANY,GERZ,HINGED PEWTER TOP,TAVERN
SCENE... 25.00
STEIN,BEER TASTERS,SIGNED,BLUE & GREY,ANCIENT WARRIORS...... 13.00
STEIN,BLUE & GREY,CAVALIER EMBRACING MAIDEN IN RELIEF....... 30.00
STEIN,BLUE-GREY,7 IN. TALL,PEWTER TOP,MARKED GERMANY 0.5-L,. 16.00
STEIN,BLUE-GREY,PEWTER TOP,GERMANY,...................... 7.50
STEIN,BOHEMIAN IN RUBY & CLEAR WITH DEER & TREE ETCHED,METAL
LID... 60.00
STEIN,BROWN,INDIAN HEAD ON HANDLE,RAISED DESIGN............ 7.50
STEIN,CHARACTER,10 IN. TALL,MONKEY IN BROWNS,PEWTER LID..... 45.00
STEIN,CLEAR GLASS,FLORAL DECORATION,PEWTER TOP,HANDLED...... 27.50
STEIN,CLEAR GLASS,PEWTER LID,ENAMELED..................... 30.00
STEIN, COPPER & PEWTER , MANNING & BOWMAN................ 21.00
STEIN,CUT GLASS,PEWTER TOP ,HANDPAINTED PORCELAIN INSERT.... 32.00
STEIN DATED 1787,1 LITRE,PEWTER TOP,WHITE WITH YELLOW &
GREEN... 55.00
STEIN,EGYPTIAN HEAD OF LADY,GERMANY....................... 25.00
STEIN,FARMERS LITHOPHANE,JACOB WILD,LION THUMBREST.......... 75.00
STEIN, GERMAN, 8 IN. PEWTER COVER, RAISED DESIGN........... 15.00
STEIN,GERMAN,16 IN. TALL,SIGNED GERMANY,MAID SERVING
MINSTREL.. 45.00
STEIN,GERMAN BEER,BLUE GREY, 14 IN. HIGH.................. 35.00

STEIN,GERMAN BEER,PEWTER TOP,PRE-1920......................	25.00
STEIN,GERMAN,IRONSTONE,PEWTER TOP,GRAY WITH DESIGN..........	27.50
STEIN,GERMAN MARKED.......................................	32.50
STEIN,GERMAN,PEWTER TOP...................................	28.00
STEIN,GERMAN,PEWTER TOP,8 IN. TALL,CATSKILL MOUNTAIN SOUVENIR...	20.00
STEIN,GERMAN REGIMENTAL,WRITING IN GERMAN,HORSES...........	55.00
STEIN,GERMAN STONEWARE CHRISTMAS,GRAY WITH BARMAID.........	35.00
STEIN,GERMAN,WEDDING,PEWTER TOP,COUPLE STANDING IN GRAPE ARCH...	55.00
STEIN,GERMAN,WHITE PORCELAIN,BAVARIAN PIONEER 3RD BATTALION COMPANY..	100.00
STEIN,GERMAN,WHITE PORCELAIN,PEWTER TOP & FINIAL,2 GENTLEMEN	85.00
STEIN,GERMAN,WINE JUG,PEWTER TOP,NOAH PLANTING ,THE ARK.....	65.00
STEIN,GERMANY,2 1/2 LITRES,4 MEN & 3 WOMEN,BOY & GIRL........	60.00
STEIN,GLASS WITH PORCELAIN ON PEWTER TOP.....................	25.00
STEIN,GERMANY,13 IN. TALL,PEWTER TOP,DIE ERSTE LIEBE........	44.00
STEIN,GLASS,PEWTER TOP ,HANDPAINTED WOMAN....................	24.50
STEIN,GREY & BLUE,FIGURES,FLOWERS IN RELIEF.................	15.00
STEIN,GREY & COBALT BLUE ,1/2 LITRE,GERMAN WRITING,FIGURES,FLOWERS......................................	12.50
STEIN,GRES DE FLANDERS SERVING,PEWTER TOP,BLUE-GREY STONE...	55.00
STEIN,GULLINGER CLEAR ,PORCELAIN LID OF 2 GIRLS AT STREAM,MAN...	60.00
STEIN,HALF LITRE,TAN GLAZE,PEWTER LID,IMPRESSED MARKS IN BASE..	25.00
STEIN,INCISED GERMANY,0.5 LITRES,CREAM,FIGURES DRINKING.....	20.00
STEIN,INCISED GERMANY,ORANGE LUSTER,STAGE SCENE,MAN.........	25.00
STEIN,INNKEEPER OCCUPATIONAL 1/2 LITRE,DATED 1886,DANCING COUPLE..	34.00
STEIN,LITHOPHANE,1 HALF LITRE,COLORED TRANSFER PICTURE OF ESTATE..	75.00
STEIN,LITHOPHANE 1 HALF LITRE,PEWTER TOP,FIRE FIGHTING SCENE	58.00
STEIN,LITHOPHANE BEER MUG,PEWTER TOP,1 HALF LITRE,GERMAN STREET SCENE..	32.50
STEIN,LITHOPHANE OCCUPATIONAL,1 HALF LITRE,TAILORS SHOP,PEWTER COVER.......................................	55.00
STEIN,LITHOPHANE,PINK & WHITE,GOLD,TAVERN DANCE SCENE.......	45.00
STEIN,LOGGING SCENE,MARKED ALOIS HARTSMANSBERGER,1/2 LITRE,.	55.00
STEIN MARKED GERMANY,PEWTER TOP,FIGURES OF FAMILY...........	55.00
STEIN MARKED HANKE,GERMANY,PEWTER TOP,PANEL WITH FIGURES....	45.00
STEIN,MARY GREGORY AMBER,PEWTER LID,WHITE ENAMELED WOMAN WITH JUG...	89.00
STEIN,MARY GREGORY,GREEN GLASS,INVERTED THUMBPRINT PATTERN,ENAMEL BOY.....................................	47.00
STEIN,METTLACH,# 171,RELIEF,3/10 LITRES.....................	67.50
STEIN,METTLACH #485,1/2 LITRE...............................	125.00
STEIN,METTLACH #690,......................................	135.00
STEIN,,METTLACH,#783,1/2 LITRE..............................	65.00
STEIN,METTLACH #1180,1/2 LITRE..............................	75.00
STEIN,METTLACH #1221,1/2 LITRES.............................	135.00
STEIN,METTLACH # 1266,RELIEF,1/4 LITRE......................	63.50
STEIN,METTLACH NO.1400,1 HALF LITRE.........................	17.00
STEIN,METTLACH # 1477,1 HALF LITRE..........................	150.00
STEIN,METTLACH #1526/1108,1/2 LITRE,P.U.G...................	65.00
STEIN,METTLACH #1565,1 HALF LITRE...........................	160.00
STEIN,METTLACH #1655,1 HALF LITRE...........................	150.00
STEIN,METTLACH,#1727 1/2 LITRE..............................	85.00
STEIN,METTLACH,1732,1 HALF LITRE,CASTLEMARK,ETCHED & SIGNED.	135.00
STEIN,METTLACH 1909,1 HALF LITRE............................	65.00
STEIN,METTLACH NO.1909,DWARFS...............................	60.00
STEIN,METTLACH # 2077,RELIEF................................	75.00
STEIN,METTLACH # 2090,ETCHED................................	175.00
STEIN,METTLACH #2092,ETCHED.................................	175.00
STEIN,METTLACH # 2140,PUG...................................	105.00

STEIN,METTLACH,#2177/1084,1/4 LITRES,P.U.G................... 75.00
STEIN,METTLACH,#2184/966,3/10 LITRE,P.U.G................... 80.00
STEIN,METTLACH NO.2184/967,ONE HALF L,DWARFS................ 80.00
STEIN,METTLACH,#2211,3/10 LITRES........................... 75.00
STEIN,METTLACH #2250,3/10 LITRE............................ 60.00
STEIN,METTLACH # 2520,1 HALF LITRE......................... 150.00
STEIN,METTLACH,#2556,1/2 LITRE,........................... 115.00
STEIN,METTLACH # 2591,ETCHED............................... 175.00
STEIN,METTLACH # 2931,RELIEF,1/2 LITRE..................... 132.50
STEIN,METTLACH # 3078,RELIEF............................... 110.00
STEIN,METTLACH,#3095,HIRES ROOT BEER MUG,.................. 20.00
STEIN,METTLACH 1 QUARTER LITRE,ETCHED...................... 80.00
STEIN,METTLACH 1/4 LITRE,VINTAGE DECOR..................... 60.00
STEIN,METTLACH,3/10 LITRE.................................. 55.00
STEIN,METTLACH,3/10 LITRE,VILLEROY & BOCH MARK,THE BOWLDER.. 110.00
STEIN,METTLACH,4/10 LITRES,ORANGE & BLACK SHIELD,1900....... 28.00
STEIN,METTLACH,1 HALF LITRE
   65.00 TO... 125.00
STEIN,METTLACH,1 HALF LITRE,ETCHED
   115.00 TO.. 250.00
STEIN,METTLACH,1/2 LITRE,SHELL #1727....................... 82.50
STEIN,METTLACH 1/2 LITRE,TAVERN BOWLING SCENE SIGNED
   WARTH,DATE 1891... 125.00
STEIN,METTLACH,1 HALF LITRE,MERCURY MARK................... 75.00
STEIN,METTLACH 1 HALF LITRE,NO.28381 ETCHED................ 145.00
STEIN,METTLACH,1 LITRE,PUG................................. 90.00
STEIN,METTLACH,2 LITRES, ETCHED
   175.00 TO.. 300.00
STEIN,METTLACH,2 LITRES,MERCURY MARK#2890.................. 145.00
STEIN,METTLACH,3 LITRES,FROGS CAVORTING SIGNED H SCHLITT.... 125.00
STEIN,METTLACH,4 MUSICIANS................................. 65.00
STEIN,METTLACH,BROWN WITH CREAM CAMEO,VERSES IN
   GERMAN,PEWTER LID.. 125.00
STEIN,METTLACH,CASTLEMARK,TROUBADOR UNDER GLAZE PAINTING.... 65.00
STEIN,METTLACH,CASTLE MARK,WEDGWOOD TYPE,INLAY LID.......... 165.00
STEIN,METTLACH,HALF LITER.................................. 85.00
STEIN,METTLACH,MOSAIC...................................... 135.00
STEIN,METTLACH,ORANGE & BLACK SHIELD,YEAR 1900............. 28.00
STEIN,METTLACH,PLAYING CARD DESIGN......................... 110.00
STEIN,METTLACH SIGNED GUIDENUS,1 HALF LITRE................ 175.00
STEIN,METTLACH SIGNED HEINRICH SCHLITT,1 QUARTER LITRE...... 55.00
STEIN,MILITARY,LITHOPANE,SIGNED GERMANY.................... 35.00
STEIN,MUSTERSCHUTZ, .5 LITER,PIRATES HEAD STYLE............ 45.00
STEIN,ONE-HALF LITRE,GERMANY,PEWTER LID,GREEN & CREAM,ELKS &
   TEMPLE.. 22.50
STEIN,PATTERN GLASS,DATED 1880,PEWTER TOP.................. 25.00
STEIN,PEWTER TOP,GERMANY................................... 8.00
STEIN,PITCHER,CLEAR GLASS,ENAMEL,PEWTER TOP &
   THUMBPIECE,GERMAN.. 67.50
STEIN,PORCELAIN REGIMENTAL GERMAN,PEWTER FIGURE ON LID...... 20.00
STEIN,REGIMENTAL GERMAN BEER,LITHOPHANE,PEWTER LID.......... 20.00
STEIN,REGIMENTAL,SHOOTING PRIZE,PEWTER LID,JUNE 1867........ 89.50
STEIN,RUBY GLASS WITH GOLD ENAMEL,HINGED RUBY GLASS
   COVER,PEWTER RIM.. 48.00
STEIN,SAPPHIRE BLUE INVERTED THUMBPRINT,BLUE MILK GLASS
   INSET LID... 55.00
STEIN,SOUVENIR,GERMANY MARKED,COLUMBUS,OHIO,CAPITOL,TAN &
   BLUE... 4.50
STEIN,SOUVENIR,GERMANY MARKED,MASONIC TEMPLE,CHICAGO,TAN &
   GREEN.. 3.50
STEIN,STONEWARE WITH PEWTER TOP,BLUE & GREY,TUDOR FIGURES
   CIRCA 1850.. 35.00
STEIN,VILLEROY & BOCH,1 HALF LITRE,GREEN METTLACH MERCURY
   MARK... 95.00
STEIN,WEDDING SALT GLAZE,GERMAN, PEWTER TOP,BLUE PORCELAIN

INSERT	65.00
STEIN WOODEN HAND CARVED,WOODEN LID,FROM NORWAY	50.00
STEIN,YALE,1/2 LITRE,	125.00

STEREO CARDS that were made for the stereoptican viewers became popular after 1840. Two almost identical pictures were mounted on a stiff cardboard backing so that, when viewed through a stereoscope, a three-dimensional picture could be seen.

STEREO CARDS,1 CLOCK	.75
STEREO CARDS,1 GRAND PACIFIC HOTEL DINING ROOM,CHICAGO	.50
STEREO CARDS,1 VIEW OF CHILDREN PLAYING	.15
STEREO CARDS,2 HAWAIIAN	.45
STEREO CARDS,2 PALESTINE	.75
STEREO CARDS,3 ADULT COMICS	1.25
STEREO CARDS,3 ASSORTED MEXICO	.75
STEREO CARDS,3 CHILDREN IN UNIFORM IN COLOUR	1.00
STEREO CARDS,3 PHILIPINE	1.45
STEREO CARDS,3 SWEDEN	1.65
STEREO CARDS,4 ASSORTED CANADA	.95
STEREO CARDS,4 CARS	1.00
STEREO CARDS,5 FRANCE,COLOURED	1.15
STEREO CARDS,5 STREET SCENES	2.25
STEREO CARDS,7 JAPAN,COLOURED	1.95
STEREO CARDS,7 MONUMENTS	1.65
STEREO CARDS,8 COMICS	2.45
STEREO CARDS,8 GERMAN	2.00
STEREO CARDS,8 YELLOWSTONE NATIONAL PARK	1.75
STEREO CARDS,9 ADULT HUMOUROUS	4.10
STEREO CARDS,9 PANAMA	3.25
STEREO CARDS,10 SCENES WITH PEOPLE	1.55
STEREO CARDS,11 OF ANIMALS	3.85
STEREO CARDS,15 CALIFORNIA	5.75
STEREO CARDS,15 NEW YORK CITY	4.65
STEREO CARDS,17 SWEDEN	3.75
STEREO CARDS,19 ASSORTED GERMANY	5.95
STEREO CARDS,19 SPANISH AMERICAN WAR	12.50
STEREO CARDS,24 OF U S A	5.25
STEREO CARDS,24 OF SAN FRANCISCO EARTHQUAKE	8.00
STEREO CARDS,39 OF NEW YORK CITY	4.00
STEREO CARDS,60 OF SAN FRANCISCO EARTHQUAKE	20.00
STEREO CARDS,64 OF JAPAN	5.00
STEREO CARDS,72 OF ITALY	6.00
STEREO CARDS,86,DOUBLE BOOK,STEREOGRAPHIC LIBRARY	15.00

STEREOSCOPES or stereopticans were used for viewing the stereo cards. The hand viewer was invented by Oliver Wendell Holmes, although more complicated table models were used before his was placed in production in 1859.

STEREOSCOPE	9.50
STEREOSCOPE,BOX TYPE VIEWER	16.50
STEREOSCOPE,CHILD SIZE VIEWER,TIN,100 PICTURES,MARKED SYNDICATE PRESS	22.50
STEREOSCOPE,ENGRAVED	8.00
STEREOSCOPE,HAND TYPE SLIDING ADJUSTER,1875 WITH 5 CARDS	7.50
STEREOSCOPE,HAND TYPE VIEWER WITH SLIDING ADJUSTMENT	4.75
STEREOSCOPE,PENNY ARCADE,COLOURED,DROP COIN & TURN HANDLE	65.00
STEREOSCOPE,TABLE MODEL	27.50
STEREOSCOPE,TIN,CIRCA 1900,5 CARDS	8.50
STEREOSCOPE,UNDERWOOD VIEWER WITH 5 CARDS	8.50
STEREOSCOPE,VIEWER,NICKLE PLATED STANDARDS	15.00
STEREOSCOPE,VIEWER WITH 60 CARDS	15.00
STEREOSCOPE,WALNUT & ALUMINUM ETCHED,25 COLOURED & BLACK & WHITE VIEWS	8.50
STEREOSCOPE,WITH 25 CARDS	15.00
STEREOSCOPE,WITH 50 CARDS	10.00
STEREOSCOPE,WOODEN	7.50

STERLING SILVER is made with 925 parts of silver out of 1,000 parts of metal. The word "sterling" is a quality guarantee used in the United States after about 1860.

STERLING SILVER, SEE ALSO COIN SILVER, SILVER..........	
STERLING SILVER BANDS ON PEARL HANDLED STEAK CARVING SET,EMBOSSED...	19.50
STERLING SILVER BASKET FOR NUTS..............................	7.50
STERLING SILVER BASKET,PIERCED...............................	20.00
STERLING SILVER BASKET W/HANDLE,SIGNED TIFFANY & CO., 9IN. DIA..	65.00
STERLING SILVER BEADS,STRAND.................................	9.50
STERLING SILVER BELL...	7.50
STERLING SILVER BOTTLE,PERFUME,PAIR 4 IN.,REPOUSSE..........	25.00
STERLING SILVER BOTTLE,SMELLING SALTS,GREEN DEPOSIT.........	9.50
STERLING SILVER BOWL,5 IN. DIAMETER..........................	6.50
STERLING SILVER BOWL,ART NOUVEAU,800 MARK,FROM NURNBERG,FLORAL..	35.00
STERLING SILVER BOWL,FOOTED,FLORAL & LATTICE WORK...........	110.00
STERLING SILVER BOWL,INITIAL T & 1903,RAISED FLORAL DESIGN..	60.00
STERLING SILVER BOX,CIGARETTE,WOODEN FRAME,GOLD INSIDE,WEBSTER CO...	12.50
STERLING SILVER BOX,MATCH....................................	7.50
STERLING SILVER BOX,PILL,RAISED CREST ON LID................	16.00
STERLING SILVER BRUSH & HAND MIRROR..........................	15.00
STERLING SILVER BRUSH & MIRROR SET DATED 1904...............	7.50
STERLING SILVER BUREAU SET MARKED & ENGRAVED,LADIES,CUT GLASS JARS..	58.00
STERLING SILVER BUTTER PAT,PAIR,RAISED FLOWER BORDER........	3.00
STERLING SILVER BUTTER PATS, FLOWER BORDER, 2 FOR...........	5.00
STERLING SILVER BUTTER SPREADER..............................	2.50
STERLING SILVER BUTTER SPREADER,6............................	18.00
STERLING SILVER BUTTER SPREADER,SET OF 6,PEARL HANDLE,FERRULES SCROLL..	32.00
STERLING SILVER BUTTON HOOK..................................	3.00
STERLING SILVER BUTTONHOOK & SHOE HORN.......................	6.50
STERLING SILVER BUTTONHOOK,8 IN..............................	9.50
STERLING SILVER BUTTONHOOK,10 IN.,ROSE & RIBBONS............	7.50
STERLING SILVER BUTTONHOOK,GLOVE.............................	3.00
STERLING SILVER CAN,WATERING,1 IN. TALL......................	15.00
STERLING SILVER CANDELABRA,PAIR,16 IN. HIGH.................	140.00
STERLING SILVER CANDLEHOLDERS,PAIR,SQUATTY..................	8.00
STERLING SILVER CANDLE SNUFFER,TWISTED HANDLE...............	8.50
STERLING SILVER CANDLE SNUFFER WITH TRAY....................	29.00
STERLING SILVER CANDLESTICK,10 IN.,GEORGIAN 1813,LONDON.....	650.00
STERLING SILVER CANDLESTICK,PAIR,3 IN........................	4.00
STERLING SILVER CANDLESTICKS,PAIR 9 IN. BY BLACK,STAR & GORHAM...	65.00
STERLING SILVER CANDLESTICKS,PAIR,10 IN. HIGH...............	20.00
STERLING SILVER CASE,CARD....................................	18.00
STERLING SILVER CASE ,CARD,WITH CHAIN.......................	7.50
STERLING SILVER CASE,CIGAR,HINGED,HOLDS 3 CIGARS............	6.50
STERLING SILVER CASE,CIGARETTE,LADIES........................	4.00
STERLING SILVER CASE TAPE MEASURE,ENGRAVED ANGEL KISSING LADY..	5.00
STERLING SILVER CASE WITH DISAPPEARING COMB,3 IN............	4.50
STERLING SILVER CASE,WITH POCKET SIZE GLASS PERFUME BOTTLE..	8.50
STERLING SILVER CELERY,OVAL..................................	20.00
STERLING SILVER CENTERPIECE,8 IN. HIGH,DRESDEN BORDERED.....	300.00
STERLING SILVER CHATELAINE,ENGLISH HALLMARK.................	35.00
STERLING SILVER CLOTHES BRUSH................................	10.00
STERLING SILVER COASTER,PAIR TUMBLER,CUT FLOWER BASES.......	3.50
STERLING SILVER COFFEE POT,AMERICAN,IMPRESSED MARK STEBBINS,12 IN. HIGH..	275.00
STERLING SILVER COFFEE SERVICE,3 PIECES,GORHAM,REPOUSSE.....	135.00
STERLING SILVER COFFEE SET,AFTER DINNER,GORHAM CIRCA 1900,3	

```
PIECES...................................................  110.00
STERLING SILVER COMB & BRUSH.............................    5.00
STERLING SILVER COMPOTE,FOOTED...........................   20.00
STERLING SILVER COMPOTE,PAIR,STANDISH PATTERN BY HORHAM..   30.00
STERLING SILVER COMPOTE,VINTAGE MOTIF,7 IN. HIGH,GEORGE
JENSEN...................................................  235.00
STERLING SILVER CONDIMENT SET,BLOWN BOTTLES,.............   45.00
STERLING SILVER CORKSCREW,BOARS TOOTH HANDLE.............    5.50
STERLING SILVER COVER HAIR RECEIVER,CUT & ETCHED &
MONOGRAMMED..............................................    6.00
STERLING SILVER CRADLE,HOODED,2 IN. TALL.................   35.00
STERLING SILVER CREAM JUG,GEORGE III CIRCA 1769,HALLMARKED..  125.00
STERLING SILVER CREAMER & COVERED SUGAR..................   35.00
STERLING SILVER CUFF LINKS,DELFT PORCELAIN INSERTS,PAIR..   10.00
STERLING SILVER CUP & SAUCER,DEMI-TASSE,CHINA INSERT WITH
GOLD EDGE................................................   12.00
STERLING SILVER CUP & SAUCER,DEMI-TASSE,SET OF 12,LENOX
LINERS...................................................  120.00
STERLING SILVER CUP,BABY,INSCRIBED W.C.S.................   12.00
STERLING SILVER CUP,BABY,SIGNED..........................    5.00
STERLING SILVER CUP,CHILDS,CYLINDER SHAPED...............   15.00
STERLING SILVER CUP,INSCRIBED,SIGNED TIFFANY & CO.,TRAVEL...  12.75
STERLING SILVER CUP WITH FLORAL EMBOSSING,CHILDS.........   35.00
STERLING SILVER CURLER,HAIR..............................    3.75
STERLING SILVER DISH,ART NOUVEAU.........................   30.00
STERLING SILVER DISH,ART NOUVEAU,FOOTED,OPENWORK DESIGN..   30.00
STERLING SILVER DISH,CANDY,FANCY EDGE,5 IN...............   10.00
STERLING SILVER DISH,CARD,FOOTED,ENGRAVED IN & OUT.......   12.00
STERLING SILVER DISH,NUT.................................    5.00
STERLING SILVER DISPENSER,STAMP,GOLD LINED...............    7.50
STERLING SILVER DRESSER SET,6 PIECES,INITIALS E M B......   35.00
STERLING SILVER DRESSER SET,ART NOUVEAU..................   30.00
STERLING SILVER EWERS,PAIR,BAILEY & KITCHEN CIRCA 1853...1,350.00
STERLING SILVER FLASK,LADIES,4 OUNCE,SWIRLED RIBBING.....   48.00
STERLING SILVER FLASK,LEATHER COVERED,HUNT SCENE.........    5.00
STERLING SILVER FORK & SPOON,BABY,WALLACE................    3.75
STERLING SILVER FORK & SPOON,CHILDS......................    4.00
STERLING SILVER FORK,OLIVE,TIFFANY,HOLLY PATTERN.........   15.00
STERLING SILVER FORK,PICKLE
3.50  TO.................................................    4.75
STERLING SILVER FORK,PICKLE,2-TINED......................    1.75
STERLING SILVER FORK,SET OF 11,MARQUAND & CO.,SHELL,1810..  110.00
STERLING SILVER FRAME,PICTURE,ETCHED
FLOWERS,SCROLLS,OVAL,EASEL...............................   19.00
STERLING SILVER FRAME,PICTURE,OVAL,PEDESTAL,ETCHED MARTHA AT
TOP......................................................    8.50
STERLING SILVER FUNNEL,PERFUME...........................    4.00
STERLING SILVER GOBLET SIGNED TIFFANY....................   40.00
STERLING SILVER GRAVY BOAT,FOOTED,TIFFANY,CIRCA 1870.....  175.00
STERLING SILVER GRAVY BOAT SIGNED BIGELOW & KENNARD & CO.
1916.....................................................   20.00
STERLING SILVER HANDLE SPOON FOR MAKING TEA..............    9.00
STERLING SILVER HANDLE WAX SEAL,LETTER D.................    2.00
STERLING SILVER HANDLED HAT BRUSH........................    2.00
STERLING SILVER HAT PIN..................................    1.25
STERLING SILVER HATPIN,FLOWER............................    3.00
STERLING SILVER HOLDER,CUP,LACY,EMBOSSED FLOWER,HINGED COVER  12.00
STERLING SILVER HOLDER,TEA,TEAPOT STYLE,2 PIECE..........    8.00
STERLING SILVER HOLDER,WATER GLASS,SET OF 5,FILIGREE,GRAPE &
LEAF.....................................................   25.00
STERLING SILVER INKWELL MADE BY TIFFANY..................   48.00
STERLING SILVER KNIFE,ADVERTISING,DUTCH MILK MAID........    5.00
STERLING SILVER KNIFE,CAKE...............................    9.50
STERLING SILVER KNIFE,CHEESE,TIFFANY,OLYMPIAN............   15.00
STERLING SILVER KNIFE,DINNER,PEARL-HANDLE,MADAM ROYALE...    2.00
```

STERLING SILVER KNIFE,DINNER,SET OF 5,PANSY PATTERN,INTERNATIONAL....................................	25.00
STERLING SILVER KNIFE,FORK & SPOON,SHELL PATTERN,CHILDS,DATED 1893.................................	15.00
STERLING SILVER KNIFE,FRUIT.......................................	5.00
STERLING SILVER KNIFE,FRUIT,PEARL HANDLE......................	4.00
STERLING SILVER KNIFE,FRUIT,SET OF 6,MOTHER OF PEARL HANDLED	30.00
STERLING SILVER KNIFE,FRUIT,SET OF 6,PEARL-HANDLED..........	18.50
STERLING SILVER KNIFE,HOLLOW HANDLED & FORK,SET OF 6........	64.50
STERLING SILVER KNIFE,PIE,STAINLESS STEEL BLADE.............	3.00
STERLING SILVER KNIFE,SET OF 4,HANDLES ONLY.................	4.00
STERLING SILVER LADLE,CREAM................................	5.00
STERLING SILVER LADLE,GRAVY................................	8.50
STERLING SILVER LADLE,GRAVY,ENGRAVED HANDLE,MARKED RW & S...	6.00
STERLING SILVER LADLE,PUNCH,EGG SHAPE,HALLMARKED 1750,WOOD HANDLE..	45.00
STERLING SILVER LADLE,PUNCH,GOLD WASHED BOWL,W & H MARK.....	39.00
STERLING SILVER LADLE,PUNCH,HALLMARKED,BEADED EDGE HANDLE...	25.00
STERLING SILVER LADLE,SOUP,HOLMES & EDWARDS,SCALLOP EDGE BOWL...	22.00
STERLING SILVER LADLE,SOUP,TIFFANY,AUDUBON PATTERN..........	37.50
STERLING SILVER LADLE WITH POURING LIP,6 IN................	10.00
STERLING SILVER LAMP,SEALING WAX,SIGNED TIFFANY & CO........	40.00
STERLING SILVER MANICURE SET,5 PIECES,FLEUR DE LIS..........	15.00
STERLING SILVER MATCH SAFE,POCKET..........................	4.75
STERLING SILVER MATCH SAFE,POCKET,FOR LONG MATCHES,CURVED,STRIKER..	9.75
STERLING SILVER MENDER,GLOVE...............................	7.50
STERLING SILVER MIRROR,HAND,REED & BARTON,MONOGRAMMED ON BACK..	18.00
STERLING SILVER MIRROR,VANITY,PINK,WHITE & RED CABBAGE ROSE DATE 1903...	20.00
STERLING SILVER MUG,SHAVING,IRIS IN RELIEF,REMOVABLE SOAP INSERT...	45.00
STERLING SILVER MUG,SHAVING,SCUTTLE TYPE...................	22.50
STERLING SILVER MUSTARD POT,FILIGREE,CRANBERRY LINER........	27.50
STERLING SILVER MUSTARD POT,OVAL,BOAT SHAPED...............	30.00
STERLING SILVER MUSTARD POT WITH CRANBERRY GLASS LINING,OPEN WORK...	17.50
STERLING SILVER MUSTARD POT WITH SPOON,FOOTED,ROUND,LOW.....	35.00
STERLING SILVER NAPKIN HOLDER,FLAT,ELEPHANT.................	5.00
STERLING SILVER NAPKIN RING,9 SCENIC MEDALLIONS.............	9.00
STERLING SILVER NAPKIN RING,EMBOSSED FLORAL.................	4.50
STERLING SILVER NAPKIN RING,HORSESHOE......................	6.50
STERLING SILVER NAPKIN RING WITH RAISED RABBIT FIGURE.......	6.50
STERLING SILVER ON BRONZE BOWL DATED 1912,GREEN,BRONZE LINING,..	8.00
STERLING SILVER ON CRYSTAL CANDLESTICK,PAIR,9 IN.,SPIRAL STEMS..	45.00
STERLING SILVER OPENER,LETTER,BLACK HANDLE.................	1.25
STERLING SILVER PEN STOCK,EMBOSSED........................	3.50
STERLING SILVER PEN,STRAIGHT,ORNATE.......................	9.50
STERLING SILVER PEN,STRAIGHT,PLAIN........................	7.50
STERLING SILVER PENCIL,MECHANICAL,RETRACTABLE,BROWN JEWEL AT TOP..	8.50
STERLING SILVER PERFUME FALCON,AMBER TOP...................	10.00
STERLING SILVER PICK,NUT,TIFFANY..........................	3.50
STERLING SILVER PIN,STICK,SCENE PIKES PEAK,DENVER 1895......	3.75
STERLING SILVER PIN,WATCH.................................	7.00
STERLING SILVER PITCHER & TRAY,ICE WATER...................	145.00
STERLING SILVER PITCHER,HELMET,ENGLAND 1900................	17.50
STERLING SILVER PLATE,10 IN...............................	40.00
STERLING SILVER PLATE,BREAD & BUTTER,SET OF 8,6 IN.........	100.00
STERLING SILVER PLATE,ROUND,A MASONIC PRESENTATION PIECE....	15.00
STERLING SILVER PORRINGER SIGNED BARBARA ANN MALCOM........	10.00

```
STERLING SILVER RIM FOR CUSPIDOR,ENGRAVED CAMP DORALJO MAY
  1914.............................................................   20.00
STERLING SILVER ROSARY,2 IN. CRUCIFIX.......................   10.00
STERLING SILVER SALT & PEPPER
  2.00  TO.......................................................   11.00
STERLING SILVER SALT & PEPPER SHAKERS,PAIR,3 IN..............    6.50
STERLING SILVER SALT & PEPPER SHAKERS,PEDESTAL...............   15.00
STERLING SILVER SALT & PEPPER SHAKERS,RIBBED.................    2.75
STERLING SILVER SALT,2,HALLMARKED,BOAT SHAPE................   14.00
STERLING SILVER SALT DIP & SPOON,SET OF 6
  18.00  TO.....................................................   25.00
STERLING SILVER SALT DIP,COBALT GLASS LINER.................    2.50
STERLING SILVER SALT DIP,FLAT BASE...........................    4.50
STERLING SILVER SALT,FOOTED..................................    5.00
STERLING SILVER SALT,FOOTED,OPEN,COLLAR,COBALT BLUE INSERT..   25.00
STERLING SILVER SALT HOLDER WITH MASTER SALT FROM
  HOTEL,COBALT INSERT..........................................   12.00
STERLING SILVER SALT,INDIVIDUAL..............................    5.00
STERLING SILVER SALT,INDIVIDUAL,FOOTED,GORHAM...............    3.00
STERLING SILVER SALT,MASTER,FOOTED WITH COBALT GLASS LINER..   15.00
STERLING SILVER SALT,OPEN,FOOTED,COBALT BLUE GLASS
  LINER,PAIR....................................................   23.00
STERLING SILVER SALT,OPEN,FOOTED,PAIR,COBALT BLUE GLASS
  LINERS........................................................   23.00
STERLING SILVER SALT,PAIR INDIVIDUAL,COBALT LINERS..........   12.00
STERLING SILVER SALT,PEDESTAL................................    3.50
STERLING SILVER SALT SHAKER,SET OF 5,INDIVIDUAL.............   10.00
STERLING SILVER SALT,SHELL SHAPED,FOOTED WITH SPOON.........    5.00
STERLING SILVER SCOOP,SUGAR..................................    4.50
STERLING SILVER SERVER,CHEESE................................    3.50
STERLING SILVER SERVER,NUT,7 PIECES..........................    8.00
STERLING SILVER SERVER,VENISON...............................  300.00
STERLING SILVER
  SERVICE,COFFEE,CREAMER,SUGAR,WASTE,FOOTED,REED & BARTON...   85.00
STERLING SILVER SHEARS,GRAPE
  15.00  TO.....................................................   27.50
STERLING SILVER SHERBERT,6,GLASS INSERTS....................   30.00
STERLING SILVER SHIP,VIKING,MINIATURE.......................   15.00
STERLING SILVER SHOE BUCKLES ON BRASS MARKED IW8PAIR........  125.00
STERLING SILVER SHOE HORN....................................    4.50
STERLING SILVER SHOE HORN,BEADED EDGE........................    3.75
STERLING SILVER SKEWER,10 IN.,ENGLISH,JOHN LAMB,LONDON,CIRCA
  1780..........................................................   65.00
STERLING SILVER SPOON & TONGS,SIGNED HESTER BATEMAN.........   75.00
STERLING SILVER SPOON,BABY,CIRCLE HANDLE,RUNNING DISH &
  SPOON IN BOWL.................................................    4.00
STERLING SILVER SPOON,BABY,CURVED HANDLE,LITTLE TOMMY TUCKER    3.75
STERLING SILVER SPOON,BABY,RAISED DESIGN DUTCH GIRL FEEDING
  DUCKS.........................................................    4.75
STERLING SILVER SPOON,BAR,WITH FORK COMBINATION.............    7.50
STERLING SILVER SPOON,BERRY,PRELUDE BY INTERNATIONAL........    2.50
STERLING SILVER SPOON,CHEESE.................................    8.00
STERLING SILVER SPOON,CHILDS,CURVED HANDLE..................    3.00
STERLING SILVER SPOON,CHINESE EMBROIDERY....................   10.00
STERLING SILVER SPOON,CHRISTMAS,DENMARK 1941................   15.00
STERLING SILVER SPOON,DEMI-TASSE,COUSIN JOE,GOLD WASHED BOWL    4.00
STERLING SILVER SPOON,DEMITASSE,ENAMELED,BROWNIE............    3.00
STERLING SILVER SPOON,DEMITASSE,FIDDLE & THREAD,SET OF 7....   30.00
STERLING SILVER SPOON,DEMI-TASSE,GOLD WASHED BOWL,UNCLE
  BILLY.........................................................    4.00
STERLING SILVER SPOON,DEMI-TASSE,LILLIAN IN GOLD WASHED BOWL    4.00
STERLING SILVER SPOON,DEMI-TASSE,PALMER COX BROWNIE TOP OF
  STEM..........................................................    5.00
STERLING SILVER SPOON,DEMITASSE,SET OF 6....................   12.00
STERLING SILVER SPOON,DEMI-TASSE,STATE FAIR OF TEXAS........    1.25
```

```
STERLING SILVER SPOON,DEMI-TASSE WITH ROSES.................   4.00
STERLING SILVER SPOON,DESSERT,ARABESQUE DESIGN..............   4.50
STERLING SILVER SPOON,DESSERT,SET OF 11,MARQUAND &
   CO.,SHELL,1810......................................... 110.00
STERLING SILVER SPOON,ERIE,POPPY HANDLE.....................   4.00
STERLING SILVER SPOON,FEBRUARY FLOWER OF MONTH..............   7.50
STERLING SILVER SPOON FOR MAKING TEA,ROSE HANDLE............   9.50
STERLING SILVER SPOON FOR MASTER SALT.......................   2.00
STERLING SILVER SPOON,GOLD BOWL,ZODIAC......................   9.00
STERLING SILVER SPOON,GOLD WASHED BOWL,ENAMELED GLASS HANDLE   8.50
STERLING SILVER SPOON,GRAPEFRUIT,FLEUR DE LIS...............   3.00
STERLING SILVER SPOON,GRAPEFRUIT,SET OF 6...................  16.00
STERLING SILVER SPOON,HALIFAX,CANADA,GILT ENAMEL............   6.00
STERLING SILVER SPOON,MARMALADE JAR.........................   9.00
STERLING SILVER SPOON,NUT,GOLD WASH BOWL WITH STAR SHAPED
   PERFORATIONS..........................................    6.00
STERLING SILVER SPOON,OLIVE.................................   8.00
STERLING SILVER SPOON,OLIVE,GOLD WASHED BOWL,DATED 1895.....   3.50
STERLING SILVER SPOON,ORANGE................................   1.25
STERLING SILVER SPOON,PRESIDENT MC KINLEY...................  12.50
STERLING SILVER SPOON,SALT..................................   3.00
STERLING SILVER SPOON,SALT,PAIR,OVAL TIP,4 IN.,CIRCA
   1829,ENGLISH..........................................   15.00
STERLING SILVER SPOON,SALT,SET OF 6
   18.00  TO.............................................   20.00
STERLING SILVER SPOON,SET OF 6,PLAIN........................  18.00
STERLING SILVER SPOON,SERVING,M.G.WOOD,SHELL DESIGN.........   6.95
STERLING SILVER SPOON,SERVING,SLOTTED,MASONIC ORIENTAL LODGE   9.00
STERLING SILVER SPOON,SUGAR,PETALLED EMBOSSED BOWL,BEADED
   FAN TOP...............................................    8.50
STERLING SILVER SPOON WITH ENGRAVED BOWL....................  12.50
STERLING SILVER SPOON WITH FIGURE OF OLD TIME GOLFER WEARING
   KNICKERS..............................................    3.50
STERLING SILVER SPREADER,BREAD & BUTTER,SET OF 12,LILY
   PATTERN...............................................   35.00
STERLING SILVER STAND,CAKE,PEDESTAL,LACE EDGE...............  24.50
STERLING SILVER STICK PIN RAISED FIGURE OF GIRL WEARING BIG
   HAT...................................................    2.50
STERLING SILVER STICK PIN SHAPE OF CLAM SHELL...............   2.50
STERLING SILVER STRAINER,TEA,WOODEN HANDLE..................  22.00
STERLING SILVER SUGAR & CREAMER
   8.00  TO..............................................   35.00
STERLING SILVER SUGAR SHELL.................................   7.00
STERLING SILVER SUGAR SHELL,PAT. 1897.......................   4.50
STERLING SILVER TABLE CRUMBER,HORN HANDLE...................   7.50
STERLING SILVER TABLESPOON IN OLIVE LEAF PATTERN............   7.00
STERLING SILVER TABLESPOON PAT.1870 ,INITIAL P.............   4.75
STERLING SILVER TABLE SPOONS,19TH CENT.,SIGNED,EACH.........   7.00
STERLING SILVER TAG,DECANTER,OVAL WITH ENGRAVED BORDER,WORD
   GIN...................................................    7.50
STERLING SILVER TAG,DECANTER,WORD SCOTCH,ENGLISH............   9.50
STERLING SILVER TEA BALL ON CHAIN
   3.50  TO..............................................    6.50
STERLING SILVER TEA BALL ON CHAIN,HINGED COVER..............   5.00
STERLING SILVER TEA CADDY...................................   6.00
STERLING SILVER TEA CADDY,3 PIECE,CHINESE CIRCA 1800........ 800.00
STERLING SILVER TEA CADDY MINIATURE TEAPOT ON CHAIN.........  15.00
STERLING SILVER TEA SERVICE................................. 185.00
STERLING SILVER TEASPOON,BEADING AROUND HANDLE,MONOGRAM
   L.L.M.................................................    3.00
STERLING SILVER TEASPOON,BUFFALO ON HANDLE..................   6.00
STERLING SILVER TEASPOON,DAFFODILS DOWN HANDLE,MINNEAPOLIS
   IN BOWL...............................................    4.75
STERLING SILVER TEASPOON,HALLMARKED,ENGRAVED W.W...........   2.00
STERLING SILVER TEASPOON,SET OF 5,FLORAL DESIGNS,INITIAL B..  13.00
```

STERLING SILVER TEASPOON,SET OF 6,COLONIAL PATTERN........... 24.00
STERLING SILVER TEASPOON,SET OF 8............................ 36.00
STERLING SILVER TEASPOON,SET OF 9,MARQUAND & CO.,1810........ 63.00
STERLING SILVER TEASPOON,SHELL DESIGN ON HANDLE & BACK OF
BOWL,PAT.1901.. 4.50
STERLING SILVER TEASPOON,WELLS & GUNDE,FLORAL & MONOGRAM.... 3.00
STERLING SILVER TEASPOON,ZODIAC,FEBRUARY..................... 7.00
STERLING SILVER TEASPOONS,6,BLANCHE ON HANDLE............... 15.00
STERLING SILVER TEASPOONS,19TH CENTURY,SIGNED,30 PIECES.EACH 4.50
STERLING SILVER THIMBLE,BEADED BAND.......................... 6.50
STERLING SILVER THIMBLE,CHILDS,BLUE PLUSH BOX............... 5.00
STERLING SILVER THIMBLE,FRANCE............................... 3.00
STERLING SILVER THIMBLE,SIZE 7............................... 5.00
STERLING SILVER THIMBLE WITH CARVED GOLD BAND............... 10.00
STERLING SILVER TONGS,11 IN. LONG........................... 22.50
STERLING SILVER TONGS,SUGAR,3 IN............................ 20.00
STERLING SILVER TONGS,SUGAR,OPEN WORK & ENGRAVING........... 11.50
STERLING SILVER TOOL,CUTICLE................................. 3.75
STERLING SILVER TOOL,LACE MAKERS,11 PIECES.................. 25.00
STERLING SILVER TOOTHPICK HOLDER,SHAPE OF TALL SILK HAT,REED
& BARTON.. 22.00
STERLING SILVER TRAY,14 IN. ROUND,LATTICE WORK.............. 80.00
STERLING SILVER TRAY,CARD,OVAL,FOOTED,CIRCA 1791,ENGLISH.... 250.00
STERLING SILVER TRAY,OVAL,BEADED BORDER..................... 7.00
STERLING SILVER TRAY,PEN.................................... 12.50
STERLING SILVER TRAY,PIN.................................... 2.00
STERLING SILVER TRAY,ROUND,DRESDEN BORDERED,13 IN. DIAMETER. 300.00
STERLING SILVER VASE,ENGLISH,EMBOSSED & SCALLOPED........... 35.00
STERLING SILVER VASE,GORHAM CIRCA 1860,ENGRAVED,PAIR RAMS
HEAD HANDLES.. 75.00
STERLING SILVER VASE,SET OF 4,FLOWER,DRESDEN BORDERED....... 360.00
STERLING SILVER VASE,TRUMPET,7 IN. HIGH..................... 8.50
STERLING SILVER VIAL,PERFUME,TIFFANY........................ 35.00
STERLING SILVER WARMER,BRANDY,WOOD HANDLE,SAMUEL LAUNDRY.... 60.00

STEUBEN GLASS was made at the Steuben Glass Works of Corning, New York.
The factory, founded by Frederick Carder and Mr. Hawkes, was purchased by
the Corning Glass Company. They continued to make glass called "Steuben."
Many types of art glass were made at Steueben. The firm is still producing glass
of exceptional quality.

STEUBEN, SEE ALSO AURENE.................................
STEUBEN ATOMIZER,GOLD....................................... 85.00
STEUBEN BASKET,COBALT BLUE WITH ROPE HANDLE,FLEUR DE LIS
MARK.. 100.00
STEUBEN BERRY BOWL & SAUCER,YELLOW JADE..................... 110.00
STEUBEN BIRD,CLEAR GLASS.................................... 45.00
STEUBEN BOWL,2 IN. TALL..................................... 5.00
STEUBEN BOWL,12 IN.,BRISTOL YELLOW.......................... 37.50
STEUBEN BOWL & CANDLESTICKS,CLEAR........................... 95.00
STEUBEN BOWL & PLATE,ROSALENE DESSERT....................... 130.00
STEUBEN BOWL,AMETHYST SHADED................................ 95.00
STEUBEN BOWL,AURENE,FLARED TOP,2 IN. HIGH,GOLD.............. 125.00
STEUBEN BOWL,BUBBLY GLASS,THREADED TOPAZ EDGE............... 75.00
STEUBEN BOWL,CALCITE,7 IN.,GOLD AURENE LINING,APPLIED DOME
BASE.. 120.00
STEUBEN BOWL,CALCITE & GOLD AURENE,5 IN. DIAMETER........... 65.00
STEUBEN BOWL,CALCITE,GOLD AURENE LINING,ROSE & BLUE
HIGHLIGHTS.. 150.00
STEUBEN BOWL,CANDY,WITH HAND GRIP,AIR TRAP,RUFFLED,ROSE &
YELLOW.. 22.50
STEUBEN BOWL,CELESTE BLUE,FLEUR DE LIS MARK................. 45.00
STEUBEN BOWL,CENTER PIECE,JADE GREEN ROLLED INWARD.......... 61.00
STEUBEN BOWL,CLEAR TO PURPLE,FLUTED TOP..................... 110.00
STEUBEN BOWL,CONE SHAPED,FLARING TOP,GREEN JADE WINE........ 40.00
STEUBEN BOWL,FINGER,& PLATE,GREEN........................... 28.00

```
STEUBEN BOWL,FINGER,AMETHYST,PEDESTAL........................      35.00
STEUBEN BOWL,FINGER,AURENE,GOLD WITH ROSE,BLUE & GREEN.......     135.00
STEUBEN BOWL,FINGER,FOOTED,TOPAZ & FRENCH BLUE..............      25.00
STEUBEN BOWL,FISH OR PUNCH,TOPAZ.............................      40.00
STEUBEN BOWL,FOOTED,BLUE AURENE,6 IN. ACROSS TOP............     250.00
STEUBEN BOWL,GOLD CALCITE,4 IN.,............................     135.00
STEUBEN BOWL,GOLD CALCITE....................................      65.00
STEUBEN BOWL,GOLD WITH STRETCHED EDGE,BLUE BOTTOM...........     160.00
STEUBEN BOWL,GREEN-CINTRA DOUBLE WAFER & BAND CRYSTAL.......     175.00
STEUBEN BOWL ON BLACK GLASS STAND,GOLD CALCITE LINED........      85.00
STEUBEN BOWL,ROSALINE........................................     135.00
STEUBEN BOWL,RUBY............................................      29.50
STEUBEN BOWL,SET OF 6,COLOUR SERIES.........................     200.00
STEUBEN BOWL,SQUARE GROTESQUE,CAT...........................      62.50
STEUBEN BOWL-VASE,CALCITE & BLUE IRIDESCENT,RODDED CUT RIM..     450.00
STEUBEN BOWL,WIDE-RIM,FLEMISH BLUE...........................      57.50
STEUBEN BOX,POWDER,COVERED,RED WITH ALABASTER,ROSE DU
  BARRY,3 IN.................................................     250.00
STEUBEN BOX,PUFF,COVERED,5 IN.,IVORY,BLACK FINIAL,SILVER
  STEUBEN LABEL..............................................     225.00
STEUBEN BUD VASE,IVORY BODY,BLUE JADE BASE..................     135.00
STEUBEN CANDLESTICK,12 IN.,TOPAZ TWIST STEM,GREEN BASE......      85.00
STEUBEN CANDLESTICK,FRENCH BLUE.............................      25.00
STEUBEN CANDLESTICK,GOLD CALCITE,MUSHROOM...................     180.00
STEUBEN CANDLESTICK,PAIR 10 IN.,TOPAZ FOOT,SOCKET INVERTED..      59.00
STEUBEN CANDLESTICK,ROSALINE WITH ALABASTER,10 IN.,BALUSTER
  STEM......................................................      95.00
STEUBEN CANDLESTICK WITH TWISTED STEM,PAIR GOLD AURENE,10
  IN........................................................     275.00
STEUBEN CANDLESTICKS,AMBER,PAIR.............................      65.00
STEUBEN CHAMPAGNE,FOOTED....................................      25.00
STEUBEN CHAMPAGNE WITH GREEN STEM,ORIENTAL POPPY...........     225.00
STEUBEN CHAMPAGNE WITH TWISTED STEM,GOLD AURENE.............     105.00
STEUBEN COLOGNE,FRENCH BLUE,THREADED,STOPPER OF 5 LEAFED
  FLOWER....................................................      17.00
STEUBEN COMPOTE,AURENE BUTTERFLY BLUE,TWISTED STEM..........     325.00
STEUBEN COMPOTE,GREEN,TWISTED STEM..........................      48.00
STEUBEN COMPOTE ON STANDARD,GOLD CALCITE,RIBBED.............      55.00
STEUBEN COMPOTE,PAIR,SWIRLED CERISE RUBY BASE & TOP.........     130.00
STEUBEN COMPOTE,PEDESTAL,AMBER,8 IN. DIAMETER...............      39.00
STEUBEN COMPOTE,SIGNED CELESTE,BLUE,TEARDROP STEM...........      50.00
STEUBEN COMPOTE,SWEETMEAT,ENGRAVED..........................      45.00
STEUBEN COMPOTE,TOPAZ.......................................      25.00
STEUBEN COMPOTE WITH UNDERPLATE,AMETHYST....................      32.00
STEUBEN CONSOLE SET,BLACK JADE WITH FLINT WHITE RIM,SILVER
  BASE,.....................................................     159.00
STEUBEN CREAMER & SUGAR WITH BLUE HANDLES,AMBER.............      60.00
STEUBEN CUP,NUT,GOLD-LINED CALCITE WITH STRETCHED &
  SCALLOPED RIM.............................................      60.00
STEUBEN DARNER,BLACK CRYSTAL................................      27.50
STEUBEN DARNER,GOLD AURENE,MIRROR GLAZE.....................      85.00
STEUBEN DEMI-TASSE IN STERLING SILVER HOLDER,GOLD LINED
  CALCITE...................................................      85.00
STEUBEN DISH,CANDY,CLEAR CRYSTAL WITH COVER,SIGNED WITH
  FLEUR DE LIS..............................................      60.00
STEUBEN FLOWER BLOCK,CLEAR WITH BLACK SCALLOPED RIM.........      32.50
STEUBEN FOOTED SALT.........................................      39.50
STEUBEN GLASS,LEMONADE,JADE WITH ALABASTER HANDLE...........      35.00
STEUBEN GOBLET & PLATE,GREEN WITH CLEAR TWISTED STEMS.......      45.00
STEUBEN GOBLET,GREEN-CINTRA FLEUR DE LIS WAFFLE PONTIL......     175.00
STEUBEN GOBLET,SET OF 4,FLEMISH BLUE PANELED,VASELINE WAFER
  BASES.....................................................      30.00
STEUBEN GOBLET,SIGNED,GREEN WITH CLEAR CRYSTAL STEM.........      54.00
STEUBEN GOBLET,WATER,ENGRAVED CRYSTAL,TWISTED STEM.........      11.50
STEUBEN GOBLET,WATER,PEDESTAL STEM,TOPAZ....................       9.00
```

```
STEUBEN GOBLET WITH GREEN STEM,ORIENTAL POPPY..............   225.00
STEUBEN HORSE,PAIR CLEAR CRYSTAL...........................    40.00
STEUBEN INKWELL,PAPERWEIGHT GLASS,IRIDESCENT...............   100.00
STEUBEN LAMP,CAMEO GLASS,GOLD PURPLE FLORIDA CUT BACK TO
  ALABASTER................................................   525.00
STEUBEN LEMONADE GLASS,JADE WITH ALABASTER HANDLE..........    30.00
STEUBEN LEMONADE,SET OF 6,TOPAZ-BLUE,HANDLED GLASSES.......   135.00
STEUBEN PARFAIT WITH ALABASTER FOOT,ROSALINE,CONICAL SHAPED.   65.00
STEUBEN PITCHER,ICE TEA,IVORU WITH BLACK HANDLE,9 IN. HIGH..  135.00
STEUBEN PLATE,AURENE,GOLD & BLUE...........................    62.50
STEUBEN PLATE,CALCITE & GOLD AURENE,6 IN...................    65.00
STEUBEN PLATE,CLEAR,CRANBERRY THREADING,STEMMED SHERBERT....   35.00
STEUBEN PLATE,DINNER,GREEN JADE,8 IN.......................    51.00
STEUBEN PLATE,FLEUR-DE-LIS,BLUE,..........................     30.00
STEUBEN PLATE,GOLD AURENE,6 IN.,..........................     65.00
STEUBEN PLATE,GREEN.......................................     45.00
STEUBEN PLATE,GREEN-CINTRA,8 IN...........................     95.00
STEUBEN PLATE,JADE........................................     45.00
STEUBEN PLATE,JADE,6 IN...................................     25.00
STEUBEN PLATE,ORIENTAL POPPY,8 IN.........................    175.00
STEUBEN PLATE,SALAD,FRENCH BLUE...........................     12.00
STEUBEN SALT,BLUE,1 IN. HIGH,SHAPED LIKE MINIATURE BOWL....    20.00
STEUBEN SALT,FOOTED,BLUE AURENE...........................    165.00
STEUBEN SALT IN GOLDEN AMBER,FOOTED.......................     28.00
STEUBEN SHADE,3,GOLD LEAF ON IVORY........................     90.00
STEUBEN SHADE,AURENE CALCITE GOLD LINED,ACID CUTBACK......     35.00
STEUBEN SHADE,CALCITE,CUTBACK GARLAND DESIGN..............     25.00
STEUBEN SHADE,CALCITE,OPENING FLEUR DE LIS MARK...........     22.50
STEUBEN SHADE,GOLD & GREEN FEATHER,PAIR...................     45.00
STEUBEN SHADE,GOLD IRIDESCENT
  22.50  TO...............................................     35.00
STEUBEN SHADE,GOLD,PINK,BLUE,SILVER,PAIR..................     40.00
STEUBEN SHADE,PAIR GOLD CALCITE RIBBED....................     35.00
STEUBEN SHADE,RIBBED,GOLD WITH BLUE HIGHLIGHTS............     31.50
STEUBEN SHADE,SET OF 5,GOLD ON CALCITE,GOLD FEATHER.......    150.00
STEUBEN SHERBET & PLATE,GOLD AURENE,.....................     110.00
STEUBEN SHERBET & UNDER PLATE,CALCITE & GOLD AURENE.......    135.00
STEUBEN SHERBET,CALCITE & GOLD AURENE.....................     65.00
STEUBEN SHERBET,GREEN.....................................     45.00
STEUBEN SHERBET WITH GREEN STEM,ORIENTAL POPPY............    225.00
STEUBEN SHOT GLASS,GOLD AURENE............................     85.00
STEUBEN SNAIL,CLEAR GLASS.................................     45.00
STEUBEN SWAN,.............................................    175.00
STEUBEN SWAN,CRYSTAL,PAIR,5 IN. LONG......................     45.00
STEUBEN TAZZA ON ALABASTER PEDESTAL FOOT,GREEN JADE.......     93.00
STEUBEN TUMBLER,JADE,6 IN. TALL...........................     47.50
STEUBEN UNDERPLATE,GOLD PURPLE,SWIRL PATTERN..............      6.00
STEUBEN VASE,AMBER CRYSTAL,VERTICAL RIBBED................     22.00
STEUBEN VASE,AMETHYST,10 IN...............................     48.00
STEUBEN VASE,AURENE,FOOTED BASE,GOLD WITH BLUE HIGHLIGHTS..   175.00
STEUBEN VASE,AURENE,GOLD WITH RED HIGHLIGHTS..............    250.00
STEUBEN VASE,AURENE SIGNED & NUMBERED,BLUE TRUMPET,LEAVES &
  VINES...................................................    550.00
STEUBEN VASE,BLUE AURENE..................................    375.00
STEUBEN VASE,BLUE AURENE,RIBBED,FOOTED....................    375.00
STEUBEN VASE,BLUE IRIDESCENT AURENE,BLUE,10 IN. TALL......    395.00
STEUBEN VASE,CABINET,BLUE AURENE,PEACOCK IRIDESCENCE......    195.00
STEUBEN VASE,CARDERS GREEN BUBBLED PATTERN................     75.00
STEUBEN VASE,CLEAR CRYSTAL,3-PRONG,RUSTIC.................     85.00
STEUBEN VASE,CLEAR TO AMETHYST,SCALLOPED..................     75.00
STEUBEN VASE,CLUTHRA,GREEN................................    450.00
STEUBEN VASE,EMERALD GREEN,SIGNED,FLAT & SQUARE,FLEUR DE LIS   35.00
STEUBEN VASE,FAN,8 IN.,ALABASTER ACID CUT BACK,CARVING OF
  FLOWERS.................................................    425.00
STEUBEN VASE,FAN,BLACK THREADING..........................     25.00
```

```
STEUBEN VASE,FAN,GREENISH CLEAR BUBBLE GLASS,GREEN THREADING    40.00
STEUBEN VASE,FRENCH BLUE.....................................   65.00
STEUBEN VASE,GREEN CRYSTAL,3 PRONG RUSTIC....................   75.00
STEUBEN VASE,GREEN,FOOTED,9 IN.,BUBBLY STEM..................   50.00
STEUBEN VASE,IRIDESCENT BLUE,PEDESTAL,6 IN.,FLARING TOP.....   350.00
STEUBEN VASE,JADE GREEN......................................  115.00
STEUBEN VASE,PAIR MATCHING,FLEUR DE LIS,FAN SHAPED..........    32.00
STEUBEN VASE,PEDESTAL STEM,AURENE...........................   155.00
STEUBEN VASE,PEDESTAL STEM,ROSALINE & ALABASTER.............   110.00
STEUBEN VASE,RIBBED,AURENE,6 IN.............................   110.00
STEUBEN VASE,RUBY CERISE,FEATHER TRACERIES IN SILVER,BLUE...  165.00
STEUBEN VASE,SIGNED IVRENE..................................   195.00
STEUBEN VASE,URN SHAPED,BLUE AURENE ON CALCITE,12 IN. TALL..  225.00
STEUBEN WINE,BLUE,2 PANEL....................................   15.00
STEUBEN WINE,PANELED THISTLE.................................    8.00
STEUBEN WINE,YELLOW JADE,ALABASTER STEM & FOOT..............   110.00
```

STEVENGRAPHS are woven pictures made like ribbons. They were manufactured by Thomas Stevens of Coventry, England, and became popular in 1862.

```
STEVENGRAPH BOOK MARK.......................................   18.00
STEVENGRAPH BOOKMARK THE OLD ARM CHAIR......................   14.75
STEVENGRAPH BOOK MARK,TWINKLE,TWINKLE,LITTLE STAR...........   20.00
STEVENGRAPH FRAMED,THE LADY GODIVA PROCESSION...............   65.00
STEVENGRAPH, HOME SWEET HOME................................   17.00
STEVENGRAPH,SIGNED,1 IN. BY 6 IN.,FOR A GOOD BOY...........    35.00
STEVENGRAPH,SILK,LONDON BRIDGE..............................    9.50
STEVENGRAPH,UNSIGNED,1 IN. BY 6 IN.,NEW YEARS GIFT..........   15.00
STEVENGRAPH,UNSIGNED,2 IN. BY 8 IN.,COLUMBUS...............    25.00
STEVENGRAPH,UNSIGNED,3 IN. BY 15 IN.,ODE BY TENNYSON,1862...  35.00
STEVENGRAPH,WOVEN SILK 1892 COLUMBUS 400 ANNIVERSARY........   12.50
STEVENGRAPH,WOVEN SILK OF ARE YOU READY.....................   20.00
STEVENGRAPH,WOVEN SILK,STAR SPANGLED BANNER.................   15.00
```

STEVENS AND WILLIAMS of Stourbridge, England, made many types of art glass.

```
STEVENS & WILLIAMS 8 IN. VASE,BLUE,APPLIED CAMPHOR GLASS
  HANDLES...................................................   40.00
STEVENS & WILLIAMS APPLIED DECOR VASE,WHITE BRISTOL FAN
  SHAPE....................................................   32.00
STEVENS & WILLIAMS APPLIED EWER,7 IN. TALL,GREEN OPALESCENT
  STRIPED..................................................   23.00
STEVENS & WILLIAMS AZURE BLUE SATIN GLASS EWER,THORN CRYSTAL
  HANDLE...................................................   40.00
STEVENS & WILLIAMS BLUE SATIN VASE,CAMPHOR SATIN HANDLES....   40.00
STEVENS & WILLIAMS CLEAR VASE WITH APPLIED GREEN THREADS....   17.00
STEVENS WILLIAMS FRAMED SWIRL VASE,GREENISH BLUE TO YELLOW..  600.00
STEVENS & WILLIAMS GLASS BOWL,APPLIED CRANBERRY LEAF,AMBER
  HANDLE...................................................   45.00
STEVENS & WILLIAMS PAIR VASES,BRASS LACY FEET,SWIRL AMETHYST
  TO CLEAR.................................................  175.00
STEVENS & WILLIAMS WINE GLASS,ROSE WITH CAMPHOR BASE,SIGNED.   55.00
STOCK TICKER BY THOMAS A. EDISON CO.,BRONZE WITH TICKER TAPE  100.00
STONEWARE BOX,SALT,BLUE,WORD SALT ON FRONT,WOOD TOP.........    7.50
STONEWARE CROCK MARKED IN BLUE,HIRAM ROCKER 2 GALLON.......    12.00
STONEWARE JAR,BLUE HORSE HEAD...............................    8.00
STONEWARE JAR,COOKIE,BARREL.................................    8.50
STONEWARE JUG,BLUE,5 GALLON,TREE TRUNK,PASTURE,FENCE & COW..   50.00
STONEWARE JUG,BLUE DESIGN,2 GALLON,EDMONDS..................    9.00
STONEWARE JUG,BLUE LETTERING & STRIPING,1 GALLON,HANDLED....    8.00
STONEWARE JUG,GREY & BROWN,OVOID............................   32.00
STONEWARE JUG,SYRUP WITH PEWTER LID,GREEN,MARKED VICTORIAN
  REGISTRY.................................................   42.00
STONEWARE MORTAR & PESTLE...................................   10.00
STONEWARE MUG,GREY WITH COBALT BANDS,5 IN.,ALE,B & D GERMANY  10.50
STONEWARE MUG,WORLDS FAIR CHICAGO 1893......................   15.75
STONEWARE PITCHER,BLUE,GRAPE DESIGN IN RELIEF ON LATTICE
```

```
BACKGROUND..............................................  16.00
STONEWARE PITCHER,BLUE STENCIL DESIGN......................  18.00
STONEWARE PITCHER WITH FIGURES & COLOUR....................  28.00
STONEWARE PLATE,BLUE,ERFORD,10 IN..........................   8.00
STONEWARE PLATE,PEARL,THE TEMPLE...........................   8.50
STONEWARE PLATTER,19 IN.,MARKED MADDOCK &
   CO.,BURSLEM,ENGLAND....................................  12.50
STONEWARE SUGAR BOWL,COVERED,APOSTLE,REGISTERED MARCH
   17,1843.............................................  78.00
STONEWARE VASE,URN STYLE,BLUE & GREY,PAIR,GERMAN,DOUBLE
   HANDLED.............................................  65.00
   STORE, SEE ALSO CASH REGISTER, COFFEE GRINDER, FIRE,
   MACHINE, SCALE,......................................
   TIN BOX............................................
STORE,ADDING MACHINE,LITTLE GIANT.......................  15.00
STORE,APOTHECARY BOX,ORIGINAL BOTTLES & LABELS...........  45.00
STORE,APOTHECARY WEIGHTS,11 BRASS IN BLOCK OF WOOD.......  10.00
STORE,BASKET WITH HANDLE,WICKER,EGG......................   8.00
STORE,BEATER,CARPET,WIRE.................................   1.00
STORE,BOX,CAMEL FLAT 50,TIN..............................   1.50
STORE,BOX,COLLAR & CUFF,6 IN. TALL,SEMI-OVAL.............  25.00
STORE,BOX,WOODEN EGG FOR 12 EGGS,PATENT 1906.............   3.50
STORE,BOX,WOODEN EGG FOR 24 EGGS,PATENT 1906.............   5.00
STORE,BUCKET,SUGAR,10 IN.................................   4.50
STORE,BUCKET,SUGAR,PAINTED,5 IN..........................   3.50
STORE,CABINET,DIAMOND DYE,OAK,COLOURFUL,TIN FRONT........  55.00
STORE,CABINET,DYE,18 X 32 X 10 IN.,N.SPENCER THOMAS,ELMIRA
   NEW YORK...........................................  47.50
STORE,CABINET,EMBROIDERY THREAD,WALL-MOUNT,RICHARDSONS WASH
   SILKS..............................................  60.00
STORE,CABINET,PUTNAM DYE,STENCILS.......................   9.00
STORE,CABINET,PUTNAM DYE,TIN,LITHOGRAPH OF MAN ON HORSE..  18.00
STORE,CABINET,RICHARDSON SILK CO.,DOUBLE SPOOL,13 GLASS
   FRONT DRAWERS......................................  75.00
STORE,CABINET,SPOOL,BELDINGS SILK,3 DRAWER,GLASS FRONT...  30.00
STORE,CABINET WITH LIFT-UP GLASS TOP,CLARKS MILL END SPOOL..  47.50
STORE,CAN,COCOA-CRUSH,A RICH MILKY CHOCOLATE DRINK,EMBOSSED
   TIN................................................  18.00
STORE,CAN,COFFEE,PEAK,BLUE,BLACK,MOUNTAIN STENCIL.......   2.00
STORE,CAN,COFFEE,SUPERBA,BLUE WITH GOLD TRADE MARK......   2.00
STORE,CAN,COLUMBIA PEANUT...............................  22.50
STORE,CAN,KINGS SEMI-SMOKELESS POWDER...................   6.50
STORE,CAN,LAFFIN & RAND,INFALLIBLE SMOKELESS POWDER.....   6.50
STORE,CAN,ROUND 1 POUND COFFEE,STENCILLED MC LAUGHLINS
   BANKERS MOCHA......................................   1.50
STORE,CAN,TIN TOBACCO,BENSON & HEDGES...................   1.50
STORE,CAN,TIN TOBACCO,BOOT JACK TOBACCO.................   2.50
STORE,CAN,TIN TOBACCO,CENTRAL UNION CUT PLUG WITH GOLD LADYS
   HEAD...............................................   2.00
STORE,CAN,TIN TOBACCO,FLAT CHESTERFIELD CIGARETTE.......   1.00
STORE,CAN,TIN TOBACCO,OLD BRIAR.........................   2.50
STORE,CAN,TIN TOBACCO,OVAL,CAVALIER CIGARETTE,RED WITH
   CAVALIER...........................................   2.00
STORE,CAN,TIN TOBACCO,ROUND BABYS BOTTOM,2 RAISED BABIES
   BOTTOMS............................................   2.00
STORE,CAN WITH LID,MILK,10 GALLON.......................   6.50
STORE,CANNISTER WITH LABEL,AMERICAN POWDER..............   4.00
STORE,CARPET BEATER
   2.50   TO.........................................   4.50
STORE,CASE,CIGAR CARRYING,BRASS,LEATHER COVERED,SALESMANS
   SAMPLE.............................................  12.00
STORE,CASE,METAL,BOYE NEEDLES & SHUTTLES................   5.00
STORE,CHEST WITH 12 COMPARTMENTS,WALNUT,LATTICE SLAT
   COVER,GOLD EAGLE...................................  35.00
STORE,CONTAINER,CANDY,TIN WITH GLASS FRONTS.............   4.50
```

STORE,CONTAINER,TIN,ALLSPICE,MUSTARD GRAINING WITH GOLD
   STENCIL.. 30.00
STORE,CRATE OPENER,KELLOGS TOASTED CORN FLAKES.............. 3.50
STORE,CROCK,WARDS ORANGE JUICE DISPLAY..................... 14.75
STORE,CUP,QUASSIA WITH CAPTIVE RING,PAMPHLET EXTOLLING
   REMEDIES... 18.50
STORE,CUTTER,CHEESE,CIRCULAR TURNTABLE,BLADE............... 15.00
STORE,CUTTER,CIGAR
   12.00 TO... 35.00
STORE,CUTTER,CIGAR,COUNTERTYPE............................. 28.75
STORE,CUTTER,PLUG TOBACCO,PAINTED.......................... 14.00
STORE,CUTTER,TOBACCO
   6.50 TO.. 10.00
STORE,CUTTER,TOBACCO,LORILLARDS CLIMAS,WOOD BASE........... 4.50
STORE,DIPPER,CHICLET PENNY CANDY........................... 1.00
STORE,DIPPER,ICE CREAM,TIN................................. 2.50
STORE,DISPENSER,DRUG STORE LEMONADE,1 GALLON,WARDS LEMON
   CRUSH.. 30.00
STORE,DISPENSER,ICE CREAM SCOOP,BRASS WITH WOOD,GILCHRISTS
   NO. 31.. 3.00
STORE,DISPENSER,MATCH BOX,IRON TOP......................... 12.50
STORE,HARNESS,DRIVING...................................... 20.00
STORE,HEAD,LADIES,SALLY CLOVER,SILVER WITH BLACK........... 2.00
STORE,HOLDER & CUTTER,PAPER ROLL........................... 10.00
STORE,HOLDER,ICE CREAM GLASS............................... 3.50
STORE,HOLDER,PAPER,COUNTER................................. 5.00
STORE,HOLDER,STRING,CAST IRON,10 IN........................ 18.00
STORE,HOLDER,STRING,IRON COUNTER CONE...................... 9.00
STORE,HOLDER,STRING,IRON,FOR TABLE COUNTRY STORE........... 8.50
STORE,HOLDER,TIN,BOYLES NEEDLE & SHUTTLE................... 25.00
STORE,HORSE-BLANKET,MILLERS BEER ADVERTISEMENT............. 12.00
STORE,ICE CRUSHER,DRUG STORE............................... 2.00
STORE,JAR,CANDY,GLASS GROUND TOP,12 IN. HIGH............... 5.50
STORE,LAB,DOCTORS TESTING,OAK CABINET...................... 45.00
STORE,LUNCH PAIL,6 IN. BY 8 IN............................. 6.00
STORE,MATCH SAFE,PAIR OF SHOES............................. 6.00
STORE,MIRROR ADVERTISING MENNENS TALCUM POWDER............. 6.00
STORE,MUG,HIRES ROOT BEER.................................. 14.00
STORE,NET,FLY,LEATHER...................................... 5.00
STORE,POST OFFICE.. 75.00
STORE,POST OFFICE WINDOW,U S A............................. 27.50
STORE,PUMP,50 GALLON WOODEN VINEGAR........................ 12.50
STORE,PUMP,SKINNY FOR VINEGAR BARREL....................... 15.00
STORE,SAUSAGE STUFFER...................................... 7.00
STORE,SCALE,1772 PENNSYLVANIA HANGING GROCERY,BRASS RODS &
   PANS.. 60.00
STORE,SCALE,BLACK,BRASS TRAY,7 WEIGHTS..................... 25.00
STORE,SCALE,BRASS PAN & 3 WEIGHTS,RED PAINT................ 20.00
STORE,SCALE,COUNTER WITH MAMMOTH SCOOP,RED PAINT........... 45.00
STORE,SCALE,EASTMAN KODAK AVOIRDUPOIS WEIGHT............... 18.00
STORE,SCALE,EGG,METAL WITH MILK GLASS EGG.................. 3.50
STORE,SCALES,1 CENT WEIGHING,PATENT 1918,5 FEET X 9
   IN.,MARBLE BASE... 38.50
STORE,SCALES,APOTHECARY,PENNSYLVANIA....................... 20.00
STORE,SCALES,BALANCE IN OAK CASE,GLASS ON 4 SIDES,BRASS PANS 32.50
STORE,SCALES,BRASS,WEIGHTS,10 MG TO 100 GRAMS............. 9.00
STORE,SCALES,BRASS,WOODEN BASE & DRAWERS.................. 45.00
STORE,SCALES,EGG
   2.50 TO... 4.50
STORE,SCALES,FAIRBANKS & MORSE POSTAGE,10 OUNCES,IRON &
   BRASS... 12.50
STORE,SCALES,FAIRBANKS,SLIDING BRASS WEIGHT ON CALIBRATED
   SCALE... 15.00
STORE,SCALES,GROCERY COUNTER,IRON,TIN BASKET.............. 50.00
STORE,SCALES,HOWE COUNTER,SCOOP & WEIGHTS................. 12.00

```
STORE,SCALES,IRON,2 BRASS PANS..............................    25.00
STORE,SCALES,IRON,CAST,COUNTER,2 CAST IRON TRAYS............     9.00
STORE,SCALES,JEWELERS,WOODEN BOX,MARBLE TOP,BRASS PANS......    25.00
STORE,SCALES,MILK,30 POUND..................................     5.00
STORE,SCALES,SHALER,IRON,TO 12 POUNDS,TIN SCOOP,PATENT
   11/18/1868..............................................    28.50
STORE,SHOOTING GALLERY TUNNEL,CAFE,3 SECTION STEEL,10 FEET
   LONG....................................................    35.00
STORE,SIGN,BEER DATED 1904,PABST BLUE RIBBON,HORSES & RIDERS   18.00
STORE,SIGN,FIREHOUSE,FIREMANS HAT WITH EAGLE................   165.00
STORE,SIGN,FROSTED GLASS,CIGARS,13 X 10 IN..................     4.50
STORE,SIGN,GLASS EYE,TAN PEBBLY GLASS WITH EYE IN
   CENTER,METAL RIM........................................    60.00
STORE,SIGN,LADIES BOOT,CAST IRON,WEIGHT 6 POUNDS...........    65.00
STORE,SIGN,METAL ADVERTISING LASHS KIDNEY & LIVER BITTERS...   15.00
STORE,SIGN,MISSION ORANGE SOLD HERE........................     7.00
STORE,SIGN,NORITAKE FIRE INSURANCE CO.,PORCELAIN ADVERTISING   12.50
STORE,SIGN,PAWN SHOP,FORGED STEEL ROD WITH ARROW POINT,3
   GILDED.................................................    185.00
STORE,SIGN,PORCELAIN,DE LAVAL SEPARATOR....................    25.00
STORE,SIGN,SILK,FLOWERS FOR SALE BY MRS.E H ATKINS.........     6.50
STORE,SIGN,TEXACO POST GLOBE...............................   125.00
STORE,SIGN,THE CAPITOL FIRE INSURANCE
   CO.,PORCELAIN,ADVERTISING...............................    12.50
STORE,SIGN,TIN OF WATCH CLOCK REPAIRER.....................    10.00
STORE,SIGN,TRADE...........................................    75.00
STORE,SIGN,TRADE,COPPER FISH MARKED TACKLE.................    60.00
STORE,SIGN,TRANSLUCENT GLASS DISPLAY,MORE MILES WITH
   MANSFIELD TIRES.........................................    15.00
STORE,SIGN,WATCH,METAL OCTAGONAL ..........................   185.00
STORE,STOOL,CAST IRON PATTERN COUNTER......................    15.00
STORE,STOOL,SHOE FITTERS,OAK TOP,TWISTED WIRE BASE.........    20.00
STORE,STOVE,CAST IRON POT BELLY COAL.......................    25.00
STORE,SUGAR CUTTER ON WOODEN STAND,IRON & BRASS IMPLEMENTS..   75.00
STORE,TIN,BLANKES TEA & COFFEE,HINGED COVER................     2.50
STORE,TIN,EDGEWORTH TOBACCO,20.............................     4.50
STORE,TIN,SWEET CUBA CHEWING TOBACCO.......................    22.50
STORE,WHEEL,WOODEN WITH 8 COMPARTMENTS FROM JEWELRY STORE
   FOR TOOLS...............................................     3.00
STORE,WINDOW,STAINED GLASS,20 X 25 IN......................    22.50
STORE,WRITER,CHECK,SAFEGUARD,1917..........................    10.00
STOVE,FOOT,BOX TYPE,PANEL,WOOD FRAME.......................    22.50
STOVE,FRANKLIN COAL,PARLOR.................................    35.00
STOVE,IRON.................................................    58.00
STOVE,RAILROAD POT BELLIED,PASSENGER CAR,EMBOSSED MKT.......   55.00
         STRING HOLDER, SEE STORE, HOLDER..................
STUFFED EAGLE HEAD MOUNTED ON PLACQUE......................    12.50
```

SUNBONNET BABIES were first introduced in 1902 in the SUNBONNET BABIES PRIMER. The stories were by Eulalie Osgood Grover, illustrated by Bertha Corbett. The children's faces were completely hidden by the sunbonnets, and had been pictured in black and white before this time. The color pictures in the book were immediately successful. The Royal Bayreuth China Company made a full line of children's dishes decorated with the sunbonnet babies.

```
       SUNBONNET, SEE ROYAL BAYREUTH......................
SUNBONNET BABIES 7 IN. PLATE...............................     7.00
SUNBONNET BABIES MILK PITCHER..............................    65.00
```

SUN-COLORED GLASS has been exposed to strong sunlight until the color of the glass has changed to purple, amber, or other shades.

```
SUN-COLOURED GLASS PURPLE CANDLE HOLDER....................     3.50
SUN-COLOURED GLASS PURPLE FAN VASE.........................     7.00
SUN-COLOURED GLASS PURPLE PATTERNED SUGAR BOWL.............     4.50
SUN-COLOURED GLASS PURPLE POWDER JAR.......................     4.00
SUN-COLOURED GLASS PURPLE SWIRL VASE.......................     7.50
```

```
SUN-COLOURED GLASS,PURPLE TUMBLER............................    7.00
SUN-COLOURED GLASS PURPLE WATER JUG..........................    8.00
```

SUNDERLAND LUSTER is a name given to a characteristic pink luster made by Leeds, Newcastle, and other English firms during the nineteenth century. The luster glaze is metallic and glossy and sometimes appears to have bubbles as a decoration.

```
    SUNDERLAND LUSTER, SEE ALSO LUSTER.......................
SUNDERLAND LUSTER,BLACK TRANSFER OF JOHN PAUL JONES,WASHBOWL
  & PITCHER..................................................  300.00
SUNDERLAND LUSTER COMPOTE,PICTURE SUNDERLAND BRIDGE &
  TYNEMOUTH HAVEN............................................   40.00
SUNDERLAND LUSTER CREAMER...................................   60.00
SUNDERLAND LUSTER PINK CHILDS CUP,SAUCER & PLATE MARKED.....   40.00
SUNDERLAND PINK MUG.........................................   32.00
SUN DIAL,POCKET SIZE,CLOSED FACE,IN CASE....................   40.00
```

SWANSEA POTTERY was made at the Cambrian pottery in Glamorganshire, Wales. It was founded by 1765 and worked until 1870. The early wares were of a fine-quality soft paste. All types of Staffordshire wares were also made.

```
SWANSEA MATCHING PAIR TUREENS CIRCA 1780....................  170.00
SWANSEA TEA & COFFEE CUP & SAUCER,PINK ROSES & GOLD ,CIRCA
  1825......................................................   55.00
SWORDCANE LONG BLADE,NICE HANDLE,COMPLETELY DISGUISED,FINE
  ORIG.COND.................................................   12.00
SWORDCANE...................................................   13.00
```

```
    TAFFETA GLASS, SEE CARNIVAL GLASS.......................
```

TAPESTRY PORCELAIN was made by the Royal Bayreuth factory of Germany during the late nineteenth century. The surface of the ware feels like cloth.

```
    TAPESTRY, SEE ROYAL BAYREUTH............................
TAPESTRY,FLEMISH,6 FEET SQUARE,FRENCH COURT SCENE...........  300.00
TAPESTRY,FRAMED,OUTDOOR SCENE,MARKED FRANCE.................   85.00
TAPESTRY HAIR RECEIVER,2 PIECE,GOLD ,FOOTED.................   43.00
TAPESTRY,ROYAL BAYREUTH GOLD FOOTED COVERED POWDER & HAIR
  RECEIVER..................................................   95.00
    TEALEAF, SEE IRONSTONE, TEALEAF.........................
TEA TILE,DRESSED LADIES DANCING,CUPID PLAYING HARP..........   15.00
TEA TILE,HANDPAINTED PANSIES,SIGNED.........................    8.50
TELEGRAPH KEY,RAILROAD STATION..............................   50.00
TELEGRAPH SOUNDER,RESONATOR BOX & PEDESTAL..................   22.00
TELEGRAPHER KEY ON WOOD BASE................................   10.00
TELEPHONE,8 IN. BY 8 IN.,WALL CRANK.........................    7.00
TELEPHONE,1949 SQUARE BASE..................................   10.00
TELEPHONE,BLACK UPRIGHT DESK................................   15.00
TELEPHONE,BRASS PAIR UPRIGHTS...............................   35.00
TELEPHONE,CRADLE-TYPE DIAL..................................    7.50
TELEPHONE,DIAL UPRIGHT......................................   20.00
TELEPHONE,GERMAN DIAL.......................................   15.00
TELEPHONE,MODEL 1925,OVAL BASE & DIAL,BELL BOX..............   10.00
TELEPHONE,OAK,WALL..........................................   35.00
TELEPHONE,OAK WOOD WALL,BELLS...............................   22.00
TELEPHONE,PUSH TO TALK HANDSET..............................    5.00
TELEPHONE,STEAMSHIP,6X7X5 IN................................   10.00
TELEPHONE,TABLE.............................................   15.00
TELEPHONE, UPRIGHT..........................................   10.00
TELEPHONE,WALL,WESTERN ELECTRIC.............................   35.00
TELEPHONE,WALNUT WALL TYPE,BELLS............................   49.00
TELEPHONE,WALNUT WOOD WALL,BRASS BELLS......................   49.00
TEPLITZ AMPHORA 6 IN. BULBOUS VASE,JEWELLED,WEBS,ENAMELED
  DRAGONFLIES...............................................   45.00
TEPLITZ SIGNED VASE,7 IN. TALL,FIREFLIES & FLOWERS,TREES....   58.00
TEPLITZ VASE,MOTTLED GOLD,BEIGE,HANDPAINTED ROSES,14 IN.
  TALL......................................................   12.00
```

```
THREADED AND ENAMELED VASES,GREEN WITH GOLD AND WHITE,PAIR..      40.00
THREADED GLASS, CLEAR TO AMETHYST WINE JUG, METAL COLLAR....      60.00
THREE CROWN CHINA CRACKER JAR,GREEN ON WHITE WITH PINK
  ASTERS.................................................      12.00
THREE CROWN GERMANY PLATE,HOLLY LEAVES & BERRIES............       7.50
  TIFFANY-TYPE LAMP, SEE LAMP...............................
```

TIFFANY GLASS was made by Louis Comfort Tiffany, the American glass designer who worked from about 1876 to 1933. His work included iridescent glass, art nouveau styles of design, and many original contemporary styles. He was also noted for his stained glass windows, his unusual lamps, and his bronze work.

```
TIFFANY BELL,STERLING,SIGNED................................      29.50
TIFFANY BONBON,FOOTED,GOLD,ROUND,SIGNED.....................     115.00
TIFFANY BOWL,12 IN.,PINK & PURPLE HIGHLIGHTS................      95.00
TIFFANY BOWL,CHARTREUSE,SIGNED LCT FAVRILE..................     225.00
TIFFANY BOWL,COLOURED ART NOUVEAU PURPLE GLASS..............      35.00
TIFFANY BOWL,FINGER,& PLATE,SIGNED,GOLD.....................     120.00
TIFFANY BOWL,FINGER & UNDERPLATE,SIGNED,IRIDESCENT GOLD.....     150.00
TIFFANY BOWL,FINGER,PLATE,SIGNED,BLUE.......................     165.00
TIFFANY BOWL,FINGER,SIGNED,RED TOP,GREEN BASE...............     190.00
TIFFANY BOWL,FINGER,SIGNED,RUFFLED & STRETCHED
  EDGE,IRIDESCENT..........................................     105.00
TIFFANY BOWL,FINGER,WITH UNDERPLATE,GOLD WITH SCALLOPED
  EDGES...................................................     160.00
TIFFANY BOWL,NUT SIGNED FAVRILE,SCALLOPED TOP,BLUE,GREEN &
  PINK....................................................      90.00
TIFFANY BOWL ON BRONZE TRIPOD,9 IN.,CRIMPED EDGE,INVERTED
  DIMPLES.................................................      80.00
TIFFANY BOWL,ROUND,BLUE LINED,GOLD WITH VINE DESIGN.........     300.00
TIFFANY BOWL,SIGNED,5 IN. DIAMETER,GOLD WITH RED...........      65.00
TIFFANY BOWL,SIGNED,7 IN. DIAMETER,3 IN. HIGH,GOLD.........      75.00
TIFFANY BOWL SIGNED FAVRILE,GOLD,10 IN. AT FLARED RIM.......     200.00
TIFFANY BOWL SIGNED FAVRILE,RIBBED & SCALLOPED,GOLD WITH
  SILVER,ORCHID...........................................     245.00
TIFFANY BOWL,SIGNED,GOLD....................................     110.00
TIFFANY BOWL,SIGNED,GOLD RIBBED,SCALLOPED EDGE..............     155.00
TIFFANY BOWL,SIGNED,GREENISH GOLD...........................      97.00
TIFFANY BOWL SIGNED LCT,4 IN.,GOLD & GREEN TONES............      95.00
TIFFANY BOWL,SIGNED,OPAL GREEN,UNDERSIDE AZURE BLUE.........     385.00
TIFFANY BOWL,SIGNED,RIBBED,FLARED & SCALLOPED...............     210.00
TIFFANY BOWL,SIGNED,RIBBED,GOLD & BLUE & RED................      95.00
TIFFANY BOX,CUT CRYSTAL,COVERED,TRINKET,STERLING SCREW ON
  COVER,SIGNED............................................      22.00
TIFFANY BOX,LEATHER ALLIGATOR COVERED,TURQUOISE VELVET
  LINED,DATED 1891........................................      25.00
TIFFANY BOX,STAMP,METAL,MOTHER OF PEARL DECORATION..........      45.00
TIFFANY BUTTERFLY,LEADED GLASS,MULTI-COLOURED...............      47.00
TIFFANY CANDLE HOLDER,SIGNED,BRONZE,3 FOOTED,SHAPED LIKE
  LEAF....................................................      30.00
TIFFANY CANDLE HOLDER SIGNED,OCTAGONAL,GOLD,BLUE............      97.00
TIFFANY CANDLE LAMP SIGNED FAVRILE L.C.T.,GOLD,BLUE TWIST
  STEM....................................................     225.00
TIFFANY CANDLESTICK,BRONZE,COMMEMORATIVE,FIRST PANEL
  SHERIFFS JURY...........................................      35.00
TIFFANY CANDLESTICK,SIGNED,BLUE & GOLD......................     130.00
TIFFANY CANDLESTICK,SIGNED,BLUE IRIDESCENT..................     110.00
TIFFANY CANDLESTICKS,PAIR,SIGNED 1927,L.C.TIFFANY-FAVRILE,4
  IN. TALL................................................     200.00
TIFFANY CANDLESTICKS,PAIR,SIGNED,BRONZE BASE...............     300.00
TIFFANY CANDLESTICKS,PAIR,SIGNED,GOLD FINISH,3-PRONGED.....      98.00
TIFFANY CANDLESTICKS,PAIR,SIGNED,SWIRLED,GLASS CANDLE
  SOCKETS.................................................     235.00
TIFFANY CANDLESTICK SIGNED LCT FAVRILE,GOLD IRIDESCENCE,9
  IN. HIGH................................................     250.00
TIFFANY CASE,EYEGLASS,14K GOLD..............................      89.00
```

```
TIFFANY CHAMPAGNE,SIGNED,LILAC COLOUR,KNOB STEM,OPALESCENT
   WHITE FOOT.............................................    470.00
TIFFANY CHANDELIER,CURVED BELL SHAPED TYPE,GREEN & PINK.....    325.00
TIFFANY CLOCK & MATCHING PAIR OF CANDELABRA,DORE
   BRONZE,SIGNED......................................... 1,200.00
TIFFANY CLOCK SIGNED,CHIME WIND ALARM,LEATHER CASE..........    325.00
TIFFANY COCKTAIL GLASS,SIGNED,4 IN. HIGH....................     90.00
TIFFANY COMPOTE,BLACK SATIN FINISH.........................     20.00
TIFFANY COMPOTE,LOW,SIGNED,METAL BASE,GOLD
   IRIDESCENCE,PINK,BLUE..................................    300.00
TIFFANY COMPOTE,OVAL,3 IN. TALL,SIGNED,GREEN IRIDESCENT.....    175.00
TIFFANY COMPOTE,SIGNED,3 IN. TALL,GOLD IRIDESCENCE WITH
   GREEN.................................................    190.00
TIFFANY COMPOTE,SIGNED,COPPER COLOURED,PURPLE HUES..........    240.00
TIFFANY COMPOTE,SIGNED,GOLD,RUFFLED,FLORIFORM,STRETCHED
   ONION EDGE............................................    210.00
TIFFANY CONSOLE SET,3 PIECE,SIGNED,FOOTED,GREEN TO CLEAR....    750.00
TIFFANY CORDIAL,2 IN. TALL,APPLIED LILY PAD DECOR,GOLD......     75.00
TIFFANY CORDIAL GLASS,CLEAR SWIRLED ON GREEN STEM,7 PIECES..    125.00
TIFFANY CORDIAL,GOLD,1 IN..................................     32.50
TIFFANY CORDIAL,LILY PAD,SIGNED,BLUE-GOLD IRIDESCENCE.......    125.00
TIFFANY CORDIAL,SIGNED,IRIDESCENT..........................     87.00
TIFFANY CORDIAL,SIGNED LCT,CORSET SHAPE WITH THREADING IN
   MIDDLE...............................................    115.00
TIFFANY CORDIAL,SIGNED,PINCHED SIDES,GOLD-BLUISH IRIDESCENCE     85.00
TIFFANY CORDIAL,STEM,SIGNED,IRIDESCENT,5 IN.................     69.50
TIFFANY CUP & SAUCER,SIGNED FAVRILE,GOLD...................    165.00
TIFFANY CUP,MARRIAGE,SIGNED,GOLD,3-HANDLED.................    185.00
TIFFANY CUP,NUT,GLASS,SIGNED..............................     70.00
TIFFANY CUP,NUT,SIGNED FAVRILE,ROUND,FLUTED,GOLD IRIDESCENCE     47.50
TIFFANY CUP,NUT,SIGNED,SERPENTINE RIM.....................     72.00
TIFFANY CUP,SALT,HANDLED,SIGNED LCT,BLUE,PURPLE & GOLD......     58.00
TIFFANY DEMI-TASSE SET,POT HOLDS 1 QUARTER PINTS,STERLING,3
   PIECE................................................     25.00
TIFFANY DESK PAD,SIGNED,SHIP & SEAHORSE...................     30.00
TIFFANY DESK SET,6 PIECES,SIGNED,ZODIAC PATTERN.............    125.00
TIFFANY DESK SET,7 PIECES,SIGNED,DORE GOLD WITH CARAMEL
   GLASS................................................    150.00
TIFFANY DESK SET,MARKED,BRONZE,BYZANTINE STYLE IN 9TH
   CENTURY PATTERN......................................    250.00
TIFFANY DESK SET,SIGNED & NUMBERED,GOLD BRONZE ZODIAC,3
   PIECES...............................................     60.00
TIFFANY DESK SET WITH CARAMEL SLAG GLASS,DORE BRONZE,COBWEB
   DESIGN...............................................    150.00
TIFFANY DISH,NUT,PASTEL,SIGNED,BLUE STRETCH EDGE...........    175.00
TIFFANY DISH,NUT,SIGNED,4 IN.,GOLD,FLUTED RIM..............     95.00
TIFFANY DISH,NUT,SIGNED,5 IN.,FLUTED TOP,GOLD IRIDESCENCE...     75.00
TIFFANY DISH,NUT,SIGNED,GOLD HIGHLIGHTS....................     75.00
TIFFANY DISH,NUT,SIGNED LCT,IRIDESCENT,PEDESTAL BASE........     97.50
TIFFANY DISH,NUT,SIGNED,RUFFLED EDGE,2 IN. DIAMETER,3 IN.
   HIGH.................................................     47.50
TIFFANY DISH,SAUCE,SIGNED,ON 6 IN. PLATE,BLUE HIGHLIGHTS....    150.00
TIFFANY DISH,VEGETABLE,OVAL WITH REEDED BORDER.............     85.00
TIFFANY EASEL,MENU,PORCELAIN,WHITE & GOLD..................     35.00
TIFFANY FAN,WHITE OSTRICH FEATHER,MOTHER OF PEARL RIBS,14K
   GOLD RING............................................     90.00
TIFFANY FLASK,SIGNED,LADYS,STERLING BASE & TOP,BASKETWEAVE
   GLASS................................................     60.00
TIFFANY FLOWER FORM IN BRONZE HOLDER,SIGNED,GREEN & WHITE...    275.00
TIFFANY FORK,PICKLE,FLORAL.................................      7.00
TIFFANY FROG,SIGNED,DOUBLE TIERED,2 ROWS OF LOOPS,GOLD......     85.00
TIFFANY GAS SHADE,SET OF 6,MOTTLED GOLD,OPALINE............    240.00
TIFFANY GOBLET,ENGRAVED GOLD..............................    175.00
TIFFANY GOBLET,SIGNED,GOLD IRIDESCENCE....................    160.00
TIFFANY GOBLET,SIGNED L.C.T. GOLD IRIDESCENCE.............    165.00
```

```
TIFFANY GOBLET,SIGNED,RED,GOLD,BLUE IRIDESCENCE,GRAPE
  PATTERN,6 IN.......................................... 185.00
TIFFANY HOLDER WITH GREEN FLOWER FORM,SIGNED,BRONZE........ 275.00
TIFFANY HUMIDOR,SIGNED,BLUE IRIDESCENCE,7 IN. HIGH......... 650.00
TIFFANY INKWELL,BLUE & GREEN IRIDESCENCE,BRASS TOP,GLASS
  INSERT................................................  27.00
TIFFANY INKWELL,SIGNED,PYRAMID SHAPE,HINGED LID............  40.00
TIFFANY INKWELL,ZODIAC DESIGN.............................  40.00
TIFFANY JUICE GLASS,SIGNED,3 IN. TALL,PINCHED SIDES,GREEN &
  BLUE..................................................  75.00
TIFFANY LAMP,3 LIGHT,BRONZE BASE..........................  75.00
TIFFANY LAMP,3 LIGHT DESK,GOLD SHADES..................... 275.00
TIFFANY LAMP,ACORN,GREEN SHADE WITH YELLOW ACORNS,SIGNED.... 338.00
TIFFANY LAMP BASE SIGNED,GLASS,ETCHED GREEN LEAVES ON GOLD.. 200.01-
TIFFANY LAMP,BEDSIDE,LEAD GLASS SHADE.....................  35.00
TIFFANY LAMP,BRONZE,FLOOR,SIGNED,61 IN. HIGH.............. 275.00
TIFFANY LAMP,CANDLE,BASE & SHADE SIGNED,16 IN. HIGH....... 250.00
TIFFANY LAMP,DAFFODIL,SIGNED SHADE & BASE................. 900.00
TIFFANY LAMP,DESK,PEAR-SHAPED FRAME ON BRONZED BASE.........  75.00
TIFFANY LAMP,DESK,SIGNED,BRONZE,CARAMEL GLASS,FILIGREED
  SHADE................................................. 150.00
TIFFANY LAMP,DRAGON FLY,SIGNED,GREEN BRONZE BASE,AMBER JEWEL
  SHADE................................................3,500.00
TIFFANY LAMP,FLOOR,5 FOOTED BASE,SIGNED,BRONZE STEM &
  FIXTURE............................................... 385.00
TIFFANY LAMP,FLOOR,SIGNED,12 LILY LITE...................1,900.00
TIFFANY LAMP,GERANIUM,SIGNED,BLUE,GREEN,PURPLE,16 IN. SHADE.1,800.00
TIFFANY LAMP,GREEN RIBBED WITH WHITE LINING,SIGNED.......... 450.00
TIFFANY LAMP SHADE,6 IN..................................  25.00
TIFFANY LAMP,SIGNED,16 IN. DIAMETER SHADE,TURTLEBACK WITH
  GREEN................................................. 650.00
TIFFANY LAMP,SIGNED,19 IN.,IRIDESCENT,YELLOW,GREEN.......... 210.00
TIFFANY LAMP,SIGNED,BRONZE,PEARL CONCH SHADE,12 IN. HIGH.... 159.00
TIFFANY LAMP,SIGNED,DORE BRONZE,MUTED GREEN SHADE,GOLD ACORN
  MOTIF................................................. 395.00
TIFFANY LAMP,SIGNED,GREEN IRIDESCENT & DECORATED,BRONZE BASE 225.00
TIFFANY LAMP,SIGNED,TABLE,NASTURTIUM,BRONZE BASE...........1,000.00
TIFFANY LAMP,STUDENT,SINGLE LIGHT,SIGNED,GREEN LEADED....... 425.00
TIFFANY LAMP,TABLE,16 IN. DIAMETER GREEK KEY SHADE,GREEN.... 600.00
TIFFANY LAMP,TABLE,BELL SHAPE DESIGN,GOLD BRONZE &
  SIGNED,GREEK KEY...................................... 225.00
TIFFANY LAMP,TABLE,CROCUS ,SIGNED,YELLOW & GREEN SHADE...... 750.00
TIFFANY LAMP,TABLE,LOTUS,SIGNED,CARAMEL SHADE,ORANGE WITH
  GREEN................................................. 650.00
TIFFANY LAMP,TABLE,SIGNED,16 IN. DIAMETER,BLUE & ORANGE
  CROESUS SHADE......................................... 750.00
TIFFANY LAMP,TABLE,SIGNED,GREEK KEY SHADE IN LEADED GREEN... 600.00
TIFFANY LAMP,TURTLE BACK,TABLE,GREEN...................... 750.00
TIFFANY LAMP,WITH LEADED SHADE,GOLD FINISH................ 450.00
TIFFANY MEMO PAD,BRONZE,SEA HORSE DECOR...................  15.00
TUFFANY MUFFINEER,PURPLE.................................  35.00
TIFFANY NUT DISH SIGNED LCT FAVRILE,3 IN.,GOLD,GREEN &
  PURPLE................................................  52.00
TIFFANY PAPERCLIP,SIGNED.................................  15.00
TIFFANY PAPERWEIGHT,SIGNED,RED,DARK CIRCLES,ENGRAVED
  IRIDESCENCE........................................... 985.00
TIFFANY PAPERWEIGHT,SIGNED,RED IRIDESCENT.................  95.00
TIFFANY PICTURE FRAMES,SIGNED,BRONZE,SAILING SHIPS.........  30.00
TIFFANY PIN HOLDER,SIGNED,ROUND,OPEN,SILVER SOLDERED DESIGN.  10.50
TIFFANY PLATE,5 IN.,BORDERED,STERLING SILVER..............  15.00
TIFFANY PLATE & FOOTED COMPOTE,SIGNED,YELLOW OPALESCENT
  PASTEL................................................ 225.00
TIFFANY PLATE ,SIGNED,6 IN. ,TURNED EDGE,GOLD IRIDESCENCE...  60.00
TIFFANY PLATE,SIGNED,BRONZE,9 IN. DIAMETER................  55.00
TIFFANY PLATE,SIGNED,GOLD WITH BLUE REFLECTIONS...........  97.00
```

```
TIFFANY SALAD SET,REPOUSSE DESIGN ON SHELL,DATED 1883........      95.00
TIFFANY SALT,3 FOOTED,BLUE IRIDESCENCE.....................      60.00
TIFFANY SALT,BLUE,SIGNED...................................      55.00
TIFFANY SALT CUP SIGNED LCT FAVRILE,CRIMPED BORDER,2 IN.....      48.00
TIFFANY SALT DIP,GOLD,THORN PATTERN........................     110.00
TIFFANY SALT DIPS,GOLD.....................................      75.00
TIFFANY SALT,FOOTED,SIGNED,GOLD WITH BLUISH-GREEN
   IRIDESCENCE.............................................      72.50
TIFFANY SALT,MASTER,GOLD INTO BLUE IRIDESCENCE,SIGNED.......     185.00
TIFFANY SALT,MASTER,SIGNED LCT,GOLD IRIDESCENCE.............      85.00
TIFFANY SALT,OPEN,GOLD,CRIMPED EDGE........................      65.00
TIFFANY SALT,OPEN ON 3 FEET,SIGNED,ROUND,GOLD IRIDESCENCE...      47.50
TIFFANY SALT,OPEN,SIGNED,THORN PATTERN WITH GOLD IRIDESCENCE      58.00
TIFFANY SALT,RUFFLED,MARKED................................      55.00
TIFFANY SALT,SIGNED,4-FOOTED,BLUE-GOLD IRIDESCENCE.........      75.00
TIFFANY SALT,SIGNED,FOOTED,GOLD & BLUE.....................      55.00
TIFFANY SALT,SIGNED,GOLD,THORN PATTERN.....................      48.00
TIFFANY SALT SIGNED LCT FAVRILE 617........................      30.00
TIFFANY SALT,SIGNED LCT FAVRILE,GOLD,BLUE RIM..............      69.00
TIFFANY SALT,SIGNED,RUFFLED EDGE,GOLD......................      65.00
TIFFANY SALT,SIGNED,RUFFLED,GOLD...........................      47.50
TIFFANY SCONCE,PAIR BRONZE WALL,SIGNED,GREEN FEATHERED LILY
   LITE..................................................     650.00
TIFFANY SCONCE,WALL,PAIR,SIGNED,3 GREEN LILY SHADES........     575.00
TIFFANY SCOOP,CHEESE,MARQUISE..............................      24.00
TIFFANY SCREEN,FIRE REFLECTOR,LEADED GLASS,BRASS FRAME......     110.00
TIFFANY SHADE ,18 IN.......................................      15.00
TIFFANY SHADE,LEADED,RED JEWELED & SCALLOPED,BACKGROUND SAGE     325.00
TIFFANY SHADE,LEADED,SIGNED,GREY,RED,PINK & BLUE...........     325.00
TIFFANY SHERBERT,4 IN. TALL,GOLD WITH BLUE HIGHLIGHTS,SIGNED     140.00
TIFFANY SHERBET SIGNED FAVRILE,GOLD,GRAPES & VINES IN
   INTAGLIO CUT...........................................     145.00
TIFFANY SHERBET SIGNED ,HOLLOW STEM,GOLD WITH IRIDESCENCE...     125.00
TIFFANY SHERBERT WITH TWISTED PRUNTS,SIGNED,GOLD IRIDESCENT.      70.00
TIFFANY SHOE HORN,STERLING SILVER..........................      25.00
TIFFANY SPOON,DEMI-TASSE,SET OF 6,SILVER WITH GILT,1916.....      35.00
TIFFANY SPOON,SOUVENIR,STERLING,THE HUDSON-FULTON
   CELEBRATION 1909.......................................      15.00
TIFFANY TAZZA,PEDESTALED,SIGNED,5 IN.,GOLD.................      95.00
TIFFANY TOOTHPICK,2 IN. HIGH,SIGNED,GOLD..................      75.00
TIFFANY TOOTHPICK HOLDER,SIGNED,BRONZE.....................      25.00
TIFFANY TOOTHPICK IN GOLD SIGNED LCT,DIMPLED,2 IN..........      95.00
TIFFANY TOOTHPICK,SIGNED,LILY PADS,BLUISH-GOLD.............      60.00
TIFFANY TRAY,BRASS,14 IN...................................      65.00
TIFFANY TRAY,BREAD,STERLING,MONOGRAM.......................      37.50
TIFFANY TRAY,CARD,GOLD BRONZE,SIGNED.......................      18.00
TIFFANY TRAY,PEN,SIGNED,ZODIAC PATTERN,BRONZE PATINA........      10.00
TIFFANY TUMBLER,SIGNED,GOLD................................     115.00
TIFFANY UMBRELLA HANDLE,STERLING...........................      10.00
TIFFANY VASE,5 IN.,PURPLE..................................      17.50
TIFFANY VASE,6 IN. HIGH,APPLIED LILY PADS,SIGNED,BLUE & GOLD     285.00
TIFFANY VASE,12 IN.,SIGNED FAVRILE,GOLD....................     120.00
TIFFANY VASE,BLUE IRIDESCENT,CLASSIC GREEK COLUMNAR.........     134.00
TIFFANY VASE,BLUE,PINCH SIDE...............................     285.00
TIFFANY VASE,BOWL TYPE,GOLD ART GLASS......................      30.00
TIFFANY VASE,BUD,6-SIDED,SIGNED............................      95.00
TIFFANY VASE,BUD,SIGNED,13 IN. METAL BASE,GREEN,GOLD,PINK...     125.00
TIFFANY VASE,BUD,SIGNED,JACK IN THE PULPIT TOP,GOLD & BLUE..     175.00
TIFFANY VASE,CONICAL,FEATHER DESIGN,SIGNED,15 IN.,BRASS BASE     245.00
TIFFANY VASE,FLOWER-FORM,SIGNED & NUMBERED,3 IN. HIGH,GOLD &
   GREEN.................................................     135.00
TIFFANY VASE,GOLD,14 IN.,METAL BASE........................     150.00
TIFFANY VASE,GOLD CYPRIOT,SIGNED,8 IN.,PURPLE HIGHLIGHTS....1,400.00
TIFFANY VASE,IRIDESCENT,SIGNED,GOLD & MAGENTA..............     265.00
TIFFANY VASE,JACK IN THE PULPIT,SIGNED,GOLD IRIDESCENT,BLUE
```

```
& RED............................................... 900.00
TIFFANY VASE,LILY PAD,SIGNED,RUFFLED TOP,GOLD
  IRIDESCENCE,BLUE HUES.............................. 285.00
TIFFANY VASE,MARKED LCT FAVRILE,GOLD.................. 165.00
TIFFANY VASE,MARKED LCT FAVRILE,GOLD DECORATED....... 400.00
TIFFANY VASE,MILLEFIORI,MINIATURE,WHITE FLOWERS ON
  GREEN,SIGNED...................................... 475.00
TIFFANY VASE,MILLEFIORI,SIGNED & NUMBERED,BLUE,PINK & GOLD.. 400.00
TIFFANY VASE,PAIR,SIGNED,11 IN.,METAL WALL HOLDERS........... 125.00
TIFFANY VASE,PAIR,SIGNED,11 IN.,ROLL OVER TOPS,GOLD & BLUE
  IRIDESCENCE....................................... 350.00
TIFFANY VASE,RED,4 IN. HIGH,FLARED TOP,BASKET SHAPED........ 850.00
TIFFANY VASE,SIGNED & NUMBERED,BLUE,APPLIED CURLED & REEDED
  EARS.............................................. 400.00
TIFFANY VASE,SIGNED & NUMBERED,BLUE GOURD SHAPED............ 250.00
TIFFANY VASE,SIGNED & NUMBERED,GOLD,CUT LEAVES IN GREEN WITH
  STEMS............................................. 500.00
TIFFANY VASE,SIGNED & NUMBERED,GOLD IRIDESCENT............... 175.00
TIFFANY VASE,SIGNED,4 IN.,BUTTERSCOTCH...................... 600.00
TIFFANY VASE,SIGNED,5 IN. HIGH,RIBBED...................... 310.00
TIFFANY VASE,SIGNED,14 IN.,EXPERIMENTAL,BLUE,RED & ENGRAVED
  GOLD.............................................. 650.00
TIFFANY VASE,SIGNED,16 IN. TALL,TRUMPET SHAPED,GOLD WITH
  BLUE.............................................. 275.00
TIFFANY VASE,SIGNED,BLUE,8 IN. HIGH......................1,000.00
TIFFANY VASE,SIGNED,BLUE,DOUBLE GOURD SHAPE................ 325.00
TIFFANY VASE,SIGNED,BLUE WITH DECORATED NECK,8 IN.........1,000.00
TIFFANY VASE,SIGNED,BUTTERSCOTCH.......................... 600.00
TIFFANY VASE,SIGNED,DECORATED,8 IN. HIGH.................. 175.00
TIFFANY VASE,SIGNED,DECORATED,IRIDESCENT DAMASCENE ON BLUE.. 525.00
TIFFANY VASE,SIGNED,DEEP CUFF NECK,12 IN. TALL.............. 225.00
TIFFANY VASE,SIGNED FAVRILE,5 IN.......................... 375.00
TIFFANY VASE,SIGNED FAVRILE,7 IN.,GOLD IRIDESCENCE.......... 150.00
TIFFANY VASE,SIGNED FAVRILE,10 IN.,GOLD,DECORATED........... 400.00
TIFFANY VASE SIGNED FAVRILE 1836,GOLD,8 IN................ 130.00
TIFFANY VASE ,SIGNED FAVRILE,CASED GREEN,DECORATED,GOLD
  FEATHER........................................... 410.00
TIFFANY VASE SIGNED FAVRILE,DOUBLE GORED,3 IN. TALL,BLUE.... 245.00
TIFFANY VASE,SIGNED,FLOWER FORM PEDESTALED,STRETCHED LEAVE
  DECOR............................................. 525.00
TIFFANY VASE,SIGNED,FOOTED,RIBBED,GOLD-BLUE................ 97.00
TIFFANY VASE,SIGNED,GOLD & GREEN WITH MILLEFIORI........... 600.00
TIFFANY VASE,SIGNED,GOLD & ORANGE DECORATED................ 950.00
TIFFANY VASE,SIGNED,GOLD,11 IN.,CAMEO & INTAGLIO GREEN
  LEAVES............................................ 650.00
TIFFANY VASE,SIGNED,GOLD & BLUE HIGHLIGHTS,15 IN............ 375.00
TIFFANY VASE,SIGNED,GOLD,BLUE,BRONZE ENAMELED HOLDER........ 310.00
TIFFANY VASE,SIGNED,GOLD,BUTTON PONTIL.................... 190.00
TIFFANY VASE,SIGNED,GOLD CYPRIOT,8 IN....................1,100.00
TIFFANY VASE,SIGNED,GOLD,FOOTED,GREEN LEAVES MEETING AT
  BOTTOM............................................ 165.00
TIFFANY VASE,SIGNED,GOLD IRIDESCENT,THREADED............... 125.00
TIFFANY VASE,SIGNED,GOLD WITH MILLEFIORI,4 IN............. 600.00
TIFFANY VASE,SIGNED,GREEN CAMEO CUT LEAVES ON FROSTED
  BACKGROUND,5 IN..................................1,400.00
TIFFANY VASE,SIGNED,GOURD SHAPE,CREAM WHITE WITH POLYCHROME
  FEATHER........................................... 435.00
TIFFANY VASE,SIGNED,MINIATURE,URN SHAPED,SILVERY BLUE....... 225.00
TIFFANY VASE,SIGNED,ORANGE,5 IN. HIGH....................1,000.00
TIFFANY VASE,SIGNED,PULLED GREEN FEATHER DESIGN............ 750.00
TIFFANY VASE,SIGNED,TRANSPARENT GOLD,GREEN & PURPLE
  PAPERWEIGHT....................................... 900.00
TIFFANY VASE,SIGNED,YELLOW IRIDESCENT,GOURD............... 159.00
TIFFANY VASE,STERLING SILVER TRUMPET SHAPED,PANELED SIDES... 45.00
TIFFANY VASE,TULIP,10 IN. HIGH,BLUE WITH GOLD............. 145.00
```

```
TIFFANY WATCH,GOLD & BLUE ENAMEL,GOLD BAND...................     200.00
TIFFANY WINE SIGNED FAVRILE,GOLD WITH SILVERY BLUE
   IRIDESCENCE.................................................     150.00
TIFFANY WINE,SIGNED,LILY PAD DECORATION.....................     100.00
TIFFANY WINE,STEM,SIGNED,GOLD IRIDESCENCE. ..................      69.00
TIFFANY WINE,STEMMED,SIGNED,PASTEL PINK.....................     325.00
TIFFIN WARE BOWL,BLACK SATIN FINISH.........................      15.00
TILE CALENDAR,1914,WITH SCENE...............................      12.50
TILE DOG POTTERY SIGNED RUBY,10 IN. HIGH....................     100.00
TILE,OCTAGONAL 6 IN. WHITE & GOLD POST OFFICE,SIOUX
   FALLS,S.D..................................................       6.00
            TIN, SEE ALSO ABC, TOLE, TRAY, STORE, ETC...............
TIN & COPPER MOLD,SCALLOPED.................................       9.00
TIN & LEAD WEATHERCOCK......................................      35.00
TIN BOX,BREAD,STENCILLED,7 X 7 X 11 IN......................       5.00
TIN BOX,CANDLE,WALL TYPE,2 STRAP HANGERS....................      45.00
TIN BOX,CANDY,EUROPEAN,MARBELIZED WITH OVAL PORTRAIT OF
   WOMAN.....................................................      16.50
TIN BOX,CIGAR,HINGED LID....................................       2.00
TIN BOX,CRACKER.............................................       8.00
TIN BOX,HINGED,STENCIL A GIFT...............................       8.00
TIN BOX,LUNCH,FOLDING,4 X 4 X 9 IN..........................      10.00
TIN BOX,LUNCH,PLAID.........................................       5.00
TIN BOX,MATCH,HANGING,WALL..................................       4.50
TIN BOX,MATCH,WALL,LIFT UP COVER............................       2.00
TIN BOX,MELACHRINO CIGARETTE................................       2.50
TIN BOX,MIRIAM,COLLINS & DEXTER DRY MUSTARD,HINGED LID......      15.00
TIN BOX,NBC CRACKERS WITH WINDOW............................      10.00
TIN BOX,ROUND,HINGED,COVERED,ASPHALTUM FINISH & STENCIL.....      15.00
TIN BOX,SOAP,OVAL,PARROT & FLORAL DECOR LID.................       1.50
TIN BOX,SPICE,6 ROUND CONTAINERS,GRATER.....................       9.50
TIN BOX,SPICE,COVERED,COMPARTMENTS & HANDLE.................       8.75
TIN BOX,SPICE,HANDLE AT TOP,2 LIFT UP COVERS,6 COMPARTMENTS.       8.75
TIN BOX,SPICE,LID,6 SQUARE SPICE HOLDERS....................      12.50
TIN BOX,STORE,COLOUR LABEL,YUKON MASCOT PARLOR MATCH........       8.50
TIN BOX,TINDER..............................................       8.00
TIN BOX WITH COVER PAT.FEB.1,1910...........................       1.00
TIN BREAD MAKER.............................................       7.00
TIN BREADPAN................................................       4.50
TIN BUCKET WITH BAIL & LID..................................       3.50
TIN CAN,FIVE GALLON MILK....................................       7.50
TIN CAN,HAZARDS GUNPOWDER WITH LABELS.......................       8.50
TIN CAN,KEROSENE,SPOUTED,FLUTED.............................       3.50
TIN CAN,MILK,2 QUART........................................       3.75
TIN CAN,MILK,PINT...........................................       2.00
TIN CAN,TOBACCO,TIGER.......................................       2.00
TIN CANDLE MOLD,12 TUBE,HANDLE..............................      32.00
TIN CANDLEBOX,WALL,10 IN....................................      45.00
TIN CANDLEHOLDER & TRAY,FOOTED..............................      12.50
TIN CANDLEHOLDER,CHRISTMAS TREE CLIP-ON,SET OF 11...........       4.75
TIN CANDLEHOLDER,PUSH UP....................................       4.50
TIN CANDLEHOLDER,TIN SAUCER PUSHUP,.........................       5.00
TIN CANDLESTICKS,PAINTED MUSTARD WITH RED HEARTS............       1.50
TIN CANDLESTICK,SIGNED SHAW,PUSH UP.........................      12.50
TIN CANNISTER,SPICE,7 CANS INSIDE...........................       5.00
TIN CAR WITH DRIVER,RUNABOUT,FLYWHEEL MECHANISM,RED COLOUR..      12.50
TIN CASE,CARRYING,FOR CLAY PIPE,MARKED......................       5.00
TIN CASE,CIGAR,3 CIGARS.....................................       2.50
TIN CASE,COMB...............................................       3.50
TIN CASE,COMB & 2 MATCH HOLDERS ON EACH SIDE OF MIRROR......       3.75
TIN CASE,VASELINE,STORE.....................................      14.50
TIN CHEST,DOMED,9 X 6 X 7 IN................................      28.00
TIN CHURN,19 IN. HIGH,8 IN. DIAMETER,DASHER TYPE............      17.50
TIN CHURN,WOODEN INSIDES, 14 IN. HIGH.......................       8.00
TIN COAL SCUTTLE
```

```
  3.00  TO.......................................................  18.00
TIN COFFEE POT
  2.50  TO.......................................................  10.00
TIN COFFEE POT,10 IN.,DUTCH,COPPER BOTTOM.....................  12.00
TIN COFFEE POT,HINGED LID,WOODEN KNOB.........................   6.75
TIN CONTAINER,MATCH,STANDING,4 IN. HIGH,CIRCULAR BASE.........   5.75
TIN CONTAINER,SPICE FOR STORE.................................  50.00
TIN CREAM SKIMMER.............................................   1.50
TIN CUP,1880 US...............................................   2.00
TIN CUP,FOLDING...............................................   2.00
TIN CUTTER,COOKIE,BEAR........................................   2.00
TIN CUTTER,COOKIE,CAT.........................................   2.00
TIN CUTTER,COOKIE,DIAMOND,HEART,SPADE & MOON..................   1.25
TIN CUTTER,COOKIE,DUTCHMAN....................................   2.00
TIN CUTTER,COOKIE,ELEPHANT,PENNSYLVANIA.......................  12.50
TIN CUTTER,COOKIE,FISH........................................   2.00
TIN CUTTER,COOKIE,HORSE.......................................   2.50
TIN CUTTER,COOKIE,LION........................................   2.00
TIN CUTTER,COOKIE,MAILMAN.....................................   2.50
TIN CUTTER,COOKIE,PONY........................................   2.00
TIN CUTTER,DO-NUT.............................................   1.25
TIN DIPPER,CREAM..............................................   2.00
TIN DISH & 4 INDIVIDUAL DISHES,PLANTERS PEANUT................   3.50
TIN DOUBLE BOILER,TOLEWARE....................................  17.50
TIN DUST PAN,SMALL............................................   3.50
TIN FLOUR SHAKER,GRATER & 2 SCOOPS............................   3.00
TIN FOOT WARMER,CARPET COVERED OVAL...........................   7.50
TIN FOOT WARMER,PIERCED,HEART DESIGN..........................  18.00
TIN FOOT WARMER,PIERCED,WOOD-FRAME............................  18.50
TIN FOOT WARMER ,WOOD TRIMMED.................................  20.00
TIN FORK......................................................   5.50
TIN KETTLE,WATER,COPPER BASE,PATENT 1871,STRAIGHT SPOUT.......  15.00
TIN LADLE.....................................................   5.50
TIN LANTERN,CANDLE............................................   5.00
TIN LANTERN,CANDLE,FOR CHRISTMAS TREE,4 PANES COLOURED GLASS     5.00
TIN LANTERN,CANDLE,FOR CHRISTMAS TREE,8 PANES COLOURED GLASS     5.00
TIN LANTERN,PIERCED,PAUL REVERE TYPE..........................  35.00
TIN MATCH CONTAINER,HANGING,ADVERTISING AMERICAN STEEL FARM
  FENCES......................................................   3.50
TIN MILK STRAINER,9IN. DIA....................................   3.00
TIN MOLD,CANDLE,4 HOLE........................................  16.00
TIN MOLD,CANDLE,6 HOLE........................................  17.00
TIN MOLD,CANDLE,8 HOLE........................................  15.00
TIN MOLD,CANDLE,72 HOLES...................................... 175.00
TIN MOLD,CANDLE,HANDLED.......................................  12.50
TIN MOLD,CHOCOLATE,CHICKEN....................................   5.50
TIN MOLD,CHOCOLATE,HOBBY HORSE................................   5.50
TIN MOLD,CHOCOLATE,HORN.......................................   5.50
TIN MOLD,CHOCOLATE,PIPE.......................................   5.50
TIN MOLD,CHOCOLATE,SWAN.......................................   9.00
TIN MOLD,PUDDING..............................................   4.50
TIN MOLD,RABBIT...............................................   4.00
TIN MUFFIN TIN,6 HOLE.........................................   2.00
TIN NUTMEG GRATER.............................................   3.50
TIN NUTMEG GRATER,HINGED LID..................................   3.75
TIN OVEN WITH SPIT,ROASTING...................................  65.00
TIN PAIL,BAIL-HANDLED,QUART,EMBOSSED ELEPHANT & PATENT DATE
  1881........................................................   4.00
TIN PAIL,PURE LARD,8 IN. HIGH.................................   2.00
TIN PAPER CLIP,IMPRESSED SPENCERIAN HORSESHOE.................   3.00
TIN PITCHER,PONTIPOOL,COLLARED FOOT,YELLOW,BLUE & WHITE
  FLOWERS,RED.................................................  12.50
TIN PLATE,10 IN.,BASEBALL.....................................   4.00
TIN PLATE,10 IN.,BASEBALL SCENE...............................   9.00
TIN PLATE,10 IN.,DUCKS RISING TO FLIGHT.......................   8.50
```

```
TIN PLATE,10 IN.,MOOSE-MOUNTAIN SCENIC.......................      9.50
TIN PLATE,10 IN.,OLD TIME BASEBALL ACTION SCENE.............      10.00
TIN PLATE,10 IN.,QUEEN LOUISE PORTRAIT......................      8.50
TIN PLATE,CHILDS,8 IN.,RABBITS RADIO PARTY..................      8.50
TIN PLATE,ELK IN CENTER DATED 1907,PHILADELPHIA.............      6.50
TIN PLATE,PORTRAIT..........................................      7.50
TIN POWDER FLASK,9 IN.,BRITISH COAT OF ARMS & BRASS PLATE
  1851 DATE................................................     14.50
TIN POWDER FLASK,POUND,HAZARD POWDER WITH LABEL.............      4.50
TIN POWDER FLASK,RUST RED PAINT,HAND HEWN WOOD STOPPER......      8.00
TIN RATTLE,FOR A GOOD CHILD,EAGLE,ABC,WHISTLE HANDLE........      7.50
TIN REFLECTOR..............................................      1.00
TIN RETABLO,HANDPAINTED,MEXICAN,RABID DOG BITING...........      7.00
TIN RIM EYE GLASSES IN CASE................................      1.50
TIN SCONCE,CANDLE,11 IN. HIGH..............................      5.00
TIN SCONCE,CANDLE,VERTICAL CRIMPED.........................     45.00
TIN SCONCE,CANDLE,WALL.....................................     45.00
TIN SCONCE,PAIR 7-BRANCH,ASPHALTUM-COATED..................    150.00
TIN SCONCE,WALL,18TH CENTURY...............................     42.00
TIN SCOOP,ICE CREAM,PATENT 1876............................      7.50
TIN SKIMMER................................................      4.00
TIN STEAM COOKER, 3 SECTIONS...............................      6.00
TIN STRAINER...............................................      5.50
TIN TEA CADDY,ROUND,EMBOSSED CHINESE FIGURES...............      3.00
TIN TEAPOT,HINGED LID OF BRASS.............................     14.00
TIN TOBACCO,UNION LEADER,5 IN..............................      3.00
TIN TOY,SINGING BIRD ON TREE BRANCH........................     20.00
TIN TRAY,4 IN.,TAFT-SHERMAN 1908,GRAND OLD PARTY...........     15.00
TIN TRAY,6 IN.,NATIONAL CIGARS.............................      3.75
TIN TRAY,CHIPPENDALE.......................................      7.00
TIN TRAY,JOHN HOHENDAEL BREWERY............................      6.50
TIN WATER COOLER ,HANDLES,BRASS SPIGOT,BLUE,20 IN. H.......     14.50
TOBACCO JAR,PORCELAIN ,AUSTRIA,3-SIDED,RAISED FIGURE NEGRO
  BOY......................................................     26.00
```

TOBY JUGS have been made since the seventeenth century.

```
TOBY JUG IN POLICEMAN DESIGN,BROWN,GOLD,BLUE & TAN.........     10.00
TOBY JUG,MAN HOLDING PITCHER & GLASS.......................    150.00
TOBY ROCKINGHAM 5IN. BROWN ON BUFF.........................     22.50
TOKEN,COAL COMPANY SCRIP,DOLLAR............................      4.00
TOKEN,LOVE ON SEATED DIMES.................................      5.00
TOKEN,LUCKY BUCK 1878 FROM BUCKET OF BLOOD SALOON VIRGINIA
  CITY,NEV.................................................      4.00
TOKEN,ONE FARE 1871 ,FRUITVALE R.R.CO......................      8.00
TOKEN,U.S.GRANT FOR PRESIDENT,DATED 1872,H.WILSON ON REVERSE   25.00
TOLE APPLE BASKET..........................................     12.50
TOLE BETTY LAMP STAND......................................     55.00
TOLE BISCUIT TRAY, SLEIGH ENDS, ORIG. DECOR................     23.00
TOLE CANNISTER,GREEN PAINT WITH YELLOW BANDS...............     12.50
TOLE CHANDELIER WITH 9 CANDLEHOLDERS.......................    550.00
TOLE,CHIPPENDALE TRAY,HANDPAINTED RED,YELLOW ROSES & MORNING
  GLORIES..................................................     39.00
TOLE FRENCH OVAL TRAY,HANDPAINTED OVAL MEDALLION OF
  APPLES,PEARS.............................................     39.00
TOLE NURSERY LAMP..........................................     20.00
TOLE PAIR CHIPPENDALE TYPE TRAYS...........................     12.50
TOLE PAP WARMER............................................     27.00
TOLE RED CANDLESNUFFER & TRAY,PONTYPOOL....................     48.00
TOLE SPICE BOX WITH GOLD DECORATION & LETTERING............     14.00
TOLE TIN PARADE TORCH ON STICK.............................      8.50
TOLE TRAY,BLACK OVAL.......................................      6.00
TOLE TRAY,PAINTED RED......................................      6.00
TOLE TRINKET BOX...........................................     14.00
TOLE,WATER COOLER,2 HANDLES,SPIGOT.........................     30.00
TOLEWARE CANISTER,PAIR.....................................     12.00
```

```
TOOL, SEE ALSO KITCHEN, STORE, WOODEN...................
TOOL,ADZ,FOOT.............................................     3.75
TOOL,ADZE FOR WORKING TIMBER,SHIPWRIGHT LINE..............    17.50
TOOL,ADZE,HAMMER LIKE,COOPERS............................      5.00
TOOL,ADZE WITH MAKERS NAME,29 IN.,CARPENTERS.............      8.50
TOOL,ANCHOR,SCHOONER....................................      50.00
TOOL,ANVIL,BLACKSMITHS..................................      37.50
TOOL,APPLE CORER,ALL-WOOD...............................       6.00
TOOL,APPLE CORER,IRON MARKED C.E.HUDSON..................      8.50
TOOL,APPLE DRYER,CHEESE CLOTH BETWEEN 3 LAYERS OF CROSS
 PIECES.................................................      20.00
TOOL,APPLE PARER,WOODEN.................................       6.50
TOOL,ARC MEASURE FOR SPOKES.............................      17.50
TOOL,AUGER..............................................       3.75
TOOL,AUGER,WOODEN HANDLE................................       2.00
TOOL,AXE,BROAD..........................................       4.00
TOOL,AXE,BROAD,CURVED HANDLE............................      12.50
TOOL,BARREL HOOD,PORK,HANDWROUGHT HOOK...................      6.00
TOOL,BELLOWS,BLACKSMITHS WITH CAST IRON FORGE HEAD.......    105.00
TOOL,BELLOWS BY BUFFALO DENTAL MFG. CO...................     12.50
TOOL,BELLOWS,BEE,A-1 ROOT CO. MEDINA,OHIO,PATENT 1907,COPPER
 TANK..................................................      10.00
TOOL,BELLOWS,FIRE,EMBOSSED BRASS,17 IN..................      28.00
TOOL,BELLOWS,FIREPLACE,EMBOSSED BRASS PLATE OF FIDDLER &
 DANCERS...............................................      27.50
TOOL,BELLOWS,FIREPLACE,MAPLE WOOD,14 IN. LONG,LEATHER & IRON  20.00
TOOL,BELLOWS,FIREPLACE,PINE,20 IN. LONG WITH IRON END......   22.50
TOOL,BELLOWS,FORGE,FOOT OPERATED........................      10.00
TOOL,BELLOWS,FORGE,HEAVY BOARDS,RED PAINT................      65.00
TOOL,BELLOWS FROM CHATEAU IN FRANCE,BRASS RELIEF FIGURES....   35.00
TOOL,BELLOWS,LATE VICTORIAN PERIOD......................      18.50
TOOL,BELLOWS OF BLACKSMITH,GIANT........................     125.00
TOOL,BELLOWS WITH HAND-HAMMERED BRASS ON TOP............      28.50
TOOL,BELLOWS,WOODEN FIRE SIDE...........................       8.00
TOOL,BINNACLE COVER,BRASS...............................      35.00
TOOL,BIT BRACE,IRON.....................................       2.50
TOOL,BIT BRACE WITH BRASS PLATES,WOODEN.................      18.50
TOOL,BIT BRACE,WOOD,18TH CENTURY,CHERRY WOOD CHUCK WITH WOOD
 SET SCREW.............................................      35.00
TOOL,BIT BRACE,WOODEN,BEECHWOOD WITH BRASS..............      14.50
TOOL,BORER,BUNG HOLE,FACTORY MADE,IRON..................       3.50
TOOL,BRACE..............................................       1.25
TOOL,BIT BRACE WITH BRASS PLATE,WOODEN,EAGLE PLATE ON TOP...   19.50
TOOL,BRANDING IRON,COPPER WITH IRON WROUGHT
 HANDLE,GEO.H.HALL.....................................      10.50
TOOL,BREAST PUMP & NIPPLE SHIELD........................       7.50
TOOL,BROAD AXE..........................................       3.50
TOOL,BROADAXE,A.CRUPPE,31 IN. CURVED LEFT HANDED HANDLE.....    9.50
TOOL,BROAD AXE,SIMMONDS,10 IN. FACE,23 IN. HANDLE........       9.50
TOOL,BUTTON GRIPS FOR REINS OF RACING HORSE.............       4.00
TOOL,CAGE,SQUIRREL,24 X 14 X 18 IN.,ONE PADDLE WHEEL.......    20.00
TOOL,CAN,OIL,2 GALLON,METAL FRAME,HANDLE................      17.50
TOOL,CAPPER,BOTTLE,1920.................................       5.00
TOOL,CHERRY PITTER......................................       7.50
TOOL,CHERRY SEEDER......................................       4.00
TOOL,CHISEL,HAND FORGED SLATERS.........................       2.00
TOOL,CHISEL,JOINERS.....................................      20.00
TOOL, CHISEL MALLET.....................................       1.50
TOOL,CHISEL,PINKING,IRON................................       2.00
TOOL,CHISEL,SLICK,WITHERBY CARPENTERS & FARMERS.........      18.00
TOOL,CHISEL,STEEL,OVAL..................................       2.00
TOOL,CHOPPER,FOOD,SINGLE BLADE..........................       3.00
TOOL,CHOPPER,HAND FORGED SINGLE BLADE,WOODEN HANDLE.......     3.50
TOOL,CHURN,BARREL TYPE..................................       8.50
TOOL,CHURN,BUTTER,PUMP,BLUE PAINT.......................      85.00
```

TOOL,CHURN,BUTTER,ROUND.	22.50
TOOL,CHURN,BUTTER,WOODEN.	12.00
TOOL,CHURN,GLASS.	8.50
TOOL,CHURN,UP & DOWN,23 IN. HIGH,LID & DASHER.	28.00
TOOL,CHURN,WOOD,SIDE WHEEL.	12.50
TOOL,CLEANING ROD,RIFLE,HAND WROUGHT,51 IN.	6.00
TOOL,CLIPPER DEVICE SHARPENS BAMBOO RECORD NEEDLES.	5.00
TOOL,COMPASS,ENGINEERS,POCKET.	3.50
TOOL,CORER,APPLE,BONE.	3.50
TOOL,CORER,APPLE,CLAMP-ON TYPE.	15.00
TOOL,CORKSCREW,FOLDING.	4.00
TOOL,CORN PLANTER.	2.50
TOOL,CORN SHUCKER MACHINE.	8.50
TOOL,CRANBERRY PICKER.	58.00
TOOL,CRANBERRY SCOOP WITH METAL TEETH.	20.00
TOOL,CRIMPER,GUN SHELL.	3.25
TOOL,CROZE,COPPER,REINFORCED WITH SHEET IRON.	17.50
TOOL,CULTIVATOR,WOODEN WHEEL,HAND.	8.50
TOOL,CURLER,MUSTACHE,IRON,9 IN. LONG.	20.00
TOOL,CURLER,MUSTACHE,STERLING SILVER HANDLE,MOTHER OF PEARL.	5.00
TOOL,CURLING IRON LAMP OF TIN,ROD HOLDERS.	17.50
TOOL,CURRY COMB FOR HORSE.	2.00
TOOL,CUTTER,WEED,PREDOMINATELY WOOD.	5.00
TOOL,DARNER,BLOWN OPALESCENT GLASS.	10.00
TOOL,DARNER,STOCKING,WOOD MUSHROOM SHAPED.	2.00
TOOL,DARNING BALL,STERLING SILVER.	3.75
TOOL,DARNING EGG WITH STERLING SILVER HANDLE.	9.00
TOOL,DENTAL,6 PIECE SET,1900.	30.00
TOOL,DOCTORS CASE,INSTRUMENTS.	27.50
TOOL,DOCTORS SATCHEL.	3.00
TOOL,EMBALMERS OUTFIT,TRAVELING,LEATHER SATCHEL,2 CASES INSTRUMENTS.	16.50
TOOL,EXTRACTOR,RIFLE BULLET,ROD TYPE TWISTED END.	2.00
TOOL,FIREPLACE TOOLS & STAND,BRASS.	10.00
TOOL,FLAIL,2 SECTION,FARM TYPE,WOODEN.	7.50
TOOL,FLAX WHEEL.	50.00
TOOL,FOOT STOVE,BOX TYPE,WOOD & TIN.	22.50
TOOL,FOOT WARMER,CREAM & BROWN RAISED LEAF DESIGN.	12.50
TOOL,FOOT WARMER,OVAL.	20.00
TOOL,FOOT WARMER,SOAPSTONE.	3.00
TOOL,FOOT WARMER,SQUARE WOOD FRAME WITH HANDLE.	13.50
TOOL,FOOT WARMER,SLEIGH,WOOD CASED SOAPSTONE.	8.00
TOOL,GAMBOL STICK,PAIR HICKORY WOOD,FOR SPREADING HIND LEGS OF ANIMALS.	5.00
TOOL,GIMLET FOR CARPENTERS.	3.00
TOOL,GLOVE STRETCHER,IVORY.	3.50
TOOL,GOUGE FOR WOOD CARVING.	2.00
TOOL,GOUGE,SET OF 7 WITH LIGNUM VITAE HANDLES.	10.00
TOOL,GRINDER,COFFEE,WALL,ARCADE.	7.50
TOOL,GRINDSTONE SEAT,PEDAL,IRON FRAME.	11.00
TOOL,GROOVER,WOODEN.	4.00
TOOL,GRUBBING HOE.	3.75
TOOL,GUTTING INSTRUMENT,FISH CLEANERS,INLAID PEWTER LEG.	10.00
TOOL,HAIR CURLER,ROD STOCK SCISSORS TYPE.	5.00
TOOL,HAME,HARNESS,PAIR,BRASS KNOBS.	6.75
TOOL,HAMMER,BELTMAKERS DATED 1874.	7.50
TOOL,HAMMER,RAP-RENCH & 10 IN. PIPE WRENCH.	5.00
TOOL,HAMMER,SHOE COBBLER.	5.00
TOOL,HAMMER,WOOD.	8.50
TOOL,HAND REAPER.	3.75
TOOL,HANDCUFFS.	8.50
TOOL,HATCHET HEAD,CRUDE HAND FORGED,18TH CENTURY.	3.50
TOOL,HEARING AID,EAR TRUMPET,SIDE TUBE.	7.50
TOOL,HELIOTELLUS ASTRONOMICAL APPARATUS PAT.1868.	110.00
TOOL,HITCHING WEIGHT,ROUND.	6.00

```
TOOL,HONE,WHETSTONE,6 IN.............................................   1.50
TOOL,HOOK,FISH,FLINT.................................................   4.50
TOOL,HOOK FOR BUCKET,SHOULDER,43 IN. LONG............................  22.50
TOOL,HOOK,HAY,METAL.................................................   1.00
TOOL,HOOK,ICEMANS...................................................   2.50
TOOL,HOOK,LOOM,WOOD HANDLED BRASS FERRULED..........................   2.00
TOOL,HOOK,S,TO HANG POT TO FIREPLACE CRANE..........................   4.00
TOOL,HYDROMETER IN HUMBLE TUBLAR TIN CASE,SILVER....................  17.50
TOOL,HYDROMETER OF SILVER IN TIN TUBE CASE..........................  17.50
TOOL,ICE TONGS......................................................   3.00
TOOL,ICE TONGS,IRON GRIPS...........................................   6.00
TOOL,ICE TONGS,WOODEN HANDLES.......................................   6.00
TOOL,JACK,AUTO......................................................   3.00
TOOL,JACK,BOOT,WOOD.................................................   4.50
TOOL,JACK,METAL WAGON OR BUGGY......................................  10.00
TOOL,JACK,RATCHET,TRUCK.............................................   3.50
TOOL,KNIFE,CHAMFERING...............................................  17.50
TOOL,KNIFE,DRAW,HAND MADE,BRASS FERRETS.............................   3.00
TOOL,KNIFE,DRAW,SPOKESHAVE,WOOD HANDLE..............................   3.50
TOOL,KNIFE,GREEN RIVER,12 IN. BLADE.................................  19.00
TOOL,KNIFE,HAY,33 IN................................................   4.00
TOOL,KNIFE,HAY......................................................   8.00
TOOL,KNIFE MARKED CLYDE,BEET KNIFE..................................  12.00
TOOL,KNIFE MARKED REVERE & CO.......................................  12.00
TOOL,KNIFE,TIMBER SCRIBING..........................................   3.00
TOOL,LAST,SHOE,WOODEN...............................................   1.00
TOOL,LAST,SHOEMAKERS................................................   5.50
TOOL,LEVEL,28 IN....................................................   6.00
TOOL,LEVEL,LONG ,WOODEN.............................................   5.00
TOOL,LEVEL,MAHOGANY,30 IN.,STANLEY,FULL BRASS BOUND & SIDE
  PLATES............................................................   6.50
TOOL,LEVEL,MAHOGANY & BRASS BOUND...................................   3.50
TOOL,LIGHTER,CIGAR,MANNING BOWMAN...................................   5.00
TOOL,LIGHTING DEVICE,FIRE,CIRCA 1860,TIN TUBE & TORCH...............  17.50
TOOL,LOG PICK.......................................................   2.00
TOOL,MACE...........................................................   9.00
TOOL,MAUL OR MALLET,STUDDED.........................................   7.50
TOOL,METRONOME......................................................   8.50
TOOL,MOLD,CANDLE,6 TUBE.............................................   8.00
TOOL,MOLD,CANDLE,8 HOLE.............................................  22.50
TOOL,MOLD,CANDLE,10 HOLE............................................   8.00
TOOL,MOLD,CANDLE,11 HOLE............................................  25.00
TOOL,MOLD,CANDLE,24 HOLE,PEWTER IN PINE BENCH....................... 185.00
TOOL,MOLD,CANDLE,24 TUBE............................................  49.00
TOOL,MOLD,CANDLE,35 HOLE,2 HANDLES.................................. 110.00
TOOL,MOLD,CANDLE,ROUND,12 TUBE,CONE & RING TOP...................... 165.00
TOOL,MOLD,CANDLE,TIN,4 BARREL.......................................  16.50
TOOL,MOLD,CANDLE,TIN,6 TUBE.........................................  16.50
TOOL,MOLD,CANDLE,TIN,12 HOLE........................................  22.00
TOOL,MOLD,CANDLE,TIN,18 TUBES.......................................  35.00
TOOL,MOLD,CANDY,PAIR,3 IN. HIGH.....................................  15.00
TOOL,MOLD,CHEESE,DUTCH,WOODEN.......................................  15.00
TOOL,MOLD,CIGAR.....................................................   3.50
TOOL,MOLD,CIGAR,20 HOLES............................................   8.00
TOOL,MOLD,CIGAR,WOOD,10 CIGARS......................................  18.50
TOOL,MOLD,JELLY,HAND MADE POLISHED COPPER,TIN LINED,2...............  18.00
TOOL,MOLD,MAPLE SUGAR...............................................  30.00
TOOL,MOLD,MAPLE SUGAR FROM NEW HAMPSHIRE,ROOSTER WITH FAN
  TAIL,WOOD.........................................................  35.00
TOOL,MOLD,MAPLE SUGAR,STRIP OF 8 CUT HEARTS ON BIRCH................  25.00
TOOL,MOLD,MAPLE SUGAR,PRIMITIVE DOUBLE HEART ON PINE................  25.00
TOOL,MOLD,MAPLE SUGAR,WOOD,6 PIECES.................................  35.00
TOOL,MOLD,POTTERY...................................................   6.00
TOOL,MOLD,SHOE,WOOD.................................................   2.00
TOOL,NAIL,20 HAND MADE FLAT IRON....................................   1.00
```

TOOL,NET TO KEEP FLIES OFF A HORSE,WOVEN CORD................ 6.00
TOOL,OILER FOR FARM ENGINE,BRASS............................ 5.00
TOOL,OILER FOR GAS ENGINES WITH REGULATOR,GLASS & BRASS
  RESERVOIR... 7.50
TOOL,OX SLING,10 FEET LONG FOR SHOEING HORSES OR OXEN....... 250.00
TOOL,PENCIL SHARPENER,CHIGAGO 1918......................... 4.00
TOOL,PENCIL SHARPENER MARKED AUTOMATIC PENCIL SHARPENER
  CO,PAT.1906.. 12.00
TOOL,PENCIL SHARPENER,TURNING CUTTING BLADES............... 7.50
TOOL,PICK,LOBSTER,2 PRONGED,EMBOSSED LOBSTER............... 3.00
TOOL,PICKS,NUT,IN ROUND WOODEN BOX,SET OF 6 METAL SQUIRREL.. 12.00
TOOL,PILL ROLLER OF A DOCTOR,WALNUT & BRASS................. 20.00
TOOL,PLANE,BLOCK,HIGH-SIDED................................ 3.00
TOOL,PLANE,BLOCK,WOODEN,10 IN. LONG........................ 5.00
TOOL,PLANE,CROSS GRAIN..................................... 4.50
TOOL,PLANE,HAND,WOODEN,6 IN. LONG.......................... 4.00
TOOL,PLANE,HAND,WOODEN,16 IN. LONG......................... 5.00
TOOL,PLANE,MOLDING... 9.00
TOOL,PLANE,MOLDING,SET OF 25............................... 40.00
TOOL,PLANE,PLOW,.. 4.00
TOOL,PLANE,PLOW,ADJUSTED BY WEDGES,BEECHWOOD............... 8.50
TOOL,PLANE,PLOW,FENCE ADJUSTED BY BOXWOOD NUTS,BEECHWOOD.... 12.00
TOOL,PLANE,PLOW,WOODEN WITH GROOVED BLADE FOR VENEER WORK... 5.50
TOOL,PLANE,PLOW,WOODEN WITH WEDGE ADJUSTED FENCE............ 7.50
TOOL,PLANE,SET OF 3 MAPLE WOODWORKERS MOLDING.............. 10.00
TOOL,PLANE,WOOD,31 IN. LONG................................ 10.00
TOOL,PLANE,WOOD,MAPLE...................................... 3.00
TOOL,PLANE,WOODEN,15 IN. LONG,LIBERTY BELL DESIGN ON METAL.. 4.00
TOOL,PLANE,WOODEN,20 IN.................................... 4.50
TOOL,PLANE,WOODEN ,22 IN................................... 4.75
TOOL,PLANE,WOODEN,22 IN. LONG,SIGNED ABBOTT................ 8.00
TOOL,PLANE,WOODEN,24 IN.................................... 5.00
TOOL,PLANE,WOODEN,28 IN.................................... 5.50
TOOL,PRESS,APPLE CIDER..................................... 8.50
TOOL,PRESS,CHEESE,50 IN. HIGH.............................. 15.00
TOOL,PRESS,CIDER... 45.00
TOOL,PRESS,LEATHER HINGED LARD BAG......................... 5.00
TOOL,PRESS,MEAT & JUICE,COLUMBIA,LANDERS,FRARY & CLARK...... 10.00
TOOL,PROTRACTOR BY BROWN & SHARPE IN VELVET LINED
  CASE,DRAFTSMANS.. 20.00
TOOL,PULLEY,MILL,LAMINATED WOOD............................ 12.50
TOOL,PUMP,TIRE,BICYCLE,HAND TYPE........................... 2.00
TOOL,QUILTING FRAME,1 COMPLETE............................. 12.00
TOOL,RACK,BAKERS... 199.00
TOOL,RACK,PIE COOLING...................................... 12.50
TOOL,RAKE,CRANBERRY,HAND-MADE.............................. 30.00
TOOL,RAZOR & STRAP & BLADE IN METAL CASE,1937 ROLLS RAZOR
  LTD.. 22.50
TOOL,RAZOR,ROLLS... 6.00
TOOL,RAZOR,STRAIGHT EDGE................................... 3.00
TOOL,RAZOR,STRAIGHT IN CASE,NAME ON BLADE HENRY CLAY........ 9.00
TOOL,RAZOR WITH STROPPER IN ORIGINAL BOX,KRISS KROSS........ 7.50
TOOL,REAPER,HAND... 2.00
TOOL,RULE,BOXWOOD,LUFKIN BRAND,DOUBLE FOLD,24 IN............ 5.00
TOOL,SANDER FOR POUNCE,TIN................................. 10.00
TOOL,SAW,HAND,13 IN.. 10.00
TOOL,SAW WITH 12 IN. BLADE & EAGLE STAMP,DOVETAIL.......... 4.50
TOOL,SCALE,BALANCE,2 BRASS PANS............................ 25.00
TOOL,SCALE,IRON,WHEELRIGHTS TRAVELLER...................... 11.50
TOOL,SCALE,LUMBER,45 X 20 IN.,10 SPOKED WHEEL ON ONE END.... 80.00
TOOL,SCALE,UNIVERSAL FAMILY,BRASS FACE,MOSS DECOR,PATENT
  1865... 12.00
TOOL,SCALES,16 IN.. 2.75
TOOL,SCALES,BRASS,GOLD..................................... 4.50
TOOL,SCALES IN CASE.. 18.00

```
TOOL,SCALES,KITCHEN...........................................  10.00
TOOL,SCALES,KITCHEN,WHITE MARBLE TOP,1906....................   6.00
TOOL,SCALES,POCKET IN CASE WITH 2 WEIGHTS,GOLD...............  12.50
TOOL,SCALES WITH BRASS PANS,KITCHEN..........................   7.50
TOOL,SCORPER FOR STAVE JOINTS,HAND FORGED....................   4.50
TOOL,SCRAPER,FOOT............................................  27.50
TOOL,SCRAPER,HOG,WOODEN CENTER,ROUND TIN DISC................   6.50
TOOL,SCRAPER PLANE IRON WITH ROSEWOOD SOLE...................   6.50
TOOL,SCUTTLE,COAL,DELFT HANDLES..............................  22.00
TOOL,SEALER,WAX,BONE-HANDLED,FORGET-ME-NOT...................   2.00
TOOL,SEALER,WAX,CROSS HATCH,INNER CHAMBER FOR SEALS..........   5.00
TOOL,SEPARATOR,CHINA,WHITE WITH BLUE & ROSE DECOR,MADE IN
   GERMANY..................................................  14.00
TOOL,SHAVE,SPOKE,2 HANDLED...................................   4.50
TOOL,SHEEP BRANDER,RAISED CT ,WOOD HANDLE....................   5.00
TOOL,SHOE LAST..............................................   5.00
TOOL,SHOE SHINE BOX,HINGED COVER,CARVED ENDS,IRON FOOT REST
   INSIDE...................................................  16.00
TOOL,SHOVEL,BREAD,53 IN. WOODEN PEEL OVEN....................  15.00
TOOL,SHOVEL,GRAIN,WOOD.......................................  45.00
TOOL,SHOVEL,STEAM,TIN,IRON WHEELS,20 POUNDS..................  40.00
TOOL,SHOVEL,WOODEN,HAND CARVED...............................  15.00
TOOL,SHUTTLE,WEAVING,HAND CARVED WOOD,11 IN..................   5.00
TOOL,SICKLE OR CORN KNIFE,FARMERS............................   6.00
TOOL,SINGLETREE.............................................   3.50
TOOL,SLICK WITH BLADE & MAPLE HANDLE WITH KNOB,30 IN.........  14.50
TOOL,SPEAR,FISHING,5 TINED...................................   2.00
TOOL,SPIKE,CAST BRONZE,SQUARE HEAD,MAINE SHIPBUILDING ITEM...   3.50
TOOL,SPREADER STRAP,COLOURED RINGS,12 RING...................  10.00
TOOL,SPUD,BARK PEELING,LOGGERS,HAND FORGED,18 IN.............   4.50
TOOL,SQUARE,BEVEL,ROSEWOOD WITH BRASS........................   3.50
TOOL,SQUARE,BUILDERS STEEL...................................   2.50
TOOL,SQUARE,TRY,ROSEWOOD WITH BRASS..........................   3.50
TOOL,STAND & 5 LASTS,SHOEMAKERS,IRON.........................   5.00
TOOL,STAND & LAST,SHOE REPAIR,COBBLERS.......................  20.00
TOOL,STEEL YARDS,3 PAIR......................................  10.00
TOOL,STOVE LID LIFTER,CAST IRON..............................   1.25
TOOL,STOVE-LIFTER WITH COIL SPRING HANDLE....................   1.50
TOOL,STRETCHER,GLOVE,BRASS,IVORY,7 IN........................  20.00
TOOL,STRETCHER,GLOVE,CARVED BONE.............................   3.00
TOOL,STRETCHER,GLOVE,PAIR,WOODEN.............................   5.00
TOOL,STRETCHER,SHOE,WOODEN...................................   4.50
TOOL,STRIKER FOR TINDER BOX,HAND WROUGHT.....................  15.00
TOOL,SURVEYORS OUTFIT CIRCA 1860,GURLEY & CO................. 135.00
TOOL,SWEEPER,CARPET,STENCILLED HARTMANNS COMBINATION SWEEPER    5.00
TOOL,TAPE MEASURE IN SHAPE OF ALARM CLOCK....................  18.50
TOOL,TELESCOPE,SHIPS,EXTENDED,17 IN.,BRASS WOVEN BAND........  75.00
TOOL,TONGS,ICE..............................................   3.00
TOOL,TONGS,PIPE,EMBER........................................   9.00
TOOL,TONGUE & GROOVING SET...................................   7.00
TOOL,TRAMMEL HANDWROUGHT.....................................  15.00
TOOL,TRAP,BEAR WITH CHAIN & RING,HAND FORGED.................  35.00
TOOL,TRAP,MOUSE,CAGE,WIRE....................................   6.00
TOOL,TRAP,MOUSE,TIN,E-Z MFG. CO..............................   3.50
TOOL,TRAP,OTTER.............................................   6.00
TOOL,TRAP,QUEEN BEE..........................................   4.50
TOOL,TRAP,RAT,WIRE...........................................   7.00
TOOL,TRAP,RAT,WIRE DOMED,17 IN. LONG.........................   6.00
TOOL,TRAP,RUSTY STEEL........................................   2.00
TOOL,TRENAIL OR JOINING PEG,TIMBER...........................   1.00
TOOL,TRENCHER,PLATEAU-EDGED GROOVED WOOD FLAT................  35.00
TOOL,VISE,SAW,CAST..........................................   8.00
TOOL,WARMER,BED,COPPER,BRASS & IRON..........................  32.50
TOOL,WARMER,BED,COPPER,WOODEN HANDLE.........................  65.00
TOOL,WARMER,CARPET WRAPPED TIN,WITH CHARCOAL.................  10.00
```

TOOL,WARMER,MUFFIN,TOLE DOUBLE SHELF........................... 35.00
TOOL,WASHBOARD,BENNINGTON-TYPE................................. 38.00
TOOL,WASHBOARD IN WOOD... 3.50
TOOL,WASHBOARD,OLD FASHIONED................................... 2.00
TOOL,WASHER,1911,PLUNGER....................................... 3.00
TOOL,WASHER-WRINGER CIRCA 1870................................. 10.00
TOOL,WHEEL BARROW,WOODEN....................................... 12.50
TOOL,WRENCH,FORD WITH SCRIPT................................... 1.00
TOOL,WOOD SANDER.. 7.50
TOOL,WOOL CARDER,PAIR... 6.00
TOOL,WOOL CARDER,WOOD... 1.50
TOOL,WHEEL OFF FLAX WHEEL...................................... 6.00
TOOL,WHETSTONE.. 6.00
TOOL,WINCH FOR DRAWING WATER OUT OF WELL....................... 28.00
TOOL,WINDER,.. 17.50
TOOL,WINDER,YARN,TABLE MODEL,IRON CLAMP TO FASTEN,20 IN.
   HIGH... 10.00
TOOL,WRENCH,BUGGY & WAGON...................................... 2.00
TOOL,WRENCH,BUGGY... 2.00
TOOL,WRENCH,MODEL T SPARK PLUG................................. 2.50
TOOL,WRENCH,PLOW,3.. 2.75
TOOL,WRENCH,WAGON... 2.00
TOOL,YARN WINDER.. 22.00
TOOL,YARN WINDER WITH COUNTER ,IVY............................. 27.50
TOOL,YOKE,30 IN.,WOODEN....................................... 30.00
TOOL,YOKE,NECK,BUGGY.. 2.00
TOOL,YOKE,NECK,HAND MADE,MAPLE SYRUP........................... 10.00
TOOL,YOKE,OXEN
   37.00 TO... 45.00
TOOL,YOKE,SHEEP NECK,HAND CARVED WOOD.......................... 5.00
TOOL,YOKE,SHOULDER,PINE,ROPES AND HOOKS ON EACH END........... 20.00
TOOL,YOKE,SHOULDER,WOODEN,FOR CARRYING WATER,BLUE............. 6.00
   TOOTHPICK, SEE ALSO OTHER CATEGORIES SUCH AS BISQUE,
   PRESSED GLASS,..
   SLAG, ETC...

*TOOTHPICK HOLDERS are sometimes called "toothpicks" by collectors. The
variously shaped containers made to hold the small wooden toothpicks are found
of glass, china, or metal. Most of the toothpicks are Victorian.*

TOOTHPICK,ALABASTER URN SHAPED,SCALLOPED TOP,FLOWERS........ 4.75
TOOTHPICK,ALABASTER,WHITE..................................... 3.75
TOOTHPICK,AMBER BARREL.. 8.25
TOOTHPICK,AMBER BARREL WITH BAND,SCALLOPED TOP................ 7.50
TOOTHPICK,AMBER CANE PATTERN,3 LEGGED KETTLE................. 12.75
TOOTHPICK,AMBER DAISY & BUTTON,3 FOOTED KETTLE............... 2.75
TOOTHPICK,AMBER DAISY & BUTTON ANVIL.......................... 12.50
TOOTHPICK,AMBER DAISY & BUTTON V ORNAMENT..................... 12.00
TOOTHPICK,AMBER GLASS CLEAR HOBNAIL TO AMBER TOP............. 8.25
TOOTHPICK,AMBER DIAMOND POINT AROUND BASE,PLAIN TOP.......... 9.25
TOOTHPICK,AMBER GLASS IN METAL HOLDER......................... 6.50
TOOTHPICK,AMBER HOBNAIL....................................... 7.25
TOOTHPICK,AMETHYST GLASS,BARREL SHAPE,RIBBED,SCALLOPED TOP.. 7.50
TOOTHPICK,AMETHYST GLASS,CHERRY WITH THUMBPRINT.............. 8.25
TOOTHPICK,AMETHYST GLASS,DELAWARE............................. 7.50
TOOTHPICK,AMETHYST GLASS,SCALLOPED TOP,THUMBPRINT........... 15.00
TOOTHPICK,APPLE GREEN,SOUVENIR................................ 5.00
TOOTHPICK,BEAR IN WELL,3 IN. HIGH,ROOF OVER WELL SHADED
   GREEN.. 7.00
TOOTHPICK,BISQUE BATHING GIRL READY TO TAKE A DIVE........... 8.75
TOOTHPICK,BISQUE DOUBLE,TAN,MARKED CZECHOSLOVAKIA........... 4.75
TOOTHPICK,BISQUE GIRL RIDING ON SLED,4 IN. LONG,MARKED...... 14.75
TOOTHPICK,BISQUE,RAISED FLOWERS ,JAPAN........................ 2.00
TOOTHPICK,BISQUE SATIN,2 IN. HIGH,FLARED...................... 3.75
TOOTHPICK,BLACK PIG SITTING,2 IN. HIGH,RING DESIGN........... 7.00
TOOTHPICK,BLUE BEAR HEAD...................................... 6.50

TOOTHPICK,BLUE BISQUE & SHELL WITH GIRL DRESSED IN WHITE.... 10.50
TOOTHPICK,BLUE DAISY & BUTTON HAT........................... 12.00
TOOTHPICK,BLUE FINE CUT ANVIL.............................. 12.75
TOOTHPICK,BLUE,FLARE TOP,WHITE ENAMEL FLOWERS & LEAVES...... 9.25
TOOTHPICK,BLUE GREEN DESIGNS,6 SIDED,3 LEGGED,3 IN. HIGH,... 7.50
TOOTHPICK,BLUE GYPSY POT & LID,DAISY & BUTTON.............. 4.50
TOOTHPICK,BLUE LINCOLN HAT,FINE CUT CROWN & UNDER
  RIM,ENGLISH HOBNAIL...................................... 9.75
TOOTHPICK,BLUE MILK GLASS,BEADED EDGE...................... 8.75
TOOTHPICK,BLUE SADDLE & BLANKET ON BARREL.................. 14.50
TOOTHPICK,BRASS,SHAPED LIKE MORTAR,2 HANDLES,MARKED ST.LOUIS
  EXPOSITION.. 4.75
TOOTHPICK,BULL,BROWN,MARKED AUSTRIA,3 IN. HIGH............. 14.75
TOOTHPICK,BUTTERSCOTCH COLORING,HAND HOLDING URN ,MARKED.... 12.75
TOOTHPICK,CARMEL,SLAG,SQUARE & FOOTED...................... 14.50
TOOTHPICK,CHINA,2 IN. HIGH,BASKET WEAVE BASE,2 TAN LUSTER
  STRIPES... 4.75
TOOTHPICK,CHINA BLACK RAVEN,SOUVENIR SARATOGA SPRINGS NEW
  YORK.. 8.50
TOOTHPICK,CHINA HAT,APPLIED FLOWERS........................ 5.00
TOOTHPICK,CHINA,MATCH HOLDER,RAISED DESIGN,2 SPRAYS OF PINK
  ROSES... 5.50
TOOTHPICK,CHINA,ORIENTAL MAN,WHITE COAT,GREEN VEST,YELLOW
  PANTS MARKED.. 7.75
TOOTHPICK,CHINA,OVAL,YELLOW LUSTER,GILT HANDLES,SHIP THE
  SHELL PICTURE... 4.50
TOOTHPICK,CHINA,PINK ROSES................................. 4.75
TOOTHPICK,CHINA,WHITE & PINK FROG.......................... 5.75
TOOTHPICK,CHINA,WHITE TO GREEN,DESIGN RAISED OF WHITE ON
  BLACK,GOLD.. 5.00
TOOTHPICK,CHINA WITH RAISED CHERRIES & LEAVES,GOLD TRIM..... 6.75
TOOTHPICK,CLEAR,2 IN. HIGH,GOLD,RAYED BASE,DIAMOND & ENGLISH
  HOBNAIL... 6.75
TOOTHPICK,CLEAR,2 IN. HIGH,NEW JERSEY TYPE PATTERN,SCALLOPED
  EDGE,GILT... 4.75
TOOTHPICK,CLEAR,2 IN. HIGH,SQUARE,WIDE GOLD BAND AROUND..... 5.50
TOOTHPICK,CLEAR,2 IN. HIGH,WIDE PANELS NEAR BASE........... 4.00
TOOTHPICK,CLEAR,3 FOOTED,RAISED SEMICIRCULAR INTERLOCKING
  DESIGN.. 7.50
TOOTHPICK,CLEAR,3 HANDLED,2 IN. HIGH,GILT,SCALLOPED EDGE,... 6.75
TOOTHPICK,CLEAR ANVIL...................................... 11.00
TOOTHPICK,CLEAR BARRELS WITH DIAMOND BAND.................. 2.75
TOOTHPICK,CLEAR,BOOK
  6.50 TO... 11.75
TOOTHPICK,CLEAR BOTTOM,RUBY TOP,SAWTOOTH TOP & BOTTOM OF
  RUBY.. 6.25
TOOTHPICK,CLEAR,BUCKET..................................... 1.25
TOOTHPICK,CLEAR,BULBOUS AT BOTTOM,BEADING,BAND AT TOP....... 4.75
TOOTHPICK,CLEAR,CANNON BALL AROUND BOTTOM,DIAMONDS IN CENTER 4.75
TOOTHPICK,CLEAR CIRCLE..................................... 4.75
TOOTHPICK,CLEAR,COAL BUCKETS,FROSTED STRIPE BETWEEN RAISED
  LINES... 3.75
TOOTHPICK,CLEAR,CORDOVA PATTERN............................ 4.75
TOOTHPICK,CLEAR,CUSPIDOR SHAPE,BEADED EDGE,CHAIN FOR HANGING 5.75
TOOTHPICK,CLEAR CUT GLASS,ROUND,DIAMOND SMOCKING........... 5.75
TOOTHPICK,CLEAR,CUT GLASS,SQUARE,RIBBED & FACETED.......... 6.00
TOOTHPICK,CLEAR DAISY & BUTTON CAT......................... 12.75
TOOTHPICK,CLEAR,DAISY & BUTTON,FAN TOP..................... 5.50
TOOTHPICK,CLEAR,DAISY & BUTTON COAL SCUTTLE................ 5.75
TOOTHPICK,CLEAR,DAISY & BUTTON GYPSY POT,3 FOOTED.......... 5.00
TOOTHPICK,CLEAR DAISY & BUTTON HAT......................... 8.00
TOOTHPICK,CLEAR,DAISY & BUTTON,SCALLOPED................... 6.75
TOOTHPICK,CLEAR,DAISY & BUTTON TALL HAT.................... 6.75
TOOTHPICK,CLEAR,DAISY VARIANT.............................. 4.75
TOOTHPICK,CLEAR,DOUBLE,TULIP EDGE.......................... 6.75

```
TOOTHPICK,CLEAR,ELEPHANT.......................................   16.50
TOOTHPICK,CLEAR,FINE CUT BAND IN CENTER.......................    2.50
TOOTHPICK,CLEAR,FROSTED RIBBON,SQUARE.........................    7.50
TOOTHPICK,CLEAR,GOLD BANDS & SCALLOPED TOP....................    5.75
TOOTHPICK,CLEAR,GRAPE PATTERN.................................    5.50
TOOTHPICK,CLEAR,GYPSY PATTERN.................................    4.50
TOOTHPICK,CLEAR,GYPSY POT,CANE PATTERN........................    4.50
TOOTHPICK,CLEAR,HAT,..........................................    4.75
TOOTHPICK,CLEAR HOBNAIL.......................................    2.00
TOOTHPICK,CLEAR,HOBSTAR.......................................    4.25
TOOTHPICK,CLEAR,HONEY COMB TYPE PATTERN.......................    3.50
TOOTHPICK,CLEAR,KEG,FINE CUT BAND IN CENTER...................    2.50
TOOTHPICK,CLEAR,MORTAR,BEADED UNDERSIDE BASE..................    6.50
TOOTHPICK,CLEAR,OVAL & PANEL DESIGN...........................    4.90
TOOTHPICK,CLEAR,PAIL WITH METAL BAIL..........................    6.50
TOOTHPICK,CLEAR,PANEL IMPRESSED ROSE IN BOTTOM................    4.25
TOOTHPICK,CLEAR,PANELLED......................................    4.00
TOOTHPICK,CLEAR,PANELED CANE PATTERN..........................    3.85
TOOTHPICK,CLEAR,PEDESTAL BASE ,CLOCK TYPE PATTERN.............    3.75
TOOTHPICK,CLEAR,PLAIN POT WITH BAIL...........................    3.85
TOOTHPICK,CLEAR,RAYED BASE,OVAL THUMBPRINTS...................    6.75
TOOTHPICK,CLEAR ,REVERSIBLE,PANEL TOP.........................    5.50
TOOTHPICK,CLEAR,RUBY FRONT MARKED MINNIE 1920.................    6.75
TOOTHPICK,CLEAR SADDLE & BLANKET ON BARREL....................    9.75
TOOTHPICK,CLEAR,SCALLOPED EDGE,THUMBPRINT AROUND RAYED BASE.     5.50
TOOTHPICK,CLEAR,SCALLOPED RIDGED EDGE,GOLD BAND...............    4.25
TOOTHPICK,CLEAR,SCALLOPED TOP & BASE,PANELLED.................    3.75
TOOTHPICK,CLEAR,SNAKE AROUND TREE STUMP.......................    6.50
TOOTHPICK,CLEAR,STAR & FINE CUT WITH FAN......................    4.75
TOOTHPICK,CLEAR,SWIRL & HOBNAIL...............................    5.25
TOOTHPICK,CLEAR,THREADED BASE.................................    2.75
TOOTHPICK,CLEAR  WITH RUBY & CLEAR PANELS.....................   12.50
TOOTHPICK,CLOISONNE,BLUE WITH FLOWERS.........................    7.00
TOOTHPICK,COPPER,ATTACHED BRASS SAUCER,MARKED ENGLISH.......      2.75
TOOTHPICK,COPPER,ATTACHED TRAY,...............................    4.00
TOOTHPICK,CRANBERRY TOP,CLEAR BULBOUS PANEL EFFECT BOTTON...     14.50
TOOTHPICK,CUSTARD GLASS,ADVERTISING WITTY COMPLIMENTS CA
   KEBBE & SON................................................    6.75
TOOTHPICK,CUSTARD GLASS,INVERTED BEADING,BAND.................    8.25
TOOTHPICK,CUSTARD GLASS RIBBED THUMBPRINT FLOWER & LEAF
   DESIGN.....................................................    4.75
TOOTHPICK,CUT GLASS
   7.50  TO...................................................   13.50
TOOTHPICK,CUT GLASS,SCALLOPED TOP,6 SIDED PAPERWEIGHT TYPE..     7.50
TOOTHPICK,DELFT PATTERN,BLUE SAILBOAT,RAISED FLEUR DE
   LIS,WHITE..................................................    9.50
TOOTHPICK,EMERALD GREEN PATTERN GLASS,RAYED BASE.............    14.50
TOOTHPICK,FLAT TRAY,SILVER & GILT,RAISED INDEPENDENCE
   HALL,PHILADELPHIA..........................................    3.75
TOOTHPICK,FROG,WHITE,3 IN. HIGH,GREEN & GOLD PAINT...........    4.00
TOOTHPICK,FROSTED DOG HEAD....................................   18.00
TOOTHPICK,FROSTED ELEPHANT WITH FOOTED BASE..................    15.00
TOOTHPICK,GREEN GLASS 4 LEGGED,BEADED SCALLOPED RIM.........     9.75
TOOTHPICK,GREEN GLASS,BULBOUS & FLARED SCALLOPED TOP,GOLD
   BANDS......................................................    5.85
TOOTHPICK,GREEN GLASS COLORADO...............................    8.75
TOOTHPICK,GREEN GLASS GYPSY POT..............................    5.50
TOOTHPICK,GREEN GLASS,PAKIN,BULBOUS BOTTOM,FLARE TOP.........    6.75
TOOTHPICK,GREEN GLASS PLAIN..................................    2.75
TOOTHPICK,GREEN SNOWFLAKE PATTERN,SCALLOPED TOP..............    5.75
TOOTHPICK,HARD RUBBER,4 LEGGED...............................    4.75
TOOTHPICK,HAT,HOLDER,ROYAL SAXE,GERMANY......................   10.50
TOOTHPICK,HORN ON WOODEN BASE WITH METAL WREATH AROUND EDGE.     2.50
TOOTHPICK,JAPAN,BARREL SHAPE,PINK FLOWERS & GREEN LEAVES....     1.25
TOOTHPICK,KETTLE,CHINA,3 FEET,MARKED DOMINION OF CANADA.....     4.50
```

```
TOOTHPICK,KINGS CROWN.................................   6.50
TOOTHPICK,LACY MEDALLION,CLEAR BOTTOM,RUBY TOP..............   8.50
TOOTHPICK,MAJOLICA,BASKET DESIGN,GREEN OUTSIDE,PINK INSIDE..   4.75
TOOTHPICK,MAJOLICA,DOG,DRESSED,CREAMISH COLOUR..............   9.75
TOOTHPICK,MAJOLICA,MATCH SCRATCHER ON SIDE,GREEN,BLUE &
  WHITE....................................................  14.85
TOOTHPICK,MAJOLICA,OBLONG,2 HANDLES,BROWN & TAN,FLOWERS IN
  RELIEF...................................................   5.75
TOOTHPICK,MAJOLICA,SIGNED,WHITE WITH GOLD DABS,JARDINERE
  SHAPE....................................................   6.50
TOOTHPICK,MAJOLICA,WHITE WITH FLOWERS & GOLD...............   7.75
TOOTHPICK,METAL,CHICKEN ON SIDE,SCALLOPED TUREEN TOP.......   4.50
TOOTHPICK,MILK GLASS BARREL WITH BOW.......................   6.50
TOOTHPICK,MILK GLASS,FAN SHAPE,CANE PATTERN................   8.75
TOOTHPICK,MILK GLASS FOOTED WITH SCROLL BASE & AROUND TOP...   7.75
TOOTHPICK,MILK GLASS ON BASE,CORNUCOPIA WITH SCROLL........   9.25
TOOTHPICK,MILK GLASS,SQUARE,FOOTED,RAISED DESIGN,SCALLOPED
  TOP,GREEN................................................   5.25
TOOTHPICK,MILK GLASS SWAN,3 HEADS MAKE HANDLES.............  11.25
TOOTHPICK,MILK GLASS UNCLE SAMS HAT........................   7.85
TOOTHPICK,MILK GLASS WHITE,SCALLOPED EDGE,SQUARE..........   7.75
TOOTHPICK,MUG,SILVER PLATE,MARKED KEEKUK ON SIDE..........   2.50
TOOTHPICK,OPEN CAR,COBALT BLUE,SOUVENIR OF WASHINGTON
  RADIATOR.................................................   7.75
TOOTHPICK,PAPERWEIGHT GLASS,TRIANGLE
  SHAPE,VARI-COLOURED,TURQUOISE IN.........................  45.00
TOOTHPICK,PARIAN TYPE,2 SWANS & BOY IN COLONIAL COSTUME.....  15.00
TOOTHPICK,PEDESTAL TYPE,FISHES DESIGN & BIRDS..............   8.50
TOOTHPICK,PIG IN BATH TUB,CHINA,GREEN,WHITE,TAN............  12.75
TOOTHPICK,PIG STANDING BESIDE GREEN GILT EDGED POT MARKED
  BAKED BEANS..............................................  12.75
TOOTHPICK,POMONA AMBER GLASS ,RAISED FLOWER,CENTER
  FROSTED,AMBER LEAVES.....................................  12.50
TOOTHPICK,PURPLE SLAG,OBLONG RIBBED BASE,FLOWERS & BERRIES..  15.50
TOOTHPICK,PURPLE SLAG,SQUARE,FOOTED........................  14.75
TOOTHPICK,RIBBED HAT,SATIN FINISH MILK GLASS...............  12.50
TOOTHPICK,RUBY MUG WITH CLEAR GLASS HANDLE MARKED JUANITA...   3.75
TOOTHPICK,RUBY THUMBPRINT,SOUVENIR,SYRACUSE 1906...........   9.75
TOOTHPICK,RUBY TOP,CLEAR BASE WITH CIRCLE & HOB............   6.75
TOOTHPICK,RUBY TOP,DATED 1903,CLEAR BOTTOM WITH UPSIDE DOWN
  HEART....................................................   6.75
TOOTHPICK,RUBY WITH CLEAR RIBS NEAR BOTTOM,CLEAR BASE,.....   4.75
TOOTHPICK,SHELL,BLUE LUSTER................................  12.50
TOOTHPICK,SHELL,BROWN & WHITE,FLOWERS & LEAVES
  PAINTED,SOUVENIR.........................................   4.85
TOOTHPICK,SHELL,GREEN & WHITE,SCALLOPED TOP,FROM LOS ANGELES   4.85
TOOTHPICK,SHELL WITH MARKED RAISED CARVED MATCHES PAN
  AMERICAN 1901............................................   4.85
TOOTHPICK,SILVER PLATE,FLOWER BAND AT BOTTOM...............   3.75
TOOTHPICK,SILVER PLATED,BEADED TOP,MARKED ROCKFORD.........   1.75
TOOTHPICK,SILVER PLATED,WILCOX SILVER CO,SCALLOPED EDGE.....   2.20
TOOTHPICK,SILVER COLOUR,SCALLOPED EDGE,SCRATCHING SURFACE...   2.65
TOOTHPICK,SILVER QUADRUPLE PLATE,FLOWER & LEAVES DESIGN.....   5.75
TOOTHPICK,SOAPSTONE OVAL,TREE STUMP ON ONE SIDE,BIRD.......   4.25
TOOTHPICK,SOFT PASTE BIRDS & MONKEY........................   8.00
TOOTHPICK,SQUARE,CLEAR TO BOTTOM,RUBY TOP..................   8.00
TOOTHPICK,STAFFORDSHIRE,CORSET,WHITE WITH FLOWERS ON FRONT..  18.25
TOOTHPICK,STAFFORDSHIRE,GREEN TOP,WHITE BOTTOM,BLACK ENDS...   4.50
TOOTHPICK,STERLING SILVER,MARKED UDALL & HALL.............   6.60
TOOTHPICK,STRIPPED GLASS,CLEAR & MILKY COLOUR.............  45.00
TOOTHPICK,SWAN,CHINA,BROWN,WHITE MOTTLED,,2 IN. HIGH.......   9.75
TOOTHPICK,THIN LEAF,2 IN. HIGH,WHITE WITH RAISED PINK
  STRIPES..................................................   4.00
TOOTHPICK,VASELINE GLASS DAISY & BUTTON HAT................   8.50
TOOTHPICK,VASELINE GLASS DAISY & BUTTON URN,PEDESTAL TYPE
```

```
BASE.............................................................  12.00
TOOTHPICK,WHITE CHINA OVAL,2 IN. HIGH,SCALLOPED TOP,GOLD,2
  HANDLED........................................................   4.75
TOOTHPICK,WHITE MILK GLASS 2 HANDLED PATTERN GLASS..............   6.50
TOOTHPICK,WHITE MILK GLASS COAL HOD WITH BAIL,SOUVENIR OF
  NIAGARA FALLS..................................................   5.75
TOOTHPICK,WHITE MILK GLASS FAN DESIGNS.........................   4.50
TOOTHPICK,WHITE MILK GLASS FLORAL..............................   4.50
TOOTHPICK,WHITE MILK GLASS HOBNAIL.............................   5.00
TOOTHPICK,WHITE MILK GLASS MILK BOTTLE.........................   3.75
TOOTHPICK,WHITE MILK GLASS TREE TRUNK..........................   7.75
TOOTHPICK,WHITE MILK GLASS UNCLE SAM HAT,STARS ALL AROUND...   11.50
TOOTHPICK,WHITE MILK GLASS URN,RAISED ROSES....................  14.00
TOOTHPICK,WHITE POTTERY,2 IN. HIGH,BULBOUS AT BOTTOM,GOLD
  BAND...........................................................   3.75
TORCH OF THE 1888 CAMPAIGN.....................................  10.00
```

TORTOISESHELL GLASS was made during the 1880's and after by the Sandwich Glass Works of Massachusetts and some firms in Germany. Tortoiseshell has been reproduced.

```
TORTOISE SHELL & INLAID IVORY TOP BROWN & WHITE BOX.........  16.00
TORTOISE SHELL BASKET,OPEN WORK,3 BRASS BALL FEET...........  18.50
TORTOISE SHELL CHINESE SNUFF BOTTLE,PEOPLE AND BUTTERFLY
  CARVED.........................................................  55.00
TORTOISE SHELL GLASS BOWL,FRUIT,9 IN.......................... 125.00
TORTOISE SHELL GLASS CUP WITH SAUCER,COVERED.................  45.00
TORTOISE SHELL ORNATE HAIR COMB...............................   5.00
TORTOISE SHELL TEA CADDY,SILVER SHIELD & FILLETS,CIRCA 1820. 165.00
TORTOISE SHELL TEA CADDY WITH WATERFORD MIXING GLASS........ 150.00
TOTEM POLE,7 FEET TALL,CIRCA 1870............................. 750.00
TOY,ACROBAT,WINDUP,WOOD & BRASS,AMERICAN MECHANICAL TOY CO..  75.00
TOY,AIRPLANE,IRON.............................................   9.00
TOY,AIRPLANE,TRAVEL AIR MYSTERY,IRON..........................   1.00
TOY,AMOS & ANDY WITH DOG IN OPEN TAXI,TIN,WIND UP............  25.00
TOY,AUTO,TIN,BUCKET SEAT,LONG HOOD............................  50.00
TOY,BASE BALL BAT,WHITE ASH,30 IN.............................   2.00
TOY,BATH TUB,TIN,CHILDS.......................................  25.00
TOY,BEAR,CELLULOID............................................   1.00
TOY,BED,BUNK,DOLL,WOODEN,2....................................  15.00
TOY,BED,DOLLS,FOLDING,WALNUT..................................  19.00
TOY,BED,DOLLS,FOLDING,WIRE....................................   5.00
TOY,BED,DOLLS,IRON,CATHEDRAL PATTERN HEAD & FOOT.............  23.50
TOY,BED,DOLLS,MAHOGANY 4 POSTER WITH COLONIAL HEAD & FOOT...  45.00
TOY,BED,HANDMADE DOLL,WOOD SPOOL,ROPE SPRINGS................  25.00
TOY,BEDROOM SET,TOOTSIE,METAL.................................  24.00
TOY,BED,WOODEN DOLL,WHITE & GOLD..............................   7.50
TOY,BED WARMER,DOLLS,HOT WATER,OVAL...........................   2.50
TOY,BENCK,FOLDING,DOLL,FRUIT WOOD.............................   6.50
TOY,BIKE & RIDER,TIN..........................................  12.00
TOY,BIRD IN CAGE,YELLOW CANARY,CELLULIOD,WIND UP.............  12.00
TOY,BIRD WHISTLE,LEAD.........................................   1.75
TOY,BIRD,WIND UP,TIN,DATED 1927,5 IN..........................   7.50
TOY,BLOCKS,NEST OF CARDBOARD..................................   5.00
TOY,BOAT WITH TIN MAN MARKED LINDSTROM,TIN...................   6.00
TOY,BOAT,WOODEN,KEYSTONE,B-15 U S BATTLESHIP.................   8.50
TOY,BOBBY,3 IN.,METAL,PALMER COX.............................   8.00
TOY,BOWL,CEREAL,HOPALONG CASSIDY.............................   1.50
TOY,BUBBLE PIPE,LEAD,HELMETED OFFICER........................   3.50
TOY,BUBBLE PIPE,LEAD,RABBIT...................................   3.50
TOY,BUGGY,CAST IRON...........................................  18.00
TOY,BUGGY,DOLL,WOOD WHEELS....................................  10.00
TOY,BUGGY,WICKER,DOLL,WIRE SPOKE WHEELS,RUBBER TIRES........  25.00
TOY,BUGGY,WICKER,IRON WHEEL...................................  75.00
TOY,BUGS BUNNY RUBBER DOLL....................................   4.00
TOY,BULL DOG,CELLULOID........................................   1.50
```

```
TOY,BUREAU,OAK,DOLLS,3 DRAWER,SWINGING MIRROR...............     15.00
TOY,BUS 8 IN.,TWIN COACH,IRON..............................     17.50
TOY,BUTTERFLY,FRICTION,ACTION WINGS,TIN....................      3.50
TOY,BUTTERFLY,GIANT,TIN,PUSH...............................      8.00
TOY,BUTTERFLY ON CAST IRON WHEELS,TIN & LITHOGRAPHED,PUSH
   TYPE...................................................      8.00
TOY,CALLIOPE WHISTLE,CHILDS,WOODEN,MULTI-TONED,MUSIC IN A
   SINNERS EAR............................................      7.50
TOY,CANNON,11 IN. SHOOTER,BRASS BARREL,IRON CARRIAGE.......     15.00
TOY,CANNON,IRON,7 IN.......................................     20.00
TOY,CAP GUN,IRON,COLT,PATENT JUNE 17,1890..................     12.00
TOY,CAP GUN,INVINCIBLE,50 SHOT,IRON........................      5.00
TOY,CAP PISTOL,8 IN.,1923 SUPER,IRON.......................      6.00
TOY,CAP PISTOL,CAST IRON,HERO,REPEAT ACTION................      8.00
TOY,CAP PISTOL,MODEL PAT. JUNE 17,1891.....................      7.50
TOY,CAP PISTOL,RONSON,TIN,1921.............................      6.00
TOY,CAP PISTOL,SPORT.......................................     10.00
TOY,CAP SHOOTER,ANIMATED,LIGHTNING EXPRESS.................     67.50
TOY,CAP SHOOTER CANNON MOUNTED ON WOOD,CAST IRON...........     20.00
TOY,CAR,1908 KLAXON,MOTOR DRIVEN,BRASS.....................     45.00
TOY,CAR,8 WINDOW,IRON......................................     17.50
TOY,CAR BY ARCADE,CAST IRON,4 IN...........................      5.50
TOY,CAR,CHARLIE MC CARTHY,WIND UP..........................     12.00
TOY,CAR,IRON,5 IN. HIGH....................................     10.00
TOY,CAR,MARX,DICK TRACY....................................      6.00
TOY,CAR,ROADSTER,CAST IRON,WHITE RUBBER TIRES,YELLOW BODY...    12.00
TOY,CAR,STREET,RED & YELLOW,STEEL..........................     35.00
TOY,CAR,TIN FRICTION COUPE.................................     12.00
TOY,CAR,TIN,SEDAN,11 IN. LONG,FRICTION.....................     24.00
TOY,CARRIAGE,DOLL,METAL,WOODEN WHEELS......................      5.00
TOY,CARRIAGE,IRON,OPEN,HORSE DRAWN.........................     28.50
TOY,CART,HOSE REEL,IVES,RED & GOLD WHEELS,2 HORSE,1 DRIVER..   225.00
TOY,CART,JAUNTING,TIN......................................      2.00
TOY,CAT,RAG STUFFED,11 IN. HIGH............................      6.50
TOY,CATCHERS MASK,BASEBALL.................................      5.00
TOY,CHAIR,DOLLS,PAIR.......................................      6.00
TOY,CHAIR FOR 8 IN. DOLL,WOODEN,STROMBECKER................      2.00
TOY,CHAISE LOUNGE,WOOD,DOLL................................     10.00
TOY,CHICKEN,FRICTION.......................................      7.50
TOY,CHINA CLOSET,DOLLS PINE,MIRROR ON TOP..................     16.00
TOY,CHINA CUPBOARD,CHILDS,HANDMADE.........................    160.00
TOY,CIRCUS ANIMALS,GERMANY,METAL,8.........................     35.00
TOY,CIRCUS,SCHOENHUTS HUMPTY-DUMPTY,4 CLOWNS,1 MULE,2
   LADDERS...............................................     32.00
TOY,CIRCUS SEESAW PERFORMERS,TIN...........................     12.00
TOY,COACH WITH HORSES MOUNTED ON BOARD,SCHOENHUT OF GEORGE
   WASHINGTONS...........................................     60.00
TOY,COFFEE GRINDER,LAP,DOLL,LITTLE TOT.....................     10.00
TOY,COW,TIN,MOOS...........................................      6.00
TOY,COW MOUNTED ON WOODEN BASE WITH WHEELS.................     18.50
TOY,COW WITH DEVICE TO MILK,COMPOSITION....................      6.00
TOY,CRADLE,DOLL,ASH WOOD WITH ROCKERS......................     12.00
TOY,CRADLE,DOLL,SPOOL,BLUE PAINT WITH BLACK................     11.50
TOY,CRADLE ON STAND FOR DOLLS UP TO 17 IN.,COLONIAL SWINGING     4.29
TOY,CRADLE,PINE,DOLL.......................................     12.50
TOY,CRADLE,WOODEN..........................................      3.00
TOY,CRIB,DOLL,HARD WOOD,WHITE..............................     12.00
TOY,CROQUET,4 MALLETS & 4 BALLS & WICKETS IN PINE BOX......     55.00
TOY,CUPBOARD,KITCHEN,CHILDS................................     27.00
TOY,CUPBOARD OF PINE,DISH,CHILDS...........................     85.00
TOY,DARKIES DANCING ON PLATFORM BOX,MECHANICAL,CLOCKWORK....    110.00
TOY,DENTAL CABINET WITH INSTRUMENT TRAYS,DOLL HOUSE.........    125.00
TOY,DINNER SET,LITTLE MAID PICTURE,PINK LUSTER BORDERED.....     35.00
TOY,DISH SET,25 PIECES,MADE IN JAPAN.......................     15.00
TOY,DISHES,HANDPAINTED,JAPAN...............................      4.50
```

```
TOY,DOG,CELLULOID...........................................  1.00
TOY,DOLL,BISQUE,2 IN.,MOVEABLE ARMS,OCCUPIED JAPAN..........  1.00
TOY,DOLL HOUSE,PAPER ON WOOD................................ 15.00
TOY,DOLL ON TRICYCLE,METAL,WIND UP.......................... 39.00
TOY,DOLL RIDING 3 WHEEL BICYLCE,MECHANICAL METAL,WIND-UP.... 37.50
TOY,DOUBLE BARREL DERRINGER CAP PISTOL MARKED NAVY,IRON..... 12.75
TOY,DRESSER,DOLL,4 DRAWERS.................................. 14.00
TOY,DRESSER,DOLL,PINE,2 FEET HIGH,SWIVEL MIRROR,3 DRAWERS...125.00
TOY,DRESSER,DOLLS VICTORIAN,WALNUT,3-DRAWERS,TIN MIRROR..... 35.00
TOY,DRUM MAJOR,TIN,WIND UP,13 IN. HIGH..................... 28.50
TOY,DUCK,TIN,FRICTION DRIVE................................ 11.50
TOY,DUCK,WALKING,WINDUP.....................................  3.50
TOY,DUSTPAN,DOLLS,TIN.......................................  2.00
TOY,ELEPHANT,CAST IRON,PULL................................ 10.00
TOY,ELEPHANT,TIN,WIND UP,3 IN..............................  7.50
TOY,FERRIS WHEEL WITH 6 CARS,TIN........................... 18.00
TOY,FIRECHIEF & SIREN COUPE,GIRARD,WIND UP................. 30.00
TOY,FIRE ENGINE & 2 HORSES,PULL,CAST IRON,STEAMER.......... 60.00
TOY,FIRE ENGINE-HOOK & LADDER,IRON,1 LADDER,1 DRIVER....... 40.00
TOY,FIRE ENGINE-RED ROVER,WOOD............................. 20.00
TOY,FIRE HOUSE,DOLLS....................................... 37.50
TOY,FIRE PATROL,IRON......................................145.00
TOY,FIRE TRUCK 10 IN. LONG,LADDER ON TOP,RUBBER WHEELS
    MARKED................................................ 15.00
TOY,FIRE TRUCK,IRON,ELEVATION AERIAL,WATER TANK WITH
    ELEVATED TOWER........................................ 50.00
TOY,FLAGMAN,LIONEL.........................................  4.00
TOY,FRYPAN,IRON............................................  2.00
TOY,FRY PAN,IRON...........................................  2.00
TOY,FURNITURE,2 PIECES DOLL WOODEN.........................  6.00
TOY,FURNITURE,DOLL,4 PIECES................................ 15.00
TOY,FURNITURE,DOLL HOUSE,PINE.............................. 50.00
TOY,FURNITURE,SET DOLL HOUSE,8 PIECES...................... 19.00
TOY,G.I.JOE,TIN,WIND UP,WALKING............................ 12.50
TOY,GOOSE,TIN,RED & GOLD,PUT IN MARBLE AND IT LAYS AN EGG...  8.00
TOY,GOOSE,WIND UP,MARX.....................................  7.00
TOY,GRAF ZEPPELIN,STEEL ON WHEELS,25 IN. LONG.............. 30.00
TOY,GUN,COPPER,BUCK ROGERS DISINTEGRATER...................  6.50
TOY,HEN,LAYING,TIN......................................... 12.50
TOY,HIGHCHAIR,IRON.........................................  8.50
TOY,HOBBY HORSE............................................ 12.00
TOY,HOOK & LADDER,3 HORSE,2 DRIVERS........................ 70.00
TOY,HOOK & LADDER,3 HORSES,4 FIREMEN....................... 75.00
TOY,HORN,TIN WITH PORCELAIN TIPS...........................  3.00
TOY,HORSE & COWBOY,METAL...................................  5.00
TOY,HORSE & SULKY,TIN,HORSE WOOD WITH TIN LEGS THAT MOVE.... 15.00
TOY,HORSE,IVES,BELL,BROWN,TIN,IRON HEART WHEELS............ 48.00
TOY,HORSE,MERRY GO ROUND WOOD SIZE OF LIVE PONY DATED 1870..350.00
TOY,HORSE ON WHEELS,TIN....................................  2.75
TOY,HORSES,PAIR RUBBER.....................................  4.00
TOY,HORSES PULLING AMMO TRUCK & CANNON,7 MEN RIDING,WORLD
    WAR I................................................. 87.50
TOY,HOSE CART.............................................. 25.00
TOY,HOUSE,FIRE ENGINE,LITHOGRAPHED TIN.....................  7.50
TOY,HOUSE,VICTORIAN DOLLS,WOOD,2 ROOMS DOWN,1 UP........... 59.00
TOY,ICE SKATES,ADULT,LEVER CLAMP...........................  4.50
TOY,ICE SKATES WITH CURVED RUNNERS DATED 1852..............  9.50
TOY,IRON,DOLL CLOTHES DATED MAY 22,1900....................  8.75
TOY,IRON IN SHAPE OF GOOSE WITH TRIVET,CHILDS.............. 12.50
TOY,IRON SHAPE OF SWAN,CHILDS..............................  3.00
TOY,IRON,STOVE,CHILDS,STOVE PIPE,SKILLET,KETTLE,TOASTER.... 25.00
TOY,KALEIDOSCOPE ON WALNUT TRIPOD BASE..................... 65.00
TOY,KIDDY CYCLIST,TIN,WIND UP.............................. 20.00
TOY,KITCHEN SET,TOOTSIE,METAL.............................. 24.00
TOY,KITCHEN,TIN............................................ 38.00
```

```
TOY,LAMB ON WHEELS,TIN................................................  16.50
TOY,LAMB,WOOLLY TYPE CLOTH,MOUNTED ON WOODEN ROCKERS.........  14.50
TOY,LAWN SWING,DOLLS,WOODEN..................................  15.00
TOY,LEAD SOLDIER,WORLD WAR I.................................   1.50
TOY,LEAD SOLDIERS,MATCHED SET OF 8 WORLD WAR I
   4.00  TO.................................................   5.00
TOY,LEAD SOLDIERS,SET OF 5,3 IN.,WORLD WAR I................   4.50
TOY,LEAD SOLDIERS,SET OF 10,CIVIL WAR.......................  10.00
TOY,LEAD SOLDIER,SET OF 12,WORLD WAR I,2 IN. TALL...........   4.00
TOY,LEAD SOLDIERS,10 MATCHED,WORLD WAR I....................   2.50
TOY,LOCOMOTIVE,STEEL,RED & GOLD,FRICTION....................  35.00
TOY,MAMMY,TIN,WIND UP.......................................   8.00
TOY,MARBLE,2 IN. CANDY STRIPE...............................  10.00
TOY,MARIONETTE,QUEEN VICTORIA............................... 150.00
TOY,MERRY-GO-ROUND FERRIS WHEEL,TIN.........................  32.50
TOY,MILL RACE,TIN,GERMANY...................................   7.00
TOY,MIRROR,HAND,DOLLS,BEVELLED GLASS........................   3.50
TOY,MONKEY,DANCING,MECHANICAL,CARVED WOOD FEET..............  85.00
TOY,MOTORCYCLE,HUBLEY,INDIAN................................  22.00
TOY,MOTORCYCLE,MAN RIDER,IRON...............................   7.50
TOY,MOTORCYCLE POLICEMAN,L.MARX.............................   6.50
TOY,MOTORCYCLE WITH RIDER,SELF KEY WINDUP...................   8.00
TOY,MOTORCYCLE WITH SIDE CAR,HUBLEY,INDIAN..................  12.00
TOY,MULE ON WHEELS,TIN......................................   2.75
TOY,PHONE,METAL UPRIGHT DIAL................................   3.00
TOY,PIANO INSTRUCTOR,SCHOENHUT..............................  12.00
TOY,PIANO,SCHOENHUT
   10.00  TO...............................................  22.50
TOY,PIANO,SCHOENHUT,CUPID DESIGN,6 IN. HIGH.................  22.50
TOY,PIANO,SCHOENHUT GRAND...................................  13.00
TOY,PIN BALL GAME...........................................   7.00
TOY,PISTOL,1932,SUPER CAP,HAMMER............................   3.00
TOY,PISTOL,CAP,NATIONAL.....................................   2.50
TOY,PISTOL,KILGORE INVINCIBLE 50 SHOT CAP...................   5.00
TOY,POPEYE EXPRESS,TIN,WIND UP..............................  14.00
TOY POPEYE PUSHING WHEEL BARROW,TIN,MECHANICAL..............  10.00
TOY,PORTER WITH SUITCASES,TIN,WIND-UP.......................  15.00
TOY,PRINTING PRESS..........................................  25.00
TOY,PUMPER-TYPE FIRE ENGINE,3 HORSES,IRON...................  45.00
TOY,PUNCH BOWL,CHILDS,2 CUPS................................  12.50
TOY,PUPPET SHOW 1910,18 HAND CARVED PUPPETS,WOOD & PAPIER
   MACHE.................................................... 400.00
TOY,RABBIT,EASTER,PETER,WOOD,FISHER-PRICE...................   8.00
TOY,RANGE RIDER WITH LARIAT,TIN,WIND UP.....................  18.00
TOY,RATTLE,MUSICAL,NURSERY,WOOD HANDLE,EMBOSSED WITH BOY &
   DOG......................................................   5.00
TOY,RIFLE,DAISY REPEATER AIR,BREAK ACTION,PATENT 1880-1891..  15.00
TOY,ROAD GRADER 12 IN. LONG,BRASS CHASSIS,CORRUGATED RUBBER
   TIRES....................................................  15.00
TOY,ROCKER,DOLLS............................................  18.00
TOY,ROYAL CANADIAN MOUNTIES,2...............................   3.00
TOY,SADDLEHORSE & TRAINER,TIN,19TH CENTURY.................. 165.00
TOY,SADIRON,CHILDS
   1.00  TO................................................  10.00
TOY,SADIRON,CHILDS,DOUBLE POINT.............................   3.50
TOY,SADIRON,WOODEN HANDLE,CHILDS............................   2.00
TOY,SEWING MACHINE FOR GIRLS 1922,SINGER....................  20.00
TOY,SEWING MACHINE,GERMANY,CHILDS...........................  10.00
TOY,SEWING MACHINE,GIRLS WITH ORIGINAL
   INSTRUCTIONS,BOX,SPOOL OF THREAD.........................  10.00
TOY,SEWING MACHINE,IRON,CHILDS..............................  12.50
TOY,SEWING MACHINE MADE IN GERMANY,HAND,CHILDS..............  10.00
TOY,SEWING MACHINE,SINGER...................................   8.50
TOY,SKATES,DUTCH WOODEN,BRASS TIPS IN UPSWING ENDS..........   6.00
TOY,SKATES,WOODEN WITH IRON RUNNERS.........................   4.50
```

```
TOY,SLATE WITH WOODEN BACK.....................................    7.00
TOY,SLED,BABYS PUSH............................................   18.50
TOY,SLED,CHILDS,WOODEN RUNNERS WITH METAL STRIPPING,BELLS....   16.00
TOY,SLED,DOLL..................................................   12.50
TOY,SLED,HAND MADE.............................................   30.00
TOY,SLED,RED,CHILDS............................................   12.00
TOY,SLEIGH,DUTCH...............................................  375.00
TOY,SOFA,DOLLS WHITE PAINTED,ROCKER & CHAIR...................   16.00
TOY,SOLDIERS MARCHING,2 IN. HIGH,12 MADE IN FRANCE...........   45.00
TOY,SOLDIERS ON HORSEBACK,3 IN.,MADE IN FRANCE...............   45.00
TOY,STAGE COACH MODEL..........................................   15.00
TOY,STATION HOUSE,LIONEL METAL,RAILROAD......................   22.00
TOY,STEAM ROLLER,WIND-UP,TIN...................................   17.00
TOY,STOVE,CAST IRON,VENUS,CHILDS,3 COVERS,HOT WATER TANK ON
   END.........................................................   22.50
TOY,STOVE,CHILDS,ELECTRIC,KINESTON LITTLE LADY...............   12.00
TOY,STOVE,GAS,IRON,EAGLE,BLUE & WHITE PAINT..................   28.00
TOY,STOVE,IRON,6 COVERS,ROYAL,SHOVEL,POTS,FRYING PAN........   34.00
TOY,STOVE,LITTLE ORPHAN ANNIE..................................    9.50
TOY,STOVE,POT,SKILLET..........................................   16.75
TOY,STOVE,TIN..................................................    9.50
TOY,STOVE,VENUS,CAST & TIN.....................................    5.00
TOY,STREET CAR,TIN,WIND UP.....................................   15.00
TOY,SUIT CASE,TIN,CHILDS.......................................    7.00
TOY,SURREY WITH FRINGE ON TOP,STANLEY,2 HORSE,DRIVER &
   PASSENGER...................................................   15.00
TOY,TABLE,CARD,EMPIRE,DOLLS,PEDESTAL BASE....................   22.00
TOY,TABLE,DOLLS OVAL WALNUT DROP LEAF.........................   24.50
TOY,TEAPOT,CREAMER,SUGAR,4 CUPS & SAUCERS,2
   PLATES,WHITE,CHILDS.........................................   12.50
TOY,TEA SET,CHILDS,WILLOW BLUE & WHITE........................    5.95
TOY,TEA SET,CHILDS,HANDPAINTED.................................   15.00
TOY,TEA SET,DOLLS,13 PIECES,BLUE & WHITE WILLOW LIKE DESIGN.    3.99
TOY,TEA SET,DOLLS,PINK ROSES ON WHITE.........................    8.50
TOY,TEDDY BEAR,WHITE...........................................    5.50
TOY,THE RANGE RIDER,TIN........................................   22.50
TOY,TIN DUCK,WINDUP,PAT.1924,LOUIS MARX......................   12.50
TOY,TOP,19TH CENTURY WOODEN CHILDS,HOLDING HANDLE WITH PULL
   STRING......................................................    7.00
TOY,TOP,1920 SYRO SPINNING WITH STAND & STRING...............    5.00
TOY,TRACTOR,STRUCTO,4 IN. X 8 IN.,1920 LINK TREADS,RUNS.....   30.00
TOY,TRACTOR,TIN,WIND-UP,GERMANY................................   18.50
TOY,TRAIN,AMERICAN FLYER WIND-UP ENGINE & 2 COACHES.........   15.00
TOY,TRAIN,CAST IRON,ENGINE,COAL CAR & 2 PASSENGER CARS......   35.00
TOY,TRAIN ENGINE,IRON..........................................   18.00
TOY TRIVET,HANDLED,CATHEDRAL...................................    4.75
TOY,TRIVET NO. 154 LACY DOUBLE POINT,IRON....................    3.75
TOY,TROLLEY,TIN,BLUE,5 IN. LONG................................    6.50
TOY,TROMBONE,KAZOO.............................................    2.00
TOY,TROMBONE,TIN...............................................    2.00
TOY,TRUCK,BRITISH TRI-ANG,WIND UP,2...........................   22.00
TOY,TRUCK,FLAT BED,IRON,3 IN. HIGH,9 IN. LONG................    7.50
TOY,TRUCK,IRON,CAST,RUBBER WHEELS..............................    6.50
TOY,TRUCK,LIFT,1938............................................   10.00
TOY,TRUCK VAN ADVERTISING WRIGLEYS SPEARMINT GUM,BUDDY L....   12.00
TOY,TRUMPET WITH 4 KEYS,TIN....................................    3.95
TOY,TRUNK,DOLLS,10 X 18 X 10 IN.,BURLAP FABRIC...............   12.00
TOY,TRUNK,DOLL.................................................   14.00
TOY,TRUNK,DOLLS WARDROBE,BROWN OILCLOTH COVERED,BRASS BOUND.   23.50
TOY,TRUNK,DOMED COVER,DOLL,GOATSKIN LEATHER & BRASS STUDDED.   18.00
TOY,TRUNK,HIGH DOME,DOLLS,4 COMPARTMENTS.....................   15.00
TOY,TRUNK,PINE,DOLL,DOME TOP...................................    7.50
TOY,TRUNK WITH DOLLS CLOTHES,BRASS TRIM......................   18.00
TOY,TUB & RUBBING BOARD,CLEAR GLASS............................   16.75
TOY,TURTLE,WALKING,WINDUP......................................    3.50
```

TOY,VENTRILOQUIST DUMMY,HAND MADE...........................	45.00
TOY,WAGON,1939 WORLDS FAIR SOUVENIR........................	1.00
TOY,WAGON & 2 HORSES & 1 MULE,IRON........................	18.00
TOY,WAGON,CAST IRON,PULL,4 IN. HIGH.......................	5.50
TOY,WAGON,CIRCUS,IRON,KENTON,HORSE DRAWN...................	59.50
TOY,WAGON,COVERED,IRON WHEELS.............................	11.00
TOY,WAGON,COVERED,WOOD WITH IRON..........................	18.00
TOY,WAGON,DRAY,CAST IRON..................................	47.00
TOY,WAGON,DUMP,2 HORSES,DRIVER,IRON WHEELS,EMBOSSED PANAMA..	95.00
TOY,WAGON,FARM,IRON,TEAM & DRIVER.........................	45.00
TOY,WAGON,FIRE PATROL,RED & GOLD,2 HORSES,3 MEN............	100.00
TOY,WAGON,IRON,4-WHEEL,STAKE,2 HORSES,DRIVER,RED BODY,YELLOW	75.00
TOY,WAGON,IRON...	9.00
TOY,WAGON,IRON,CONTRACTORS DUMP...........................	45.00
TOY,WAGON,IRON,STAKE,2 WHEEL,HORSE........................	40.00
TOY,WAGON,IRON,WESTERN,COVERED............................	49.00
TOY,WAGON PULLED BY HORSE WITH RIDER,2 WHEELS,IRON,COAL.....	15.00
TOY,WAGON,SHEFFIELD FARMS PULL............................	69.50
TOY,WARDROBE,DOLL,WOOD,2 DOORS,SHELF,RACK,2 HAND MADE	
HANGERS...	6.00
TOY,WASHER,CHILDS WRINGER-TYPE,WOLVERINE..................	10.00
TOY,WASH TUB,DOLLS,TIN,ROUND..............................	2.25
TOY,WHEELBARROW,TIN.......................................	3.50
TOY WHEELBARROW,TIN,RED PAINT.............................	10.00
TOY,ZEPPELIN DIRIGIBLE,IRON,5 IN..........................	6.00
TRAIN,#1688 PRE WAR LIONEL ENGINE TENDER,3 CARS,O GAUGE.....	12.50
TRAINS,LIONEL,IRON,GREEN,LOCOMOTIVE & 3 PASSENGER CARS......	35.00
TRAIN,O GAUGE AMERICAN FLYER,ORANGE & BLACK ENGINE &	
TENDER,3 CARS...	12.50
TRAY,1907 ROUND ADVERTISING...............................	18.00
TRAY,BUDWEISER,RED COATED MEN AT TABLE,ARTIST SIGNED........	12.50
TRAY,BUDWEISER,ST.LOUIS LEVEE IN EARLY SEVENTIES............	13.75
TRAY BUSCH BEER...	2.00
TRAY,KOPPITZ-MELCHERS,DETROIT,DATED 1911...................	18.50
TRAY STAG BEER..	2.00
TRAY,STORZ & SCHULITZ.....................................	3.00

TRIVETS are now used to hold hot dishes. Most of the late-nineteenth- and early-twentieth-century trivets were made to hold hot irons. Iron or brass reproductions are being made of many of the old styles.

TRIVET,& PRONGED C.I.ACORN HOOKS,RAISED S IN CENTER.........	1.00
TRIVET,18TH CENTURY HAND WROUGHT IRON,WOOD HANDLE,10 IN.	
LONG..	18.00
TRIVET,18TH CENTURY HAND WROUGHT IRON TRIANGULAR,RAT-TAIL	
HANDLE..	18.00
TRIVET,A.O.OF F...	11.50
TRIVET,ADVERTISING PSF CO.................................	3.00
TRIVET,BRASS 4 FOOTED,OPENWORK DESIGN MARKED CHINA..........	2.75
TRIVET,BRASS 4 LEGGED,ENGLISH,1830........................	28.00
TRIVET,BRASS,4 PEG FEET,SCROLL TOP TO CIRCLE IN	
CENTER,ENGLISH..	16.75
TRIVET,BRASS & IRON.......................................	12.50
TRIVET,BRASS,FOOTED,CHASED,SPIDER WEB,MARKED INDIA..........	4.50
TRIVET,BRASS FOOTED ,U S IN CENTER........................	3.00
TRIVET,BRASS,PEG FEET,POINTED END,ENGLISH.................	11.00
TRIVET,BRASS THREE LEG,CAST...............................	13.00
TRIVET,BRASS,WOOD HANDLE,IRON BAND LIP....................	8.75
TRIVET,CAST IRON,GEORGE WASHINGTON........................	27.00
TRIVET,CHILDS IRON..	6.00
TRIVET,CHINESE FOOTED BRASS...............................	4.00
TRIVET,COLEBROOKDALE CROWN & MALTESE CROSS.................	2.95
TRIVET,EAGLE HORSESHOE,G.A.R..............................	15.00
TRIVET,ENTERPRISE...	3.50
TRIVET,ENTERPRISE BAR.....................................	2.95
TRIVET,ENTERPRISE BIG E IN CENTER.........................	5.00

TRIVET,FIREPLACE,FOOTMAN,BRASS.................................. 85.00
TRIVET,FIREPLACE,FOOTMAN,STEEL.................................. 35.00
TRIVET,FIRESIDE,12 IN. HIGH,BRASS,3 IRON LEGS,WOOD HANDLE... 34.50
TRIVET,FOOTED BRASS,SLIDING,12 IN. LONG,OVAL.................. 10.00
TRIVET,HANDLED HEART WITH W..................................... 4.75
TRIVET,HORSESHOE & EAGLE,2.0.0.F. ODD FEWWOWS................. 10.00
TRIVET,I WANT U COMFORT IRON.................................... 7.50
TRIVET,I WANT YOU... 5.50
TRIVET,IRON.. 5.00
TRIVET,IRON,BEST ON EARTH...................................... 5.00
TRIVET,IRON,COLT.. 15.00
TRIVET,IRON,ENTERPRISE E....................................... 5.00
TRIVET,IRON,IRREGULAR SPIDER................................... 3.50
TRIVET,IRON,LACY RUN... 5.00
TRIVET,IRON,LETTER B... 4.00
TRIVET,IRON,MULE SHOE.. 3.00
TRIVET,IRON,OBER MFG.CO.. 6.50
TRIVET,IRON,ODD FELLOWS....................................... 12.50
TRIVET,IRON,PLAIN.. 1.00
TRIVET,IRON,SPIDER WEB... 3.50
TRIVET,IRON SQUARE,EAGLE & CREST.............................. 15.00
TRIVET,LANTZ 6... 3.95
TRIVET,LETTER H.. 4.75
TRIVET,MULE SHOE... 3.95
TRIVET,OBLONG WITH OPENWORK ,1 IN. LEGS,9 IN. LONG.......... 10.00
TRIVET,PAINTED ,SHAPE OF GAS IRON INSIDE,.................... 7.50
TRIVET,PLAIN IRON.. 1.00
TRIVET,ROUND,BRASS,OPEN HANDLES,ROOSTER IN CENTER,3 PEG
  FEET,MARKED.. 14.50
TRIVET,ROUND ON HALF IN. LEGS.................................. 6.50
TRIVET,RECTANGULAR PANEL WITH INITIALS H W.................... 4.75
TRIVET,U NEED IT,ROSENBAUM MFG. CO............................. 3.95
TRIVET,WOODEN HANDLE INITIALED SAD IRON TRIVET................ 9.00
TRIVET,WOODEN HANDLED,3 FOOTED,INITIALED...................... 10.00
TRIVET,WROUGHT IRON,ROUND HEART................................ 5.00
TRUNK,DOMED TOP PINE,DOVETAILED,13 BY 12 BY 24................ 30.00
TURKS-HEAD PUDDING MOLD,AMERICAN REDWARE POTTERY.............. 22.00
TYPEWRITER 1892... 40.00
TYPEWRITER,HAMMOND... 15.00
TYPEWRITER,OLIVER NO.5... 35.00
TYPEWRITER,OLIVER ,NO. 9,PAT.1912............................. 30.00
TYPEWRITER,OPEN KEYS,OLD PRINT TYPE OLIVER.................... 15.00
TYPEWRITER REMINGTON WITH TIN COVER........................... 20.00

VAL ST.LAMBERT CLARET PITCHER SIGNED,GREEN,FROSTED
  BACKGROUND.. 100.00
VAL ST. LAMBERT SIGNED OVAL BOWL,BLUE FLORAL MOTIF.......... 35.00

*VAN BRIGGLE POTTERY was made by Artus Van Briggle in Colorado Springs,
Colorado, after 1901. Mr. Van Briggle had been a decorator at the Rockwood
Pottery of Cincinnati, Ohio, and he died in 1904. His wares were original and had
modeled relief decorations with a soft dull glaze.*
VAN BRIGGLE ASH-TRAY,SIGNED,ROSE & BLUE...................... 35.00
VAN BRIGGLE BOWL,FLOWER,BLUE,SHAPE OF MANS BUCKLED SLIPPER.. 8.50
VAN BRIGGLE BOWL,SIGNED,2 SHADES OF BLUE..................... 12.00
VAN BRIGGLE BOWL,SIGNED,2 SHADES OF BLUE,LEAVES FALL OVER
  TOP... 20.00
VAN BRIGGLE BOWL,SIGNED,ROSE WITH RAISED PETALS,ROSE & BLUE. 25.00
VAN BRIGGLE FIGURINE,INDIAN MAID HOLDING WATER VESSEL ON
  SHOULDER.. 85.00
VAN BRIGGLE PLAQUE,INDIAN HEAD,OVAL,SIGNED,BLUE & GREEN..... 7.50
VAN BRIGGLE VASE,3 INDIAN FACES AT TOP,MAROON & BLUE,SIGNED. 50.00
VAN BRIGGLE VASE,4 IN.,SIGNED,LIGHT MATT BLUE TO ROYAL BLUE. 7.00
VAN BRIGGLE VASE,4 IN. TALL,BLUE WITH FLOWER & LEAVES,SIGNED 12.00
VAN BRIGGLE VASE,6 IN. TALL.................................. 15.00

```
VAN BRIGGLE VASE,BLUE.......................................    7.50
VAN BRIGGLE VASE,BOWL TYPE,SIGNED,MAGENTA WITH 3 BUTTERFLIES   15.00
VAN BRIGGLE VASE,PAIR INDIAN HEAD,SIGNED,MAROON REDS & BLUES  250.00
VAN BRIGGLE VASE,SIGNED,2 SHADES OF BLUE,RAISED LEAVES......   15.00
VAN BRIGGLE VASE,SIGNED,BLUE LEAVES ON ROSE................    4.50
VAN BRIGGLE VASE,SIGNED,BROWN WITH GREEN IN LEAVES AT TOP...   10.00
VAN BRIGGLE VASE,SIGNED,HANDLES,BLUE PETALS SHADED TO ROSE..   25.00
VAN BRIGGLE VASE,SIGNED,MAGENTA BOTTOM TO BLUE.............    12.00
VAN BRIGGLE VASE,SIGNED,MAROON & BLUE,WOMANS HEAD & BODY
  INSIDE....................................................  100.00
```

VASA MURRHINA is the name of a glassware made by the Vasa Murrhina Art Glass Company of Sandwich, Massachusetts, about 1884. The glassware was transparent and was imbedded wtih small pieces of colored glass and metallic flakes. Some of the pieces were cased. The same type of glass was made in England. Collectors often confuse vasa murrhina glass with adventurine, spatter, or spangle glass. There is much confusion about what actually was made by the Vasa Murrhina factory.

```
VASA MURRHINA BASKET OVAL BASKET,PINK......................   58.00
VASA MURRHINA BASKET,PINK BORDER ,SILVER MICA,CRYSTAL LOOPED
  HANDLE....................................................   35.00
VASA MURRHINA BASKET,YELLOW,PURPLE,GOLD....................    35.00
VASA MURRHINA BLUE BASKET,SILVER MICA.....................     38.00
VASA MURRHINA CREAMER & OPEN SUGAR,GREEN,PINK &
  WHITE,CRYSTAL FEET........................................   35.00
VASA MURRHINA ROSE BOWL,BLUE WITH SILVER FLAKES............    35.00
VASA MURRHINA ROSEBOWL,FOOTED,MELON RIBBED SWIRL...........    45.00
VASA MURRHINA TUMBLER,BLUE,RED,PINK & GOLD,WHITE LINING....    17.50
VASA MURRHINA TUMBLER,YELLOW OUTSIDE WITH GOLD FLECKS.......   30.00
VASA MURRHINA URN VASE,9 IN. TALL,PEDESTAL
  BASE,GREEN,WHITE,OX-BLOOD.................................   28.00
VASA MURRHINA VASE,CASED,ROBINS EGG BLUE,MELON SHAPED BASE..   35.00
VASA MURRHINA VASE,JACK IN THE PULPIT,BLUE,6 IN. TALL.......   55.00
VASA MURRHINA VASE,MULTI-COLOURED SHARDS,SILVER MICA &
  OVERLAY,9 IN..............................................   42.50
VASA MURRHINA VASE,PAIR 9 IN.,MULTI-COLOURED SHARDS WITH
  SILVER...................................................    75.00
VASE MURRHINA VASE,PAIR 11 IN.,PINK,GREEN,YELLOW ,MAROON &
  SILVER...................................................    85.00
VASE MURRHINA VASE,PAIR,SWIRLED,CRANBERRY INSIDE,GOLD
  FLECKED..................................................    85.00
VASA MURRHINA VASE,PINK,7 IN.,SILVER MICA..................    28.00
VASA MURRHINA VASE,PINK,WHITE LINING,SILVER FLECKS.........    37.00
VASA MURRHINA VASE,ROBINS EGG BLUE,MELON SHAPED BASE.......    35.00
VASA MURRHINA VASE,RUFFLED TOP,PINK CASED IN WHITE BLOWN
  SILVER MICA..............................................    65.00
VASA MURRHINA VASE,SPANGLED,OXBLOOD WITH WHITE OPALESCENT
  FLECKS...................................................    47.00
```

VASELINE GLASS is a greenish yellow glassware resembling petroleum jelly. It is not an indication of age, and some vaseline glass is still being made in old and new styles. Pressed glass of the 1870's was often made of vaseline-colored glass. The old glass was made with uranium, but the reproductions are being colored in a different way. (See PRESSED GLASS for more information about patterns that were also made of vaseline-colored glass.)

```
VASELINE GLASS BASKET,BLOWN,RUFFLED & CRIMPED EDGE.........    22.00
VASELINE GLASS BERRY BOWL,SET OF 3,DAISY & BUTTON.........     25.00
VASELINE GLASS BERRY SET,7 PIECES,DAISY & BUTTON,TRI-CORN
  SHAPE....................................................    65.00
VASELINE GLASS BOTTLE,BLOWN STOPPER.......................      9.00
VASELINE GLASS BOTTLE,COLOGNE.............................     10.00
VASELINE GLASS BOWL,4 X 9 IN.,LEMON YELLOW,WHITE EDGE......    20.00
VASELINE GLASS BOWL,9 IN.,IMPERIAL JEWELS.................      7.50
VASELINE GLASS BOWL,BERRY,MOON & STAR....................      10.50
VASELINE GLASS BOWL,FINGER,DAISY & BUTTON WITH V ORNAMENT...   10.75
```

```
VASELINE GLASS BOWL,FLAT,2 PANELED..........................   12.50
VASELINE GLASS BOWL,FOOTED..................................   20.00
VASELINE GLASS BOWL,FOOTED,DAISY & BUTTON WITH CROSSBARS....   12.50
VASELINE GLASS BOWL,FOOTED,DIAMOND QUILTED..................   15.00
VASELINE GLASS BOWL,FOOTED,ROSE SPRIG,SCALLOPED.............   12.50
VASELINE GLASS BOWL,SET OF 8 TRI-CORNERED SHAPED,DAISY &
 BUTTON....................................................   65.00
VASELINE GLASS BOWL,WASTE,DAISY & BUTTON WITH THUMBPRINT....   18.50
VASELINE GLASS BOWL,WASTE,DIAMOND QUILTED..................   18.50
VASELINE GLASS BOWL,WASTE,WILDFLOWER........................   17.50
VASELINE GLASS BUTTER,COVERED,ROPE & THUMBPRINT.............   28.50
VASELINE GLASS BUTTER,COVERED,SUGAR,CREAMER & SPOONER,PALM
 BEACH.....................................................   95.00
VASELINE GLASS BUTTER DISH,CLEAR TOP........................   25.00
VASELINE GLASS BUTTER DISH,COVERED,OPALESCENT,SCALLOPED EDGE   15.00
VASELINE GLASS BUTTER DISH,PLEAT & PANEL....................   18.50
VASELINE GLASS CAKE SERVER,LOOP HANDLE,CUT FLOWERS & LEAVES.   22.50
VASELINE GLASS CAKESTAND,11 IN..............................   35.00
VASELINE GLASS CANDLE HOLDER,NAILSEA,5 IN. TALL,CUP BASE....  125.00
VASELINE GLASS CANDLESTICK,7 IN.............................   37.50
VASELINE GLASS CANDLESTICK,PAIR 7 IN.,OCTAGON SHAPE.........   25.00
VASELINE GLASS CANDLESTICK,PAIR,8 IN.,TWISTED STEMS.........   15.00
VASELINE GLASS CANDLESTICK,PAIR,OCTAGONAL SHAPE.............   18.00
VASELINE GLASS CANDLESTICK,PAIR SANDWICH,FLINT..............   66.00
VASELINE GLASS CANDLESTICK,PAIR,TWIST STEM..................   45.00
VASELINE GLASS CANDLESTICK,ROSE SPRIG.......................   27.50
VASELINE GLASS CANOE,DAISY & BUTTON.........................   22.00
VASELINE GLASS CASTOR,PICKLE,IN SILVER PLATED HOLDER,DAISY &
 BUTTON....................................................   35.00
VASELINE GLASS CASTOR,PICKLE,SILVER PLATE FRAME WITH
 TONGS,DAISY BUTTON........................................   65.00
VASELINE GLASS CASTOR SET,4 BOTTLE,.........................   57.50
VASELINE GLASS CELERY,DAISY & BUTTON WITH CROSSBAR..........   22.50
VASELINE GLASS CELERY,ROSE SPRIG............................   16.50
VASELINE GLASS COMPOTE,BLOWN,PURPLE APPLIED TO LIP,BASE.....   18.00
VASELINE GLASS COMPOTE,CANDY,OPALESCENT,SCALLOPED EDGE......   15.00
VASELINE GLASS COMPOTE,COVERED,FOOTED,RAINDROP..............   14.00
VASELINE GLASS COMPOTE,OPEN,THOUSAND EYE....................   30.00
VASELINE GLASS COMPOTE,OPALESCENT,4 WAY STEM................   10.00
VASELINE GLASS COMPOTE,OPALESCENT HOBNAIL,RUFFLED...........   25.00
VASELINE GLASS COMPOTE,ROUND................................   37.50
VASELINE GLASS COMPOTE,SQUARE,DAISY & BUTTON WITH THUMBPRINT   45.00
VASELINE GLASS CONSOLE SET,CANDLESTICKS & BOWL..............   25.00
VASELINE GLASS CREAMER,LION LEG.............................   27.50
VASELINE GLASS CREAMER,PRESSED DIAMOND PATTERN..............   22.00
VASELINE GLASS DISH,BASKET,OPALESCENT HOBNAIL...............    3.75
VASELINE GLASS DISH,CANDY,8 IN. DIAMETER....................    3.00
VASELINE GLASS DISH,CANDY,ARGONAUT SHELL,ON STANDARD........   22.50
VASELINE GLASS DISH,CANDY,DIVIDED,NICKEL STAND..............   10.00
VASELINE GLASS DISH,CANDY,FOOTED,6 IN. DIAMETER.............    4.00
VASELINE GLASS DISH,CANDY,FOOTED,OPALESCENT.................   12.50
VASELINE GLASS DISH,COVERED,DAISY & STAR....................   35.00
VASELINE GLASS DISH,MEDALLION...............................   12.20
VASELINE GLASS DISH,PEDESTAL,OPALESCENT.....................    8.00
VASELINE GLASS DISH,PEDESTAL,SEAWEED & SHELL PATTERN ON BASE    8.00
VASELINE GLASS DISH,ROUND,4 SECTIONS........................    3.00
VASELINE GLASS DISH,SAUCE,2-PANELED FLAT....................    3.60
VASELINE GLASS DISH,SAUCE,PANELLED DAISY & BUTTON CLOVER
 LEAF......................................................    2.00
VASELINE GLASS DISH SAUCE,ROUND DAISY & BUTTON.............    4.00
VASELINE GLASS DISH,SAUCE,SQUARE,FOOTED,PANELED & CANE......    5.50
VASELINE GLASS EPERGNE,REEDED,OPALESCENT EDGES,3 JACK IN
 PULPIT LILIES.............................................   65.00
VASELINE GLASS GOBLET,2-PANELED.............................    9.00
VASELINE GLASS GOBLET,BASKETWEAVE...........................   15.00
```

```
VASELINE GLASS GOBLET,DAISY & BUTTON WITH CROSSBAR..........    21.50
VASELINE GLASS GOBLET,DIAMOND QUILTED.......................    15.00
VASELINE GLASS GOBLET,FINE CUT..............................    15.00
VASELINE GLASS GOBLET,FINE CUT & PANEL,CANE.................    10.50
VASELINE GLASS GOBLET,INVERTED THUMBPRINT...................     8.50
VASELINE GLASS GOBLET,OHIO THUMBPRINT.......................    15.00
VASELINE GLASS GOBLET,PEDESTALED,BERRY & LEAF DECOR.........    29.00
VASELINE GLASS GOBLET,SHORT STEM,CLEAR BASE,NARROW PANEL....     3.00
VASELINE GLASS GOBLET,WATER,INVERTED THUMBPRINT.............    15.00
VASELINE GLASS GUM STAND,BEECH NUT..........................     8.00
VASELINE GLASS GUM STAND,TEABERRY...........................     7.50
VASELINE GLASS GUM STAND,TEABERRY,PEDESTAL..................    15.00
VASELINE GLASS JAR,CANDY....................................     6.00
VASELINE GLASS JUG,SYRUP,PEWTER TOP,INVERTED THUMBPRINT.....    35.00
VASELINE GLASS MUG,DEER & PINE TREE.........................    22.50
VASELINE GLASS PAPERWEIGHT,AMBERINA CHICK ON TOP............    35.00
VASELINE GLASS PITCHER & CREAMER,DAISY & BUTTON.............    32.50
VASELINE GLASS PITCHER,DEWEY JEWEL..........................    18.00
VASELINE GLASS PITCHER,PEDESTAL BASE,THUMBPRINT.............    29.50
VASELINE GLASS PITCHER,WATER & 5 TUMBLERS,OPALESCENT,FOOTED.    85.00
VASELINE GLASS PITCHER,WATER,OPALESCENT,6 TUMBLERS,GOLD
  FLOWERS...................................................   200.00
VASELINE GLASS PITCHER,WATER,RAINDROP.......................    15.00
VASELINE GLASS PITCHER,WATER,WILDFLOWER.....................    36.50
VASELINE GLASS PLATE,COOKIE,IMPERIAL JEWELS IRIDESCENT......    13.50
VASELINE GLASS PLATE,IMPERIAL JEWELS,6 IN.,PANELED..........     5.00
VASELINE GLASS PLATE,PLEAT & PANEL,7 IN.....................    22.50
VASELINE GLASS PLATE,SQUARE,STIPPLED BLOCK..................     8.75
VASELINE GLASS PLATTER,OPEN HANDLES,DAISY & BUTTON..........    22.50
VASELINE GLASS RAMEKIN SET,LUTZ THREADED....................    37.50
VASELINE GLASS RAMEKIN SET WITH ROSE THREADING.............     49.50
VASELINE GLASS RELISH BOAT,ROSE SPRIG.......................    12.50
VASELINE GLASS ROSEBOWL,INVERTED FAN & FEATHER,4 IN.........    28.50
VASELINE GLASS ROSEBOWL,SPANISH LACE,RUFFLED TOP............    17.50
VASELINE GLASS ROSEBOWL,TALL STEM,OPAL EDGE.................    15.00
VASELINE GLASS SALT SHAKER,THOUSAND EYE.....................     8.75
VASELINE GLASS SALT SHAKER,WILDFLOWER.......................     7.50
VASELINE GLASS SAUCE,DAISY & BUTTON,8 SCALLOPS..............     7.50
VASELINE GLASS SAUCE,FLAT,HOBNAIL,THUMBPRINT BASE...........     7.75
VASELINE GLASS SAUCE,FOOTED,DAISY & BUTTON..................     7.50
VASELINE GLASS SAUCE,FOOTED,SQUARE,FINECUT & PANEL..........     4.50
VASELINE GLASS SAUCE,MAPLE LEAF.............................     6.25
VASELINE GLASS SAUCE,SET OF 6,HARTLEY,FOOTED................    36.00
VASELINE GLASS SHADE........................................     3.50
VASELINE GLASS SHADE,FLORAL.................................     3.50
VASELINE GLASS SHOE,SLOUCHY.................................     7.00
VASELINE GLASS SLIPPER,DAISY & BUTTON,6 IN..................    21.00
VASELINE GLASS SPOONER,AMBER & GREEN........................    18.00
VASELINE GLASS SPOONER,DAISY & BUTTON.......................    11.00
VASELINE GLASS SPOONER,DAISY & BUTTON WITH THUMBPRINT.......    18.00
VASELINE GLASS SPOONER,DIAMOND QUILTED......................    15.00
VASELINE GLASS STEIN,PEWTER TOP.............................    65.00
VASELINE GLASS SUGAR BOWL,PRESSED DIAMOND PATTERN,COVERED...    22.50
VASELINE GLASS SUGAR,COVERED,BRACKET & SWAG,OPALESCENT......    22.50
VASELINE GLASS SUGAR,COVERED,DAISY & BUTTON CROSS
  BAR,PEDESTAL BASE.........................................    20.00
VASELINE GLASS SUGAR,OPEN,DEWEY.............................     9.50
VASELINE GLASS SYRUP,OPALESCENT TO CLEAR....................    18.50
VASELINE GLASS TOOTHPICK,DAISY & BUTTON TOP HAT.............     8.50
VASELINE GLASS TOOTHPICK HOLDER,HONEYCOMB...................    11.00
VASELINE GLASS TOOTHPICK,HORN OF PLENTY.....................    17.50
VASELINE GLASS TOOTHPICK,KITTEN ON PILLOW...................    22.50
VASELINE GLASS TOOTHPICK,THOUSAND EYE.......................    12.50
VASELINE GLASS TRAY,BREAD,DAISY & BUTTON....................    24.50
VASELINE GLASS TRAY,CARD,IMPERIAL JEWELS....................     7.50
```

VASELINE GLASS TRAY,COLUMBIA SHIELD...........................	45.00
VASELINE GLASS TRAY,FAN SHAPE ,DAISY & BUTTON................	9.00
VASELINE GLASS TRAY,FOOTED,CLARKS TEABERRY GUM..............	5.50
VASELINE GLASS TUMBLER,DAISY & BUTTON........................	16.00
VASELINE GLASS TUMBLER,OPAL RIM.............................	8.00
VASELINE GLASS TUMBLER,PEARS...............................	3.50
VASELINE GLASS TUMBLER,WILDFLOWER..........................	12.50
VASELINE GLASS VASE,11 IN.,FLUTED..........................	12.50
VASELINE GLASS VASE,14 IN.,OVERLAY,FLARED TOP...............	28.00
VASELINE GLASS VASE,BUD,10 IN..............................	12.00
VASELINE GLASS VASE,BUD,12 IN..............................	15.00
VASELINE GLASS VASE,BUD,13 IN..............................	15.00
VASELINE GLASS VASE,CAR,HOLDER.............................	15.00
VASELINE GLASS VASE,FAN,IMPERIAL JEWELS,PEDESTAL FOOT.......	11.00
VASELINE GLASS VASE,FLUTED TOP,GROUND PONTIL...............	8.50
VASELINE GLASS VASE IN SHAPE OF OLD LANTERN,MILK WHITE TOP	
TRIMMED RED..	7.75
VASELINE GLASS VASE,JACK IN THE PULPIT,CRIMPED TOP..........	16.00
VASELINE GLASS VASE,OVERLAY,FLARED TOP,10 IN. HIGH..........	22.00
VASELINE GLASS VASE,SQUARE PLATFORM BOTTOM,2 HANDLED,7 IN.	
TALL..	12.00
VASELINE GLASS VASE WITH APPLIED BROWN LILY PADS WITH RED...	35.00
VASELINE GLASS WINE,AUSTRIAN...............................	15.00
VASELINE GLASS WINE,CLARET,DIAMOND QUILTED.................	7.50
VELES SIGNED 7 IN. VASE,GREEN WITH BROWN LEAVES,ACID CUT....	80.00

VENETIAN GLASS was made near Venice, Italy, from the thirteenth to the twentieth century. Thin, colored glass with applied decorations was favored, although many other types were made.

VENETIAN GLASS BLUE TUMBLER,HANDPAINTED WHITE DAISIES,GOLD	
FERN..	15.00
VENETIAN GLASS CLEAR DOLPHIN WINE DECANTER..................	50.00
VENETIAN GLASS PERFUME BOTTLE WITH GILT DESIGN WITH RED	
PANELS..	55.00
VENETIAN GLASS SET OF 6 GLASSES,FISH STEMS,PINK & GOLD......	75.00

VERLYS GLASS was made in France after 1931. Verlys was also made in the United States. The glass is either blown or molded. The American glass is signed with a diamond-point-scratched name but the French pieces are marked with a molded signature.

VERLYS 12 IN. BOAT SHAPED CENTER PIECE WITH 4 RAISED OPAL	
DOVES...	65.00
VERLYS BOWL,CENTER PIECE,FRENCH,11 IN.,3 OPALESCENT BIRDS...	67.50
VERLYS BOWL,SIGNED,AMBER,SHEAFS OF WHEAT DESIGNS............	125.00
VERLYS BOWL,SIGNED,AMETHYST,ELONGATED AIR TRAP DESIGN.......	90.00
VERLYS CANDLESTICK HOLDER,PAIR SATIN FROSTED,SIGNED.........	35.00
VERLYS FRANCE SIGNED SMOKY COVERED BOX,CHRYSANTHEMUM........	38.00

VERRE DE SOIE GLASS was first made by Frederick Carder at the Steuben Glass Works from about 1905 to 1930. It is an iridescent glass of soft white or very, very pale green. The name means glass of silk and it does resemble silk. Other factories have made verre de soie, and some of the English examples were made of different colors. Verre de soie is an art glass and is not related to the iridescent pressed white carnival glass mistakenly called by its name.

VERRE DE SOIE BOTTLE,PERFUME,PINK MARBELIZED SPOPPER........	38.50
VERRE DE SOIE BOWL,FOOTED,PURPLE,GOLD & GREEN..............	42.00
VERRE DE SOIE BOWL,RUFFLED,6 IN.,SIGNED BY CARDER..........	35.00
VERRE DE SOIE BOWL,SPANISH GREEN EDGE,SIGNED STEUBEN........	72.50
VERRE DE SOIE CABINET PIECE,CONCH SHELL ON BED OF GREEN	
SEAWEED...	22.00
VERRE DE SOIE COLOGNE.....................................	50.00
VERRE DE SOIE COMPOTE,JELLY,ROLLED EDGE...................	35.00
VERRE DE SOIE DESSERT SET WITH MATCHING SERVERS,RANDOM	
THREADING...	150.00
VERRE DE SOIE GOBLET,STEMMED,SIGNED.......................	17.50

```
VERRE DE SOIE JAR,POWDER,ROSE-PINK KNOB....................   35.00
VERRE DE SOIE PLATE WITH ENGRAVING,6 IN.,SIGNED HAWKES......   32.00
VERRE DE SOIE ROSEBOWL,3 IN. DIAMETER,GREEN FLORAL..........   15.00
VERRE DE SOIE SALT,PEDESTALED..............................   40.00
VERRE DE SOIE SHERBETS & PLATES,4..........................   37.50
VERRE DE SOIE SHERBET,STEMMED,SIGNED.......................   17.50
VERRE DE SOIE TUMBLER......................................   45.00
VERRE DE SOIE VASE,7 IN.,RIBBED,GREEN BINDING ON TURNED DOWN
  RIM.....................................................   49.50
VERRE DE SOIE VASE,9 IN.,STERLING..........................   63.00
VERRE DE SOIE VASE,10 IN.,PINCH TOP,GOLD WITH ENAMEL........   25.00
VERRE DE SOIE VASE,11 IN...................................   75.00
VERRE DE SOIE VASE,BUD,PAIR................................   40.00
VERRE DE SOIE VASE,FLARE TOP,BLUE AURENE THREADING..........   53.00
VERRE DE SOIE VASE ON STEMMED FOOT,RUFFLE TOP..............   45.00
VERRE DE SOIE VASE,PEDESTAL BASE,APPLIED HANDLE WITH 7
  PLEATS..................................................   19.00
VERRE DE SOIE VASE,PEDESTAL BASE,FLARE TOP,POLISHED PONTIL..   18.00
VERRE DE SOIE VASE SIGNED F.CARDER,THREADED IN GREEN........  115.00
VERRE DE SOIE VASE,WHITE SATIN,SPRAY DAISIES, 10 IN.........   20.50
VERRE MOIRE DISH,BON-BON,FOOTED,RUFFLED
  TOP,NAILSEA,CRANBERRY & WHITE............................   95.00
```

VILLEROY AND BOCH POTTERY of Mettlach, Germany, was founded in 1841. The firm made many types of pottery including the famous Mettlach steins.

```
VILLEROY & BOCH BLUE & WHITE PLATE,12 IN.,CLASSICAL
  SCENE,PIERCED...........................................   19.50
VILLEROY & BOCH CAKE PLATE,BLUE & WHITE ONION PATTERN,MARKED  10.00
VILLEROY & BOCH CREAMER,BLUE & WHITE.......................    7.50
VILLEROY & BOCH DINNER PLATE,BLUE & WHITE ONION
  PATTERN,MARKED..........................................    7.50
VILLEROY & BOCH MARKED DINNER PLATE,9 IN.,BLUE & WHITE ONION
  PATTERN.................................................    7.50
VILLEROY & BOCH MARKED STEIN,BROWN WITH TAN DECOR...........   35.00
VILLEROY & BOCH METTLACH CANDLESTICK WITH HEXAGONAL SAUCER
  BASE....................................................   20.00
VILLEROY & BOCH PAIR 7 IN. PLATES,BEARDED DWARFS PICKING
  GRAPES..................................................   15.00
VILLEROY & BOCH PITCHER,7 IN. HIGH,BLUE & GRAY,VIKING FACE
  ON SPOUT................................................   68.60
VILLEROY & BOCH PLATE,MARKED,YELLOW BREASTED LONG BILL BLUE
  BIRDS...................................................    9.00
VILLEROY & BOCH PLATE SIGNED,GIRL & TURKEY.................   12.50
VILLEROY & BOCH PLATE,WHITE,7 IN.,FLOWERS IN CENTER.........    6.00
VILLEROY & BOCH PLATTER MARKED DRESDEN MADE IN GERMANY,BLUE
  & WHITE.................................................   12.00
VILLEROY & BOCH SHAVING MUG,MERCURY MARK,TAN BAND TOP &
  BOTTOM..................................................   16.00
VILLEROY & BOCH STEIN,1 HALF LITRE,PEWTER TOP,SIGNED........   57.00
VILLEROY AND BOCH TUMBLER,BERLIN,LEIPZIG & STUTTGART,3......   29.00
VILLEROY & BOCH WALL PLATE,12 IN.,MOUNTAIN & VILLAGE........   28.00
VINCENNES DATED 1765 MUSTARD POT,BONNETED GIRL..............   75.00
      VINEGAR CRUET, SEE CRUET.............................
VIOLIN,LABELED STRADIVARIUS,COPY...........................   35.00
```

WARWICK CHINA was made in Wheeling, West Virginia, in a pottery factory founded in 1887.

```
WARWICK BULBOUS VASE,RED POINSETTIAS.......................   25.00
WARWICK CHINA TUREEN,COBALT LEAVES,ORANGE FLOWER............    7.00
WALRUS TOOTH,8 IN. LONG,CARVED INTO A CRIBBAGE BOARD........   21.50
WALRUS TUSKS,2 POLISHED....................................   16.00
WATCH,7 JEWEL ELGIN,14K ROLLED GOLD PLATE..................   12.50
WATCH,7 JEWEL RELIANCE SILVEROID CASE......................    6.00
WATCH,7 JEWEL WALTHAM,14K GOLD PLATE.......................   10.00
WATCH,14K DIAL WATCH FACE PIN PENDANT,SAPPHIRE & ENAMEL.....  150.00
```

```
WATCH,14K GOLD CASED MANS ELGIN.............................   65.00
WATCH,14K HUNTING CASE LADIES...............................   50.00
WATCH,15 JEWEL COIN SILVER GOLD-FILLED TRIM CASE............   12.50
WATCH,15 JEWEL ELGIN MANS THIN GOLD FILLED HUNTING CASE,RUNS   18.00
WATCH,15 IN. DIAL...........................................   65.00
WATCH,16 SIZE HUNTING CASE WALTHAM ENGRAVED.................   30.00
WATCH,16S 19J BURLINGTON SPECIAL DISPLAY CASE...............   50.00
WATCH,16S OPEN FACE,BUNN SPECIAL MONTGOMERY DIAL............   50.00
WATCH,17 JEWEL,20 YEAR CASE.................................   15.00
WATCH,17J SIZE 16 HALLMARKED SILVER CASE....................   30.00
WATCH,18K GOLD MANS HUNTING CASE,15 JEWEL WALTHAM...........   44.00
WATCH,18 KEYWIND OPEN FACE WALTHAM,RUNS,SILVEROID CASE......   17.50
WATCH,18K ,LAPEL,GOLD FLOWER GARLAND,PENDANT FESTOON........   95.00
WATCH,18 OPEN FACE KEYWIND,RUNS,SILVEROID CASE..............   17.50
WATCH,18 SIZE OPEN FACE ELGIN KEY WIND,GOLD FILLED..........   30.00
WATCH,18S OPEN FACE KEY WIND................................   25.00
WATCH,1910 HEW HAVEN POCKET,PANAMA PACIFIC INTERNATIONAL
  EXPO.,1915................................................   15.00
WATCH,20 YEAR GOLD CASE,ENGRAVED............................   35.00
WATCH,23 JEWEL WALTHAM VAN GUARD,CASE WITH ELK..............  150.00
WATCH,BOREL & COUVOISIER HUNTING CASE SIZE 18,KEY WIND & SET   37.50
WATCH,COIN SILVER ELGIN MANS OPEN FACE,KEY WIND.............   20.00
WATCH,COIN SILVER OPEN FACE MANS,ROCKFORD,ILL.,KEY WIND.....   29.00
WATCH,ELGIN 15 JEWEL ,COIN SILVER ENGRAVED HUNTING CASE.....   12.00
WATCH,ELGIN 18S OPEN FACE KEY WIND..........................   25.00
WATCH,ELGIN COIN SILVER HUNTER CASE.........................   11.00
WATCH,ELGIN COIN SILVER HUNTING CASE........................   18.00
WATCH,ELGIN GOLD FILLED LADIES HUNTING CASE,CHAIN & SLIDE...   75.00
WATCH,ELGIN IN ENGRAVED FLORAL & ARCH WITH SCENE,18K GOLD
  CASE.....................................................   27.50
WATCH,ELGIN NATIONAL WATCH CO.,NO.476848 COIN SILVER
  CASE,KEY WIND............................................   27.50
WATCH,ELGIN POCKET 15 JEWEL,25 YR.,14K CASE.................   12.50
WATCH,ELGIN,RUNS,18 SIZE KEY WINDER.........................   27.50
WATCH,ELGIN SIZE 16 MOVABLE WINDING STEM 1884...............   25.00
WATCH,ENGLISH FUSEE KEYWIND,SILVER OPEN FACE CASE WITH
  HALLMARK.................................................   25.00
WATCH,ENGLISH KEYWIND SILVER HUNTING CASE,RUNS,ARNOLD
  ADAMS,LONDON.............................................   15.00
WATCH,ENGRAVED WALTHAM LADIES HUNTING CASE,CHAIN & GARNET
  SLIDE....................................................   85.00
WATCH,FISHER SIZE 18 SILVER CASE,LEVER-SET,................   37.50
WATCH,FLEUR DE LIS PIN......................................    4.25
WATCH,FLEUR-DE-LIS PIN WITH RED ENAMEL ON FACE..............   12.50
WATCH, GOLD ELGIN HUNTING CASE, RUNS........................   24.50
WATCH,GOLD ELGIN HUNTING CASE,ENGRAVED,REPOUSSE EDGES.......   67.50
WATCH,GOLD FILLED MANS HUNTING CASE AMERICAN WALTHAM
  TRAVELER.................................................   21.50
WATCH,GOLD FILLED,RAISED APPLIED GOLD NUMBERS &
  HANDS,WALTHAM PERMIER....................................   40.00
WATCH,GOLD HUNTING CASE.....................................   55.00
WATCH,GOLD HUNTING CASE WALTHAM.............................   85.00
WATCH,GOLD WALTHAM,RUNS,OPEN FACE...........................   38.00
WATCH, HAMILTON, 23 JEWELS,OPEN FACE,14 KT.WHITE GOLD CASE..   40.00
WATCH,HAMILTON RAILROAD WATCH,21J,SIZE 16,..................   42.50
WATCH,HAMPDEN LADIES GOLD FILLED HUNTING CASE,ENGRAVED......   16.50
WATCH,HAMPDEN SIZE 18 OPEN FACE SILVER CASE KEYWIND ,RUNS...   17.50
WATCH,HENRY BEGUELIN SIZE 18,17J,STERLING SILVER CASE,LEVER
  SET......................................................   37.50
WATCH,HOWARD,23 JEWELS,OPEN FACE,14 KT.GOLD CASE............   55.00
WATCH,HOWARD OPEN FACE MANS POCKET,RUNS.....................   75.00
WATCH,HUNTING CASE ELGIN,20 YEARS,ENGRAVED & STIPPLED.......   54.00
WATCH,HUNTING CASE GOLD 20 YEAR WALTHAM.....................   27.50
WATCH,HUNTING CASE LADIES ENGRAVED 14K......................   75.00
WATCH,HUNTING CASE WALTHAM,3 SIX,20 YEAR CASE...............   55.00
```

```
WATCH,HUNTING CASE WITH WORCESTER ON DIAL...................    35.00
WATCH,KEY-WIND 185 GOLD HUNTING CASE,ENGRAVED,CIRCA 1820....    37.50
WATCH, KEYWIND , HUNTING CASE, WORKS.......................    14.50
WATCH,LADIES 3/0 SIZE OPEN FACE WALTHAM,GUN METAL CASE......    30.00
WATCH,LADIES 3/0 SIZE WALTHAM,ENGRAVED 20 YEAR HUNTING CASE,    40.00
WATCH,LADIES 6 SIZE GOLD HUNTING CASE WALTHAM..............    40.00
WATCH,LADIES 14K GOLD ELGIN,ENGRAVED CASE,HUNTING,RUNS......    45.00
WATCH,LADIES 14K GOLD HUNTER CASE,RUNS,FLOWERS & SCROLLS....    85.00
WATCH,LADIES 14K GOLD HUNTING CASE WALTHAM,RUNS............     3.00
WATCH,LADIES 25 YEAR GOLD HUNTING CASE WALTHAM,BIRDS &
  FLOWERS..................................................    85.00
WATCH,LADIES 40 YEAR OLD HAMILTON,SILVER...................    12.00
WATCH,LADIES CLOSED CASE ELGIN,GOLD FILLED CASE,ENGRAVED
  BIRDS & VINES............................................    35.00
WATCH,LADIES CLOSED FACE HUNTER CASE ELGIN,ENGRAVED CASE....    35.00
WATCH,LADIES COIN SILVER OPEN FACE,ENGRAVED................    15.00
WATCH,LADIES CROWN HUNTING CASE,ENGRAVED FLOWERS,COUNTRY
  CHURCH,20 YEAR...........................................    50.00
WATCH,LADIES ELGIN 11 JEWEL,GOLD FILLED HUNTING CASE........    30.00
WATCH,LADIES ELGIN HUNTING CASE 20 YEAR GOLD FILLED CASE....    25.00
WATCH,LADYS ENGRAVED GOLD CLOSED CASE ELGIN ON ROPE CHAIN...    85.00
WATCH,LADIES GOLD ELGIN,ENGRAVED..........................    29.00
WATCH,LADIES GOLD FILLED,ENGRAVED.........................    17.50
WATCH,LADIES,GOLD NASSAU,HUNTING CASE,ENGRAVING...........    65.00
WATCH,LADIES GOLD OPEN FACE,CHAIN WITH 3 JEWEL SLIDE.......    65.00
WATCH,LADIES HUNTER CASE GOLD.............................    48.00
WATCH,LADIES HUNTING CASE SWISS,GOLD,ENGRAVED.............    25.00
WATCH,LADIES MARKED 14K AMERICAN WALTHAM,HUNTER CASE.......   150.00
WATCH,LADIES OPEN FACE,14K GOLD...........................    29.50
WATCH, LADIES OPEN FACE LAPEL,............................    15.00
WATCH,LADIES WALTHAM,20 YEAR GOLD CASE,ENGRAVED...........    50.00
WATCH,LADIES WALTHAM,20 YEAR GOLD CLOSED CASE,............    45.00
WATCH,LADIES WALTHAM 20 YEAR GOLD FILLED HUNTING CASE,RUNS..    27.50
WATCH,LADIES WALTHAM GOLD FILLED HUNTING CASE,7 JEWEL......    28.50
WATCH,LADIES WALTHAM OPEN FACE,GOLD FILLED CASE...........    12.00
WATCH,LADIES WALTHAM,PINK,GREEN,YELLOW  GOLD..............    46.50
WATCH,LADIES WRIST,GOLD WALTHAM,RUNS......................     9.50
WATCH,MANS 14K GOLD HOWARD,OPEN FACE......................    65.00
WATCH,MANS CLOSED YELLOW GOLD ELGIN,ENGRAVED..............    41.00
WATCH,MANS ELGIN 15 JEWEL GOLD 18K HUNTING CASE,ENGRAVED....    42.00
WATCH,MANS GOLD ENGRAVED CLOSED CASE ELGIN................    18.00
WATCH,MANS GOLD-FILLED HUNTING CASE WALTHAM,DOG DESIGN......    27.00
WATCH, MANS HUNTING CASE WALTHAM..........................    17.00
WATCH,MANS HUNTING CASE WALTHAM,GOLD-FILLED,FLORAL DESIGN...    25.00
WATCH,MANS OPEN FACE AMERICAN WALTHAM,25 YEAR GOLD CASE.....    10.00
WATCH,MANS OPEN FACE ELGIN,SCREW BACK,RUNS................    12.50
WATCH,MANS OPEN FACE KEY WIND POCKET,COIN SILVER CASE,MARKED    35.00
WATCH,MANS OPEN FACE WALTHAM,STEM WIND,ENGRAVED COIN SILVER
  CASE....................................................    15.00
WATCH,MANS YELLOW GOLD CLOSED ELGIN,ENGRAVED..............    42.50
WATCH,OPEN FACED AMERICAN,WALTHAM CO......................    18.00
WATCH,OPEN FACE,ENGRAVED SILVER,KEY WIND,MEDALLION ON BACK..    50.00
WATCH,OPEN FACE LADIES GOLD FILLED........................    14.50
WATCH,OPEN FACE SETH THOMAS MENS 20 YEAR CASE.............    18.00
WATCH,OPEN FACE WALTHAM,20 YEAR CASE......................    25.01-
WATCH,OPEN FACED WALTHAM,SILVEROID WITH DEER ON BACK,RUNS...    28.00
WATCH,SILVER CASE KEY WIND,KEY WIND,OUTER HALF HUNTING CASE
  COVER...................................................    20.00
WATCH,SILVER KEY WIND.....................................    14.50
WATCH,SILVER POCKET,LOCOMOTIVE ON BACK....................     5.00
WATCH,SILVER R & G BEESLEY LIVERPOOL,KEY WIND.............    45.00
WATCH,SIZE 0/18 MANS SILVER CASE OPEN FACE ,LOCOMOTIVE ON
  BACK....................................................    30.00
WATCH,SIZE 18 ELGIN.......................................     8.00
WATCH,SIZE 18 ELGIN 17 J COIN SILVER CASE.................    37.50
```

WATCH,SIZE 18 HUNTING CASE KEYWIND,SILVER CASE..............	7.50
WATCH,SIZE 18 ROCKFORD OPEN FACE STEMWIND,RUNS,GOLD CASE....	12.00
WATCH,SIZE 18 WALTHAM KEYWIND OPEN FACE COIN SILVER CASE,RUNS..	18.50
WATCH,STUDEBAKER POCKET......................................	14.00
WATCH,TRAVEL IN STERLING SILVER CASE.........................	15.00
WATCH,WALTHAMS 7 JEWEL.......................................	8.00
WATCH,WALTHAM,18 KEY SIZE WINDER.............................	27.50
WATCH,WALTHAM ENGRAVED HUNTING CASE,14K GOLD.................	50.00
WATCH,WALTHAM HUNTING CASE ,ENGRAVED GOLD FILLED.............	25.00
WATCH, WALTHAM OPEN PORCELAIN FACE,CASE,DATE 1891............	18.50
WATCH,WALTHAM SHIELD SHAPED CASE,TWIN HOUR HANDS.............	30.00
WATCH,WALTHAM WITH ENGRAVED GOLD FILLED HUNTING CASE,15 JEWEL..	32.00
WATCH,WOMANS HUNTING CASE,RUNS...............................	30.00
WATCH,WM.ELLERY WALTHAM KEY WIND,STENCIL CASE................	45.00
WATCH,YELLOW ENAMEL SWIVEL PENDANT ON BLACK ENAMEL FRAME....	59.00

WATCH FOBS were worn on watch chains. They were popular during Victorian times.

WATCH FOB,BUICK...	3.00
WATCH FOB, ECHO SPRINGS WHISKEY.............................	2.00
WATCH FOB,EUCLID NO STRAPS..................................	2.50
WATCH FOB,FORD..	3.00
WATCH FOB,MARBLEHEAD,MASS. 300 ANNIVERSARY..................	2.00
WATCH FOB,MAXWELL...	3.00
WATCH FOB, NEWPORT,MAINE, CENTENNIAL........................	2.50
WATCH FOB,UNCLE SAM,WITH U.S.FLAG DATED 1914................	4.50
WATCH FOB WITH LEATHER STRAP,POLL PARROT SHOES,COLOR........	7.50

WATERFORD-TYPE GLASS resembles the famous glass made in the Waterford Glass Works in Ireland. It is a clear glass that was often cut for decoration. Modern glass is still being made in Waterford, Ireland.

WATERFORD TYPE CRUET SET,HAND FINISHED WOODEN HOLDER........	32.00
WATERFORD TYPE DECANTER,3 COLLAR NECK.......................	15.00

WAVECREST GLASS is a white glassware manufactured by the Pairpoint Manufacturing Company of New Bedford, Massachusetts, and some French factories. It was then decorated by the C. F. Monroe Company of Meriden, Connecticut. The glass was painted pastel colors and decorated with flowers. The name "Wavecrest" was used after 1898.

WAVECREST BISCUIT JAR,WHITE TO ROSE,SILVER RIM,COVER,BAIL HANDLE..	62.00
WAVECREST BOTTLE,SIGNED,METAL TOP...........................	25.00
WAVECREST BOWL,MARKED,6 IN.,ORMOLU HANDLES,PINK TINT,SATIN LINED...	65.00
WAVECREST BOWL,SIGNED,3 IN.,SWIRLED,BLUE & WHITE ENAMEL BUDS	25.00
WAVECREST BOWL,SIGNED,SIDE HANDLES,FLORAL DECOR.............	37.00
WAVECREST BOX,COVERED,HINGED,ENAMEL.........................	35.00
WAVECREST BOX,GLOVE,COVERED,HINGED,SIGNED...................	65.00
WAVECREST BOX,GLOVE,HINGED COVERED,SIGNED,BLUE & WHITE,FLORAL DECOR...	75.00
WAVECREST BOX,HINGED,5 IN. DIAMETER,4 IN. TALL,FLORAL DECOR.	87.50
WAVECREST BOX,HINGED..	85.00
WAVECREST BOX,HINGED COVERED,OVAL SHAPED,SIGNED,RED BANNER MARK...	88.00
WAVECREST BOX,HINGED COVER,ROUND,2 CUPIDS MARKED............	65.00
WAVECREST BOX,HINGED,JEWELRY................................	65.00
WAVECREST BOX,JEWEL,BRASS HINGED,SCROLLS,ENAMELLING.........	42.50
WAVECREST BOX,JEWEL,PINK BLOSSOMS & DOTTED ENAMEL,BRASS BINDINGS & FEET..	175.00
WAVECREST BOX,JEWEL,SIGNED,OPEN,FOOTED,PINK FLOWERS ON BLUE.	26.00
WAVECREST BOX,JEWELRY,FOOTED & HINGED IN SHINY BRASS,SIGNED.	85.00
WAVECREST BOX,OVAL,SIGNED,5 IN. LONG,3 IN. HIGH,WHITE FLOWERS..	55.00

WAVECREST BOX,ROUND,HINGED,MARKED,ROBINS EGG BLUE BACKGROUND	65.00
WAVECREST BOX,SIGNED,ENAMELED ROSE FLOWERS...................	125.00
WAVECREST BOX,SIGNED,HINGED,COVERED,STUD,PINK HANDPAINTED SCENE..	75.00
WAVECREST BOX,SIGNED,HINGED,PORCELAIN SET IN PEWTER..........	87.50
WAVECREST BOX,SIGNED,OVAL,BLUE & PINK FLORAL DESIGN..........	92.50
WAVECREST BOX,SIGNED,SQUARE & SCALLOPED,YELLOW & CREAM,BRASS BAND..	55.00
WAVECREST CANDY OR NUT BOWL,OCTAGON WITH SILVER BAND,HANDPAINTED...	45.00
WAVECREST COOKIE JAR,QUILTED,SQUARE,SATIN FINISH.............	55.00
WAVECREST COOKIE JAR,SIGNED,SILVER RIM & LID & HANDLE........	65.00
WAVECREST CRACKER JAR,GREEN & PINK FLOWERS...................	79.50
WAVECREST CRACKER JAR,PINK FLORAL CLUSTERS & GREEN LEAVES,SILVER.......................................	35.00
WAVECREST CRACKER JAR,PINK WITH WHITE MEDALLIONS.............	39.00
WAVECREST CREAMER,SUGAR & SPOONER,FLORAL DESIGN.............	67.50
WAVECREST DISH,OPEN,SIGNED,BLUE & WHITE ENAMEL,PINK & WHITE FLOWERS...	22.00
WAVECREST DISH,PAIR,JEWEL,SIGNED,OVAL........................	45.00
WAVECREST DISH,PIN,SIGNED....................................	20.00
WAVECREST EWER,14 IN. TALL,CUPID FIGURE IN TAN,BROWN & GREEN	55.00
WAVECREST FERNERY ,BAROQUE EMBOSSING,MARKED,BLUE,RUST&GREEN.	125.00
WAVECREST JAR,SIGNED,AQUA WITH WHITE MEDALLIONS.............	70.00
WAVECREST JAR,SIGNED,COVERED,WILD ROSES,WHITE DOTS,GREEN LEAVES...	60.00
WAVECREST JAR,SIGNED,OPEN,BRASS RIM & HANDLES,BLUE & PINK FLOWERS...	80.00
WAVECREST JEWEL CASKET,SIGNED,GREEN,HINGED,4 IN. ROUND......	50.00
WAVECREST LETTER HOLDER,ENAMELLED ROSES......................	75.00
WAVECREST LETTER HOLDER,FLORAL DECOR,SIGNATURE...............	45.00
WAVECREST PLANTER,SIGNED,SQUARE,BLUE DECOR...................	60.00
WAVECREST PLATE,SIGNED,HANDPAINTED YELLOW ROSES..............	12.50
WAVECREST SALT,BEIGE & YELLOW................................	5.00
WAVECREST STATIONERY HOLDER,SIGNED,BLUE WITH EMBOSSED SCROLLS...	125.00
WAVECREST STATIONERY HOLDER,SIGNED,RAISED SWIRLS,BLUE & YELLOW FLOWERS...	49.00
WAVECREST SUGAR & CREAMER,SILVER TOP.........................	55.00
WAVECREST SYRUP PITCHER,SWIRL RIB WITH BLUE SCROLL DESIGN...	75.00
WAVECREST TOOTHPICK HOLDER,SIGNED,FLOWERS....................	43.00
WAVECREST TRAY,PIN,OPEN,BRASS COLLAR & HANDLES,ENAMELLED FLORAL...	59.50
WAVECREST TRAY,PIN,ROUND,MARKED,HANDLES......................	18.50
WAVECREST VASE,10 IN. HIGH,GOLD,FLOWERS & BIRDS,WHITE BACKGROUND..	88.00
WAVECREST VASE,SIGNED,9 IN.,WHITE BACKGROUND,BLUE FORGET-ME-NOTS...	40.00
WEAPON,ARROWHEAD,3..	1.00
WEAPON,AXE,FLUTED,GROOVED....................................	15.00
WEAPON,AXE,GROOVED..	5.00
WEAPON,BAYONET,FRENCH,SCABBARD,SIGNED & DATED,BRASS FITTINGS	27.50
WEAPON,BAYONET IN SHEATH,ENGLISH TYPE SPIKE..................	3.50
WEAPON,BAYONET WITH SCABBARD,SPIKE,BRITISH...................	1.50
WEAPON,BILLY,ENGLISH TYPE POLICE.............................	3.00
WEAPON,BILLY,POLICEMANS,12 IN...............................	4.00
WEAPON,BLUNDERBUSS,ENGLAND CIRCA 1770,CONVERTED INTO PERCUSSION...	350.00
WEAPON,BOLO SIGNED MOLE & SONS,ENGLAND,LEATHER SCABBARD.....	15.00
WEAPON,BULLET MOLD,COLT PERCUSSION...........................	6.50
WEAPON,BULLET MOLD,KENTUCKY RIFLE ROUND BALL.................	3.00
WEAPON,CANNON,11 IN. SHOOTER,BRASS,IRON CARRIAGE.............	15.00
WEAPON,CANNON,SHIPS...	130.00
WEAPON,DAGGER,GERMAN ARMY OFFICERS...........................	30.00
WEAPON,DAGGER,PERSIAN IVORY HANDLED,SILVER & WOOD SHEATH....	20.00

```
WEAPON,FLINT BUFFALO.....................................    2.00
WEAPON,FOIL,PAIR FENCING..................................   12.50
WEAPON,FOLSUM POINT.......................................    5.00
WEAPON,GORGET,BRASS,COPPER INLAYED DESIGN.................   45.00
WEAPON,GUN,ALLEN PEPPERBOX................................   65.00
WEAPON,GUN,BURNSIDE CIVIL WAR BREECHLOADING PERCUSSION
    CARBINE...............................................   67.50
WEAPON,GUN,CAP & BALL MUSKET..............................   35.00
WEAPON,GUN,COLT SINGLE ACTION 45,NICKEL,PEARL.............  175.00
WEAPON,GUN,DERRINGER,PHILA.,PERCUSSION....................  150.00
WEAPON,GUN,DOUBLE BARREL PERCUSSION PISTOL................   25.00
WEAPON,GUN,E.WHITING,NEW HAVEN,CAP & BALL NAVY
    REVOLVER,OCTAGON......................................  160.00
WEAPON,GUN,FLINTLOCK BUCCANEER PISTOL.....................  110.00
WEAPON,GUN,HARPERS FERRY MUZZLE LOADING MUSKET DATED
    1836,EAGLE & US.......................................   72.50
WEAPON,GUN,HARPERS FERRY US MUSKET DATED 1822,PERCUSSION
    LOCK..................................................   27.50
WEAPON,GUN,KENTUCKY RIFLE,WALNUT,41 CALIBRE,19 GERMAN SILVER
    INLAYS................................................   90.00
WEAPON,GUN,LADYS KENTUCKY RIFLE,WOOD STOCK,34 CALIBRE BORE..  175.00
WEAPON,GUN,MANHATTAN 36 CAP & BALL........................   90.00
WEAPON,GUN,PAIR EUROPEAN FLINTLOCK PISTOLS SIGNED CLAUDE
    NIQUET................................................  450.00
WEAPON,GUN,PARKER SHOT GUN,12 GAUGE,DAMASCUS BARREL,PATENT
    1876..................................................  100.00
WEAPON,GUN,PINFIRE REVOLVER...............................   35.00
WEAPON,GUN,PISTOL,3 IN. BARREL,HAMMERLESS GRIP,SQUEEZE
    SAFETY 1890...........................................   35.00
WEAPON,GUN,REMINGTON ROLLING BLOCK MILITARY RIFLE.........   75.00
WEAPON,GUN,SMITH & WESSON 45 PISTOL,1917 U.S.ARMY,BLUE STEEL  75.00
WEAPON,GUN,SPRINGFIELD 45/70 RIFLE........................   60.00
WEAPON,GUN,STEVENS 22 VISABLE LOADER RIFLE................   35.00
WEAPON,GUN,STEVENS 44 32/40...............................   50.00
WEAPON,GUN,U S FLINTLOCK MILITIA MUSKET CIRCA 1820........  135.00
WEAPON,GUN,WINCHESTER 40-60...............................  175.00
WEAPON,JANG MOLD CASTS 8-30 CALIBRE BULLETS...............   12.00
WEAPON,KNIFE,1918 U.S.ARMY,7 IN. LONG.....................    1.50
WEAPON,KNIFE,CIRCLE REMINGTON POCKET,2 BLADES.............   16.50
WEAPON,KNIFE,ITALIAN FASCIST TRENCH,SHEATH WITH INSIGNIA..   16.00
WEAPON,KNIFE,SAILOR,CIRCA 1800,CARVED BONE HANDLE.........   10.00
WEAPON,KNIFE,WORLD WAR II BRASS-KNUCKLE
    COMBAT,HOMEMADE,DATED 6-10-43.........................   18.00
WEAPON,MACHETE DATED 1912 IN CASE,U.S.....................    9.00
WEAPON,MUSKET,1835 SPRINGFIELD............................  150.00
WEAPON,PIKE,POINTED,PREVENTS PIRATES BOARDING SHIP........   50.00
WEAPON,POWDER FLASK,DEAD GAME PARTRIDGE & RABBIT,COPPER...   18.00
WEAPON,POWDER FLASK,FLOWER WITH VINES,COPPER..............   12.00
WEAPON,POWDER FLASK HORN SCRIMSHAW........................  150.00
WEAPON,POWDER FLASK,LEATHER...............................   10.00
WEAPON,POWDER FLASK WITH EAGLE,COLTS PATENT...............   85.00
WEAPON,POWDER FLASK WITH RIBBED DESIGN,BRASS MEASURE SPOUT..   12.50
WEAPON,POWDER HORN,8 IN. LONG,FOLK TYPE SCRIMSHAW
    WORK,MERMAID & DOG....................................   16.50
WEAPON,POWDER HORN,9 IN. LONG,CARVING OF ROOSTER,3
    FISH,MASONIC EMBLEM...................................   19.00
WEAPON,POWDER HORN 9 IN. LONG,OCTAGON SHAPE IN CROSS SECTION  18.00
WEAPON,POWDER HORN,10 IN.,INITIALED.......................    6.50
WEAPON,POWDER HORN,BRASS RING AT NECK AND BASE,16 IN. LONG..   22.00
WEAPON,POWDER HORN,BUFFALO................................   15.00
WEAPON,POWDER HORN,DICKLE.................................   10.00
WEAPON,POWDER HORN,KENTUCKY,8 IN.,FOR RIFLE,DATED 1846....   12.50
WEAPON,POWDER HORN,REVOLUTIONARY,OCTAGON & DOUBLE
    RING,CARVED...........................................  295.00
WEAPON,POWDER HORN,RING & FACETED NECK....................   30.00
```

```
WEAPON,POWDER HORN,TIN LID................................  10.00
WEAPON,POWDER HORN WITH CHARGER...........................   9.00
WEAPON,POWDER HORNS WITH POWDER MEASURE....................  12.00
WEAPON,POWDER HORN WITH TIP CHARGER.......................   7.50
WEAPON,PRIMING FLASK OF FLUTED ZINC,BRASS TOP,HUNTERS.......  22.50
WEAPON,RIFLE MARKED LONG RIFLE,22 CALIBRE,DATED 1913........  18.00
WEAPON,SHELL,BRASS,4 IN...................................  10.00
WEAPON,SHOT POUCH,LEATHER,BRASS MEASURING SPOUT............   8.00
WEAPON,SPEAR,10 IN........................................  15.00
WEAPON,SPEARHEAD..........................................   2.50
WEAPON,SWORD,CHINESE TEMPLE,DRAGON & SIGNATURE ON BLADE,WOOD
  SCABBARD................................................  40.00
WEAPON,SWORD,CURVED PRUSSIAN,ENGRAVED SILVER ON SCABBARD....  55.00
WEAPON,SWORD,DYAK HEAD HUNTERS CIRCA 1800,CARVED BONE HANDLE  40.00
WEAPON,SWORD,GERMAN ARMY,CHASED BLADE,BRASS GUARD & LION
  HEAD...................................................  30.00
WEAPON,SWORD,KNIGHTS MALTA LODGE WITH BELT & SCABBARD.......  12.00
WEAPON,SWORD,KNIGHTS TEMPLAR,SILVER WITH INSIGNIA,SCABBARD..  20.00
WEAPON,SWORD,MASONIC WITH IVORY HANDLE....................  25.00
WEAPON,SWORD,MASONIC WITH SCABBARD,WIRE WOUND LEATHER GRIPS.  25.00
WEAPON,SWORD,NATIONAL GUARD...............................   9.00
WEAPON,SWORD,NICKEL TRIM,SCABBARD,SASH & KNOT,CHASED BLADE..  25.00
WEAPON,SWORD,WHALE BONE,26 IN. LONG,6 LAND & SEASCAPE SCENES
  IN COLOUR...............................................  40.00
WEAPON,SWORD WITH SCABBARD DATED 1913,US CAVALRY...........  17.50
WEAPON,SWORDCANE..........................................  13.00
WEAPON,SWORDCANE,COMPLETELY DISGUISED.....................  12.00
WEATHERVANE,5 FEET,ARROW WITH SCROLLS,GOLD LEAF...........  235.00
WEATHERVANE,AUTOMOBILE,TIN,MILK GLASS WHITE BALL,IRON ARROW.  35.00
WEATHERVANE,CLIPPER RUNNING HORSE,18 X 31 IN..............  200.00
WEATHERVANE,COPPER ROOSTER................................  375.00
WEATHERVANE,FULL BODIED HORSE,DIRECTIONAL LETTERS.........  200.00
WEATHERVANE,HORSE,COPPER,RUNNING TROTTER..................  175.00
WEATHERVANE,SULKY,36 X 21 X 13 IN.,WHEELS.................  450.00
```

WEBB GLASS was made by Thomas Webb & Sons of Stourbridge, England. Many types of art and cameo glass were made by them during the Victorian era.

```
WEBB ALEXANDRITE VIOLET VASE,WIDE BLUE EDGE,1 & 1 HALF
  IN.HIGH.............................................1,000.00
WEBB BASKET,CHARTREUSE OUT & PINK INSIDE,ENAMEL FLOWERS.....  72.00
WEBB BURMESE 5 IN. VASE,LEMON YELLOW TO PINK..............  125.00
WEBB BURMESE 10 IN. STICK VASE,ACID FINISH................  245.00
WEBB BURMESE ACID FINISH BOWL,...........................  200.00
WEBB BURMESE DECORATED BOWL,6 SIDED,CORAL FLOWERS & GREEN...  295.00
WEBB BURMESE DECORATED BOWL,GREEN LEAVES & RED BERRIES......  300.00
WEBB BURMESE FAIRY LAMP,6 IN. TALL,ENAMELED
  DECORATION,MARKED CLARKES..............................  250.00
WEBB BURMESE FAIRY LAMP,DOME SHADE,CLEAR MARKED CLARKE......  95.00
WEBB BURMESE FAIRY LAMP,SIGNED CLARKES PATTERN GLASS BASE...  150.00
WEBB BURMESE ROSE BOWL,CRIMPED TOP,LEAVES & VINES..........  230.00
WEBB BURMESE ROSE BOWL,RUFFLED TOP.......................  215.00
WEBB BURMESE TOOTHPICK HOLDER,SALMON COLOURING............  180.00
WEBB BURMESE VASE,PETAL FLOWER FORM TOP,SALMON TO YELLOW....  195.00
WEBB CAMEO PERFUME BOTTLE,4 IN. LONG,V SHAPE,LYING DOWN.....  180.00
WEBB CAMEO RECLINING PERFUME FLASK,FROSTED CRANBERRY &
  OPAQUE.................................................  250.00
WEBB CAMEO VASE,BLUE SHADED,WHITE MORNING GLORIES,4 IN. HIGH  275.00
WEBB LAY DOWN SCENT BOTTLE,GOLD ON IVORY..................  85.00
WEBB MOTHER OF PEARL VASE IN DRAPE PATTERN................  72.00
WEBB OVERLAY FOOTED BOWL,3 APPLIED CLEAR FEET.............  57.50
WEBB PEACHBLOW DECORATED MUSTARD JAR ,SILVER HINGE TOP......  185.00
WEBB PINK SATIN GLASS COMPOTE,SILVER PEDESTAL BASE.........  50.00
WEBB PINK VASE,ACID FINISH,PINK CASING,GOLD DECOR.........  200.00
WEBB RIBBON SATIN VASE,PINK,COIN GOLD FLOWERS,LEAVES &
  STEMS,4 IN. TALL.......................................  95.00
```

```
WEBB ROSEBOWL,SIGNED..........................................   370.00
WEBB SATIN 3 IN. BUD VASE,TAN GROUND WITH ENAMEL COLOURED
  BIRDS.......................................................    95.00
WEBB SATIN GLASS BOWL,PINK INSIDE,GOLD ,ROSES,BUDS,LEAVES &
  STEMS.......................................................    75.00
WEBB SATIN GLASS CIRCA 1890 VASE,WATERMELON
  COLOUR,GOLD,BROWN...........................................   485.00
WEBB SATIN GLASS MOTHER OF PEARL VASE,GOLD COLOUR,RAINDROP
  PATTERN.....................................................    55.00
WEBB SATIN GLASS VASE,5 IN. TALL,PINK TO APRICOT,WHITE LINED     40.00
WEBB SATIN GLASS YELLOW PITCHER,APPLIED CAMPHOR SHELL HANDLE     75.00
WEBB SATIN VASE IN ALTERNATING VERTICAL RIBBON STRIPES OF
  PINK........................................................   100.00
WEBB SIGNED 10 IN. VASE,CLEAR & ETCHED........................    45.00
WEBB SIGNED SUGAR SHAKER,CLEAR WITH SIMPLE CUTTING...........     20.00
WEBB TYPE VASE,PAIR,11 IN. TALL..............................    145.00
WEBB VASE,CABINET,BURMESE,ENAMELLED BLUE & WHITE FLOWERS....     295.00
WEBB VASE,CASED,GOLD ENAMELLED BUTTERFLY,GOLD & WHITE
  FLOWERS & STEMS.............................................    65.00
WEBB VASE,FLOWER FORM,BURMESE,SILVER HOLDER..................    195.00
WEBB VASE,GOLD SATIN GLASS,TURQUOISE BLUE ENAMEL.............     87.50
WEBB VASE,MARKED,6 IN. HIGH,SHINY BLUE TO WHITE,GOLD FLORAL
  & VINE......................................................   155.00
WEBB VASE,OPAL BASE,GOLDEN MIRROR IRIDESCENT.................     40.00
WEBB VASE,SATIN GLASS,ROSE RED TO PINK AT BASE,ENAMEL.......     85.00
WEBB VASE,WHITE TO BLUE,IVORY LINING,COIN GOLD MATSUNOKE
  DECORATED...................................................    85.00
WEBB YELLOW SATIN COMPOTE,4 CAMPHOR SATIN FEET,.............     48.00
```

*WEDGWOOD POTTERY has been made at the famous Wedgwood factory in Eng-
land since 1759. A large variety of wares have been made including the well-
known jasper ware, basalt, creamware, and even a limited amount of porcelain.*

```
WEDGWOOD BARREL,BISCUIT,BLUE,GRECIAN FIGURES,SILVER PLATE
  HANDLE......................................................    35.00
WEDGWOOD 18 PIECES,BLUE & GOLD WORK,EDWARDIAN,PORCELAIN.....     300.00
WEDGWOOD BARREL,BISCUIT,BLUE,SILVER PLATE COVER & HANDLE....      60.00
WEDGWOOD BARREL,BISCUIT,BLUE WITH WHITE FIGURES.............      55.00
WEDGWOOD BARREL,BISCUIT,GREEN WITH WHITE CLASSIC
  FIGURES,SILVER LID..........................................    95.00
WEDGWOOD BARREL,BISCUIT,JASPER,BLACK WITH WHITE CLASSICAL
  FIGURES.....................................................   125.00
WEDGWOOD BASKET,CHESTNUT,QUEENSWARE CIRCA 1890-1900.........      80.00
WEDGWOOD BASKET,JASPERWARE,BAMBOO WITH GREEN LEAVES & GRAPES
  IN RELIEF...................................................    75.00
WEDGWOOD BOWL,BASALT,BLACK,FLAT,2 IN. HIGH,9 IN. DIAMETER...      50.00
WEDGWOOD BOWL,BASALT,BLACK,IMPRESSED WEDGWOOD................     75.00
WEDGWOOD BOWL,BASALT,RIBBED,FOOTED...........................     40.00
WEDGWOOD BOWL,BLUE WITH WHITE,SILVER RIM,FLAT...............      60.00
WEDGWOOD BOWL,GREEN,3 FOOTED,MARKED WEDGWOOD-ENGLAND........      65.00
WEDGWOOD BOWL,JASPERWARE,GREEN WITH WHITE LEAVES IN
  RELIEF,IMPRESSED............................................    65.00
WEDGWOOD BOWL,PEDESTAL BASE,BASALT,BLACK.....................    325.00
WEDGWOOD BOWL,SALAD,BLUE,SILVER-BORDERED TOP,MARKED WEDGWOOD      85.00
WEDGWOOD BOWL,YELLOW GLAZED WITH BLACK OVERLAY VINE DECOR...      25.00
WEDGWOOD BOX,COVERED,CIRCULAR,JASPER,BLUE,IMPRESSED WEDGWOOD
  & YZX.......................................................    45.00
WEDGWOOD BOX,MATCH,JASPERWARE,BLUE & WHITE,MARKED WEDGWOOD
  ENGLAND.....................................................    20.00
WEDGWOOD BOX,PATCH,BLUE WITH WHITE RELIEFS,SIGNED...........      25.00
WEDGWOOD BOX,ROUND,JASPER,BLUE WITH WHITE CLASSICAL
  MEDALLIONS..................................................    35.00
WEDGWOOD BUCKET,BLUE WITH WHITE,SILVER RIM & BAIL...........      52.50
WEDGWOOD BUTTER DISH,BLUE WITH WHITE CLASSICAL
  FIGURES,SILVER COVER........................................    37.00
WEDGWOOD CANDLESTICK,BLUE WITH WHITE CLASSICAL
```

```
DESIGN,IMPRESSED ENGLAND.................................   25.00
WEDGWOOD CANDLESTICK,JASPERWARE,BLUE,WHITE FIGURES,SIGNED...   42.00
WEDGWOOD CANDLESTICK,JASPERWARE,GREEN & WHITE,MARKED
   ENGLAND...............................................   43.00
WEDGWOOD CANDLESTICK,JASPERWARE,MARKED WEDGWOOD ENGLAND.....   38.00
WEDGWOOD CANDLESTICKS,PAIR,JASPERWARE,COBALT BLUE & WHITE...  125.00
WEDGWOOD COMPOTE,SIGNED,REBECCA GIVES PIECE OF MONEY TO
   GURTH................................................   28.00
WEDGWOOD CREAM & SUGAR,BLUE & WHITE PORCELAIN..............   12.50
WEDGWOOD CREAMER,5 IN.,ENGLAND............................   18.00
WEDGWOOD CREAMER,BLUE WITH WHITE CLASSIC FIGURES,IMPRESSED..   28.00
WEDGWOOD CREAMER,BLUE WITH WHITE RAISED CLASSIC FIGURES.....   22.00
WEDGWOOD CREAMER,DARK BLUE,ENGLAND........................   28.00
WEDGWOOD CREAMER,JASPER,BLUE ,MARKED WITH WHITE CREST OF
   ENGLAND...............................................   32.00
WEDGWOOD CREAMER,JASPERWARE,BLUE WITH WHITE FIGURES,SIGNED..   20.00
WEDGWOOD CUP & SAUCER,GOLD EMBOSSED.......................   12.50
WEDGWOOD CUP & SAUCER,GREEN,1958..........................   13.00
WEDGWOOD DISH,CHEESE,BASALT,BLACK WITH WHITE CLASSIC FIGURES  175.00
WEDGWOOD DISH,CHEESE,COVERED,ROUND,BLUE WITH WHITE
   FIGURES,FERNS.........................................   85.00
WEDGWOOD DISH,CHEESE,COVERED,WHITE FERN LEAVES & FLOWERS....   89.00
WEDGWOOD DISH,COVERED,FISH-HANDLED........................   17.50
WEDGWOOD DISH,GREEN MAJOLICA LEAF FORM,19TH CENTURY.........   17.50
WEDGWOOD DISH,NUT,PEDESTALED,WHITE LEAF ON BLUE WITH
   CLASSICAL FIGURES.....................................   50.00
WEDGWOOD DISH,VEGETABLE,COVERED,HANDLED,BLUE & WHITE,MARKED.   10.00
WEDGWOOD EGG CUP,HANDLED,BROWN,CALIFORNIA..................    6.00
WEDGWOOD FIGURINE,BASALT,BLACK,SPRING,WOMAN & DOVE,10 IN....  300.00
WEDGWOOD FIGURINE,CAT,BASALT,BLACK,4 IN. HIGH.............  150.00
WEDGWOOD HAIR RECEIVER,JASPER,BLUE,MARKED ENGLAND..........   45.00
WEDGWOOD JAR,BISCUIT,JASPERWARE,BLUE & WHITE,SILVER
   TRIM,MARKED...........................................   62.00
WEDGWOOD JAR,BISCUIT,JASPERWARE,BLUE WITH WHITE CLASSIC
   FIGURES,MARKED........................................   90.00
WEDGWOOD JAR,BISCUIT,SILVER COLLAR & TOP..................   60.00
WEDGWOOD JAR,CRACKER,BLUE.................................   85.00
WEDGWOOD JAR,CRACKER,BLUE & WHITE,SILVER PLATE OVER BRASS
   FRAME.................................................   38.00
WEDGWOOD JAR,CRACKER,BLUE,NICKEL PLATED RIM,BAIL & COVER....   47.50
WEDGWOOD JAR,CRACKER,BLUE,SILVER COVER & 3 BALL FEET,8 IN.
   TALL..................................................   52.00
WEDGWOOD JAR,CRACKER,BLUE WITH WHITE CLASSICAL FIGURES......   50.00
WEDGWOOD JAR,CRACKER,BLUE WITH WHITE FIGURES IN RELIEF......   75.00
WEDGWOOD JAR,CRACKER,DARK BLUE WITH WHITE,SILVER LID,MARKED.   70.00
WEDGWOOD JAR,CRACKER,GREEN,NUT FINIAL & LEAVES & STEMS IN
   WHITE.................................................   60.00
WEDGWOOD JAR,CRACKER,JASPERWARE,BLUE & WHITE CLASSIC
   SCENE,RELIEFS.........................................   60.00
WEDGWOOD JAR,CRACKER,JASPERWARE,BLUE WITH CLASSIC
   FIGURES,SIGNED........................................   50.00
WEDGWOOD JAR,MUSTARD,JASPERWARE,BLUE & WHITE,SILVER
   TOP,MARKED............................................   28.00
WEDGWOOD JAR,SUGAR,BLUE WITH SILVER LID...................   19.50
WEDGWOOD JAR,TOBACCO,BLUE WITH WHITE CLASSIC FIGURES,ACORN
   FINIAL................................................   45.00
WEDGWOOD JAR,TOBACCO,WHITE LEAF ON BLUE,COVERED,SIGNED......   75.00
WEDGWOOD JARDINIERE,GREEN WITH WHITE CLASSIC FIGURES........  125.00
WEDGWOOD JARDINIERE,IMPRESSED MARK........................   50.00
WEDGWOOD JUG,TOBY,ELIHU YALE,6 IN. HIGH...................   75.00
WEDGWOOD JUG,SYRUP,HINGED PEWTER COVER,BLUE WITH WHITE
   GRAPES................................................   48.00
WEDGWOOD JUG,SYRUP,LAVENDER,SILVER FINIAL,HINGED SILVER
   COVER.................................................   65.00
WEDGWOOD JUG WITH SILVER PLATE TOP,JASPER,BLUE &
```

WHITE, IMPRESSED.. 48.00
WEDGWOOD MATCH HOLDER, GREEN WITH WHITE RIBBED CENTER
  STRIKER, 3 IN. HIGH.. 30.00
WEDGWOOD MATCH HOLDER, WHITE ON BLUE............................. 12.50
WEDGWOOD MATCH SAFE, BLUE.. 17.50
WEDGWOOD MOLD OVAL IMPRESSED EAGLE, DUCK, PIGEON................. 65.00
WEDGWOOD MOLD, SOAP, POTTERY, LEAVES & BERRIES, IMPRESSED........ 10.00
WEDGWOOD MUFFINEER 6 IN. HIGH MARKED WEDGWOOD.................... 49.50
WEDGWOOD MUFFINEER, JASPERWARE, BLUE & WHITE..................... 50.00
WEDGWOOD MUSTARD, 2 SALTS & PEPPER SHAKERS, STERLING TOPS....... 35.00
WEDGWOOD PERFUME, BLUE & WHITE, FALCON........................... 25.00
WEDGWOOD PIN, BLUE IN GOLD MOUNT, MARKED......................... 45.00
WEDGWOOD PIN, OVAL, SAFETY CLASP, ROLLED STERLING FRAME, LADY
  WITH LYRE... 15.00
WEDGWOOD PITCHER, BLUE, 7 IN. HIGH............................... 85.00
WEDGWOOD PITCHER, BLUE & SILVER RESIST, BULBOUS, FALLOW DEER.... 12.50
WEDGWOOD PITCHER, BLUE & WHITE, 8 IN., MARKED................... 95.00
WEDGWOOD PITCHER, BLUE & WHITE CLASSICAL SCENE, GRAPES &
  CUPIDS, 8 IN.,.. 38.00
WEDGWOOD PITCHER, BLUE, MARKED WEDGWOOD ENGLAND................. 35.00
WEDGWOOD PITCHER, GREEN & WHITE, ROPE HANDLE, MARKED WEDGWOOD
  ENGLAND... 57.00
WEDGWOOD PITCHER, JASPER, BLACK, ROPE HANDLE, MATERMAN
  AFFECTION, MARKED... 85.00
WEDGWOOD PITCHER, JASPERWARE, BLUE & WHITE, MARKED, CLASSICAL
  FIGURES... 27.00
WEDGWOOD PITCHER, JASPERWARE, GREEN & WHITE, MARKED WEDGWOOD
  ENGLAND... 50.00
WEDGWOOD PITCHER, LAVENDER WITH WHITE TREES & FIGURES, 4 IN.
  TALL, ENGLAND... 35.00
WEDGWOOD PITCHER, MILK, BASALT, BLACK WITH SHAMROCKS, LYRE &
  SUNFLOWERS.. 70.00
WEDGWOOD PITCHER, POWDER BLUE WITH WHITE CLASSICAL FIGURES... 38.00
WEDGWOOD PITCHER, TANKARD SHAPE, GREEN WITH WHITE RAISED
  GRAPES & LEAVES... 48.00
WEDGWOOD PITCHER, WHITE WITH BLUE, 7 IN. TALL, SIGNED.......... 22.50
WEDGWOOD PITCHER, WHITE WITH BLUE RAISED FOXHUNT SCENE, 19TH
  CENTURY... 75.00
WEDGWOOD PLATE, 9 IN., U.T.C. OF AMERICA & FIRST
  CHURCH, QUINCY, MASS.. 7.00
WEDGWOOD PLATE, 10 IN., IVANHOE SERIES, FRIAR TUCK ENTERTAINS
  BLACK KNIGHT.. 16.50
WEDGWOOD PLATE, 10 IN., ST. LAWRENCE SEAWAY 1959............... 3.50
WEDGWOOD PLATE, 1909, YE KING OF CLUBS DOTH MAKE DECREE....... 15.00
WEDGWOOD PLATE, 1909, YE KNAVE OF HEARTS DOTH TEND EACH
  THOUGHT... 15.00
WEDGWOOD PLATE, BLUE, 9 IN., COMMEMORATIVE OLD CITY
  GATEWAY, ST. AUGUSTINE.. 8.50
WEDGWOOD PLATE, BLUE & WHITE, 8 IN., CONNECTICUT CHURCH........ 10.00
WEDGWOOD PLATE, BLUE & WHITE, 9 IN., COMMEMORATIVE ERIE CANAL
  DATE 1899... 7.50
WEDGWOOD PLATE, BLUE & WHITE, 10 IN., COMMEMORATIVE WEST POINT
  1933.. 9.00
WEDGWOOD PLATE, BLUE & WHITE, COMMEMORATION HOWE TAVERN........ 9.50
WEDGWOOD PLATE, BLUE & WHITE, COMMEMORATION, IMPRESSED, MARKED
  ETRURIA... 15.00
WEDGWOOD PLATE, BLUE & WHITE, COMMEMORATION OLD STATE HOUSE
  BOSTON.. 9.50
WEDGWOOD PLATE, BLUE & WHITE, COMMEMORATION THE RED HORSE..... 9.50
WEDGWOOD PLATE, BLUE & WHITE, COMMEMORATION THE WAYSIDE INN
  1883.. 9.50
WEDGWOOD PLATE, BLUE & WHITE PORCELAIN, 8 IN.................. 6.50
WEDGWOOD PLATE, BLUE & WHITE, COMMEMORATION SARATOGA BATTLE
  MOMUMENT.. 10.00
WEDGWOOD PLATE, BLUE CENTER TRANSFER, RIM GRAPES & WHEAT, 10

IN.,MARKED... 9.50
WEDGWOOD PLATE,BLUE,COMMEMORATIVE ARLINGTON HOME OF ROBERT
E.LEE... 12.00
WEDGWOOD PLATE,BLUE,COMMEMORATION,OLD MAN OF THE MOUNTAINS.. 9.50
WEDGWOOD PLATE,COMMEMORATION PILGRIM EXILES.................... 7.50
WEDGWOOD PLATE,BLUE ENGLISH COUNTRY SCENE..................... 10.00
WEDGWOOD PLATE,BLUE,FORT TICONDEROGA,SIGNED.................. 8.50
WEDGWOOD PLATE,BLUE-GREY WITH VINE & GRAPE BORDER,9 IN.,1875 12.00
WEDGWOOD PLATE,BLUE,LONGFELLOWS HOME IN PORTLAND
MAINE,MARKED... 6.50
WEDGWOOD PLATE,BLUE ON WHITE,9 IN.,OLD BOSTON THEATRE 1794.. 15.00
WEDGWOOD PLATE,BLUE,WORLDS FAIR 1939,10 IN.,GEORGE
WASHINGTON... 12.00
WEDGWOOD PLATE,BROWN,COMMEMORATION JOHN QUINCY ADAMS HOUSE.. 9.50
WEDGWOOD PLATE,CALENDAR,BLUE & WHITE,JANUARY................. 22.50
WEDGWOOD PLATE,COLUMBIA UNIVERSITY,MARKED ETRURIA,ENGLAND... 9.00
WEDGWOOD PLATE,COMMEMORATION BOSTON COMMON & STATE HOUSE
1836... 12.00
WEDGWOOD PLATE,COMMEMORATION CITY HALL,HARTFORD.............. 5.50
WEDGWOOD PLATE,COMMEMORATION NIAGARA FALLS................... 8.00
WEDGWOOD PLATE,COMMEMORATION PILGRIM MEMORIAL MONUMENT...... 9.00
WEDGWOOD PLATE,COMMEMORATION,OLD BOSTON STATE HOUSE EAST END
1890... 10.00
WEDGWOOD PLATE,COMMEMORATION,OLD WINDMILL NANTUCKET ISLAND.. 12.50
WEDGWOOD PLATE,COMMEMORATION,THE BOSTON PUBLIC LIBRARY...... 12.00
WEDGWOOD PLATE,COW.. 22.50
WEDGWOOD PLATE,DINNER,9 IN.,BOSTON,MARKED ETRURIA ENGLAND... 12.00
WEDGWOOD PLATE,DINNER,SET OF 10 10 IN.,BLUE,LANDSCAPE
PATTERNED... 45.00
WEDGWOOD PLATE,EDWARD VIII CORONATION......................... 5.00
WEDGWOOD PLATE,GAME,BIRD OF PARADISE CENTER................... 9.00
WEDGWOOD PLATE,GAME,WILD TURKEY,GREEN,SIGNED.................. 8.50
WEDGWOOD PLATE,GREEN VINE & PINK FLOWER BORDER,MARKED,7 IN.. 7.50
WEDGWOOD PLATE,HANGING,BLUE,OLD STATE HOUSE,BOSTON........... 7.50
WEDGWOOD PLATE,LONGFELLOWS HOME COMMEMORATION................ 8.00
WEDGWOOD PLATE,PINK,NEW YORK UNIVERSITY....................... 7.00
WEDGWOOD PLATE,RED,10 IN.,WORLDS FAIR 1939,GEORGE WASHINGTON 12.00
WEDGWOOD PLATE,RED RIDING HOOD,WOLF IN BED,ETRURIA,ENGLAND.. 25.00
WEDGWOOD PLATE,ROSE DESIGN....................................... 3.00
WEDGWOOD PLATE,SET OF 9,COW,10 IN.............................. 22.50
WEDGWOOD PLATE,SEPIA,1930 BICENTENARY,9 IN.................... 18.00
WEDGWOOD PLATE,WASHINGTON ELM,CAMBRIDGE....................... 6.50
WEDGWOOD PLATE,WORLDS COLUMBIAN EXPOSITION,ELECTRICAL
BUILDING.. 5.50
WEDGWOOD PLATES,10 HARVARD TERCENTENARY....................... 40.00
WEDGWOOD PLATTER,COW,17 IN....................................... 45.00
WEDGWOOD PLATTER,OVAL,BOSTON,MARKED ETRURIA ENGLAND.......... 30.00
WEDGWOOD RING TREE,BLUE WITH WHITE FIGURES & HORSES.......... 35.00
WEDGWOOD SAUCER,BASALT,CANADA,ENGLISH.......................... 5.00
WEDGWOOD SAUCER,GREEN VINE & PINK FLOWER BORDER,MARKED...... 3.50
WEDGWOOD SHAKER,PEPPER,JASPER,BLUE WITH WHITE FIGURES....... 29.50
WEDGWOOD SOUP DISH,IVANHOE SERIES............................... 10.00
WEDGWOOD SOUP PLATE,BOSTON,MARKED ETRURIA ENGLAND........... 12.00
WEDGWOOD SUGAR & CREAMER,COVERED,JASPERWARE,BLUE............. 65.00
WEDGWOOD SUGAR,BASALT,BLACK,SHEAF OF WHEAT FINIAL........... 67.50
WEDGWOOD SUGAR BOWL,BASALT,SHEAF OF WHEAT FINIAL............ 55.00
WEDGWOOD SUGAR BOWL,COVERED,EASTERN FLOWERS PATTERN......... 6.00
WEDGWOOD SUGAR,COVERED,GREEN WITH WHITE CLASSICAL
FIGURES,SIGNED.. 32.00
WEDGWOOD SUGAR SHAKER WITH SILVER PLATE MOUNT,JASPER,BLUE &
WHITE,.. 40.00
WEDGWOOD SYRUP,JASPERWARE,CLASSIC FIGURES,IMPRESSED WEDGWOOD 55.00
WEDGWOOD SYRUP WITH COVER,3 COLOUR.............................. 185.00
WEDGWOOD TEAPOT,BASALT,4 LIONS & WHITE CROSS,IMPRESSED
WEDGWOOD.. 45.00

WEDGWOOD TEAPOT,BLUE... 50.00
WEDGWOOD TEAPOT,BLUE & WHITE PORCELAIN.......................... 8.00
WEDGWOOD TEAPOT,GREEN,ENGLAND................................... 35.00
WEDGWOOD TEAPOT,GREEN WITH WHITE CLASSIC FIGURES............... 55.00
WEDGWOOD TEAPOT,JASPERWARE,BLUE & WHITE,MARKED WEDGWOOD
  ENGLAND... 36.00
WEDGWOOD TEAPOT,JASPERWARE,BLUE WITH WHITE CLASSIC
  FIGURES,IMPRESSED... 45.00
WEDGWOOD TEA SET,BASALT,BLACK................................... 87.50
WEDGWOOD TEA SET,BASALT,BLACK WITH WHITE CLASSICAL FIGURES,3
  PIECES... 110.00
WEDGWOOD TEA SET,BLUE,MARKED WEDGWOOD-ENGLAND.................. 110.00
WEDGWOOD TEA SET,BLUE WITH CLASSIC FIGURES,3 PIECES,ENGLAND. 75.00
WEDGWOOD TILE,ROUNDTABLE,BLACK & WHITE......................... 42.00
WEDGWOOD TRAY,BLUE... 46.50
WEDGWOOD TRAY,BLUE,CIRCA 1891.................................. 30.00
WEDGWOOD TRAY,BLUE WITH WHITE CLASSICAL FIGURES,10 X 7
  IN.,SIGNED.. 65.00
WEDGWOOD TRAY,LIGHT BLUE....................................... 32.50
WEDGWOOD TRAY,PICKLE,FLORAL.................................... 3.50
WEDGWOOD TUB,BLUE WITH WHITE,SILVER RIM........................ 42.50
WEDGWOOD URN WITH HANDLES & COVER,BLUE,WHITE & GREEN......... 225.00
WEDGWOOD VASE & COVERED DISH,TAN,MADE IN ENGLAND.............. 20.00
WEDGWOOD VASE,BASALT,BLACK,WHITE FLOWER BORDER,ENGLAND....... 25.00
WEDGWOOD VASE,BASALT,BLACK WITH GOLD PLUME LIKE LEAVES,12
  IN... 300.00
WEDGWOOD VASE,BLUE & WHITE CLASSICAL FIGURES,5 IN. HIGH..... 75.00
WEDGWOOD VASE,BLUE & WHITE PORCELAIN,PORTLAND,SHIP CENTER... 6.50
WEDGWOOD VASE,BUD,JASPER,BLACK,MARKED.......................... 75.00
WEDGWOOD VASE,CYLINDER,BLUE & WHITE............................ 32.50
WEDGWOOD VASE,JASPER,BLUE & WHITE FIGURES,5 IN............... 37.50
WEDGWOOD VASE,RED FAIRYLAND LUSTER,PORTLAND MOTIF,DRAGON.... 125.00

WELLER POTTERY was made in Fultonham, Ohio, from 1873 to 1900. The most famous pottery made at the factory was art pottery that resembled Rookwood, and a type of gold metallic luster pottery.

WELLER ART NOUVEAU FEMALE ON VASE,PURPLE & GREENS,DOLPHIN... 75.00
WELLER ART NOUVEAU VASE,9 IN.,SIGNED........................... 19.00
WELLER ART NOUVEAU VASE,SIGNED,4 FOOTED,JEWELED............... 75.00
WELLER BASKET,HANGING,POTTERY,TAN & GREEN WITH APPLIED
  FLOWERS.. 6.50
WELLER BASKET,SIGNED,2 HANDLED,ROSES........................... 12.00
WELLER BOWL WITH CATTAILS & WATER LILIES,GREEN & BROWN,12
  IN.. 25.00
WELLER CANDLE HOLDER,GREEN,3 IN. HIGH,POTTERY................ 2.50
WELLER CANDLE HOLDER,WHITE,5-HOLE,8 IN. AT CENTER,ARC OF
  PINK ROSE BUDS... 15.00
WELLER CANDLEHOLDER SHAPED LIKE JUG,HANDLED,FLORAL DECOR.... 25.00
WELLER CANDLESTICK,POTTERY..................................... 3.00
WELLER CONSOLE,3 PIECE,9 IN. DIAMETER BOWL.................... 10.00
WELLER DICKENSWARE MUG,INCISED DESIGN INDIAN & TAME WOLF.... 50.00
WELLER DICKENSWARE VASE,9 IN.................................... 45.00
WELLER DICKENSWARE VASE,11 IN. HIGH,OVOIDAL,PORTRAIT........ 75.00
WELLER DICKENSWARE VASE,BOTTLE SHAPED,11 IN. HIGH........... 85.00
WELLER DICKENSWARE VASE,BOY GOLFER............................. 78.00
WELLER DICKENSWARE VASE,SIGNED,HEART SHAPE,MONK ON FRONT... 40.00
WELLER DICKENSWARE VASE WITH INCISED SCENE OF 2 GOLFERS &
  CADDY... 100.00
WELLER FISH STANDING ON TAIL................................... 25.00
WELLER FLOWER BOWL WITH FROG,BROWN & FLORAL................... 35.00
WELLER FLOWER FORM SHAPED LIKE LOBSTER,SIGNED................. 8.00
WELLER FLOWER FROG,IMPRESSED CIRCULAR.......................... 4.75
WELLER FLOWER FROG,MARKED,LOBSTER.............................. 9.00
WELLER FLOWER FROG SHAPED LIKE TURTLE,INCISED................. 9.00
WELLER FRUIT BOWL,12 IN. ACROSS, 3 IN. HIGH,LILY LEAF

```
PATTERN.................................................  24.00
WELLER JARDINIERE,BROWN DESIGN IMPRESSED PINEAPPLE..........  10.00
WELLER JUG,SIGNED,ROUND,HANDLED,GLOSSY BROWN,YELLOW EAR OF
  CORN....................................................  30.00
WELLER LAMP BASE,SIGNED,BRASS BASE,CAP & CENTER ROD,SCENIC..  39.00
WELLER LAMAR VASE,RED WITH BLACK TREES & BIRDS.............  75.00
WELLER LASA SIGNED VASE,5 IN. HIGH........................  55.00
WELLER,LOUWELSA 6 IN. VASE,GLOSSY,ORANGE TO BROWN,YELLOW
  FLOWER & GREEN..........................................  23.00
WELLER ,LOUWELSA CABINET VASE,TOP BROWN,BOTTOM AMBER.........  18.00
WELLER LOUWELSA CHERRY VASE,2 HANDLES......................  25.00
WELLER LOUWELSA JARDINIERE................................  30.00
WELLER LOUWELSA MUG,BROWN TONES,CHERRY DECORATED...........  22.00
WELLER LOUWELSA VASE,6 IN.,BROWN & ORANGE..................  25.00
WELLER LOUWELSA VASE,BROWN WITH YELLOW FLOWERS,8 IN.........  22.00
WELLER MUG,BEER FROM LANCASTERS LTD.,5 IN.,LAMP POST HANDLE.  12.50
WELLER MUG,HANDLED,GREY GROUND,PURPLE GRAPES...............  25.00
WELLER MUG,MARKED,6 IN.,CHERRIES DECOR....................  16.00
WELLER PITCHER,CREAM WITH BLUE BAND........................   4.50
WELLER PITCHER,PAIR,WATER,SIGNED..........................  17.50
WELLER PITCHER,SIGNED,6 IN.,GREY TO PINK,PINK FLOWERS.......  15.00
WELLER PITCHER,WATER,7 IN.,CREAM COLOURED BASKETWEAVE DECOR.   8.50
WELLER PLANTER,11 IN.,OAK LOG WITH LEAF DECOR,AUTUMN
  COLOURS,FOOTED.........................................   8.00
WELLER PLANTER,MARKED,FOOTED,LOG..........................   9.50
WELLER PLANTER,MARKED,TREE BARK...........................   7.00
WELLER PLAQUE,SIGNED,4 IN.,LINCOLN........................  18.50
WELLER PUNCHBOWL,3 FOOTED,SIGNED,BROWN WITH AMBER LEAVES &
  FRUIT..................................................  72.00
WELLER SICARD SIGNED 7 IN. VASE...........................  75.00
WELLER SICARD 11 IN. IRIDESCENT POTTERY,FLORAL,SIGNED
  WELLERWEAR.............................................  75.00
WELLER SICARD SIGNED 6 IN. VASE,STAR & STRIPE DESIGN.......  65.00
WELLER SICARD SIGNED BULBOUS VASE,GREEN & SILVER SHAMROCKS
  ON REDDISH.............................................  75.00
WELLER SICARD,SIGNED,PURPLE BACKGROUND WITH BLUE FLOWERS....  47.00
WELLER TANKARD SIGNED ETNA,GREY-BLUE TO OFF WHITE,PURPLE
  GRAPES.................................................  47.50
WELLER TEAPOT,PINEAPPLE SHAPE.............................  15.00
WELLER TOBACCO HUMIDOR,SIGNED,PIPE ON BROWN...............  65.00
WELLER TUMBLER,POTTERY,4 IN.,MARKED,PINK & WHITE FLOWERS....  22.50
WELLER UMBRELLA HOLDER,IMPRESSED,20 IN.,BROWN TO GREEN TO
  PINK...................................................  35.00
WELLER VASE,4 HANDLES AT NECK,GRAY WITH PURPLE GRAPES.......  30.00
WELLER VASE,7 IN.,6 SIDED,APPLE BLOSSOMS ON BROWN...........  10.00
WELLER VASE,7 IN. HIGH,IVORY COLOUR,ROSES,LEAVES,HANDLE.....  18.00
WELLER VASE,7 IN.,MARKED,BLUE WITH YELLOW FLOWER...........   6.50
WELLER VASE,8 IN. HIGH....................................   4.00
WELLER VASE,9 IN.,GREEN & BROWN...........................   4.00
WELLER VASE,9 IN. HIGH,GLOSSY BROWN,WHEAT,MARKED...........  18.50
WELLER VASE,9 IN. TALL,GREY TOP TO PINK BOTTOM,ROSE IN
  RED,POTTERY............................................  19.00
WELLER VASE,10 IN.,BLUE,GREEN,SYLVAN SCENE.................  18.00
WELLER VASE,BLUE,7 IN. TALL,SIGNED........................   4.00
WELLER VASE,BUD,POTTERY,MARKED,GREEN,PINK & BLUE FLORAL.....  12.50
WELLER VASE,GREY,GREEN....................................   4.50
WELLER VASE,GREEN,DOUBLE,HANDLED,WHITE FLOWER..............   5.50
WELLER VASE,GREEN,WHITE FLOWER............................   4.50
WELLER VASE,GREEN WITH WATER LILIES & CATTAILS.............   7.50
WELLER VASE,INCISED,14 IN. HIGH,PINK,HANDLES,MARKED H.ADAMS
  ARTIST.................................................  20.00
WELLER VASE,MARKED,2 HANDLED,BLUE,YELLOW FLOWER...........   4.95
WELLER VASE,MARKED,2 HANDLED,GREEN WITH WHITE FLOWER.......   4.50
WELLER VASE,MARKED,12 IN.,BEIGE...........................   8.00
WELLER VASE,MARKED,BLUE,WALL,PINK ROSES...................   7.00
```

```
WELLER VASE,MARKED ,GLOSSY BROWN WITH ROSES IN GOLD & CORAL.      15.00
WELLER VASE,MOTTLED BLUE...........................................   8.00
WELLER VASE,PAIR 8 IN.,POTTERY....................................  15.00
WELLER VASE,POPPIES,BUTTERFLIES,POTTERY...........................  35.00
WELLER VASE,RIBBED,GUN METAL BROWN................................  12.00
WELLER VASE,SIGNED,2 IN.,ORANGE,YELLOW & GREEN FLORAL.......       27.50
WELLER VASE,SIGNED,8 IN.,2 HANDLED,PEACH COLOUR,FLOWER DECOR        9.50
WELLER VASE,SIGNED,9 IN. TALL,FLORAL DECOR,LOOP HANDLES.....       15.00
WELLER VASE,SIGNED,13 IN.,SATIN FINISH,RAISED FRUIT DESIGN..       22.50
WELLER VASE,SIGNED,APRICOT SHADINGS,2 PRIMROSES & GREEN
  LEAVES..........................................................  10.00
WELLER VASE,SIGNED FLORETTE,6 IN.,EMBOSSED FLOWERS...........      12.50
WELLER VASE,SIGNED,GREEN & BEIGE,APPLE TREE TRUNK WITH OWL..       35.00
WELLER VASE,SIGNED,PAIR 8 IN......................................  45.00
WELLER VASE,SIGNED,WALLFLOWER,GREEN WITH ROSES...............      16.00
WELLER WALL VASE,9 IN. TALL,MOTHER BIRD FEEDING YOUNG ON
  BOUGH...........................................................   9.00
WICKER LUNCH BASKET...............................................   3.00
WIREWORK FRUIT COMPOTE............................................   8.50
WITCH BALL, 2 IN. , BRILLIANT CRYSTAL.............................  50.00
WHEELOCK GERMANY 3 IN. COVERED SUGAR,GREEN & PURPLE,ROSE
  DECOR...........................................................  12.50
WHEELOCK GERMANY 9 IN. BOWL,GOLD SCALLOPED RIM,RED ROSE
  DECOR...........................................................  20.00
WHEELOCK,PRUSSIA PLATE,CREAMY ROSES,BUDS,GREEN LEAVES ON
  PINK............................................................  19.50
WHEELOCK PRUSSIA RELISH DISH,BLUE & GREEN WITH WATER LILY
  DECOR...........................................................   9.50
WHEELOCK TRADE MARK PRUSSIAN 4 FOOTED 2 HANDLED COVERED
  SUGAR...........................................................   9.50
     WILLOW, SEE BLUE WILLOW......................................
     WOODEN, SEE ALSO KITCHEN, STORE, TOOL.......................
WOODEN BARREL,BISCUIT,OAK,PORCELAIN LINED,SILVER PLATED
  COVER & HANDLE..................................................  25.00
WOODEN BENCH,COBBLERS,PINE,DRAWER & SHOES..................       150.00
WOODEN BITSTOCK,14 IN.,BRASS SETTINGS & BOUND,SHEFFIELD
  ENGLAND.........................................................  25.00
WOODEN BOARD,BREAD,DECORATED......................................  35.00
WOODEN BOARD,CHESS,BLACK,GOLD SQUARES.............................  16.50
WOODEN BOARD,SKIN DRYING,ARCHED TOP,FLATTISH..................       2.00
WOODEN BOTTLE,24 IN. TALL,JACK KELLYS BLUE GRASS 1865.......       35.00
WOODEN BOTTLE,AMBER,FROM OLD DRUG STORE,1/2 GALLON..........        3.00
WOODEN BOTTLE,ROUND SIDE,AQUA,EMBOSSED COCA COLA &
  SAVANNAH,GEORGIA................................................   2.75
WOODEN BOTTLE,SOUTH CAROLINA DISPENSARY,WHISKEY,CLEAR W WITH
  EMBLEM..........................................................   9.50
WOODEN BOWL, 12 IN.,BURNT GRAPE DESIGNS...........................   5.00
WOODEN BOWL,BURL,12 IN. DIAMETER.................................. 110.00
WOODEN BOWL,BIRDS EYE MAPLE.......................................  12.50
WOODEN BOWL,BUTTER,OBLONG,HAND HEWN...............................  30.00
WOODEN BOWL,BUTTER,ROUND..........................................   4.50
WOODEN BOWL,CHOPPING,BIRDSEYE MAPLE...............................  22.50
WOODEN BOWL,HANDMADE,RECTANGULAR..................................  20.00
WOODEN BOWL,MAPLE.................................................  22.50
WOODEN BOWL,OVAL,COUNTRY PAINTING OF ACORNS & LEAVES.........       6.00
WOODEN BOWL,ROSEWOOD BURL.........................................  25.00
WOODEN BOWL,ROUND,CHOPPING,HAND MADE..............................  22.50
WOODEN BOX,ALMS,1840 PERIOD,MAHOGANY,CARVED LID,SILVER
  MALTESE CROSS...................................................  89.50
WOODEN BOX,AMERICAN PINE CANDLE,HAND DOVETAILED CORNERS.....       16.50
WOODEN BOX,CANDLE,PINE,DOVETAILED,SLIDING COVER,MUSTARD
  COLOUR..........................................................  22.00
WOODEN BOX,CIGAR & TOBACCO,CROTCH MAHOGANY,CIRCA
  1850,AMSTERDAM..................................................  30.00
WOODEN BOX,CIGAR,BLUE CURLS,1901..................................   3.00
```

WOODEN BOX,CIGAR,MAHOGANY.................................	15.00
WOODEN BOX,CIGAR,MAHOGANY WITH TORTOISE SHELL	
VENEER,EDWARDIAN......................................	58.50
WOODEN BOX,CIGAR,NOVELTY,BIRD & CIGAR ON BASE..............	3.00
WOODEN BOX,CUTLERY,2 SECTION..............................	3.50
WOODEN BOX,HANDKERCHIEF,SATIN LINED,1900..................	3.50
WOODEN BOX,HANDMADE WITH HANDMADE SHOT....................	9.00
WOODEN BOX,HERB,OVAL,5 IN.,COPPER TACKS..................	5.00
WOODEN BOX,JEWEL,HAND CARVED WITH MORNING GLORIES IN	
RELIEF,LOCK & KEY.....................................	19.00
WOODEN BOX,KNIFE,WALNUT,3 COMPARTMENTS....................	18.50
WOODEN BOX,MAIL,WALNUT WITH KEY,9 IN. HIGH...............	8.00
WOODEN BOX,PEGGED,ROUND,LAPPED FINGERS....................	9.00
WOODEN BOX,PENCIL WITH METAL SCROLL ON TOP................	6.50
WOODEN BOX,ROSEWOOD WITH INLAID TOP.......................	7.50
WOODEN BOX,SALT,BARREL SHAPE,WALL.........................	22.00
WOODEN BOX,SALT,BOARD ON BACK TO HANG,SCALLOPED..........	10.50
WOODEN BOX,SALT,CIRCA 1890,WORD SALT,FLOWERS & LEAVES......	12.50
WOODEN BOX,SALT FOR HANGING,PINE..........................	5.00
WOODEN BOX,SALT,PINE,FOR HANGING,WORD SALT ON FRONT.........	9.00
WOODEN BOX,SALT,WALL.....................................	4.00
WOODEN BOX,SEA CAPTAIN DITTY,WALNUT FINISH,SILVER MEDALLION	
TOP..	5.00
WOODEN BOX,SNUFF,METAL DECOR.............................	8.50
WOODEN BOX,TRINKET,LINED MAHOGANY,SHELL DECOR.............	19.00
WOODEN,BOX,WALNUT,13 X 20 X 5............................	15.00
WOODEN BREAD BOARD,CURLY MAPLE,ROUND......................	18.00
WOODEN BREAD PEEL,CHIMNEY OVEN...........................	15.00
WOODEN BUCKET,5 GALLON PICKEL TAPER,PUSH-ON LID............	9.00
WOODEN BUCKET,6 IN. TALL, DECORATED......................	4.00
WOODEN BUCKET,STAVED MAPLE SUGAR,WOOD LAPPED HOOPS..........	10.00
WOODEN BUTTER CHURN,14 IN. HIGH,RED STENCILLED COW ON SIDE..	13.75
WOODEN BUTTER CHURN,DASHER TYPE..........................	35.00
WOODEN BUTTER CHURN,VERTICAL STAVED,HOOPED................	50.00
WOODEN BUCKET,KEROSENE...................................	6.00
WOODEN BUCKET,MILK.......................................	6.00
WOODEN BUTTER PRINT,SQUARE,FLOWER........................	4.50
WOODEN BUCKET,SAP..	6.00
WOODEN BUCKET,SEWING,CORD HANDLE,SPOOL RACK...............	9.00
WOODEN BUCKET,SUGAR,REFINISHED...........................	9.00
WOODEN BUCKET,SUGAR,WOODEN HOOPS,HANDLE,MARKED SARATOGA.....	18.00
WOODEN BUCKET,WATER......................................	6.00
WOODEN BUCKET WITH HANDLE,HORSE RADISH...................	8.00
WOODEN BUTTER MOLD,FLORAL................................	9.00
WOODEN BUTTER STAMP,PATTERNED,FLOWERS-FERNS..............	7.50
WOODEN BUTTER STAMP,SHEAF OF WHEAT.......................	5.00
WOODEN BUTTER STAMP WITH FERN & LEAF DESIGN..............	4.75
WOODEN CANDLESTICK,PAIR,TURNED,WHITE PAINT,FROM QUEBEC	
CHURCH...	45.00
WOODEN CANDLESTICK,PAIR,TURNED WITH TIN SPIKES,PAINTED WHITE	25.00
WOODEN CANDLESTICK,WALNUT,8 IN..........................	8.50
WOODEN CANE HANDLE,EAGLES HEAD,CARVED WITH INLAID EYES.....	7.50
WOODEN CARVING,COMEDY & TRAGEDY MASKS,CARVED ON RED CEDAR	
KNOTS..	6.50
WOODEN CARVING,ELEPHANT WITH IVORY TUSKS,HANDCARVED.........	4.00
WOODEN CARVING,HAND CARVED BEAR,GLASS EYES,39 IN. HIGH......	625.00
WOODEN CARVING,HAND CARVED HORSE.........................	10.00
WOODEN CARVING,ORIENTAL BOATS,PEOPLE,RED.................	50.00
WOODEN CARVING,PINE BIRD.................................	15.00
WOODEN CARVING,SLEEPING LAMB ON CLOSED BOOK,WHITE & GOLD	
LEAF...	45.00
WOODEN CIGAR STORE INDIAN,6 FEET HIGH....................	450.00
WOODEN CIGAR STORE INDIAN,HAND CARVED,29 IN. TALL............	500.00
WOODEN CLOTHES WRINGER,PAT.1898..........................	3.00
WOODEN COFFIN,PINE.......................................	45.00

WOODEN COOKIE BOARD,BOXER DOG................................... 16.00
WOODEN COOKIE BOARD,GINGERBREAD MAN & WOMAN.................. 12.00
WOODEN COOKIE BOARD,KITTEN CUT OUT FIGURE.................... 5.00
WOODEN COW POKE.. 10.50
WOODEN CUTTER,COLESLAW,ADJUSTABLE............................. 4.50
WOODEN CUTTER,DOUGHNUT.. 9.00
WOODEN CUTTER,SAUERKRAUT...................................... 4.50
WOODEN DARNER... 2.00
WOODEN DOUGH BOARD WITH ROLLING PIN,5 PIECES,POPLAR,WALL
TYPE.. 25.00
WOODEN DRILL,HAND... 5.00
WOODEN DUMBELLS WITH SILVER PLATED KNOBS..................... 12.00
WOODEN EAGLE,WING SPREAD 21 IN............................... 60.00
WOODEN FIGURE,ANGEL,HANDCARVED,GOLD LEAF..................... 80.00
WOODEN FIGURE,CANNON MODEL,MAHOGANY.......................... 195.00
WOODEN FIGURE,CARVED ALPINE MAN,14 IN. HIGH................. 28.00
WOODEN FIGURE,CARVED OWL,JAPANESE............................ 48.00
WOODEN FIGURE,CHINESE IMMORTAL,HARDWOOD,CARVED,4 IN. HIGH... 32.50
WOODEN FIGURE GOD SHISHI TEMPLE GUARDIAN,CAMPHOR WOOD,CIRCA
1700-1750.. 120.00
WOODEN FIGURE,HAND CARVED BROWN BEAR,INSET GLASS EYES,42 IN.
TALL... 350.00
WOODEN FIGURE,PAIR CARVED FOO DOGS,CIRCA 1870,9 IN.
LONG,JAPANESE.. 120.00
WOODEN FIGURE,PAIR HORSES.................................... 10.00
WOODEN FIGURE,RELIGIOUS,HAND CARVED,POLYCHROME,CIRCA 1650... 135.00
WOODEN FIGURE,WINGED,8 FOOT,HAND CARVED,MEXICO,SAN RAFAEL... 350.00
WOODEN FIGURINE,MADONNA & CHILD,PAINTED,1820................1,800.00
WOODEN FIGURINE,PAIR CARVED WITH SILVER WIRE INLAYS......... 165.00
WOODEN FLAX CARDER... 10.00
WOODEN FOOT WARMER... 12.00
WOODEN FORK,3 TINE,9 IN...................................... 2.00
WOODEN FORK,CLOTHES,HAND MADE,32 IN. LONG................... 6.50
WOODEN FRAME,14 IN.,OVAL,WALNUT.............................. 8.00
WOODEN FRAME WITH GOLD LINER,OBLONG,WALNUT.................. 17.50
WOODEN FRAME WITH GOLD LINER,OVAL,WALNUT................... 12.50
WOODEN FRAMES,PAIR 12 IN.,OVAL,WALNUT...................... 12.00
WOODEN GRIPS,PAIR FOR REINS FOR RACING HORSE............... 4.00
WOODEN HANDLE DINING FORK.................................... 1.00
WOODEN HANDLE DINING KNIVES,7................................ 5.00
WOODEN HASTY PUDDING STICK,HOME MADE,21 IN.................. 4.00
WOODEN HEAD,WIG MAKERS FOR NET.............................. 10.00
WOODEN HOLDER,TOBACCO & PIPE,CARVED IN SHAPE OF LONG-LEGGED
MAN,JAPAN.. 50.00
WOODEN HORSE HOBBLE.. 8.00
WOODEN ICE SKATES,PAIR RACING STYLE,STRAIGHT STEEL RUNNERS.. 7.50
WOODEN INK SANDER USED WITH QUILL PENS
5.00   TO... 7.50
WOODEN JACK,BED,TO TIGHTEN ROPE BEDS........................ 7.50
WOODEN JACK,WAGON.. 8.00
WOODEN JEWEL BOX,CHASED BRASS MOUNTINGS,SHANGHAI CHINA...... 200.00
WOODEN KEY,BED,FOR TIGHTENING ROPE BEDS..................... 7.50
WOODEN LANTERN,CANDLE,9 IN................................... 75.00
WOODEN LETTER OPENER,CARVED HEAD AT END..................... 5.00
WOODEN MALLET.. 3.00
WOODEN MEASURE FOR GRAIN,FARM PECK SIZE..................... 5.00
WOODEN MEAT POUNDER.. 2.00
WOODEN MOLD,BUTTER,1 HALF POUND,FLOWER...................... 6.50
WOODEN MOLD,BUTTER,1 POUND,PINEAPPLE........................ 7.00
WOODEN MOLD,BUTTER,2 POUND,DESIGNS.......................... 9.00
WOODEN MOLD,BUTTER,PINEAPPLE DESIGN......................... 12.00
WOODEN MOLD,BUTTER,PLUNGER TYPE,SHEAF OF WHEAT,1 POUND...... 12.50
WOODEN MOLD,BUTTER,RECTANGULAR.............................. 3.50
WOODEN MOLD,BUTTER,ROLLER-TYPE,WHEAT,MARKER................ 12.50
WOODEN MOLD,BUTTER,ROUND,PINEAPPLE,1 POUND................. 8.50

```
WOODEN MOLD,BUTTER,ROUND,PLUNGER TYPE,LEAF DESIGN...........     8.00
WOODEN MOLD,BUTTER,SWAN.......................................    19.00
WOODEN MOLD,BUTTER,STAR & SHEAF OF WHEAT.....................     8.50
WOODEN MOLD,CIGAR,CLOSED,10 IN. CIGAR........................    10.00
WOODEN MOLD,HAT,2 PARTS......................................    20.00
WOODEN MOLD,MAPLE SUGAR,SOLID BLOCK,DOG......................    15.00
WOODEN MOLD,MAPLE SUGAR,SOLID WOOD BLOCK,2 CARVED STARS......    19.00
WOODEN MOLD,MAPLE SUGAR,SOLID WOOD BLOCK,HORSE...............    15.00
WOODEN MOLD,SQUARE,HINGED,4-PART,GEOMETRIC DESIGN............     6.00
WOODEN MORTAR & PESTLE,7 IN. HIGH...........................     14.75
WOODEN MORTAR & PESTLE,PINE.................................      1.50
WOODEN MORTAR & PESTLE,MAPLE................................      8.00
WOODEN MORTAR & PESTLE PAINTED RED..........................     20.00
WOODEN MORTAR,LIGNUM VITAE..................................     27.50
WOODEN MORTAR WITH PESTLE,MAPLE.............................     22.00
WOODEN NAPKIN RING,SOUVENIR,FLUME HOUSE.....................      1.25
WOODEN OPENER,LETTER,DATED 1869,CASED,FOLDING,POCKET........      3.00
WOODEN OX YOKES,27 IN. STOCK................................     12.00
WOODEN PADDLE,FLAT,25 IN....................................      9.00
WOODEN PADDLE FOR BREAD IN OUTSIDE OVEN.....................     20.00
WOODEN PATTERNS FOR INFANT CASKETS..........................     10.00
WOODEN PITCHER..............................................     32.00
WOODEN PLANE,BLOCK..........................................      5.00
WOODEN PLANE,MOULDING.......................................      5.00
WOODEN PLANTER STAMPED WAKEFIELDS PATENT....................     12.50
WOODEN PLAQUE,BURNT,BUST OF LOVELY LADY.....................      5.00
WOODEN PLAQUE,SET OF 4 WITH INLAID BASE OF COLOURED WOOD....    150.00
WOODEN PLAQUE,WALL WITH 10 POINT DEER HORNS.................     10.00
WOODEN PLATE,WALL,PAIR,HANDCARVED...........................     30.00
WOODEN POTATO MASHER........................................      2.00
WOODEN POWDER FLASK,DOT DECORATION..........................     30.00
WOODEN PULLEYS..............................................      5.00
WOODEN RACHET,WATCHMANS.....................................      5.00
WOODEN RACK,PIPE TO HANG ON WALL,HOLDS 10,18TH
   CENTURY,ENGLISH OAK......................................    150.00
WOODEN RAT TRAP.............................................      3.00
WOODEN RING.................................................      7.50
WOODEN ROLLING PIN..........................................      4.00
WOODEN ROLLING PIN,CURLY MAPLE..............................     12.00
WOODEN ROLLING PIN FOR MAKING DESIGNS.......................     12.00
WOODEN ROLLING PIN,NOODLE...................................      7.00
WOODEN ROLLING PIN,PINE.....................................      8.50
WOODEN SADDLE,CAMEL,SHAPE OF SAW HORSE WITH PAD.............     22.50
WOODEN SALAD FORK & SPOON,STERLING HANDLES..................      3.00
WOODEN SCOOP,BUTTER,MADE OF CURLY MAPLE.....................     12.50
WOODEN SCOOP,CRANBERRY,TINED................................     35.00
WOODEN SEWING BIRD WITH MIRROR & PIN CUSHION................      9.00
WOODEN SHIP,CARVED,23 IN. X 18 IN.,OLD SPANISH,5 CANVAS
   SAILS,RIGGED.............................................     20.00
WOODEN SHOE,HAND CARVED,CHILDS SIZE.........................      3.50
WOODEN SHOVEL,56 IN. LONG...................................     35.00
WOODEN SIGN,BARBERS ADVERTISING,STRAIGHT RAZOR..............     15.00
WOODEN SKATES,PAIR..........................................      5.00
WOODEN SPOON................................................      2.00
WOODEN SPOON,RUSSIAN ENAMELED HANDLE........................     45.00
WOODEN SPOON WITH 2 SLITS...................................      2.00
WOODEN STICK,BLEACHING,LONG HANDLED.........................      3.00
WOODEN STIRRER,APPLE BUTTER KETTLE,LONG HANDLED,37 IN.......     10.00
WOODEN SUGAR SCOOP,REFINISHED...............................      7.00
WOODEN TEA CADDY,MAHOGANY COFFIN SHAPE,11 IN. HIGH..........     35.00
WOODEN TOBACCO JAR,CARVED,BARREL SHAPE,HANDCARVED ROOSTER...     25.00
WOODEN TRAY CARVED AS A LEAF,12 X 20 IN.....................      6.50
WOODEN TRAY,KNIFE,WALNUT....................................      7.50
WOODEN TRAY,MEAT,FARMERS....................................      7.00
WOODEN TRAY,PINE KNIFE......................................     10.00
```

```
WOODEN TRAY,WALNUT KNIFE.....................................   12.00
WOODEN TRENCHER,CHESTNUT.....................................   38.00
WOODEN TRUNK,CHILDS,BRASS BOUND,21 X 12 X 9 IN..............    4.50
WOODEN TUB,BUTTER,STAVED OPEN TOP...........................   12.50
WOODEN WARE,BEE BOX.........................................    4.00
WOODEN WARE,BLOCK,CUTTING,MEAT,HOMEMADE.....................   25.00
WOODEN WARE,BOARD,BREAD,PORCELAIN KNOB,MAPLE...............    10.50
WOODEN WARE,BOARD,DOUGH OR BREAD,MADE OF SLATE,CUT HAND HOLE   15.00
WOODEN WARE,BOARD FOR IRONING SHIRTS,BOSOM,1874 PATENT......    9.00
WOODEN WARE,BOARD,PLEATING OUTFIT WITH 85 STEEL RODS........   12.50
WOODEN WARE,BOARD,SCOURING..................................   11.00
WOODEN WARE,BOWL,BUTTER.....................................    6.00
WOODEN WARE,BOWL,CHOPPING...................................   22.50
WOODEN WARE,BUTTER PRINT,EAGLE,INITIALED B.C...............    30.00
WOODE WARE,BUTTER PRINT,MAPLE...............................    2.50
WOODEN WARE,DUMBELLS,VICTORIAN..............................    6.50
WOODEN WARE,MOLD,BUTTER,1/2 POUND,BLOSSOM..................     8.50
WOODEN WARE,MOLD,BUTTER,1 POUND,PLUNGER TYPE...............     8.50
WOODEN WARE,MOLD,BUTTER,8 SQUARES ON PANEL,CLOVER DESIGN....   30.00
WOODEN WARE,MOLD,BUTTER,ACORN..............................     8.50
WOODEN WARE,MOLD,BUTTER,BOX TYPE,FLOWER PATTERN............     5.75
WOODEN WARE,MOLD,BUTTER,GLASS,WOODEN HANDLE,COW DESIGN......   35.00
WOODEN WARE,MOLD,BUTTER,HINGED,4 FLORAL-PETAL QUARTERS......    7.50
WOODEN WARE,MOLD,BUTTER,POUND,SWAN..........................    8.50
WOODEN WARE,MOLD,BUTTER,ROUND,PLUNGER TYPE,ACORNS...........    8.50
WOODEN WARE,MOLD,BUTTER,ROUND,WOOD..........................   10.00
WOODEN WARE,MOLD,BUTTER,ROUND,WOOD,PLUNGER TYPE,FIGURE OF A
SWAN.........................................................   15.00
WOODEN WARE,MOLD,BUTTER,SQUARE,4 SECTION,WOODEN............     5.00
WOODEN WARE,MOLD,BUTTER,WOOD,PLUNGER TYPE,PINEAPPLE.........   10.00
WOODEN WARE,MOLD,BUTTER,WOODEN,PLUNGER TYPE.................    4.00
WOODEN WARE,MOLD,COOKIE,FARMER BOY WITH HAT.................   11.00
WOODEN WARE,MOLD,COOKIE,SOLDIER WITH SWORD..................    8.50
WOODEN WARE,PADDLE,BUTTER...................................    4.00
WOODEN WARE,PADDLE,BUTTER,WOOD,CARVING......................    6.00
WOODEN WARE,PADDLE,PAIR RIBBED FOR DAIRY TABLE..............    2.00
WOODEN WARE,PADDLE TYPE APPLE BUTTER STIRRER,43 IN..........    7.50
WOODEN WASHER,ELECTRIC,1915 MODEL...........................   20.00
WOODEN WELL WHEEL,OAKEN BUCKET..............................    8.00
WOODEN WRITING BOX,SATIN INLAID,FELT WRITING SURFACE........  100.00
WOODEN YARN WINDER,OAK......................................   22.00
WOODEN YOKE,SHOULDER........................................   10.00
WORCESTER PLATE IN COBALT BLUE WITH GOLD BORDER MARKED
W.DR.WALL.................................................... 125.00
WORLD WAR I COMMEMORATION MEDAL.............................    5.00
WORLD WAR I GERMAN BELT BUCKLES,2...........................    2.00
WORLD WAR I GERMAN POLICE LEATHER SHAKE.....................   24.00
WORLD WAR I PENNA.VICTORY MEDAL WITH RIBBON.................    3.00
WORLD WAR I TOY LEAD SET OF 8 SOLDIERS......................    4.50
WORLDS FAIR 1904 ST.LOUIS CHINA BOOT, 3 IN. TALL...........    7.50
WORLDS FAIR TUMBLER,HORTICULTURAL BLDG......................    2.25

YELLOW MOUNTAIN STONE PAIR BOOK ENDS,CARVED WITH FOO
DOGS,BROWN..................................................   65.00
YELLOW WARE BABY SITTING BY TREE STUMP HOLDING BOTTLE,2
CHICKENS....................................................   10.00
YELLOW WARE PAIR MOLDS,EAR CORN.............................    8.00
```

ZSOLNAY POTTERY was made in Hungary after 1855.

```
ZSOLNAY BOWL,BLUE AND GOLD IRIDESCENCE,7IN.DIA..............   60.00
ZSOLNAY-PECS SIGNED IRIDESCENT COMPOTE,GREEN & ROSE
IRIDESCENCE.................................................   37.50
ZSOLNAY VASE,RED & GREEN IRIDESCENCE, 10IN. DIA............   175.00
ZSOLNAY VASE,4 IN.,IRIDESCENT PATTERN,BLUE & GREEN,SIGNED...   48.00
```